Published by: Shopping Business, Inc.
1079 W. Round Grove Rd, PMB 428, Suite 300
Lewisville, TX 75067

Distributed by Curtis Distributing

The entries appearing in this book were selected based on a number of criteria, including their appearance of being "less than retail," the personal value judgements of the author, her staff and a team of trained shoppers who visited each listing. The Underground Shopper is the culmination of many years of experience in shopping the metropolitan area and additional research from national shopping directories by the author.

The Underground Shopper is a registered trademark of Sue Goldstein

10 9 8 7 6 5 4 3 2 1

ISBN 1-879524-10-4

Printed in The United States of America

the UNDERGROUND shopper

The Underground Shopper Is Back!

Over $7,000 In DIVA Dollar Certificates Inside!

Best 100 SHOPPING DESTINATIONS

www.undergroundshopper.com

SUE GOLDSTEIN

The Underground Shopper - Since 1972

Table of Contents

Dedication

To Bob, my husband and partner, my rock when I have
been in between here, there and a hard place; to Josh and
Irina who've made me "qvell" (that means in Yiddish
bursting with pride) and to you and all of you who have
sent me in one way or another your love and support this
past year, I'm finally back where I belong. As Mike Sime-
one used to always say to me, and now I to you, "We
thank you!"

Disclaimer

Note this year we have included in the back of this book, what we are calling Diva Dollar certificates. If you like, you can think of them similarly as coupons. They are our way to separate the clutter of money-saving resources that exist today. Nobody's paying full price for anything these days. I never thought I would be saying there is a glut of so-called opportunities to save money so this is my way of giving to a select few an additional incentive for you to shop them first. Another way of saying it --- I'm making good deals even better.

We start with a team of researchers who shopped to and fro, in and out of storefronts and back rooms all year long. With about 3,000 store visits, we narrow it down to a mix of geographic and categorical opportunities that we think make for a balanced book of money-saving opportunities. Then because of space restraints, we eliminate certain ones when we have so many good ones already to choose from; or for one reason or another chose to not include. A few had serious complaints on file. Some were down right rude to us. And one or two scammed readers out right this past year and were reported to authorities, when necessary.

Lastly, we have a sales person who picks their favorite listings from those that we rated in the 100 BEST (You don't have to count them, we already know we have more than 100!) and call on them to join our Diva Dollar coupon program, our photo op in the book, or our advertising program in our monthly magazine or have us as radio advertisers on our call-in show. Merchants have supported us for years and with this added feature, I know you'll appreciate their additional generosity with additional incentives to shop them first.

Remember, though there was money that exchanged hands (yes they paid to print their coupon), they were asked, not demanded. There are plenty of 5 star and 5 diamond merchants who said "NO" and their ratings or their inclusion in the big book were not affected. I would never promote stores that I find disreputable, despicable, disgusting, degrading or undeserving, period. Nobody pays for a good write-up. I shop and my shoppers shop and write their reviews as they see them. They are paid researchers. And as readers and fans of The Underground Shopper ®, you always let me know when you were disappointed. We take all of your emails, phone calls, written letters and conversations into consideration when I do the ultimate write-up.

For those who want to know which listings got the ax for no reason except perhaps they were a periodic sale, or they were so well known that we didn't want to waste space on them. Home Depot, Lowe's, etc.) are perfect examples of them. Some were so far out of the Metro area --- but not good enough to make the drive worthwhile. Sorry, Charlie, you just weren't good enough to warrant the long ride, so, "Adios!"

Soon after the publication of the book, we will be announcing our SHOPWHO® database, where every listing will appear online. All of the deleted listings that didn't get printed plus more each month that I find will be added to our database and available for a monthly access fee. Right now, all you can see online are those that made it into the 100 BEST. Obviously, with multi-thousands of stores in the Metroplex, plus the multi-thousands that will be appearing in the big national book, The Underground Shopper/Online®, some shoppers will still want to know everything that I know. And so, soon you will be able to get it all with a click of the mouse. For a small fee, our database will become available to members of the Diva Club. You've heard of the M.O.D. Squad? Well, we have one, too. Members of the Diva Club (MOD) will have special deals. And we don't even have to be related. More about that later.

We always try to ensure a perfect write-up. We verify everything at the last minute. When we shop a store or service, our criteria has remained constant over the 33 years we've been writing the book. We look at the following for the STAR ratings:

- Quality of the merchandise

- Selection

- Service

- Amenities

- Convenience

- Price

- Something out of the ordinary that makes them special

The same holds true for services, though we used diamonds for ratings. The consideration for services, though, is different because being the lowest price is not always the main ingredient for the highest service ratings. We look at the following for the DIAMOND ratings:

- Quality of their service

- Integrity of their warranty; Do they ensure complete satisfaction?

- Professionalism of their technicians

- Prices compared to their competitors

- Do they go the extra mile? Do they do something extra special that others don't?

- Time factor? Do they show up when they say they are? Will they not charge you if they find they can't help you or it's something so minor that it only requires turning on a switch?

Granted, there's nothing scientific about the process we use. We could calculate to the minutest detail, but we don't. Chances are, you don't either. We can smell a good deal. We can smell a raw deal. Occasionally we're wrong on both, but take it in our stride that sometimes it doesn't turn out as it appears on the surface.

No doubt, our ratings are for the most part "subjective" though we do try to put personal feelings aside and be objective. Let's face it, even the greatest store, with the greatest prices and the greatest selection can have an "off" day. Merchandise can get strewn about the showroom floor or all of the top sales personnel were off sick on the day of our visit. But that's the price you pay for being in retail; and it's the price you pay for our one-time shopping experience. We wish we could have given you a second chance. But there's always next year.

We certainly can claim to be the longest lasting bargain-shopping book printed continuously in this country, perhaps even the world. Though we made a detour for two years with another name that we're still proud of (Bigger Better Bargains), we have decided to return using the name that we were born (to shop) with. And since I own the name again, we're glad to be back to being The Underground Shopper!

Log on to our website, www.undergroundshopper.com and put your two cents worth. After all, what's a shopping guide book without your input and comments? We may one day add a "Chat Button." We're trying out our version of a product that you can bid on all week and we'll announce whoever buys it at the highest price they've bidded the following week. Can't be sure it'll work, but we like to try new things. We also have lots of other buttons to click.

ASK THE DIVA --- if you have a question or want to talk shop with me. I answer all of them every day, most days. The 100 BEST BUTTON is our searchable 100 (plus) BEST. The SPEAKERS' BUREAU has all kinds of programs club groups who have always invited me multiple times to be a guest speaker can look to others in the "underground" for their respective expertise in a fun and informative program of their very own. LIVE is where I will be appearing with either a public appearance or an on-location radio remote. Don't miss our SATURDAY FREEBIES button either because it will tell you what prizes we'll be giving away on that Saturday show; or it will tell you by not calling in, what you missed on last Saturday's show. Of course, we have a DEAL OF THE WEEK where we feature one particular product all week, that all you have to do is tell them the Diva sent you and it's yours for that special price. Talk about "insider trading."

And that's just for starters. Do hop aboard our gravy train and gobble up the savings. Remember, you don't have to be cheap to love a bargain, you just have to be smart.

Online Shopping

When you shop any of our online stores, you can trust we know these merchants well. At the time of publication, all met our criteria for inclusion in the book, including having a secure shopping site, relationships with professional organizations such as the Better Business Bureau, a toll-free number for easy communication, an easy return policy, a variety of delivery options and, of course, quality merchandise.

Ratings, Codes, and Designations

The Shoppers voted and the results are in. When you see this logo, it means they are the cream of the crop and have joined our marketing family.

Star Ratings: Merchants of Goods & Products

Please see the disclaimer for the criteria of these ratings.

★★★★★★ TOP DOG

★★★★★ ALMOST

★★★★ NOT QUITE, BUT CLOSE

★★★ DEFINITELY WORTH A TRIP

★★ NOT BAD

★ DON'T BOTHER

NO STARS: UNLESS IT'S A TYPO, BEWARE!

Diamond Ratings: Merchants who perform a service

Not every entry is judged on price alone. A merchant who provides a service that is superior to others in the same business is given the highest rating (5 diamonds); sometimes, they also charge a little less but give you a lot more. You know what I mean. Those special touches are like music to my ears. For example, when a merchant will go the extra mile … a moving company who works into the wee hours of the night to make sure you get every box inside; the printer who will make a second press check to make sure that the color pages are just right; the plumber or a/c man who says, "Ah, it was nothing. Just turn on the switch. No charge, ma'am!"

◆◆◆◆◆◆ SPECTACULAR AND WELL BEYOND THE CALL OF DUTY

◆◆◆◆◆ ALMOST

◆◆◆◆ NO COMPLAINTS, WHATSOEVER

◆◆◆ GOT WHAT I PAID FOR

◆◆ ADEQUATE

◆ WOULDN'T RECOMMEND THEM TO MY MOTHER-IN-LAW

NO DIAMONDS: BOTCHED THE JOB, BEWARE

To Die For

Ever walked into a store and said, "This is to die for?" Sorry, but it may be a sexist-only phrase, but somehow women understand it implicitly. We couldn't resist including some of our top crop "to die for" picks.

Look for the heart symbol with the cupid's arrow puncturing through. It's a few we wanted you to know about and may eventually become its own stand-alone book. You never know what we're up to.

There are lots of fabulous finds out there in the big city. Sometimes money is not the ONLY object that propels us to shop one store over another. It's always in the back of my mind, but every once in a while, you walk into a "To Die For Store" and shout, "Wow!" Something is drop-dead gorgeous so you'll throw abandon to the wind. Who cares what it costs? I want what I want. And so you buy it and pay the consequences later. (The Diva won't get mad, I promise. I do it myself every now and again!)

Online Bargains

There are lots of websites associated with brick and mortar stores. Some just give static information at their site with their locations, history, investor relation's information and such. Think of it like an online brochure. Too, if you have a problem and want to return the merchandise, they encourage you to exchange it in person at the store nearest you.

Ah ha! Another ploy to get you into their store. Then again, you save on the postage and packing it back up to mail.

On online sites, there are downloadable coupons. What a boon to extra savings. It's so convenient and still another way to entice you. It works for me. Some tout their promotions as well. So if you miss their ad in the paper or their commercial on TV, you might be drawn to their store this way.

When you see an online store that we designate with a computer screen, the only way you can access their merchandise is online, and there is no physical store for you to shop at. We've included them because they sell online exclusively. To be successful as a strictly online storefront, it means they are good enough to stand alone. You don't need to be lured or romanced with soft-sounding music or the smell of pot-pourri. You either like the price or you don't. You either want the product or you don't. And with certain safeguards in place on their site you feel secure ordering from this company --- or you don't!

Some online sites were chosen because there were no comparable discounters in the Metroplex for their products. One such site comes to mind --- www.goknobs.com. Hundreds of thousands of drawer pulls make them a serious category killer. Too, their prices are the best. Another site I love for all the right reasons is www.overstock.com. For price, selection and service, they just can't be beat. It's just the best. Name brand and designer items covering a wide range of merchandise, superb customer service, a top notch management team, plenty of solid financing and a history of at least one year of personally shopping them, well, you can tell I'm a happy looker who is a regular shopper who has bought it all ... hook, line and sinker.

Where we had no one locally to recommend for pool supplies, besides Wal-Mart or Leslie's, it was necessary to look elsewhere for discounted pool supplies. That's why we included several pool supply discounters in the category of Pools and Yards. They only sell online and you don't want to miss them. They represent the best the web has to offer that speaks to quality, integrity and discounts that lower overhead (no store front) allow. Enjoy the savings without ever getting wet. But if you're like me, you'll want to jump in and save a bundle. Really, the water's fine and you'll never drown by going overboard.

It's another carrot we've thrown in to the Dallas/Fort Worth book to show you that we take bargain shopping seriously, wherever it takes us. The world is now your marketplace. Join us so we can take you from one underground find to another. Yes, we will even take you there --- by train, by plane or by ship. Turn to our website for trip itineraries and you will be able to go "Saling with the Diva!" Of course, we'll help you save some money and get you a whole lot more. The days of camping out of a bunker and riding cargo class are over for me.

I watch your money as I watch mine. So you need to watch for our national Underground Shopper/Online book coming to a bookstore near you and to our website. We hate to leave a bargain unturned.

So whether it's across town, across the country, the continent, the world, welcome to the wonderful world of bargains. Now isn't it time you went "underground" so you will continue to live the good life - at half the price! (SM)

Other Codes

Some codes you may run across in the headers or write-ups include:

MO   **Mail Order**

PQ   **Price Quote**

PS   **Periodic Sale**

NV   **Not Visited, maybe just a rumor**

How We Do a Few Other Things

Credit Cards

All merchants listed take credit cards. If they only take cash, we'll indicate in their heading with a $ sign. However, instead of wasting space, we've eliminated the signs for credit cards because they all accept them these days. If they don't, we'll tell you.

Addresses

To conserve space, we usually list three store addresses. If there are more than three stores, find the one nearest to you by going to: www.switchboard.com, www.whitepages.com, or www.yellowpages.com; or check directory assistance if we haven't listed all locations.

Toll Free Numbers

We just used the area codes of 800, 888, 877, 866 without the one before it. We assumed you knew to dial it.

Prices Listed

Prices that are listed in the write-ups are *strictly* illustrative of the prices and the savings at the time of our visit. As you well know, they change. Don't expect to see that item with that price tag on when you shop.

Blanket Apology

Up front, I admit we might have goofed. Inadvertently there may be a typo or incorrect information. In spite of proof reading 'til we're blue in the face, we may still have egg on our face. But at least it's Egg Benedict! Consider this my overall "I'm sorry."

To conserve space, though, it was necessary to draw the line on the number of listings we ultimately printed in the book. Believe it or not, there are still more and they will be available to Diva Club members online. Some we missed, some we dropped intentionally, and others we just don't know about. We admit it --- we don't know it all. So, if your favorite store is missing, send me an email at diva@undergroundshopper.com and let me have it! Always tune in to our radio show and visit our website often so you will always have a heads up on the latest and greatest.

As for brand names, which appear in the text like this—**BRAND A**—we may have missed a few here and there but we're sure you can pick them out of the lineup anyway.

When special sales are on, you'll hear about it on the air or read about it on our website. Since they come and go at whim, we decided to alert you when we hear them. If we know about them in advance, we will post them in plenty of time.

Shopping Tours

I hate riding on busses. I get bus sick and I have trouble getting up and down the steps. But if you want an Underground Shopping Tour, I will design a custom itinerary for your group and provide a kick-off breakfast or luncheon speech on the history of Underground Shopping. For information and availability, call our offices at 469/293-SHOP (7467). Same for speeches and shopping bazaars; yes, I still do them and yes, I'm still cheap. Call and see why club groups continue to invite us back year after year.

Diva Dollars New This Year

For the first time in the history of The Underground Shopper, we've included money-saving coupons at the back of the book. Yes, coupons. What better incentive is there but to offer a "dollar-off" to get you to that store? Too, with the coupon, we can certainly say "With the Underground Shopper, you are guaranteed the lowest prices, period!" Everybody else pays the discounted price. When you include the Diva Dollar offer, you'll be saving even more; hence, nobody can beat the price that you get by utilizing your dollars off coupon. If you start with those that are offering a Diva Dollar, not only will you be shopping at a merchant that was voted into the 100 BEST, but you will be receiving the lowest price. Plain and simple. They're also dangling the possibility of saving you collectively more than $7,000 off their already discounted prices. No kidding. But these DD are only available to those who have purchased this book. How can you not want to put them to good use (and put those savings in YOUR pocket)!

Now, calculate the economic impact Underground Shopping is really having on the economy? (Hey, maybe I should replace Alan Greenspan?) It's safe to say, UNDER-GROUND SHOPPERS ALWAYS GET THE BEST PRICES! Take us with you whenever you get ready to shop. Put us in your purse or your glove compartment and never leave home without us!

Photo Ops

At the last minute, I decided I wanted to offer some pictures of various merchants so you can get a sense of what they look like. We hired Larry Hayles who is a professional photographer and off he went—from the Dallas Sample Sales to G & S Sales. On occasion, he brought his wife helper and guess what? She shopped everywhere he went. We'd like to do this again in next year's book so if you liked the pictures and would like to see more, just drop me a line and let me know. (diva@undergroundshopper.com)

LA DIVA LATINA

Lastly, if you or someone you know were of Hispanic descent, perhaps they would prefer reading this book in their native language. Even if they are fluent in English, it doesn't hurt to deliver the deals in Spanish. Watch for The Underground Shopper/Espanola edition coming soon to a bookstore near you. For your copy, Spanish editions will also be available at select Spanish-Speaking merchant stores and by clicking a button on our website if you prefer to access the database in Spanish. We are very proud to announce our first foray into this untapped and underserved market and to introduce you to our representatives, a duo of very talented bi-lingual Divas and Divos. La Diva Latina and La Divo Latino – we just made up those names so forgive us if they're improper in Spanish. We thought they were fun.

FOREWORD

Since 1972, I've been writing these kinds of books. This year marks the return to my birth name, The Underground Shopper ®. Until I sell it (for real) again, it remains my trademark forever and a day.

There are some rules of thumb (and feet) when it comes to shopping for bargains.

Don't shop when you're hungry --- especially in a grocery store. When your stomach is growling, "Feed me", you'll make terrible choices. Same with other shopping categories. Funerals, for example. Don't shop for one when you're grieving. You'll generally wind up buying something that's way too expensive; or something you could better do without. Don't overlook our chapters on Funerals and Caskets.

2. Don't shop in stiletto heels. Unless you want to make a podiatrist very rich, wear comfortable shoes and attire. You're not out to impress anybody and especially the merchant. This is very dangerous especially at a flea market. They may get the impression you can actually afford the prices marked!

3. Leave your credit cards at home. If you don't have the cash, it's just too easy to put it on a credit card. Save them for a rainy day or in an emergency. You'll be glad you did.

4. Make a list of things you need. Browse for comparison purposes only; then buy when you can really afford it.

5. Shop alone. You don't need a group experience to convince you that you really need that fuchsia chair.

6. Be conservative. Just because something's cheap, doesn't mean you have to buy it. What if you get it home and you have nothing to wear with it? Then, you'll run to the corner neighborhood retailer and spend even more for a blouse to go with it. You know you'll regret it in the morning, Same with furniture. Always carry a tape measure when shopping. But even so, you always think your room is bigger than it is and when you get that chair home that you couldn't live without, you discover that it won't even squeeze through the front door much less have a place with elbow room in your living room.

7. Plan a shopping route that is efficient. Combine bargain shops and make your time and gas go a long way.

8. Don't buy something because some movie star wore it to the Academy Awards or because everyone's got one and you should, too.

9. Read ads so you'll be familiar with what things cost. At least when a store is claiming it's on sale or marked down, you'll be armed with some information that could prove them wrong.

10. Lastly, if it's too good to be true.... read the book. If it's a great buy, it's more than likely within these pages. If not, let us know.

Enjoy your finds.

Sue Goldstein

Acknowledgements

The years of 2001-2002 may have been my transition years to bigger and better everything. After all, the name Bigger Better Bargains was the name I chose when the trademark of The Underground Shopper ® was in dispute. Rather than spending any more money fighting the good fight, I finally decided to move on with my life. A lawsuit ensued and though I won, what I wanted back more than anything was my name. Well, I've got it back now and the bad guys have been indicted and it's out of my hands (and heart) at last.

But first, may I indulge in dispelling some of the rumors that have been floating around the Metroplex these past few years. Some are so funny, I can't resist.

Funniest was that my ex-partner was my husband. Wrong! I HAVE a wonderful husband and his name is Bob Blair and trust me, I was NEVER married to the man who joined me for a few years that I made a partner.

Another rumor that I heard these past few years was that another man has claimed to taken over The Underground Shopper; plus he, too, was my husband. Lordy be, this isn't Utah, is it?

I'm the founder of The Underground Shopper. Since 1972, I have been publishing the book; written over 70 market-specific books on bargains, a dozen or so national books, been on hundreds of TV shows, locally and nationally, and the same with radio. Competitors or not, none of these guys can match my prowess in the subject of bargains. No one, even imitators who use similar names can compete with our knowledge and our delivery. But it's a free world and once the information is published and repeated in a number of different ways on the web, the information is there for all to see. It is very disheartening to have others capitalize on what was once your domain. But that is how the cookie crumbles, I guess. So, I'll try to be a chip off the old block and dismiss them without giving them a second look.

We find new stores and new services every month to supplement the annual publication of the paperback book. You shouldn't shop without it. Even if you are not computer literate and keep up to date via our website, you can get the FREE magazine at various merchants around town. If not, we will be happy to mail you one with a subscription to our newsletter. The magazine, thought, is always a great pick-me-up.

So is listening every Saturday from 11-1 to my call-in radio show on Legends 770 KAAM. Plus, you know we are famous for giving great prizes to callers. From Zoom teeth whitening procedures that were given FREE (a $700 value) to four lucky listeners during a radio live remote from Dr. Steven Titensor's spa-like dental office in Flower Mound to a FREE digital hearing aid from Hearing Aid Express in Dallas. These are typical grand prizes for listeners. Expect lots of goodies on our Saturday Freebies button. Ergo candles to a 17-pound slab of beef ribs, you are always rewarded for being a good shopping doo bee.

So between a website that gets so many hits a month, that we had to go to the biggest server possible to handle the volume, a radio show, a best-selling paperback book, over a hundred personal appearances to area clubs and organizations, our own Speakers Bureau, our own Closeout Store, a TV show in the works, you can readily see we are very different from any other publication who provides a one dimensional approach to the subject matter. Agreed?

We stand alone. And alone we stand for giving you the biggest bang for your buck.

Now that I've gotten this off my chest, let me now count the blessings that have crossed my path this year. And there were many. I'll try to make sure I thank everybody but before I start, I know I'll forget somebody and will toss and turn all year because of it. So first and foremost, let me thank those that I will forget. Thanks a million.

As you know, I was a single parent for 29 years raising my son alone. Only after Josh got settled into his role as a happily-married young man to his beautiful Russian bride, Irina (pronounced with the E sound), did I have room in my heart to welcome a man into mine.

As usual, how we met was unusual. But to have found my soul mate at this late date in life (at 300 pounds no less) was probably the first of all miracles. We met three months after my beloved father died in 1997 when I first read Bob Blair's name online. Yes, I did meet my future husband on the Internet because he was a free-lance writer looking for a job and I was a publisher looking for a writer. The fact that he was born on my Mother's birthday really caught my eye first. Then, when I saw the year in which he was born, I knew we were the same age. And then, like all single ladies, I looked through the computer to see if he was wearing a wedding band. (Just kidding, but I did look to see if he were married.) After seeing his picture, I was hooked - he was a handsome dude with salt and pepper hair (now all silvery white), the son of a preacher man. I just knew it was the beginning to the rest of my life and he was the one to share it with me.

A year later after thousands of emails and hours of phone calls, he said something on the phone to me that only my DAD ever said. He had never said anything like that before, but after that, I knew my Dad had sent him to me. If anybody out there doesn't believe in serendipity, here it was in all its glory. My daddy was still looking out for me by sending me Bob. Though my heart still belongs to Daddy, it now has room for Bob, too.

And Josh approves.

The next major event that has had a dramatic impact on my life was Gastric Bypass Surgery. It's been almost three years since I've lost over 140 pounds and life has been oh so much better. I still feel I'm on a mission to share this surgery with every morbidly obese person out there. If you are one of them (and need to lose 100 pounds or more), please call me. If I insult you because I tell you you're fat and this surgery will save your life, forgive me. I just want to help. It has helped me "get a life!" The quality of my life has improved so - like now I can walk, shop, and even get a good night's sleep, cheap! (Well, my adjustable latex mattress from City Mattress helps, I must admit.)

Next, in line to thank is KAAM radio, a legend in its own time and to my two Jacks who can't be beat --- Jack Davis and Jack Bishop, two professionals in the business that are superb broadcasters and dear friends. Behind every successful broadcaster is a team of engineers, voices and production specialists. These two make our show what it is today. Fun. Lively. Loving. And I thank them for being an integral part of our sags to rags saga..

Too, you can listen to Bargain Buylines (Monday-Friday) where I give my money-saving shopping tips during drive time mornings and afternoons and on Friday mornings, promptly at 8:45 AM, I announce the "Deal of the Week" every Thursday at 5:15 on the Jack Bishop show. That deal is repeated twice a day for the entire week until the next Thursday when I announce the new Deal of the Week. These are special deals for Diva fans and KAAM listeners. It makes good sense to shop the "underground." It makes even greater sense to buy the Deals of the Week! For more deals, you can also call me on the radio show and be awarded FREE prizes just for your call to 972/445-0770 or 877/272-KAAM. From theater tickets to restaurants, furniture to bedding, it's all there to talk about at the lowest prices in town. Tune in every Saturday from 11-1 on only on Legends 770 on your AM dial. It's the only show that caters to an older, more sophisticated listener who, like me, remembers the good old days where Sinatra and Streisand ruled the airwaves and music was listenable, danceable, huggable and memorable. During the week, around noontime, they even play a patriotic hour of music. I kid you not, it's really moving. Some days I even get goose bumps. Don't we all hope for a better tomorrow? This kind of music is really hopeful.

So sit down and stop rocking the boat and turn to Legends 770 KAAM (that's 770 on the AM dial.)And on the weekends, it's all talk. You can Talk! Shop with the diva (that's me, the "diva of discounts.")

Lastly, I must thank the people who I work with day in and day out. My staff has stood behind me all the way. (Sometimes to even pick me up when I start to fall!) Even with some of their idiosyncrasies (and mine, too), they have always been ready to tackle the next crisis. We've all weathered this year, some good and some not so, but we can't give up - there's too much good stuff yet to buy and for us to find at a discount.

Merchants in the underground save you money from the "getgo" and in doing so, should be a reward all onto themselves. If you're sick and tired of paying high prices for a decent mattress, even the best mattresses that you've see advertised on TV for $3,000, we love referring you to City Mattress who makes them and can save you 50-60-70 percent. No kidding. So, the joy goes around to everyone. The merchant. The shopper. And the liaison between the two…me! Ah, sleep tight, all you tightwads!

G & S Sales is another example that does my heart good. They have many of the exact items that you'd see at Home Depot - at half the price. An AMERICAN STANDARD pedestal sink, for example, was priced elsewhere for $1,100 yet G & S had the same sink in the box, brand new for $199. If you're a Weekend Warrior, where should you head to this weekend? Five acres of half price home improvement supplies makes perfectly good sense in my book.

And it goes on and on. But the reason I know so much about what is happening with these merchants is because they've been voted into the 100 BEST.

That's where you come in. Thanks for an occasional recommendation. That's how we find some of these jewels. Others, we read about elsewhere. But mostly, we are instinctive snoopers and shoppers and we find them ourselves. In fact, I think our noses are super-sensitive and we can even smell them.

There are a few helpers, though, that contribute to our research staff that are consistently thinking "cheap chic." Margaret McCann is one who not only introduced us to Carrabbas, but finds places for us to check out on a regular basis. She is also a devoted fan who can't do enough for us --- from remotes to research, she's been there and done that.

Maureen Popp came to us in a similar fashion. She was a fan who invited me to speak at her woman's club in Colleyville and was hooked thereafter. She is a fabulous shopper who takes being cheap to the lowest level with the highest sense of integrity. She tells it like she sees it but always backs it up with facts. Just the facts, ma'am, only the facts.

Then we have almost an entire family on our side. When they come to work, Garland residential population is reduced considerably. The Kraft family of workers all come from good stock, so there's something to be said about the gene pool. (No, not THAT Gene Pool who's the Farmers Insurance Agent in Garland.)

The Krafts are not THE Krafts from the food company, either. No, they don't sell cheeses. But Ken Kraft is the big cheese when it comes to our database, our website, our funnyman on the radio, our sometime designer and sometime producer. In otherwords, he's kind of a guru of it all. He's also stubborn. But he's the most talented mule I've ever schooled. He's usually up half the night in pain or having a problem with swollen hands or some other medical calamity and the guy just won't quit. Even when he was bitten by a spider, he continued to weave our Saturday Freebies on our web … site, that is.

He was the first to jump on board when the big company went down and has been here ever since. You can thank him for our wonderful website and all of the buttons that I insist on. You can thank him for the database. You can thank Steve Walker and Ken Kraft for getting the paperback book out. (Remember, I'm the writer and shopper - everything else is dumped into their laps.)

And now Ken's sister and niece are full-time gluttons of punishment by driving every day cross town from Garland to come to work. I couldn't turn out the quantity and quality of work is it wasn't for Susan and Heather Kraft, a mother/daughter duo who handle running the office without a glitch. From books to speeches, fliers to freebies, they do it all. I am very lucky to have found this family. Even their father/grandfather has presented us with his hand-carved name plates and his mother shops like she means it at every remote.

They are like my family, too, being behind the scenes everywhere I go and therefore will be there when we move into the big leagues with private executive bathrooms that we can call our own.

Oh, did I also mention they are great little writers, proof readers, PR agents, flyer makers, hair and makeup artists, speech helpers, cooks — just about anything we need done can be handled by this dynamic duo — no, I mean trio.

There's a reason why the Saturday Freebie button gets so many hits? Same with the Deal of the Week. Susan is in charge of them and really gets some whoppers. Hopefully, it has resulted in a loyal and dedicated following. Remember when each caller got a Microwave oven? Or sirloin steaks or a 17-18 pound rack of beef ribs from Dallas Food Depot? What about those frou-frou pillows from Bedroom Solution? Or those Limoges Plates for $59 from Cabbage Patch? These are just a few of the prizes that Susan secures each and every week. Not one, not two, but often five or six prizes to each caller. And then Ken posts them on our website under the Saturday Freebie button. See, you can get something for nothing!

Lee Evans is the designer behind the magazine who's ahead of the times. He does all of our design work, from posters to the paperback book, the magazine to our Botox Parties. We ask plenty and he delivers more. Whether it our new logo or a hand-made scroll that accompanied our donation to the Flower Mound Fiesta Charity Auction, Lee is one of the most talented designers out there. Too, I really like his wife Denise and his bulldog Higgins. He's got a wonderful calming influence over us when we start to feel harried. His temperament is soothing which is unusual for an artist. Need design work for a website or other advertising materials, he is the one to log on to: lee@evansandhamlin.com.

Steve Walker's another anomaly. He's never very far away from any of my book projects. There have been years where he and I did the books all by ourselves. Then there are books that major publishers have published that I didn't have to worry about production. Either way, Steve is not far from the maddening crowd of manuscripts. He may be the publisher of Vince Vance's successful new book called the Rock & Roll Reader, but it's on the Underground Shopper that Steve has built his seniority. How long has it been Steve, 20 years? Though he works full time for a major radio organization, it will be Steve who will be building our radio studio when the time comes. Right now, he's our desktop guru trying out a new publishing program. He loves a challenge. It should prove very workable and important for next year's book as well. When it comes to publishing books, he knows his stuff. I bet in a year or so, he'll be heading up either our publishing arm or our radio department. Betcha. Betcha. We have always loved working together, even during the days when I would sleep over on his couch and watch the fish swimming in the lit-up tanks rather than having to drive all the way home to Flower Mound after a grueling 20 hour clip art session. Remember those days, Steve? Well, now that you have a home in Rowlett and a wife and two kids, I am still staying up all night during deadlines but at least I'm sleeping in my own bed and so are you. But we since we still pull all-nighters closer to deadlines, I guess we haven't really come a long way, baby, after all.

Lue Lue (not her real name) is our bookkeeper. She works full time elsewhere so we bother her at nights and on the weekends. She is the best. She can keep the books but she also has been there for us when we needed it most. In fact, she bent over backwards to provide not only counseling when we needed it but financing when we REALLY needed it. She's a tough cookie with a heart as big as the Grand Canyon. She help us save a fortune as well as the day. She is our money (wo)man who has the good fortune to tell us when we're not making a fortune. But like those other cookies, we haven't crumbled yet! It also helps to have a great CPA, Nick Mayrath. Thanks to Nick, too.

Then, lastly, I've got to thank the glue that makes it all work and the person I'm most grateful to - my husband for being there when I needed him most and who never made me feel like I couldn't achieve whatever I set my mind to as long as we stayed a team. Granted, living and working together presents its own problems and I can attest to each and every one of them. Sometimes we fight like cats and dogs (though we're loving to all of our cats and dogs) over the many control issues that arise daily. Why? Because we are both controlling individuals and want the last say. Thought sometimes we can be reasonable and discuss it, often we can't. We both protest too loudly but are always ready to forgive and forget before we say good night. He has taken the reigns of running the company -- and does a great job, if I'd let him. Please grant me the serenity to let him do it without having to put in my two cents.

Bob can stand back and see the writing on the wall — long before it smacks me in the face. He can spot a con man a mile away. He usually sends them away before I start to build an addition onto my house. I'm the sucker who feels sorry for every lost soul. He is the one who makes sure we have enough money in the bank to delivering the magazines himself to save money. He is my angel in a pair of jeans. He bought a blue truck this year for himself, his very own truck because somewhere I had given his car away to a new employee who didn't have transportation. (See, I would give away the ship if I had a ship, whether it would be a canoe or a yacht!)

He's still afraid I'm going to give away his truck though he's been in hog heaven tooling around town in his blue and silver gray Cowboy-type truck. But the novelty has worn off since it gets lousy mileage. Now he wants to sell it. Anybody want to buy it?

Though he'd rather be out on the golf course than delivering magazines, recording the DIY guy, negotiating the best price with our printers and all the myriad of things he does that I don't always given him credit for doing, I am hoping this year will give him some breathing room to at least play a round of golf on a regular basis. Since he volunteered to work as a Marshall on a golf course to receive the benefit of free golf at country clubs around the country, if he doesn't have a day off to play, why bother? So, here's to him having a day off? Otherwise, he stays teed off. And here's to me to have my nails done or a facial on occasion. I need to remember, too, to practice what I preach and that is to always "live the good life ... at half the price!" I never said I'd pay full price for my facials, did I?

Enjoy your shopping spree and remember, "You don't have to be cheap to love a bargain, just smart!"

Antiques & Auctions

★★★★★ **Accent Antiques**   **972/226-9830**

616 Hwy. 80   Mon-Sat 9-5; Sun 11:30-5:30
Sunnyvale, TX 75182

Don't you just love it when they claim that their success is all due to "word of mouth"? Do they not realize whose mouth it is that starts the ball rolling? In fact, shoppers headed to Sunnyvale are often heard saying, "Je ne fais que regarder," which when translated means, "I'm just looking." But still, there are plenty of shoppers, both Monsieurs and Madames, who say, "Oui, Oui!" After 25 years in the business, these folks may not speak fluent French, but they certainly know their French antiques. Welcome to Accent Antiques, a 14,000 square foot showplace specializing in French and Italian antiques. Save yourself a trip to the Eiffel Tower and discover the French antiques of owner Ron Robinson. Don't expect tourist class prices, though. These are jet-setting, Concorde prices all the way. His jewels reign supreme in his worldly warehouse. However, the ambience is hardly regal. The selection is stellar, from French to country French, **CONTINEN-TAL**, bombe'secretaries and chests, Louis XV and XVI armoires, rush chairs, gilt armchairs and treasures, all pricey but discounted dramatically. Since most of his clientele are dealers, you might as well shop where the dealers shop. Pocket their commission and have a bite next door at the Eastfork Restaurant.

★★★★ **Affordable Antiques**   **214/741-2121**

1201 N. Industrial Blvd.   Mon-Wed & Fri-Sat 10-5; Sun 12-5; Closed Thurs
Dallas, TX 75207

Looking for a complete suite at a sweet price? Then try Affordable Antiques, a 20,000 square foot warehouse where **CHIPPENDALE** meets **DUNCAN PHYFE**. That's not your style? Then, what about Mission? Or a solid pine armoire? Or a walnut chest of drawers? Or a mahogany sideboard? Or an oak washstand? Nothing is left to the imagination. If you are looking for French, English, Americana, Victorian, or, like me, you covet Art Deco, then you're in the right setting, especially if you like one matching roomful. Then, throw in an accent mirror, a piece of stained glass or a table lamp and you've completed your search for some affordable antiques. Dining rooms and bedroom suites are their specialty alongside all the above. Dealers welcome. A free 90-day lay-away if your taste exceeds your budget.

★★★★ Antique Co. Mall   972/548-2929

213 E. Virginia St.   Mon-Sat 10-5:30; Sun 11-5
McKinney, TX 75069

Frankly, my dear, foo dogs make the best house pets. No mess. No fuss. No barking. To buy them, you'd be barking up the right tree shopping at the largest antique mall in McKinney. With 120 dealers and two nearby restaurants (The Pantry serving sandwiches and quiche and The Sweet Tomato with an outdoor deck), this 22,000 square foot emporium provides merchandise and buried treasure galore. Look and see tons of furniture plus glassware, toys, rhinestone tiaras, roll-top desks, pottery to pipes, autographed memorabilia to antique coins, jewelry and old-time photographs. For the country touch, add a weathervane, a rusty porch chair, a washed fence post, various cows, screen doors, faded quilts, granny's lace, old crockery and cast iron skillets. Hang out at their smaller Lewisville location at 201 S. Mill Street in Lewisville, 972/219-1335.

★★★★★ Antique Sampler Mall & Tearoom   817/461-3030

1715 E. Lamar   Mon-Sat 10-7; Sun Noon-6
Arlington, TX 76006

Arlington is home to the Rangers, Six Flags and the Antique Sampler Mall & Tearoom. Want proof in the pudding? Well, take a seat at my gorgeous solid black cherry dining room suite, six chairs, china cabinet and bar. Snagging this dining room ensemble at a terrific price, I was full of it before I even made the deal. That's right, I first enjoyed a marvelous tearoom lunch complete with their famous mango tea. Forget that it's a bargain-hunter's full course meal all unto itself. Forget the hundreds of vendors that offer a myriad of antiques and not-so-antique collections with contemporary service. It's also a great way to spend the day. The tea room is open Mon-Fri 11-3; Sat 11-4 and Sun 12-3. Before you leave, be sure to stop by one of their newest offerings—a collection of original watercolor paintings matted and framed or just matted at low prices. A group of Arlington area artists got together and pooled their artistic resources to open a space at this mall. You may even be privy to one of the artists painting in real time right in front of your eyes!

★★★★★ AntiqueLand   972/509-7878

1300 Custer Rd. @ 15th   Mon-Wed 10-6; Thurs-Sat 10-8; Sun 11-6
Plano, TX 75075
www.antiquelandusa.com

AntiqueLand is a Plano landmark with over 85,000 square feet of opulent shopping. Shop the almost 400 vendors, and be sure to grab a bite at their Palm Court Restaurant. But though they recently declared Chapter 11, JoAnn informed me that reorganization had nothing to do with the Metroplex locations as they were all doing fine. It's those out of state Antiqueland's that were needing some breathing room. But the Denton Mall surely is not flourishing as it should. This is one of our favorite antique malls. Their restaurant can accommodate tea for two or a party of 100. The pies are worth spooning over. When have you ever seen meringue a mile high? Gourmet dining doesn't stop at lunchtime. Three days a week they are open for dinner when the mall stays open, too, for your dessert....though it doesn't cost a dime! No wonder it's such a popular site for bridal and baby showers, birthday parties and other special gatherings where your guests can dine. Lunch is daily from 11-2:30 and dinner is Thurs-Sat 5-8. Brunch is a special menu, so who says "Never on Sundays!" About half of the mall is split with 80 percent antiques and 20 percent reproductions. The other half houses antiques and designer furnishings representing American, French, English and Primitive furniture and collectibles. There are also design-related spaces, a TV lounge for couch potatoes and a meeting/classroom for seminars. Go ahead, take a class or ask an expert. They have both. And don't miss their special events: from antique appraisal fairs to an Elvis festival, you can return to the days of splendor, with the looks of today at prices of days gone by. Their newest location is at the Denton Factory Stores. Don't miss their showcase gallery and interior design studios. From estate jewelry to an Oriental rug gallery, a gardenland of fountains to furniture to fill any niche or corner, this land is yours at AntiqueLand. Manager Jean Allread and her band of bargain sleuths will lead you by the hand while you strike up the band. Ah....music to my ears.

★★★★★ Antiques & Moore   817/543-1060; 817/548-5931

3708 W. Pioneer Pkwy.   Mon-Sat 10-6; Sun Noon-6
Arlington, TX 76013
www.antiquesandmoore.com

Sometimes more is not better. In this case, this **MOORE** is. One of the originators of the antique mall craze, expect Sue Moore to be leading the pack (rats) with the myriad of merchants who are part of Antiques & Moore. Since 1993, her ability to hand-pick a unique blend of over 175 individual dealers and put together a showcase gallery of collectibles all within a 50,000-square-foot emporium is testimony to her antique acumen. One particular favorite is the western boutique featuring Double D Ranch wear for the lady desiring a contemporary southwest wardrobe, including **DIAN MALOUF** jewelry. Other favorites include glass, china, crystal, Dresden dolls, birdhouses by Sharon Holmquist, lamps made from teapots. Stop by the Tea Room, open 7 days a week, Mon-Sat 11:30-4; Sun 12-4. From Fort Worth, take I-30 West, exit East Chase Parkway. Go south three miles to Pioneer Parkway, then east 1 mile. They're at the southeast corner of Park Springs and Pioneer Parkway. (Reverse these directions coming from Dallas. Take I-30 East.) They're at the southeast corner of Park Springs and Pioneer Parkway. Interested in getting an appraisal? Call Dr. Adelia Hale-Stanley, Ph.D., 817/265-8990. Sue Moore's husband, Otis Moore, is the one to call if you want Antiques & Moore to consider buying your entire estate. Call Otis at 817/543-1060. Lori Airheart is the specialist in charge of the sale and repair of estate and contemporary jewelry. And for reservations for parties of 10 or more for The Tea Room, or to arrange a more extravagant affair, room availability, menus or catering services, call The Tea Room at 817/795-3093. Bon Appetit!

★★★★ Antiques & More   972/323-1092; 972/418-9092

1015 S. Broadway
Carrollton, TX 75006

If you're an old and new jewelry fan, you've met your match at Antiques & More. Both old beauties from years' past and new replicas that would pass the part are waiting in one of many cases for a new home in your jewelry box. Then mix in a pot pourri of antique collectibles and bric brac and you've got the picture. There's always a discount on an entire category of something plus their usual sale merchandise to count on for savings. A gorgeous pair of blue and green glass earrings with a matching pin that I intend to wear as a necklace was a knockout and I succumbed to its charms at a mere $19; then I got a coordinating snake-wrapped glass bracelet for $20 to make an ensemble worth noting. Too, I couldn't resist an exquisite faux gold with black jet ring for $12, a lavender/green wrought iron hat stand that holds one of my wigs and a wrought-iron with glass beads easel to hold a treasured picture for $8. Two doors down from Mary Lou's in historic downtown Carrollton and across from the Skin Spa, what a way to spend a day. You'll see plenty of other knick-knacks as well as one of the largest collections of Victorian christening gowns I've ever seen. A certified appraiser is on location, to uncover the treasures. Owner Beverly Morris is an accredited member of the ISA (International Society of Appraisers) and can provide a written appraisal of most anything you have of value that you need for insurance purposes, obtain a value price in a divorce proceeding, probate, charitable contribution or to attain a replacement value for something that was lost or damaged in transit, a fire or other natural disaster. Beverly charges by the hour and not by a percentage of the value. Beverly also will provide a written appraisal for one-two items as well as a whole household full, if requested.

★★★   Antiques & Uniques   817/485-9632

8053 D Grapevine Highway   Mon-Sat 10-6; Sun 1-5
North Richland Hills, TX 76180-7100

If thumbing through old magazines is what Life is all about, you'll find a life's worth of Life Magazines in pretty good shape here. For a unique birthday present, find one with the recipient's birth date and you've got yourself a memory for a lifetime. However, finding one over 50 years old was like finding a needle in a haystack....near to impossible. For those who might be coming up on a 25-30-40-45 year old milestone, you may be able to snag one for $5-$6. Also, there's an "Earth to Art" pottery studio inside with a selection of $20 and under gifts which is hard to beat, especially since the artist used to sell her pots through a high-end Southlake gallery and had to charge twice as much. Though this antique mall may be small in size, it still packs a wallop on certain specialty items like colored glass and COCA-COLA ® memorabilia.

★★   Antiques Etc. Mall   972/436-5904

201 S. Mill St., Suite 180   Mon-Sat 10:30-5:30; Sun 1-5
Lewisville, TX 75057

Stroll down memory lane and remember when these items were selling as new. Don't you just hate the fact that you remember them when? That in itself will jolt you back to reality. But what's nice is that, at today's prices, you can NOW afford them. One step above a garage sale on some booths while others were priced as legitimate antiques, it's really a mixed bag, but a fun place to walk the aisles. If you're looking for an heirloom from the Kimball Museum, forget it here. If you're looking for some old furniture that will suit your purposes, and you prefer not to pay an arm and a leg, this is a good mall to start your journey. There are lots of tables and chairs, all with fully functional arms and legs. Much of it is priced as typical used furniture, while much else is priced higher. Though housed in the Historic Old Town of Lewisville, most of their goods are not historically-challenged—old, but still in good shape. Around for almost 20 years, this mall features a wide variety for the wide-eyed optimist. A real chip off the old block off Main Street.

★★   Artifacts Antique Gallery   972/723-1411

210 W. Avenue F   Thurs-Sat 10-6
Midlothian, TX 76065

Good day ole chap, tallyho and all of that. You old blokes will find knick-knacks and patty whacks and maybe even a paddy wagon with prices at such a steal. Furniture abounds with most pieces uncovered from the 1940s and 1950s from merry ole England. But don't despair. American classic antiques from Duncan Phyfe can be uncovered and you won't have to dig too far. Artifacts define history, so let a few of these define your home. Now they don't close for afternoon tea, but they do close Sunday through Wednesday, so if you need to stop by then, be sure to have an appointment.

★★★   Bargain House   972/288-9151

1839 N. Galloway   Mon-Fri 10-5; Sat 11-5
Mesquite, TX 75149

Marie McBride is a legend in her own time. For more than 20 years, collecting and selling someone else's castoffs has made her the maven of Mesquite. Her 7,000 square foot shop is brimming with antique and flea market booths. If you're in the mood for love (seats) and other furniture finds, you should have no trouble furnishing your entire house with bargains from here. Consider outfitting the following rooms: dining room, living room, master bedroom, kids'rooms, guest room, dinette, entryway, library...they've got it all. Then check out all the little chatshkas (those are knick-knacks in Yiddish). They also are blooming with flowers, both silk and dry, to bring the outdoors in with little or no maintenance. The other part of McBride's is where you'll find lots of housewares to spruce up your home. China, glassware, vases, figurines—and it figures that birds of a feather stick together singing, "Cheep, Cheep!"

★★★★   Berry's Antiques & Collectibles, Etc.   903/509-3527

5615-H Troup Hwy.   Tues-Sat 10-5:30
Tyler, TX 75707
www.berrysantiques.com

It's the Berry's. Cherry-picked by owners Johnny and Carolyn Berry, here is where to buy or sell antiques, from total estates to individual pieces of furniture, stained glass, pottery, art, china, stamps, coins, even old books and other fine collectibles. If you want something old to be appraised, take it in before you are showcased on the Antiques Roadshow. After all, what if it's worth only a few bucks? How embarrassing on national TV. If you're interested in **ANCHOR HOCKING**, **FENTON** or **FOSTORIA** glass, here's where to buy it or sell it. As an incentive, they offer three-month layaways where you can make payments monthly and then when it's paid off, it's yours. You can even order online, but that's easier said than done as there are only pictures of their total inventory and not individual items. You can get an idea, though, of their wall-to-wall pieces. To get a better look, go in person. They are located across from the Train Manufacturing Plant on Hwy. 110 south towards the Whitehouse. (No, not THAT Whitehouse!) *Call toll-free: 888/249-1425*

★★★   Betty's Antiques & Cotton St. Mall   903/753-8204

414 E. Cotton   Mon-Sat 10-5
Longview, TX 75601-7523

I wish I was in the land of Cotton....where antiques and such should not be forgotten. Thanks to Betty, they are not. With over 10,000 square feet of space, you can browse 'til the cows come home. English and American antiques, pottery, glassware—you know, the full regalia of antiques and collectibles. The Cotton Patch is nearby if you get hungry or your feet give out, whichever comes first. Expect legitimate antiques but pretty contemporary prices.

★★★★★★   Cabbage Patch Antiques   972/272-8928

901 S. Jupiter Rd.   Tues-Thurs 10-5; Fri & Sat 10-6; Sun 12-5 (no Sun during July & August)
Garland, TX 75042

 If you didn't fall off a cabbage truck, you'll marvel at the mirth of merchandise here. But never on Monday. Leave your troubles at the doorstep and smile when you enter this patch of good cheer. Some authentic antiques (over 100 years old) and some reproductions are in mixed company, but would still feel comfortable in anybody's home. Blooming beautiful floral arrangements, candles, stained glass, potpourri and home decor items complete this idyllic scene. Join their buying club for $30 and receive discounts on all purchases. Layaway and interest-free financing add additional incentives for buying here. They're on Jupiter near the Forest Lane intersection, between Forest and Miller Roads. Note they are closed to the public on Monday which is when they are open for designers and wholesalers only. For an appt. on Monday, call 214/536-4961. The English accent and English accents are only the beginning touches inside the veritable and varied cabbage patch. As you wander through room after room, vignette after vignette, you will lose yourself in the myriad of objects laid out waiting to be unearthed to your patch. On the day of our visit, prices were negotiable if we were club members and would pay by cash or check. We're still thinking about that 18th century claw and ball dining room table and four Victorian high back chairs if it weren't for the scratch. Then again, they'd fix it and take off even more from their low, low prices. I'd say, "this patch is a match made in heaven!" Natch? There's even a full-time handyman on site to help create custom vanities for those drop-in sinks, or to fix a drawer, or help carry purchases to your car. Whatever's needed, this store provides incredible service. That's why we call Josephine, the Queen Mum and the rest of us, the **PRINCE** and Princesses of Sales!

★★★★★★ China Heirlooms   972/365-3608

4800 Lakawana   By Appt. Only
Dallas, TX 75247-6712
www.operationchinaschild.com

 Take 35 to Inwood, then go west on Inwood to Irving Blvd. Turn right on Irving Blvd. and then left on Lakawana if you want to save a fortune, cookie, on authenticated Chinese antiques. One-of-a-kind, hand-carved bombe'chests, tables, armoires, baby beds, chaises, chairs....complete with papers at prices at least 40 percent off comparable goods elsewhere. Actually, in a Design District showroom, you're probably saving a whole lot more. But what's so special about this warehouse is where the profits go - all benefit the Chinese orphans that are discarded by parents who honor the one-child rule. So, if they give birth to girl babies, those babies soon wind up at an orphanage. Furthermore, if the child is flawed in some way, due to malnutrition or a birth defect, they are surely not prime for adoption. David Carl and his wife had other ideas. Just see their three daughters and know how blessed they are. Also, on their website, you can link to overseas travel and save up to 60 percent. Refundable tickets are available - if once you get over there you discover the paperwork is not in order and your plans are delayed, your ticket is refunded. These special Adoption Fares make the process a whole lot easier, and cheaper, too.

★★★ Christie's Collectibles Antique Mall   903/234-0816

111 W. Tyler   Mon-Sat 10-5
Longview, TX 75601-6318
www.christiescollectibles.com/

It may be a long view to see the intricate details of the **FENTON** glassware, so you're better off getting up close and personal. Since 1994, Christie's has been a Fenton Showcase dealer. But if you'd rather stay home and shop, they've been blowin'and goin'online for the past three years. Note the Fenton Stars & Stripes collection, Annalee-Annalee Mobilitee Dolls, Fenton Family Signature Series, Fenton Historic Collection, Fenton Connoisseur Collection, Fenton Limited Editions, Fenton General Catalog, Fenton Older Pieces - and that's just for Fenton collectors. They also carry other antiques and collectibles should you choose to venture out beyond Fenton. Additional collectibles highlighted included: It's a Keeper, Cookie Stamps, Button Babies, Heritage Lace, Cottage Collectibles and many others from days of yesteryear, as they say. Fell in love with the Elvis piano for $150 but instead, stuck with the $3-$20 Coke memorabilia items....perfect for my print tray collection.

★★   Clements Antiques of Texas   972/564-1520

206 E. Hwy. 80, Bldg. A   Mon-Fri 9-5; Sat 10-5; Sun 1-5
Forney, TX 75126

I know, how can you not rate this old-timer just out of respect higher than a two star? Well, simple. Older doesn't necessarily mean better. And though you may be a die-hard fan of antique shopping and Clements, you know his prices hit below the belt. Clements is one of the originals on "the strip"—the formidable founding father of antique shopping in the Metroplex. Just 25 miles east of downtown Dallas, you can't miss them: they're the first shop on the left, with statuary welcoming you in. There are more than 60,000 square feet of antiquity, some in need of repair, others in perfect shape, some museum-quality, others just treasures in your own mind. Auctions and estate sales are legendary and usually the prices open within reason. They're very cordial to novices and well-stocked for the demanding antique shopper. You can trust a legend, but expect their reputation to command prices worthy of the upper crust. European, English and French antiques predominate, with some crystal, bronze and statuary, but all worth the trip to Forney, for there is strength in numbers.

★★★★★   Cobwebs Antiques Mall   972/423-8697

1400 Ave. J   Mon-Sat 10-6; Sun 1-5
Plano, TX 75074
www.cobwebsantiques.com

Weaving a web of possibilities, this 15-year-old mall can entangle you even if you aren't looking for anything in particular. Located in historic downtown Plano, just east of Central Expressway (US 75), there's something for everyone, from estate jewelry to vintage clothing. One of the oldest antique malls in the Metroplex, many of the dealers are celebrating a decade or more in business without cobwebs in Cobwebs. And just when you think you've exhausted the inventory, The French Hen tea room appears. Now open 11-3, Monday-Saturday, it came just in the nick of time. Shoppers appreciate a time-out, too. Take a step back in time in historic old Plano, right off 15th Street, and remember the good ol'days when shopping was affordable and an antique mall was walkable (without having to participate in a marathon). With over 35 dealers, the mall offers a unique selection of **AMERICAN** oak, cherry and walnut furniture, country primitives and accessories, clocks and clock repairs, fine china and porcelain, holiday collectibles, antique quilts and linens, antique and vintage jewelry, toys and dolls, old books, glassware, antique tools, ephemera and scrap advertising and political memorabilia, all alongside lots of other collectibles. But back up to ephemera and scrap advertising - what on earth is it? Anybody out there have a clue? It sounds like either a diet pill ingredient or an advertising agency for a metal yard. But don't miss a Miss Prissy Party Place, the home of The Chocolate Teacup. (www.thechocolateteacup.com) for dress up parties and accessories for girls ages 4 and up. Mini make-up sessions, tea sandwiches, cake and beverage served on china complete with linens and silver, story telling, photos and party favors for that perfect little Miss Muffet's birthday. Call 469/693-3413 for more information.

★★★★★★   De Marco Collection   214/366-0000

2606 Manana Drive   PS
Dallas, TX 75220-1302
www.demarcocollection.com

 This "strictly to the trade" operation has opened its wholesale warehouse to the public and has slashed prices to the Tuesday Morning standard—50-80 percent off. And off we ran to the DeMarco Collection, a fine line of recreated antique furniture and accessories. Looking for a lookalike? Then here's the place that replicates European antiques. The only difference is that you're not paying for antiquities or the first class passage on the QE 2. These artisans use the tools and techniques that were employed by their predecessors decades, even centuries past. Often, too, they've utilized old materials that they've reclaimed from demolitions or wherever. But who's looking for all the t's to be crossed as long as the effort results in a stunning reproduction? Their warehouse showcased hand-crafted and one-of-a-kind items, everything from pottery and bronzes to accents for our garden's path. Furniture and accessories that look the part without the museum price tags are our cup of tea. Ta Ta. Let's hope they stay open to the public. I am certainly wishing them well.

★★★★   Dusty Attic, The   972/613-5093

3330 N. Galloway, #225   Mon-Sat 10-6; Thurs 10-8; Sun 1-6
Mesquite, TX 75150
www.antiquelandusa.com/dustyattic/

Going up to the attic doesn't mean having to bring the Kleenex®. You won't sneeze when visiting here because there's not an ounce of dust in spite of their name. Just down the street from Town East Mall, this attic is the combined efforts of almost 500 vendors jam-packed into this 30,000-square-foot plethora of possibilities. From crafts and SOUTHWEST items in one half to antiques in the other, you'll see it all—but never together. On the crafts side, you'll see clothes, ceramics, yard art, birdhouses and such; on the antiques side, you'll see everything from FENTON glass and art deco furniture to Victorian hats, primitive accents to PRECIOUS MOMENTS. Nice synergism. Nice shopping at this dusty attic.

★★★★   Englishman's Antiques & Interiors   972/386-5996

14655 Midway Rd.   Mon-Sat 10-5:30; Sun 11-6
Dallas, TX 75001
www.englishmans.com

At the northwest corner of Midway and Proton, Englishman's Interiors has raised the bar several notches. What a showplace. Opened in June, 1999, it's just north of the Crown Plaza Hotel Suites, and is 30,000 square feet of English tea and crumpets. It's one of the most breathtaking showrooms in the city, sure to make a trip to London a close second to shopping at a British marketplace for antiques. Their forte is antique reproductions. As seen on the Ainsley Harriott Show, no one could identify the real Staffordshire Foo Dogs from the repro dogs. You'll find yourself wandering the ever changing inventory being brought in from England and Europe almost daily. There are at least two 45-foot containers being unloaded monthly, and they're always on the lookout for deals throughout the U.S. Some of the more outstanding objects noted were: grandfather clocks, antique partner's desks, Crown Derby porcelains, ROYAL DOULTON and a huge selection of antique FLOW BLUE. Bob was particularly enamored of the bronzes and the walking stick. Shoppers looking for perfect shower or wedding gifts should rally around the pine blanket boxes, the pine chests and the period mahogany chests for starters. Lastly, don't miss the MAJOLICA, a favorite, the hundreds of gilt mirrors, the stained glass, the wall sconces, the militaria and more just waiting for a new home. As for reproductions, there's none better than those created by the manufacturers that Englishman's has commissioned to make reproductions for shoppers looking for a real bargain. These repros look the part, but are often better made and a lot cheaper. They can custom make almost anything and they ship worldwide. Don't forget, too, that they make reproductions of Staffordshire pottery. Though they sell the real stuff, very few of us can afford it. Staffordshire copies are a different story. To read all about how they do it, head to their website, but you must swear not to ever resell them as the real McCoys. Promise?

★★   Finishing Touch Antique Mall   972/446-3038

1109 Broadway   Mon-Fri 10-5; Sat 10-5:30; Sun 1-5
Carrollton, TX 75006

When considering those finishing touches for transforming a house into a home, a visit here may be in order. Whether it's an antique or a collectible, join in the quest for the best by topping off a luncheon treat in any of the several tea-rooms in historic downtown Carrollton, and skipping dessert. Instead, shop. It's better for your waistline and there are no calories, remember? No crafts at this mall—this is strictly a 30-vendor collection of antiques, primitives, kitchen gadgets from days gone by, clocks, glassware, jewelry and dolls (oh, you beautiful dolls). As a doll collector, I personally put them everywhere so I always have company. Since I didn't collect them as a child, I'm making up for lost time. I've got them on window sills, up the stair cases, on the beds, in the chairs and on a myriad of shelves. I'll never grow up!

★★★★   Forestwood Antique Mall   972/661-0001

5333 Forest Lane   Mon-Sat 10-7; Sun Noon-6
Dallas, TX 75244
www.justtherightthing.com

This Austin, Texas-based company took off in 1998, acquiring antique malls all over the country. Today, they own 20 malls doing $40 million in sales and already are the largest antique mall owner in the U.S. Forestwood is one of them, which means you have access to buying and selling online as well. There are around 200-300 dealers. Half is serious antiques, expensive French armoires, English antiques, china, pottery and collector books, for example; the other side is less pricey with French beds, armoires, bookcases, costume and Victorian jewelry and more. Dine in the Garden Tea Room, Mon-Sat from 11-3 and "Salud!" Shoppers will find an extensive selection of furniture ranging from 18th and 19th century American, English and French to an unusual collection of primitives, art deco, and 50's pieces. Other specialties include depression and cut glass, Majolica, crystal, sterling and silver plate, china, chandeliers and other lighting, clocks, Roseville, art pottery, Oriental rugs, books, paintings, estate jewelry, vintage costume jewelry, linens, toys, architectural relics, textiles, whew! Too, they have some unusual specialists on board such as a clock and rug repair expert and, occasionally, they will have someone on site to repair porcelain. Custom framing is also available. Jayroes Antiques specializes in French furniture, designer accessories and bed conversions. The Village Goldsmith specializes in estate jewelry as well as custom design and repair of jewelry.

Found Antiques   214/741-5533

1225 N. Industrial @ Leslie   Mon-Sat 10-5; Sun 1-5
Dallas, TX 75207-4001
www.foundantiques.com

 I found it! I found it! Inside you will find it, too. Many antique dealers have found their way to collaborate by pooling their talents and opening all under one roof. A specialty antique mall, where dealers with their own following and own area of expertise have a symbiotic relationship with the Mother Found-ry. And is it a find. One, for example, is J.P. Wolfe (info@jpwolfeantiques.com.) Expect to see upscale groupings catering to the trade but open to the public as well. Found Antiques is also the sister store to Debris Antiques, both brainchild's of Joey Edwards of Dallas. Cafe Danielle, though, has moved to 1080 Dragon Street inside Connie Williamson Antiques. And you'll definitely want to imbibe there since the resurrection of the two-martini lunch (though not of the kind you would imbibe, these are entrees and desserts inside martini glasses. A nice twist to something that brings after- lunch ruminations back at the water cooler.)

You'll have plenty of room now to enjoy the shopping without feeling stuffed. But expect the antiques to be pretty pricey so there may have to be a limit to your indulgence.

★ Gold Leaf Antique Mall   903/665-2882

207 North Polk St.   Mon-Fri 10-5; Sat 10-6
Jefferson, TX 75657

Every once in a while, you get a gem of a recommendation. This one, however, was too far away to check out in person this late in the game. So, it's up to you, Sweetpea, to check it out yourself. If nothing else, its name should enlighten you somewhat. There are six dealers under the Gold Leaf banner owned by Hazel and Bill Williams. (I wonder if his parents named him William William at birth?) Anyway, while you're scouring the wonders of the city of Jeffferson and all the B 'n B's and antique shops, here's one that has been recommended for antiques, collectibles, furniture, books, coins, Vaseline Glass and jewel tea dinnerware. They buy entire estates and sell them off one piece at a time. Vaseline Glass? It's a particular shade of yellow-green (hence the name "Vaseline Glass"), and the only certifiable way of determining whether it's actually Vaseline Glass is by shining a blacklight on it—the real thing will turn a bright fluorescent green, thanks to its chemical makeup. This place should be a soothing balm to collectors.

★★★★ Grandmother's Treasures, Inc.   972/488-2313

2740 Valwood Pkwy., Suite 147   Mon-Sat 10-6; Sun 1-5
Farmers Branch, TX 75234

To Grandmother's house we went. And boy, were we surprised what big bargains were laying in wait. About 40 vendors are housed in this strip center mall that's just chock-full of stuff. Lots of stuff. Not all antiques, but bric-a-brac, collectibles, glassware, dishes, chairs, rocking chairs, lamps, sports memorabilia and so much more, I'm getting a cramp in my fingers just thinking about it. Grandmother's Treasures, Inc., is owned by Catherine Abercrombie, maybe a grand-mother, maybe not. Maybe even part of the Abercrombie and Fitch empire. Who knows? But what I do know is that this place is a treasure trove for bargain shoppers. Like one big garage sale, with everything priced accordingly.

★★★★★★ Harris Antiques & Classic Design   817/246-8400

7600 Scott St.   Mon-Sat 8:30-5:30
Fort Worth, TX 76108

 Fort **WORTH** and antiques are synonymous with the Harris family. Separated by real and unreal (antiques and reproductions), this wholesaler offers the real McCoy and the look-alikes, too. Since retail stores buy from them, what's good for the goose is good for the gander, right? The selection is staggering: hundreds of chairs, armoires, tables, headboards, hand-carved desks, china cabinets, leaded-glass lamps and even **CHIPPENDALE** items within their 445,000-square-foot showroom and warehouse. Miles and miles to go before you sleep, so you'd better get going.

★★★ Jayroe's Premier Antiques   972/960-8516

5333 Forest Lane   Mon-Sat 10-7; Sun Noon-6
Dallas, TX 75244

Located at Forestwood Antique Mall, between Inwood and the Tollway, Jay Jayroe's the name, have odd-size bed, will travel. He's not just an antique dealer, but he offers the service of convert-ing that odd-size antique bed into a double, queen or sometimes a king. If you buy the bed from him, the conversion costs $100, or $150 if you bring in another bed. The conversion, by the way, won't detract from the value of the antique or do any damage to the bed. Plus, it's completely reversible. Just think—what if you were a basketball player and seven feet tall? That's not reversible. But it's nice to have a bed fit the frame, right? There's more—like restored French-imported antiques (armoires in particular), mirrors, clocks and tables, too.

★★★★★ Linda's Treasures & Affordable Antiques 214/824-7915

1929 Greenville
Dallas, TX 75206
www.lindastreasures.com

Mon-Sat 11-7; Sun 1-6

This Perdue's not into chickens. Instead, Linda Perdue sells used furniture "cheep, cheep!" Named as the best used furniture store for years by *The Dallas Observer*, Linda's shop won't disappoint you. The possibilities are endless. Head up to lower Greenville for English or Art Deco armoires, vanities, chests, tables, buffets, dining room tables, chairs and beds. Into collectibles? Pick up a unique gift, a piece of collectible pottery, china, or jewelry, both old and new. Then bump into original artwork, paintings, pottery and carousel horses, then hop aboard an assortment of anything and everything for the bar. Drink up! This year I noticed an even greater variety of home furnishings and decorator accessories. Too, vintage clothing is now a popular feature. But their stand alone treasure is still the Art Deco English Furniture, especially the armoires that can be converted to entertainment centers, computer workstations, bars or storage cabinets.

★★★★★ Little Red's Antiques 972/564-2200

10274 W. Hwy. 80
PO Box 128 Forney, TX 75126

Mon-Tues, Thurs-Sat 9-5; Sun 1-5; Closed Wed

What do you get when you open the doors to 40,000 square feet of European antiques and reproductions? Little Red's, that's what. Richard Whaley is behind Little Red's (dad was the original **RED**) and has located his treasure-trove in the groves of Forney's Antique Row. Whatever your pleasure, whether antique or a reproduction, they've got it. Even if you don't have a cast-iron stomach for wandering down the many miles of aisles, if you're looking for cast-iron, it's one of their specialties. Looking for something to flank your entryway? This is where I bought my two stately Great Dane guard dogs....ceramic, of course. From majestic armoires to MAJORCA pottery, patio sets to old-fashioned street signs, urns to yard ornaments, sideboards to pianos, it's their outdoor lamps for $250 (wired and ready to glow) that light my fire. One of the highlights in the Forney strip—if you can tolerate no air-conditioning. Whew! It's hot in there.

★★★★ Lone Star Antiques 817/503-0441

6601 NE Loop 820
North Richland Hills, TX 76180-6040

Mon-Fri 10-6; Sat 10-8; Sun 1-6

In the old Sears Homelife store, this antique mall is soaring with a department store-like selection of antiques and stuff that wouldn't qualify except that it's old. Each dealer, when available, was open to negotiation, so if you've got the chutzpah, give it a try. Practice at home, "Will you take less for this?" and hold your expression taut. Don't move a muscle as they'll think you're going to rescind your original offer. This will begin the process of haggling. It worked for us when we found a pair of mahogany round end tables that were marked $300. We got them down to $125 and then the dealer threw in another 10 percent off without us even asking. We decided to forge ahead and continue on our winning streak. When we saw a beautiful credenza in excellent condition for $250, we decided that was a fair enough price and left it at that. See, it all comes out in the wash. Watch for mall-size sales periodically where everything in the whole place goes for less.

Enjoy the fare at their Tea Room—a particularly delicious chicken salad was had by a trio of hungry ladies. But on Friday is when they serve their famous tortilla soup. And it is outstanding. Slurp, slurp. But only on Fridays.

★★★★   Love Field Antique Mall   214/357-6500

6500 Cedar Springs @ Mockingbird   Mon-Sat 10-7; Sun 12-7
Dallas, TX 75235
www.lovefieldantiquemall.com

Since 1989, Love Field Antique Mall has been home to over 250 antique shops, a showcase gallery, lots of unique gifts, and seventy cars ready for a new "Minnie driver". If you can find Love Field, you can find this 65,000-square-foot mall. If you're looking to store your antique car, they have climate-controlled spaces with security (ADT) to protect your classic. And for your next meeting, luncheon, shower or get-together, why not indulge your guests with a home-cooked feast in their private dining room? Groups up to 20 can be accommodated. If you're just shopping and working up an appetite, Cafe Avion (214/351-9989) will sate your hunger pains. Open Mon-Sat 11-2:30.

★★★★★★   Maude & Murel's   972/658-4536

610 W. State Street.   Mon-Thurs 10:30-5:30; Fri-Sat 10:30-6:30
Garland, TX 75040

 Janet and Chris are the epitome of the survival of the fittest when the subject of "Mom and Pop" antique businesses are concerned. Moving "down" from a small shop of resale clothes to an even smaller shoppe with antiques does make for interesting fodder around the lunch table next door at Patricia's. The duo destination locations—Maude & Murel's and Patricia's, well what a delicious past and repast. Now, back to the antiques. Wait 'til you hear who Janet is related to? Would you believe Robert E. Lee? (Yes, THAT Robert E. Lee! One visit to quiet little Garland's downtown historic district will bring you to your knees of history. Her past also includes showing registered Appaloosa horses in the circus, riding in full American Indian costume in the 4th of July Milwaukee Parade with the entire entourage of Barnum and Bailey circus (even though she was the only blue-eyed Indian in the show) and other memorable activities sure to be told to you while you're shopping. She and her husband Chris met over 30 years ago fighting over who was going to ultimately buy the antique that they both wanted. (I wonder who won?) Her family history is based around her great grand father xs2 General Robert E. Lee. Combining their love of history and family heritage has instilled in both a true love of our nations art forms in glass, furniture and collectibles. The shoppe is named after their grandmothers: Maude is Robert E. Lee's great granddaughter and Murel is Janet's Gram as well as her friend who is family to Mary Todd Lincoln. Her Dad's family are the Lees who stayed in the North during the Civil War and married into the family who owned the Blair House in Washington and established the Congressional Library. Wow! If you don't fall in love with her antiques, you'll fall in love with her history. Imagine the stories she can tell. Ten years ago, she started an upscale clothing resale shoppe in an antique store at the Old Garland Antique Mall. That was short lived because after she went to her first estate sale and bought her first piece of vintage jewelry, she was hooked. Forget the clothes, she wanted to buy and sell antiques and collectibles. The rest is history. Both Chris and Janet love to shop for quality furniture and Chris does all the touch-ups if needed. Join the fun in Garland's Downtown "walk around" district. As their new shop is a 650-square-foot space, they jokingly refer to as a curio cabinet. Since Janet has arthritis, she can sit in her favorite chair and talk to all her customers at one time considering the size of her store. Talk about getting to know your customers all in one fell swoop. Have a seat and rock the day away. What they lack in space, they make up for in authentic antiques and collectibles. Their motto is, "You

CAN afford the real thing!" They know their business, research it to the hilt and are rarely fooled by a reproduction. About 30 percent of their customers are other dealers who buy from them and then resell it. Now, I've worked up a sufficient appetite just talking about them, I think I'll go next store to Patricia's for some pie and pickles.

★★★★★ Montgomery Street Antique Mall   817/735-9685

2601 Montgomery at I-30
Fort Worth, TX 76107
www.300-antiques-4sale.com

Mon-Sat 10-6; Sun Noon-6

You might feel Bewitched if you try to visit the website of Montgomery Street Antique Mall. The site was not operative when we recently checked and no new info was available. So wiggle your nose, put the key in the ignition and get out those jogging shoes because the only way you might be doing any buying is to stop in and see for yourself. Here's where you'll find over 240 dealers, all wheelin'and dealin'under one roof. No doubt the biggest antique mall you're going to find in Fort Worth, it's well worth the trip. Besides all the antique deals and steals on everything from furniture to glass and pottery, advertising to books, porcelains, housewares, toys, sporting goods, metals and jewelry, you'll also find an area filled with reproductions. Even **BEANIE BABIES** and **DEPARTMENT 56** (What is Department 56 you may ask? Well, Deptartment 56 is houses and villages with people, bridges, etc. For more information, go to www.villageminiatures.com/index.php/d56.html and see what's popping up in this special section). Amenities at the mall include strollers and wheelchairs so everybody can navigate with ease. Be sure to savor a few moments and gloat over your purchases with a stopover at The Secret Garden Tea Room. And since the early bird catches the worm, you'd better get there before the 4 PM closing.

★★★ Nicole's Antiques and Tobacco Shop   214/821-3740

3611-A Lower Greenville Ave.
Dallas, TX 75206

Mon-Thurs 10-7; Fri-Sat 11-8; Sun Noon-6

You won't need coal to get this fire going. Cigars are hot and Nicole's Antiques and Tobacco Shop knows it. That's why they're currently planning on starting up their own cigar factory. But in the meantime, you can get a mean cup of Joe, stretch out on a leather sofa and so far, there hasn't been a fight over the remote. Relax and enjoy some of the finest cigars available. Still feel you need more to burn—money included? Then check out the candle selection for yourself or to give as gifts. Other gifts include humidors, picture frames, lighters, cutters, silver jewelry and more. Oh, not satisfied yet? Good, because there's more to see with art deco dining room tables, pop-up bars, wardrobes, vanities, clocks, lamps and antique martini sets. Don't turn green with envy. These deals will probably turn you ashen if you smoke after every meal. Really, it's an antique shop with cigars thrown (or is it flown or blowin'in?) Delivery is extra.

★★★★ Nicole's Estate Resale   972/392-2100

6959 Arapaho, Suite 503
Dallas, TX 75248-4061

Wed-Sat 10-5:30; Sunday 12-5

Nicole is no nickel and dime kind of place. Rather, it's a consignment shop for the hoi polloi with the added advantage of managing estate sales on location (that's if you have an entire mansion to unload, from floor to ceiling.) If you just have a chandelier or an Oriental rug, something over the top, and something for the floor, you're better off letting Nicole Aaron Blue sell it in her store. Limited store hours so be sure not to shop on Monday or Tuesday, but those are good days to probably negotiate what merchandise is acceptable for her to take on consignment. Nicole is the president-elect of the Consignment Association of Dallas (CAD) so she's in the know about what others are doing, too. Go to CAD's website at www.consignmentdallas.com for a list of Dallas-area stores.

★★★★★★ Nostalgia Warehouse   817/572-5012
Mon-Fri 9-5; Sat 11-3

7801 U.S. HWY 287
Arlington, TX 76001
www.nostalgiawarehouse.com

Three and one half miles south of I-20, it's back to the future, part 1-2-3. Easy does it. Take the Turner Warnell exit (not business 287) and see if you can find Nostalgia Warehouse. If you are a fan of the 30s, 40s, 50s and 60s, you should be in hog heaven, squealing with delight, when you take a peek at the sleek advertising signs or the full size jukeboxes. This company's the largest WURLITZER dealer in the country with three locations in the Metroplex. No doubt about it, if you're decorating a media room, rec room, family room, gameroom or bar, you'll want something from here. Trust that the real antiques are tagged "real" and you'll not be duped into believing one of the reproductions is the real McCoy. They have quite the Pandora's box of offerings: CROSLEY RADIOS, HARLEY-DAVIDSON ROADHOUSE, KIT CAT Clocks and WURLITZER are the brand names you'll recognize. But if you want any auto-mobilia, CDs and 45s, hot rods, soda machines, pedal cars, signs, stools and ice cream tables, you'll never see a better selection .... well, except for Past 'n Presents. Love those gas pumps or a coke machine that'll accept the small bottles? These are good investments as they appreciate upwards over the years. Past 'n Presents has 'em, too, and since they're the largest retailer of nos-talgia in the world, we thought we'd given them a mention. Visit them at Grapevine Mills, across from Bed, Bath & Beyond, 972/724-9900 and the Parks Mall in Arlington, first level north of SEARS, 817/467-2910. Both stores are open 7 days a week. Prices, though, are better at Nostalgia Warehouse. Ooh Wee! Their website is a full-time browser's delight and think about this — stocks fluctuate but gameroom memorabilia both old and new remain a good investment regardless.

★★★★★ Old Home Supply   817/927-8004
Mon-Fri 8:30-5; Sat 9-5; Sun 11-5

1801 College Ave.
Fort Worth, TX 76110
www.yellowpages-ads.com/01293413Oh

Oh, give me a home, where architectural salvage and relics do roam, and I'll point you to Old Home Supply, one of the seven wonders of the world. Housed in the historic Fairmont District in downtown Fort Worth (including the Tasty Bakery Building), they have loads of stuff from the good old days. Since 1985, they have occupied four corners of downtown Fort Worth housing old home relics and architectural remains of the day. From doors to door knobs, lighting fixtures to hardware, why not make a dramatic entrance with a new entryway? Furnish your home with all the accompanying artifacts that give your house that personal touch. Pining for pedestal sinks and coveting claw-foot tubs? Choose from literally hundreds of items. Then it's off to building number two for the lights. Most are even rewired and ready to light up the town. Another building is for green thumbs who don't want to spend a finger more than necessary to accessorize their garden, patio, porch or entry way. Find objects from the past that make perfect accessories for today. Stained and bevel glass, antique cabinetry and hardware, glass doorknobs, solid wood doors (hard to find these days), ornamental crown moldings — grab a truckload and have yourself a field day. Retro is "in" and paying dearly for them is "out."

★★★   **Old Town Village Antique**   **972/938-9515**

307 S. Rodgers   Mon-Sat 10-5; Sun 1-5
Waxahachie, TX 75165

No question about it: this is how the West was won. Good old-fashioned values surround the savings that abound at this former **JCPENNEY** store (circa 1936) called Old Town Village Antiques. Churn your way through the square and find this historic landmark. With hospitality and grace (not to mention good will towards mankind), they offer one small step for shopping-kind and all's well in the end. Just don't expect a thrift shop. This antique shoppe is a complete shopping experience featuring furniture, glassware, collectibles, lamps and so much more, all tastefully displayed throughout. And if you're looking to tempt your taste buds, be sure to make plans to reel in a meal (that's a pretty good deal) at the Catfish Plantation Restaurant. Keep your hooks about you because this famous eatery was featured on "A Current Affair" and is reportedly haunted. Scare up some more fun by strolling on over to the Waxahachie Antique and Craft Mall for Belleek porcelain and Battenburg lace. Let's just make a day of it, bid adieu as the sun sets and remember a time when fanfare and leisure went hand in hand.

★   **Olde Good Things**   **888/233-9678**

124 W. 124th Street   Hours To Be Announced
New York, NY 10011 Dallas, TX
www.oldegoodthings.com

Coming soon, but they'd better hurry, otherwise I will explode with anticipation. New York's finest antique and architectural salvage and artifacts resource is blowin'and goin'across the land. From their periodic truck sales that pull up in towns all across America with their unmistakable Big Red U affixed to the backside of their trucks (log on to their website to discover its meaning), to permanent locations like their new anticipated Dallas store, you will go ga-ga over the architectural remains of the day. They call themselves "architecturologists" while traveling with their roadshows. The only problem? They won't tell me where their local store will be. Check our website and theirs for show dates and locations. That's the best I can do for the moment. See, touch, buy mantels, entry doors, decorative iron, garden ornaments, lighting and more. It won't take you long to see why they were voted "Best of New York 2003!" Come see why dealers, designers, decorators, even landscapers have been fans of their shows coast to coast. They buy architectural salvage from demolished or about-to-be-demolished buildings and they are always on the lookout for tin ceilings, wood beams, barn wood, and antique flooring. They are particularly enamored with original hardware, doorknobs, mantels, doors, bronze, brass, columns, corbels, stones, stained glass....well, almost anything that spells good, olde things. The lineup of possibilities includes benches, fountains, marble tables, medallions, reliefs, mosaic borders, mosaic tiles, pedestals, planters and vases, statues, table bases, trims and moldings....well, these added extras are the tip of the mountainous selection. In their Chelsea warehouse in New York City, it's like being on a dig. I imagine the Dallas store will be similarly inclined. Remember the Wrecking Bar, the home of Hard Rock Cafe of the 80s? Well, the subject matter of architectural salvage is returning with a vengeance. And here will be the place to score. From ornate marble mantels from Harlem brownstones to original posters from Times Square landmarks, can you imagine over 20,000 doorknobs or 300 mantels all in one place? And the best part, you won't pay retail. *Call toll-free: 888/233-9678*

★★★★   **On Consignment**   **214/827-3600**

2717 Fairmount   Mon-Sat 10-5:30
Dallas, TX 75201-1959

Looks like On Consignment is on the move this year from the Knox-Henderson area—they've finally relocated to uptown. Now what? Is it still going to be a great place to find a perfect piece for that apartment, loft, or that M Street remodel? You bet. Owner Anita Carpenter has retained the comfortable ambience conducive to browsing and manager Wanda McIntosh has the knowledge to also ensure you'll find just what you're looking for as well as to help you sell what you think would fit into their inventory mix of antiques on consignment. If not, Wanda says she'll help find another shop where your furniture may be more compatible. Now that's a generous merchant. For $75, we were able to snare a great looking Art Deco chest with a top that lifted up to sub as a perfect small-sized bar. Now, that's a small price to pay for a little addition to your home's decor. Say "thanks for the memorabilia" at this relocated haunt. One of the first antique consignment concepts in town, what comes in, goes out fast. Shop often for home furnishings and decorative accents and a nice mix of traditional and antique home furnishings. From chandeliers to armoires, iron beds to desks, tables to sofas, they've got it all, and now they're in the heart of antique row. Remember, if it's "too good to be threw" it just may have an additional lifespan with you.

★★★★★★   **Oriental Antique Furniture**   **214/366-0688**

9920 Monroe Drive   Mon-Fri 10-5; Sun 1-5
Dallas, TX 75220
www.zrmdecor.com

 Prices are Oriental-ly expressed within this authentic Oriental Antique Furniture warehouse. Experience the best of where East meets West. Lucky for us in the Metroplex, we're smack dab in the middle. Every kind of cabinet, from those shaped like a butterfly to specialty cabinets called Kang. From alter tables to coffee tables, end tables to occasional tables, you won't want to table the issue. The prices are so low, you might have room for a pair or more. Looking for the perfect Ming sideboard or chest? What about a game table for the media room? Or a wash stand that's just waiting for a drop in sink? There's so much to see but luckily, you don't need a current passport. Let Allen be your guide. He's both knowledgeable and genuine in his approach to helping customers. See all the pieces online, too, complete with prices and shipping. The antique hat boxes were painted and exquisite. The one I bought was $198 and $15 shipping. Not bad for a conversation piece that now sits atop my closet for all to see. In the rare find department, I thought I'd see pieces that would be selling for tens of thousands, but no, individual items were priced just under or over a $1,000 for very intricate pieces of furniture that were categorized as "rare finds." See, too, intricately carved screens for $278....what a steal alongside the tapestries and Oriental rugs that were all handmade. The piece de resistance, though, was the wedding bed. What a perfect gift for the bride and groom....oh, come to think of it, it would also be perfect in my room, too.

★★★   **Pease-Cobb**   **817/763-5108**

3923 Camp Bowie Blvd.   Mon-Sat 10-5:30
Fort Worth, TX 76107

The dig is on. Excavate all the rest but dust off some great deals at this site located between Virginia and Belle Place. Nestled into every corner are great finds, finding their way from their home to yours. Light the way with table lamps and lighting fixtures while you take home estate furniture, rugs, bric-a-brac and more, lovingly displayed in vignette settings to give an overall appeal. (Besides, where else can you get such hands-on decorating ideas?) Everything is priced to sell.

And if you're looking to sell, take advantage of Pease-Cobb's 60/40 split on consignment items. Dig around, turn around, pick up those items in your cellar, perch yourself in the attic and empty out those old trunks. You might be surprised how you can consign them for and get a pretty penny in return. Got too much to haul in? Simply arrange an estate sale at your very own estate. Pease-Cobb will arrange it, with pleasure. And now, see some of their high-end offerings inside the Gathering on Turtle Creek in Dallas, Pease, pretty Pease!

★★★★★★ Philbeck's Antiques & Reproductions   972/564-9842

119 E. Hwy. 80
Forney, TX 75126   Mon-Thurs 9-5; Fri-Sun 9-5:30
www.philbecksantiques.com

 Do not forsake Forney for this is the answer to faux heaven. If you're looking for the real McCoy, you'll find it here. But if you happen to be a descendent of the Hatfield's just wanting everyone to think your lineage is from the McCoys, you'll find some here as well. Randy and Gayle Philbeck will custom-make pine reproductions that look straight out of the pages of **RALPH LAUREN** to your specifications. So fire away and move along through the many rooms while you take a little of this and a little of that. Your eyes will be able to look up, over and through old stained glass, iron and horned chandeliers and if you get lost, just make your way to the back where you can take cover in the warehouse amongst armoires, buffets, desks, dressers, candlesticks and chests. To be found, is a brilliant selection of direct imports from Germany, England, the Czech Republic and Indonesia. So call a truce and head over to Philbeck's Antiques and Reproductions for a unique experience in the heart of the Antique Capital of Forney, Tx. Since they specialize in European pine antiques and Texas pine reproduction furniture, Philbeck's Antiques can offer furnishings and accessories tailored to what folks are looking for when they ask for southwest or country motifs. For small houses to large-scale contemporary estates, Hill Country ranches to that lake house or country cottage, you will find something to fit in and to cherish. In addition to all of the above, Philbeck's is chock-full of accessories and accent pieces, including its most unusual offering for the hunter and wild game enthusiast—trophy mounts. Yes, you will see full size moose, elk, bear, lion and cougar as well as many African mounts. The perfect accessory for anybody who's out for the kill.

★★★   Second Hand Rose of Tyler   903/939-8979

3717 S. Broadway   Mon-Sat 10-6
Tyler, TX 75701-8737

You may resent wearing second-hand clothes, but sitting on a chair or sofa from Second-Hand Rose, what's wrong with that? Even Barbra Streisand does not object to sitting on a settee that has been sat on before. She may even sing their praises, no? And could they be located on any more appropriate street than Broadway? This East Texas haunt may be owned by someone with a foreign accent, but he's got an all-American viewpoint on merchandising. After all, we call old furniture antiques even if they're not 100 years or older. Where he comes from, they call what he's selling used furniture. Furniture from the '30s, '40s and '50s are so "in" these days, you might want to just bring a tractor trailer and load up. If he would showcase any 18th or 19th century furniture, well, that is a legit antique and most robust families of today need furniture that can take much more abuse than delicate heirlooms. So be it. Second Hand Roses wouldn't be as cheap if sold in any other city but Tyler. You know that roses are their crop of choice, so why not Second Hand Rose home furnishings at prices that won't put a thorn in your budget?

◆◆◆◆◆   **Smith Antiques**   **817/265-7048**

3650 Garner Blvd.   Mon-Fri 8-4:30
Arlington, TX 76013

Breathe new life into that old furniture. Though Smith Antiques may no longer sell antiques, they have created a niche for themselves as antique restorers. And not to rub you the wrong way, their work is top notch. Like cosmetic surgeons, they're medical geniuses at removing nicks and filling crannies until your antiques gain a more youthful appearance. Don't you wish a face-lift was this easy? Well, at least it can be for your treasured antiques and with pick-up and delivery service available for a charge, you'll be sure each piece receives the private room TLC it deserves. And speaking of service, most work is completed within two to three weeks. If it was your face, you'd still be black and blue.

★★★★★★   **Texas Antique Connection, The**   **817/429-0922**

7429 E. Lancaster   Mon-Fri 9-5; Sat 9-Noon
Fort Worth, TX 76112

Partake in the pleasure of hunting for buried treasure. Those French ships might just have missed the New Orleans port and come ashore at The Texas Antique Collection. With Belgian and French antiques, along with hand-carved mahogany reproductions from Indonesia, your ship should set sail with the rudder in gear. Drop anchor and spend some time looking over the wide selection of authentic and reproductions "shore" to fit any decor or budget. Then when you think you couldn't possibly make it through another hour afloat, you'll want to moor—next door. Classic Designs (www.classicdesign.com) at 3701 New York Ave., No.140, Arlington, TX 76014, 817/446-3204. They offer furniture to retailers all across the Southeast plus accessories, bronzes, pottery, autographs, books and more. Bury the gold in the back yard and take along some chump change because when they advertise their inventory sales, it's time to proceed full steam ahead. Make those land lovers appreciate a good deal when you sea one. "Today's Craftsmanship....Tomorrow's Antiques!" You'll enjoy a day of strolling along Lancaster where there's a multitude of little antique stores and galleries. Look back in time and remember those days gone by.

PS   **Thomas & Assoc. Professional Auctioneers 214/632-4824**

301 Wilcox St.   Call for Times and Dates
McKinney, TX 75069-5623

Watch newspapers, get on their mailing lists, listen to the Diva because when they get to talking the talk, you better be walking the walk. Their auctions generally will net you great prices on furniture, antiques, bric 'a brac, collectibles, junk and junque that may be a treasure to others. Though you may not understand the banter once they start their chatter, just look for the dealers bidding and then when they stop bidding, you make the next bid up and quit. That's when you know for sure you're getting a good deal.

★★★   **Travis Mitchell Auctions**   **972/276-3500**

209 S. International Rd.   Mon-Fri 8-5
Garland, TX 75042
www.travismitchellauctions.com

If you're getting into or out of the restaurant business, this auction's for you. But since commercial kitchens are all the rage, the public is invited as well. Selling good used kitchen/restaurant and bar equipment, it's one of the few places that homeowners can really save on commercial products at residential prices. Consignments get the proceeds in 10 business days. In order to bid, you have to ante up a $200 cash deposit. It's refundable if you don't buy or it's applied to your purchase price if you do. The auction now takes place in a new air-conditioned warehouse on Dividend Drive. They boast they're the pinnacle of new and used restaurant and bar equipment via the auction block, and they're not far from the truth. Find everything you'd find in a restaurant or bar, including dishes, glassware, freezers, icemakers and more. Sales are held at the warehouse approximately every three weeks. Auctions start at 10 on select Saturday mornings, with previews from 1-6 the preceding Friday afternoon. You can view the inventory that is expected to arrive on the auction block during normal hours on any business day, but will not be tagged for auction until Friday. Other items that may wind up at the auction can include furniture, stereo equipment, TVs, cash registers, ceiling fans and etc. You never know what goes. That's part of the fun of the hunt for the lost cooktop, the deep fryer or built-in coolers! Auctions may also take place at another location and time if, so check the classifieds or their website often. Payment is by cash or cashier's check only. Checks accepted only with a Bank Letter of Guarantee. If you're a savvy cook and buyer, you could very well end up with a commercial kitchen at half the price. But don't get burned. Know your equipment, especially if it needs to meet certain residential electrical codes to use in residential applications. ***Call toll-free: 877/4-AUCTIO***

★★★★★★ Unlimited Ltd. Antique Mall 972/490-4085

15201 Midway Rd. (North of Belt Line)
Addison, TX 75001
www.antiquelandusa.com/unlimited

Mon-Sat 10-6; Sun 11-6

The sky's the limit at this antique mall. Over 250 vendors are all joined at the hip— displaying everything from antique and classic furniture to artwork, collectibles and more. You may feel like you're walking to the moon and back again in this 40,000-square-foot showroom, but you'll be walking on clouds after seeing some of their price tags. A bright surprise is how well some antiques are preserved in over 135 showcases. And don't let a bout with hunger rain on your parade. Pull up a tufted chair in The Copper Pan, open Tues-Sat 11-2:30 and Sun 11:30-3, especially if you have a hankerin' for a blooming treat of sandwiches and desserts. By the way, desserts are served daily until 4 PM. Then head back to seventh heaven for all those goodies that are best sat on, rather than eaten.

★★★★★ Wholesale Antique 972/564-4433

5 Forney Industrial Park
Forney, TX 75126

Tues-Sat 11-6; Sat 11-6; Sun 12-5

Older can definitely result in a bigger, better bargain stop. And stop in the name of love! This 10,000-square-foot den of antiquity is located at Hwy. 80 and Country Roads (Exit 212-217) in Forney, a favorite strip of antique wheeler dealers. You, too, can wheel and deal where the dealers deal. Shop wholesale and save the needless markups. (Hey, that has a nice ring to it!) Save money on good-looking solid mahogany, walnut or oak dining room and bedroom suites and assorted pieces to complete the 1900-1940 look. Fifteen minutes east of the LBJ freeway, they also have booths at Unlimited Antiques on Midway, Forestwood Antique Mall, Forest and Inwood and at The Colony. But this is their Mother Lode and you don't want to ignore it. Try it, you'll like it!

Apparel: Children's

★★★★ A Little Behind

2310 Virginia Parkway, Suite 180
McKinney, TX 75071-3557
www.milliondollarbaby.com

972/562-6772
Mon-Fri 9:30-6:30; Sat 10:30-6:30

Million Dollar Baby was established in 1990 as a wholesale baby furniture company in Los Angeles, CA. In 1992, Million Dollar Baby acquired Bexco Enterprises, a wholesale baby furniture company, which had been in business since 1982, in Dallas, TX. Then the distribution network was expanded to Atlanta, GA in 1993. Now what does that have to do with Dallas? Well, look ahead to A Little Behind above. It's a retail outlet where you can save from 40-70 percent on children's furniture, maternity clothes and children's clothes to size 4 T. New as well as consignment items are front and center. A Little Behind started by selling diaper supplies and disposable diapers at wholesale prices. That put them right up there in the "must-shop" league. Then, they added children's clothes from newborn to 4T with savings of 40-70 percent. Then, they hooked up with Million Dollar Baby furniture and added the component of baby furniture to the mix. Now, let's talk! Online you can see the furniture first hand including their factory direct outlet online. Their furniture line is extensive: ASHLEY COLLECTION, JENNY LIND, LAUREN COLLECTION and the SLEIGH COLLECTION offers everything from cradles to cribs, high chairs, rockers, youth beds, mattresses and convertible beds. The furniture is solid and priced accordingly. Impressive and not at all behind the times.

★★★ Carter's For Kids

3000 Grapevine Mills Pkwy.
Grapevine, TX 76051
www.carters.com

972/724-6770
Mon-Sat 10-9:30; Sun 11-8

Since 1865, Carter's is considered one of the oldest and largest manufacturers of infants'and children's apparel in the U.S. Lucky for us Texans, we've got five Carter Outlets in the state: Grapevine Mills, Allen Premium Outlets, Hillsboro's Prime Outlets, San Marcos and Conroe (outside Houston). See the popular and patented drop-seat PJ's that made Carter's For Kids as well known as its namesake liver pills. Whether it's baby's sleepwear or play-clothes, expect about 20-30 percent off and more during sales and end-of-the-season closeouts. Sizes newborn to size 7 in boys; newborn to size 6X in girls. The store's equally divided between boys and girls so we can't file any discrimination charges. But I wouldn't recommend charging anything on Saturdays as it's a madhouse with wailing babies and wall-to-wall mothers. Then when you add in mothers-to-be, you are really breaking the occupancy load requirements. Try shopping weekdays for peace of mind. ***Call toll-free: 800/253-3079***

★★ Chelsea's Tea Room & Boutique 817/276-8100

2421-C Westpark Row
Pantego, TX 76013

Mon-Sat 10-5:30

Coffee, tea, and tea parties. What a terrific combo. Ta! Ta! Chelsea's Tea Room and Boutique caters to little girls and boys in a very elegant atmosphere. Experience true southern comfort (the non-alcoholic variety), charm and grace when shopping for baby and children's clothing. Find the perfect outfit for any special occasion, whether it be a portrait or just because you're a stickler for perfection. They have boy's sizes 0-7 and girl's sizes 0-14 and have closets full of CHICKEN NOODLE, COTTON COLLECTION, NANETTE, WEEBOK, ZOODLES and more. Even pree-mie sizes and maternity samples round out (pardon the expression) their inventory. And sampling prices at 15-20 percent off retail makes that tea a little easier to swallow. Then, there's always just the tearoom....a perfect place for that tea party or any other child-like soiree. That makes shopping with the kiddos easier to take. I'll drink to that!

★★★★ Children's Orchard 214/488-2257

291 E. Round Grove Road
Lewisville, TX 75067
www.childrensorchard.com

Mon-Fri 10-7; Sat 10-6; Sun Noon-5

Talk about taking a bite out of the red apple! This resale chain is building an orchard nationwide. Their modus operandi—franchising. Go to their website for details. Only top brands are invited in with the potential of saving customers up to 70 percent. Look, see and shop for gently-used and new kids'clothing, toys, furniture, equipment, books and accessories! But the best part? They buy your castoffs up front. That means, no waiting for months to collect that check only when your castoffs sell. The only location on the website is listed for Lewisville, though we've heard rumors about stores in Plano at 7200 Independence Pkwy, Plano, 972/618-5800 and Grapevine at 2100 Northwest Highway, #215, 817/442-1257, but if the franchiser doesn't know about it, maybe they don't exist. Call before you head out the door. Another plus, this chain supports the Family Build-ers Adoption Network, helping to find supportive adoptive families for hard to place children. *Call toll-free: 800/999-KIDS*

★★★ Chocolate Soup 214/363-6981

1214 Preston Royal Plaza
Dallas, TX 75230

Mon,Thurs-Fri 10-8; Tues-Wed, Sat 10-6; Sun 1-5

With a name like this, how can they not have a can or two mentioned on a website? It's more than delicious and I have written about them for over 25 years. Too bad they didn't stick with their original concept as it was born long ago in a factory in Kansas City. But oh how delicious it is when there's a sale on. And when they created the brother and sister outfits that were perfect for portraits or church-going only, they were priced factory-direct and oh so irresistible. Today, it's just another cute children's shop with a great name and logo. Unwrap some new duds for the young ones with a variety of the Chocolate Soup label sprinkled within the other labeled goods. Don't even bother looking for CHICKEN NOODLE as a brand that you could stoop to scoop up. They don't carry that brand. Girl's sizes 0-12 and boys to size 7 can be devoured, but the reduc-tions in caloric count come only at the end of the season. Slurp, slurp! Splurge by adding some crackers to the Chocolate Soup entrees like BUSTER BROWN, CARRIAGE BOUTIQUE, HEARTSTRINGS, LE TOP, NAUTICA, S.F. BLUES, and more—all at a savings that averaged 25 percent off retail. Isn't it time you shake your bonbon down to the southeast corner of Preston and ROYAL for more Chocolate Soup...before it melts in your hands!

★★★★★ **Just Kidstuff** 972/240-5500
4125 Broadway, Suite 120
Garland, TX 75043 Mon-Sat 9-6

Twelve years in the same location is some kind of record. Maybe it's cheaper by the dozen. Be grateful there's a Just Kidstuff just around the corner. Between clothing your children and keeping them in strollers, car seats, cribs and walkers, who are you kidding? It's ain't cheap. But here's the place to save on infant's furniture, accessories, specialty items and clothing in girls'sizes O-Jr. 7 and 0-20 in boys. Since Channel 5's Sabrina Smith is a fan, why not give them a good old-fashioned try? Trading in last year's barely worn for this year's latest can be like looking a gift horse square in the eyes! This resale shop satisfies that well-known wail, "I've got nothing to wear!" Clothing and accessories arrive daily by the trunk-full. Just stop in and save up to 70 percent off retail and see why children's resale is a hot commodity every season. From the day they are born, teach them the value of comparative shopping and they'll grow up with a sense of what it takes to be fiscally responsible. Shopping the resale route is the right path to walk. After all, it's just kidstuff, and they'll outgrow it in a few months. What the heck! Indulge them with a whole new wardrobe at these prices so that when they shop the other Broadway in New York City, they will appreciate what low prices are all about!

★★ **Kids' Alternative** 817/377-4988
2823 Alta Mere Mon-Fri 10-5:30; Sat 10-5 (Closed First Monday each month)
Fort Worth, TX 76116-4112

Take the alternative route, the road less traveled. Buy resale—not retail. Kid's Alternative is a children's resale shop that dresses them up and moves them out in designer labels. See any names you know? Rub elbows with **BUSTER BROWN, CHRISTIAN DIOR, GAP, GUESS?, GYMBOREE, OSHKOSH B'GOSH, POLO, THE LIMITED, TOMMY HILFIGER** and more. And since kids are so active, they also offer after-school activewear such as dance and gymnastics wear, karate pants and sweats. Find it all in sizes ranging from 0-16. But don't forget to bring by those outgrown outfits for Kid's Alternative to buy or consign. Out with the old and in with the new, or nearly new. Find them just up the street from where their old shop used to reside. Only a block away at Alta Mere and Calmont, you're almost there.

★★★★ **Kidswap** 214/890-7927
6728 Snider Plaza Mon-Fri 10:30-6; Sat 10:30-5
Dallas, TX 75205

Shopping for deals is child's play when it's this easy. Mother May I please have a place to shop where they have my size and I won't have to worry if I outgrow the stuff practically overnight? Don't be mad at me. I can't help it if I can wear it one week and then it's too short or too tight the next. Hide and seek out designer and name brands for boys and girls in sizes infants through juniors. Rock a Bye baby in due time with maternity wear, too. Tag, you're it with tags that include Baby Guess?, **BUSTER BROWN, CARTERS, DIOR, DKNY, GAP, GYMBOREE, LEVI'S, LIMITED TOO, NIKE, POLO** and **TOMMY HILFIGER**. The stork has even given birth to a new addition to Kidswap with the arrival of overruns and brand new clothes from **FLAPDOODLES**. But there's no flap over that. Although the prices on much of the chi-chi clothes reflected a less-than country club approach to the high life, it's still important to teach your children the art of the deal. Since Kidswap is within earshot of SMU, you can expect the wardrobes to be preppy and Highland Parkish, if you know what I mean.

★★★★★ Mudpuppy

817/731-2581
Mon-Sat 10-6

5714 Locke @ Camp Bowie
Fort Worth, TX 76107-5020

Saving money is never a dirty word when you're shopping at Mudpuppy. No need to clean out the bank account when you enter the doors in need of clean designer and department store's children's clothing. Just dig in your heels and start reeling through the racks sizes 0-16 for girls and 0-20 for boys. Even maternity styles and infants' accessories can be found lining the shelves. Just because they've been worn before doesn't mean they should have to stain your budget. Jana Minter keeps her store spic-n-span so labels like Neiman's feel right at home keeping company with **CARTERS, GAP, GYMBOREE, LEVI'S, OSHKOSH B'GOSH**, and **POLO**. Who cares if they're not even wet behind the ears? To make this shop even more endearing, dog gone it, see the doggies in the window that are the adopted waifs from the Humane Society. Jana helps place these adorable puppies with new loving families. How can you resist? Bring in your children to shop and extend your family wardrobe even more so. In short order, this lady has single-handedly placed a lot of puppies and doggies. (Watch for a button on our website for similar doggie adoptions.) See what a difference one store can make? A pinafore and a puppy, a great combination for each and every child in the Metroplex.

★★★★★★ Once Upon a Child

972/874-0779;
Mon-Fri 10-7; Sat 10-6; Sun Noon-5

2311 Cross Timbers Rd., #317
Flower Mound, TX 75028
www.ouac.com

Once Upon A Child there stood a great children's resale shop with racks and racks of great names like **BUSTER BROWN** who was playing nicely with CARTER'S while **CHRISTIAN DIOR** was filling the **GAP** that was left by the hole dug by **GYMBOREE** who was dressed in LEVI'S while bouncing on his **POLO** stick. Okay, so we took some liberties while we were shopping. But remember, we were once upon a time children, too. Shelves were brimming with toys and infant accessories from **CENTURY**, EVEN-FLOE, **FISHER PRICE, GERRY, GRACO, KOLOCRAFT, IN STEP** and **SAFETY FIRST**. Everyone was very happy to be saving so much money. Then one day, a big change took place and all the world decided to shop the resale way. But at Once Upon a Child, there's no wait for your money. "Kid's stuff with previous experience" is welcomed and paid for up front — except for the new inventory discounted 20 percent. This franchised chain is building momentum and growing by leaps and bounds. Bring in your gently used items, no appointment necessary, and if it meets the store's criteria, they pay on the spot. Check directory assistance for location nearest you.

★★★★ OshKosh B'Gosh

972/551-3007
Mon-Sat 9-9; Sun 11-6

301 Tanger Dr., #103 (Tanger Outlet Mall)
Terrell, TX 75160-6653
www.oshkoshbgosh.com

After a century of doing business, **OSHKOSH** is still going strong, B'Gosh! When the going gets tough, the tough go shopping at this factory outlet. Overall, its clothes (and overalls) for kids are pretty terrific in sizes in newborn to age 10. Founded in 1895 in Oshkosh, Wisconsin, OshKosh B'Gosh has grown from a small-town manufacturer of adult workwear into an international brand of children's clothing and accessories. Though originally best known for its men's hickory-striped bib overalls, once they started making their pint size versions, they never looked back. In addition to the OshKosh B'Gosh name brand for boys and girls sizes 12 months to 6X-to 7, the OshKosh

B'Gosh family of brands now includes OshKosh B'Gosh Baby for newborns to size 6/9 months, Genuine Girl for girls sizes 7-16 and Genuine Blues for boys sizes 8-16 and includes bib overalls, pants, shorts, shirts and swimwear, as well as a complete layette line for newborns. They've also starting licensing their name onto a myriad of other products such as car seats, strollers, bedding, eyewear, plush toys, hair accessories, shoes, socks and sleepwear. The company has earned a profit every year for more than 75 years! Visit other area outlets at Grapevine Mills, Gainesville Prime Outlets and Allen Premium Outlets and enjoy the selection which is twice or three times more than you'd see at the department or specialty store where they appear retail.

★★★ Purple Pony   972/422-4500
1301 Custer Rd., #258   Mon-Sat 10-6
Plano, TX 75075-7429

It was an itsy-bitsy, teeny-weeny, yellow polka-dot bikini that every little girl at one time or another wanted to wear. And guess where I found one for Hannah? That's right — I rode all the way to the Purple Pony to unearth several bikinis for the current swim season and I bought three of them for $3 each, less than I'd pay for the cheapest one at a TJ Maxx. So there! Behind Albert-son's, here's one resale shop where you don't need an appointment to bring children's clothing, maternity clothing, or toys into the shop. Just make sure it's current, in good shape, clean and on hangers, no foolin'! And don't type in Purple Pony online and expect it to jump to a children's resale shop — that name will take you to a T-shirt company and there's no relation. Once you've found the SW corner of Custer & 15th, you can start roping in the deals.

★★ Resale Shop   972/317-9884
1297 FM 407 (Justin Rd.)   Mon-Fri 10-6; Sat 12-5
Lewisville, TX 75077-2232

It's all in the name and the name says it all. Preemie to children's size 8 clothing starts the ball rolling. But without maternity clothes, moms-to-be would feel left out of the equation. And they are important in the incubation period and beyond, wouldn't you say? So, expect a good selection of maternity clothes. Add in mommy bracelets and then fill up baby's room with furniture, bedding, toys, books and accessories. Just 1/4 mile west of I-35E at the corner of FM 407 and McGee in Lewisville, while coming back from or passing through on your way to Highland Village. Ah, the cheap smell of success!

★★★ Runt Rethreads   972/686-7007
1220 Town East   Mon-Sat 10-6
Mesquite, TX 75150

There was an old woman who lived in a shoe; she had so many children, she had way too many pairs of shoes to buy. That's why she shopped at Runt Rethreads where hand-me-downs take on a whole new appeal. Here's a shop that offers the convenience of a play area for children and resale items at a fraction of their original cost in sizes infants through pre-teen. Consignments are always welcomed, but bear in mind, if you fail to pick up your unsold items when requested, they will be donated to the Buckner Children's Home. Be sure to visit their additional location in the Country Club Square at Colonel and Broadway.

★★★★★★ **Small Fry**   **940/387-9915**
                                                  Mon-Sat 10-6
330 Sunset
Denton, TX 76201
www.SmallFryChildrensClothing.com

  Do not, I repeat, do not associate this Small Fry with Small Fry World. They are like night and day. One's full price. This one's not. Here you'll save as much as 50 percent (and more) on all the famous brands that are ogled at department and specialty stores. How do they sell for so much less? Well, for one, they are housed in two adorable clapboard cottages in Denton where the cost of doing business is less. Secondly, they buy market samples, promotional goods and make other such "good buys" as they can negotiate on current and sought-after clothing and layette items for babies, girls (preemies to 16), boys (preemies to 7) and gifts for both. Order up an entire wardrobe for your children, grandchildren or anybody's else's children and save a bundle on your little bundle. Dress your small fries and hold the ketchup in: ALLISON ROSE, AMY BYER, BABY TOGS, BISCOTTI, CALVIN KLEIN, CHICKEN NOODLE, CITY KIDS, CLAIRE LYNN, COTTON COLLECTION, DORISSA, FELTMAN, GOOD LAD, KC PARKER, KNITWAVES, LE TOP, LITTLE ME, MICHAEL SIMON, MONDAY'S CHILD, MULBERRIBUSH, SCHWAB, SIMI, TICKLE ME, TODDLE TYKE, ZOODLES and ZYNO. Shipping is available nationwide. Shoping via phone? Simply tell them what you're looking for, what size, how much you want to spend and your gift is on its way. I trust owner Nancy Cole implicitly. Just give her the dollar amount you want to spend and she picks out the perfect baby gift. From birthdays to holidays, you don't want to forget how adorable little tykes can look with the perfect outfit. This place is the award-winner in the Children's Category every year. They consistently have the biggest selection at the lowest price for the most coveted and sought-after brands plus all the matching accessories like hats, socks, ribbons, bows, baubles to bags, it doesn't get any better than shopping at Small Fry. Head north to Denton on I-35, exit Hwy. 377 (which turns into Carroll), Exit 465B. Turn right on Sunset. After one visit, you'll see why they hold the record for being in this book every year since 1972. That's 32 years of consistent blue-blooded bargains. Now all I'm waiting for is to be a grandmother so I can start all over again. *Call toll-free: 888/442-9002*

★★★★★ **Spankie's Rethreads**   **972/227-8822**
                                                  Tues-Sat 10-5
169 Historic Town Square
Lancaster, TX 75146
www.lancastersquare.com/spankies.htm

Spankie's is the perfect place to dress up those little rascals. This historic old building makes classic fashions come alive. It's the perfect resurrection. Suit up boys and girls in sizes newborn to 20. Entire wardrobes can be acquired from previously-attired kiddos who have only worn the best: BUSTER BROWN, CARTER'S, BABY GUESS? GAP KIDS, GYMBOREE, HUSH PUPPY, LEVI'S, MONKEY WEAR, NAUTICA, OSHKOSH B'GOSH, POLO, REEBOK, TOMMY HILFIGER — just like the kid's Christmas list, it goes on and on. Colored tags show even greater savings: yellow and orange tags offer an additional 50 percent off their already discounted prices. But keep your eyes peeled for pink and purple ones 'cause those are the ones that offer a whopping 75 percent off their already low, low prices. Yikes! That's practically Free. And if you're expecting, don't forget the maternity outfits, baby furniture and accessories. Toys and books, you know, are often the most welcomed gift....who cares about clothes? Gotta give whatcha gotta give!

★★★★ **St. Michael's Exchange**   **214/521-3862**

#5, Highland Park Village
Dallas, TX 75205

Mon-Sat 9:30-5

Mom and Dad, listen up. There is a better way to keep those rug rats dressed and not have to refinance your house. For a change, smile and say Cheese. Look at the zip code where this resale shop is located — Highland Park. And savings and Highland Park have not been running buddies for long, but at this shop they go hand in hand. Did you hear that? Discounts on previously broken-in (but still in great shape) children's clothing help not only the parishioners of St. Michael's Episcopal Church but others who only wish they could live in Highland Park. Dress 'em up for church, school, after-school and school dances. There's plenty to choose from, from suits to frilly dresses, but when you get home you're not alone when you break out those jeans and sun dresses. Kids go through clothes so quickly that making a stop here can become an event. Clean out the kids' closets and drawers, bag them up and drop them off for a tax credit donation. Then pick out some new (at least to the kids) clothes and re-fill those empty closets and drawers back up. Not only will you be getting a bargain, but you'll be teaching your children the value of charity. After all, charity does begin at home.

★★★★★ **Yesterdaze Kids**   **817/284-5437**

7269 Glenview Drive
North Richland Hills, TX 76180

Tues-Fri 11-5; Sat Noon-4

Okay, so they didn't get an "A" in spelling. Never you mind and Never on Sundays or Mondays, but every other "daze," this is where your children's wardrobes can be completed. From one piece to a wardrobe, this children's resale shop is like a lean, green, money-saving shopping machine. In fact, it's wishful thinking come true. What a welcome relief for the cause of parental rights. Write your own ticket. Bring in clothes that they've outgrown, despite being practically new; or buy someone else's outgrown-though-practically-new stuff so you can start to build an entirely new wardrobe. Follow the store's light brick path just minutes from North Hills Mall. Sizes newborn to 18 for both boys and girls are hanging around just waiting for a new home. Designer duds, toys, gifts, books, baby accessories and more can be bought or sold. Coincidentally, the owner's name is Sandy Parrent and she's the store's Mother. This darling little house is home to one of the best resale shops in the Metroplex, and you can huff and puff and try to blow the house down, but the store's 1,300 square feet is firmly rooted in a solid bargain-shopping foundation. Your budget will remain intact all through the shopping process and you won't believe you can fill so many bags with bargains for your kids.

Apparel: Family

★★ American T-Shirt

1228 Scyene Rd., #209
Mesquite, TX 75149
www.american-t-shirts.com

972/289-8262
Mon-Fri 9-5; Sat 10-1

As American as apple pie, American T-Shirt is in the business of helping businesses grow. Everything is available — aprons, athletic apparel, bags and totes, blankets, denim wear, flannel, fleece and golf shirts, headwear, loungewear and outerwear, sunglasses, sweaters, towels and more. Emblazon your name on these items and strut your stuff. Add to that shorts, sweaters, towels, turtlenecks and, of course, T-shirts, Get the message? Names you know were front and center: ANVIL, FRUIT OF THE LOOM, HANES, JERZEES, LEE, OUTER BANKS, RAWLINS and VAN HEUSEN. Order by the piece, the dozen or by the case. This wholesaler/distributor has no minimum order, but the more you buy, the more you'll save. They will even custom embroider most products. Call for a **FREE** brochure, their $5 catalog, or shop online. Finding them, though, will get you a gold star. Ask for Moe. Prices fair. ***Call toll-free: 800/782-0214***

★★★★ Andor's

3700 E. Lancaster
Fort Worth, TX 76103

817/531-3225
Mon-Fri 9:30-5:30; Sat 9:30-5

With new owners, there are now possibilities for expanding your horizon while supporting the foundation upon which they were born. The big seller here is their BERKSHIRE pantyhose (carried by Neiman's, Foley's and Dillard's for $6.99; Andor's price, $1.99.) They've been around more than 42 years, and at this location for 25. You can load up on underwear, scrubs and bras by PLAYTEX and VANITY FAIR. To quote them exactly, "We pile it in and sell it cheap." How much more explicit do we have to be? Slip in, slip on, slip out, though that's really hitting below the belt. But you might as well strike pay dirt while the going is dirt cheap. Pick a pair or two. There are always over 30,000 pair on the floor at all times. For the men, they offer socks, undershorts and T-shirts and occasionally, some ladies' casual tops can top off a pleasant shopping excursion. To their credit, since gaining new ownership from the former Andor's Dollar Store, they now accept credit cards (MasterCard and Visa).

Charly Calder Faux Furs   415/215-1108

Dallas, TX
www.charlycalderfauxfurs.com   🖱 *Top Online Store!*

Nobody in their right mind buys real fur these days. It's not politically correct plus it's expensive. So, go with the faux. Fur coats, throws, jackets, stoles in mink, chinchilla, sable, wolf and fox, it's all in the pelts. If you want to save some gelt, call their West Coast offices, open Mon-Fri 9-7 PST at 415/215-1108 to see up close and personal a sample of the actual faux fur. To request a sample of four different furs/$10. Keep warm. Keep cool. Do the right thing.

★★★★★   Dickies Factory Outlet   817/877-0387
                                              Mon-Sat 9:30-5:30
521 W. Vickery
Fort Worth, TX 76104
www.dickies.com

Here's a name you should know since DICKIES has been providing quality work clothes for men and women since 1922. Since uniforms can really put a dent in your budget, doesn't it make sense to shop at their outlet? What's really extraordinary is they guarantee your complete satisfaction. If for any reason you're not happy with your purchase, either now or later, just return it for a new item or complete refund. Forget getting the third degree while wearing those workpants for only $17 and khakis for $18 (either men or women.) Coveralls should fit the bill at $21 and pocket tees were $7. Children's school uniforms can be a real pain year after year. But this company can outfit yours without having to cash in your IRA. Their newly remodeled outlet store is at the northern edge of the Fort Worth Medical District. It's like shopping in a high-end contemporary chic retail setting with retro prices. Also, they've refixtured their other four outlets, in Orlando, Pigeon Forge and another in Texas at 506 Nevada St., Weslaco, TX near the border. Their website is a wealth of information regarding their history and their product line, including what's hip and who's wearing DICKIES in the celebrity star-studded world. Everything is categorized at the outlet as being "irregular," meaning something is wrong with the garment. Right? You can't see it and what you don't see, won't bother you. Like the dye lot may not be exactly perfect. If the price is right, nobody will know the difference. Can you really tell last year's jeans from this year's? Jeans to size 56/32 should keep even the biggest of bargain-shoppers covered. ***Call toll-free: 800/DICK-IES***

★★★★★★   Hamze & Sons   972/241-5556
                                              Mon-Sat 9-6; Sun 12-5
10712 North Stemmons
Dallas, TX 75220
www.hamze-sons.com

When the group decides to play ball, make sure their name is prominently displayed on their shirt, their hat, their jacket or wherever if you want to score a home run. From company spirit to a team's camaraderie, have your name emblazoned for all the world to see. From a kid's soccer team to a restaurant's wait staff (shirts and aprons, for example, with their name and restaurant is a great look to build cohesiveness and company identity). Build loyalty with identifying your logo and company name on a uniformed look by shopping at Hamze & Sons where the prices can't be beat. They are rock-bottom and the quality is solid so they can even be washed and look like new the second time around. Want something embroidered with 200 threads? Then show them a design you'd like and they can do it with their high-tech artistry. T-shirts, jackets, sweat shirts for the entire family can be bought that will last as long as they don't outgrow it. (Sorry, they can't stop growth spurts). And as an additional incentive, how does men's shoes that are actually comfortable for under $10 bucks sound? Hurry. Time doesn't stand still and neither do these shoes.

★★   Jeans Warehouse   972/247-2800

11171 Harry Hines   Mon-Fri 9-7 Sat 9-8; Sun 10-8
Dallas, TX 75229

If something has to come between you and your jeans, it might as well be a few bucks off brands such as LEVI'S 501 and **TOMMY HILFIGER**. But the rest of the jeans were less recognizable and it's so crowded, there's absolutely no breathing room between garments or even between the aisles. But frankly, it was so musty smelling, all we could think of was getting a whiff of fresh air. What we could see once we were able to maneuver the jeans on the racks didn't smack of high-end. Rather it spelled low end to moderate, even though there were some well-known brands visible, it was so crammed with merchandise and so unappealing, we didn't stay long. The clerks watched us like hawks which also made us uncomfortable. What gives? Well, not many of the waist bands, for sure. But if shopping for jeans is in your genes, try a pair of denim, dungarees, or overalls for kids, moms and dads at a few dollars off. Still, we didn't get "**LUCKY**." There were none with that label though the selection included pants, shorts, jackets, tops, Capri's....some with fake fur, others were plain Jane's. What you think?

★★★★★★   Manufacturer's Expo   469/429-6000

Ave. K & Spring Creek   Mon-Fri 10-9; Sat 10-6; Sun 11-6
Plano, TX
www.manufacturersexpo.com

It's all about you and they call it ME — Manufacturer's Expo. You start at this 15,000 square foot emporium where this importer has brought together fine jewelry, designer watches, leather apparel for the entire family, handbags, bed and bath domestics, giftware and put it all together under one big discount emporium. They even offer the services of three gemologists so if you want a piece appraised, bring it on in. What doesn't sell at these low prices are further reduced and shipped to their outlet store called Extempo at 2200 Vantage St., 214/267-1318, open Wed-Sat 10-6 and Sun 12-5. ***Call toll-free: 877/8-LEATHE***

★★★★   NBC Name Brand Clothes   817/576-0002

7563 Grapevine Hwy.   Mon, Wed - Sat 10-9, Closed Tues & Sun
North Richland Hills, TX 76180-8355

Proud as a Peacock, this NBC affiliate is also interested in ratings....ours. So here goes. Our shoppers thought it not a pretty sight. In the former Service Merchandise location, you'll uncover racks and racks of men's, women's and children's clothes from various department stores that you'll recognize instantly. Other brands mixed in were unrecognizable. (You know, some people just won't wear clothes with no name!) Seconds are clearly marked, so if you don't mind a button missing here and a sleeve missing there, you might land a whopper. Being tenacious, though, is the only way to not get discouraged. Dive into some first quality **EDDIE BAUER** shirts from $6-$56, **TOMMY HILFIGER** jeans for $15, **LIZ CLAIBORNE** cashmere sweaters marked down to $29 from $134 and men's **CLAIBORNE** dress shirts were $13, originally priced at $59. The brands were everywhere, but it's separating the chic from the ones that reeked that takes the patience of Job. Other labels to highlight included **DOCKERS**, **GAP**, **GUESS?**, **L.E.I** and **POLO**. Not a bad beginning for a season's primetime line-up, eh? Some labels remain as evidence, others are cut and some marked out or removed (like LEVI'S.) Expect a thrift store ambience with some pre-

owned garments in the back. At prom time, we saw tons and tons of wrinkled formals for $19.99-
$39.99. Even we have our limits.

★★   Socks Galore   254/582-9439

I-35 S (Exit 368 Hillsboro Outlet Center)   Mon-Sat 10-8; Sun 11-6
Hillsboro, TX 76645

Retailers can sock-it-to-you when it comes to selling socks. Did you ever stop to think where all
the designer labeled socks are made? Probably at the same major mill that make all of the name-
brand socks. But the name that goes on them determines the price. Without the designer label,
expect to slip into a pair for a lot less. At Socks Galore, you can save on more than 60,000 pairs of
socks. Wear them with or without shoes, it's your call. The only other option is to go sockless or
barefoot. Otherwise, if you're looking for knee-highs to anklets, scrunch to athletic socks, even the
store's 10-20 percent discount will help you toe the line. De-feet the agony of paying full price and
hammer away at your budget. With sock-its like these, it's a cinch at the outlet center.

★★★★★   T-Shirt Outlet   972/241-7030

14015 N. Stemmons   Mon-Sat 10-8
Farmers Branch, TX 75234

Shopping in Carrollton is a lot safer these days than traveling to China, although the language barrier still persists. The best remedy to "High-price-itis" is to shop here. Prices on shirts started at $3
each for S-M-L-XL and $4 each for 2XL-4XL, but on pricing for the whole team, that's a different
story. For custom silk-screened T-shirts, expect to pay a $35 setup charge per color to be printed.
Then it'll cost $1 per side of printing on a white shirt and $1.50 per side of printing on colored
shirts. The minimum order for printed T-shirts is three dozen, but smaller orders for just T-shirts
can be negotiated for a price slightly higher. They can either be 100 percent cotton or 50-50 (cot-
ton/polyester combination). They also have all the equipment to churn out the quantities fast, in
time for the first batter to go to bat. The children's T-shirts are five for $10 and that's the lowest
we've found in the Metroplex. Adults can get the same quantity at the same price. No kidding. But
oversized T's (2XL and 3XL) are a tad higher, three for $10, but still the lowest in town. Looks
like this is where we'll be getting our shirts that say, "We are your cheapest link!" Oh, that was
last year's popular show. Guess we'll have to get a reality show saying this year. How about,
"You're fired!"

★★★★   Tommy Hilfiger Outlet   972/874-0172

Grapevine Mills Mall   Mon-Sat 10-9:30; Sun 11-8
Grapevine, TX 76051
www.tommy.com

If Tommy is a friend of yours, you might want to stop by his store and check out deals on clothing
for men, women and children. There's no mistaking the savings with prices clearly marked an
average of 40 percent off. Sport the look complete with logo T-shirts starting at just $15. Cozy up
to one of the many clearance racks to save an extra 50 percent off their already low outlet prices.
It's like having a friend in the business when savings like this add up to a whopping 80 percent off.
So who cares if they're last year's style? Sure looks like this year's, huh? Classic good looks never
go out of style. Wholesome, all-American, clean-cut, that's a **TOMMY HILFIGER** kind of guy or
gal. Visit their other outlet store at the Prime Outlet Mall in Hillsboro, 104 N.E. I-35, Hillsboro,
TX 76645, 254/580-9204. Oh, Tommy Oh!

★★★★★★ **VF Factory Outlet**   **903/874-1503**

316 Factory Outlet Drive   Mon-Sat 9-7 Sun 10-6
Corsicana, TX 75110-9045
www.VFFO.com

 VANITY FAIR is far from being fair. It's fantastic! It's the cleanest concept for an outlet operation in the country. Take one of the most powerful names in manufacturing and put in an outlet out in the boonies and they will come. Stock up on stuff that you can mention as well as those that are unmentionable. Make this an annual excursion. It's no different than the pattern that most people fall into when shopping for lingerie in general. You generally shop for underwear and like stuff once a year. The difference here, though, it you'll save at least 50 percent off the retail price. Why? Because VF is the manufacturer. When you see the prices, you'll know from whence I came. I'm proud to be an American and at the Factory Stores of America, you can buy direct the all-American way. Many times it's 50 percent off the already lowest ticketed price. That's how it was during one of their blowout sales. How's that for a company's mission statement? Visit online to find the VF Factory Outlet nearest you. Born in "The Outlet Capital of the World, in Reading, Pennsylvania, they have spread their wings and brought forth their brand names into the hinterlands. The line-up is mind-boggling: BRITANNIA, HEALTH-TEX, JANSPORT, JANTZEN, LEE, RED KAP, RIDERS, VANITY FAIR, VASS-ARETTE and WRANGLER. So whether it's lacy or denim, it's materially coming from one of the big boys. Go online and print out a $10 coupon off a $100 or more purchase. Such a deal! Closest to the Metroplex, you can shop in Corsicana by taking I-45 S to Exit 229 to Highway 287 S.; or 4500 Highway 180 East in Mineral Wells, TX 76067-8385, 940/325-3318; from either Fort Worth or Dallas, take I-20/Highway 180 to Mineral Wells; Wichita Falls: Highway 281 S to Highway 180 E.

★★★★★★ **Wilsons Suede and Leather**   **972/681-5731**

820 West Stacy Road   Mon-Sat 10-9; Sun Noon-6
Allen, TX 75013
www.wilsonsleather.com

 Finally, Wilsons (no apostrophe) has scored a home run by establishing an outlet division to complement all of their mall-based stores. With four area outlets, you can finally enjoy the luxury of suede and leather, soft and elegant, bold and strong, timeless and contemporary. Though they have retail stores that offer value pricing in malls across the country, there's much more excitement in and around their 112 outlets. Fans can commandeer a suede or leather bomber jacket and reek of success. Who cares if it's got a scratch on the sleeve or a blemish under the arm? Or so what if it's last year's? (Sure looks like this year's to me!) But what's hot this year is their partnership with NASCAR and the Dale Earnhardt licensing program. Why? Because NASCAR is one of the premier sports brands and Dale Earnhardt, Jr. is one of the most marketable drivers. Secondly, statistics ranked the sport No. 1 in brand loyalty, No. 2 in TV ratings and No. 3 in sales of licensed products. Online, a $400 jacket was priced at $99. Step out in style, for less, in pants, tops, jackets, skirts, handbags and more, all made from quality leather and suede, some even sporting names you know like ANDREW MARK, LIZ CLAIBORNE, NINE WEST and Wilson's own private label. Visit Prime Outlets in Hillsboro, Tanger Outlet Center in Terrell and Grapevine Mills in Grapevine (now that you're part of the fringe network.) And don't forget the kaleidoscope of leather accessories. Bags, all kinds — from panel hobo bags to cross-body mini bags, buckle shoulder bags to totes, baguettes to camera bags; online, they were 50-70 percent off. Now, who gets your vote for these kind of totes? *Call toll-free: 800/967-6270*

Apparel: Men's

★★★ Apparel World

4949 Beeman Ave.
Dallas, TX 75223

214/887-8999
Mon-Fri 8:30-4:30

Jump into this apparel shop for a deal on jumpsuits. Okay, so jumpsuits aren't at the top of your shopping list? There are some guys who won't leave home without wearing their favorite — and you can snare a pair at wholesale prices at Apparel World. That's right. This really is the manufacturer's outlet (look for "LORCH" on the front of the building; once inside, you'll see the sign for Apparel World) offering a large selection of jumpsuits sure to fit men sizes 38-short to 60-long. Leap for joy with factory-direct pricing on knits and long-sleeved shirts in sizes S-2XL. You're bound to find something with this expansive inventory that includes everything from socks to sweaters. Just don't you sweat it. Finding the world of men's apparel is easy once you find the LORCH Building. Make a beeline and you'll be fine. ***Call toll-free: 800/397-3086***

★★★★ Barry Mfg. Co.

4141 Independence Drive
Dallas, TX 75237
www.bettermenswear.com

972/298-3366
Mon-Thurs 9-7; Fri 9-8; Sat 9-7; Sun Noon-5

Does same day alterations sound like just another line on a plastic surgeon's brochure? If we're lying we're dying 'cause men can size up this situation because it's true. They offer same day alterations whether they're small or tall, up to size 60. Let the fat robin sing about savings on single and double-breasted suits, rayon/linen blends, polyester and wool, all priced up to 50 percent off comparable retail, from $99-$169. Shoes by **FLORSHEIM** and **STACY ADAMS** were walking out the door for as low as $39.99. Barry's has been a family-owned company for four generations with over a century of years in business. With almost 50 factory-owned stores that sell menswear at wholesale prices to the public, you can give Abe Zeeman credit for its foundation. Immigrating from Russia in 1884 at the age of 17, he started selling sewing machines to homemakers for whom he'd get piecework from New York manufacturers. In 1898, he started manufacturing menswear that was soon sold alongside brands like **HART, SCHAFFNER AND MARX**. Soon, they began making private-labeled suits for some of the best department and specialty stores like Bloomingdales and Barney's New York. When they outgrew their Pennsylvania facility, the business moved to Georgia and they changed their name to Barry's, one of the owner's sons who is today the current President and CEO. What's next in their evolution? Could they be looking to squeeze a little business from the " I Guarantee It man!" Getting the most bang for your buck is Barry's marketing scheme so we shall see. The few changes noted on their website was sure an improvement. Try on another Barry Mfg. Co. in Fort Worth at 5700 Airport Freeway, 817/834-8413.

★★★★★ Big and Tall Fashions for Less 817/468-5900

951 W I-20, Suite 105
Arlington, TX 76017

Mon-Fri 10-8; Sat 10-7; Sun Noon-5

Don't be chained down to just one store. Big and Tall Fashions for Less has eight locations throughout the Metroplex. Shop often for big deals on big sizes all the way up to size 66 in jeans and 70 in suits. Big taste and lots of style for Texans in **ADOLFO**, **ARROW**, **DUCK HEAD**, **HAGGAR**, **HARMONY**, **IZOD**, **LEVI'S** (545s up to size 60), **PALM BEACH**, **RALPH LAUREN** and **WRANGLER** at prices less than you'd find elsewhere. Make it easy and take advantage of one-stop shopping at this location between Matlock and Cooper. Men who are super sized can be just as handsome as their big and beautiful female counterparts. Just because they're supersized doesn't mean stores can get away with upping the price-tags. Let the sales staff here treat you with dignity and fitting know-how. They know what looks good and what works when you want to be a fashion plate and you are big and tall. At last, here's one store that can deliver the real-l-l-y big bargains. Check directory for multiple locations and make some hunk one big happy fella! Add a website and they'd be upped to a 6-star. *Call toll-free: 817/467-5856*

★★★ Casual Male Big & Tall 817/784-8091

4100 S. Cooper St.
Arlington, TX 76015
www.thinkbig.com

Mon-Sat 10-8; Sun Noon-6

Now down the street (from 3200 S. Cooper to 4100), this chain has really made a comeback. Since 1973, they have catered to big and tall men who wear sizes 1X-6X and waist sizes 36-66. They now are a big chain, with over 400 stores, a new apparel catalog and a website. They even have a 4-star outlet store in Hillsboro (104 NE 1-35, Suite 201, 254/582-1920.) Look for active and casual sportswear, blazers and sports jackets, outerwear and accessories plus boots, dress and athletic shoes. Brother stores are Repp Big and Tall and B & T Factory Stores. But for now, let's just concentrate on Casual Male. See the savings on **HARBOR BAY** (comparable to **DOCKERS**), which is always a favorite. Feel the comfort of kicking back in a pair of **LEVI'S** or **WRANGLER'S**. Dress like the little guys in big boy's clothes. Prices are also lower than retail and lower still during special promotions. Check directory for multiple locations in the Metroplex but pay attention to their outlet store in Hillsboro. After all, there are approximately 20 million big and tall men in America alone but until recently, designers and manufacturers didn't pay much attention to them. Same in the women's arena. But my how things are changing. Congratulate **DOCKERS** who've done it again with their "Go Khaki" pants and shorts with what they refer to as the stain defender. That's right. They've taken their cotton blend khaki pants and shorts and made them even better with their classic fit, no wrinkles, double-pleated waist, cuffs and a permanent crease which made them so popular in the first place, and now, they are stain repellent. So, when the spaghetti drips over the plate onto your lap, it won't mean a total wardrobe loss. (See also **HAGGAR**'s new & improved fabric line of pants, too.) Another locations around the Metroplex but their outlet store that commands our 4-star salute.

★★★★★ Corporate Tradition Men's Clothing 214/638-5050

1140 Empire Central
Dallas, TX 75247
www.corptrad.com

Mon-Fri 9-5; Sat 9-2

Keep abreast of the latest trends while holding dear to basic traditions; in the end, your wardrobe will be worn by befitting a chairman of the board. Meet for lunch at The Palm, write the contract when the espresso is served and tip the waiter well. Welcome to Corporate Tradition Men's Clothing. Whether you've already arrived or are still making waves crawling to the top, remember to shop smart. Traditionally, this company pampers you with the finest in customer service while shopping for the finest men's clothing at the lowest possible price. So while taking advantage of what might feel like an employee discount, create a relationship with Anita Green and her staff. Her 4,000-square-foot showroom contains a wardrobe befitting the boardroom. Only the finest European and **AMERICAN** designers are even considered. If you don't know what the word haute couture means, you better ask before stepping foot inside. Coordinate your entire wardrobe from top to bottom, suits to shoes, shirts to belts, ties to socks, slacks to shorts....it's a one-stop source for designing men. To test your designer vocabulary, here are a few names to impress you: **ASHWORTH, AUSTIN REED, AXIS, BALLIN, BARRY BRICKEN, COOGI, CUTTER & BUCK, DESCENTE, HAUPT, JACK VICTOR, JHANE BARNES, LORD WEST, ST. CROIX, TALLIA** and **TERZOD**. Now for the more fiscally-endowed, what about an **IKE BEHAR** custom shirt? And what is your favorite shoe? **ALLEN EDMONDS, COLE HAAN** or **TIMBERLAND**? They've got them and the price is right! They also offer fashion consulting like what's appropriate and what's not for specific occasions. They'll come to your home to do a "closet audit & assessment" and will soon offer a personal shopping service online. *Call toll-free: 800/438-7848*

★★★★★★ **E. Magrath Golf Apparel Outlet**   **214/631-4582**

8941 Empress Row
Dallas, TX 75247

Mon-Fri 9-3; Sat 9-3 (through Father's Day)

During the week, they're open for business selling men's knit shirts, woven shirts, slacks, shorts, sweaters and outerwear. First quality **E. MCGRATH** and **BYRON** NELSON golf sportswear join the other secret warehouse outlets buried deep in the heart of Dallas. Hours expand to Saturdays as Father's Day and the holidays sneak up on us. Get with the program and shop at the factory where the clothes are made and save a stroke or two. (Defibrillators are not provided with any other strokes.) But if your golf game needs an injection of style, here's the place where the handicap comes to the fore.

★★★ **Far East Outlet**   **214/637-6828**

1336 Inwood Rd.
Inwood Trade Center Dallas, TX 75247

Mon-Sat 10-5:30

The Far East does not have to be far out of your way. Take time to explore new fashions in a not-so-new outlet. For more than 30 years, this store has been discounting men's and boy's clothing (sorry, they no longer offer women's) an average of 30-50 percent off retail. Dress up the little tykes in savings on boys'suits sizes 4-20, including slim and regular that retail for $99 for only $39. Fancy that! It's one of the few resources that cater to dressing up little boys like they were little men. They hope to capture them while they're young and impressionable — in other words, they're grooming customers for life. Then when they're all grown up, they'll be shopping at Far East (with no threat of SARS) for all of their men's things like an all-wool suit in sizes 36-60 (reg/long) and 36-44 (short) for $165 ($360 elsewhere). Then, why not polish it off with a dress shirt for $16, silk shirts for $12 and ties for $9? Since we're talking the Far East, expect many of the names to be unfamiliar. But what a surprise! Many of the names sounded tres Italiano: **CLASSICO UOMO, EUROPA COLLECTION, GINA CAPPELIO** and **LINEA CLASSICA**. If you don't care about familiarity, you'll get your money's worth.

★★★★★★ **Gent-ly Owned Men's Consignery**   **972/733-1115**

17721 Dallas Parkway, Suite 145   Mon-Fri 11-7; Sat 11-5
Dallas, TX 75287
www.gentlyowned.com

Ask a man where he bought his **HUGO BOSS** pin-striped suit and he's quick to respond, "Neiman's," of course. But if the truth be known, Todd Shevlin sold it to him from his ever-so-chic resale boutique at the corner of the Dallas Parkway and Trinity Mills. Check them out online, too, their website's a stunner. And you can be, too, in what they call, "Liquid Wardrobes." Fluid, ethereal, tasteful, elegant. They provide quality service and the prices are great, too! When was the last time you were REALLY waited on in a men's shop? Upscale names like **ARMANI, CANALI, COLE-HAHN, COOGI, HUGO BOSS, NICHOLE MILLER, PERRY ELLIS, POLO, TOMMY HILFIGER, VERSACE** and **ZEGNA**. Impressed yet? Business and casual wear including market samples are all wholesale priced. Smart men consign out-grown clothes immediately to generate cash flow. Smart men buy consigned clothes to maintain a cash flow. And if they're smarter still, they'll buy an entirely new wardrobe at Gent-ly Owned for the best in American and European designer labels. Don't just be a customer, be a consignor and profit from your clothes that no longer fit you or your lifestyle. Maybe you've just entered your midlife crisis? Out with the old, in with the new....new to you, anyway. And laugh all the way to the next Doc Gallagher's investment seminar. Shop at their other boutique in Oak Lawn, just north of Cedar Springs, 2926 Oak Lawn, across from the Melrose Hotel, 214/219-8588.

★★★★★★ **Haggar Clothing Factory Store**   **214/481-1929**

Sam Moon Center   Mon-Sat 10-6: 30; Sun 12-5
11818 Harry Hines Blvd., Ste. 202 Dallas, TX 75234
www.haggar.com

The HAGGAR Clothing Factory Store should make a believer out of you with savings as big as Texas! Now settled in their new corporate headquarters and their new outlet surrounds at Sam Moon, this well-bred Texas manufacturer is a staple in most Texans' wardrobes and for one simple reason: their clothes are as easy to put on as they are to wear. Everything coordinates, from modern dress-up clothes to golf attire, khakis to business casual, if there's a Friday in your work week, expect to dress the part from here. You will save up to 50 percent and more at their outlet stores. The selection is supersized with slacks, sport coats, suits, shirts, shorts, jackets, jeans and ties. Pay attention when they run their world renowned sales....savings of 70 percent off are a regular occurrence. Woven shirts for $12.99 (retail $38) and fleece tops for $12.99 (retail $40) hit our shopping carts as soon as we hit the store. Leave it to **HAGGAR** to also be inventive and innovative. Their **HAGGAR** comfort-fit waist inside their dress and casual pants, for example, is an improvement to the adjustable waistband that grows and contracts as the wearer bends, sits or stands. If you're looking for fit and comfort, and the price is right, grab a pair or two. Then, on to Microluxe ®, which is their new men's pleated dress pant that provides a smooth drape and a silky and wrinkle-free quality. Is it any wonder folks are asking, "What kind of pants are these?" Lastly, ask about their Tempra-tech ® pant, the latest fabric that pulls moisture from the skin for quick evaporation. Look for this fabric in not only their COOL 18 golf shirt line, but in some of the casual clothes as well. Other outlets at Grapevine Mills, Allen Premium Outlets and the Prime Outlets at Hillsboro. Don't be left out in the cold. Cheapness should not be associated with nakedness. Here, you can almost dress for next-to-nothing!

★★★★★　**Internation Suit & Shoe**　　　　　　　　**972/780-2599**

4030 W. Camp Wisdom Rd.　　　　　　　　　　　　　Mon-Fri 10-8; Sat 10-7
Dallas, TX 75237

It's a good thing they call this land of ours a melting pot because International Suit and Shoe Warehouse is having a meltdown. This huge liquidation center is big on private label suits and sportswear — discounted up to 70 percent. You didn't have to write the book "Dressing for Dummies," to recognize that quality doesn't have to have a designer label sewn into it's collar. Many of those fancy-shmancy suits are made for certain designers and travel down one conveyor belt and for International Suit on the another. It may even be the exact same suit. So, what are you willing to pay for a label? Double? Triple? Are you that stuck-up that you are still needing to impress your cleaners? Now we're talking my language. Shoes, too, but they have the names still on them like GIORGIO BRUTINI and STACY ADAMS. Heard of them, haven't you? And when you're buying everything from polyester to virgin wool suits for just $89-$329, you better understand what's in the mix. Shirts are a "neck" of a deal in sizes 14-22, 32-37 sleeve. Don't leave empty-handed since some alterations can be performed on the spot — just $4 for hems and $5 for cuffs. International Suit and Shoe Warehouse is owned by Big and Tall Menswear for Less and has an additional location in North Dallas at 635 Preston Road, corner of LBJ and Preston, 972/239-1984. Buy-no-mite!

★★★　**Jos. A. Bank Clothiers**　　　　　　　　**972/248-4330**

1713 Preston Rd. Suite C　　　　　　　　Mon-Fri 10-8; Sat 10-6; Sun Noon-5
Plano, TX 75093
www.josabank.com

Farewell to you fair maidens. Jos. A. Bank has returned to a Men's Only policy. After almost 100 years, they are going back to where they belong and where they established their prominence. Whether you're a banker, a baker, a candlestick maker, they can get you covered. Jos. A. Bank delivers direct from their own factory thereby eliminating the middleman. By looking down the button-downs and up to the pinstripes, men have sized up their wardrobes and concluded they could bank on Jos. A. Bank. Sizes 37S-50XL, with additional sizing available through their catalog but expect prices to be steep. Even during sales, you might shell out $375-$575 for a suit. Pull up to this bank online and shop their clearance section where they descend to as much as 60 percent off. Jos. A. Bank is legendary for their "Business Express" program which consists of a 100 percent wool suit coat (two- or three-button, or double-breasted) with a coordinating pant, pleated or plain, for $375. Step up the corporate ladder in mix 'n match separates that will match your style. Alterations are available for an additional charge and are ready in seven days. Online, explore the world of dress shirts, sports shirts made of cotton and wool blazers made of natural fibers with a touch of Lycra ® as well as all-wool trousers. These are the ones that look freshly-pressed from morning to night. Oh really? Close the deal at other Jos. A. Bank locations by checking directory assistance.

★★★★★★　**K & G Men's Center**　　　　　　　**972/438-6100**

3417 E. John Carpenter Frwy.　　　　　　　　Fri 10-9; Sat 10-7; Sun Noon-6
Irving, TX 75062
www.kgmens.com

 This chain is on the move and in the groove concurrently. With 48 Men's Only stores, twenty-one combo stores (men's and women's), expect that some changes will be in store for their Metroplex locations soon. Be sure to check out their website! Online we discovered steals for the gals, too: cargo skirts, $16.99 and 100 percent silk blouses, $19.99. Where have you seen 100 percent wool men's suits in plenty of styles as low as

$99.99? These are the kind of prices that made K & G famous (formerly T & C, remember them?) But for the moment, call the 800 number for the store nearest you or log on with your zip code and their website will lead the way. Shirts started at $14.99 and were available in both regular and big and tall sizes. And shoes, man, do they have shoes! The prices range from $49.99-$64.99, compared to $72-$100. Five area locations are open Fridays, Saturdays, Sundays, holidays and every day of the week from the day after Thanksgiving until New Years. Expect to save 30-70 percent throughout their warehouses in sizes 36 Short to 54 Extra Long. Dress like the big shots with two-button, three-button, four-button and double-breasted styles in suits and sports coats. Oxford dress shirts were only $19.99 and their tie collection (values to $30-plus) will get you all choked up marked at $7.99 each. Among the many designers were: **ADOLFO**, **CHAPS BY RALPH LAUREN**, **CHRISTIAN DIOR**, **PIERRE CARDIN**, **PURITAN** and more are dressing up their racks these days. And this location's but a mere 1/2 mile east of Texas Stadium at the Grauwyler exit right down the street from KAAM Radio Station. *Call toll-free: 800-GOSHOPKG*

★★★★★ Men's Wearhouse, The   214/369-1841

8239 Preston Rd.
Dallas, TX 75225
www.menswearhouse.com

Mon-Fri 10-9; Sat 9:30-6; Sun Noon-6

By George, I think they've bought it. If it's not one chain, then it's another. Good old George is buying them up like we buy a case of **DIET COKE**. If there's a good price one day, we buy a couple of cases. So does George. Only he buys chains of men's stores and puts them under his tutelage. Men's Wearhouse is a well-run, well-stocked, power-buying men's chain with labels like **BOTANY 500**, **CHAPS BY RALPH LAUREN**, **EVAN PICONE**, **GIVENCHY** and **PIERRE CARDIN**. Men, save 30-40 percent any way you cut it. They are a force to contend with....no matter how much you grimace at "I guarantee it!" By George, it works. Check directory for 15 Men's Wearhouse locations and tuxedos sold at most. *Call toll-free: 800/776-SUIT*

★★★ Repp Big & Tall   817/784-8091

4100 S. Cooper St.
Arlington, TX 76015
www.reppbigandtall.com

Mon-Sat 10-9; Sun Noon-5

Here's a store that will suit you just fine, no matter what your size. Size up that large loving man measuring 6'4" or taller or sporting a waistline of 36-58 and look no further than Repp Big & Tall. If he's really a BMOC, be sure to give him a wardrobe befitting his stature in sizes to 8X or waists to size 70-72. The stores in the Dallas area are all their "Premier Stores" with brands such as: **NAUTICA**, **POLO**, **RALPH LAUREN**, **TOMMY HILFIGER** and their own **REPP** label in all the classic fashions and colors for men. Designer shirts were standing tall around the store for $50 to $69.50. Find more brands represented in the Repp Big & Tall catalog including **CUTTER & BUCK**, **ENRO**, **GANT**, **HEARTLAND**, **IZOD**, **LEVI'S**, **NEW BALANCE**, **PALM BEACH**, **RALPH LAUREN**, **SEBAGO**, **WORLD TRAVELER**. **ENRO** dress shirts were $34.50, **WORLD CLASS TRAVELER** cotton trousers were $52.50, **LEVI'S** 545 jeans were $49.50 and cotton pocket T-shirts were $14.50. Alterations available should you need a few minor adjustments. Their no-hassle return policy makes shopping easy. So what if you have to wait for their sales. It's could be worth it! Check directory for store locations.

★★★★ S & K Famous Brand Menswear — 972/874-1927

3000 Grapevine Mills Pkwy.
Grapevine, TX 76051
www.skmenswear.com

Mon-Sat 10-9:30; Sun 11-8:30

Your man will look like he stepped off the covers of GQ Magazine with the current designer fashions available at S & K. And you'll even feel rich enough to rub elbows with those in Fortune Magazine knowing you saved 20-50 percent and more off everything in the store. Start cheering for S & K Famous Brand Menswear! With over 230 stores nationwide, they are in direct competition with the Men's Wearhouse, though they are headquartered in Richmond, VA and Men's Wearhouse is based in the Bay Area. Here you can join the Elite Rewards program that offers a point system for every dollar you spend during the year. In exchange, you receive valuable discounts like a $100 savings voucher, gift certificates for up to $200, pre-sale notifications and their fit for life guarantee. If you should gain or lose weight a few pounds, just bring them into any S & K and they will alter them for **FREE**....for life. Lots of sportswear and over a thousand suits in stock from names like **BILL BLASS, BRASSBRO, DANIEL HESTER, JOHNNY BENCH, JONES NEW YORK, NINO CERRITO, OLEG CASSINI, PIERRE CARDIN**, et al. Looking to save even more? Apply for their S & K credit card and receive 90 days same as cash with purchases over $299 and 10 percent off your purchases or with your first purchase with their credit card, you'll save $10 off a purchase of $50 or more. Other locations include Prime Outlets, Hillsboro, 254/582-0082 and Tanger Factory Outlet Center, I-20 in Terrell, 972/524-6034. *Call toll-free: 800/285-7848*

Apparel: Resale

★★★★★ **ACO Upscale Resale Shop**   **972/727-4751**

801 E. Main St.
Allen, TX 75002

Mon-Fri 9-5; Sat 10-4

ACO stands for the Allen Community Outreach, a United Way Affiliate. What lies behind door No. 1 are some of the best buys on gently used items, from baby things to exercise equipment. It's the "Joy of the Hunt" that makes you want to uncover what's hiding behind every nook and cranny. Proceeds benefit the Allen's Community Outreach programs, so it's all for a worthy cause. Expect to sing the ACO's praises on designer clothing with names like **ANNE KLEIN**, **CACHE**, **CAROLE LITTLE**, **GAP**, **HILFIGER**, **IZOD**, **LIZ CLAIBORNE**, **OSHKOSH B'GOSH**, **PERRY ELLIS**, **POLO** and more on the gently worn. Fashions for the entire family hang out like clothes on a line, but they are definitely not washed up. Instead, they are pressed and cleaned and selling cheap. Or shall I say inexpensively? Things for the baby, from strollers to car seats, playpens to porta-potties, keep your budget flush. Add toys, collectibles, housewares, small appliances, bridal wear and more to the mix, stir in an ounce of charity and load up the bags. Finally, being a "Bag Lady" has an entirely new meaning. Run, don't walk, when they have their famous bag sale, where you load as much as you can into a bag for only $15. Merchandise moves fast. Donations, of course, are welcomed and always needed. So clean out those closets, garages, attics and donate to a worthy cause. Tax receipts provided with every donation.

★★★★ **Backroom Raggs**   **972/227-4600**

129 Historic Town Square
Lancaster, TX 75146

Tues-Sat 10-5:30

If you're interested in one of the 8 million stories in the big city, consider the one entitled, "From Raggs to Riches." Instead of Tuesdays with Morrie, try Thursdays at the Backroom. That's when they put the pedal to the metal and win all the awards. Garments fly off the racks, in names from department store stock to designer duds, no rugs, just rags with an additional one-third off their already low prices. Mix 'em up and spit 'em out, from consigned goods to right-off-the-line new accessories, including the sought-after **BRIGHTON** belts, watches, bracelets and such. Shine on wardrobes from all the better lines from **DANA BUCHMAN** to **NEIMAN MARCUS** and many more. Lend an ear towards **LIZ CLAIBORNE** or **CAROLE LITTLE** (now owned by TJ Maxx) from $10 to $100 and fill in the gaps with great-looking accessories. Inventory moves in and out fast, so make hay while the sun shines Tuesday through Saturday. A total wardrobe can be had, so you go, girl! From the boardroom to the ballroom, the classroom to the dining room, strike a deal for your closet. Full size range available, sizes 2 to 28 are well represented.

★★★★ **Chapter Two Ladies Resale** 972/594-7722

1111 W. Airport Frwy., Suite 123 @ MacArthur
Irving, TX 75062

Mon-Fri 10-6; Sat 10-5

Sometimes you just don't get it. If so, read on. By the time you're on to Chapter Two, it all makes sense. Just because these fashions weren't housed in your closet first doesn't mean they're not perfectly acceptable now. Let somebody else do the breaking in! Evening wear, career wear, sportswear, casual wear, something to wear to the club; it's all part of the closet reorganization. Whatever needs to be worn can be done so here without wearing a hole in your pocketbook. Consider, instead, buying a new wallet. Surely when you're pulling out that credit card from your used wallet, do you think anybody will scream, "Shame, shame on you!" Accessories, shoes and jewelry add to the finished look here. Not finished looking? Okay! Skim through racks of CAROLE LITTLE, ESCADA, EMANUEL, LIZ CLAIBORNE to bring out the Texan in you with big deals on BMW and DOUBLE RANCHWEAR. You will find sizes 4 to 18 with an occasional plus size. Cash in on greater deals in the "back room" where everything is marked half price. Bring in your consignments, but be sure they are cleaned, in season, on hangers and remember there's a minimum of five items. This store is indeed a page-turner. I wonder who wrote the book?

★★★★★ **Chic to Chic Designer Resale** 972/713-7733

7529 Campbell Rd., #303
Dallas, TX 75248

Mon-Sat 10-7

Dancing chic-to-chic, you're sure to spot a real looker dressed to kill with something from this designer resale boutique. The labels are right off the runways: BCBG, BEBE, CAVALLI, CHANEL, CHLOE, DIOR, DOLCE & GABANA, FENDI, GAULTIER, HERMES, L. FERAUD, LA CROIX, MOSCHINO, PRADA, ST. JOHN, UNGARO, VALENTINO and YSL to name drop a few. Since you only go around once, you might as well go for broke and look the part. Who would know that your wardrobe didn't start with you? After all, you've gone around the block more than once, too. Sizes 0 to 16 may be well worn, or should we say, "Worn well!" No one will ever know it's not new, except you. Let's make it our little secret, just Chic to Chic. Take advantage of great discounts on eveningwear and dress it up with great shoes (sizes 5 to 10) and accessories. Putting it all together makes it a whole new look. This is a resale shop that does carry both new and pre-owned items for sale. This store is known for its boutique-shopping atmosphere and full-service staff. Returns, forget it; they're not allowed, so shop carefully. And remember, this is just between us, Cheap to Cheap.

★★★★★★ **Clothes Circuit, The** 214/696-8634

6105 Sherry Lane @ Preston
Dallas, TX 75225
www.clothescircuit.com

Mon-Fri 10-7; Thurs 10-8; Sat 10-6; Sun Noon-6

Have a glass of sherry and congratulate Clothes Circuit on their 20th Anniversary. Wearing second-hand clothes is "in"- just ask Tammy Faye, who continues to buy her ST. JOHN KNITS at a resale shop in Charlotte, North Carolina where she lives. In fact, she discovered buying them at $120 instead of $1,500 is much more appealing. She's beating the system while wearing her resale suit to visit her husband(s) in prison in years' past. She's sold on the idea of resale shopping. Me, too. So, do as the rich-and-famous do — the ones who want to keep up appearances, that is. This is one "Decidedly Upscale Resale" shop and one of the best in Dallas. Just review some of these movers and shakers: ARMANI, BCBG, CALVIN KLEIN, DKNY, DONNA KARAN, ESCADA, RALPH LAUREN .... and of course, ST. JOHN

KNITS — all priced to thrill while allowing you a dress to kill. Automatic price-downs make it imperative to shop often. Sizes, unfortunately, are limited to unheard of 2s up to 14, but the upper limit is ever-growing and maternity clothes are making their appearance regularly now. The accessories department is world renowned — where else could you find the perfect accompaniment to carry off an entire social season? Wait 'til you see the bags by **BOTTEGA**, **FENDI**, **GUCCI**, **JUDITH LEIBER** and **PRADA**; belts by **BRIGHTON**, **COACH**, **DKNY** and **JUDITH LEIBER**. No "Red Apple" sales here, but their Yellow Banana Sale is legendary. They reduce their already 30 to 40 percent off items by an additional 20 percent. Then twice a year, in late January and late July, they have their Back Room Sale, where prices are slashed to a pittance — and where last season's goods are marked another 50 percent off on the floor. (Prices as low as $5.) They also mark down items an additional 10 percent off during their Random Tuesdays sales, which are unannounced and decidedly ... at random. So, meet you Tuesday Morning, eh? Oh, did I say I saw a few **LOUIS VUITTON'S** sitting next to a **BANANA REPUBLIC**? I almost slipped and fell over. Since 1983, each day at least 50 or more consignors flock to Clothes Circuit with items (hundreds of them) to consign. With one quick glance of the evening wear section, you'll match up several dresses that were photographed the month before for D Magazine or Paper City. And now, mothers-to-be have an elegant selection to choose from as well. But the piece de resistance usually winds up around my wrist or my fingers. Their jewelry collections are the coveted ones from Neiman's such as **LAGOS** and YURMAN as well as fine jewelry from **CARTIER** and **TIFFANY**.

★★★★★★   Clotheshorse Anonymous   972/233-7005

1413 Preston Forest Sq. (Forest Ln @ Preston)   Mon-Fri 10-8; Sat 10-6; Sun 12-6
Dallas, TX 75230
www.clotheshorseanonymous.com

Being the Grande Dame of Dallas'resale shops holds quite a distinction. Jan Kennedy, one of the original founders in the early '70s is still party to the first part and continues to be a hands-on owner since buying out her partner. They hold the distinction of being world's apart from other resale shops not only in their ability to snare couturier labels from their stash of secret consignees, but because they have learned to create a chi-chi boutique atmosphere with gently worn clothes, accessories and some home decor. From the runways of Milan, to the pages of Fashion! Dallas, the labels are dreamy: **ARMANI**, **BCBG**, **CALVIN KLEIN**, **CHANEL**, **DANA BUCHMAN**, **DOLCE & GABBANA**, **DONNA KARAN**, **ESCADA**, **GUCCI**, **HERMES**, **PRADA**, **ST. JOHN**, **VALENTINO**, **VERSACE** and more. They never reveal which closets they've come from, but you can expect lines from sought-after **AMERICAN** and European designers. Their sterling line-up doesn't stop with just clothing as they also showcase hundreds of fabulous accessories in shoes, handbags, scarves and jewelry. We went nuts when we saw the prices on the **JIMMY CHOO** shoes, the **HERMES** scarf, the **LOUIS VUITTON** bag that was actually a current model, bracelets by **DAVID YURMAN**, and **LAGOS** that were the real McCoys....need I say more? Watch for an online department to open soon. They've been written up in a myriad of national magazines and local venues over the years as the premier resale shop of clothes recycled from the rich and famous. With over 17,000 consignees, surely there is at least several high society ladies that you read about in the society columns who consign (and buy) their wardrobes here. In fact, some items even sport their original price tags and have never been worn.

★★★   Consigning Women   972/769-9297

6205 Coit @ Spring Creek, #324   Mon-Fri 10:30-6; Sat 10-5
Plano, TX 75024

Designing women are Consigning Women. Make no bones about it: If you're smart, you clean out your closets each season and hand-pick those clothes that you know you'll never wear again. Too tight. Too bright. Too short. Too whatever. Then take them in and put them on consignment. Recycling helps the environment and your closet. Then with the money you make, reinvest in another wardrobe from ANN TAYLOR or the BANANA REPUBLIC. Good quality, but not exactly right from the pages of Vogue Magazine. Hardly couture but not too shabby, either. From petites to plus sizes, every body has a chance.

★★★★   Dot's Closet   214/826-4099

5810 Live Oak St   Mon-Sat 10:30-6
Dallas, TX 75214-4334

Let's take a leisurely stroll down Memory Lane and seek relief from the plain and uninviting thrift stops of the world. This particular one is a welcome addition to the East Dallas/Lakewood scene, where some of the most beautiful homes and equally lush landscaping reside. All you have to do is dot the i's and cross the t's when deciding what to buy at this charitable thrift shop. Here's where the Disciples of the Holy Trinity Church collect and resell clothing and housewares for their parishioners as well as raise money for a very worthy cause. X doesn't mark the spot but this Dot does wonders. Open the doors to this Closet and take a peek inside. Looking for furniture, collectibles, clothes or antiques? Here they are, just waiting to be adopted. Find china and stemware to impress your guests at your next dinner party or unearth a manual typewriter to pound out your next best-selling novel. Do you know how many requests I get for typewriters? Not everybody is computer literate and every once in a while, a secretary even wants to type in an address on an envelope the old-fashioned way. "Dot provides a pantry, clothing and other assistance to people with terminal illnesses," says DOT executive director Jim Davis. You can't go wrong whether you're buying or giving. It's a wonderful exchange from which ever direction you approach it.

★★★★★★   Double Exposure   817/737-8038

6205 Sunset   Mon-Sat 10-5
Fort Worth, TX 76116

Best 100 SHOPPING DESTINATIONS More than 50 years ago, the Junior League of Fort Worth opened a resale shop called "Bargain Box" for the purpose of selling gently-used clothing. Not only did its members stock the store by donating their clothing, but they also worked the store. Today, it's called Double Exposure. Do a double take and double your pleasure. Double your savings. The name has changed, but the discounts haven't. Twice the selection of men's and women's clothing, but don't overlook other great finds. Cozy furnishings for the house are the beginnings to making your house a home. Mix in an eclectic collection of artwork, vases, books, candy dishes, mirrors and lamps. Unearth a treasure chest of jewelry, then go looking for the right shoes, purse and hat to coordinate with it all. Members of the Junior League still, after all this time, stock the store with high quality merchandise and give more than 5,000 volunteer hours to make sure the place runs on a dime. All merchandise is examined carefully and if it doesn't meet the standards of excellence, it is donated to the Salvation Army. The selection of earrings is all ears. This place is doubly good when the savings double, triple, quadruple, get the picture? Just shutter to think of letting this camera get overexposed because once it's gone, it's gone. Better grab it before it disappears. Double Exposure is located just behind the Ridglea Presbyterian Church, where helping friends and family of Fort Worth's Junior League make their way. Make THEIR day by lending a hand; make YOUR day by lending a hand. One good deed deserves another. After all, don't you deserve that (tax) break today?

★★ Encore! Encore!

972/317-3772

1301 W. FM 407, Suite 104
Lewisville, TX 75077

Tues-Wed, Fri-Sat 10:30-5; Thurs 10:30-7

The audiences roared "Encore! Encore" for many years in our book. But one unhappy customer has some bones to pick with them and frankly, some of those words are better left unsaid. She claims her visit to this resale shop would be her last. With her brand new **ESCADA** pants, they placed a $199 price tag on them, netting her $8 dollars when she went to collect her take. It cost her more in gas with gas prices as high as they are. So to start off, she wasn't happy with her meager commission. Furthermore, she claims the store's personnel were rude as rude could be. Surely they were having a bad day. But when a customer takes the time to write, we take the time to listen. You might be on the alert, and your experience may be completely different. Please share you thoughts with us on our website under the Shoppers Choice Words button. You may shop them on a better day and of course, we want to hear about that, too. Command performances take place on the first Tuesday of each month, and rightfully labeled "Hot Tuesday" when most of the store's inventory is reduced 50 percent; then the remaining coats, evening wear, better leather and sterling silver is dropped 30 percent. Rise to your feet as **ANN TAYLOR, ARGENTI, CALVIN KLEIN, ESCADA, ESPRIT, ESPRIT, GOTEX, LIZ CLAIBORNE** and **TOMMY HILFIGER** take center stage. Ticket prices originally start at $80 to $110, but when it's on an Encore tag, prices descend to $5 and up. With prices this low, the consignor probably felt cheated; but the lucky lady who buys it for $5 no doubt feels like Queen of the May. Pick any seat in the house from slacks and jeans to skirts, dresses, silk shorts and more for career, casual or evening wear. There's also jewelry, accessories, designer handbags priced $20-$60 and there's even a few teenager's things, too. There's a new show every day and for those stars making recurring appearances, markdowns occur every five weeks with color tag discounts up to 50 percent. Street performances are available three times a year during their sidewalk sales in February, July and October. Write your own experience and see if it's a smashing hit or a bomb. Located on FM 407, 1/2 mile west of I-35 E but note, consignments accepted by appointment only. So no wonder this shopper was so unhappy when they couldn't give her an appointment to accommodate her picking up her unsold items before she left for a trip out of town. See, there's always two sides of the story and the merchants have their rules, too. Let's hope all is well that ends well next year.

★★ Family Treasures Resale Shop

214/823-3600

6465 E. Mockingbird Lane, Ste. 362
Dallas, TX 75214

Tues-Sat 10-6

Some heirlooms are meant to be passed on, others are meant to pass away and return some other day — elsewhere. At this resale shop, you will see a comfortable spot for that item to RIP. Proceeds from the sales in this shop benefit the Gateway-Homeless Families by providing shelter and training for mothers with young children. You can lend a helping hand by loading up items that are only collecting dust in your attic: apparel for men, women and children of things that have been in boxes and ignored for years. Donate them. Write them off so the needy can buy needed housewares and furniture at rock-bottom prices. Most items start at just $5. And if you have any items that no longer need to be kept among your Family Treasures, bring in those bags of "nicer than rags" for a tax break benefiting a very worthy cause. Furniture, clothes, housewares and appliances are particularly welcome.

★★★★★   **Fashions For Fractions Boutique**   **214/630-5611**

5554 Harry Hines Blvd.   Mon-Sat 10-5:30
Dallas, TX 75235
www.salvationist.org

Love 'em or leave 'em, either way, you can be a winner. Turn those fashions loose and let them hang out here where they will be grabbed up to serve another purpose. From your closet to God's ears, there is much to be salvaged at the Salvation Army's thrift store, Fashions for Fractions. Taking on a new outlook in life, here's where you can get some of the best designer labels at a really low price. It's almost sacrilegious. Without skirting the issue, this is where you'll find racks and racks of CALVIN KLEIN, CHAUS, GLORIA VANDERBILT, GUESS?, JONES NEW YORK, LIZ CLAIBORNE, POLO and SCOTT MCCLINTOCK. Break the mold with prices at fractions of their original retail. Spend your shopping time wisely by dividing yourself evenly between departments. Calculate the savings on clothing, sporting goods, housewares, exercise equipment, small appliances, wall decor and more. Bring your donations with you and if they can't fit through the door, such as a car, boat or motorcycle, just push three on their voice messaging system for complete details. Be sure to look for stores in Farmers Branch, Irving, Grand Prairie and two in Oak Cliff. But this is the boutique that is haute dog!

★★   **Flock Shop, The**   **817/834-2503**

2908 Layton Ave.   Fri-Sat 10-2
Haltom City, TX 76117

Blessed is she who follows the flock, for birds of a feather find discounts together. Spread those wings and glide into the savings on a wide variety of items here. Help spruce up the family nest without spending the nest egg. Find new duds for men, women and children that have come from somebody else's closet. Arrange them all in a new dresser or maybe even an armoire that's occasionally available. Then complete the package with lots of housewares, collectibles, toys, children and nursery items and even a few crafty notions if you have the notion to rummage around. Inventory in the Flock Shop is constantly changing, so stop in often. Go ahead and wing it. The Flock Shop is the Ashbury United Methodist Church Mission's resale boutique and is located between Beach and Belknap.

★★★★★   **Gavrel Furs**   **817/335-3877**

2735 W. 7th St.   Mon-Sat 10-5
Fort Worth, TX 76107
www.casualfurs.com

How can you tell that the furs aren't new? By the price, silly. No way can you buy new furs this cheap. Fort Worth is home to a lot of opportunities to dress up and look like the rich and famous. What began strictly as a storage and re-styling of furs, both contemporary and vintage, has turned into a place to find gorgeously restyled furs plus fur and cloth coats that didn't sell or sell out at specialty stores. So what you might see are racks of cashmere or angora coats that retail up to $1,500 for under $500. Now put that in your bonnet, or hat, or muff, and top off a winter's chill. Or, for lighter moments, wrap up in a boa. They have one of the country's largest selections of pre-owned furs under one roof, over 400 in stock at all times. Shopping online has also been introduced. After all, remember those wintry days in Detroit? New York? Finally, the eastern seaboard can shop in Texas and warm the cockles of their pocketbooks. Call them toll-free for additional information on all of their stock if you don't see one that appeals to you. Check out their fabulous fur teddy bears, bomber jackets and denim vests that round out their inventory. The purses alone will make you drool. Slip into a pair of fur slippers if you think luxury only begins with a coat. But remember, the furs under $1,000 sell fast, so call before even getting your hopes up with something you see on their website. It may be up one day and sold the next. Across from the old Montgomery Ward's on 7th Street, near the Will Rodgers Coliseum, this is the perfect place to secure the perfect cover up for an evening on the town. Ask for Robert Rook and trust me, you can now call it a wrap! *Call toll-free: 888/629-0100*

★★★★★ Genesis II 214/351-6394

5417 W. Lovers Lane
Dallas, TX 75209

Mon-Fri 10-5:30; Sat 10-5

Bring them your tired, your poor, your closets in dis-dress and make somebody happy. When God created the heavens, he also had a hand in creating Genesis II. Proceeds from this charitable collection of fashion dynasties make for wonderful fodder at society luncheons. Wow, what a wonderful cache of designer clothes — some new with the price tags still intact; others worn once, without a wrinkle in sight. A never-been-worn NEIMAN'S embroidered jacket was a staggering $10 (retail $100), a RALPH LAUREN silk summer dress valued at $125 was a measly $10, and a CAROLE LITTLE red skirt that retailed for $50 was marked $8. The couturier line-up sparkles with stars like: CHANEL, GIANFRANCO FERRE, ISSEY MIYAKE, MOSHINO, ST.JOHN KNITS and others. Hundreds and hundreds of women have benefited from the services offered through Genesis Women's Shelter. Many media personalities make Genesis II a regular stop on their resale route, whether they're buying or donating. Donations are accepted Monday through Friday 10 to 5 and Saturday 10 to 4:30.

★★ Genesis Thrift Store 214/520-6644

2918 Oak Lawn
Dallas, TX 75219

Mon-Fri 10-5; Sat 10-4:30

No doubt about it. These "Bargains of Eden" will have you coming and going. At the corner of Oak Lawn and Cedar Springs, this is the first of two thrift stores, one is more thrift than upscale, but more about that at Genesis II. The thrift store on Oak Lawn is jam-packed for serious bargain basement shoppers. The Lovers Lane location, Genesis II, is for serious upscale shoppers. Within their large 7,000-square-foot expanse, every item is organized, except on Saturdays, when it's hand-to-mouth. Displays wind up getting "undisplayed" so it's often your job to sort and shop with caution. Clothing for men, women and children have relocated from others'closets, kitchens, toy chests and buffets in town. There are a few pieces of furniture, shoes on the side shelves, jewelry and more to catch your attention. All proceeds benefit the Genesis Shelter, a full-service care facility serving abused women and children. Within this 14-room facility, they provide a safe temporary haven and a six to eight-week rehabilitation program that includes help in finding housing, jobs and providing 24-hour counseling (especially in the area of self-esteem). ALCOVE, the Jewish Women's Council, offers this child-care assistance facility FREE, giving women a real second chance at re-establishing a healthier lifestyle. All women are screened prior to entering the program for drugs (they're the only shelter that does so). In spite of such a worthy cause, our shopper this year was very disappointed in their store. However, for a more orderly arrangement, visit their upscale resale location at 5417 Lovers Lane. They, too, support the Genesis Shelter and accept just about anything you might have that's not currently being put to good use. This year, you can now donate your car to help save a life. By donating your car, working or not, you may be able to help a battered woman or child. Remember, all donations are tax deductible. Call 214/559-2050 for car donations. And separate the need for charity from the review of their Oak Lawn Thrift Store because everything you buy helps this most worthy cause.

★★★★   Graceful Buys   817/481-6254

201 N. Barton St.   Mon-Sat 10-6
Grapevine, TX 76051

Grapevine's upscale resale shop specializes in men's, women's and children's apparel is ready for
Freddy and any other frugal frontiersmen anxious to head out for the hunt. Most items are donated
by Colleyville, Southlake and Grapevine communities, so expect the clothes to be of designer
label quality waiting to be re-dressed for success, as would be appropriate for the climb up the corporate ladder. But man and woman do not live by wardrobes alone. So, to that end, they offer
plenty of goods for the home and hearth. Ah, Home, Cheap, Home. They also sell home decor,
electronics, computers, jewelry, linens, books, shoes, toys and more! All proceeds benefit
GRACE, the local non-profit charity. Located in downtown Grapevine, at the north of Main Street
and next to Elliott's Hardware, how can you lose?

★★★★★   Hope Chest Resale Shop   214/520-1087

4209 McKinney Ave., Suite 200   Tues-Sat 10-5
Dallas, TX 75205

You gotta have Hope. All you really need is Hope. And when you're supporting the Hope Cottage
folks, who can resist? Seasonal samples are donated, along with decorative gift items that are sure
to bring down the house. This one-stop haven for maternity, baby and children's resale items,
men's and women's clothing, toys and household items not only generates money for mothers-to-
be who are considering adoption, or families waiting to adopt, a stop here sure comes in handy
when the baby or child is ready to call John and Jane Doe, Mom and Dad. Worthy cause, agreed,
but don't forget that you like a bargain now and then, too. For a touch of Underground Shopping
history, this resale shop is now sitting where the former Oak Lawn office of The Underground
Shopper was for about 15 years before Hope Chest bought it. And now, it's probably one of the
best thrift stores in town. It must be in the water.

PS   Les Femmes Du Mond   214/350-4406

6303 Forest Park Rd.
Dallas, TX 75235-5450

This is one fabulous charity that when they hold their periodic rummage sale at Exchange Park
Mall, just off Mockingbird between Lemmon Ave and Harry Hines, you can bet Highland Park
turns out in force. After all, it's their neighbors who have donated all of their wardrobes and home
accents that have fallen out of favor only to make room for something new. Shop for fantastic bargains on gently-used couture clothes, shoes, furs, accessories, children's clothes and toys, menswear, books and potpourri that appear at a pittance of their regular prices. So, it's like a swap and
shop 'til you drop marathon for one day that has shoppers coming out of the woodwork. Since I
was asked to speak to the group this year at the Zodiac Room at North Park's Neiman-Marcus, the
least I can do is support their charitable contributions and spread the word. It's a sale that is the
talk of the town and you should be first in line when I tell you about it next. Of course, you can call
the number above if you want to be in the know before anybody else beats you to the punch. Go to
lunch and then have a field day.

★★★★★ **My Secret Closet**   **972/267-1144**

17194 Preston Rd., Suite 118   Mon-Thurs 10-7; Fri-Sat 10-6; Sun 1-5
Dallas, TX 75252
www.mysecretclosetinc.com

At the corner of Preston and Campbell, the secret is out. They have come out of your closet and into theirs. Labels include ESCADA and ST. JOHN KNITS alongside the lower-priced BCBG, BEBE and CAROLE LITTLE. Did you know some women will fill their closets with expensive clothes that are hardly, if ever, worn? Well, now you do. And when they need more room, they unload here. Welcome to My Secret Closet - a secret can be kept only so long, you know. There comes a time when you just can't keep it "in" without bursting at the seams. Merchandise is divided into three distinct groups for casual, career and couture occasions. I do know ladies who lunch and buy very expensive clothes and only wear them once or twice. That silk blouse, wool jacket or pair of fine shoes can look brand new for years — but here, it's a slam dunk deal. It's no secret that a ball gown goes to just one ball, or that the only way real people can afford CHANEL is if we're owner No. 5. This neat, petite boutique with perky blonde personnel take in consignments of only the highest caliber and resell them for the lowest prices. New VERSACE jeans were originally $98, marked down 30 percent and then another 15 percent. Suits were going for about $95; blazers, $45; blouses, $10. We found new fashions from LUCIA LUKKEN like broomstick skirts, velvet patchwork jackets and chenille sweaters selling for a little above wholesale. Belts and handbags said KATE SPADE and D & G and the tag clearly stated "faux" so....A never-worn market sample linen dress with ethnic embroidery was $24 so we grabbed it and forever held our peace. Can you keep a secret? We saw it in a famous catalog for $85 plus shipping. Seeing is believing, and I'm a believer now. Amen!

★★★ **My Sister's Room**   **903/597-8500**

216 W. 9th   Mon 10-4; Tues-Fri 10-5; Sat 10-4
Tyler, TX 75701

Sisters rejoice. Make room for new attire and retire some of the old. My Sister's Room is open for business. Ladies, welcome in a whole new look from casual wear to After 5 in sizes ranging from petite to plus and fit for everyone in between. Girlfriends include CAROLE LITTLE, DONNA KARAN, ELLEN TRACY, LANE BYRANT and even LIZ CLAIBORNE — they've all made a visit to My Sister's Room at one time or another. Consignments are accepted, but must first be cleaned, pressed and on hangers. Current styles and in-season clothing only with a consignment split of 50/50. Now open on Mondays. Anything less would be splitting heirs.

★★★★ **New Beginning Resale**   **972/487-8840**

1486 Buckingham @ Garland Rd.   Mon-Sat 11-6
Garland, TX 75042-4201
www.newbeginningcenter.org

When the charity impacts victims of domestic violence, you have a double purpose to shop. Whether you're donating or buying, you're doing a double duty. Looking for buried treasure? Start digging your way through the stacks of possibilities and see what Mothers can unearth. See donated goods of every shape, kind and value, but clothes are still the strength in numbers here, all sizes for men, women and children. This non-profit refuge benefits the New Beginning Center which is the outreach program for victims of domestic abuse and violence in the Garland and Mesquite area. Donated items are sold through the store and all proceeds are in turn recycled to the Center. For larger donations, the store will provide pick-up; otherwise, pack up your kids and pack up your car....but unfortunately, your kids are not on the welcome donation list. If so, what would you claim as your write-off? Priceless? Look for shoes, clothing, housewares and furniture in this no-frills store for a new beginning for some victim of abuse. But especially shop on Tuesdays as they pick a category each Tuesday and mark everything in that category half off their already low, low prices. It's not uncommon to walk out with a designer like a **JONES NEW YORK** suit for $6 or a **BILL BLASS** suit for a man, $10. Talk about cheap chic!

★★★   North's Plus Size Fashions   817/737-2174

5405 Birchman Ave.   Tues-Sat 10-6
Fort Worth, TX 76107

Tired of shopping on the one small rack in the back of the store at the typical consignment or resale shops? Worry warts, relax. Grow weary no more. Muster up your strength and head south to North's Plus Size Fashions. Sorry skinny mini's, unless you're a size 16 or above, there's not much here for you except accessories. But for those who represent the woman of girth, there's a world of worth waiting your visit. Rack after rack, you won't have to wrack your brain looking for an outfit that has some oomph. Fashionable wear for work and play run the gamut. Try on tops and blazers, suits and slacks, dresses and skirts. Even sweaters for the winter and cover-ups for the summer are available for zaftig women. Heat things up with a large selection of activewear, but should you need a little number for a night on the town, the numbers are pathetically few. Big girls don't cry except when they can't find a prom dress when they need it most. Other than that, North's Plus Size Fashions has everything a full-figured woman would want at a price that is certainly lean and mean.

★★★★   Prestonwood Upscale Resale   972/669-9000

300 N. Coit Rd., Ste. 153   Mon-Sat 10-6; Thurs 10-7
Richardson, TX 75080

At last, the Prestonwood Baptist Church has opened its doors to all shopping denominations. You don't have to be Baptist to love a bargain....you just have to be cheap! Within the 2,000 square feet of retail selling space, Prestonwood Upscale Resale has ladies'and junior apparel, wardrobes for expectant mothers and their eventual offspring, babies and children. Add into the mix: purses, scarves, hats and jewelry. You know you're blessed because there's something affordable for a change. Far northern lights shine on this faith-based, nonprofit retail store which generates monies to support the Prestonwood Pregnancy and Family Care (PPFC) clientele. It's a double whammy. You get to shop and save on new and gently-used merchandise and they raise much-needed monies for those in need. They have volunteer store personnel, a prayer support team and willingly accept gifts and donations from the community. Remember, all donations are tax deductible, with tax receipts available. Located on the street level between Belt Line and Arapaho.

★★★★★★   Re-Furred Vintage Furs   214/696-1381

9820 N. Central Expressway @ Walnut Hill, #507   Mon-Sat 10-5
Dallas, TX 75231

 At the Corners Shopping Center, owner Koslow's Furs has resurrected another concept to replace the failed Lilly Dobson Designer Outlet. Keeping the same location and the same phone number, this is now THE place to wear someone else's fur coat. Specializing in pre-loved furs, whether you're buying or wanting to consign yours for sale, expect to be able to save plenty of gelt on these pelts. The two European men in charge were perfect gentlemen, suave and debonair themselves. Too, they knew furs.

★★★★ ReThreads   972/233-9323

411 Preston Valley Shopping Center   Mon-Wed, Fri 10-6:30; Thurs 10-8; Sat 10-6; Sun 12-5
Dallas, TX 75230

This is the place for tired wardrobes, clothes with lots of tread still left and many miles to go - especially men's. ReVitalize, ReJuvenate, ReTaliate against high prices. Trade in, trade up, trade your old way of thinking into a more contemporary mindset about wearing someone else's wardrobe. It's in. It's smart. Who cares? Whether you're buying or selling, this is an option to consider on the road to success. Consignment men's and women's apparel, shoes and accessories are jammed into rack after rack, waiting to ReTire to your closets. Buy them by the closets full; sell them by the closets full. Both ways, you'll come out a winner with twice as much for your money.

★★★★★★ Revente-Ladies Upscale Resale   214/823-2800

5400 E. Mockingbird Lane, Suite 113   Mon-Thurs 11-7; Fri-Sat 10-6; Sun 1-5
Dallas, TX 75206
www.reventeresale.com

Dawna Derrick has quite a line-up of awards, including being voted into the 100 BEST in The Underground Shopper, being named by D Magazine as not only a best buy but as a best shop in the September and October 2003 issues and named by the Dallas Observer as the Best Women's Clothing Store and all for good reason. It's a pleasure buying and consigning at her upscale designer resale shop. There are no exuses not to shop ladies! Whether it's during a lunch break or a weekend layover, you're sure to find something new that has been worn by someone before ye. Across from the old Dr Pepper plant and now part of the resurgence of Uptown, here you'll find one of the best-laid plans for any mark-down maven. Peek into the closets of Highland Park and see BCBG, BETSY JOHNSON, CHANEL, DANA BUCHANAN, DKNY, DONNA KARAN, ELLEN TRACY, EMANUEL, ESCADA, FERRAGAMO, JIL SANDER, RALPH LAUREN, ST. JOHN KNITS, TAHARI and more. Don't shut your wallet until you've seen all the new and consigned accessories: COACH, KATE SPADE (the real ones) and PRADA handbags were in pristine condition waiting to be toted off into a new life, but some greedy long-arm grabbed Kate before I got out of the gate. Everything in the place is in tip-top shape and just waiting for their walking papers. You will find everything from career wear to After 5, from petite to plus sizes, but the concentration is in sizes 2 to 18. Consignors split 40/60 with the advantage staying in-house. There's a 60-day sale period, or else it's bye-bye. You get a check on what's sold monthly, which can be a real boon to your cash (or cache) flow, depending on whether you're buying or selling. Eight items are requested at a time to be brought in. One will also find accessories such as jewelry, shoes, scarves, hats, great smelling candles....the whole shebang. Hop online and learn a thing or two about reinventing a whole new wardrobe for less.

★★★★★ Ritzy Raggs Ladies Resale   817/377-1199

6714 Camp Bowie (Town West Cntr)   Tues-Sat 10-5
Fort Worth, TX 76116

Puttin' on the Ritz, even if it was someone else's, has never been easier or more cost-effective. Consider this shop among Tarrant County's more prestigious addresses. After all, members of the TCU theatre guild can only be seen in a dress once per opening. And with six performances a year, that's a lot of new threads. (Glitzy beaded ones, that is.) Take advantage of these designer labels and prices designed for those who are price conscious. Make an appearance in ADOLFO, AFTER FIVE, ALBERT NIPPON, ANNE KLEIN, ARMANI, BIZ, CHANEL, CRISSA, DIANE FREIS, ESCADA, HARI, KASPER, RALPH LAUREN, ST. JOHN KNITS, TERIJON, UNGARO and others of the same ilk. But there's more than meets the eye here since even the rich and famous get down and dirty (but not in these clothes, of course.) Choose from dresses, sportswear, shoes, belts, purses, active wear, suits, casual ensembles and separates. Equally impressive is the selection of coats and wraps available when the season's temperatures drop. Become a seasoned shopper and shop for any of these Ritzy Raggs. Consignments are accepted only if they're pressed, cleaned and presented on hangers. Find them hanging out in the West Town Shopping Center. Reconfirm their hours before you head out the door as we've called three times only to have silence at the other end.

★★★ Robin Hood Designer Resale   214/360-9666

6609 Hillcrest Rd.
Dallas, TX 75205

Mon-Fri 10:30-6; Sat 10:30-5

Now you can't accuse them of stealing from the rich, but rather consigning from the rich and reselling to the poor. Guilty as charged. Fair maidens can don designer suits, pants, jeans, T-shirts, dresses, blouses, blazers and the list goes on. Countrymen (and women) still sing the praises of Robin Hood and his merry band of labels including ANN TAYLOR, BANANA REPUBLIC, GAP and GAP EXPRESS, J.CREW, RALPH LAUREN, ST. JOHN KNITS, XOXO and more. Hugs and kisses to the Mustangs, this shop is located directly across the street from SMU. For all those skinny, short-skirt coeds running around campus, you will have your fill. Sizes 2 to 12 are those they cater to; those with a small frame and nothing but(t)! Anything larger and this MUSTANG runs out of gas. The selection varies from semester to semester and some of the time, they don't make the grade while other times, they go to the head of the class. It all depends, but too erratic for a much higher rating.

★★★★ S & P Trading Co.   214/369-8977

6104 Luther Ln. (Preston Cntr.)
Dallas, TX 75225

Mon-Sat 10-6

S & P is like the A & P, only for women hungry for designer clothing, resale and samples. If you're a size 2 (and in need of drink supplements) to size 16, here is a place for all things to consider. Apparel and accessories will keep you coming and going to any event, from casual to corporate, cruise to the country club....at a fraction of what they cost new. This expanded closet houses more clothes in 1,200 square feet than any other store in Preston Center. That's a fact worth noting but why, I don't know. Anyway, don't bring in an entourage of shopping buddies 'cause you all won't fit. And don't bring in a truckload of clothing expecting them to take them all in. This isn't the Humane Society. Consignments are accepted for 60 days with a 50/50 split, unless your item sells for more than $100, then you get 60 percent. You might remember that S & P could stand for being S-tylish and P-riced right. So, if you want to "trade up," this company could be your door-opener.

★★★★ Second Glance   817/581-1909

6304 Rufe Snow Drive
North Richland Hills, TX 76148-3317
www.openarmshome.org/pages/resale.html

Mon-Sat 10-6

Look, once, look twice, oh what the heck, look a third time because every time you find yourself looking, chances are, you'll find something to buy. Buying here is a two-fold experience, both positive. The diligent efforts of this shop help support programs for abused women, so be sure and give them a second chance....oops, glance. Operated by Open Arms Home, Inc., they have a reputation of doing good deeds for all concerned. Now, do yours. Clothing for the entire family is the bulk of the stock in house. Some designer clothes, some department store stock, some discount stock, and some unknown stock. Plus housewares, furniture and appliances now line their aisles, too. Wearing second-hand clothes is like giving a first-hand opportunity to a woman who has suffered from abuse. She and her children can buy what they need; proceeds of the shop benefit the entire program. You'll find plenty of resale clothing for everyone including new clothing for men, women and children. You can also find picture-perfect home furnishings, accessories, household items, bedding, appliances, collectibles and even a few antiques. Got a little extra time on Saturday? Then visit the corner of Watauga and Rufe Snow where there's an enormous rummage sale that catapults itself into a colossal savings event. Remember that shopping for charity is more than just finding a bargain, it's giving something in return. These volunteers give of themselves daily to provide a safe haven for battered and abused women along with their children. How can you help? Donations and volunteers are always welcomed. Pick-up of furniture donations available by calling 817/263-9784. Be sure to visit their other locations at the Wedgwood Shopping Center, 5314 Trail Lake Drive, Fort Worth, 817/292-8222 (Mon-Sat 10-5) and in Grapevine at 1649 West Northwest Hwy., 817/416-2953 (Mon-Sat 10-6). Se habla Espanol.

★★ Thrift Mart 972/721-1861

1131 E. Irving Blvd.
Irving, TX 75060

Mon-Sat 10-8; Sun Noon-6

Simple is as simple does. The name gives it away. Nothing to figure out. This is a marketplace of used goods, thrifty and not much more than a nickel. Sift through thrift clothing for men, women and children in a variety of shapes and sizes. Uncover **BUGLE BOY**, **CALVIN KLEIN**, **CHEROKEE**, **GIRBAUD**, **NAUTICA**, **POLO**, **TOMMY HILFIGER** and **UNION BAY** at any given visit. Put your feet up on pre-owned furniture while tuning on to your favorite station on one of the many stereos available. (If you're not tuned to Legends 770, KAAM, why not?) If you're just interested in furniture, call 972/721-9635 for the direct information line. Slip into something more comfortable and start your fitness regime to get in shape with the selection of exercise equipment for sale. But if the cross trainer is on the other foot gathering dust (although an old **STAIRMASTER** does make for an interesting plant stand), bring it in for a donation and receive a receipt for a tax write-off. You should be familiar with those by now. We're almost through with this chapter and you should know by now, it pays to give.

★★★★ Tinka's 972/716-9944

142 Spring Creek Shopping Village (NW Corner Coit & Belt Line)
Dallas, TX 75248

Mon-Sat 10-6

We're not sure where the name came from but the values speak for themselves. Tinka's consignment boutique offers an elegant shopping atmosphere for women of all ages in search of clothing for any occasion with lots of designer labels, After 5 and prom dresses, suits, skirts, blouses, pants and much more. Find new and used inventory, sizes 2 through 22 and all marked well below retail. Tinka's offers a laundry list of designer labels cleaned, pressed and ready to be dressed out and up with accessories including jewelry, shoes, handbags, hats, belts, scarves, sunglasses, did we leave anything out? Tinka, dinka, party, too.

★★★★★   Western Wear Exchange

817/738-4048
Mon-Sat 10-6

2809 Alta Mere
Fort Worth, TX 76116
www.westernwearexchange.com

Promenade your partner to and from this resale shop if you want to live the lifestyle of a Texan. A big life. A good life. For a lot less. Unlike your typical resale shop, this one is a specialty boutique celebrating a decade of delivering the deals to Dallas and Fort Worth urban cowboys. Whether you need boots or jeans everyday or just for a special event, who cares if a dude has roped in it before? See the better brands of **BANJO, CINCH, JUSTIN, PANHANDLE SLIM, RESISTOL, ROCKY MOUNTAIN, STETSON, WRANGLER** and more. Every once in a while, you'll see a chi-chi brand such as **ECR** (Ooh, la la!), **HARISTON-ROBERSON, SCULLY** and **STUBBS**. Pre-worn and new intermingle with the ambiance creating a popular hangout for ranch hands as well as ranch owners. A huge selection of the popular pearl snap shirts, long and short sleeve styles, makes any cowhand drool. Gather information on their website on how to consign, get on their mailing list, and learn the ropes. Just don't show up in chiffon and lace or you'll be skinned and tarred. This resale and consignment shop is the only one catering to western wear that we know of in the Metroplex. Gently-worn, please, not worn out. Pick through your collection and get rid of those you're not wearing. Somebody else will. Jeans, shirts, boots, belts, buckles, vests and hats for the entire family will start the ball rolling. Thank you, ma'am. Big hair, fancy skin boots and a pair of leather jeans may even be in the cards next.

Apparel: Vintage & Costume

★★★★ **Ahab Bowen**   214/720-1874

2614 Boll St.   Mon-Sat Noon-6; Sun 1-5
Dallas, TX 75204

Get in the groove at Ahab Bowen. Guys 'n'dolls can cover up in just about any vintage or classic fashion style from the '40s, '50s and '60s all the way to the '70s. Hey, just put it all together for your own eclectic ensemble and start singing, "Yesterday." Since the "Beat Goes On," a little funk with some '78s can be found casually lining the shelves. The repertoire is tagged generally about $40 or less. Frankly, my dear, I don't give a — well, actually, we do care enough to buy the very best. We do believe that paying more and getting less is for the birds. These cool cats make sure you do just the opposite. Ahab's isn't just blowing smoke screens around the fashion scene. He's breaking the molds while setting trends everywhere he goes. Break out at your next semi-formal occasion by donning a new Age of Aquarius ensemble. Authenticate the evening with hats, handbags, costume jewelry, scarves, ties, boots and even a zoot suit thrown in for good measure. Time to do the time warp again! It's no wonder it's a favorite of the uptown/downtown scene.

★★★★★★ **Buffalo Exchange**   214/826-7544

3424 Greenville Ave. @ McCommas   Mon-Sat 11-7; Sun Noon-6
Dallas, TX 75206-5806
www.buffaloexchange.com

At last, the buffalo has come home to Big D so let's give them a hand. This Arizona-based chain of used-clothing and consignment shops has finally made it to lower Greenville, making this store their third in Texas (Houston and Austin before Big D!). Named the best vintage clothing store, for example, in Phoenix and in Boise, Idaho, expect the Observer to be scouting them for some notoriety soon. Rope some perfect duds to dig for both men and women in used and vintage clothing, shoes, handbags and knick-knacks. If you're not daring enough to wear that chiffon strapless prom dress from the '50s to your next soiree, you can always use it at Halloween. Expect the traditional blue jeans from the **GAP** or a pair of overalls from **DICKIES** hanging out next to the cat-like sunglasses and fishnet stockings. As a seller, you can choose your method of payment — either 35 percent of the selling price in cash or a 50 percent credit towards merchandise. As with most resale/consignment shops, their policy is that the stuff is delivered in clean, good condition, in season and on hangers. Expect them to be "underwhelmed" if you bring in a cashmere sweater in July or a sleeveless pastel blouse in January. If you get goose bumps shopping for a retro wardrobe with socially-responsible undertones, you can enjoy their "tokens for bags" program and instead of accepting to have your purchase bagged, you can have a nickel instead donated to a charity of your choice. Nothing spectacular, but there's nothing that was not worthy of a budgetary consideration since most items are priced under $25. Born in 1974 in Tucson, Arizona near the university and supposedly the first store that bought, sold, traded and took clothing items and accessories on consignment, today this chain boasts 22 stores and six franchises in 11 states with a $24 million dollar balance sheet. Who would have thought a used clothing store would evolve into such a gold mine?

Casa Loco   214/748-5626

2639-B Elm St.   Mon-Fri 1-9; Tues-Sat 2-6
Dallas, TX 75226

 Watch out Ricky, living La Vida Loco takes on a whole new attitude here. This house is crazy. Vintage may be one way to describe the clothing, but others might use trendy, wild, fanatical. In other words, this is the place where it's hip to be square. Shape up the deal if you can, but most prices seem a little steep on clothing sized 1-10 and Small-Large. Casa Loco is a happening place for Dallas night-lifers, which is why the store doesn't open until noon. Everyone who works there is still in bed. If life for you is wild and crazy, you might just find a little solace in some new threads (though they have that old, retro look.) Think SoHo and you'll be right at home in this Deep Ellum clone. It's fun and fashionably advanced. Hip, haute and high priced.

★★★★ Garland Road Thrift Store   214/324-1010

10030 Garland Rd.   Mon-Sat 9-9; Sun 11-7
Dallas, TX 75218

This is a flea for all, a garage sale bazaar atmosphere where anything goes. But you can really capture some vintage clothing that if it would be hanging around in Deep Ellum would command a much bigger price tag. Looking to spin a few vinyl's? Need a couch for your starving-artist son, an exercise bike for yourself and a bridal gown for your daughter? It's all under one roof with prices so low you'd might want to buy by the bag full. If all else fails, the fabric alone can be recycled into great looking pillows. That's what I did with several of them....and now all my friends want me to make them what I'm calling my "Petticoat Pillows." Well, maybe in my next life. Surely you can work them into your busy schedule, they're open enough hours.

★★★★★★ Hale's Costume   817/838-7126

2902 Race   Tues-Fri 10-6; Sat 10-4; Mon By Appt.
Fort Worth, TX 76111

 Also known as Beverly & Winona's Costume & After Five Fabrics, by whatever name, they are Hale and hearty when it comes to costumes and fabrics. Even if you needed a little gore or wanted a selection that is strictly Gabor, you will find it here. This black and yellow addition to Fort Worth, off Highway 121 and Sylvania Avenue, is a stop worth making, especially if you're in the market for a non-traditional bridal ensemble. Owner/creator Beverly Hale and her daughter (Beverly & Winona) have the magic touch when finding the garment that responds to a particular theme, be it medieval, Western or surreal. No matter what is in store for the party, look the part with everything from custom-made costumes to old favorites including Dracula, Grim Reaper, Cinderella, Dorothy and her entourage, Peter Pan and a host of pirates. Costumes for saloon girls, cowboys, Indians, bank robbers and even prisoner's black and white stripes complete with a ball and chain. (Know anybody that would look perfect in a size 60 Extra Large?) But don't feel tied down due to high prices because most costumes edged out the competition at $35 to $55 a day. Children's costumes run less and rent for $25. Discover the undercover world of Hale's Costume and wear what's on your mind. Other "underground shops" at the same intersection: Judy Havelka Enterprises and Discount Building Supplies, for starters, down the street from City Mattress and At Your Service. So, the Race is on.

★★★ Puttin' on the Ritz   214/369-4015

6615 Snider Plaza
Dallas, TX 75205

Tues-Fri 11-5; Sat Noon-5

Since when does a store close for the summer and the buyers take off on a buying trip? I don't believe that for a minute. Even though they recently moved to more spacious digs, how can they get away with a vacation several month's long? I want that kind of job! Maybe owner Siri Ahearne will consider hiring me so I can go on a buying trip next summer. Wouldn't that be special? I can, at the drop of a hat, put on the Ritz, believe me. If you're blue and don't know what to do, head to Puttin'on the Ritz. Cheer up. Everything here is probably older than you because it's all vintage clothing that has been beautifully restored, including wedding gowns. Gary Cooper would drop to his knee seeing these nuptial gowns dating from the 1880s to the 1960s. But proposals run $200 to $3,000 for gowns of this magnitude. Squeeze into a size 1-10 or squash the whole idea. Finish off the bridal party in dated suits and dresses for a completed or eclectic look while time stands still. After all, when you finally say, "I do," you need all the time you can get.

★★★★ Ragwear   214/827-4163

2000 Greenville
Dallas, TX 75206

Mon-Sat 11-7; Sun Noon-7

Ever heard a "Rags to Rags" story that didn't make you cry? Well, instead of crying, go to "Rags to Riches" instead. Got a date and need something special to wear? Something that will turn heads and get their tongues wagging? Then set a world's record in making a bee-line to Ragwear. Jazz it up. Snazz it up. Steppin'out with your baby does require an extra effort otherwise you sort of fade into the woodwork. Imagine not whining, "I've got nothing to wear!" Like a good wine, these clothes get better with time. Wind up with a few outfits that reflect the good ol'days. If it's authentic and 20 years or older, you'll find it hanging out with other oldies but goodies. Problem is, the older you are the less likely you are to 1) be able to fit into them or 2) want to wear them....again! Older is indeed better. Better yet, find them at good old-fashioned prices — most were under $40. If they're trendy enough to make the cut, you might even find new fads that are all the rage. Ragwear is wearing out the competition and feeding the fashion frenzy next to Lula B's restaurant in lower Greenville across from the Arcadia Theater. Visit the second Ragwear at 13410 Preston Rd. in the old Arnold Square (in the same center as Vantage Shoes, across from Valley View Mall, at the intersection of Preston and Dilbeck.) Now you can double your pleasure. From top to bottom, dress for less.

Rich Hippie

972/991-4477

5100 Belt Line, Suite 700 (Village on the Pkwy)
Addison, TX 75240
www.richhippie.com

Mon-Fri 10-6; Sat 10-6; Sun 12-5

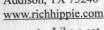

Like a cat, Eric Kimmel has nine lives, and probably has even more — just to be different. From the day we first met at El Centro College when I spoke to a group of students on Underground Shopping, Eric stood out in his orange Bermuda shorts and to date, is probably still wearing them. As usual, he's on the cutting edge of high fashion and continues to push the envelope with new angles on singing (and sewing) the old denim blues. His line of vintage clothing with the **RICH HIPPIE** label is sold in boutiques from California to Japan with the foundation being blue jeans and camo. Considered unisex, they are imaginative and in-your-face fashion-forward designs. Jeans, vests, jackets, vests with patches of bandanna, gingham, suede or macramÈ insets; I would expect nothing but creativity oozing from any venture he touches. Other jeans were jeweled or embroidered. Wow! Hawaiian shirts were transformed into drawstring skirts, suede and leather patchwork pants, vintage leather jackets, shearing coats, real fur and faux, ever so chic. Bring in any item of clothing and have their in-house seamstresses applique it or add any custom feature to create a one-of-a-kind statement to call your own. Take something old that you have grown accustomed to and for under $20, transform it into something new. Prices averaged in the $39 to $79 range with outerwear topping out under $300. Eric Kimmel may or may not be rich or a hippie, but he is sure clever as clever is!

★★★★★★   Rose Costumes

940/566-1917

521 N. Elm St.
Denton, TX 76201
www.rosecostumes.com

Mon-Sat 10-5:30

A rose by any other name just wouldn't be the same. Plant yourself here for tons and tons of costumes (over 4,000 to choose from) from the basics to the unusual. Duds you might not have ever thought to dig up may be unearthed here as you walk through a myriad of room period vignettes. Each room houses a different category, era, period, you'll see what I mean when you get there. Avant-garde to vintage, elegant or funky, you'll have more than enough to choose. In fact, it's like taking a field trip to a museum. Plan on spending hours just playing "dress up!" Pick an era, any era, but make no mistake about it, Rose Costumes is the place that will knock your socks off (and then replace them with some laced-up stiletto shoes). Almost 90 percent of their costumes are hand-made and you'll never see any other like them. Did you see me as "THE RECYCLED QUEEN" on TV last year? Complete with plastic bags, doggie bags, old cigarette packs on a specially-designed coat complete with a drum majorette matching hat. Oh, it was sensational! Did you know you can complete just about any costume with accessories such as socks, shoes, hosiery, jewelry, wigs, capes, purses, ties, suspenders, parasols, wands, canes and props for propping up whatever. Keep your wallet at bay as costume rentals start as low as $45. But what a great way to remember the day with a 1970s sherbet-tinted tux? Or maybe a zoot suit from the 1920s is more your style? Get in on the game with knights in shining armor, fair maidens, scoundrels and gypsies. Maybe Elvis isn't really dead? Wasn't he last seen hanging out with Captain Hook and Cher? Clown around with royalty. Let the fireman put out the flames from those old-time bathing suits. Just what you needed....another bag lady in your life. Oh, you'd rather it be a belly dancer? No, then go calypso as Rhett Butler, Wizard of Oz, Pinocchio or the Flintstones? Or would you'd rather don a poodle skirt? Dress as a cheerleader, car hop or glamour puss, Easter bunny, a pilgrim, a gambler, a can-can dancer, a beer can, a witch doctor, a devil, a rabbit, pink elephant, well, I'll drink to that! Make new friends and keep the old — one is sacred and the other bold. Looking for the next fashion statement? Maybe leisure suits will make a return to fashionability. Or maybe for once, you'd like your wife to come dressed as a hooker and you as her pimp? (We're just make believing, remember?) Stroll down Memory Lane with MM and Joe DiMaggio, Lucy and Ricky Ricardo, John and Lorena Bobbit (yep, you read that one right!) Father Mulcahey and Hot Lips Hoolihan. From kilts to kimonos, togas to tutus, just look for the palm tree awning out front and flamingo mural. Hey, there's nothing too bizarre for Rose's Costumes. It's the only place to shop for costumes for any occasion. And note the great website for playing dress-up before putting the dress-on. Verify address before you go. Rumor has it they may be moving to Denton Factory Stores.

★★★★★★   Zola's Everyday Vintage   214/943-6643

414 N. Bishop St.   Thurs-Sat 10-6; Sun 10-3
Dallas, TX 75208-4657

 It's so haute, it's hot. Shop the Bishop Arts District in Oak Cliff because it's a throwback to the days when people felt a sense of neighborhood and everyday was a holiday. Even with the closing of Mistletoe Boot, I still find it nostalgic to shop in Oak Cliff. My monthly treks to Dallas Food Depot for my gourmet garnishes for half price are legendary! But it's the vintage spin on retailing that is drawing crowds to the Bishop Arts District in record numbers. More and more folks with flair are looking for zoot suits and something out of the ordinary. Between Hate's Restaurant and Bishop Arts Floral, Zola's (this vintage resale shop) has something appetizing for both men and women. And prices, well, definitely a throw-back to the good old days. Though the two cousin owners named their store after their grandmother (Zola), inspiration for its panache is written at every nook and cranny. They both work in other full-time jobs, but they ooze with spirit and determination. When can you dress up in an evening dress for $50 or throw on a silk blouse for $15? Scarves from the 80s are making a comeback (just look at the PUCCI's and GUCCI's in chi-chi boutiques around town.) Mix in both old and new and what results is a total package of funk and blues. Would somebody please tell Tom Parsons of Best Fares that he can replace his usual Hawaiian shirts with some new ones here? Not as cheap as Resale at CCA in Lewisville, but still too good to be threw! And leave it to my eager beaver husband who loves to wear a different kind of hat to the golf course and my son who puts his hair under a cap or ties a scarf around his head to keep hair out of his eyes, there's actually a selection to choose from. My family thinks it's cool to wear hats like Mama does. Vintage handbags were neatly displayed on the wall with ties strewn over some table racks where it was easy to rummage through. A nice beginning to Chapter One. Watch them grow until they've written the book on Everyday Vintage clothing. Whatever Zola wants, Zola gets!

Apparel: Women's

7th Avenue Plus Size Outlet

★★★★★★ **7th Avenue Plus Size Outlet**   **214/638-9033**

1331 Inwood Rd. (Inwood Outlet Cntr.)   Mon-Wed 10-6; Thurs- Fri 10-7; Sat 10-6; Sun Noon-5
Dallas, TX 75247

If you are looking for Fay-th, Hope and Charity, shop 7th Ave. First, she's one of the best retail managers in this city and knows how to cater to her clientele. I'm talking bend-over-backwards service. Secondly, there's **HOPE** for women who need a wardrobe boost without taking out a second mortgage. Finally, the average sized American women can call upon 7th Ave. for all their wardrobe needs. Attached at the hip is their sister store, through the door and you're in their Career Outlet (sizes 2-14). So from skinny-minnies to more of the ample samples, they can provide the fashionable wardrobe including hats to match. With prices discounted up to 90 percent, brand names and service to match, it doesn't get more charitable than here. I mean, you can afford an entire wardrobe, a dress or pant suit, a suit, a sportswear outfit, a handbag, maybe even a hat for under $100. Yes, for the entire wardrobe. For $200, you can buy an embellished designer suit with a matching hat that would retail for at least $500. No more needless markups just because you're a woman of size. This is definitely an equal-opportunity merchant. Shop where the stars shop for designer fashions and accessories where styles are chic and prices are cheap. And if you like African-inspired clothing, there's even a department for it. This is the largest plus-size outlet in the Metroplex, probably the Southwest. One whopping step for womankind, no ifs, ands or butts. At last, get covered in a fashion-forward wardrobe without robbing Peter to pay Paul. From a dramatic, jewel-encrusted suit for a night out on the town to appropriate business suits, from a tailored work wardrobe to three-piece ensembles with duster, you can dress to the nines from nine to nine and transition right into a night on the town. One line, made exclusively for 7th Ave. by **R & B WOMAN**, for example, fits up to size 5X. Now, go take on the day! Located off Stemmons, two blocks west on Inwood, where all twains meet at the Inwood Outlet Center. Verify location before you head out the door. May be in a new location soon.

★★   **A & A Fashions**   **972/241-8588**

11363 Denton Drive   Mon-Sat 10-6
Dallas, TX 75229

Giddy-up gals, if you're ready to hit the trail. This outlet gets an "A" in selection, and "A" in prices, but they still flunk English 101. So, in spite of some terrific deals, we are not linguists and therefore we are sure some things get lost in the translation. This year we paid with a $100 bill and

I guarantee you, they did not know how to make change. Nothing un-American about that! Look and ye shall see a round-up of women's sportswear, including lots of denim at wholesale prices. Hours are flexible, just ask them. ***Call toll-free: 800/590-6888***

★★★   Avenue, The   214/358-5642

3701 W. Northwest Hwy.   Mon-Sat 10-8
Dallas, TX 75220
www.avenue.com

Bigger sizes usually means bigger prices at this store formerly know as Plus Sizes, Plus Savings. They've really grown, as they now number 16 locations in the Metroplex. As we say, bigger is better as long as the discounts tag along. And they do, especially on their private-labeled clothing. That way, there's no more comparison shopping, but just affordable, fashionable and upbeat wardrobes for the Ruebensque physique. Forget dowdy and drab; just because you're big doesn't mean you're not beautiful. Say hello to all the good buys inside for the fuller-figures. Take a walk down The Avenue in sportswear, dresses, coats and separates in sizes 16 to 32. Now we're talkin'! Get pampered by informed personnel who help put it all together at the best possible price. The only thing small about this store is....well, there's nothing small about any of their stores. And for additional discounts, join the club. Exclusive online shopping discounts, track your purchases, and then open your mailbox for your purchase. How easy does it get? Well, what about shopping via their **FREE** catalog? There, that's easy, too. This national specialty retailer of women's apparel and accessories is growing by leaps and bounds and only employs women of size who are walking testaments to confidence and grace — just like their customers. Then again, I have seen a few shoppers in there that didn't look THAT graceful. Check directory for the location nearest you.

★★★★   Bon Worth   940/668-0777

4321 I-35 N.(Exit 501), Suite 245   Mon-Sat 10-8; Sun 11-6
Gainesville, TX 76240
www.bonworth.com

Can you believe this is a nationally-known manufacturer and retailer of high fashions for women with over 133 stores in 30 states? Lucky ladies can shop their two area outlet stores and have an entire wardrobe of comfortable, wrinkle- and care-free clothing at factory-direct prices. Bon Appetit! Both misses and petite sizes in SM to XL and 6 to 20 are made to sell without using the traditional wholesale middleman. Therefore, they've already eliminated that layer of cost and price all of their garments for direct-to-the-public consumption. Though they certainly would not be categorized as high-fashion, you can't fault them for developing their specialty niche of embroidered down-home and casual wear at savings of up to 40 percent off comparable items. Just because it's comfortable doesn't mean it's a "Plain Jane" nobody. From denim to knit sweaters, you'll find big deals on their clearance racks offering an additional 20, 30, 40 even 50 percent off. Don't expect to eat bon bon's, though you will find some mouth-watering deals at their outlet above or at the Tanger Outlet Mall in Terrell, Suite 108, Terrell, TX 75160, 972/563-3610. Headquartered in Hendersonville, NC (where I use to work when I was a camp counselor at Blue Star Camp), that's where the flagship retail store is as well as the centerpiece of operations for design, manufacturing and distribution. They couldn't have picked a better place to headquarter — the home of "clogging" in the streets.

★★★   C'est la Vie!   214/631-4446

1303 Chemical Street   Mon-Fri 9-5
Dallas, TX 75207

How dare they close on weekends. Just when things get heated up and you want some cool clothes from Coldwater Creek. Rats! But Monday through Friday, you can say "C'est la Vie" to high prices and high-tail it to this contractor who makes clothing for the Coldwater Creek catalog. That's life. C'est la vie! Like the weather in Dallas, the merchandise selection is up and down and you never know what's comin'round. Some days it's really slim pickin's while other days, it's like traveling to the promised land. Racks and racks of samples and overruns in sportswear, pant sets, jackets, separates and fun dresses available in sizes 4 to 14 and SM to XL. You can say fare thee well to this outlet if you're a plus size, but the Coldwater Creek Catalog and online clearance store has plenty (www.coldwatercreek.com). They've said C'est la Vie to their old location and now have set up shop on what is becoming a serious invasion of specialty stores on Vantage Street. So, what are you waiting for? Then go to Vantage Shoes and match up all your outfits with a pair during their well known two-fer or three-fer, or whatever sale on designer shoes. Whew! I know a few loyal Coldwater Creek fans who would gladly work weekends just for clothes. If so, call me!

★★★★★★   Career Outlet   214/637-7702

1331 Inwood Rd.   (Inside 7th Ave.)   Mon-Wed 10-6; Thurs- Fri 10-7; Sat 10-6; Sun Noon-5
Dallas, TX 75247

 The Career Outlet is a sibling attached at the hip to 7th Ave. Plus Sizes. Walk through the opening inside the store and you've crossed over into small-size land. Sizes 2 to 14 can get outfitted to the hilt without feeling that only plus size girls have all the fun. After all, even size 2's need an new outfit for less money once in a while. Here is a great place to start. Adorable career dressing with designer names and price tags slashed practically in half. Save 40 to 60 percent on suits and dresses in sizes 2 to 16 with sizes 4 to 14 their strength. That's right. Fully-lined suits are often up to 75 percent off. Does the name KASPER suits help you climb the corporate ladder? You're practically on top and you have saved money on each rung on the way up. Who needs all those extra perks when the best part is dressing the part for less! And if moving up means spending more and more of your salary for an appropriate wardrobe, then you've missed the point. Hey, that's not even beating the system. So, girl, get with the program. Take notes. Stay ahead of the game. Be smart and shop smart. Enroll in Dressing 101 and get your outfits here. Also, since they've added several racks of petites, it sure makes the grade with these shorties! Call to verify location before you head out the door. They may be moving to another location soon and wherever 7th Ave. goes, there goes Career Outlet.

★★★   Cato   972/436-7885

724 W. Main St.   Mon-Sat 10-9; Sun 1-6
Lewisville, TX 75067
www.catofashions.com

Here's another Cato that brings women to their knees. This four-letter word gives a whole new meaning to the phrase, "a square deal." Just circle the parking lot a few times to find a spot and enter into this Alabama-based chain store to see what's really shaping up. With 24 Metroplex locations, they must be doing something right. Well, what's right is the full spectrum of sizes from misses, juniors and plus-size sportswear, career wear, coats, dresses, tops, pants, shorts, hosiery, shoes, accessories, lingerie, even children's clothing sizes 7-16 in some locations - all at very inexpensive prices. Cato just might be that diamond in the rough, like the Lerner's of a previous generation. When the budget is tight and new threads are needed, stay on the straight and narrow by shopping at Cato's. Look for their private labels, including **CAROLINA COLORS** and **STUDIO C**. Then square off with your checkbook. Mold together an entire outfit for less than $30 when prices average just $20 for dresses, $15 for pants and $10 for tops. Top off a great deal with bigger savings on their many clearance racks. Shape up or ship out to Cato this year. Check directory for one of their 24 locations in the Metroplex, available online as well as through directory assistance. *Call toll-free: 800/810-CATO*

★★★★★   Chico's Outlet   972/874-9124

3000 Grapevine Mills Parkway   Monday - Saturday 10 - 9:30; Sunday 11 - 7
Grapevine, TX 76051
www.chicos.com

Well, this popular womenswear haunt has 10 Metroplex stores in all the better malls and strip centers and one lone outlet. Which one do you think I frequent? Three guesses. You got it. It's their outlet store where I can save 30 to 70 percent, day in and day out. Chico's is successful for all the right reasons. One of the fastest growing, trendy hits in the fashion world today, they were born in a small store in Sanibel Island, Florida with one couple selling Mexican folk art and cotton sweaters in 1983. Today, there are over 400 stores and there's no stopping them. Everything in their store's in sync: Colorful, bold, dramatic, clean, crisp, fashion-forward, a bit edgy and all have accessories to match. It's the perfect combination for the klutz in the closet who doesn't know what goes with what. Wherever I'm speaking and admire an outfit of an audience member, if it's good-looking and has a matching necklace and earrings set, I just say, "There goes another chic Chico chick." The sales personnel are trained to coordinate, accessorize and help build a wardrobe on a solid foundation of good fashion sense. Joining the Passport Club provides an additional 5 percent discount on all purchases via their retail stores, but you know me, I'm off to the outlet because the savings are there. Why join the club? Then again, there are some advantages like birthday bonuses, **FREE** shipping, discounts on gift certificates and exclusive sales. Well, go ahead, you might as well join. On my last visit, I bought a $22 double eyeglass case to carry my bifocals and my sunglasses....black leather with a red heart, a favorite combination. Also, go online (or call toll-free) to request their catalog at their corporate headquarters in Fort Myers, Florida. *Call toll-free: 888/855-4986*

★★★★★★   Clothes-Out   817/731-0086

3710 West Vickery   Wed-Fri 10-6; Sat 10-5
Fort Worth, TX 76107
www.clothes-out.com

 Four days a week, ladies, Clothes-Out is still closing the deals on great clothing. The Fort Worth Star-Telegram called it one of the top 15 places to shop in the Metroplex and so do we. So there, we agree on something. There must be some validity in these reviews and you might as well know that your time will be well-spent. This designer boutique sells samples, overstocks and closeouts directly from the manufacturer. No seconds, ever. Always first quality and some one-of-a-kinds that are never even mass produced. Each week they feature a different special, so pay attention if you're a weekly cheapo. One week it may be designer handbags, another it may be shoes and boots, then jeans, sweaters, jackets, necklace sets, belts....well, you need to check in regularly. New designer dresses, **MARY STRICKLAND** suits, separates, sportswear, sweaters, denims, gifts, sterling silver, scarves, vests and more arrive weekly. This fashion broker broke the mold on retail prices. Buy the same outfits you'd buy at a department store, only here you'll pay half. For example, sterling charms may be $3 each, scarves $3.95, leather belts from $9.95 to $24. Reject those imitation outlets and find lots of designer closeouts to choose from in sizes 2 to 24 and always at 50 to 80 percent off. Then let them dazzle you with more great prices on purses, vests, belts, accessories, silver jewelry, costume jewelry and the like. Four-days a week, you can been in shopping heaven.

★★   Clothestime   214/363-8532

5500 Greenville Ave.   Mon-Fri 10-8; Sat 10-6; Sun Noon-5
Dallas, TX 75206
www.clothestime.com

Dwindling down to a manageable size, there are now 15 Clothestime stores in the Metroplex. But in place of the Clothestime's that have closed is a new and exciting concept store they're calling Eye Candy — a much more visual and trendy-looking store testing the latest and most fashion-forward merchandise. They've added an online store, too! At times, though, their site was malfunctioning; hopefully when you hit the enter key, it won't say, "Page is not available!" For junior wardrobes, Clothestime is still a favorite. If you've got a youthful figure that is sexy, smart and sassy, they've got the wardrobe to go along with it. Whether you're a teeny-bopper or a young-lady-at-heart (older, but with the figure of someone half your age), you will find brands that even the "Young and the Dressless" find appealing. Labels, though, are unfamiliar. Ever heard of BLUE THREADS, SPOILED GIRLS, X.CESS.IT? Of course Eye Candy is familiar now because it's their new concept store. Coast-to-coast, they've closed about 200 non-performing stores this year, but fortunately are weathering the storm and are still alive and resurrecting as we go to press. Teeny-boppers spend money and it appears Clothestime has a good chance at remaining a popular shopping destination. Retail prices are very affordable. Take note, there are printable coupons of in-store savings online. Check directory for multiple locations throughout the Metroplex.

★★★   Discount Dresses   214/634-3366

1304 Inwood Rd.   Mon-Sat 10-6
Dallas, TX 75247
www.discountdressesonline.com

Easy does it! Now you can shop online for all your special occasion dresses and never even travel to shop in person. This is their only remaining location since they closed Fort Worth this year with a mammoth selection of plus-size dresses up to 75 percent off. In fact, they claim they have the largest (pardon the expression) location in town. When it comes time to pull out all the stops and let the good times roll, don your dancing shoes and shimmy on down to Discount Dresses. The name says it all. Whether you're going uptown, downtown, or all around the town, this is the place to dress 'em up. Dressy suits from $39.99 to formal dresses as low as $59. Whether for a cocktail party, or your daughter's homecoming, if you hate to shop with her, have her pick what she likes online and then you're done with it. Then pick out something for yourself in a suit: church suits, embellished suits, cocktail suits — and add jewelry to accessorize. Yes, they are now carrying hats. Save up to 75 percent on dresses and suits in sizes 6 to 26. OK, they also have casual dresses, too, for $15 and up, but who's looking to dress down when the time is ripe to kick up your heels and let loose? *Call toll-free: 800/724-7319*

★★★   **Dress Barn**   **972/437-0967**

1361 W. Campbell Rd.   Mon-Fri 10-8; Sat 10-7; Sun 1-5
Richardson, TX 75080
www.dressbarn.com

With eight, I'll take an eggroll and a new outfit from Dress Barn. When you go out to eat, dress the part. After all, you didn't just fall off a turnip truck, did you? These clothes were made for going out — to the office or for play — and note, this store has a significant presence nationwide. Leave the barn doors open for business and kick back the racks of both name-brand and private-label apparel. Rake in savings of 20 to 50 percent in sizes 4 to 24. A stable selection of career and casual wear along with a few trendy styles from **ARIUM** (a **KASPER** knock-off), **ISAAC HAZEN**, **LEE DAVIS**, **SIGNA** and **WESTPORT** (their private label) as they all make for a very interesting blend in a conservative wardrobe. What separates us from the animals is our ability to accessorize. So go for it. A selection of necklaces, earrings, pantyhose, belts, socks and occasional gift items will keep you in sync. It's no bull — charge it on a new Dress Barn account and save an additional 10 percent on your first purchase. Stop stall-ing and race over to one of the Metroplex's eight Dress Barns and Dress Barn Women (down from 16 locations last year.) And don't forget to go to the barn online so you can print out in-store coupons and learn of their in-store promotions before you leave home.

★   **Euro Ladies Clothing**   **972/866-6880**

15402 Addison Rd., Suite A   Mon, Tues, Fri, Sat 9:30-5:30; Wed-Thurs 10:30-4:30
Addison, TX 75001

European styles grace many a chi-chi closet, but they may not be your cup of tea. Ta, Ta, as they say with a wardrobe that is often dripping in elegance. If you want the extravagance, expect to pay the piper. Say hello to Euro Ladies Clothing, which has been providing a steady flow of top fashions covering the map for at least a decade or more. Sail the Mediterranean without leaving the port of Big D. Couturier lines from France, Germany and Italy with labels that were as unfamiliar as the back waters of the Bering Sea. Find slacks, skirts, blouses, dresses, suits and blazers with a conservative bent for that Captain's Dinner or for when you take that walk on the Promenade Deck. The lines are especially appealing to the mature woman, but at least you'll have something to wear to that luncheon or charity event. From silks to fine linens, Euro Ladies Clothing specializes in exclusive lines, so don't walk in thinking cheap. You can, however, save money during an occasional sale. Whatever the language, Euro Ladies Clothing is in a class by itself.

★★★★★   **Fast Fashion**   **214/634-4181**

1321 Regal Row   Mon-Fri 8-6; Sat 8-2:45
Dallas, TX 75247-3615

Raise the checkered flag after arriving at Fast Fashions. Take stock, these prices are in the pits (low, that is!). Jack up a good deal on thousands of petites to plus-size dresses, pants, suits, tops and sweaters that are found racing around retail stores all over the country. Tire-d of paying those high prices? Track these fashions and start trucking around what seems to be an endless warehouse of wholesale prices. Need an instant replay? If you find it for less within 30 days of purchase, they will refund the difference or give you credit. Car-tons of handbags compete for your attention as you cheer over price tags of $15 to $20 on imported look-alikes. Sometimes it looks so close, you'll need a photo finish. Get in gear and zoom on into Fast Fashion. Hurry — you're on your way to the winner's circle. Ignore the construction, as it's well worth driving through the obstacle course. *Call toll-free: 888/LADY-WEA*

★★★ Luanna's

972/218-9114

137 Historic Town Square
Lancaster, TX 75146

Tues-Sat 10:30-5:30

Don't expect Luanna to answer on Sunday or Monday, or even to get an answering machine. They are not available to speak, period. But when Tuesday morning rolls around, the place is hoppin'. Luanna's carries mostly ladies'clothing sizes 2 to 22, but also fashion accessories like belts and purses. Of course, women do not live by clothes alone. What about candles, bath products, floral arrangements and jewelry. Okay, so a sucker is born everyday, and I am a sucker for custom jewelry which is designed and made by a stay-at-home Mom from Coppell utilizing natural stones, crystals, mother of pearl and some of nature's other offerings. The line includes earrings, bracelets and necklaces and priced from $48 to $95. If shopping makes you hungry, enjoy a relaxing respite next door at the Tea Room. A pot of tea and now you can sip and shop. Make a day of it turning back the tides.

★★ One-Price Clothing Store

972/399-1434

3402 N Buckner Blvd., #307
Dallas, TX 75228
www.411.com

Mon-Sat 10-8; Sun 1-6

Keep it simple, stupid and kiss high prices goodbye. Save substantial sums of money on casual sportswear, dresses, separates and accessories for the young and dressless. Save at least 50 percent and circle Wednesdays as a particularly good day, when stock is replenished. Easy does it! With sizes small to 3X, you can haul out a stash for a lot less cash. Sunglasses to shorts, slacks to sundresses, rompers to biker shorts, casual and cheap. Check your directory for a location near you. Don't expect to see any formalwear, this is strictly easy on and off. Locations at 125 Wynnwood Village S/C; 139 Pleasant Grove Center; 1507 E. Kiest Blvd.; 160 Medallion S/C; 220 Jefferson Davis Center; 5334 Ross Ave, No. 300 and 9751 Webb Chapel Rd., No. 300.

★★★★ Pursley Discount Fashions

972/298-3384

208 N. Main
Duncanville, TX 75116

Mon-Wed, Fri-Sat 9:30-6:30; Thurs 9:30-8

Not necessarily a source for Purses, this Pursley is a name that is recognizable to anyone from the 1950s who remembers the good ole days. Over 50 years old and still going strong, this mature and seasoned veteran of the bargain business is still a mainstay on Main Street. First quality and some irregulars (well marked) line the walls and racks of this Duncanville legend. With prices on dresses as low as $5 and up to $125, imagine averaging $60 on some of Dallas'favorites like ANN TOBIAS, JENNIFER JEFFRIES, LESLIE JEFFRIES, LESLIE LUCKS, MELISSA and others that make it from the Apparel Mart to North Main in Duncanville. When it lands at the store, it's discounted naturally. Closeouts at the end of the season are discounted to the lowest depths. One blowout sale promoted savings of 50-80 percent. Embellished suits with values to $250 were marked $49-$99. Designer fabrics were cut to 99-cents/yard and pantsuits were cut to the quick to $19.98 (retailing as high as $140.) Locations in Lancaster at 1322 N. Dallas Ave and in Hubbard at 101 E. Second. Obviously a "small town favorite with big time savings," since you're traveling to Duncanville for certain cosmetic procedures with Dr. Standefer, you might as well redo your wardrobe as well.

★★★★★　　**Sequins USA**　　　　　　　　　　　　**214/630-6988**

2200 Vantage- B & C　　　　　　　　　　　　　　　　　Mon-Sat 10-6
Dallas, TX 75207

If putting on the Ritz means slathering yourself with crackers, than this is the place to call home. Save up to 75 percent on everything from beaded dresses and gowns to After 5, sportswear, prom and designer suits a la cheap. Don't ignore those short dresses for $25 and up, gowns from $49 and up, as you don't have to show up in a snap-front house coat when the occasion calls for "After Five!" From dressy sequins and beaded dresses and gowns, in sportswear, prom and suits, you can throw casual to the wind and show up like a whirlwind. Take ad-Vantage of its larger-than-life selection and size range and then hit the social scene with wild abandon. Don't say I didn't tell you where to go to gussy up!

★★★　　**Sheryl's Basement**　　　　　　　　　　　**214/630-9499**

9011 John W. Carpenter Frwy.　　　　　　　　　　　　Mon-Sat 10-6
Dallas, TX 75247

The bottom line descends to the basement of this chain of stores. It's where the action is, make no mistake about it. This veteran retailer, like the Diva, returns in many different incarnations, but what worked once, generally works again, regardless of the name. If you're a working stiff, working 9 to 5, you'll find Sheryl's Basement offers relief from the high price spreads. Sizes 4 through 24 have the opportunity to dress up in work or play clothes, whatever the occasion, in Misses, Juniors, Petites and Plus Sizes. The inventory changes like the wind, blowing hot and cold. Some days they're swell; other days, they're not. Check directory for additional locations. Tom Spiegel's still the head honcho but no relation to the other Spiegel's from catalog fame. Remember the old Suzanne's? That's where he got most of his initial notoriety. Even before then, he was one of the first listings in the first 1972 Underground Shopper in 1972 called Original Manufacturer's Outlet on East Grand. My, how time flies when you're shopping.

★★　　**Simply Fashions**　　　　　　　　　　　　　**214/946-8929**

257 Wynnewood Village Shopping Center　　　　　　　Mon-Sat 10-7; Sun 1-5
Dallas, TX 75244
www.simplyfashions.com

I won't skirt the issue here. Simply Fashions is simply a place to buy cheap clothes at cheap prices. Quality is mediocre, though, in juniors, misses and plus sizes up to size 36 alongside inexpensive accessories. But a woman's gotta cover up and this is simply a one-stop fashion find. If you're in South Dallas, ante up some of your earnings and spend them here. A casual lifestyle commands a wardrobe of jeans, shorts, T-shirts; then shift to skirts, jumpers and dresses when play ends and your work day begins. Plenty to choose from on the clearance racks, which have even more incentives to pick and save. Nothing higher than $40 was seen and, simply put, may be overpriced. Juniors, Misses, Plus or Extended Plus Sizes is the strength on which to build a wardrobe foundation if you're singing the wardrobe blues. Based in Alabama, this chain is a sleeper with over 230 ladies specialty stores in 21 states and two in Dallas. Visit also at 3200 S. Lancaster Rd. in Dallas, 214/374-7810 if you're so inclined.

★★★   Suzanne's   214/638-8429

1335 Inwood Rd. (Inwood Outlet Cntr.)   Mon-Sat 10-6; Sun Noon-5
Dallas, TX 75247

Not connected to the original Suzanne's from Tom Spiegel above, this one-time Dallas icon has
been resurrected under new owners and management. If you knew Suzanne's like I know
Suzanne's, oh, oh, oh what a store. Suzanne's has some good days and some not such good days.
The merchandise fluctuates from simply passable to simply adorable. Some days, the labels are
impressive — **ANNE KLEIN** and **DONNA KARAN**, while other days, the labels were unfamiliar.
Go for style as some are quite chic; some are even stylish and quite cheap. Whatever day you hit
Inwood Outlet Center, you might find yourself captivated by the hundreds of moderate - to higher-
priced garments that will get you to the church and back on time and in style. Suit up at $75 and
start your day off on the right foot. Also, slip into something casual and if price is a consideration,
you can take these to the bank! It's a nice one-stop shop for an entire wardrobe. Plenty of inventory and attentive personnel to cater to your stylish needs.

★★★★★   Talbots Outlet   972/315-5900

500 E. Round Grove Rd., Suite 101   Mon-Wed 10-6; Thurs-Fri 10-8; Sat 10-6; Sun Noon-5
Lewisville, TX 75067
www.talbots.com

Shop at the Shops at Vista Ridge, especially if you're a fan of Talbot's. This all-American mall
favorite deserves your cheers for its outlet store. Rah, Rah, sis boom bah! Save 50 percent and
more on Talbot's last season's unsold inventory (though last year's sure looks like this year's!) If
you want that "au natural" look in natural fibers, there's none better. Keeping a low profile with
darkened windows allows them to sell their outlet merchandise without slapping the full price
stores in the face. Tailored and well-made slacks, the kind you used to see Kate Hepburn wear,
man-tailored shirts, shirt-waist dresses, suits and appropriate shoes make for a well-rounded
"preppy" kind of look. Think **ANN TAYLOR**. Think **RALPH LAUREN**. Think Harold's. But shop
Talbot's!! Then, when they have a clearance sale, run, baby, run. Most things are then 75 percent
off with another percentage taken off at the checkout. No kidding. A wool crepe jacket was under
$20; saw it in their catalog for $178. We did slip out (but paid for) a pair of black ballet flats that
retailed for $64 for $12. They also have baby apparel in matching fabrics and looks. A full size
range is one of their claims to fame and every dame, from infants to size 24W should find them
very appealing. Their lone star outlet in **TEXAS** is in Lewisville.

★★★★★★   Tiny Thru Plus Size Outlet   817/265-3737

705 Secretary Drive   Tues-Sat 10-5; After 5 By Appt. Only
Arlington, TX 76015

 Whatever they call themselves, Dress Outlet, Traveling with Jane, or
Tiny Thru Plus Sizes, as long as you call them for your fashion wardrobe, that's all that counts. If you're looking for variety, selection, ser-
vice and price, here's where the pedal hits the metal. This outlet represents hundreds of different
manufacturers that are sold in department and specialty stores. In fact, T Thru P may be the largest
sample buyer in the Southwest. If you're looking for garments in all the wrong places, turn around
and head to Arlington. Just ask the realtors from Ebby Halliday that I took there for a shopping
spree. And this street is gaining in notoriety with the other outlet draws and a Krispy Kreme across
the street. Thompsons Appliances is on Cooper at Secretary on the other side of the street and then
Buck n'Loons is down the street on Cooper for lunch in between shops. Head 1.5 miles north of I-
20 off Matlock, and turn left at the Texaco or has it changed to Shell? It's a gas station neverthe-

less. Turn there and you're almost there. Look for the semi-truck or the **RV** that is parked up front or look for Janie Smith who's packing up and taking the samples on her famous road trip sales. See Janie drive a semi. See Janie shift. See Jane's shifts and dresses, suits and pantsuits in sizes 2-34, plus petites and plus sizes. Everything here is priced at wholesale or below. Average expenditure, $29-$69 instead of three or four times that price. Be sure, though, to verify they're open before you head out the door. They hit the road (Jane's Traveling Dress Show) to small towns for sales on select weekends, so please get their traveling road show schedule by calling the store. And always call before you head out to their store to verify they're not on a road trip. There are no road shows in December, January, June and July. When there is a road show going on, the store is only open Tues-Thurs; then the truck leaves for the road show towns: Waco, Temple, Athens, Marshall, Nacogdoches and Longview.

Zachi's Unique Boutique   903/567-5883
131 E. Tyler (on the Square)
Canton, TX 75103

I was in such a hurry to squeeze this last-minute find into the book this year, that I forgot to find out their hours. So would you mind doing a little research for me. I'd sure appreciate it. And you will kiss me for turning you on to this unique boutique. Out of the blue, I spent a half day up in Canton waiting to speak to their director of tourism, and wound up "Oohing and Aahhing" over this boutique. In Canton, no less. Would you drive all that way and expect not to shop at Canton's First Monday? Probably not. But for those who want a fabulous store with a fashionista impresario picking only the most dramatic and head-turning outfits to buy, then you will probably make the trek like you would a mercy mission. I guarantee it. In fact, once you get acquainted with Zachi, she'll probably shop with you in mind and call you when she gets something in that you can't (or shouldn't) live without. This is a "to die for" store in Technicolor with panoramic vision. For any occasion, you'll only see the unusual, the different, the imaginative, and the must have's — at any price. Yes, even the Diva falls down on her knees and succumbs to the ever-so-gorgeous one-of-a-kind outfits. Let me know what you think and give my regards to Tyler....on the Square.

7th Avenue Plus Size Outlet
See writeup on page 63

Appliances

◆◆◆ Appliance Concepts

972/235-4231
24/7

4614 Princeton Drive
Garland, TX 75024

Well, here's an interesting concept. Available 24/7, if something breaks, they are the ones to call to give you a break. Any time, any day, $40 is what they charge for a service call. Though there's an occasional refurbished appliance available, their forte is fixing washers and dryers, dishwashers, ovens, cook tops, refrigerators....oops, there goes my ice-maker. Now I know who to call when any appliance goes belly-up! They even recommended their distributor for the sale of appliances. Call 972/991-9915 and see if you can strike a happy deal.

★★★★ Appliance Fixx

972/466-0808
Mon-Fri 9-5:30; Sat 10-4

1311 E. Belt Line Rd., #3
Carrollton, TX 75006
www.appliancefixx.com

If you were not born with a silver spoon in your mouth, but have a silver spoon stuck in your garbage disposal, this shop's your fix-it stop. Though most of their business today is selling washers, dryers, stoves, wall ovens, side-by-side refrigerators and stand-alone freezers that they've fixed up to like-new condition, imagine the savings that are offered since you're not buying new. And if yours is broken, they do fix 'em, too. Brands include **AMANA**, **DACOR**, **GE**, **HOT POINT**, **JENN-AIR**, **KITCHENAID**, **ROPER** and **WHIRLPOOL**. The basics, man, just the basics. Join the counter culture with counter top and under-the-counter microwaves, dishwashers and disposals as well. Looking for a part? This is part and parcel of their service, too. Make appointments online and save yourself a phone call. This company does it all. They service most makes and models of appliances, sell the parts, and sell you the appliances, too. Talk about meeting a need and filling it! Between Josey and Old Denton Road in Carrollton and another location at 629 E. Jefferson, Dallas, TX 75203; 214/946-WASH (9274) — just northeast of Zang Blvd. Trust these guys, they've got a decade-plus years of experience under their fix-it belts. Service calls are $39.99, but for upper-end appliances such as Sub-Zero, service calls jump to $79.99. This may be the perfect FIXX to keeping your nose and your clothes'clean.

★★★★★ Arlington Used Appliances 817/795-5966
Mon-Thurs 9-6; Fri 9-5; Sat 9-3

1105 Colorado Lane, A1
Arlington, TX 76015

Scratch and dent, do da, do da. Scratch and dent is the way to save, all the live long day. Some little scratches or dents are so small they're indistinguishable, while others are on the back, so who cares? Sales and service on all brand names for those who are willing to sacrifice perfection for function. You won't be giving up doing the dishes, keeping the beer on ice, getting rid of those rings around the collar....just the price, ma'am. Just the price. And now they sell brand-new name brand appliances as well as used. Their showroom should make a believer out of you. Owner Ed Behlau has been contributing to area residents' clean, rinse and cook cycles since 1994. But if used is not your cup of tea, turn that new unit with a scratch or dent into the deal of the century. Then, when you've concluded the transaction, grab a donut at Krispy Kreme next door.

★★★★ Arrow Appliance 817/465-5660
Mon-Fri 9-5:30; Sat 10-4

2114 Roosevelt Drive
Arlington, TX 76013

Even a used arrow does the trick. So, when making an "Overture," make sure you "Tell" them the Diva sent you - especially if you want to hit a bulls-eye. Arrow is one place to strike while the iron is hot. Often they have products that no one else does. In fact, when we were searching for a 30-inch built-in stovetop and microwave, we found it here for $399 while elsewhere, it was priced at $1,100. Now we're talkin'! Most appliances come with a one-year warranty; extended warranties available; 90-days on less expensive models. Rest assured, if it's used and reconditioned, you will get a lot of mileage out of one hit. If you don't know owner Chuck Friberger, let me introduce you: He's been buying and selling used appliances (washers, dryers and refrigerators) for years and he only carries the best brands, like GE, KENMORE, MAYTAG, WHIRLPOOL and more. Washers started as low as $99 and refrigerators at $159. Whether you need appliances for your second home or your first, consider used where you can come clean, for less. Catty-corner from the Mexican Restaurant instead of behind it (they've actually moved a few feet, changed their phone number, but stayed with the same marketing know-how) so you can hardly say they've stayed on the straight and arrow!

◆◆◆◆◆ Broward Factory Service 817/640-1772
Mon-Fri 8-5

2650 Lombardy Lane, Suite G
Dallas, TX 75220

Around since 1967, this company was born to be the authorized warranty service center for FRIGIDAIRE. But in 1974, they began offering Extended Service Agreements that would cover all manufacturers of home appliances and air-conditioners for one low annual fee. Homeowners should not buy a house without a home warranty and this one is particularly noteworthy. Though their name implies you have to live in Broward County, which covers Fort Lauderdale and Palm Beach, Florida, you can still participate in their warranty program while living in the Metroplex. An important element when buying a home that has been lived in is to insist that the seller throw in a home warranty with the sale. Don't you know that the minute you move in, the heating coil breaks, the JACUZZI® goes kaput, and the dishwasher leaks? Protect yourself for $199 a year. That gets you the necessary insurance to protect you from you and your appliances having a nervous breakdown (one or the other, or both at the same time). Service coverage for appliances, central air conditioning, refrigerators, heating (gas or electric), wall thermostats, ovens/ranges, water heaters, freon recovery, dishwashers and disposals for example are covered with a basic program. For more extensive coverage, BFS offers that, too, because they have a large fleet of fully-stocked trucks, a large parts inventory behind it and factory-trained technicians that ensure both fast and reliable repair. Depending on what you want covered (pool, sauna, pond, each bedroom, sprinkler system, etc. will determine the cost.) *Call toll-free: 877/BFS-9700*

★★★★ Capital Distributing

214/638-2681.

2910 N. Stemmons Frwy.
Dallas, TX 75247

Mon-Fri 10-6; Sat 10-5

At the last minute, we ran across this appliance distributor who was moving and liquidating about $1 million dollars worth of high end appliances. We thought too bad they're not open all the time. Then, just as we were wishing that, they announced they'd taken over the old Marshall Moody location and now our wish came true. So there. This two-story marvel can now "Marshall" your "mood" from dismal to elation. The first floor is where the ideas for every imaginable kitchen design is displayed in vignettes that will send you into overload. Which one is the most beautiful? That's for you to decide. I found one. Then, I went to the second display and said, "Oh, I think I want this one." "No, I want this one." By the time I had seen three or four, I was in serious trouble....after all, I only had ONE kitchen to remodel. Brands included ASKO, BOSCH, DACOR, FISHER & PAYKEL, FRIGIDAIRE, GAGGENAU, GE, JENN-AIR, MARVEL, MIELE, MONOGRAM, SCOTSMAN, SUB ZERO, THERMADOR, U-LINE, VIKING, WOLF....well, are you going to cross over the line and get yourself a deal on a luxury appliance or not? Here's the deal: a BOSCH stainless steel interior dishwasher that retailed for $689 was $390; a FRIGIDAIRE washer and dryer was $481 (remember, it's a pair); a 26" 5 X 5 stainless steel FRIGIDAIRE was $1,056 and a THERMADOR 30" stainless steel double oven was $1,999 (retail $3,250). Kitchens have gone upscale and prices have ascended accordingly. At least here, you'll get it for less. And this is the only source for one-stop shopping for complete kitchen remodels....appliances, countertops, backsplashes, tilework, cabinets plus the designers to guide you all rolled into one location. The second floor houses the more mundane appliances like your basic whites. Website in the works.

★★★★★ DoLittle's Appliance

972/285-1505

12840 Hwy 175 @ Edd Rd
Dallas, TX 75253

Mon-Fri 8-6; Sat 9-3

Around here we don't accept that you do little. After all, we think big. But if you want to buy at DoLittle's, then that's okay, especially if you are tired of doing nothing about saving money. This family-owned and operated (no coins required) appliance store has an amalgam of slightly new, used, scratch and dented appliances that still have plenty of miles of usage left. Save up to 50 percent on washers, dryers, refrigerators, ranges (both gas and electric), ovens (free standing and built-ins), dishwashers and freezers. If you do a lot of washing and drying, cooking and freezing and want to know where the savings are, here is a place to start. Try 'em, you'll like 'em and you'll also love the selection.

★★★★★★ Factory Builder Stores

817/410-8868

512 E. Dallas Rd.
Grapevine, TX 76051
www.factorybuilderstores.com

Mon-Fri 8-5; Sat 9-Noon

More than a decade in business does count for something. Since 1988, Factory Builder Stores has been selling to builders and remodelers, but you, too, can participate since the doors are now wide open to the public at the same builder/remodeler price. If it's an appliance, here is a source for them all. Though they specialize in KITCHENAID stainless appliances, you can also find an impressive line-up of ASKA, BOSCH, DCS, DYNASTY, JENN-AIR, MAYTAG, SCOTSMAN, SUB-ZERO, THERMADOR, WHIRLPOOL, U-LINE, VIKING and more. They just moved into their new location in Grapevine, but their warehouse/ showroom is just a hint of bigger things to come. They've spread their wings throughout the state, contributing to the expanding interest in haute cuisine. After all, you can't cook crepe Suzettes on just any ol'cooktop surfaces. Other locations in Houston, Dallas, San Antonio, Austin and Bryan. Probably the largest builder supplier in the state. If you are remodeling or building from scratch, save some serious scratch and visit one of their state-of-the-art showrooms. Ah, dream on.

## Ferguson Bath & Kitchen Gallery					817/261-2561
2220 Duluth Drive								Mon-Fri 8-5
Arlington, TX 76013
www.ferginc.com

 If you're the nation's largest distributor of plumbing supplies, pipes, valves and fittings (PVC) and the third largest for heating and cooling supplies, you must have all your little duckies in a row. Selling plumbing supplies since 1953, today there are nine other locations in the Metroplex: Grapevine, Denton, Fort Worth, Dallas, Arlington, McKinney, Rowlett, Euless, Plano. Tap into the faucets and fixtures for the bar, bidets, kitchens, lavatories, ROMAN tubs, tubs and showers. Looking for sinks with pedestals, wall mounts, bars, laundries or maybe just a new toilet, shower pan, tub or tub and shower unit, whirlpools and shower doors? Look no more. They are all displayed artfully in these warehouse/showrooms. Any of these names ring a bell? ALSONS CORPORATION, AMEREC PRODUCTS, BALDWIN BRASS, DELTA FAUCET, DUPONT CORIAN SURFACES, ELKAY MANUFACTURING CO., GROHE AMERICA, INC., JACUZZI WHIRLPOOL BATH, JADO, KALLISTA, INC., KITCHENAID, KOHLER, KWC FAUCETS, MOEN, NUTONE, ONDINE, PRICE PFISTER, PHYLRICH INTERNATIONAL, ROBERN, ROCAILLE, SEA GULL LIGHTING, STEAMIST CO., ST. THOMAS, WHIRLPOOL....don't settle for less. Now why don't you "Skip to my loo!"

## ★★ Freedom Appliance Town					214/388-8585
7016 Military Pkwy.						Mon-Fri 9-7; Sat 9-6; Sun 11-5
Dallas, TX 75227

Want freedom from high prices on appliances? Then here's a place to declare it! Just outside of Mesquite, they buy all their appliances in working order so you can secure some pretty decent buys if price is a primary consideration. Scott makes sure everything is in tip-top shape, and if need be, refurbished from top to bottom. There's nothing wrong with a "used" appliance as long as it gets the job done. Used GENERAL ELECTRIC, HOTPOINT, KENMORE, WHIRLPOOL and other washers, dryers, stoves and refrigerators are sold at decidedly discounted prices from new, but you have to shop often as the inventory blows hot and cold. During this year's stop-over, there were plenty of gas and electric ranges, no side-by-side refrigerators at the time of our visit, and never microwaves, so don't ask. Dishwashers, maybe. Don't expect to see a wall oven, he doesn't carry them either. All of the appliances here are basic plain vanilla. Right now there were lots of dryers ranging from $89 to $169 and frankly, Scott believes the less expensive models are every bit as good as the high price varieties. Dryers are the easiest to refurbish 'cause they keep going and going and going. Washers, on the other hand, because of all the moving parts, will not last as long. How's that for a quick course in Appliances 101? Washers and dryers, stoves and refrigerators and freezers get 60-day warranties. Same-day delivery available if you're in the neighborhood.

◆ **Gunn Appliance Repair** **214/823-2629**

4422 Dalny Street
Dallas, TX 75214

By Appt. Only

Hopefully, if you can hang tight, they'll be out to fix you up when your appliances have hung you out to dry — permanently. Expect service in one to two days; if you can't wait, then tough, call someone else. Even if they "Gunn" their motors, they can't be Johnny's on the spot. Sorry, just point your "Gunn" in the opposite direction. If I can't get immediate service, can you imagine how expensive it would be to replace all of my lipsticks if they melt without air-conditioning? I can't chance it, personally. I'm not the only one spoiled at my house.

★ **Hoover Co., The** **972/503-9494**

13536 Preston Rd., Suite 100
Dallas, TX 75240
www.hoover.com

Mon-Fri 9-6; Sat 10-5

Even if you're related to a former President, you'll only get a discount on discontinued, demo or reconditioned **HOOVER** models that are standing around waiting to get picked-up! Why is that? Because this is a retail store in every way. They don't take trade-ins, but they do sell new and refurbished models at full retail prices as well as service all makes, models and brands. The refurbs, of course, are your best bet though selection was limited to a few. Steam cleaners started at $199 and the popular self-propelled "WindTunnel" blew us away. Phone orders accepted. Located at the southeast corner of Alpha and Preston, you can be a sucker and pay retail or consider a refurbished model and save a hint of lint.

★★★★★★ **Jarrell Appliance Gallery** **214/363-7211**

2651 Fondren
Dallas, TX 75206
www.jarrellco.com

Mon-Fri 7:30-5; Sat 9-1

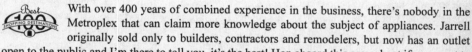

With over 400 years of combined experience in the business, there's nobody in the Metroplex that can claim more knowledge about the subject of appliances. Jarrell originally sold only to builders, contractors and remodelers, but now has an outlet open to the public and I'm there to tell you, it's the best! Hop aboard this gravy boat if you want to start cookin'! The deals are hot from this "built-in appliance" company who's been around since 1947. Buy from the experts who has over 400 years of combined experience. (Talk about being born into the business.) From vent hoods from $10, cooktops from $141, dishwashers from $149; no doubt, you'll want to shop 'em before the subdivision gets wind. Prices fluctuate. Seeing is believing. **VIKING** gas cooktop, builders'price, $1,203/warehouse sale price $471; **GE** drop-in range, builder price, $466/warehouse sale price $278. Similar appetizing discounts on uncrated, scratched and/or dented, builder returns, displays and floor models in all the best brands like **ASKO, BOSCH, CAHANA KITCHENS, DACOR, DCS, FISHER & PAYKEL, GAGGENAU, GE PROFILE, JENN-AIR, KITCHENAID, MARVEL, MAYTAG, MIELE, MONOGRAM, SCOTSMAN, SUB ZERO, THERMADOR, U-LINE, VIKING PROFESSIONAL, WASTE KING, WHIRLPOOL, WOLF** and more waiting to be turned on. Delivery and installation available. Look and see gas and electric cooktops, wall ovens, microwaves, free-standing ranges, pro-style ranges and cooktops, free-standing and under-counter refrigerators, dishwashers, ice machines, washers and dryers, range hoods, downdrafts, water filtration systems and many other upscale home appliances. If you don't have a built-in ironing center, why not? What about a hot water dispenser for your sink? Instant coffee and tea, you see! What about a separate wine storage unit? It's all possible for less. A lot less. I'll drink to that!

★★★ Maytag Warehouse Store, The   972/247-0030

11237 N. Stemmons Frwy @ Royal
Dallas, TX 75229
www.maytag.com

Mon-Fri 9-8; Sat. 10-5; Sun. 12-5

One guy is a maestro to all of the direct **MAYTAG** stores in town. Apparently business is booming, but hopefully not for the repairman. This warehouse/clearance center covers almost an entire exit on Stemmons and with the amount of "come-on's" on their building, you'd think it was some kind of warehouse savings heaven. Well, maybe (saving $30 wasn't that exciting, agreed?) The Maytag repairman, however, should soon be applying for unemployment since they've opened Maytag direct stores all over the country. Just don't expect half-price tags. In many cases, you will save hundreds on Maytag closeouts, last year's models and a guarantee that they will "meet or beat" any competitor's advertised prices. Parts are available for do-it-yourselfers and by the way, they service all brands. And for your edification, did you know Maytag also makes **AMANA, DIXIE-NARCO, DYNASTY, HOOVER, JADE RANGE AND JENN-AIR**? Other direct locations in Richardson, Plano and two in **FRISCO**. You can shop online for each direct Maytag store which is linked from their main Maytag.com website. Look for rebates. For example, the "Jetclean" was listed for $770 with $30 rebate which brought the price down to $349 at their warehouse store. But here's where the confusion comes in. Online, they show which models each store carries and their prices. But if it's a current model, prices are the same everywhere and that spells R.E.T.A.I.L.

★★★★ Oliver Dyer's Appliance   817/244-1874

8201 Camp Bowie W, State Spur 580
Fort Worth, TX 76116
www.oliverdyers.homeappliance.com

Mon-Fri 9-6:30; Sat 9-6

Since 1945, if you were in the market for a dryer, you would have thought Dyer. Then again, you may already be washed up and the only thing that will cool things down would be a refrigerator. Or maybe a room air-conditioner? Great, now that you're cookin', let's go onward and upward to the stoves, ovens or cook-tops that are required so you can transform that deal into a meal. In that case, Oliver Dyer is the place to go - especially if you're patient enough to wait until their final days when prices are slashed up to 50 percent. Whether it's seasonal or models that have been used for display, demo, got scratched or dented, it's all in the savings plan. Every brand is represented: **AMANA, BOSCH, ESTATE, FRIEDRICH AIR CONDITIONERS, FRIGIDAIRE, GE, GE PROFILE, HOTPOINT, KITCHENAID, JENN-AIR, MAYTAG, ROPER, SCOTSMAN ICE SYSTEMS, THERMADOR, U-LINE, WASTE KING, W.C. WOOD CO, WHIRLPOOL** and more. Five-year guarantees are issued, plus a small charge for delivery and installation, if needed. All makes and models of appliances are sold and serviced and used appliances come with a one-year limited warranty. The service department is open Monday-Friday 8:30 to 5:30; Saturday 9 to 2 and delivery is offered from 8 to 6.

★★★★★★ Thompson's Appliances   817/277-1131

2408 S. Cooper
Arlington, TX 76015
www.thompsonsappl.com

Mon-Fri 8-7; Sat 9-6

What started as a factory-certified service department in 1971 has grown into an all-around, one-stop shop for your kitchen, laundry room and patio grill appliances. Not only do you get it all under one roof, you'll get a JENNAIR test kitchen where you can see first-hand what cooking in the 21st century looks and feels like. Appliances at retail prices can eat your lunch, so even if you've got a healthy appetite, head to Arlington, where Thompson's Appliances can ease the indigestion of high prices. This is a family affair, second-generation Eddie Thompson is at the showroom's helm; his brother's in charge of the service department, his sister the back office and his Mother is the resident chef for cooking demonstrations. She and her husband started the company in 1971 and look at them now. The Thompsons have enough experience to orchestrate the best advice at the best prices when it comes to appliances for your home. All the brand names that are fit to print with prices suitable for buying. Have it your way with AMANA, BOSCH, FISHER & PAYKEL, FRANKE, KITCHENAID, JENN-AIR, MAYTAG, MIELE, SHARP, SUB-ZERO, THERMADOR, U-LINE, WHIRLPOOL and WOLFE and that's just the beginning to cookin'up something great. Then mix in such ingredients as kitchen vignettes so you can picture a total remodel, and you've got the beginning to a wonderful repast. From the minute you walk through their doors, until the appliances are in your home, you can expect service every step of the way. Expect, too, a three-year warranty on everything they sell. Why? Because they also service them. With three full-time service crews on the road making service calls, if you wind up buying a front-loaded MAYTAG washer and dryer after learning it uses half the water, is much gentler on your clothes, and has a delayed timer so you tell it what time to "go, washer, go," then you'll understand that an educated appliance consumer is a welcomed Thompson's Appliance customer. If you're building your home from scratch or remodeling your kitchen, you'll want to call upon their designers for advice (at builder's pricing, of course). They will orchestrate the job from start to finish and that includes custom features such as hoods, built-in refrigerators and freezers, wine cellars, under-counter ice makers, blenders or coffee makers, hot water dispensers, commercial sinks, ice machines, beer taps, commercial-style ranges, cooktops/hoods, built-in ironing centers, toasters and can openers. Just south of Arkansas Lane and west of Cooper. *Call toll-free: Metro 817/26*

PS   Travis Mitchell Auctions   972/276-3500

3821 Dividend Drive   Mon-Fri 8-5
Garland, TX 75247
www.travismitchellauctions.com

Know anybody getting out of the restaurant business? Know anybody wanting to get into the restaurant business? Then this auction is one sure bet either way. You might be able to snare something for 50 percent off that is almost brand new at a Travis Mitchell Auction. Selling good used kitchen/restaurant and bar equipment, why not put your hand up at this auction that specializes in kitchens. But in order to bid, you have to ante up a $100 cash deposit. It's refundable if you don't buy or applied to the purchase price if you do. The auction now takes place in a new warehouse on Dividend Drive. They are tops in the new and used restaurant and bar equipment via the auction block where you'll find everything you'd find in a restaurant or bar. Sales are held at the warehouse approximately every three weeks. Auctions start at 10 on select Saturday mornings, with previews from 1 to 6 the preceding Friday afternoon. Auctions are usually held at their warehouse, but sometimes on location at the restaurant being liquidated. If you are considering industrial or commercial kitchen equipment, make sure you've check with your utilities provider to see that the equipment will work in a residential setting. You don't want to blow a fuse, or start a major Forest (Ave.) fire! *Call toll-free: 877/4-AUCTIO*

★★★★★★   **Walt's Appliance**   **972/263-3751**
                                                  Mon-Fri 9-6; Sat 9-4
2336 E. Main
Grand Prairie, TX 75050

Walt's and Rick McDonell are synonymous with appliances beyond their territorial roost in Grand Prairie. Folks from hundreds and hundreds of miles away "schlep" to this unremarkable site in Grand Prairie featuring 35,000 square feet of brand name appliances, both new and used, perfect and not so. With more than 40 years of experience, what do they have going that others do not? Well, low, low prices is one. People are coming from every county around the Metroplex and some coming now from other counties outside the Metroplex — word spreads fast. Brands include **AMANA**, **FRIGIDAIRE**, **HOT POINT** and **MAGIC CHEF**. When my icemaker collapsed one day, I called their service department and they were literally at my front door knocking in less than 5 minutes. Well, truth be known, they just happened to be on another sales call in Flower Mound when I called in. Since they're all radio-dispatched, they were there in a flash — for a whole lot less cash. My ice-maker was putting out the ice in no time. My new motor was installed, my vents were vacuumed and all was accomplished for just over $100, with a mere $39 service call charge. In fact, their service department is by far not only the lowest price, but the workers are top-notch. These guys know their stuff! They're known as the shelter for abandoned, abused, neglected, worn, torn, scratched or bruised appliances so why not adopt an appliance this year as your charitable contribution to *your* own home improvement project. Tell Rick The "SuperJew" sent you. That's his nickname for the Diva and the only difference, I don't fly to Grand Prairie to shop. If you want my thoughts on the subject of low prices on both appliances and servicing those appliances, Walt's is *the* place to shop three acres and 35,000 square feet under one roof. Surely you'll find something to buy whether new or refurbished.

Art & Collectibles

★★★★ **A & G Framing Studio and Gallery** **972/404-8899**

6959 Arapaho Rd., Suite #216
Dallas, TX 75248

Mon-Fri 10-6; Sat 10-5

New owners. Same location. Same service. Not nearly as pleasant an experience, sorry to say. Language is part of the problem, but still we were able to get our message across. The minute you walk through their doors in the Albertson Center, you'll recognize that this is a custom framing shop complete with computerized mat cutting, specialized frames like shadow boxes, French mats and needlecraft frames for those one-of-a-kind masterpieces. Their claim of being able to save you 50 percent and more on framing, shadow boxes and custom matting remains to be seen, however. But what you will see is so overwhelming, you'll be awash in the sea of selections. More than 2,500 moldings alone will leave you boxed in with plenty to choose from, as well as canvas transfers and affordable prints. They boast a 10 percent discount off custom framing price quotes from Michaels and MJDesigns. Well, every snip helps. At least you won't get framed (in the pejorative sense, at least.)

★★★ **Art & Frame** **817/442-1211**

304 S. Park Blvd., Suite 200
Grapevine, TX 76051

Mon-Fri 10-7; Sat 10-6

This shop has more names than a leopard has spots. Formerly Warehaus Gallery, then Kangoo Gallery, they have finally settled in for the past three years as Art & Frame. Plain & Simple. Easy & Out. If you're tired of searching the outback for an outlet just for in-stock custom framing, as well as framed art at good prices, here's a place to take in lock, stock and painting. The owner has taken great pains to hang it, frame it, then you claim it. Wander through their stock of thousands of prints by G. HARVEY and KINCADE, to name-drop a few popular ones. Then have it framed at prices lower than the going rate on frames and framing materials at the big boys, including matting, glass, etc. Custom framing also available. Art & Frame works almost entirely in wood frames, with a wide variety available. Low prices and good workmanship keep the customers coming back.

★★★ **Art USA** **972/491-2441**

7000 Independence Pkwy.
Plano, TX 75025

Mon-Tues, Thurs-Fri 10-7; Wed & Sat 10-6; Sun Noon-5

See the USA in your **CHEVROLET**, but America is also calling you to stay home and hang out. To that end, the framers of the constitution would be pleased to note that this chain (some franchised and some not) is located at the northeast corner of Independence and Legacy (next to Kroger), and it's here that you are granted the inalienable right of saving 25 percent on framing. If you're looking for proof of your "Frame and Fortune," check it out against other framers in the area, then bring in your quote and Art USA will match the materials, then cut the price by 25 percent. When a promotion's going on, that's the time to truly strike it rich. There are plenty of posters and framed art for sale. Multiple locations in the Metroplex for your artistic pleasure.

★★★★★   **Art-Frame Expo**   **214/824-1214**

Mon-Sat 10-7; Sun Noon-6

5620 E. Mockingbird Lane
Dallas, TX 75206
www.artframeexpo.com

There is nothing like a frame, and here's a dame who found this gallery and went artistic! Frame a poster for $34.95, or use their "buy one, get a second at half-price" as a beginning to the end of framing elsewhere. There are also thousands of oil paintings, mirrors, prints and posters to reflect on this country's competitive spirit. Low prices offered similarly at their other locations: 3501 E. McKinney Ave., 214/219-2242; 17390 Preston Rd., 972/373-8449; Frisco, 3311 Preston, E No. 14, 972/668-7480 and in Plano, 1725 N. Central Expressway. Go, Expo, Go! Check out coupons online and rest assured, they provide the lowest price guarantee, claiming if you find a comparable order at a competitor, whether it's on sale or not, they will match the price PLUS deduct an additional 10 percent.

★★★★★★   **Artists' Showplace (Art Gallery & Studio Lofts)**

972/233-1223

Mon-Fri 10-6; Thurs 10-9

15615 Coit Road, Suite 230
Dallas, TX 75248
www.artistsshowplace.com

Spanish Village Shopping Center may not be the Louvre or the Kimball, it's still a treasure-trove awaiting your viewing pleasure. Conceived by several local artists, the gallery is a consortium of 15 of them who bonded into an artist-run gallery showcasing paintings. They also offer other artistic mediums such as from photography, digital art, jewelry, sculpture, pottery, glass designs and mosaics. See the works of the emerging artists who are all waiting to be discovered. Located at the southwest intersection of Arapaho and Coit in far north Dallas, some of the artists use the gallery as their working studio where you can see their creativity in action. Most mediums represented — oils, pastels, modern, Southwest, wood carvings, sculptures and bronzes. Among the artist/coop partners are: Stan Allen, Cecie Borschow, Robin Walker and Dovie Wu. Frankly, each took my breath away. Stan Allen's photography was very crisp and appealing. The pastel portraitures of Daggi Wallace were so real looking, I thought they were photography; and Dee Mayes....well, she paints fish and I fell in love with them hook, line and sinker. I saw a wonderful hand-crafted semi-precious necklace and matching earrings ensemble for under $100 and some great chips off the old block mosaic pottery. Enjoy custom print-making and framing services as well. It's really a one-stop source for the artfundingly endowed. As Degas once said, "A painter out of Monet is worth supporting!"

★★★★ **Dallas Visual Art Center**   **214/821-2522**

2917 Swiss Ave.   Tues-Fri 10-8:30; Sat 10-5
Dallas, TX 75204
www.immedia.net

Boasting over 14,000 square feet with a large workshop and conference room, two gallery spaces, a resource room and staff office, leave it to Swiss Avenue to house the culturally enriched. This non-profit art center is located in the hub of the Wilson Historic District and houses some of the best cultural bargains in the Metroplex. The center is Free and open to the public. See original works of art by up-and-coming Picassos and Monets. Don't miss their annual Critic's Choice Juried Show that features artists from all over the state of Texas. Seeing is believing at this Visual Art Center in Dallas. Literally hundreds of artists participate with the hopes that their works will be shown at the Center. Multiple forms of media presented, from pottery to photography, oils to water color, '40s retro images to minimalist abstract paintings; it's all a visual treat to behold. Special summer hours are Tuesday, Wednesday and Friday 10 to 5; Thursday 10 to 8:30; Saturday 10 to 5. Make a trip to East Dallas where you'll find this Swiss location much easier to climb than the Alps. Established in 1981, the center is dedicated to encouraging and promoting art and artists of Texas, y'all.

★★ **Deck The Walls**   **972/315-1808**

Vista Ridge Mall   Mon-Sat 10-9; Sun 11-7
Lewisville, TX 75067
www.deckthewalls.com

Log on to their website if you're looking for corporate information. Visit their stores if you're looking for custom framing and a huge selection of original limited editions, framed prints and out-of-stock paintings. When your walls are naked and you're in need of a quick cover-up, framed prints start as low as $30; framed original oils were all over the place, from $75 to $3,500. Then, don't hold your breath when you see their selection of framed limited editions priced from $500 to $5,000, as you might choke! Then again, you might see a "Portrait of an Artist as a Young 'un," but you'll pay for his formal education and it doesn't come cheap. Circle the months of February, September and October, as they are sale months which is the time that all smart shoppers come to shop. Other months, don't expect any special deals except personal care and attention to all your framing needs. Well, service counts for something. Deck your walls from stores in Hulen Mall, The Parks at Arlington and Ridgmar Mall. Check out online coupons before you go to save some dough.

★★★ **DJL Antiques and Custom Framing**   **972/864-0278**

10500 W. Hwy 80   Tues-Fri 10-5; Sat Noon-4
Forney, TX 75041

Looks like they've given up their long-standing real estate site next to Vikon Village and Wholesale Art & Frame is now, DJL Antiques and Custom Framing in Forney. Well, perhaps now, we'll take them seriously and they'll answer their phones on a regular basis. From wholesale art and framing, looks like they have now added antiques to the mix. Now it makes two reasons to stop by and buy. How can you lose? Located right in the middle of antique row in Forney, combining two driving forces to drive to Forney, antiques and wholesale framing, he sure has expanded his target audience. Now maybe he's hit a bullseye! Shoppers looking for antiques and shoppers looking for a deal. Look for him in the big white building with red lettering proclaiming DJL Antiques and Custom Framing. So, what's the problem? Maybe no problem, as he's probably settled down and decided he really wants to be available to the public. Anyway, you can have whatever you like framed at pretty good prices. You also can take advantage of his wide selection of posters, prints and limited editions in Southwestern or classic designs, mostly; and choose from ready-made frames or custom framing, it's your call. That's all, y'all!

★★★★★★   Dulce & Art Gallery   214/219-5656

2914 Oak Lawn Ave.   Mon-Sat 10-7
Dallas, TX 75219
www.mydulce.com

At the end of a crowded little strip center is a consignment shop with a very discriminating clientele and a high-end merchandise mix. Neither stuffy or expensive, at Dulce you'll see the most exquisite antiques, furniture, art, accessories and gifts that have relocated from homes in the Park Cities. Calling themselves an interior consignment showplace and art gallery, you will love their stuff (and the prices.) This place is a perfect way to submerge yourself in the myriad of artsy and affordable antiques and accessories while playing the artful dodger when it comes time to pay Peter without robbing Paul. Looking for antique, retro or contemporary furnishings? Look no further than La Dulce Vita. Ah, the sweet life at a great price. Original artwork from $800-$1,500 appeared to be every bit as good as one would see in a more expensive gallery setting with champagne and crumpets. We enjoyed the ambience of their gallery complete with stained concrete floors and dramatic chartreuse walls. A gorgeous pecan-finished cocktail table with solid aluminum legs and glass top was $990 (a Cantoni-lookalike was priced at $3,500.) I bought some '50s vintage aluminum office armchairs at $115 each. A steal! From art glass to jewelry starting as low as $30, this is an impressive respite from the hum-drum and bustle of Oak Lawn. Since everyone admires their painting savoir faire, they decided to offer their talent after hours by appointment only.

★★★   Electronic Boutique   972/788-5487

14902 Preston Rd., Suite 410   Mon-Fri 10-8; Sat 10-6
Dallas, TX 75240

Right when you think you are omnipotent and nobody can stump you, you get a call for something that I didn't have the foggiest idea where to get, let alone at a good price. That's when I had to pull out all the stops and send the caller to the Electronic Boutique. Don't expect it to come cheap, but these kind of callers will pay any price to get what they want when they want it. So be it. You gotta have what you gotta have, right? I understand that, especially in the category of sports memorabilia. Since, as a kid I didn't collect trading cards, I didn't consider it significant as an adult. But that was all before my son met Mickey Mantle and started collecting them himself. On eBay, he has supported himself buying and selling them....so who would have thought they would someday save his day? And that's where these guys come in. At the southeast corner of Preston and Belt Line, here's where it all begins - and ends. Whether you're buying or selling trading cards or collectibles, they'll be there. Autographed sports memorabilia include all-time favorites like BABE RUTH, PUDGE RODRIGUEZ, TROY AIKMAN, MICHAEL JORDAN and others who are traded back and forth. Then for the non-sports crowd, you can fill in the gaps with POKEMON, STAR WARS, G.I. JOE and other collectible figures. Before you head to an online auction, see for yourself why Electronic Boutique is the ultimate collector's Nirvana. Imagine the madhouse if they decide to open their own auction siteÖ

★★ Frames 'n Graphics Warehouse   817/488-5511

6301 Colleyville Blvd.   Mon-Fri 8:30-6; Sat 9-3
Colleyville, TX 76034

Near the old Grapevine Highway is a little blue house set far back off the thoroughfare with "warehouse" in its name. Quaint and cozy, this is where you'd think low overhead would translate into low prices. Wrong. Though they claim to be competitive (as they find the word discount unappealing), they are not. So, seeing as we don't like to be boxed in over our heads, you may want to put a pencil to the numbers once a quote is delivered to make sure they are, indeed, competitive. Previous work has all been excellent, though you're paying for their artistry. It's hefty. But what price, art? If you're still willing to give it a try, if you've passed the Bluebonnet Cemetery, you've gone too far. Though appearing much smaller from the outside, there are still tons of frames to choose from plus original art by **G. HARVEY**, **SKY JONES** and **CYNTHIA BRYAN**, limited editions and posters. Now, speaking of posters, that's really where they shine. Since they are a poster manufacturer, they surely can sell you a poster factory-direct. Then, when it's framed, that's where they can stick it to you. I guess then it's a wash and I'm not talking water colors! In addition to prints, serigraphs, original limited editions and custom framing, they do Qwik signs and color graphics, decals, banners, neon vehicle graphics, channel letters, magnetic signs, real estate signs, menu boards, screen printing, logos and graphics.

★★★★★★ Framing Warehouse/ArtHouse Gallery   972/416-3626

2760 E. Trinity Mills, Suite 126   Mon-Fri 10-6; Thurs 10-8; Sat 9-5
Carrollton, TX 75006
www.framingwarehouse.net

 Nowhere else but here will you find the true "art of a deal!" The hunt for the best framers is over. At the southwest corner of Trinity Mills and Marsh, once you've found this unobtrusive shopping center framing studio/warehouse/art gallery, you won't have to look elsewhere for custom framing. Framing Warehouse and Arthouse Gallery offers custom framing at "Wholesale (prices). They do deliver. I counted about 100 frames in just one kind of pewter alone. Owner Chris Grimes has been the creative force behind this retail showroom and studio for the past 18 years. He's a renowned artist, painter, sculptor, metal and woodworker, designer and craftsman; Glenda Smith, his talented manager/designer-in residence has also contributed her own personal artwork to the gallery portion as did the other artisans who are in the back doing the day-to-day framing. It was Grimes' vision to bring multi-talented artists together to stimulate enough synergy to energize each others' creative juices. The artists have both their framing and their individual choice of mediums to express their talent; you have the benefit of more than just another frame shop. Their frames are masterpieces all unto themselves. Believe it or not, it doesn't cost extra for them to deliver a one-of-a-kind work of art, be it the frame, or the artwork that goes inside the frame and at such low prices. Since Glenda holds a degree in Interior Design, she is on location a lot making sure each picture is hung with a plan in mind and often lends a hand with installation and custom work like no other shop I know. If it requires a specialty mat, she has even hand painted one. She will rearrange, reframe, reformat whatever it takes to create a conversation wall or an entire house full worthy of a blue ribbon at The Hall of Frames. Alongside Chris and Glenda there's Alexis Justice (Ali) who's a budding dress designer. Soon her wearable art creations may be appearing in the gallery as an example of her talent as well. Lastly, don't miss the metal and wood sculptures, they're striking and a personal favorite. But it's their framing that sets them apart from the crowd (museum-quality) with equally impressive prices. Each frame is tailored-made to fit the work and the wall in question be it a diploma or a "Medal of Honor." Restoration of fine works of art, yes siree. On-site consultations, name the time and place! And still, at wholesale prices? That's right, bargain inquis-itor!

Helene's Fine Art and Framing

972/867-1733

2001 Coit Rd., Suite 305
Plano, TX 75075

Mon-Sat 10-6 (Late By Appt. Only)

 Helene's is supreme when you're looking for original pieces of fine art, paintings, limited edition prints and custom framing all rolled into one. Her sense of adventure and taste for the sublime result in an eclectic mix of artistic intentions. What a fun turn to take when your cupboards are bare and you're looking to fill it with collectibles. For example, if you want to start with collectibles and objects d'art, consider GIUSEPPE ARMANI sculptures or MARK HOPKINS bronzes. No, not your type? Then gaze at some SWAROVSKI crystal, or smile at some WALT DISNEY Classic Collections. For Dad, dear LARRY DYKE is America's most collected golf artist. If he's good enough for Pope John Paul II, Ronald Reagan and Jack Nicklaus, isn't it good enough for your Tiger wannabe? Helene's also shows many local and national artists' original oils, water colors, lithographs, sculptures and bronzes and can be considered an expert custom and museum-mounted framer. If you've never heard of a local wunderkind artisan who has created a series called "Pocket Dragons," you will. Their little faces are enchanting and sure to be in demand as a work to be collected. Pay attention - eBay, remember? *Call toll-free: 800/ 410-4278*

◆◆◆◆◆◆ International Galleries, Inc.

972/318-1020

3744 Arapaho Road
Addison, TX 75001-4311
www.SAA.igi-art.com

By Reservation or online 24/7

Who wants to make extra money? I do. I do. Combine the love of artwork with the love of helping artists and youíve got a winning combination for a business model. Enter International Galleries, Inc....an Addison art gallery that showcases limited edition reproductions which are produced in the back of their sizeable gallery at Arapaho and Marsh in Addison. Call Sue for a reservation for lunch on the house, Mon thru Thurs. If you buy something at the gallery, she gets credited with points for your purchase but so do you. Then you refer somebody and that's how the world gets artwork for their home and office. Build a bank of rewards which means in everyday vernacular cash - moolah - money, honey. Paid Daily. One guy has already made close to a million dollars in less than 9 months. No kidding. Buy artwork at their local gallery or online (and yes, millions of dollars are being sold online). Then, you set up your own online gallery and sell artwork online, too, making money with every sale. You also share in the total sales efforts getting a piece of the action of the global sales. Like any customer reward program, you buy something, you earn rewards but with IGI, it's cash that is transferred into your Electronic-bank account called an e-Wallet (Ooh, how I like this kind of wallet that bulges with money so I can buy more.) You can cash out or buy more....artwork. Remember, much of these original reproductions will appreciate in value. So now you, too, can build a portfolio of net worth and maybe even become a millionaire. IGI has sold over $9 million in artwork in the past eight months and in turn paid over $4.5 million back to members. You get your own free online gallery which enables IGI to track all of your referrals and know how much Reward money to pay you. (It's very well organized and sophisticated). The prints are very limited editions on artist canvas that tend to increase in value second only to originals and are called Giclee Reproductions (pronounced gee-clay).Welcome to the 21st century in buying and selling art. Make money. Support talented artists who have never before had a forum to sell their work worldwide. Welcome to International Galleries, Inc. (IGI). Log on to www. Saa.igi-art.com or call Sue Prue at 972-318-1020. To get to their physical gallery and headquarters for lunches. Sue Prue is your sponsor on behalf of the Smart Art Associates of Highland Village. What an opportunity to earn money as well as enjoy artwork at the same time for yourself or your club group. One of the best money generating opportunities I've ever seen. Buy the art you love and receive nearly five times the monetary amount back in cash. Plus, you not only earn directly from your referrals but you share in the rewards of the total company's efforts.

★★★   Julie's Custom Frames   214/341-1631

By Appt. Only

Dallas, TX 75243

When Bob Blair won a college award, secured his college diploma, and was cited by President Clinton, who did he entrust his precious documents to? That's right....Julie Forsyth. This entrepreneur has a full-blown framing shop right in her home. Keeping the overhead low, she's in a better position to pass the savings onto the ultimate end user. But don't think because her showroom is in her house that there's only a few frames or mats to choose from. No, no, NANETTE. Quite the contrary. This gal's got lots. It all started when she was asked to frame some pictures for the Black-eyed Pea Restaurant, followed by Mary Kay's Corporate Offices. By that time, she was in the pink and started to think she'd like to be in business for herself. More than 20 years ago, Julie was framing needlework projects for herself and her friends and it all came together like a flash of light. Though she's still a one-woman show, churning out custom-framed works one picture at a time, she is a sought-after framer taking special care of each and every picture as if it were her own.

★★★★★   Lone Star Sportscard Co.   972/245-8884

2150 N. Josey, Suite 100   Mon-Fri Noon-7; Sat 10-6; Sun Noon-5
Carrollton, TX 75006
www.lonestarsportcard.com

Blake Meyer has been specializing in unopened boxes, signature cards and rookie cards since the late '70s. Since 1990, he's been holed up at his current location and standing alone, head and shoulders above the rest of the sports card collector fanatics. Where do they go when they want to "collect" their thoughts? To Lone Star Sportscard Co., that's where. Where, oh where did those Mickey Mantle cards go? Well, let's find out. Located at the northeast corner of Josey and Keller Springs in Carrollton, if it's sports cards you covet, you'll love it here. Sports cards, POKEMON mania and autographed memorabilia is the stash that'll bring you increased cash one of these days, Mama. Let them have at it. Whether you're buying or selling major trading cards such as STADIUM, TOPPS or UPPER DECK, young or old, male or female, there's something of value here. And if you're the kind who likes to don the wardrobe of the stars, trek out with jerseys, or memorialize the actual sports equipment that made history, here's another reason to head to Lone Star Sportscard Co. Can you imagine owning one of the original TROY AIKMAN or MICHAEL JORDAN jerseys? You might be able to retire and never work again. Maybe TIGER WOOD'S first set of clubs or PETE SAMPRAS'S first tennis racket? It's all Greek to me, but it could mean money for you. The better the condition, the rare the collection, the more valuable. You never know what the future holds.

★★★★★   **Moses Gallery**   **214/421-4842**

1409 S. Lamar, Loft 237   Wed-Fri Noon-6; Sat 11-6; Sun 1-5
Dallas, TX 75215
www.mosesart.com

Now open Wednesday through Sunday, Moses Gallery has nothing to do with leading more than a
half million shoppers through the desert of the Metroplex. Actually this Moses has other talents.
He can paint. Yea, though we walk through the valley of other galleries, there is none so impressive online or in person. As a one-man art gallery, he is an empire all unto himself. Think a combination of Andy Warhol and **PETER MAX**, only less expensive. Well, I hate to ascribe such an
unworthy characteristic as less pricey, but in this book, that's what it's all about. Forget starving
artists. This one probably eats, but at least he doesn't have to sing for his supper (or for us either!)
Now settled into his artist's loft, you won't see the wailing wall, but you will find his unique style
of painting oversized objects with super-bright neon colors outlined all in black a very appealing
style for your walls. His one-man gallery is like being inside a candy store. One of his specialties
is called a **GICLÈE** Print. Like offset lithographs, **GICLÈE** prints start with an original painting
that is scanned into a computer, where it can be color corrected and stored digitally. A series of
tiny nozzles spray the paper with a fine stream of ink — more than four million droplets per second. Because there are no screens involved, GiclÈe prints have a higher resolution than offset
lithographs. The inks are sprayed as droplets rather than dots; each droplet bleeds into the paper,
creating more of a continuous tone rather than a dot pattern. Moses chose GiclÈe prints over other
forms of reproduction because he felt it best reproduced his works. The GiclÈe process, because of
its high resolution and color range, captures the subtleties of each stroke of the artwork. GiclËe
Prints range from $325 for a 20 by 20-inch to $550 for a 36 by 36-inch shipped in a tube and
unframed. Well worth every stroke of genius! Okay, so I like his stuff. What's it to ya? I also like
that he paints animals, foods, abstracts, flowers — things that I dig. So there. But dig this, he also
has select prints on tote bags, mugs, BBQ aprons, sweatshirts, lunchboxes, teddy bears, T-Shirts,
and even boxer shorts and thongs. But granted, in boxer shorts, I look more like a lady heavy-
weight wrestler who's over-the-hill.

Photosynthesis   **206/931-4858**

By Appt. Only

Seattle, WA 98125

www.photographersseattle.com    *Top Online Store!*

Shutter at the thought of paying through the nose for original art. This award-winning national photographer is a Dallas transplant who makes his work available on
the internet. I keep wondering, though, why he and I have the same last name? Perhaps like Mother, like Son? He's one of the most talented lens crafters in the business and can
make even the most boring of shots stand out from the crowd. Architectural shots, landscaping
shots, album covers, magazine covers, he's not cheap but you'll get more bang for your buck with
every shot he takes. With an eye for the minutia in life, Joshua spends hours just to achieve the
right lighting, the right angle, be it for a poster or a black and white shot. Order online; then take
his work to be framed at Framing Warehouse for half the price. Then, all that's left to do is find a
place to hang it. Enjoy it. Marvel at the details, the shadows, the images and dream on. You'll be
getting a work of art at a fraction of its worth 25 years from now. So buy now while he's still
affordable (and then I can stop sending him his allowance.) Just kidding, Josh. Why wait until he's
recognized as the next Ansel Adams? The time is right...because the price is right. And now, he's
printing museum-quality **GICLEE** prints, the latest technique in the photographic world.

★★★★★★ **Sandaga Market** 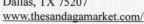 **214/747-8431**

1325 Levee St.
Dallas, TX 75207
www.thesandagamarket.com/

Mon-Fri 9-6; Sat 10-6; By Appt.

If you want a taste of Africa, then head to the Levee, where you'll find Darrell Thomas' Sandaga Market. This is one show of artistry. The African imports are intoxicating. One dose, and you're drunk with pleasure. Unless you travel the continent, you'll never see such tribal tribulations west of the Congo. It's like being on a safari, capturing a bird's-eye view of jungle artisans and craftsmanship. It's certainly the best selection of African imports in the Metroplex. Taste the distinctive array of tribal art and textiles from Ghana, the Ivory Coast and Mali. Savor the dogon stools, masks, mud cloths, sculptures, fetishes and fine art. Whether it's one piece or one hundred, accent your home with ethnic treasures from Africa. At these direct prices, you might be able to outfit an entire house. To get to Sandaga Market, take I-35 E. southbound to Continental, turn right, turn right again at Industrial, go four blocks to Cole, then turn left to the end of the block and look for a big white sign with red letters — To Market, To Market, you've found "Sandaga Market."

★ **Treasure Aisles** **940/484-6161**

1220 W. Hickory ST
Denton, TX 76201

Mon-Sat 10-6; Sun 12-6

Bali high, it's not. But if you want to unearth something from the Treasure Isles, try this Treasure Aisle. Don't expect them to pick up the phone on the first ring. Actually, it took 10 on the first try and nine on the second. Well, they are getting faster on their feet. If you're looking for comic books, antiques, collectibles, model planes and games, this is a hobbyist hideout. However, like many of the stores in this genre, it's a hodge-podge, with nary a semblance of order. If you like to rummage, dig through, get dirty, and have fun, this is the perfect place to start. Thanks for the memorabilia.

★★★★ **Weber's Nostalgia Supermarket** **817/534-6611**

6611 Anglin Drive
Fort Worth, TX 76119
www.weberspump.com/

Mon-Fri 9-5

Since 1917, Weber's Nostalgia Supermarket has known there are many things in life that are "too good to be through." Thanks, Weber, for the largest repository of gas pump restoration supplies, globes, signs, decals, photos, books, clocks, magnets, novelties and gifts all related to the good old days. Nostalgia continues to play an ever-increasing role in Baby Boomer's home decor (or for any age group, come to think of it). From game room to garage hobby shops, these are great items for a conversation piece, a movie prop or a restaurant decoration. Ever wonder where all of these trendy restaurants get their wall and shelf decor? Probably Weber's. We eyed a '58 CADDY porcelain sign, $5; TEXACO FIRE CHIEF glass mini globe, 9" on a 3" base, $50; a MCDONALD'S refrigerator magnet, $2; nostalgic black and white photos, $2.50; a barber shop thermometer, $17; DR PEPPER dominoes, $24; and a trailer that I could pull to Canton should I decide to go into the concession stand business, $5,000. Now I'm not so miffed to have to pay for the catalog, $10 (though it will be deducted from my purchase.) Returns are accepted with a receipt within two weeks on catalog items. Mailing charges: 10 percent of purchase with a $3.50 minimum (but that's subject to change, so be sure to check). And get pumped!

Arts, Crafts, Kits

★★ Aidaworks   972/436-5999
1134 W. Main
Lewisville, TX 75067

Mon-Fri 10-6; Sat 10-4:30

Jodi and Sandy Lynch are enterprising owners who promise not to needle their customers. Furthermore, let me assure you, this is no Verdi opera, but rather a neat little neighborhood cross-stitch shop. What makes them special, though, is that there isn't another like them in the Metroplex. I guess you could consider them at the crossroads of the cross-stitch capital of North Texas. If you're a cross-stitcher (not a cross-dresser), you will be able to get the tools of the trade, including all the different kinds of threads and fabrics such as specialty threads, over-dyed fabrics, needles, gadgets, books and charts from all your favorite designers; well, this is the store that has it all. Going into their store is like entering one giant display case of possibilities. AIDA fabrics and linens is just one line they carry alongside plenty of patterns and supplies. They also do custom framing of cross-stitched finished works. If you're looking to learn the art of the stitch, there's how-to books and personalized instruction. Meet new friends, even if they're sew and sews. Some of the classes included Beginning Cross Stitch, Beginning Linen, Beginning Hardanger, Intermediate Hardanger, Beginning Drawn Thread, Just Nan Class Project, and a Patriotic Hardanger Doily. Now I'll need a translator to explain. *Call toll-free: 888/761-2342*

★★★ Beacon Foam Company   214/528-8534
4438 McKinney Ave.
Dallas, TX 75205

Mon-Sat 9-5:30

When you're itching to create a project that requires a special-sized foam to be custom cut, here's the place to call. For me, though I don't sew, I do love gorgeous fabrics. One day, I decided to make some decorative pillows. I had the fabric, but am not nimble with a thimble. So, I bought some LIQUID THREAD (a fabric glue) and then needed some foam for stuffing. I bought three for $34, not bad, eh? And now I'm the bargain beacon in my neighborhood. Bring in your dimensions and they will cut the foam to fit while you wait. Prices depend upon the size of pieces required, but it could launch you into an entirely new business. Check the Fabrics Chapter to buy your fabrics and you're practically there.

★★★   Beadworks   972/931-1899
7632 Campbell Rd., Suite 309   Mon-Sat 10-6; Thurs 10-7; Sun Noon-5
Dallas, TX 75248
www.beadworks-dallas.com

Get her in a choker hold and string her along until she's green with envy. How? Take a jewelry class at Beadworks. Every kind of bead imaginable is waiting for you; you don't even need a line. Crystal, glass, wooden, bone, seed, pearls, quartz, it's up to you and your artistic inclination. Learn to make the latest jewelry designs, from a lariat necklace to a flat peyote. Let Linda Hoffman guide you every step of the way when it comes to jewelry and doing it your way. Located at Campbell and Coit, this is the place where they'll teach you the ropes. Go online to redeem discounts for classes and join the club, "The Circle Club," when registering. Completed cards will pay for a $25 class or provide $15 off more expensive classes. Save money by buying in large quantities therefore reducing your cost per item. These prices are per bead of the same size, color and shape and is not meant for a mix and match assortment unless otherwise noted. Then for beads sold by the strand, if you purchase one to nine strands, you pay the list retail price. The more you buy, though, the more they discount the prices and then you can mix and match strands. Shop on Thursday evenings 'cause that is their sale night and every bit helps.

PS   Christmas Warehouse   214/638-7867
1331 Regal Row   Varies
Dallas, TX 75247
www.zipcode.com

Watch for the billboards to proclaim their large, perhaps the largest selection of pre-lit trees and Christmas decorations in all of the Metroplex. Custom floral designers are ready to cut and create a floral arrangement that will glow and show; and why not? It's the season to have a reason to go all out, isn't it? Store opens in early September for the upcoming season. Watch for sale dates on billboards and get with the greenery for holiday scenery.

★★★★   Coomers Craft Mall   972/931-3073
2661 Midway (Midway & Trinity Mills)   Mon-Sat 10-7; Sun Noon-5
Carrollton, TX 75006
www.coomers.com

Often imitated, but never duplicated, Coomers was the originator of the crafts mall craze 15 years ago, with variety being the operative word here. They're the biggest of their genre (over 20 locations nationwide: Arizona, Houston, Nevada, Colorado, Ohio and Dallas/Fort Worth, Carrollton (above), Plano, Arlington, Fort Worth and North Richland Hills. This retailer holds the distinction of being the first and many the only chain of craft malls in the country based on unique and handmade crafts and home decor. But they also provide an outlet for America's crafters and artisans who beforehand, had nowhere to go and nowhere to show. Doctors, lawyers, teachers and secretaries have turned their after-hour activities into full-time works of art, finally putting their heart where their art is. You can also hop aboard their online site to learn how you could also be a major display artist. Then, you as the shopper can shop direct from the maker. In most cases, the merchandise is indeed handmade; but there are many booths that show readymade craft items as well. And if you're a do-it-yourselfer yourself, they carry a complete line of **AILENE** craft supplies. After all, if you want the tools of the trade, where can you buy them? Here, of course. Online, they reveal how you can open a craft store, tour their stores, sign up for a crafter's newsletter and more.

Enterprise Art

PO Box 2918
Largo, FL 33779

www.enterpriseart.com

800/366-2218
24/7 (Office Hours: Mon-Fri 9-5 EST)

 *Top Online Store!*

When in Florida, you've got to see this three and one half acre site for all kinds of crafts. Located in several barns for each of your crafty projects, wear comfortable shoes and walk 'til you drop out of ideas. Or better yet, shop online and never get blisters or fall victim to exhaustion. Enterprise Art is the numero uno source for all things for craft lovers. Over 100 different patterns for projects including items that have never even been seen in stores. This catalog has over 350 full-color pages to ooh and ah over and if you are looking to create AND save money, this is the perfect place to put your energy. Whether you're a jewelry designer or a home-maker looking to decorate for the holidays, brilliantly faceted beads accented by a delicate beaded garland and crisp red bead ornament topper in an easy-to-assemble kit could be right up your alley. Or what about making an elegant glass bead watch from a kit that offers graceful styling in all the classic materials. You see them up and down Harry Hines but making your own will save you at least 50 percent. A lovely mother-of-pearl watch face finish was encased in a classic silver design with a durable stainless steel back that I saw for $29.95 that would cost you $14.95 to make yourself. Watch out! But it doesn't stop there. Tons of beads and beaded accessories, bead kits including Austrian, Cateye, Faceted, Fossil, Glass, Pony, Shapes, Starflake beads are available for purchase. Plus charms, clay, cord, dolls, finishes, glues, jewelry, all kinds of Austrian jewelry kits, paints, pearls, pewter, pins, rhinestones, rings and wire. If you're never heard of Throw Beads, go to www.throwbeads.com if you want to connect to a direct import source for parade and party throwers owned and operated by Enterprise Art as well. Think Mardi Gras and parties of all kinds that you could buy the cheapest throw-away beads you can find. If you need to talk to someone, call during office hours at 727/536-1492 Eastern Standard Time. The toll free number is strictly for ordering the catalog or product information and not for chit-chat or "how-to" advice. ***Call toll-free: 800/366-2218***

★★★★★   Garden Ridge

2727 Towne Center Drive
Mesquite, TX 75150
www.gardenridge.com

972/681-5006
Mon-Sat 9-9; Sun 9-7

This ridge is so big, you get dizzy looking down the aisles. But if you're looking for home decor objects, surely you can find something here. Why spend a fortune getting organized at The Container Store? You can get twice as much for your money here and still be able to put things in their place. Add artwork and picnic totes, porcelain bowls and bean bags, ornaments and ordinary wrapping paper, and if you can't get your holiday shopping done within a normal 12-hour period, they'll keep the doors open 24 hours just for you as the holidays get closer. Seven area locations provide you multiple opportunities for a fresh approach to home decorating while making only one stop. Starting with one lone store in San Antonio in 1979, they've grown into a leadership role in the home-decorating/accessories business with 44 stores in 13 Midwest and Southeast States. Part of their appeal is variety, but it's the silk florals and greenery that have gotten into my veins. Too, it's the place to go for their incredible selection of pottery, crafts, housewares, baskets, art, frames, mirrors, home textiles....well, I am a big fan. I've got the perfect place for that 6-foot ficus that for once, I can't kill (at a killer price of $18.88).

★★★★★   Hobby Lobby   972/772-5021
                                                    Mon-Sat 9-8
2004 S. Goliad
Rockwall, TX 75087
www.hobbylobby.com

Can you believe that they were born the same year and month as the Underground Shopper, in 300 square feet of retail space in north Oklahoma City? Shopping was my hobby initially but I had to move out of my home's lobby and into an office just as they were establishing their miniature picture frame business in a 1,000 square foot house. Today, I'm still the Underground Shopper with one product and several by-products. They, on the other hand, are a chain of 308 stores with sales in excess of $1 billion (according to records revealed in 2001 — and that was two years ago. They stock over 60,000 items of arts and crafts supplies, fashion fabrics, baskets, silk flowers, needlework, wearable art, picture framing, cards, party supplies, furniture and a large department devoted to seasonal merchandise. You may not know that Hobby Lobby also owns the Greco Frame & Supply Company, Crafts, Etc!, Mardel Christian Books Stores, HL Realty and now the sensational Hempisheres. Significant savings on everything you've ever thought of making with supplies to satiate your every creative bone in your body. When the urge overtakes you, splurge on all the little doodads that will result in personalizes your one-of-a-kind home decor. Accent the positive with perfectly crafted masterpieces that are just plain cheap. Be it a silk or dried flower arrangement, a perfectly packed picnic basket, a needlepoint design or any other project that will allow your imagination to soar. Load up with readymade picture frames and furniture. Check directory or their website for multiple locations. You will be impressed, even if there's no hobby involved.

PS   Importers Warehouse   469/635-0190
                                        Watch Newspapers for Sale Dates
1990 Lakepointe Drive
Lewisville, TX 75067

Looking for fleurs-de-less? Then catch this periodic sale months leading up to Christmas and another at springtime, leading right up to Mother's Day weekend. Expect to fall in love with savings of 40-70 percent on over 200 types of trim-a-tree ornaments and over 90 styles of Christmas trees. Thousands of Santas, angels, snowmen, nativity sets, figurines, designer arrangements, holiday centerpieces, wreaths and mantel sprigs that add that special holiday charm. Designer arrangements can be bought readymade, or custom-made with floral designers standing by. Stem flowers for under $1 a piece was planted in my shopping cart as fast as I could dig it out of the box; potted plants for as low as $3.99, silk bushes for as low as $2.49, well, I still had a little room left in the cart, so why not? Don't expect this to be kin to a dollar-store variety. This importer caters to upscale home decor with high-end quality merchandise. They clean out their warehouse (400,000 sq. ft.) of excess inventory at these two big clearance sales. Take 35 north to Exit 3040 in Lewisville/Flower Mound. Turn east two blocks to Lakepoint and turn left at the light at Lakepoint (behind Super Target), and enjoy a large quadrant of this importers warehouse when it opens to the public. Head to the "Designer's Corner" if you're all thumbs when the subject is decorating. Buy floral arrangements, wall hangings, wreaths, kitchen accents, trees and bushes that make for a spring fling like there's no tomorrow. Then in springtime, you can start the Christmas balls rolling with artificial trees as low as $19.95 and up. One-of-a-kind designer pieces and hundreds and hundreds of home accents. What they lack in duration, they make up for it with creation.

★★★   Marshall Moody   214/631-5444

1348 Motor Circle   Mon-Fri 8:30-5; Sat 8:30-Noon
Dallas, TX 75207-5910
www.marshallmoody.com

What started in 1926 as an art supply company in Fort Worth soon grew into a palette of colorful
options that spoke to most of our holiday decorating needs. Marshall Moody is a display source for
local retail stores looking for just the right vignette. Even though they've help decorate store windows and displays for biggies like Saks Fifth Avenue, Dillards, Bloomingdales and others, what
about YOUR home at Christmas time? This is when smart shoppers turn to Marshall Moody. For
custom designs that have been available only to decorators, interior designers, florists, or others
that'll pay for the day, you can also turn to this Marshall for seasonal decor. From Hollywood to
retail display helpers like mannequins and clothes racks, you can see that if an occasion calls for
decorations, MM is the place to do it up right. From topiary forms to display turntables, artificial
foods to spray paint, photographic supplies to giant flowers, why not have a party tonight? Just tie
a yellow ribbon 'round that old oak tree in memory of someone overseas? What about some columns for a wedding? They've got it all, and it's just as easy to shop online. If you insist on shopping in person, exit Motor St. off I-35E and head south. Turn left on Motor Circle. Motor Circle is
located between I-35E and Irving Blvd. *Call toll-free: 800/627-0123*

★★★★   Old Craft Store, The   972/242-9111

1110 W. Main St.   Mon-Sat 10-5; Thurs 10-7
Carrollton, TX 75006
www.theoldcraftstorequilting.com

For the dedicated Queen Bee, this is the Old Downtown Carrollton Square hive to flock to. After
nearly 30 years in business, they are spinning the same philosophic bent: Offer the latest items at
the best prices while educating customers on all the current trends and timely traditions in the art
of quilting. They have all the necessary tools to complete a project from rulers, needles, threads,
quilting stencils, supplies for hand and machine quilting, well, anything that has to do with quilting without feeling guilty. The "Discount Quilting Club" will really have you buzzing. Join for
$25 a year and receive discounts throughout the year but during your birthday week, enjoy savings
of 30 percent, honey. Bee a dear and don't cross the line into the other room because it's a fully
functional U.S. Post Office where they ship anywhere in the world. In another room, if you're not
mailing something or are not into quilting, you might buy something that you'll ultimately mail (or
take home yourself.) This is the old country store, a throw-back to days gone by with items that
perhaps your grandparent's may have coveted. Antique spice cans, advertising tins, soap and
cleaning products such as OXYDOL — it may be nostalgic enough to want to buy a box or two.
Lastly, make sure to check out the fabric room. Manufacturers such as MARCUS BROS., MODA
and RJR were available but there was so much, I gave up counting. Samples can be secured with a
phone call or an email. Either way, they're happy to accommodate you. *Call toll-free: 800/
576-4251*

★★★★★   Prime Time Treasurers   214/369-7446

9845 N. Central Expressway   Tues-Sat 10:30-4:30
Dallas, TX 75234

Now is the time for all good grandmas and grandpas to come to the aid of their leisure time. Fill 'er
up with creative projects and earn money at the same time. This non-profit Assistance League of
Dallas is home to many senior artisans - from quilt makers to aprons, all hand-made by folks over
the age of being carded at the hip joints (not the arthritic kind anyway!) Support this worthy cause

and buy some terrific-looking appliqued T-shirts, purses, paintings or painted furniture, gifts for yourself or others, toys, as all are prime-time creations. New items are accepted the first and third Mondays at noon. Don't bring them in any other time, please.

★★★★★★   Rock Barrell, The   972/231-4809

13650 TI Blvd., Suite 104
Dallas, TX 75243-1452
www.rockbarrell.com

Mon-Tues, Thurs-Fri 9-6; Wed 9-8; Sat 9-5

Since 1972, the first year the Rock Barrell opened its doors, it has been on solid ground. Rock around the clock in this 4,000-square-foot, one-of-a-kind store whose premise is "Sharon the Stone" (semi-precious, of course). They can offer incredibly low prices because they are direct importers of much of their merchandise. Secondly, they buy closeouts all over the world. Dig in to their stretch bracelets made from 4mm bi-cone glass crystals with your choice of a large assortment of colors. Ever hear of stone cross beads? These beads are drilled top to bottom and are great additions for either bracelets or necklaces. They can also be used as individual beads. Use a head pin and attach them to an ear wire or for drops on a necklace. You won't have to scrape the bottom of the Rock Barrell, either. (Oh, by the way, I know how to spell Barrel, even if they don't! It's a way to stand out from all the others who want to roll out the barrels.) Choose Silver Leaf, Fancy Agate, Yellow Jasper, Poppy Jasper, Picture Jasper, Leopardskin Jasper, Red Jasper, Red Aventurine, Turquesite. Looking for precut, polished, raw stones or cabochons? The word cabochon refers to the shape of the polished stone. It has a flat back and a polished domed top. Each stone is unique so color and pattern may vary from what is shown on their website. Adopt an Agate, Aventurine, Carnelian, Malachite, Mother of Pearl, Onyx, Papua, Quartz, Tiger Eye or Unakite, for example, as they are all available in sizes 5 by 3 mm up to 38 mm. Lastly, my favorite, the SwarovskiÆ crystals is just "raring" to go. Nothing common about these. There's none so brilliant. It's time to add some glitz to your life and put on the ritz. For over 100 years, these crystals have been glistening in the cosmos all to themselves. Made in Austria, these crystals are flawlessly machine cut. You can order them through the Rock Barrell in any size and cut. So, if you want to impress someone, 40 carats should do it. The **MILLIFIORI** solid glass crosses are handmade using ancient glass. In Italian, it means "thousand flowers." These are ready to wear as a pendant and will certainly bring about a thousand smiles. Too, love the one-inch AMBERLITE hearts for $4.50. Love amber since my daughter-in-law brought me back some amber from Russia, it's one of my favorites now.

Smashing Times   214/363-2088

308 Preston Royal Shopping Center
Dallas, TX 75230
www.smashingtimes.com

Mon-Fri 10-6; Sat 10-5; Sun 12-5

Giving new meaning to getting "smashed," this most unique creative shop is the only one of its kind in Big D, maybe in the universe. Since 1999, Tracy Graivier Bell (yes, Pauline's daughter) and Robin Oldham (yes, Todd's sister) have been joined at their artistic hips to provide this most imaginative addition to the custom handicraft scene. Buy something ready-made, commission the gals to do something special (a dining room table, a kitchen backsplash, a swimming pool mural, a chandelier, a dog house....just some of theirs and other artists' works showcased on their website) and let them choose the mosaic and tile medium. They take broken china, dishes, ceramic tile and glass and see what materializes. Too, if you'd like to learn the craft yourself, come on in. From beginners who want to learn how to make their own vases, candles, flowerpots or coasters, for example, to those who've been there and done that, yet still want to learn a thing or two, by appointment or walk-right-in, either way, you can play. What a way to tile away the hours, whether grown-up or not. How about having your 10-year-old little girl's birthday party inside Smashing Times. (Sure beats Medieval Times!) Ensure a good time without getting smashed! What a sobering thought!

★★★★★★ **Wood Finishers Source**   **972/226-8822**

613 Highway 80 East @ East Fork Road   Mon-Fri 9-5 (CST)
Sunnyvale, TX 75182
www.woodfinisherssource.com

Allen Shuttleworth has a wonderful store for hard-to find professional wood finishing and touch up supplies as well as replacement hardware for antiques. If you are handy with your hands and have a knack for restoration, you are often left in the dark when it comes to supplies. That's why we applaud this store — it's probably the only one that specializes in these hard-to-locate supplies. Half the store is wall-to-wall supplies for professional wood workers and the other half is for the decorator kind looking for a huge selection of drawer pulls. Since 1995, Wood Finisher's Source has supplied materials and tools to the trade: for furniture restoration, picture and frame restoration plus specialized materials to those interested in repair and restoration. Things like specialty glues for even museum-quality items. Anything wood that needs repair or restoration, here is your source for improvement. I recommend "**FIDDES SUPREME FURNITURE POLISH**" because it's one of the best wax polishes for antiques and other important wood pieces. Then there is **HOWARD'S** "Feed 'n' Wax" products which enhance the natural beauty and depth of grain in finished and unfinished wood products that will prevent drying and deterioration of all wood finishes. There is a wealth of information at this store and website if you want to fix it yourself and save. Of course you do. And with the money you save, down the street is Direct Buy, the only Membership Club that can get you everything ready-made at wholesale prices. *Call toll-free: 888/822-0974*

★★★★★ **Woodworks Outlet Store**   **817/581-5240**

4521 Anderson Blvd.   Mon-Fri 8:30-5
Haltom City, TX 76117

www.woodworks.com    *Top Online Store!*

Want to shop by the book? Well, here's your chance. They've closed their little retail store and now offer their sales strictly through their catalog. However, if you're a navigator with a penchant for finding remote places in the world, you can order by phone and drive to their will-call window. I prefer to do it by the seat of my pants and stay put. You, too, can continue to keep your finger on the pulse of carved wooden objects. A random sampling included: angels, animals, apples, bells, birdhouses, blocks, bowling pins, golf tees, miniature lamps, milk bottles, mushrooms, Noah's ark, rocking horses, school houses, snowmen, trees, watermelons and more; you can keep busy 'til kingdom comes. They are the largest supplier of American-made wood parts with over 25 million stock pieces. Wow! Wooden it be lovely if they also sold them at wholesale prices? Well, they do. Order their catalog and start pining away for a time when you can whittle away those leisure hours. It'll cost you $5.50 plus the item's price to order from their catalog but you'll still be saving a tree-load of money. Isn't it time you carved out your creative niche? *Call toll-free: 800/ 722-0311*

Baby & Mom

★★★ Babies 'R' Us
3850 Belt Line
Addison, TX 75001-4303
www.babiesrus.com

972/247-4229
Mon-Sat 9:30-9:30; Sun 10-7

Sister store to Toys 'R'Us, if you are expecting, you'll spend a majority of your pre-and post-natal months and years straddling between these two. Looking for an toy, piece of equipment, clothing, furniture, or an accessory for a baby, toddler or older? Well, at Babies 'R'Us, they cut you off at the terrible two's or three's. Then, you have to move over to Toys 'R'Us. It is described as the largest baby store in the USA and one run through will leave you panting. Shop for essentials like strollers, cribs, high chairs, car seats, play pens, DIAPER GENIES, etc. as well as all of the new-fangled items that today's new parents can't live without. There's even a baby registry that moms-to-be can register their wishlist. Locations in Plano, Mesquite, Lewisville, Arlington and Fort Worth, they've got the Metroplex covered, but fortunately not with dirty diapers. The brands are formidable, but the outlet online stinks. The discounts across the board were generally in the 20 percent range but in person, it's definitely a one-stop destination mecca. Great gear, special savings, travel tips and more. Though adorable in every aspect of its design, and mammoth in its selection, prices are much better elsewhere. The best part, though, is definitely the baby registry, the ability to shop for over 30 brands and 2,500 maternity styles, the vast compendium of educational opportunities and downloadable coupons. If you're looking for a car seat, every configuration seemed to be available, except for those that have been recalled. Whether you're looking for an infant seat, a convertible model, or a booster, you'll find just the right stuff to keep your baby safe while on the go. All the gear, all the play centers and walkers, swings and bouncers, stuff for bathing, diapering and potty training, everything you'll need if you're breast-feeding (including the entire MEDELA line), bottle-feeding, solid feeding and high chairs. Everything, no kidding. Grandparents love the ability to point and click when gifts are expected for grandchildren who live thousands of miles away. Then, if they don't like what they get, there's a store in their home town to return it. *Call toll-free: 888/869-7932*

★★★★ Baby and Beyond
204 N. Greenville, Suite 250
Allen, TX 75002

972/396-1004
Mon-Fri 10-5; Sat 10-5

In the CiCi's Shopping Center, when you're looking for a quality children's and maternity resale and gift boutique, this is the place to go. Turn your childrens' outgrown castoffs into a place that'll pay cash up front. Why wait for items on consignment to sell? You've got things to do, places to go, and money to burn. They also carry jewelry, bows, mother and baby bracelets, socks, candles and new giftie-type items to fill in the gaps (so you won't have to shop at The Gap!) As the say, they are for babies and moms-to-be, but they are picky, picky. So examine items carefully. Pablum-ladened bibs are not acceptable. A far northern outpost that is a breath of fresh air for babes in toyland.

★★★★★★   Baby Bedding   817/419-0088

3415 S. Cooper St., Suite 102   Mon-Sat 10-6; Sun Noon-6
Arlington, TX 76015

For the custom look in the baby's room, this is the hand that rocked the cradle. Expect custom fabric, yours or theirs, and then watch them sew. Next door, you'll see sewers needling every project as they cater to every mother's dream. Catering to the boom in babies, nobody beats their prices on custom baby bedding and matching accessories. Direct from the factory, the quality of their workmanship doesn't come without some loose strings attached. It's not like buying readymade so don't expect the prices to be down and dirty. Come clean and welcome your li'l one home from the hospital to a room brimming with the finest trims plus matching linens, lamps, wall hanging, pillows, cradles and cribs, highchairs, changing tables, gliders and rockers. What makes this outlet so enticing is its ability to pull the entire room together with fabric. And do they have fabric; lots and lots of fabric. Whether you buy one piece or the entire ensemble, your baby will enjoy being in the "lap" of luxury — for less. Their prices often beat those in resale shops and these items are all brand new, in the box. Shop their weekend location at Traders Village, 2600 Mayfield Rd. in Grand Prairie.

★★★★★   Baby Delights   972/291-7844

610 Cedar St.   Tues-Sat 10-5:30
Cedar Hill, TX 75104

This shop is beyond conception. When the time comes to welcome baby into this world, mommies and daddies will be delighted with the hand-made bedding and bumper pads here. It doesn't stop with the delivery, either: They offer adorable apparel, furniture, and nursery doodads for infants through 6X. Make sure your baby sleeps tight while visions of sugarplums dance overhead. Cribs in the $250 range available in traditional finishes like oak, white or natural. Everything can be mixed and matched from the MILLION DOLLAR BABY line. Don't you know your baby is priceless and even a million dollars won't cut it? But as long as you're dressing their room in the MILLION DOLLAR BABY line, it shouldn't have to cost you a million. Calling all girls, ages 4 to 9 for their renowned "dress-up tea parties." What a great idea for a birthday celebration.

★★★★   Baby Depot @ Burlington Coat Factory   972/613-1333

2021 Town East Blvd.   Mon-Sat 10-9; Sun 11-6
Mesquite, TX 75150
www.bcfdirect.com

Ooh, baby, ooh baby, ooh! Choo-choo your little caboose over to this offspring within Burlington Coat Factory. This is one-stop shopping for the expectant mom, infants and toddlers at its bargain best. In fact, shopping here should carry you through your baby's needs for several years, at best, without a pregnant pause. There's a huge selection of car seats, cribs, bedding, bumper pads, strollers, play yards, swings, dressers, changing tables, rockers, layette items, infant apparel, baby gifts and more from all the leading manufacturers. Check out: APRICA, BASSETT, CHILDCRAFT, GRACO, LAMBS & IVY, NOJO and SIMMONS; there's not too many others out there to consider. In fact, we heard through the grapevine that SIMMONS hand-makes all of their furniture. If true, it sure beats the assembly line. Baby, let's face it, a wonderful wicker bassinet and matching lace skirt caught our eye and it soon went "Buy, Buy!" If you're expecting, don't forget to sign in, please, to the gift registry. See, even with discount prices, you can expect all the little extras that make shopping a pleasure. Other Baby Depots located in Burlington Coat Factory outlets at Webb Chapel and Forest; in Plano, Central Expressway and Parker; in Euless, Industrial Blvd. and 183; at Grapevine Mills Mall; and in Arlington, at I-20 and S. Cooper St. And this little mommy cried (with joy) all the way home. Type in Baby Depot and you'll be taken to the bcfdirect.com website.

◆◆◆◆ Castleguard Child Safety Consultants 972/509-1610

By Appt. Only

Plano, TX 75074
www.castleguard.com

If you care enough to protect the very best, then consider baby-proofing your home and your pool with these professionals. Ward off the spiral staircase, plug up the plugs, gate off the kitchen and most importantly, install the removable pool safety fence that will keep babies and kids safe from unexpected dips. These are the removable-in- minutes, see-through varieties that are self-closing, self-latching and with key lockable gates that ensure you against tragic consequences. A lifetime warranty is offered. These folks are the distributors for the official POOL GUARD and BABY GUARD products. They also offer in-home safety evaluations for your home and CPR and First-Aid Instruction. You never know when a life will be in your hands.

★★ Diaper World   817/459-3843

Mon-Sat 9-6

1417 E. Abram St.
Arlington, TX 76010

Ever catch a dad on a grumpy day? Well, this is how it was at Diaper World when we visited. In spite of offering great prices on diapers direct from the factory (package of 100 diapers for newborns was $15.99), the guy was as cordial as a smacked mackerel. Unfortunately, on the phone, his English is halting; in person, he does better, but still, almost non-verbal. And his body language says, "Don't talk to me!" Perhaps he needs the Dale Carnegie course or to read a book on "How to Win Friends and Talk to Shoppers!" What was perfectly clear, however, were the prices on these diapers. Guaranteed to be the lowest prices in town, delivered the same day....but from then on, you're on your own. Wash and dry, wash and dry, wash and dry, the wetlands before thee was the lullaby were singing on our way out the door. They also can get everything the baby needs for his/her room except a gourmet meal and another roof over its head. Diaper World can handle baby furniture, clothing, shoes, swings, bikes, walkers, strollers, cribs, bedding, toys, equipment — a little of this and a little of that. Don't expect them to compete with the likes of the big boys. They pale by comparison. Look for the gas station on E. Abram between **COLLINS** and **BROWNING**. Last time we were there it was a Diamond Shamrock station, but who knows what it is today?

★★★★★★ Kid to Kid   817/468-1995

Mon-Sat 10-8; Sun 1-5

1201 W. Arbrook Blvd., Suite 115
Arlington, TX 76015
www.kidtokid.com

Can we talk, kid to kid? Face it, clothes don't make the child, but we can't send them back-to-school looking like a ragamuffin, now can we? Why spend a fortune on kids'clothes when, for a few bucks, you can outfit them in style, including their rooms when they start out. This Arlington franchised children's resale shop has a finger on the pulse of quality used kids'clothes, furniture, toys, even equipment. They accept both consignment resale as well as buy the clothes outright, it's up to you. Mom-to-be are not left out in the cold either; they can get covered, too. Find gifts for babies including infant toys, baby furnishings, nursery sets and linens, car seats and strollers, cribs, cradles, bassinets, play pens and port-a-cribs, infant swings and walkers, swimwear, shoes, the list is exhaustive enough to tire even a day-care school director. They buy used children's items six days a week, just make sure they're clean, pressed and on hangers, if required. Right across from The Parks of Arlington Mall, have yourself a field day if you want to save serious money. What started as one store in Sandy, Utah in 1992 is an amazing rags-to-resale success story. Kid to Kid uses a state-of-the-art computer program that appraises your kids'stuff which helps in establishing uniform resale prices and provides the store with guidelines for how much to pay you. Your cash payment is determined by the brand, style, condition and demand for the item. You receive either cash, or get up to 20 percent more in store credit. Fort Worth, 4750 Bryant Irvin Rd., #802, 817/263-4660; Bedford at 2200 Airport Freeway (Hwy. 183 @ Central), Suite 540 A, 817/283-6364; Allen at 2035 W. McDermott, 972/390-1117 and in Plano at 6405 W. Parker @ Midway, 972/781-2543. A new one's just opened in McKinney at 4900 Eldorado Parkway, #158, 972/529-6131. They also have stores in Austin and San Antonio. *Call toll-free: 888-KID 2 KI*

★★   Kiddo's Kloset   817/460-1746

2223 W. Park Row Drive, Suite E   Mon-Sat 10-6
Arlington, TX 76013
www.kiddoskloset.com/

Just when you think your kiddo couldn't possibly fit another item into his or her closet, you find Kiddo's Kloset and manage to squeeze in just a few more things. This dual-role resale shop offers children's and maternity wear together, giving parent and child an equal opportunity to participate. Mothers can shop for kids'clothes from boys'sizes 0 to 16, girls'0 to juniors, women's and maternity sizes 4 to 16 and S-XL. No department left naked. Even shoes and bedding for babies was available alongside toys, hair bows and other accessories. Kids never have enough of a good thing. Take I-30 to Fielder and go south, past Allan Saxe Stadium (UTA's baseball field), then turn right on Park Row. Kiddo's Kloset is at the bottom of the hill in a strip center with CiCi's Pizza. If you get to Bowen Road, you've gone too far. Have you noticed how many of the children's resale shops are located close by a Cici's Pizza? It's probably no coincidence. Cheap pizza and cheap clothes are the perfect pairing.

★★★   Kids Too   817/656-2919

8214 Grapevine Hwy.   Tues-Fri 11-6; Sat 11-5
North Richland Hills, TX 76180

If you've got kids, too, you know that they cost a pretty penny. How to outfit them in style is as easy as learning the ABC's. Start at the very beginning of the alphabet with elementary resale shopping, my dear. Two lights north of I-820 on Grapevine Highway just before Harwood Road, begin your lesson in Frugal Shopping 101. Babies, kids and moms-to-be can be outfitted in someone else's wardrobe and nobody will know the difference. Consider resale in uniforms, too. Why buy new, when someone else's will do? Department store labels, worn once or twice, look new to me and you. So, who are you kidding? Girls'sizes 0 to 16 and boys'0 to 12 can expand your children's wardrobe by a mile. You'll smile, too, if you recycle what's in their closet, make a few bucks, and apply it to something else. Keep the ball rolling. That's what it's all about via the resale network. New and used maternity clothing alongside shower invitations and custom birth announcements, all at discounted prices. Nursing moms can rent or buy MEDELA breast pumps from LACTATION CONNECTION. Life is good with Kids, too.

★★★★★★ **Motherhood Outlets**   **972/539-2154**

3000 Grapevine Mills Pkwy.   Mon-Sat 10-9:30; Sun 11-8
Grapevine, TX 76051
www.motherhood.com

Let's vote for motherhood. Whoever you campaigned for, all women, regardless of their affiliation, deserve a break today. At this outlet, you can save more on your maternity wardrobe than if you had shopped at any of their retail stores. Yes, they have retail stores all over the city, so its name should be familiar. Their outlets, however, show-case their castoffs, closeouts, discontinued styles and last season's merchandise with plenty of mileage left. Brands such as **MATURNITEE, MIMI, MOTHERHOOD** and **PEA IN THE POD** are potential candidates for the next nine months. At the end of their rope, we saw skirts as low as $1.50, some ensembles as low as $3 and designer private-labeled Motherhood dresses for $138. There were also cotton knit dresses for $19, a two-piece career knit dress with short sleeves with a matching long jacket for $49, T-Shirts under $10, nursing apparel, other intimate apparel and plus sizes all at a savings of 30 to 75 percent. Visit their other outlets at Katy Mills, outside Houston, Gainesville Factory Shops, Prime Outlet Center in Hillsboro and San Marcos Factory Shops for savings throughout the state or shop online for everything, from accessories to sundresses, jumpers to swimwear, it's all available. FREE newsletter and camaraderie available. Now that BeBe Maternity bit the dust, the Motherhood Outlets are the only new Lone Star Maternity outlet left.

◆◆◆◆◆◆ **Neighborhood Diaper Delivery**   **817/652-0477**

2320 Superior Drive   By Appt. Only
Arlington, TX 76013
www.diaperdelivery.net

What goes wee-wee all the way home? You guessed it! At last, the time has come for all good parents to stay put when they run out of diapers. This disposable diaper service delivers anywhere in the Metroplex and the delivery is **FREE**. Wee! If you live outside of the Metroplex, deliveries are handled by independent dealers or by mail. Stock up with a few extras, just in case, and buy your diapers by the caseload. Small, medium, large and extra large diapers are available along with the necessary baby wipes and the potential training pants. Day care deliveries, too. What's so new about a diaper delivery service? Well, the ones we used years ago were all cloth diapers, so delivery allowed us the luxury of not having to wash them. Here, they're all disposable. They are produced by one of the leading diaper manufacturers who shall remain nameless. They are all top-quality and have all the special features such as elas-tic waistbands and inner-leg cuff barriers. Small diapers were $22.95 for a package of 136, extra large diapers were $31.99 for 120 and training pants were $32.99 for 90. They even carry swim diapers plus baby gifts, too, to round out their inventory offerings. If you're not completely satis-fied, they will refund your money less the shipping and handling fees. Adult diapers are now delivered by the case count to your home, office or daycare facility for anybody suffering from incontinence. How more convenient does it get? *Call toll-free: 888/391-1356*

★★ **Oh Baby!**   **817/460-2229**

612 Lincoln Square   Mon-Sat 10-7; Sun 12-6
Arlington, TX 76011

Woe is me. This north Arlington arsenal can arm parents with a bunker full of bargains, but they're not ready for prime time yet. Their selection, though, could win the battle for a baby's wardrobe. Unique baby clothes and gifts — and a lot of them. Plus, an occasional good price. Therein lies the rub. Prices. Sizes 0 through 4T for both boys and girls, as well as new furniture and a few toys though a neighborly approach doesn't replace good old-fashioned discount prices. It makes sense to take a deep breath and a pregnant pause before buying everything you see. It could add up and maybe even burst your bubble (and if you're not ready to deliver, that could be a problem!) Located on N. Collins, just south of I-30, it also stands to consider their maternity clothes, but their prices are similarly non-plus. What to wear to a gala is part of their menu of mark-downs, though. Here's what's good. Why buy when you can rent? That's right. For a one-night stand, just rent a gown and then return it the next day. Enjoy them all from lingerie to play clothes, workout clothes to work clothes, but these are not rentable. Can you imagine going to an aerobic class and then returning what you wore for someone else to wear? Don't sweat it. They don't do it.

R.B.J. Manufacturing

PO Box 353
Burleson, TX 76097
www.johnny-light.com

Remember, we found it first. The invention called the Johnny-Light was first discovered by one frustrated mom in our office with three little boys. What a clever idea, we thought. Then before we knew it, the Johnny-Light was being touted on national talk shows, from "Regis" to "Leeza" and in magazines and newspapers everywhere. We thought we were letting you in on our little secret, but no, in 1996, this Burleson group called R.B.J. (Richie, Bill and Jack) had to promote it everywhere. They're the originators who thunk it up. A DHC (domestic harmony commodity) can be achieved with the Johnny-Light, an easily installed light to help eliminate late-night fall-ins and help in toilet training. This battery-powered device lights up when the seat is down to remind users to return the seat to its full down position after late-night use. The light also reportedly helps potty-training efforts by giving a visual aid. Also a handy reminder if you sleepwalk or are groggy when you first wake up. You know the old saying, "We aim to please, you aim, too, please!" You don't have to be flush to afford it, either. It only costs $12 and is available through the mail only (batteries included). It's simple to install, no tools necessary. It's ready to go when you are! ***Call toll-free: 888/566-LITE***

★★★★★★ You & Me Babe   972/669-2110

870 N. Coit Rd., Suite 2651   Mon-Fri 10-6; Sat 10-5
Richardson, TX 75080
www.youandmebabe.com

Surely the Sonny and Cher theme song was never intended as a name for a baby and mom's resale store, but who cares as long as you're on board. You've Got Me, Babe, lock, stock and bargains. So what else is new? Well, maternity clothes, that's what's new. Sizes 2 to 26 in Petites to size 3X can get covered. You go, girl. While you're shopping for the baby, you can load up on undergarments, lingerie, hosiery and more. These items are often ignored by other outlet stores so it's a welcomed sight to behold. Need a bathing suit? A cover up for a cruise? Maybe you'd like to take a swim class with baby? Don't worry, this is one-stop shopping for both you and your babe-y! New items are co-mingled with the used, which is especially helpful when thinking about nursing moms. Buy what you want — from apparel and supplies or rent as the need arises. When it comes time to outfit the nursery, you must opt for the latest in cribs, bedding and accessories, of course. Bring the new baby home to the life to which they will soon become accustomed. They need to get off on the right booties, you know! ***Call toll-free: 888/258-4552***

Elegant Salon

Beauty

Back-n-Time Antique Barber Shop — 972/724-2278

3501 Long Prairie Road, Suite 104
Flower Mound, TX 75022-2780

Mon-Fri 9-7; Sat 8-6 (Walk-ins Welcome)

Shave and a hair cut, two bits! Well, maybe not THAT cheap but it's certainly a close shave nevertheless. Nostalgia is written all over the place the minute you walk through the doors. Yes, walk-in's are welcome. Back to the good old days where the red-striped barber poles beckon you to sit back, gramps, for a good old-fashioned razor cut. Enjoy relaxing in the old antique barber chairs that have all been lovingly restored to like-new condition. See the magnificently refurbished oak work stations, juke box and don't overlook the collection of old shaving mugs and other barbershop memorabilia. Ah, thanks for the memorabilia. The owner (Ace is the man) has spent a lifetime collecting only authentic examples of an era that conjures up the warm fuzzies. Though he shops online, to date he hasn't put together his own online store yet. However, he's the one to compliment for refinishing some of the items himself coupled with the old-fashioned service that he delivers personally at his shop. Return to the days of yesteryear when men were men and children were welcomed. Hey, anybody up for a crew cut? A duck tail? A Mohawk? Yes, today's latest styles are also cut and dried. Any which way and just up? Have it your way!

◆◆◆◆◆◆ Beauty Brands Salon Spa Superstore — 972/231-4573

2060 N. Coit
Richardson, TX 75080
www.beautybrands.com

Mon-Sat 8-9; Sun 10-6

Separate the fray from the frizz with professional hair care products at amateur prices at this over 10,000 spa- and salon-quality products that line the shelves of this beauty mega store. Relax, or perm it with everything from rods and rollers to hair-brushes and combs. Decorate with barrettes, beaded bobby pins, scrunchies, hair bands, bandanas, clips and more. Clean up with **FUDGE, GRAHAM WEBB, H2O, MATRIX, REDKIN, SEBAS-TIAN** and all the shapes and styling products you'd ever need to create salon looks at home. Don't want to go home? Hop into a chair at the spa and salon where waxing, massaging, manicuring nails and facials are all part of the process. Expect to pay $35 for hair cuts, but only $15 for mani-cures. Either one should cure the blues. One spa pedicure will put you out, way out. Exfoliate, soak, shape and polish and then sink into oblivion with a foot and leg massage and mask plus an upper body chair massage. It does it to me every time. And kids are welcome for their haircuts, too. Visit their other locations at Park Blvd. and the Tollway in Plano (972/248-1480) or their newest in **FRISCO** at 3211 Preston Rd. (972/668-4290). A little dab will do ya!

★★★   Beauty Smart   972/596-2673

3100 Independence Pkwy.   Mon-Fri 9:30-7; Sat 9:30-6; Sun Noon-5
Plano, TX 75025

Banish those blemishes. With savings of up to 40 percent, they just might get you to blush. Bob Berliner's new gig is called Beauty Smart, the official new name of the former Beauty Mart. Carrying an oasis of mainstream beauty products as well as some new ones you might not have heard of. At these prices, you should be willing to give them a try. If not, stick to your same ol', same ol', like L'OREAL, **PAUL MITCHELL**, **REDKIN** and TONI & GUY — all with fabulous price tags. I remember when Toni & Guy first came to Dallas, and look at them now! They're everywhere, they're everywhere, blowin'and growin'! But if doing your own thing is not your style, try Beauty Smart's full-service salon. That should "do" it! Sales will net you the greatest savings, but there's always something going on that you can't resist a spritz or two.

◆◆◆◆◆◆   Beauty Store & Salon   972/608-4444

5964 W. Parker @ Tollway   Mon-Fri 9-8; Sat 9-7; Sun Noon-6
Plano, TX 75093

 Want to turn heads? Then get the look that gets you noticed. Beauty Store and Salon has services for men and women, so get with the program. Step right up ladies and gentlemen and let's get on with the transformation. From the bath to the vanity, head to toe, you can look smart as well as shop smart. The buzz is they're even carrying the **BUMBLE & BUMBLE** line. Located at the southeast corner of the Tollway and Parker Rd., next to Tom Thumb, specials are always ongoing and brands are some of the best: **BIOLAGE**, **PAUL MITCHELL** or **TIGI**, for starters. Ask for Michael if you need to add hair extensions, and there's even an Eco (AVEDA) Spa and Salon attached (972/422-8332) for all the sought-after day spa services such as Vichy showers, massages, facials, body wraps, waxing, cuts and colors. The extensive line-up of products is stellar, especially because you don't see these everywhere: **AHAVA**, **DERMAOLGICA**, **JACK BLACK** (skin care), **DIRTY GIRL** products, **TOCCA** and **VOTIVA**; makeup by **JANE IREDALE** (a personal favorite because its mineral based), hair care by PHYTOLOGIE and **PUREOLOGY**, and **STRIVECTIN-SD**. See what else the Beauty Store & Salon has up their sleeve at their second location at the southeast corner of Park Boulevard and Preston Road behind Chili's, 972/867-6888.

Bodyworks   817/416-7361

6201 Colleyville Blvd., Suite 200   Tues-Thurs 9-8; Fri- Sat. 9-5 (By Appt. Only)
Colleyville, TX 76034
www.dayspapackage.com

 Shopping is hard work and in order to de-stress, here's one solution — head to Bodyworks in Colleyville. Their day spa packages can be delivered the next day wrapped up in a beautiful gift box. Then, all it takes is for you to bring your body to get the works. Whether it's a facial, hydro-therapy tub treatment, a massage or a pedicure, life can be good and in sync, once you get your tootsies in one of their sinks. Consider the combos, too, from 1½ hours to 3½ hours that range from $149 to $285 for both men and women. How about a Swedish, deep tissue sports, hot rock couple's massage? Come on down. There's a myriad of facial options: for teens, acne, oxygen, moisturizing, anti-stress and anti-aging procedures which are all available from $50 to $95. Hydrotherapy tub treatments include seaweed, mineral, aroma or rice soak that costs $60-70. Lastly, for Body Treatments, they can scrub you down with salt, mud, seaweed or sea enzymes for $60 to $80. Get the perfect tan like the girl from Ipanema and her St. Tropez Tan without any of the UV rays. For $75, you can be exfoliated, covered in a self-tanning lotion and buffed to a beautiful bronze. Look for holiday specials for Mother's Day, Father's Day, Valentine's Day and, for sure, when asked what you'd like for your birthday, just do it! Here's the perfect gift for a Diva. And it sure is "to die for."

★★★★★★ CBI Laboratory Skin Care Outlet   972/241-7546

4201 Diplomacy Row   Fri 12-3; Sat 10-5
Fort Worth, TX 76155

 OK, so it's no longer convenient. So it's not nearly as big. So the hours are miniscule. But it's still CBI and beggars can't be choosy. So, stop complaining. They're back, smaller and limited in what they can display in a teeny-weenie outlet store, but if you want to make a clean sweep of things, say those dirty words to yourself. You can still make a clean sweep of their outlet. If you shop, load up, they will expand. So double the bubbles and let's all drown in savings of up to 90 percent. No, they didn't throw in the towel, they just moved from the location at Luna and Valwood in Carrollton. I clocked more than a thousand emails from past CBI'ers who were crying the blues when the outlet closed. Me, included. It was like a long-winded soap opera —"How your Bath Bubbles Turned." But now that they're back, life is good clean fun again and you can have your bath salts and liquid soaps, too. They're starting back up small and concentrating on skin care and body products that they produce for department and specialty stores. These are their overruns and over-produced items. Look for the map on our website to their new location. Go to www.undergroundshopper.com and click on the 100 BEST button and we'll show you the way. What woman would turn her back on their bulk bubble bath salts? Not too many in this day and age — especially when they can scoop it up to 90 percent off. You can stoop and scoop at this itsy-bitsy, teeny-weenie yellow-polka dot outlet bathpost. Buy beauty — at the least. Load up for yourself, make custom gift baskets, just don't look a gift horse in the mouth because you may blow nothing but bubbles. Products such as skin care, bath products, children's bath products, bath salts, shower gels, body lotions, gift bags, facial skin care, candles, sponges, room sprays and more can be scooped up and enjoyed by bargain bath shoppers without drowning in debt. You're all wet if you don't shop here. Closeouts from famous private label bath products for department and specialty stores across the country are shipped from here and you can really scoop up a windfall. Soak, sink and swim your way into every marble tub fantasy. Be it skin care or bath gels, you can double the bubble without getting soaked. No dirty tricks. Make a clean sweep of things here but bring your own shopping bags. There are no more shopping carts.

NR Cute 'n Country   817/560-7294

8255 West Camp Bowie   Tues-Sat 10-5
Fort Worth, TX 76116

All I'm going to say is....it's rumored to be possibly the outlet for the largest direct seller of beauty products in the world. But I'm taking the "fifth" and am sworn to secrecy. Remember, it's only a rumor from one of our shoppers in the Fort Worth area and since I didn't see it with my own eyes, I refuse to put my life on the line for a lip liner or some bath oil. But if you tell me it's true, you'll make a believer out of me and I'll meet you there in the morning. But keep this treasure under wraps otherwise the owner, who is purported to be the largest seller of these products in the region (that seven or eight states), maybe the country, could get into hot water if you go blabbing every-where about what you've discovered. Why wait for your order to come in the mail? Get your hands, feet and face into current products right now; or last season's products for sizeable discounts. You will love it. Let's "face it," their product lines are already some of the best in the business and the most affordable. Imagine discounting what's already some of the best buys out there. But remember, "You've got to keep a secret!" Let me know if I'm just dreaming.

★★ Debbie's Fragrance & Gift Shop   972/278-9747

2840 S. Jupiter, #103   Wed-Sat 10-5; Sun Noon-6
Garland, TX 75041

How much more scents-ible does it get when you can spritz and spray the day away for at least 20 percent less? If beauty calls, Debbie answers. If your scents of smell calls for designer fragrances, consider these: GIORGIO, JOOP, PASSION, RED or WHITE DIAMONDS, WINGS on the woman's side and COOL WATER, HALSTON, LAGERFELD, POLO, LAGERFELD on the men's. Prices varied between packages and individual perfumes, but at least 20 percent off is better than nothing. Load up on gift baskets and those little gift packages you get when buying something at regular price. Enjoy a day of shopping at Vikon Village, then stop in next door for a whiff. Exit from LBJ east onto Jupiter-Kingsley and turn left on Jupiter.

◆◆◆◆◆◆ Electrolysis & Laser Studio   972/276-3799

1446 Belt Line Rd., Ste. 141   Tues-Sat By Appt. Only
Garland, TX 75044-6800
www.lightspeed-electrology.com/dallas

If you're looking for permanence in your life, then contact Carol Manning, probably the longest plucking electrologist in town (specializing in Thermolyis and Blend modalities.) But she is not just for hair removal any longer — she does the works. If you want to wake up as fresh as you went to bed, why not go for broke and consider permanent makeup, too.

◆◆◆◆◆◆ Elegant Salon Suites   972/406-9406 x 210

3812 Belt Line Rd.   By Appt. Only
Addison, TX 75001

Not only is this salon elegant but it's economical, too. Imagine, enjoying the benefits of a day spa of services in an European villa setting with experienced personnel and being charged half of what the competition is charging. No kidding. Why look like a shar-pei when you can look like a sharp-ie with the best Microdermabrasion facial ever. Only the finest medical skin care products are used, but without the brand name, you will be paying less. Enjoy the camaraderie of all the personnel who've been with owner Marjan for years and years and become one of the family. From the old cut and curl to the state-of-the-art hair and color do's, each stylist has their own special contribution. And if it's solar nails you want, there are two talented technicians at your service for manicures and pedicures. Why not put your best face forward and look and feel your best. I do. And though I wasn't sanforized at birth and actually have shrunk a bit, with regular Microdermabrasion facials and the specialized treatments that are given as needed (and not sold but given freely), my face looks like a million bucks (on my pauper's paycheck!!) Pampering at its best. Oh, by the way, ask them to tell you why the Brazilian wax is the hottest thing going. And while you're at it, why not get an air-brush tan? Or permanent make-up? This is indeed a one-stop overhaul operation for a complete beautification package.

Fragrance Junction   972/240-0931

Dallas, TX

www.fragrancejunction.com   🖱 *Top Online Store!*

 From $3.99 to $10.99, you can have your cake and smell it, too. That's right. From the smell of an angel food cake to a After Dinner Mint (24 oz.) candles are just the beginning to an aroma orgy. In fact, at this site, there were over 1116 fragrant candles to select from and even more than that in their selection of male and female fragrances. Bet you didn't even know there were that many to smell? I almost fell over, but my list of favorites were long and it was in the middle of the night, so I keep going and going and going. From LIZ CLAIBORNE to AQUA FLORE, DRAKKAR NOIR to STILL, ADOLFO COUTURE to ALEXANDER JULIAN, ALLURE to CONTRADICTION, CALVIN KLEIN ETERNITY to well....everything is 20-50 percent off, so you might as well climb aboard the sweet smell of success. It goes on forever. There were 1087 different women's fragrances and 455 different colognes for men. Thank goodness there were only 36 gift box sets to wade through and I didn't miss a one. If you want to put it all together in a boxed set for gift-giving, you're but one spritz away from putting on the Ritz! Call if you want to meet in person. Otherwise, just order by phone or online. Website easy to navigate you can almost smell the fragrances right through the screen.

★★★★ Fragrance World/Fragrance Outlet   972/241-9696

2588-A Royal Lane   Mon-Sat 9-6:30
Dallas, TX 75229

"A rose by any other name wouldn't smell this cheap," so says one happy customer....me! One of the best smelling outlets in the Metroplex, expect a cosmetics counter ride of a lifetime for fragrances and cosmetics at close to wholesale prices. Crammed with product floor to ceiling, in the middle aisle, in and out of the glass counter cases and on the wall shelves, there's perfume and cosmetics everywhere. And the sales staff is watching every move you make. Broken English spoken but they know their stuff so you better watch your P's and Q's. I was never comfortable when shopping in their store since their beady eyes never left me — not for a minute. I think they must have lots of thefts because he watched me like a hawk. If you're playing the "Face Card," you'll make the sacrifice and let them stare all they want. After all, you will save 25 to 60 percent on cosmetics and skin care products from CLINQUE, ELIZABETH ARDEN, ESTEE LAUDER, LANCÔME, LA PRAIRIE, YSL and more. Then, add on layers of perfume at up to 70 percent off from ESCADA, GIORGIO, PASSION and WHITE DIAMONDS (how do you think Liz got eight husbands going on nine?) For girls who love sweet-smelling guys, dab on a little ARAMIS, LAGERFELD, JOOP!, even old MACKIE'S back and see what spell can be cast. Be careful, there's POISON lurking on a top shelf. Stop, I want to get off Stemmons, east of Harry Hines. Sure smells like a sweet deal but the staff are too intense for me. They are like used car salesman with perfume and cosmetics as their product of choice. Lots of gift sets, though, keep me coming back for more.

★★★★ Hair Colour for the World   972/726-8776

14990 Landmark Blvd.   By Appt. Only
Dallas, TX 75240

Color me beautiful, but make sure you cover the gray. That is my mantra for all of us who are 40 plus. Here is the place for panache when it comes to a great cache for cover-ups. Retouching, $20, foil highlighting, $35 and try-on hair colour for $20....bet you haven't seen prices like this since the Dark Ages. All spa services performed by a board-certified colorist. I thought I'd heard of every board-certification, but this is the only time I've heard it for a cosmetologist. What do you have to lose except a few gray hairs? A few blonde streaks? A few fried strands? Colour them gone.

◆◆◆◆   **Images International**   **972/404-0101**
                                                                    By Appt. Only
12655 N Central Expy., Suite 430
Dallas, TX 75243-1743
www.laserhairgrowing.com

One block south of 635 and Coit Road, you can be hair tomorrow if it's been gone since yesterday. This leader in the Hair Replacement Industry for more than a decade probably has a swelled head (of hair) over the many accolades given to him for his service. No pain, no surgery, and no side effects and hair is restored to a lush condition without surgery. Sine 1993, Images opened their first office in Indianapolis, Indiana using the innovative techniques learned in over 25 years experience in the industry. In addition to Indianapolis, centers are now located in Chicago, Dallas, Detroit, Lansing and Milwaukee. It is anticipated by 2005, additional centers will be located in New Orleans, San Antonio, Houston and San Diego. It's a lucrative business since both the aging boomers are now entering the "Age of Vanity" is upon us. Where looking old is out and thinning hair is something of the past. Utilizing a new kind of laser, both men and women can benefit from this treatment with some of the most advanced techniques in corrective hair loss. The most sophisticated technique used is similar to the cold laser treatments being performed by Glenn Smith, D.C. for pain. In this case, the exclusive "Cool" Laser Hair Therapy is what they call it. I have not any reason to doubt this if it weren't for my own success story. Well, I'll let you know if it's done anything for my thinning hair. And is it really cool? First developed in Europe and through years of research, Images has perfected this latest technology in correcting hair loss. This particular therapy has been seen on national TV newscasts. With tens of thousands of satisfied clients, let me know how it goes. Do you or don't you have more hair? With certified technicians, the procedure is relaxed and in a professional environment. So, if you have thinning hair, baldness or problems with your scalp, LHT (Laser Hair Therapy) may be just what the doctor ordered. Simply put, the laser light stimulates the cells'metabolism and causes damaged cells to be repaired. It first was used over ten years ago in Europe to treat diseases of the skin and scalp. Now, it's being recommend by doctors. The best candidates are men in the early stages of male pattern baldness and women who are generally thinning throughout. The Laser Hair Therapyô device is approved by the FDA and is classified as a Certified Class IIIA cosmetic laser approved for cosmetic use in the U.S. It's perfectly safe.

◆◆◆   **José Eber**   **214/696-4074**
                                                            Wednesday Evenings Only
8201 Preston Road, #110
Dallas, TX 75225
www.joseeberatelier.com/index.html

At the Dallas Preston/Sherry Plaza location (above), get a lock on prices from this famous stylist. Chances are it won't be Jose himself tending to your hairdo, but on Wednesday nights, patrons can get a $25 hair cut. Any other day, you'll fork out $85 at this Hollywood hair stylist's namesake. (Can you really trust a guy whose hair is longer and thicker than yours and who wears a cowboy hat on top of it?) Well, you can try. There's also an opportunity to get yours coifed in Plano at The Shops at Willowbend, 6121 West Park Blvd., Space D-206, Plano, Texas 75093. Women have for years clamored for José's special touch. His signature look has talk show hostesses crooning, "More, More." It's no wonder he took sedate Dallas by storm flying in on a whirlwind media blitz from the opening of his first Beverly Hills Salon located on Rodeo Drive. If you buy into the philosophy of creating individual looks by analyzing each woman's personality, lifestyle and facial structure, I guess you will be able to see her inner beauty, too. Of course, just remember that he created the Farrah Fawcett look and look where she's at now? Anyway, Jose welcomes house-wives, students, business men and women, just like you and me. Right?

◆◆◆◆◆◆ Light Touch Laser & Anti-Aging Center 817/361-8838

6351 Oakmont Blvd., Ste. 151
Fort Worth, TX 76132
www.laserhairremoval.com

By Appt. Only

Attention Fort Worth Females (Men are welcome, too!) But first, let's ask the ladies this question. Do you have a beard and don't consider it one of your best features? Well then, you're a perfect candidate for the Queen of Lasers, Jeannie Lee (C.L.T.). This former kindergarten teacher decided to try something new and when it worked for her, she considered it a miracle. She knew then she wanted to help others whose body hair caused them to experience any discomfort, especially emotionally. Trained at the most prestigious school for laser therapies, Jeannie Lee uses the "Candela Gentle Laser Plus" and hundreds of satisfied clients swear by their new and improved hairless face and other body parts. Men who never wanted to be seen without a T-shirt because their back looked like a gorilla were first in line. Jeannie has clients all over the Metroplex who swear by her thoroughness and her ability to make this procedure affordable. After all, it changed her life and now she wants it to change yours. New this year is the Smoothbeam Laser, which is the latest eradicator for sufferers of acne. Whether you're a teenager and mortified when a zit pops up on prom night; or you're a mother who can't believe her hor-mones are STILL raging, this non-invasive treatment takes only about 30 minutes. But what got my attention is that it's also applicable for wrinkles. Try it but only if you want to look younger, more beautiful, more rested and awake! Call for an appointment and be sure to verify her location as she may be moving.

◆◆◆◆ Ogle School of Hair Design 214/821-0819

6333 E. Mockingbird, Suite 201
Dallas, TX 75214
www.ogleschool.com

Tues-Fri 8:30-5:30; Sat to 5; Appt./Walk-ins

For less pomp and circumstance, primp and take your chances at the Ogle School of Hair Design. If you've survived the school of hard knocks, then have your locks done here for less. Senior stu-dents, ready to make the grade and go out into the cruel, real world and triple their price, offer manicures, haircuts, perms, facials, pedicures, the whole nine yards. Expect services to start as low as $8.50 for a haircut, hair color to start at $17 and perms, $27. For a plain manicure, $6. Not bad. Save at least 50 percent over the full salon menu. Teachers hover overhead so you're never alone with the students and their scissors. All services, though, are provided by students. Prices vary due to length and/or thickness of hair, however. Procedures that you've grown accustomed to, like a shampoo, are priced separately, $1.25. How about a basic braid, $8.25? Shampoo and blow-dry, $7? Wig Styling, $7? Neck or bang trim only, $3? Comb out, $3.50? Long-hair spiral perm, $50? Foil Frost (Bleach or color), $35? How about a French Manicure for $9 or a set of sculptured nails for $15? (Hey, I pay less than that at Tip Top Nails in Lewisville!)

◆◆◆   Oriole Barber Shop

214/651-0019
Mon-Fri 7-5:30

1923 Commerce
Dallas, TX 75201

Return to the days of the buzz of a razor and the price of an old-fashioned haircut for under $10. Dream on, this is just for the cut. No facials, no manicures, no day spa extras. Just the plain vanilla snip-and-go. Yes, a decent haircut is what you'll get. But if you want a shampoo, expect to shell out some more money. This barber shop has defied the 21st century sophisticated marketing campaigns and all the ambience you've come to expect in the unisex salons of North Dallas. Definitely a step back into a time warp and particularly popular with the no-frills downtown executive. Sing your own tunes and get yourself a haircut for a song. Tra-la-la-la-la, la-la-de-da!

◆◆◆◆◆   Parfumelle

817/731-6633
Mon-Sat 10-6

6441 Southwest Blvd.
Fort Worth, TX 76132
www.parfumelle.com

If your favorite fragrance has been discontinued, lost for years, changed its packaging or name and you are hooked and can't live without it, who can you turn to? Parfumelle are the folks who specialize in finding those long-lost scents that have gone by the wayside. Even if they've gone stateside, they still can find it. Their selection of perfumes and colognes is astounding. Almost every brand known to man kind (and woman) is available. This beauty tracer takes time, but it's worth it if they find it. Shipping's **FREE**. Now, for the new stuff that smells like a winner — it's called the **LAMPES BERGER**. It's a magnificent crystal, porcelain and ceramic object d'art in the form of a miniature bottle/vase that captures and destroys odors in a room with the addition of perfume. These vases also purify the atmosphere and frankly are much more elegant than a **GLADE** plug-in. Parfumelle also carries an exquisite line of handbags that are both luxurious and egalitarian. Large bags, small bags, shoulder bags, bags of all shapes and sizes. *Call toll-free: 800/874-1118*

★★★★★★   Paris Fashions

214/630-7622
Mon-Fri 10-6; Sat 10-5

2629 Stemmons Frwy., #108
Dallas, TX 75207

 Oui, oui, monsieur. Shopping for Paris Fashions in Dallas is a whole lot quicker than hopping aboard a 747 and landing at Orly Airport. Tres chic, ooh la la. Want a Pashmina shawl? How about one at 20-70 percent off retail alongside everything else? What a mix of inventory to choose from....some apparel, but not a lot. Here's the source for funky handbags, fashion jewelry and perfume. Do they have perfume! All are priced at wholesale-to-the-public prices. Think of it like "off Harry Hines" just like the store "Off Rodeo Drive." I couldn't wait to finally be smelling like the rich and famous. Get some knockout Parisian scents for 50 percent off and knock 'em dead at Les Femmes du Mond luncheon. Name brand fragrances were here at up to 70 percent off, though the discount varies with the fragrance. They have one of the best selections at the lowest prices, if not THE lowest in town. They also carry fashion handbags. And reading glasses galore. Well, if you need a reason to energize your shopping list, here's a place to really check off a number of different items all under one roof. Across from the Ninfa's Mexican Restaurant on Stemmons on the service road.

Paula Young Wigs

800/343-9695

PO Box 483
Brockton, MA 02303

Mon-Fri 7 AM-Midnight, Sat 9-6 EST

www.paulayoung.com   *Top Online Store!*

 You'll flip your wig when you order through their catalog or shop online. They are the best priced-wig source in America. Since 1978, they've been splitting hairs over their low, low prices. With 100's of wigs (starting at $29.95) and hair pieces to choose from, it's no wonder they can keep you ahead of the crowd (even on a windy day.) Women of all ages and lifestyles can find a change of hairdos at a moment's notice, from short to long, smooth to curly, blonde to brunette, highlights or not, and make a quick transformation without spending hours in a beauty salon. **PAULA YOUNG, CHRISTINE JORDAN, GABOR** and **RAQUEL WELCH** Collections are their star performers. Too, be sure to check out their luxurious 100 percent human hair styles which are versatile and so natural looking as low as $49. Yes, human hair wigs for this low price. Curl them, blow dry them, style them, color them — and forget that standing appointment at the beauty shop. Great for travel. Great for last-minute dates. Great for emergencies of any kind. Great for chemo patients. And great for TV divas. You can also add a hair piece in for variety. Why not? You are a woman of independent means and that means you can change your look on command. It's so easy to do so online. Shop for wigs by lengths, styles, sizes, brands, features, colors. My favorite, though, is still the **RACQUEL WELCH** styles, though in spite of my fantasy, I'll never look like her even when I have her hair on! Shop for wig accessories, too. For more than 20 years, they have covered more heads than all the salads in Texas and saved even more green. With more than one million active customers, why not be one million and one? And the latest? They are now carrying their own line of cosmetics, from lipstick liners for $4.99 to lipsticks, $5.99, eyeshadows and eyebrow liners. Link to their other online catalog called Especially Yours Æ. You will flip (but hopefully not your wig!) *Call toll-free: 800/343-9695*

★★★★ Perfumania

940/665-4124

4321 I-35 North, #285
Gainesville, TX 76240
www.perfumania.com

Mon-Sat 10-8; Sun 11-6

It's always nice to have your perfume precede you when you walk into the room or have it linger on after you've gone. That means **PERFUMANIA** and Perfumania.com. Online, it's one of the premier discount fragrance retailers and wholesale distributors specializing in the sale of genuine designer fragrances, bath and body products, cosmetics and skin care treatments and related gifts and accessories for men, women and children. The three S's are very much the operative words at this company: service, selection and savings on quality perfume, fragrances and related products. You can shop in Gainesville, or go online and save 20 to 60 percent. I saved on women's **NOA** by **CACHAREL, THEOREMA** by **FENDI** (to match my handbag), **FERRE** by **GIANFRANCO FERRE, ANIMALE** by **ANIMALE PARFUMS** and **CABOTINE** by **PARFUMS GRE**. Hey, right now it's 50 percent off online. Then, for the bath, I had to have a pair of bath gloves and a long back brush by **JEROME PRIVEE**. Here's to "Smelling the good life....at half the price. Closer to home, Grapevine Mills is now home to Perfumania Numero 2, at 3000 Grapevine Mills Parkway, Suite 303, 972/724-6803. So in person or online, it all smells the same when the day is done. *Call toll-free: 800/927-1777*

◆◆◆◆◆   **Prestige Electrolysis & Laser Hair Removal Center**

972/386.9082
Mon-Sat By Appt. Only

6757 Arapaho Road, Suite 763
Dallas, TX 75248
www.laserhairremoval.com

Answer just a few easy questions online and in seconds, you'll have your answer as to whether you're a good candidate for laser hair removal. Owner Carol Crowley is a board Certified Medical Electrologist and holds a certificate of teaching in electrolysis. She is active in all the professional societies those in her profession hold in high regard included being a member in good standing at the Dallas Better Business Bureau. Since 1981, Carol has been one of the leaders of the pack. And today, all of the latest high-tech treatments are part of her repetroire offering needle electrolysis, laser hair removal, facial treatments including Microdermabrasion, Jessner peels and Foto Facialô skin repair — all state-of-the-art and medically sponsored. Her office is one of the biggest in the business with seven technicians and two receptionists. For the past 20 years, hair removal specialists have been removing hair permanently with electrolysis. But today, they are now removing hair with the **GENTLELASE ALEXANDRITE** laser. You can be hair free in a few appointments include a man's full back, chest and ladies can secure hair removal to both arms and both legs if they want. Almost any body area can have hair removal and men and women are both candidates. All Prestige "lasertrologists" (this is a new word in the dictionary, for sure) are certified and work under medical direction. They are one of the most experienced professional groups in the Metroplex who have been performing laser hair removal for more than three years. For the best hair removal results, don't take chances — go to the pros. It'll hurt less in the long run. Other area locations are privately owned. Call for appointments to Duncanville Electrolysis & Laser Clinic, 122 W. Center, 972/298-1575; Laser Centers of Denton at S. I-35E, Denton, Texas 76205.

◆◆◆◆◆   **Rhiannon's Closet & Gallery Salon Suites**

972/503-3330
By Appt. Only (Tues-Sat)

14833 Midway Rd., #205
Addison, TX 75001
www.rhiannonscloset.com

Take one feisty redhead who's bursting with creative energy, give her a blank slate, and see what materializes. Well, that's exactly what Diane Delahunty did and continues to do - all outside the box. This is not just another grouping of salon suites. This is the Gallery Salon Suites, an approach that is strictly Diane. Once inside the Suites (on the second floor above the Stone Trail Restaurant), you'll "Ooh and ahh" and rightfully so. Stop in at Rhiannon's Closet, which is Diane's hair and color room and take advantage of her expertise when it comes to hair color. Give Diane the credit for the decorative panache. If I am the Princess of (Price) Cuts, what do you suppose we should call Diane? She is a discount decorator, she is a masterful colorist, she is a classic entrepreneur catering to lots of other talented stylists under her Gallery Salon Suite Banner and she plays in a woodwind orchestral and if that weren't enough, she's writing a series of children's book. But first and foremost, she can do hair — cut, styling and color. She also has introduced drama and color throughout the Gallery. It's a one-of-a-kind palette at each stylist's individual room, complete with different faux elements everywhere....all on a budget, but you'd never know it. Unusual chandeliers in each stylist's area complete with moldings, shelving, unusual thematic accents — you will want to know every trade secret (from beauty tips to decorating). She's a bubble ready to burst on the scene with other projects: a series of "Princess" How-to books, while taking perhaps a

detour or two onto the concert stage as a flutist. Redheads are not only beautiful, but they're determined. If you need more convincing, see her website, read her trade secrets newsletter, and make a
hair and color appointment.

♦♦♦♦♦♦ Salon de Joie   972/392-1919

14817 Inwood Rd.   By Appt. Only
Addison, TX 75001-3721

She loves him, she love him not, only her hairdresser knows for sure. She does or
she doesn't color her eye brows? Are those her nails or those are sculptured? She
looks relaxed enough to have just had the best massage she's had in her life? Well,
welcome to this Salon de Joie for the real royal beauty treatments. Debra Storie has plenty of stories to tell about patrons who have been coming to this salon for years. Of course being next door
to Delicious Cakes and down the street from the Tuesday Morning's main store doesn't hurt. But
it's the stylists, aestheticians, massage therapists and manicurists/pedicurists that makes them
come back for more. Make an appointment and see for yourself, glamour puss.

♦♦♦♦♦♦ SoZo Hair Salon   214/522-7600

4524 Cole Ave.   Tues-Sat By Appt. Only
Dallas, TX 75205
www.SoZoHair.com

Ron and Jody Blevins had a better idea. After extensive training with Toni & Guy,
Ron decided to soar on his own recognizance. Meaning, he wanted to "do his own
thing." As a hair stylist with experience as a cutting and color specialist, he knew his
life's work was in the hair business but to him, the meaning of owning a hair salon was not just to
be there with instruments and knowledge in his hands but he really wanted to make a difference in
each client's life. (Of course, that is the purpose of the other 12 talented stylists he has on board,
too.) No, this isn't a one-stop fits all day spa. They do not pamper you all day with a myriad of spa
treatments. SoZo cuts, colors, perms and straightens hair. Period. They do have, though, the Thermal Hair Straightening procedure that does take all day and really straightens your hair right down
to the roots. So, if you've always been a little Orphan Annie, why not try this for a change. How
many curly heads have always dreamed of long straight hair hanging down the middle of your
back? Jody, Ron's wife, on the other hand was a manicurist but they decided they did not want to
offer manicures but to be strictly a hair salon. Simple is as simple does. This salon is based on the
theory that if you provide the best service at a fair price and put forth the effort to serve your clientele well, they will come. Well, this shop certainly has the right focus. What also sets them apart of
being just another hair salon is their consignment art gallery where they showcase talented artists
work for sale. A nice decorative touch to the salon. Enjoy the museum-like, yet hip atmosphere
while having some of the best stylists making you a new "do." They have plenty of requests for
"updo's" so if you are a bride or a prom gal, this is the place to have it done with aplomb. (Many
salons refuse to do updo's these days.) Too, they even make house calls and will go on location for
catalog shoots. See why the concierge at the Mansion refers all of their guests to SoZo. Oh, if
you're wondering where they got their name, it's Greek and means "Saved." Does that tell you
that their intentions are indeed honorable.

Susan's Soaps & More   1/972/452-8965

Scurry, TX

www.susansoaps.com   🐭 *Top Online Store!*

 Want to lather up with handmade soaps, lotions and other healthful things? That's what Susan wanted when she developed a serious case of eczema and nothing the dermatologists could prescribe gave her any relief. So, when there's a need, she created first Body Butters. Then she added a face scrub which does triple duty: It cleanses, lathers and exfoliates so you don't have to buy three different products. A gift pack for $19 is about as beautiful a custom gift to give at a bridal shower, a teacher at the holidays, the Mother-in-Law who does nice things for you all year long — well, you get the picture. For such a low price, the package consists of a jar of salt glow crystals, one of body butter and a hand-made soap all tied up with raffia in a beautifully ensconced package. From salt glows to solid perfume, lotion bars to bath salts, this is handcrafted luxury made affordable. Only pure essential oils are used — no synthetic fragrances, colorants or preservatives. You'll get true aromatherapeutic benefits without the threat of any kind of allergic reactions. Susan's soaps are all hand-made which means they will not strip your skin of its natural oils the way commercials soaps do. All the glycerin remains naturally in the soap. Your skin will feel softer and smoother. In all products, Susan uses only pure vegetable oils such as olive and coconut. No lanolin or peanut oil because of possible allergic reactions. And she lives in Scurry, TEXAS and there probably isn't another pure clean activity to keep her busy 24/7. So she built a website and now you can wash your troubles down the drain.

◆◆◆◆◆   Tip Top Nails   214/488-5292
Mon-Sat 9:30-7:30

1071 W. FM 3040, #400
Lewisville, TX 75067

Once I get hoisted into the spa pedicure chair and my feet feel the rush of the JACUZZI-like waves, I drift off to never-never land. When I awake, my feet, calluses and bunions have gone bye-bye and my feet now are actually presentable in public. I have reminded you for 32 years to never step foot outside your house without your toenail polish on; you never know who you may run into and that little extra effort elevates you to the upper crust, trust me. For $15 to $20 bucks, be a sport. You can look rich and your feet will be forever grateful. Same with a set of solar nails. I love them and won't leave home without them. The prices charged at Tip Top Nails are hands down typical of the Vietnamese monopoly on inexpensive nail salons all over the Metroplex. I paid more for my nails 20 years ago than I do today. And, too, they are much more attractive than my glue and go do-it-yourself nail jobs. They do all the latest techniques, including the solar nails, which I personally recommend. My nails look so natural and are so strong, I never have a chipped or broken nail....ever, well, almost never. Do it cheaper, faster, and as good if not better than at the fancy salons. Why not? The only thing I won't let them do is paint stars or an AMERICAN flag on my pinkie. There's a limit to my 5-star regimen.

◆◆◆◆◆   Toni & Guy Academy   972/416-8396
Mon 9:30-5; Tues-Sat 8:30-5 (By Appt. Only)

2810 E. Trinity Mills
Carrollton, TX 75006
www.toniguy.com

The only way to achieve "Beauty at the Least" at Toni and Guy's is to get your name on their Academy's special hair sessions list. Otherwise, you'll pay on an escalating schedule for their services, depending on the level of training of your stylist. Is he a Creative Director or an Apprentice, as services are priced accordingly. You will pony up no less than $40 at the bottom of the totem-pole hierarchy. Color for medium-length hair can run $50 to $80 and that's for partial color. For full color, well, expect to pay $65 to over $100. The Toni & Guy Academy is located at Marsh and Trinity Mills in the Mills Point Shopping Center (look for Tom Thumb and Mr. Gatti's). For a hair-blowing experience, haircuts are $15, $21 for highlights, $41 for coloring short hair, perms are $44 - but for chemical treatments, you need to make an appointment for a consultation first. Dye jobs are priced upon request, after the review session. Call for an appointment. And if you haven't tried any of the Toni & Guy products (TIGI), you've had your head buried beneath a shower cap too long!

★★★★ Ulta   972/612-6031

2432 Preston Rd., Suite 320   Mon-Sat 10-9; Sun 11-6
Plano, TX 75093
www.ulta.com

There's always a flier in my mailbox that lures me into the doors of an Ulta store. FREE gift. I'm no fool when it comes to sharing my Beauty Secrets. Shop here for all your favorite cosmetics, fragrances, skin care, hair and salon care products to bath and body stuff and small appliances. If it's related to keeping your up-do's up and your toe and nail polish down, consider one of the more than 1,500 products that are neatly organized and displayed by manufacturer and category. Load up on **CALVIN KLEIN, CONAIR, COTY, ELIZABETH ARDEN, FREEMAN, GIVENCHY, MAYBELLINE, MURAD, NEUTROGENA, REMINGTON, SALLY HANSEN, SASSOON, YVES ST. LAURENT** and more. From nail polish to tips, lipsticks to Q-TIPS, there's so much to choose from you'll be able to lather up a storm. Hair products by **GOLDWELL, IMAGE, JINGLES, NEXXUS, PAUL MITCHELL, TIGI, TRESSA** and more are waiting to be tried. Then give yourself a hand with **CREATIVE NAIL, POI, PEAU DE PECHE** or **ZOOM**. Mix in a few other brands like **FRANCIS DENNY, ULTIMA II** and more. You can also get a manicure or haircut. Watch for inserts for great specials and gifts with purchase. Check directory for location near you. *Call toll-free: 800/968-5823*

Vicki's Making Faces   817/692-6639

Arlington, TX
                                                         By Appt. Only

 Vicki Hansen's the Florence Nightingale of Permanent Cosmetics was voted the #1 permanent makeup artist for the 2005 shopping season. She's not only a medical aesthetician with a dozen plus years of experience, but a magician when it comes to her touch of genius. Forget the daily ritual of putting on eyebrows, eye liner, even lipliner much less lips. Pucker up and don't be a sucker by letting just anybody do permanent makeup on you without credentials or years of experience. Yes, Vicki uses only the best dyes that are void of iron oxide (important to know if you ever need an MRI, for example. You can't have an MRI if you are wearing permanent makeup with iron oxide.) Once under her spell, and your face part is properly numbed, the results of her artistry will leave you spellbound. Have eyes that are alluring, dramatic and perfect 24/7. Shave 15 minutes off your morning make-up ritual and have a leisurely cup of coffee instead. Have those fading brows restored to the arches de triumph. Yours will be feathered rather than drawn across your brow with a straight black line. You'll feel better as a result. That's why one plastic surgeon flies Vicki to Houston every three weeks to tend to his patients. Vicki also works in the offices of select area plastic surgeons so you can expect her work to measure up to the highest of standards. Expect this former makeup artist to transform you from plain Jane to super Sue. Next time you see me, you'll see the difference. If you've had reconstructive breast surgery and want a realistic areola, she can make it so even your husband won't know the difference. Whether you are wanting

permanent makeup for beauty's sake or for medical reasons, her references read like a Who's Who in the Metroplex. You won't make a face after Vicki makes yours. Trust me. She also does facials and make-up, if requested. With five kids, four of them daughters, she has plenty of experience with what girls who ultimately grow up want. And she is the best in this business. Let he do your face and face the day with permanent makeup. Look for her "before and after" pictures on our website at www.undergroundshopper.com

Elegant Salon

See wirteup on page 108

Beds & Mattresses

★★★★★★ **City Mattress Factory Outlet**   817/834-1648

900 S. Haltom Rd.
Haltom City, TX 76117
www.onlinesleep.com

Mon-Fri 8-5; Sat 8-3

While it doesn't take a Ph.D. in cartography to find this place, it takes some effort, (off 121, exit Haltom Road and go south a half mile, across the railroad tracks, then around a curve) but your back will be forever grateful.) The entire staff of The Underground Shopper sleeps cheap thanks to City Mattress. Experience their version of the **TEMPURPEDIC** mattresses that have been clinically proven to relieve back pain, neck pain, and insomnia. They make their own visco-elastic, temperature-sensitive material that adjusts to body weight and temperature as well as an adjustable bed that you can raise and lower at whim. I personally sleep on an adjustable mattress system from City Mattress and it has saved my life. Really. Have remote, will go (up and down as the activity dicates.) Sleep apnea sufferers and snorers, take note. If you raise the back of an adjustable mattress, you can generally open your airways. Save plenty of restless nights on any of **ROYAL SLEEP**'s products. And if you don't want to invest in an entirely new bedding system, try their Whopper Toppers®, a topper layer that you can throw over your current mattress to give you a hint of that latex pleasure. It will also protect your current mattress making it last longer. Remember, latex is hypo-allergenic and doesn't allow the infiltration of mites or anything close to a bed bug. If you want to be lulled to sleep on any other kind of bedding option, City Mattress carries a vast variety of pillowtops, futons, inner spring mattresses for at least half the price at twice the value. Buy direct and save up to 70 percent. Go to their website and see first-hand how to pick your next best night's sleep cheap and have it delivered. Just call their toll-free number above or place your order online. Visit their website at www.beddingtoppers.com until their new website is up and operational. It will ultimately link to their full mattress website. This year, there were literally 1,467 "thank you" emails to me about the City Mattress mattresses. *Call toll-free: 800/834-2473*

★★★★★   Factory Mattress Outlet & Futons   817/346-4893

6236 McCart Ave.   Mon-Sat 10-6; Thurs 10-8; Sun 1-5
Fort Worth, TX 76133
www.factorymattressoutlet.com

Not even a **PRINCESS** could find a pea under these mattresses. In 1973, Marvin and Ava Beleck created the Factory Mattress Outlet in their first 2,700-square-foot building in Dallas. Three years later, they expanded to 16,000 square feet across the street. There, they created one of the largest displays of nationally-advertised bedding at discounted prices in the U.S. Now that's something. See 50 sofa sleepers and over 100 different models of mattress sets made by the top manufacturers: **BEMCO, BASSETT, ENGLANDER, KING KOIL, NATIONAL CHIROPRACTIC, RESTONIC, SEALY, SERTA, SIMMONS, SPRING AIR, THER-A-PEDIC** and more. Models were displayed in foam, innerspring, air and water. When the waterbed craze was in its heyday, Factory Mattress Outlet saw explosive possibilities so reduced their sofa sleeper display to 12 models and placed 50 models of waterbed frames and accessories on the sales floor. When they started to wane, they reversed the display presence to what's hot and what's not. In 1987, Marvin Beleck sold the Dallas property and moved the store operation and showroom to 6236 McCart, where they are continuing to enjoy their status as one of the five-stars in The Underground Shopper. Shipping nationwide. Remember, "They Sell Sleep at Savings."

★★★   Heavenly Sleep Shoppe   817/595-4205

1133 W. Pipeline Rd. @ Melbourne   Mon-Sat 10-6; Sun 1-5
Hurst, TX 76053
www.heavenly-sleep.com

Since 1986, this family-owned and operated business has been helping Hurst residents sleep at a discount. Especially strong in brands **SEALY** and **SIMMONS**, if you are contemplating some heavenly-sleep ahead (or a foot, too.) Pull up a cloud and drift off into never-never land. Prices may not be exactly what you expect to find at the pearly gates, even if they do claim that "nobody sells for less." So what, if they're pennies from heaven and not quarters. After all, a penny saved is a penny earned. But for sure, the angels here will go out of their way to provide divine customer service. FREE delivery. FREE setup. FREE financing. And FREE removal of your old mattresses. Also carrying dinette sets, headboards, bar stools, futons, chairs and rockers, computer desks, entertainment centers and more at not so heavenly prices, but at least, down-to-earth. New this year, shop their Arlington outpost at 2544 E. Abram St., 817/795-2900.

★★★★   Mattress Firm Clearance Store, The   972/401-9665

10699 N. Stemmons Frwy.   Mon-Fri 10-9; Sat 10-8; Sun Noon-6
Dallas, TX 75229
www.mattressfirm.com

Nobody sells **SEALY** for less than this **SEALY**-owned chain of stores named as the industry's most resourceful and profitable retail chain in the country. In fact, The Mattress Firm is the fastest growing bedding retailer in the U.S. Founded in 1986 in Houston, today it has over 300 stores in 41 markets. Revenues for 2000 exceeded $220 million. **SEALY** Mattress is the most recognized bedding brand in the world and has been in existence for over 100 years. The Mattress Firm is also the largest retailer of **STEARNS AND FOSTER**, their luxury line with prices from $899 to $1,999 for queen and king-size, sometimes less at their Clearance Store above. Online, print out $25 to $75 coupons from their website and shop the more than 29 stores in the Metroplex, including the two newest on Skillman and in Frisco. FREE delivery or bed frame with premium set purchase.

One-year Free financing with approved credit available and appreciated. And all with three-hour express delivery, same-day, next-day, any day you want delivery. Join the many other firm believers in this mattress kingpin.

★   Mattress Giant   972/960-2337

4900 Belt Line Rd., Suite 100   Mon-Fri 10-9: Sat to 9:30-8; Sun 11-6 PM
Addison, TX 75240
www.mattressgiant.com

Since there are more than nine major brands of mattresses to choose from, this **SIMMONS**-owned giant is a force to reckon with. The only bone I have to pick with them, is don't expect anything really to be discounted. Instead, expect to pay $1,799 to $2,199 for a queen or king-size SERTA Perfect Night Jupiter. Go to the smaller discounters or the Simmons outlet (World of Sleep) and do a lot better in my wrack-ridden back's opinion. Oohing and aahing aside, someone's got to pay for their million-dollar advertising campaign and their multi-million dollar corporate headquarters.There are so many Metroplex locations, that I've stopped counting. They are considered the fastest growing "specialty" bedding retailer in the country as compared to The Mattress Firm, the fastest growing mattress retailer in the country. Really, what's the difference? Order by phone, online or in person, a plus. Headquartered in Addison on Midway, there are over 250 stores in 14 states. "Shop Smart. Sleep Better." H-m-m-m! And to think that I knew the founders, back then. And now, who's retired as multi-millionaires? And who's still working 7 days a week? Then again, I'm no giant. *Call toll-free: 800/442-6823*

★★★   Mattress USA   972/424-0474

811 E. 15th St.   Mon-Sat 10-7; Sun Noon-6
Plano, TX 75074
www.mattressusa.com

If you've been shopping for mattresses lately, you know how difficult it is to compare "apples to apples" since many manufacturers produce the same mattress under different labels. It's a challenge when every one of them claims to be the lowest price, don't you agree? Well, here's a place where you can get a good deal that we guarantee. Not great, but good. With up to 50 percent off and more, it's as American as apple pie. All mattresses are new and unused. In fact, I've always heard it's against the law to sell a used mattress in Texas. Who'd want to anyway? Top it off with a large selection of futons, daybeds, bunk beds, iron beds, canopy beds, even futon and sofa accessories. Create your own comfort with custom-made mattresses that are available upon request. Choose from the ready-mades by Chiropractic by **SPRINGWALL**, **KING KOIL**, **POSTURE BEAUTY** and **SIMMONS BEAUTYREST**. Take Central to 15th Street in Plano, one red light east to old town Plano. See the USA at the northeast corner but don't forget there's also a store in Garland at 417 N. Garland Ave.

★★★★   Mattressland   972/423-5656

6000 N. Central   Mon-Fri 10-7; Sat 10-6; Sun 12:30-5
Plano, TX 75074

In a world all onto their own, Mattressland will lull you to sleep with their dreamy prices alone. Just because they're factory seconds, closeouts, liquidations or blemishes doesn't mean they'll induce nightmares. Instead, take advantage of the savings. Believe me, a slight discoloration on the underside will not keep you awake at night. Hey, dreams are in black and white anyway. And so are these prices. It's clear to see that when **BASSETT** pillow-top sets start at just $250, your dreams are finally coming true. But this is no fairy tale with **KING KOIL, SIMMONS BEAUTY-REST, SPRING AIR** and **SPRINGWALL** stacked high in a plain-Jane showroom. Besides, that's how us plain Jane's sleep well without worrying about paying a fortnight for our mattresses.

★★★   Rick's Bedrooms   972/840-3000

3010 S. Jupiter   Mon-Fri 10-8; Sat 10-7; Sun 12-6
Garland, TX 75041
www.ricksbedrooms.com

At Rick's Bedrooms, they are selling more than waterbeds, but waterbeds are sure what brought them fame and fortune. Expanding this empire to include budget bedroom furnishings, beanbags, mattresses, futons, leather and youth bedroom sets makes for an expanded menu of options. You can order online or at any of their Metroplex locations with Free delivery. At a recent Home and Garden Show, they were showcasing a queen-size Tempurpedic mattress. That's the one that has been clinically proven to relieve back pain, neck pain, and some common sleep disorders such as insomnia with that visco-elastic, temperature sensitive material that adjusts to your body weight and temperature. From futons, waterbeds, waterbed accessories, bedroom furniture and name-brand mattresses, you should be a sleeping beauty in no time. Inexpensive bedroom furniture, **SIMMONS BEAUTYREST** mattresses and more are available in any of their four locations; Addison, 15300 Midway Road, 972/991-9811; Mesquite, 3501 Gus Thomasson, 972/681-5878; Plano, 901 W. Parker, #117, 972/422-4401 and their distribution center above, 866/742-5723 (RICK'S BEDS). Since you're visiting Vikon Village nearby and down the street from Cabbage Patch, you're in the area, so why not stop in. *Call toll-free: 866/RICKS BE*

★★★★★   Sweet Dreams Bedding Co.   817/790-8510

4125 S. I-35 W   Mon-Fri 9-5
Alvarado, TX 76009
www.sweetdreamsbedding.com

No need for soothing lullabies, Sweet Dreams Bedding Company is all the comfort you'll need. No need to fuss over several labels because Sweet Dreams is the manufacturer of futons as well as mattresses used in the hospitality industry. Your questions and comments are always welcomed, since production of these mattresses meets and exceeds the industry standards for quality name brands. If you remember having a good night's sleep while staying at a Marriott hotel, you've slept on a **SWEET DREAMS** mattress. See, I told you. When you're tired, the last thing you're looking for is the designer's name, right? What you want is some shut-eye without getting poked in the back with some loose spring. The quality of their mattresses generally exceeds industry standards established by the major brands anyway. Have any mattress delivered Free in the Metroplex. Just call for a price quote. A pillow top king mattress set was $602, delivered. Not bad, eh? Besides carrying mattresses, frames and rails, they are now carrying bedroom sets, leather sofas, wing chairs, rustic armoires, French-like furniture, rustic bookcases and coffee/end tables, occasional tables, oak curious, misting fountains and accent furniture. Visit closer to town, CDI Warehouse, 2810 Ave. E., Arlington, TX 76011, 817/608-0073; 888/236-5835.

★★★★ **United Mattress Company**   **940/565-1914**

220 W. Oak   Mon-Fri 9-6; Sat 10-5
Denton, TX 76201-4112
www.unitedmattress.com

United we stand, and united we fall — into bed. This manufacturer makes quality bedding without the big price tag. Test-sleep one on location to see what a difference buying factory direct makes. There's a factory showroom and warehouse in downtown Denton off I-35, exit West Oak to the second block off the downtown square. Then, for the more adventurous, go to their new Gainesville store called United & Holland Mattress, 427 N. Grand Avenue in Gainesville, TX 76240, 940/668-6700. Drive a little, save a lot may be an overused cliche, but in this case, we're talking saving quite a lot, not just a lot. You can even call for special appointments after hours, toll free, if you can't make it in during regular business hours. *Call toll-free: 800/833-1914*

★★★★★ **World of Sleep**   **214/631-3257**

1290 Conveyor Ln. (Inwood Trade Center)   Mon-Fri 10-7; Sat 10-6; Sun Noon-5
Dallas, TX 75237
www.wosmattressoutlet.com

Hopefully, you're lucky in love and lucky in — bed, with a good night's sleep. Well, if you shop at the SIMMONS Outlet, now called World of Sleep Mattress Outlet, off Inwood and Stemmons, at the Inwood Outlet Center, you will rest easy. This company has been manufacturing bedding and inventing products we consider commonplace today. They are credited with being the first mattress company to introduce a Super Size mattress in 1958. Two years later, **SIMMONS** began manufacturing both queen and king-size mattresses that today outsell twins and doubles. They offer their Do-Not-Disturb famous "Beautyrest" mattress as well as their other models such as the "**BACK CARE**," "Maxipedic" and "Ultimate Supreme" and it's common to see savings of hundreds of dollars. Queen sets started as low as $199; king sets started at $350. Get a good night's sleep by buying overstocks, mismatched sets, mattresses with a blemish or two, mattress orders that have been cancelled in all sizes. Visit their second location at 1144 Plano Rd., Suite 100, Richardson (Arapaho Station), 972/690-4270. Same hours and same great products.

City Mattress
Factory Outlet

See writeup on page 119

Boots & Western Wear

★★★ Affordable Western Store   817/237-7111
1179 Southeast Pkwy   Mon-Sat 10-7; Sun 12-6
Azle, TX 76020

You don't have to cross over the border into Texas to look like real cowboys, but it helps. That's how it feels to travel to Azle, but since it's affordable western wear, right down to the spurs, you might make an exception. Looking for hats, hats and more hats? Good, because they have hats and boots, coats, belts, buckles, tack, rodeo shirts, vests, jeans, purses, chaps and more. Here's the more: jewelry, mugs, wallets, money clips, hat bands, bolos and lots of items that clearly say "Texas." Even children's wear for those li'l wranglers can be rounded up. The hats come in many configurations and materials — felt, wool and beaver in the $49 to $349 range and straw from $20 to $70. Hats are creased by professional hatters and for another $9 to $29, you can add a band. These boots were made for walking so slip on a pair from $39 to $200. Brands included: **ADOBE ROSE, AMERICAN HAT CO., BANJO, BARSTOW, BILLY COOK, BLAZE, CIRCLE Y SADDLES, COWTOWN BOOTS, ELY WALKER, LARADO, LAWMAN, MILLERS, MO BETTA, MONTANA SILVERSMITHS, PANHANDLE SLIM, RED RIVER BITS, RESISTOL, ROCKY MOUNTAIN, RUDDOCK BROS., STETSON, SUPREME WESTERN, WOLVERINE** and many more. Jeans were limited to **ROCKY MOUNTAIN** and **WRANGLER'S** from $20 to $50. There is nothing that adds more to the mystique about a cowboy than his hat. And it's hats off here, where prices are always a little less when the storefront's in Azle, Texas. *Call toll-free: 800/270-2621*

★★★★★★ Beads Beautiful/Wanted   940/627-7394
106 W. Walnut   Mon-Fri 9:30-5 Sat 10:30-5
Decatur, TX 76234

WANTED! Well-bred or alive! Never heard of this label, WANTED? Well, it's the name that will open the right doors for you in all the right Southwestern circles. If you're looking for the perfect western outfit to wear to the Cattle Baron's Ball, look toward Decatur for a look that separates the women from the girls. Shop Beads Beautiful's outlet store for factory pricing on ladies'dresses, skirts, jackets, vests, fringed outfits and silk broomstick skirts, all hand-painted or decorated by on-site artists. Look for **BRIGHTON, MICHAEL LOO** and handcrafted Indian jewelry, for example, that will indeed add that extra oomph. If you're clamoring'for a western wedding, what about a shawl and a skirt to say your "I do's"? Expect to see these western-flared duds in specialty stores only that cater to high-fallutin'rodeo queens. To look like one, save the money and drive a bargain here — up to 75 percent off. Their on-the-square historic boutique is brimming with bargains and one-of-a-kind gifts. I was going to say oozing with bargains, too, because their custom Coozies are the talk of the town. Doesn't everybody you know what to quench their thirst sipping from a real cowhide and fringed coozie? A perfect stocking stuffer for the displaced Texas or the natives who have everything. And there's no whar else in Texas to get these. Rodeo queens and society genes know a good thing when they see it. Now, buy it! *Call toll-free: 800/959-WANT*

★★★★   Boot Town Superstore   972/243-1151

2821 LBJ Frwy. @ Josey   Mon-Sat 9-9; Sun 11-6
Farmers Branch, TX 75244
www.boottown.com

Kick up your heels and move 'em on out. Boot Town is the premier discounter in this part of the woods. It's business as usual and time for you to step out in a pair of boots, as these boots were made for walkin': **CHIPPEWA, CORRAL, DURANGO, HARLEY** (men's and women's), **JUSTIN** Boots and **JUSTIN** Original Work Boots, ORIGINAL and 2000, **TONY LAMA, NOCONA, RESISTOL, WOLVERINE, WRANGLER** — it goes on and on. All the accessories, too, including **FORCE TEN** Leather Collection, Buckles, Belts, Jewelry and Watches, Public Safety Footwear and Black Jack Boots. All of the best brands are represented from plain to exotic skins (lizard, snake, ostrich and more) in sizes that'll knock your socks off! Add in all the extras, from clothing to key rings, dusters to wallets, wrist bands to hats, say, "Howdy, pardner!" Boots and shoes in sizes 6¾ to 13 for men, 4 to 10 for women and children's sizes, too. Boot Town has been kicking up its heels for the well-heeled with 10 Metroplex locations, combined with their brother/sister stores, Western Warehouse. Order from their **FREE** catalog. Locations throughout Texas, in Houston, San Antonio and Austin, too. *Call toll-free: 800/222-6687*

★★★★★★   Boots for Less (Just Justin)   214/630-2858

                                                    Mon-Fri 10-8; Sat 10-7; Sun Noon-6
Dallas, TX 75207
www.bootsforless.com

 No longer a store front, but for the time being, you can order whatever you want online until a new home is found. This Wycliff discounter has closed its doors and is out looking for a new home on the range. But until then, you can shop online or via their Free catalog. Call the number to get yours. While you're waiting for it, here's an interesting fact I bet you didn't know about when buying boots: You take a half size less than you normally wear in street shoes. I thought it was just the opposite. Even kids can kick up their heels in a pair of **JUSTIN** boots for as low as $39. They will be selling by phone or catalog until a new physical location is founb. Expect discounts anywhere from 40 to 70 percent off list. More than 20,000 pairs in stock. Don't expect any other brand but JUSTIN and if truth were known, **TONY LAMA** and **CHIPPEWA BOOTS** are also owned by JUSTIN. Ask for their FREE catalog and try your hand at ordering for your feet and de-feet the high cost booting up your shoe wardrobe. They know how to fit you sight unseen just by knowing your shoe size. In fact, they were picked by CNBC as "one of the four best mail order companies" in the country. Returns are accepted if you are ever dissatisfied and boots are unworn. However, if you wear them and discover a defect, that's a whole other story. They will gladly accept them back for a refund or exchange. All JUSTIN boots sold at Boots for Less are first quality. With over 20 years in the business and the solid name of JUSTIN behind them, you can bet your sweet booty that these boots are made for walkin'. *Call toll-free: 800/292-2668*

★★★   Cavender's Boot City   817/589-7311

857 W. Pipeline Rd.   Mon-Sat 9-9; Sun 11-6
Hurst, TX 76053
www.cavenders.com/

When James Cavender started his western wear store in 1957, little did he know that he and Elvis would be both riding high. This began as a little store in Pittsburg, Texas that first was a Dairy Mart. In 1967, another store was opened, but this time it was a retail western wear business for men and boys. Thirty-five years, 40-plus stores and some 800 employees later, the Cavenders still have a family-owned and operated store that truly is a Texas dream come true. Today, it's one of the largest boot companies in Dallas. Synonymous with Texas, they have it all: boots, western wear, jeans, home accessories, purses, wallets and stuffed animals. There's always something on sale at this City round-up. Stomp 20 percent off all WRANGLER oxford shirts or a pair of TONY LAMA smooth ostrich boots for $178. You needn't be a scavenger when you look for boots at Cavender's as you'll find ACME, ARIAT, NOCONA and TONY LAMA starting as low as $49. Racks and racks of western duds like shirts and jeans by CINCH, LAWMAN, PANHANDLE SLIM and WRANGLER as well as women's duds by LAWMAN, ROCKY MOUNTAIN and WRANGLER. Check directory for multiple Metroplex locations.

★★★★   Circle C Western Wear   817/237-7111

7640 Jacksboro Hwy.   Mon-Wed, Sat 10-8; Thu-Fri 10-9; Sun Noon-6
Fort Worth, TX 76135

You can circle the Metroplex, but you'll always land a square deal at Circle C Western Wear in Fort Worth. Their men's department and boots (COWTOWN, DIAMOND J, DOUBLE H, JUSTIN, REDWING, RHINO and WOLVERINE) make it worth your while. But they've also surrounded themselves with western home accents, Montana jewelry, belts, buckles, hats and a hat bar that creases hats right on the spot. Lest women think they've been forsaken, there's women's clothing, purses, western furniture and a line-up of restaurants to keep your appetite filled to stuffed. So, if you're looking for clothes in all the wrong places, this may well be the place to head. Turn down Jacksboro Highway just northwest of I-820 if you want to detour from high prices on western wear. Not only that, they sure are friendly in them thar parts!

★★★   Foster's Westernwear/Saddle Shop   940/383-1549

6409 N. I-35   Mon-Sat 9-6:30;
Denton, TX 76207

Located just north of Denton Factory Stores and Loop 288 on I-35, while heading north to the ranch, foster a relationship with Foster's. This family-owned ranch store is especially rope-worthy if you're living, learning or "lariating" in Denton County. When classes resume at North Texas and TWU, there's usually a line outside their door. DOUBLE D and WRANGLER clothes take a front-and-center position for the entire family. Leather coats and jackets, a must. And of course, you've got to have a pair of boots from DAN POST, JUSTIN and TONY LAMA, be it a pair of ropers, lace-ups or full-quill ostrich, it's your call. Add in the saddles and tack, DOUBLE D outfits, a leather coat, a KISS department for kid's clothes, and you are ready for a well-rounded ride into the sunset. Last, but not least, encircle their western jewelry. You can't leave home without something turquoise. It's back. What will the neighbors think? Look after those feet and cultivate an entirely new western look from Foster's Western Wear and Saddle Shop. They'll treat you like one of the family.

★★ Horse & Rider

972/542-4162
Mon-Sat 10-8; Sun 1-5

123 N. Central Expwy.
McKinney, TX 75069

This ride 'em cowboy store is the retail outpost of America's largest saddle maker. No horsing around here. Saddle up with **ABETTA, ACTION, BILLY COOK, LONGHORN, SADDLESMITH** and others — they're just waiting to be harnessed. Is your preference Western or English? You have your choice here. Be it English or Western tack, English riding clothes, Western boots, saddles, everything for the horse and rider but not decidedly discounted. (Come to think of it, Horse & Rider's a really good name for a chain of stores, don't you think? And it may be the best thing this chain has to offer — save the selection.) Discounts, no. Nearby, restaurants, yes. So at least won't be driving home on an empty stomach. This is steak country, you know. If you log on to www.horseandrider.com, you'll get connected to the magazine of that name but not this store's online site. Sorry about that. Gallop away without saving the day. *Call toll-free: 800/436-8742*

★★★★ Justin Boot Outlet Store

817/654-3103
Mon-Fri 9-5:30; Sat 9-5

717 W. Vickery Blvd.
Fort Worth, TX 76104-1142
www.justinboots.com

When this hometown favorite shut down its manufacturing site in Fort Worth, we were a little nervous they'd move the outlet store to El Paso, too. Thank goodness they didn't. Just off I-30 in downtown Fort Worth, exit Commerce to Jennings, then turn left. Continue on to West Vickery and turn right. Buy boots for the entire family. And the prices, well, it just doesn't get better than shopping at the outlet. Slip into a stupendous selection, but there's nothing but irregulars, small blemishes and defectives. Sure could have fooled me. They support the Justin Cowboy Crisis Fund (their non-profit organization that helps injured rodeo athletes), giving 100 percent of all donations to this group. And that's straight from the horse's mouth — George Strait's, that is. What started by H.J. Justin in 1879 is still going strong today. **JUSTIN** boots are handcrafted today with each pair built and inspected one at a time to ensure quality with every stitch. JUSTIN boots is Texas for Texans going places. Take your pick from Western Ropers, Chukkas and their Gear-styled boots for men, women and children.

★★★ Justin Discount Boots

940/648-2797
Mon-Sat 9-6

101 FM 156 (PO Box 67)
Justin, TX 76247

Even if a new pair of boots is only a stone's throw away in the Metroplex, you owe it to yourself to drive to **JUSTIN**, past the Texas Motor Speedway, to the JUSTIN Discount Boot Outlet just to see where over $60 million dollars of boots are sold. They have a wide selection of EVERYTHING JUSTIN! Not only do they offer a great selection, but SOME of the prices are equally appealing. But remember, it's just as easy to spend a little money on a great pair of boots as it is to drop a bundle. Which way would you prefer to go? Spend a lot or save a lot? Order without even leaving home, this is where they shine. No website. No mail orders any more. So, it's to the store or nothing. Why? Building their business with mail order customers all over the world, why would they stop doing what they did best? Well, 'tis not for me to say. Shop at their store in Justin and that's it for aspiring Roy Rogers and Dale Evans. If you don't wear it or scuff the soles, you can return your boots within 30 days for a refund or exchange. Their extensive western collection of apparel, accessories and boots is surely how the West was really won — from work boots, ropers or exotic skins (bull hide, lizard, ostrich and shark) in men's, women's and children's boots. Since 1978, they have been rustling up these boots at the historic old Wallace Building in Justin including all the famous brands and styles. Though some first-quality items were full price, some irregulars were 30 to 60 percent off. But it's not consistent so you may have to go to Boot Camp to learn the ropes on how to separate the men from the boys. A trip back in time would be one small step for the nostalgic kind. *Call toll-free: 800/677-BOOT*

★★★   Master Hatters   972/276-2347

2355 Forest Lane   Mon-Sat 10-6
Garland, TX 75042
www.masterhatters.com

Hey, Mister Hatter, how many hats can the mad hatter have if the mad hatter bought his hat from the Master Hatter? Well, at these prices, probably twice as many. Please don't be mad but this is a family matter. The Cook family offers the perfect topper for a sunny day. Straw hats for men and women are their forte, starting as low as $24.95. But if you want to call forth the big guns, they also carry a variety of cowboy hats in sizes 6 3/4 to 7 5/8. Whether you've got a big head or not, you can protect your scalp with a sun shade made in Texas. You'll also go wild for the western wear selection. From the **WRANGLER** brand to less familiar names, you'll find that all of their jeans come from good genes. All are first-quality and sell for $20 to $25, with irregulars as low as $15. Just look for them through the forest on Forest just east of **SHILOH**. Founded the same year as The Underground Shopper, 1972, when the Urban Cowboy craze hit the movie screen. They finally took over like a bull in a china shop. When that fad faded, they added fur felt hats to their product mix and then acquired the WRANGLER license for hats. True to form, they continue making WRANGLER hats to this day. Find the perfect shade protector at this hat factory. And the top of the morning to you, too!

★   Resistol Hats Outlet Store/Arena Brands   972/494-0337

721 Marion Drive   Mon-Sat 10-5:45
Garland, TX 75042
www.stetson.com

A real true blue outlet store with years of history behind it has finally exploded into a tourist desti- nation. After all, every transplant or visitor to Texas can't wait to buy a cowboy hat. And where are they made? That's right, in Garland at the **RESISTOL** and **STETSON** hat factory under the cor- porate umbrella Hatco. Unfortunately, saving 20 percent is no big deal in Big D. Waiting until Christmas or the end-of-the-season for the savings of up to 75 percent was like leading a horse to water and then pulling the trough out from under him. Bargain shoppers want instant gratification. So, to top it off, there wasn't much of a savings even on RESISTOL top-quality hats. Hey, isn't that what the appeal of a factory outlet's suppose to be? Furthermore, straw hats started at $39.95, which didn't appear drastically reduced either. So what gives? Are they just another retail western store with a large selection of hats by **CHARLIE 1 HORSE** and **STETSON** and jeans by **CINCH**, **ROCKY MOUNTAIN** and **WRANGLER** plus shirts, belts and jewelry? You might do better price- wise ordering from a discounter like www.westernhats.com. Sorry, that's just the way it is! For more information on STETSON hats, go to their website and learn where to buy them retail since their outlet has few.

★★   Rowan's Western Wear   903/887-3618

Highway 90 at 175 (PO Box 571)   Mon-Sat 9-5:30; Fri 9-7
Mabank, TX 75147

Being a proud sponsor of the Texas Wildfire Express Drill Team, Rowan is still goin'and growin'and staying involved in the Mabank community. This year they moved about a quarter of a mile up the road on the right. You can't miss them. They still have the same big sign with the horse on it. Since things were moving right along, they decided to move to bigger and newer digs. Instead of being satisfied with a new store, though, they bought the entire shopping center and leased out the excess space. These Rowans are smart. And you can benefit from their sharp buying power. Head down scenic U.S. Highway 175 until it turns onto Highway 90 and you're practically there. Western wear is the specialty at this house, including **NOCONA**, **TEXAS** and **TONY LAMA** boots at a savings of 20 to 25 percent. JUSTIN lace-ups were placed at the check-out counter for $89.95 and ropers were just $79.99 (at least $20 less than most Dallas stores). It pays to shop away from the maddening crowds that attract those big city slickers. Instead, head to the outskirts and snag straw hats for $29.95, a pair of **RED WING** work boots for $99.95 or a pair of **WRANGLERS** for $19.95. Lots of casual wear as they cater to lake goers in the area. Donnie and Sheila Rowan are still firm believers in the meaning of a fair and square deal.

★★★★★★   Sergeant's Western World Outlet   972/484-9988

13600 Stemmons Frwy.   Mon-Thurs10-7; Fri-Sat 10-8
Farmers Branch, TX 75234
www.sergeantswestern.com

Attention Sergeant fans: This location has been transformed into their outlet and talk about a tornado when the world catches on. Get a whiff of what Sergeant's Western World is all about first by logging on to their fabulous website to sniff out the bargains. This is where to shop for high-end clothing, accessories, tack and saddles. It's where I brought Dr. Laura to shop when she was in town. And since Sergeant's ensures they will meet or beat anybody else's prices, what do you have to lose? Now with the name "outlet" in their game plan, there is no room for contemplation. Lucky for us there is everything imaginable under one large rodeo-size building: from western apparel to show clothing, saddles to tack, horse equipment and everything in between. We found the mix intoxicating and far from ordinary. Sergeant's Western World also has a superstore in south Arlington just south of I-20 at 4905 S. Cooper St. and their newest at their corporate offices in Pilot Point at 8767 S. Hwy 377, Pilot Point, TX 76258, 940/440-9307. For catalogs, call 817/784-8085 or their toll free number and start shopping right away. *Call toll-free: 800/383-3669*

★★★★   Sheplers Westernwear   972/270-8811

18500 LBJ Frwy.   Mon-Sat 10-9; Sun Noon-6
Mesquite, TX 75150
www.sheplers.com

Even if you're a "schlep," you can still shop at Sheplers Western Wear. With more than 50 years under their belt buckle, this western wear department store has some of the best buys west of the Pecos River. Popular brands included **BAILEY HATS**, **CARHARTT WORKWEAR**, **CRUEL GIRL**, **LEE JEANS**, **LEVI'S**, **ROCKIES**, **WRANGLER** and many more including Sheplers private label. If you're a modern-day cowboy or a gal who's a rugged individualist, you will find Sheplers a place to be seen and outfitted. It's also a place to locate appropriate artifacts for accenting your home with western decor. And online, it's surely one of the largest selections of westernwear in the world. Off line, their brick and mortar stores have over an acre of selling space under one roof. Browse the racks of $10 shirts, jeans, closeouts on hats and boots, that's when you become the leader of the pack and rack in the savings. Recently, they were rated among the top 10 catalog retailers for customer satisfaction. So, jump aboard. Call toll-free to order via their catalog rather than online. Visit also at 2500 Centennial Drive in Arlington, 817/640-5055. *Call toll-free: 888/835-4004*

★★★★ Western Warehouse   214/634-2668

2475 Stemmons Frwy.   Mon-Sat 9-9; Sun Noon-6
Dallas, TX 75207
www.boottown.com

Different names, but it's the same folks that own Boot Town so don't let the name fool ya. The Pink family is legendary in the boot and western wear business that will keep you in the green while keeping themselves in the black (or is it in the red, I never know which is the good one to be!) Downtown visitors coming to Market love to make a stop at the Western Warehouse near the Market Center. Check it out. Savings on jeans, western wear and boots, yes, they do have boots! We found **ABILENE**, **ACME**, **ARIAT**, **JUSTIN**, **LARRY MAHAN**, **LUCCHESE**, **NOCONA**, **PANHANDLE SLIM** and **TONY LAMA** boots ready to roll out the barrel. Next, it's western apparel. You won't walk out naked if you pick a pair of jeans by LEVI'S, WRANGLER'S or **ROCKY MOUNTAIN** for women in every color imaginable. We never counted, but there are claims of more than 50,000 pairs of boots in stock. Rope other good deals in Dallas at 10838 Central Expressway in Dallas (214/891-0888), 2501 Centennial in Arlington (817/640-2301) and Grapevine Mills (972/355-8312). Ten area locations so your feet will be able to take a seat. Put your feet up and show off your new boots-for-less. *Call toll-free: 800/222-6687*

★★★★★ Western Wear Exchange   817/738-4048

2809 Alta Mere   Mon-Sat 10-6
Fort Worth, TX 76116
www.westernwearexchange.com

You can count the consignment western wear stores on one hand - no, with one finger. In fact, just today I answered a lady who wanted to know who might be interested in procuring all of her western wear dance costumes and imagine what a transaction that's going to be? This is the one and only westernwear resale shop and for that reason, give them some rope. If you have something western and want to turn it into cash, there's no need for an appointment, just bring them in — in good condition, freshly laundered or cleaned and on hangers. This is the "Cadillac" of resale stores that specializes in western wear. Why not make some money on items that are still hanging in your closet (yours or anybody else) and going unworn? Then, with that money, you can buy something else. What goes around, comes around. See? At least with the resale route, it's new to you. Whether it's a pair of jeans or that leather vest, duster coat or a pair of Ropers, hats to shirts, boots to zoot scooters (isn't that something that cowboys wear or drive or something like that?) this is the place to take them - or buy them. Whether you're a kid or a grown-up, there's something here for you. They've also expanded into home decorative western accents and jewelry. Still, the big deal is on the clothing, hats and boots. Rustle them up and tote them home. Your wardrobe and your budget will yell, "Whoopee!"

★★★★★ Wild Bill's Western Store   214/954-1050

603 Munger St., Suite 321   Fri-Sat 11 AM-Mid.; Mon-Thurs11-10; Sun Noon-6
Dallas, TX 75202
www.wildbillswestern.com

Meet Bill Dewbre. Bill's the Wild Bill in the name and has been at the helm since 1977. Anybody that locates on the third floor of the West End Marketplace and guarantees the lowest prices in writing, even after the sale, must have a sure thing. "Whether you need a $5 souvenir to bring back to your Aunt Martha in Rochester, New York or a pair of custom-made-to-measure boots for yourself, you'll find what you're looking for at Wild Bill's." Prior to opening in the West End, they were located across from NEIMAN MARCUS in downtown Dallas for 10 years, specializing in the convention, visitor and tourist business, which included supplying merchandise to meeting planners, associations and corporations and gifts to the VIP's. So, they've got a feel for the tourist as well as the local yokels. You will enjoy the southern hospitality here! They custom make boots for some celebrities as Sylvester Stallone, Bruce Willis and Chuck Norris. Now that's kickin'some booty! Wild Bill's carries belt buckles, boots for kids, men and women, cowboy hats, dusters and outerwear, home dÈcor, MONTANA cowboy boots, ROCKMOUNT ranch wear, SCULY LEATHER, T-shirts and vests. Did I miss anything?

Bridal

★★★★★★ **All for Less Wedding Svcs** **972/509-5368**

Windy Meadow Drive
Plano, TX 75023-5004
www.allforlessweddings.com

24/7 online; By Appt. In-House (Mon-Fri 10-7:30); Sat 11-2

 If I have but one party left to plan, let me call Sharon Nichols at All for Less to help me make it through the night. Her attention to detail since 1994, the savings of 20 to 40 percent off every kind of invitation and all the extras that she makes available in person or online turns you into a fool if you fool with it yourself. Leave your name and she'll return your call. Grooms are not neglected as they rent tuxedos, too. Just bring in your correct measurements (and don't lie); then they do the rest (except for pick up and return of the tuxedo.) Expect only the finest invitations and accessories at THE BEST discounts in town. They also do Floral/Gown Preservation (at less than retail) with connections to other services a bride may be looking to purchase. Take a walk down her aisle of wedding products: invitations, accessories, veils, engagement announcements, bridal shower invitations, rehearsal dinners, plus the full spectrum of greeting cards including anniversary, birthday (for kids and grown-ups), calendars, congratulations, a new line of Courage CardsÆ, get well, sympathy, thank-you cards and more. Then, for personal or business use, what about letterhead, business cards, envelopes, mailing envelopes, customized stamps, advertising labels, Post-it Notes, shipping labels, personalized labels, memo pads; well, make a note to call Sharon ASAP! And if you are looking for specialty and premium items, don't forget to peek at her selection: address books and planners, pens, T-shirts, mugs and cups. If you want to promote your business, here's the place to place your bets. Remember, they do MUCH more than invitations! Member of Association Of Bridal Consultants and the Association of Wedding Professionals International. Also call 469/569-2893.

★★★★ **Anderson's Schmalzreid Formal Wear** **972/423-4233**

1201 E. Plano Pkwy.
Plano, TX 75074

Mon-Fri 8:30-6; Sat 9-1

Though it may be a long name to remember, lest you forget it, tie a string around your finger when you're ready to place a ring upon her finger. Grooms and After 5 shoppers, this is where to don a tux for that special day, or any special occasion for that matter. A prom, an anniversary, a cruise? (See Eagle Travel for our Diva Cruises under Travel.) Whenever it calls for pulling out all the stops, here's the place to land. Shabby chic is not "in" when it comes to a formal affair. But shopping the "out-let" for designer tuxedos are where you be chic on the cheap. Say "I do" from Anderson's Schmalzreid Formal Wear and make your dreams come true. Don't worry about pronouncing their name, just remember that the price is right. Whether you're walking down the aisle or taking a trip across the red carpet, don't forget to strut your stuff. This star-studded cast hangs out with the best: **CHRISTIAN DIOR, PIERRE CARDIN, OSCAR DE LA RENTA** and others who command the star treatment. One mile east of Central Expressway on Plano Parkway, pull up in the front lot and start thinking penguins! They are one of the largest tuxedo rental retailers in the country so it makes perfect sense to sell them off when their usefulness has been exhausted. Either rent them again or buy them. With a name like Anderson's Schmalzreid, they've got to be good. *Call toll-free: 800/729-3718*

★★★★★★ Anonymously Yours   214/341-4618

204 Abrams Forest Shopping Center   Mon-Fri 10-6; Sat 10-5:30
Dallas, TX 75243
www.AYresale.com

 Now that your secret admirer has revealed his true feelings and "finally" popped the question, pop on over to Anonymously Yours for big savings on resale gowns. Their catchy phrase, "Everything from Business to Bridal" tells you there's more than just bridal in store, but bridal is still what gives them the clout in the city. Resale is the serious way to save and if you think about it, these gowns have only been worn once. So why not take advantage of saving 50 percent or more? Put the savings towards your honeymoon. Who'll know that it was somebody else's dream gown first? Lots of styles to fit any occasion and just about any waistline. Sizes ranging from 0 to 44. In addition, they also have bridal veils, formals, Mothers-of-the-Bride dresses — the complete bridal ensemble and more. The bridal labels are impressive: **ALFRED ANGELO, MORI LEE, MAGGIE SOTTERO** and others all hanging out to take the plunge co-mingled with closeouts and sample gowns, too. Consignments are accepted weekdays only from 10 to 11 AM Incoming items must be cleaned, pressed and on hangers. Current styles only, please. Accessories are welcome, too, in excellent condition only. Torn gloves, pearl-less bodices, ragged sleeves or other disasters to the dress's condition should be left to someone else (who shall remain anonymous) as Renee will flatly reject it.

★★★★ Ascot Tuxedos   214/520-8897

3400 Oak Lawn Ave.   Mon 10-7; Tues-Thurs 10-6; Fri-Sat 9-5
Dallas, TX 75243
www.ascottuxedos.com

Ladies, no matter what the occasion, be sure to make an entrance with an appropriately dressed man draped over your arm. And that man would be in a tux, no less. No, a tux, for less. Sizes range from a boy's 3 to a men's 70. Find all the tux stars: **AFTER 6** with **ANDREW FEZZA, RALPH LAUREN, CHRISTIAN DIOR, DONI BARRASI, FUBU, PERRY ELLIS** and **OSCAR DE LA RENTA**. If it's a wedding party you'll be dressing, the groom's tux is free and you'll get $30 off attendant's tuxes with five or more rentals. And the groom's tux with these five rentals can be upgraded to a designer tux for FREE. Then, if you access their promotions or their website, you can get a coupon of 20 percent off any purchase. From their first 1,000-square-foot location in downtown Houston, Alan and Lillian Gaylor have grown to well over 100 stores in the surrounding four states with future stores on the drawing board. They've made their name on last-minute rentals. Their two distribution centers have state-of-the-art dry cleaning plants, an alteration staff that is computerized to be able to turn around that tux in a matter of hours. They are the parent company to BridesMart, Ascot Tuxedos, Louise Blum, A.B. Graham Formal Clothiers and Ascot Formal Wear. Check directory for multiple locations.

★★★★★   **Bridal-Tux Shop**   **972/303-9022**

6527 Duck Creek Drive   Mon-Thu 10-7; Fri 10-6; Sat 10-5
Garland, TX 75043

It's very simple. Shop at Bridal-Tux Shop for, you guessed it, bridal wear and tuxedos. But what you didn't imagine were rock-bottom prices. Make your wedding a no-brainer with gowns starting at just $149 and racks of dresses for the bridal party and mothers-of-the-bride for only $39. Feeling lucky? Then you might just walk out with one of these great names at a great price: **ALFRED ANGELO, AMY LEE, BILL LEVKOFF, BRIDAL ORIGINALS, FOREVER YOURS, MA CHERIE, MORI LEE, T.R. THORNTON** and more. Ah, the sun is shining, oh happy days. And this year, happy days are here again. Alterations done on the premises, a nice insurance policy that it won't get lost in the transaction.

★★   **Bridals by Sue Ann**   **817/926-0297**

5201 McCart Ave   Mon-Sat 10-6
Fort Worth, TX 76109

Romeo, Romeo wherefore art thou, Romeo? Move over, Juliet because Sue Ann is in town. And unless your true love is looking to shower you with the finer things in life, you'd better start planning that nest egg now by taking advantage of the savings at Bridals by Sue Ann. No, it won't put your kids through college (Kids! What kids?) but with savings of 20 percent off retail, the old home front might just get a new face lift. Getting a little ahead of ourselves? Then go ahead and dress the bride, the groom, the bridal party, the bride's mothers, oh, just about anybody that's coming or going to the church. But be on time and save the day. How about getting the groom's tux for FREE? Just rent the other five for the groomsmen and fathers and the sixth one is at no charge. Pretty typical, eh? Size up the women from 4 to 46 and that should blanket the potential target audience. Nothing spectacular, but note there is a savings and every little bit helps.

★★★★★★   **Brides Rejoice**   **214/727-1123**

2817 S. Jupiter (In Vikon Village)   Sat Only 10-6
Garland, TX 75041
www.BridesRejoice.com

 When you are ready to say, "Do you take this woman to be your lawful wedded wife," you better tell her she better have bought her dress here if she knows what's good for her. After all, a smart wife is a frugal wife. Gowns here cost as little as $99. Hallelujah and say, "Amen Brother." Brides Rejoice is a breath of fresh air catering to a bride on a budget with three booths at Vikon Village all rolled into one. You've got to start somewhere so it might as well be where you can shop for gowns priced from $99-$199, and a huge collection of tiaras, jewelry — you know, all the accessories that you MUST have when you're a bride. With the savings you'll realize, you'll have enough left over for the cake and all the trimmings. Mostly they sell NEW wedding gowns (though there were a few on consignments — who cares? After all, wedding gowns are worn only one time (unless of course you remarry several more times and wear the same dress!) So why not consider one that has taken the walk before? Take the Jupiter/Kingsley exit off LBJ (635) in Garland and see if you can't say "I do" for under $100. If you've got a bridal gown you want to sell, well Brides Rejoice has the best consignment split in the Metroplex — they keep 25 percent of the sale (that means, you keep 75 percent.) And that's a very good thing. There is plenty to choose from. So, although you've narrowed it down to one choice for a husband (and that is a very, very good thing), the least you can do is have plenty of choices in dresses. If you don't shop on Saturdays, you won't be able to buy.

★★★★　BridesMart

817/784-1171

Mon-Thu 10-8; Fri-Sat 10-6; Sun Noon-5

4648 S. Cooper St.
Arlington, TX 76017
www.bridesmart.com

Brides who are smart-alecks need not shop here. Only brides who are smart are welcome. It doesn't take a Ph.D. to get a deal 'cause all the work's already done for you. As corny as it sounds, you don't want to write the *Bridal Book for Dummies*, do you? Get the skinny on real deals on real designer dresses starting at just $199. Find occasional clearance dresses for any occasion at just $30 and up. I know one bride who got dressed with shoes, slip, veil and dress for under $100. Now we're talking smart! Inflation won't stop the deals at BridesMart. For years they've offered such great names as **ALFRED ANGELO, BRIDAL REPLACEMENTS, FOREVER YOURS, ILISSA** by **DEMETRIOS, MON CHERE, MORI LEE** and more at savings up to 70 percent off. No matter what shape your wedding budget is in, you'll fit into these dresses in sizes 1 to 44. Part of the Al's Formal Wear of Houston (see their history under the Ascot Tuxedoes write-up at the beginning of this chapter), when the owners got wind of the shift in shopping, from "anything goes" to "prices count," the chain of BridesMart and Ascot was born. Now, watch out as they blanket the Southwest and expand their reach. They're neck-and-neck with David's Bridal as the two fastest growing chains. I wonder who will get to the church on time....first? Dumb, de-dumb dumb.

NR　Castle Douglas

469/223-8678 (Tours & Reservations)

By Reservation Only

2071 Clem Road Extension
Rockwall, TX 75087
www.CastleDouglasTexas.com

Take one happily married couple, John and Charlotte Dumford, and then catapult yourself into their dream-castle just outside Dallas, Texas. Why jet to Scotland when you've got a castle right over the bridge in Rockwall? Chivalry's not dead at Castle Douglas, a full-service wedding venue and a personalized wedding and event planning business that will make any event one that will be etched in your memory forever. A one-of-a-kind event that will have guests talking for years. (Though it doesn't always have to be a wedding that you're celebrating. They also provide party planning and catering for corporate parties, political fundraisers, charity balls, and a wide range of private social gatherings. Maybe even a "Shoppers Choice Awards banquet." But for a bride looking to be treated to a Cinderella dream come true, what better place to start than at the castle, my lord. Yes, there's an armory, a pub, a library, chapel, a ballroom, kitchen, great hall (serving up to a party of 600) and acres and acres of pastoral grandeur (the castle sits on 71 acres). Just don't look for King Arthur to coming riding over the glen. This is a "knight" to remember. Create the perfect fairytale wedding as you take the plunge into matrimony. You won't be banished to the dungeon, though they do have a basement for a home theatre set up and wine cellar. This 7 bedroom/14 bath castle will also be living quarters (top three floors) for this 38-year old lawyer and his Castle manager wife. There is over 23,000 square feet of air-conditioned space and a twin four story tower; 1,500 square feet of roof terraces surrounding the fortress in this quiet rural setting that is, to say the least, secluded. The price tag to build? Just under $10 million. And that's a lot of weddings to recoup their investment. But as is inscribed as you enter, "Amor Vencit Omnia" — "Love Conquers All!"

◆◆◆◆◆◆ **Chapelle des Fleurs**   **972/317-2632**

2701 Corporate Drive   By Reservation Only
Flower Mound, TX 75028
www.chapelledesfleurs.com

 Getting to the chapel on time is now twice as easy since Janice Orndorf opened a second facility catering to weddings and other special occasions in Flower Mound. Her first, though, is smaller and called The Orndorf Haus in Highland Village (almost Flower Mound). Vive la difference! But her big venture is at the corner of Corporate Drive and College Parkway in collaboration with builder/developer/friends of hers, The Hodges. It's a one-stop shop for everything — wedding as well as on - off - premise catering for any occasion or function, from a bar mitzvah to a corporate party. Expect at least 30 percent less for similar quality florals and that's the start of something terrific. Think of how many occasions call for flowers, followed up with food to order in. Think funerals and you get the picture. Want to celebrate an anniversary or 25 years in business? Then think event planning. Think big. Think limos and elaborate cakes — what about the all important QuiÒceaneras or a corporate seminar? Carve out an ice sculpture and leave the driving to this one-stop elegant facility that will ease your mind of the details. By reservation only, you won't have to worry about a thing. Take a virtual tour of their chapel and wind up at the buffet table. You will be impressed.

◆◆◆◆◆◆ **David Clark Videography**   **972/539-0842**

                                                                   By Appt. Only
Flower Mound, TX 75028
www.davidclarkvideography.com

 Have camera, digital, state-of-the-art video — all the latest and greatest and David Clark will be your Johnny-on-the-spot. His quality photographic offerings with his internet coupon specials probably are the best money can buy. He does such neat stuff you'll want to order the whole shebang. Wedding productions, legal videos, editing and duplication are available via this video guy, too. Generations to come will have a visual record of their family tree LIVE on Saturday Nights! One package includes a wedding video for $1,150, but you can download a coupon and take $50 off for the internet discount and another $50 off if you say the Diva sent you. This is a $100 off. He can record on a DVD (with chapters included) and have a permanent memory of a memorable occasion to live on in infamy.

★★★★★ **David's Bridal**   **972/458-2211**

5525 Arapaho Rd.   Mon-Fri 11-9; Sat 10-6; Sun Noon-6
Dallas, TX 75248
www.davidsbridal.com

You'll love David's Bridal. Maybe even more so than your betrothed. But he doesn't need to know about the other man in your life. David's will pamper you with a huge selection of over 1,400 bridal gowns. Save big on designer show-offs from just $199. Wait around for their $99 sales and put the savings toward your veil, shoes, jewelry, gloves, purse, card pouch, hosiery and garter. Check their website for the latest promotions; one deal may net you $50 to $300 off every gown. You wouldn't turn the other cheek with a discount like this, now would you? Another may net you 50 percent off invitations. You can literally put your entire wedding party's ensembles together without stepping foot inside their stores. David's is the largest bridal retailer with close to 200 locations nationwide. Having trained consultants who are familiar with the bride's needs and the emotional turmoil that the entire family is undergoing is crucial to a smooth transaction. One trip and you'll see why they've been around for more than 50 years. Two additional superstore locations besides the one above are 2508 South Stemmons Freeway in Lewisville's Lake Pointe Crossing, 214/488-3347; and in the Mid-Cities at 804 Northeast Loop 820, Hurst 76053.

Imperial Gown Restoration

Fairfax, VA   24/7

www.gown.com   🖰 *Top Online Store!*

 Since 1947, they have been preserving a bride's most cherished of items (besides her husband, we hope,) and that is her gown. Utilizing the same textile processes that are used by museums so that there is no possibility of damaging the fragile fabrics (as is the case so often with your neighborhood dry cleaners.) They specialize in cleaning and caring for delicate fabric and trims, then shape and package your gown and accessories into an acid-free archival box. They offer an unmatched fifty-year, replacement value warranty with every gown they preserve, even if the bride opens the box to inspect it. That means, you can unseal and inspect your gown at any time so as not to worry about damage. Still located in the Washington, D.C. suburb of Fairfax, Virginia, the same family that founded the company is still running the company. Steven Saidman and his wife Susan is the third generation to look to for taking care of business. Since their proximity to the nation's capitol, they regularly clean lots of formalwear befitting the dignitaries that regularly dress to the nines. Imperial arranges a No-Cost, No-Obligation, fully-insured Free pickup and delivery of your wedding gown from anywhere in all fifty United States and Puerto Rico. Brides in Canada and the Caribbean may also take advantage of Imperial's quality preservation services for a nominal shipping charge. Imperial will provide you with all packaging materials and handling charges so that you may receive a FREE consultation and quote on having your gown handled safely and properly. They can not quote you a price without seeing your gown first. This is their only business now (they sold their chain of dry cleaning stores to concentrate exclusively on bridal restoration and preservation.) They serve brides all over the county and Canada including the families of three U.S. Presidents. (Well we know Clinton or Bush haven't married off their daughters yet, so I guess we can guess at which daughters' gowns are preserved here.) Too, many of the top gown designers, bridal boutiques, and even the Smithsonian Institution call upon Imperial. They are the best, you might as well go for broke. They've been featured in Martha Stewart Living as well as all of the bridal magazines and Steven and Susan Saidman are often called upon as an industry expert for national TV segments. Prices start at $400. *Call toll-free: 888/469-6888*

★★★★   Invitation Warehouse   214/381-6367

PO Box 570368   By Appt. Only
Dallas, TX 75357-0368
www.invitationwarehouse.com

Lois knoweth the invitation business and can save you 30 percent across the pages of a myriad of albums. Wedding invitations and all the other printed matter can be etched into the occasion without gouging your budget. More than 35 albums to choose from in all the popular brands. **BIRCH-CRAFT, CARLSON CRAFT, CLASSIC, ENCORE** and **ENCORE STUDIOS, MASTERPIECE, MCPHERSONS, NU ART, REGENCY, STYLART, TATEX** and others are waiting to be engraved RSVP Graduations, anniversaries, thank you notes, bat/bar mitzvahs, QuiÒceaneras, birthday parties, anniversaries, greeting cards, graduations, rehearsal dinners, birth announcements — if it's a paper invitation or announcement, all that is yet to do is address and stamp. Monogrammed stationery also is available online or make an appointment to see what's in the books. With so many albums to browse through, you may miss the party. Delivery, if it's coming from a Waco-based company, takes three to five days; engraved invitations from the finest factories take three weeks, so plan accordingly. *Call toll-free: 866/381-6367*

★★★ Isis Bridal & Formal   972/681-5939

1032 Town East Mall
Mesquite, TX 75150   Mon-Sat 10-9; Sun Noon-6

Simply say, "I do" when you're in the market for formal wear at Isis. I is, I is. To have and to hold, from this day forward, hold any dress for just a $20 deposit. For richer or poorer, either way you'll get a deal on gowns over $500. Consider this an incentive: The headpiece, veil, gloves, petticoat and shoes are **FREE**. Have you ever tried to add up all those extras? Consider it sold. Bridal packages include tuxedos and/or bridal party wear as well as other formal occasion attire. Plenty of QuiÒceaneras dresses and coronas. The cup runneth over at this store. So get over to Isis Bridal and Formal before taking that all-important step down the aisle. You won't regret it. You will, though, if you don't!

★★★★ Lasting Impressions Bridal Boutique   972/991-7498

15056 Beltway Drive
Addison, TX 75004   Mon-Thurs 11-7; Fri 11-6; Sat 11-5

Since the day only lasts only a moment but tomorrow, it's a lifetime, try to make the memories last forever. Every bride wants her day to be special, unique and truly her own (oh yeah, and the groom should last forever, too). But why buy? Afterall, it's only a ceremony that lasts minutes and the party's a one night affair. Instead, rent beautiful gowns from $185 to $500 instead. They make a statement all of their own. Or get the entire wedding package for $300 and up. After all, you only wear it once. Or would you rather spend up to $500-$1,000 on a so-so gown you'll just store away at the end of the day. Instead, rent a fabulous, to-die-for gown for the same price and save the storage fees for something else? It's all up to you! But if you go this route, you'll probably end up flying off to **BALI** or taking a cruise to the Greek Isles. Not a bad exchange for not owning a wedding gown, I'd say, "I do (or I did!)"

◆◆◆◆◆ Le Renaissance Wedding Facility   214/692-8442

8041 Walnut Hill Lane, Suite 820
Dallas, TX 75231   Mon,Tues,Thurs & Fri 11-6; Wed 1-7:30
www.lerenaissance.com

Planning a big hoop-de-do? Want to create your own backdrop for your wedding day? How about a beautiful courtyard garden, quiet, secluded and intimate. Listen to the bridal march on their website. View the dramatic balcony where you can throw the bouquet and entertain guests in a separate reception area. Choose some of the finest chefs, bakers, uniformed wait staff and all because you've chosen Le Renaissance as your wedding facility. This is one of Dallas' best-kept bridal secrets. Prices are generally 30 to 60 percent under the going rates charged by traditional hotel facilities plus your event will be handled by experienced bridal consultants. Whether it's a small gathering of close friends and family or up to 200 guests who crawl out of the woodwork, this family-owned business can supply everything to make your day a dream come true. Let them handle all the details. Let them do their thing and arrange it all, from caterers, bakers, limos and florists to paper products, make-up experts, musical and video artists. And if you want to feed the brood, have them bring on the food! Check out their website complete with photos.

★★★ **Milliners Supply Co.**   **214/742-8284**
                                                    Mon-Fri 8:30-5

911 Elm St.
Dallas, TX 75202
www.milliners.com

You've got the guy of your dreams, you've got the ring you've always wanted and the gown your friends won't forget. So what's missing? Complete the picture with a trip to Milliners Supply Co. Take the stress out of any wedding ensemble by stepping through these doors and back in time. Good old-fashioned prices are ripe for the picking. See shelves of bridal ribbon, flowers, garters, ring pillows, accessories and even hoop skirts. Founded in 1911 by Martin and Charlotte Weiss, it's still in the same location with nary a change. Hear the floor creak and brides from years past echo their recommendations. Today, it's run by the third generation of its founding family and continues to serve the millinery industry and bridal and wedding accessory stores in all 50 states, Puerto Rico, Canada and Mexico. Lucky they're in Dallas and you get a taste of an old-fashioned business that exists today. With all the decorative pillows and lamps popular these days, shop here for decorative trims, feathers, boas and the like, but consider this shop a resource for other craft projects, too. It's a trip. *Call toll-free: 800/728-3962*

★★★★★ **Mockingbird Bridal Boutique**   **214/823-6873**

5602 E. Mockingbird Lane   Tues,Wed,Fri 10-5:45; Mon & Thurs 10-7:45; Sat 9:30-5
Dallas, TX 75206-5346
www.mockingbirdbridal.com

Longevity counts in the bridal business. The longer you stay open, the more brides you can outfit and after 40 years, you've got to give them credit for trying. The labels are impressive enough: AMALIA CARRERA, BARBARA ALLIN, COUTURE BRIDAL, DIAMOND BRIDE, EMANUELLE, EVA HAYNAL, FORSYTH, GINZA, DEMETRIOS, JASMINE, MAGGIE SOTTERO, MARISA, EVE OF MILADY, MON CHERI, MONIQUE LUO, MOONLIGHT, STEPHEN YEARICK, TOMASINA, VICTORIAS....how many more do I need to reveal to get your attention? Oh, you want to know about other formals for the bridesmaids, flower girls or mothers-of-the-bride? Here goes: AFTER SIX, BARI JAY, BELSOIE, BILL LEVKOFF, CHAMPAGNE FORMALS, DESSY CREATIONS, VERA WANG, WATTERS AND WATTERS, W-TOO and others. They carry two-piece dresses that are certainly more daring than the fussier and more sedate gowns worn by conservative first-timers. Three blocks east of Central Expressway, between Central and Greenville Ave. Next to Campisi, so grab a pizza and some crab claws before you try on your dress and hopefully, you will enjoy it more than trying to find a parking place. Over 600 styles carried with abou5 95 percent of those featured in all the bridal magazines from prices as low as $249 to $6,000. All coupons and specials from competitors honored so why not get the selection and the savings while you're at it. *Call toll-free: 877/823-6873*

◆◆◆◆◆ **Rabbi Marc Ben-Meir, Ph.D**   **817/831-9512**
                                                    By Appt. Only

3541 Garwood Drive
North Richland Hills, TX 76117
www.askrabbi.com

Looking for a non-denominational wedding official? Or will only a traditional Jewish ceremony do? Either way, Rabbi Marc of the North Tarrant Jewish Fellowship has the words and the way anywhere in the Metroplex. In fact, have ceremony, will travel, Bible and all. This traditionally-ordained Jewish rabbi is a member of the Rabbinical Fellowship of America, the International Federation of Rabbis, and is a Jewish Chaplain (Lt. Col.) in the U.S. Air Force. Whatever's your pleasure, he can deliver a proper union, even if you're not affiliated with a synagogue or church. Mazel-tov!! Bet you didn't even think I'd get some questions about a mobile rabbi. Well, I did and so now you know, too.

★★★★★ Resale Gallery   817/285-0633

724-A E. Pipeline Rd.   Mon-Sat 10-6
Hurst, TX 76053

Prince Charming will fall to his knees and bless the ground you walk on when he learns that you were smart enough to save some extra cash for the honeymoon and shop for your dress here. The dresses may have made their debut elsewhere, but a grand re-entrance is still in order. Think of how many times a new gown has been tried on in the bridal shop — but you don't pay for that fact in a new gown, now do you? So, what do you have against saving money for the honeymoon? Highway 183, south on Brown Trail to Pipeline, left two blocks. It's behind the Grandy's in the Village Square Shopping Center. You found it. You might as well enjoy it. Of course, you could be renting the same gown you sold back to the consignment shop several years before, and in return, it was rerouted here again, and again. You never know. It could be your original gown that you're buying back. Then again, marrying your first husband again is not unheard of either!

★★★★★★ Saleplace, The   972/557-7747

3641 Shepherd Lane   Mon-Fri 10-8; Sat 10-6; Sun Noon-5:30
Balch Springs, TX 75180
www.weddingsuperstore.com

 You've got the church, the hall, the caterer, the dress, the bridal party. The groom. What else do you need? How about confetti, bubbles, ring pillows, flower baskets, unity candles, pew bows, veils, garters, gloves, cake toppers and charms. The Saleplace has almost everything you will need within their 22,000 square feet of wedding essentials and "I wants!" The Saleplace has it all, from heart-shaped bubble bottles to wands, ring pillows, flower baskets, gloves, veils, headpieces, canopies, unity candles, and all the other little things that make the big event a hit. Since 1977, the Reid family has provided the only one-stop wedding store in town. "I'll drink to that!" Not as difficult to find as you might suspect, it's a hop, skip and a jump off LBJ (I-635) and the Elam Road exit. It's the largest of its kind in the Metroplex — that's why they call themselves a superstore. Wholesale customers can call and speak to Greg Reid at the number above if you'd like to resell these items for your own business, catering or otherwise. Or the public is welcome at deep discounted prices. Discount to the public, wholesale to the trade, and everybody comes out a winner. This wedding superstore is a do-it-yourself haven for brides on a budget, without looking chintzy.

◆◆◆ Timeless Blooms   972/530-1909

                                                                     By Appt. Only
Garland, TX 75044
www.timelessblooms.com

This is it, I think. The only remaining source to have your florals preserved for a lifetime. After all, a wedding IS a once-in-a-lifetime event, isn't it? For those sentimental souls who want to keep those special memories alive with, if nothing else, the flowers from that memorable day, meet Timeless Blooms. This home-based business will freeze-dry your flowers a few weeks after your wedding and then return them to you decorated in an attractive framed acrylic dome with other mementos from your wedding (if you choose), such as your marriage license, an invitation, garter, photo or any other special item. The folks at Timeless Blooms are proven pros at flower freeze-drying, so you're in good hands. Frame displays are available in a variety of shapes and sizes starting around $75 and go up to $575, depending upon the size of the arrangement. This price includes pre-treatment of your flowers, freeze-drying, post-treatment, designing, ribbon and display container. Visit their website and be sure to contact them in plenty of time for a reservation so they'll get to the church on time.

◆◆◆◆◆ **Wedding Cottage, The**   **972/771-2340**

Mon-Fri. 9-5; Sat. (By Appt. Only)

730 S. Goliad St.
Rockwall, TX 75087
www.theweddingcottage.com

Even if you decide to hold your wedding at the City Dump, folks will still think you were beautiful. However, let me propose a more perfect setting. Why not consider the bright and airy chapel of The Wedding Cottage? You'll have your choice of an intimate ceremony or one of their complete packages which includes the ceremony and reception. On staff are wedding specialists to guide you every step of the way. The Wedding Cottage can accommodate up to 150 guests. The Dream Package includes: the bride's cake, the groom's cake, punch, gourmet coffee, nuts, mints, bride's bouquet, one attendant's bouquet, a boutonniere for the groom and his best man, a bouquet to throw, fresh flowers for the cake topper, single rose for the mothers, engraved napkins, engraved toasting glasses, a Victorian wedding certificate, birdseed and bubbles, limo service to one destination in the Metroplex. Spend more and you'll get more — like a photograph in a bridal portrait studio, etc. All the specialists are on hand for you to book, including photographers, ministers, musicians, florists — and prices are available online upon request.

◆◆◆◆◆◆ **Weddings Today Chapel**   **972/620-9357**

By Reservation Only

2415 Fruitland Ave.
Dallas, TX 75234
www.weddingstodaychapel.com

 When it comes to saying "I do," you only need to do it at Weddings Today. Their chapel, their packages, and their prices spell "right on" for today's budget-conscious couples. Quietly nestled in Northwest Dallas, their beautifully decorated chapel makes the perfect place to join this man and this woman. Officiating, if you wish, owner Rev. Paul Tatum joined by the hostess with the mostest, his wife Anne, whether it's a quickie or a year-long planned event, they can make it happen. Want the 7-Eleven special? They're open 24/7 where you can drive through and say your I do's! Since they are a full-service wedding facility, they have all the credentials including a licensed and ordained minister on the premises. Ceremonies can be performed at your place or theirs, there's a wedding planning coordinator on board, indoor and outdoor reception areas and seating for up to 35 persons. Can't afford a beach setting at sunset? What about a western motif? Want a package for $150? Or want to plan a large outdoor reception complete with a deluxe buffet? They'll do it all with your budget in mind. And now, even if you want to rent your gown, and order two dozen white roses at www.2dozenroses.com at the lowest prices on the net, you'll be set for life by starting off on the right track — not in debt up to your eyeballs.

★★★★ **Yvonne's Bridals**   **214/467-2870**

Mon-Fri 10-7; Sat 9:30-5:30

2550 W. Red Bird Lane, Suite 410
Dallas, TX 75237

The belle of the ball rings here. Now that you've found your prince, what are you going to do? Cinderella could have made it to the party on time if she'd just stopped by Yvonne's Bridal first. This little gem will make any girl sparkle in beaded, satin, chiffon, taffeta or silk. Prices begin as low as $200. This diamond in the rough will have you stepping right out of the pages of your favorite bridal magazine. Immerse yourself in the warm, friendly, pampering service that's been perfected by Yvonne's for nearly 20 years. Yvonne provides all the accessories, too. Then, if you decide to rent, you'll save 40 to 50 percent. Even flower girl dresses, mothers-of-the-bride and formal selections are ripe for the picking. Want to save up for that perfect day? Layaway's available with a 25 percent deposit. They're a **SWEETHEART** of a bridal salon, with other labels like **ALFRED ANGELO** to dress that little daughter angel who's all grown up now and ready to "take on the day!"

Cameras & Optical

★★★★★★ **Arlington Camera**

817/261-8131

544 W. Randol Mill Rd.
Arlington, TX 76011
www.arlingtoncamera.com

Mon-Sat 9-6

 Arlington Camera has focused on keeping one of the best selections of cameras in the Metroplex for over 15 years. New or used, co-owner Bill Porter can make taking great pictures a snap whether you want a high-end **NIKON** or **MAMIYA** or just want to take snapshots with a little **KODAK** or **POLAROID** disposable camera, or anything in between. They also carry **BRONICA**, **CANON**, **HASSELBLAD**, **MINOLTA**, **OLYMPUS** and **PENTAX** though the list goes on from there. There is a complete selection of film and darkroom supplies, too. The employees pride themselves on being professionals with the highest level of customer service. No gray market cameras sold ever, no warranties in foreign languages, no substituting your request with something they want to get rid of, or any other games merchants play. This store is legit. So smile for the camera! *Call toll-free: 800/313-6748*

B & H Photo-Video-Pro Audio

800/947-9950

420 Ninth Ave.
New York, NY 10001

Mon-Thurs 9-7; Fri 9-1; Sun 10-5; Sat Closed

www.bhphotovideo.com ⌒🖱 *Top Online Store!*

 If you can tolerate the abruptness of the New York sales approach, you'll be over the hump 'cause this is the best photographer's resource in the world....hands-down. (Camera World may be a close second, but our experts still voted B & H as numero uno online.) They've been serving photogs for more than 25 years and describe their pricing as competitive. Ha! They're the lowest in the world and photographers know it! But low prices do not make a business strong all by itself. You've got to have service before, during and after the sale. Order by phone, online, by fax, or via their catalog (it's Free and it's a whopper!) Imagine a store as large as a football field and imagine warehouse space even larger; now, do you get the picture? It's a snap. They have the most extensive inventory in the industry, both new and used. Trade in, trade up, get it fixed, or sell yours outright; if it was made for a photo shoot or if it's professional audio/visual equipment, this is the best of the best. More than 130,000 items are available including some that are considered classic or collectors'items. It's like visiting a camera museum. Every name in the business is represented, so just go online and see for yourself. It's a snap! *Call toll-free: 800/947-9950*

Class A Photography   **214/607-0913**

Dallas, TX   By Appt. Only

www.classaphoto.com

       You can't get any more candid than this. Class A Photography gets an A for class.
And affordability. If you are scouting around for a great photography package for
your little guy or gal who's into scouting, look ma, no hands! Put the troop into the
hands of these talented photographers who can make every boy or girl look handsome in a uniform. We found that this website is most ingenious. Point, shoot and click onto your favorite scout
master, a troop on an outing, inaugural events, presentation of awards, whenever you want to com-
memorate an activity, here are the photographers who've put their talent where their lens is at. A
variety of packages and frames are available at your fingertips. Each time you purchase a print,
frame or package from Class A Photography, a portion of your purchase will go to your Scout's
unit. It's a great way to support Scouting and your unit in particular. Join the troop online; then
view the images of your Scout(s). Signing in is easy. They give you a user name and a password
and you're there in Technicolor. If your photo gallery is available, it will appear on your screen
when you log in. Talk about proud. It should warrant a special gift from Grandma when she sees
you in uniform. (Grandmas can't resist a guy in uniform. They do it every time.) If you want an
idea of what you'd look like should you decide to sign up, take a look at their DEMO photo album
and get ready to "puff" out that chest with pride. Who's behind this ingenious photolog? Why
none other that Class A photographers Larry Hayles and Steve Walker. If you want to book a
photo shoot, email steve@classaphoto.com and then smile when he says PLEASE....or is it
cheese? Extra! Extra! Read all about them on their website. Last we heard they were starting to do
youth sports photography, too.

★★★★★   **Competitive Cameras**   **214/744-5511**

2025 Irving Blvd., #107   Mon-Fri 9-5:30; Sat 9-4

Dallas, TX 75207

www.competitivecameras.com

Eugene and Ramsey Jabbour click. Their store is notorious for being THE resource for serious
shutterbugs or those just starting out. Since 1982, they have been delivering the goods with name-
brand lenses as opposed to substituting a lesser quality lens to cut costs. Yes, expect the lens to be
what the manufacturer intended. Personalized service by knowledgeable photographers makes it
easier to buy the camera that is right for the job. Located in the "photographic district" where
many professional camera buffs have their studios, CC continues to direct you to the camera that
gives you your money's worth. Name brands are the best: BRONICA, CANON, CONTAX, HAS-
SELBLAD, KODAK, MAMIYA, MINOLTA, NIKON, OLYMPUS or PENTAX including film,
lenses, flashes and lighting supplies. They have a complete line of darkroom equipment and carry
KODAK and FUJI professional film and paper. If you're looking for video cameras or high-tech
anything relating to cameras, this is the place to target your shoot. Even OLYMPUS underwater
cameras won't drown your budget. If you want information on the latest and greatest or a deal on a
pre-owned model, just say "cheese" and put the squeeze on Competitive Camera. They also buy,
trade and sell your cameras.

David Clark Videography   **972/539-0842**

Dallas, TX   By Appt. Only
www.davidclarkvideography.com

 With camera, digital, state-of-the-art video....all the latest and greatest, Dave Clark will be your **JOHNNY** on the spot. His quality photographic offerings and his internet coupon specials probably are the best money can buy. Don't expect a plain vanilla package for your special event, though. This guy can record on DVD with chapters and video included. He does such neat stuff you'll want to order the whole shebang. Wedding productions, legal videos, editing and duplication are available via this video guy, too. He's the one to call for it all. Why? Because he's the best and gave us the best price, silly. I'm no dummy, you know. Remember, a video can capture almost everything....the sights, sounds and emotions of your special day. Dave Clark, take 5. You will be glad you did. Generations to come will have a visual record of their family tree LIVE on Saturday nights! Whether it's a high school reunion or a business training seminar, get a seamless professional video complete with flying animated titles and appropriate special effects timed with music. Cecil B. DeMille, he is. Or if you already have something recorded, but it stinks — needs to be lightened, darkened, volume adjusted, maybe you'd like to add titles — Dave is a photographer who will capture the moments in time for a lifetime.

★★★   **Don's Used Photo Equipment**   **214/630-4062**

2731 Irving Blvd.   Mon-Fri 10-6; Sat 10-3
Dallas, TX 75207-2307

For the minimalist, if you want to buy a camera, plain and simple, Don sells them and buys them. Like a garage sale, you've got to go in and see what's cooking at any given time. Lighting and darkroom equipment, too. He's got a variety and if you'll lens him your ear, he'll talk you through each one's good points and limitations.

PhotoSynthesis   **206/931-4858**

Seattle, WA 98125   24/7 online; Office Hours Mon-Fri 10-6
www.photographersseattle.com/ 🖱 *Top Online Store!*

 As the mother of the greatest photographer on earth, if you want museum-quality shots for your brochures or annual report, or black and white architectural shots for the lobby of your office, this guy is a square shooter. Have **HASSELBLAD** will travel. Expensive, but you get what you pay for. Go to his website above and read his reviews of cameras or order a print. Then take it to Framing Warehouse in Carrollton for the best prices and the best framing in the city. (See their write-up in the Art & Collectibles Chapter.)

★★★★   **Warehouse Photographic**   **972/416-7110**

2255 E. Belt Line Rd., Suite 301   Mon-Fri 9-6; Sat 9-5
Carrollton, TX 75006
www.warehousephoto.com

Just about everything you need or want for your camera and darkroom can be secured at this 30-year plus veteran of the photo business. Equipment and supplies, cameras and accessories, lenses, camera bags, darkroom equipment and supplies, filters, negatives, ink jet paper, books and more. Shop online through the pages of their *Photo Equipment Catalog* for used equipment, film processing and more. Consign your equipment and let them sell it for you. Great prices on used equipment such as the **CANON** AE-1 for $219, a **KODAK** digital camera for $299, an **OMEGA** D-2 lens board for $29.95 and a PELOUZE darkroom scale for $49.95. Lots more such as an ELMO T-3 slide timer for $15 and a MAESTRO meter for $399. How about 80 different models of point-and-shoot cameras by CANON, KODAK, KONICA, MINOLTA, NIKON, OLYMPUS, POLAROID, VIVITAR and more? Prices run anywhere from $7.49-$399.99. They also carry some excellent digital cameras and equipment. The KODAK Create-a-Print machine lets you do your own enlargements in minutes, and the latest machine from KODAK does "picture-to-picture" up to a final image of 8 X 10 inches, all in seconds, no negative required. Hopefully you'll have a photographic memory and will remember where to head when you're looking for a camera. *Call toll-free: 800/400-8203*

★★★★★   **Wolf Camera Clearance Center**   **972/874-1662**

3000 Grapevine Mills Pkwy., Suite 501   Mon-Thurs 9-9; Sat 9-6; Sun 10-5
Grapevine, TX 76051
www.ritzcamera.com

Make no snap judgments. The wolf has gobbled up the Ritz and all store names are changing to Wolf Camera. Bye, bye putting on the Ritz; say hello to the good buys at this big box merger. Reckon you'll see notable changes? Watch this space; other than their name, there probably won't be dramatic shifts in their retail philosophy. At this particular location, there were a few "outlet" type refurbished cameras, but not nearly as extensive as the Wolf Clearance Store on Harry Hines. Decades and decades of service and a combined buying capacity should speak volumes about their net worth that are now one and the same. Their clearance centers at Grapevine Mills and on Harry Hines are where the savings are, thought, up to 80 percent on photo, digital and video equipment. Instant passport photos, camera and video repair, digital big print/five minute enlargements and low prices on name brand camera and video equipment makes for an all-around development worthy of recommendation. Check directory for other locations in Hurst, Irving, Lewisville, Mesquite and Plano but don't expect dramatic discounts. For the lowest prices, turn your focus to Grapevine Mills and 11171 Harry Hines, Dallas, 972/241-0582. End of discussion. *Call toll-free: 800/52-FOCUS*

Carpets & Floors

S&H Carpet Distributors

◆◆◆◆◆◆   **a-abc Chem Dry**   **972/490-1977; 817/712-2345**

14001 Distribution Way   24/7
Dallas, TX 75234-3438
www.aabcservices.com

"Do I do windows?" No! "Do I do floors?" No! Why? Because I've turned all my dirty work over to Dave Katz and the Chem-Dry team. With a motto like, "If you're not delighted with our service, you won't owe as a dime — guaranteed," what do I have to lose? To me, I consider their unique patented process of carbonated bubbles to be the PERRIER of carpet cleaning companies. You will soon discover why a-abc is a member of the exclusvie President's Club — meaning they are in the top 1 percent of the ChemDry franchises worldwide. I love that their unique products and techniques use only ingredients from Mother Nature. No harmful chemicals are used to lift the soil and stains from your carpet or upholstery. It's amazing. Watch those pet stains go bye-bye. (Remember to use your Diva Dollars for additional savings on all three of their specialties: carpet cleaning, pet removal and upholstery cleaning.) Out, damn spot, out! For more than 20 years, Chem-Dry has been the leader of the pack. a-abc has been cleaning up since 1994. They move furniture routinely and can put it back in place before they leave. They also wipe down the baseboards. See why I love them? They do it all without any hidden surprises plus you're getting the best in water damage restoration, carpet repairs, spot dyeing, Oriental rug cleaning, auto interior detailing, leather and vinyl cleaning and yes, on-site drapery cleaning. I've even had dinner parties later that night after they've cleaned up in the morning. See their little red vans (similar to the the a-abc Appliances'red trucks — a company founded by Katz's father.) Note the separate numbers for Dallas, Southern Collin and Tarrant counties. Call for appointments 7 days a week and emergencies are handled immediately. But now you can even schedule appointments online. And they show up when they say they are (within a two-hour window.) I can count on them every time. I love it. No more waiting on the phones. No more waiting for the tech to show up. It's a pleasure doing business with a company who's work ethic is in sync with mine. I can schedule it in the middle of the night when I'm working on a deadline. If a spot returns, so do they (at no charge to you.) They offer a 30-day guarantee. Lots of good information via their website including products for sale. I am now cleaning up inbetween visits with The Razor, one of the revolutionary products I bought online. The Razor Floor Tool is soooo cool. Industrial strength with a cleaning solution that really works with a padded handle and ergonomic design. Me, doing floors? It's so much fun with my new toy. And it's not just for hard surface floors either. It can clean spots on carpet, too. You can't beat their spot removers. I'm hooked.

★★★★★★   **AAA & Broadway Vacuum**   **214/348-1620**

9845 Kingsley   Mon-Fri 9-6; Sat 9-4
Dallas, TX 75238
www.aaavacs.com

 Let's beat on the Tom-Tom-Tomi when the subject of buying a vacuum cleaner is discussed. This second generation family (by the name of Tomi) with twenty-five years of experience has a handle on state-of-the-art vacuum cleaners, right down to the best marble polisher or carpet cleaning spot remover money can buy. The Tomi's could have written THE book on vacuums; maybe even clean up the Dust Bowl in the process. They offer some of the lowest prices and the best service, including delivery to your front door if need be. They also have a great website for additional learning aids. From residential to commercial, they have every brand name made, including some exotic models imported from Europe like **MIELE**. The proof is in the power puffs: **BOSCH**, **HOKY** Floor and Carpet Sweep, **HOOVER**, **KENT COMMERCIAL**, **ROYAL POWERCAST** 9200 (maybe the ultimate in vacuum cleaners on the market), **PANASONIC**, **PRO TEAM**, **SANITAIRE**, **SANYO**, **SHARP**, **STEAM FAST** and **WEST-INGHOUSE**, just to name a few. Online they are one of the leaders of the pack. Remember, they charge NO shipping, NO taxes outside Texas AND they are the lowest prices. Visit the other Tomi brother at Broadway Vacuum, 4401 S. Broadway, Garland, TX 75043, 972/240-7971. *Call toll-free: 866/822-8868*

AAA Vacuums   **325/795-0954**

3462 Catclaw Drive   Monday - Saturday 9 AM to 6 PM Central Time
Abilene, TX 79606
www.aaavacuums.com   ◌⊟ *Top Online Store!*

 Who would have thought the center of the universe for vacuum cleaners would be in the Lone Star State, let alone Abilene? Good thing you don't have to go any farther than your computer! Save up to 50 percent on all the best in the cleaning business. Suck up to **PHANTOM**, **FILTER QUEEN**, **HOOVER**, **KIRBY**, **PANASONIC**, **SANYO**, **SHARP**, **TRISTAR** and more. You'll be floored at not only the selection but the prices — from canisters to uprights, convertibles to mini-models plus floor buffers and rug shampooers all there to do your dirty work. Clean up when you shop online: All products are shown with photos, delivery fees, descriptions, everything you need for a clean sweep. If you don't see the model you're looking for, don't hesitate to call. All products come with an additional AAA parts and service guarantee plus the manufacturer's warranty. If not happy, returns are accepted within 10 days or you can call me a dirtbag! *Call toll-free: 800/533-8227*

◆◆◆◆   **ABC Air Duct**   **972/404-8873**

Dallas, TX   By Appt. Only
www.abcairduct.com

ABC Duct Control — oops, I'm singing the wrong song — that one's for ABC Pest Control. Still, dirty carpets and dirty ducts are another kind of pesky situation. And these guys do have their ducts in a row. Cleaning air ducts as well as carpet, serving both the Dallas and Fort Worth areas, consider all those sleepless nights with itchy, watery eyes, sneezing, coughing, catching that runny nose....well, all the headachy symptoms that a good duct cleaning would eliminate. Their profes-sional technicians are bonded and insured and will vacuum, as well as brush, those ducts to the bone, eliminating bacteria, smoke, dangerous chemicals, mold and dust. If it's not supposed to be there, they'll shout "Out, damm mold, out!" If you're a senior citizen, expect a 10 percent discount. A recent current special when we shopped was for $7.50/duct. If you wanted all vents that are connected to the furnace cleaned, the price was $99. With that price, a four-year warranty ($100 value) was thrown in for Free (a nine-vent cleaning). Carpet cleaning prices panned out as follows: Two rooms, $45; three rooms, $55; four rooms, $65; five rooms, $75 or a whole house up to seven rooms, $120. As always, read the FINE PRINT. These are very good prices, but make sure they don't get you for "pre-spotting" or "moving furniture" or something else that you haven't thought of, but they have! In Dallas call 214/341-0159 and in Fort Worth call 817/471-6336

American Terrazzo Co.   972/272-8084

309 Gold Street   By Appt. Only
Garland, TX 75042
www.americanterrazzo.com

Talk about a perfect floor! How does this sound? Holds up to bulldozer traffic, doesn't show wear and tear, and can be cleaned with a damp mop with a little soap and water? Since it is seamless, you can also use it on countertops with ease and, by the way, it's also bacteria-resistant, stain and scratch-free. It's recycled terrazzo glass. Since 1931, founder Mattia Flabiano (Mike) has created his dynasty with terrazzo. Being a stickler for perfection, his company is considered one of the foremost terrazzo companies in the United States with the third generation of Flabianos running the show. Sons Luighi (Tony) and Mattia, Jr. are at the helm, alongside their sons, to continue in the tradition of artistry and craftsmanship. It's right up there price-wise with other materials such as marble, hand-painted tiles and granite. Terrazzo is from the Italian word for terraces and has been around for several hundred years. It's origin began in Europe where Venetian workers discovered a new use for discarded marble remnants. Since that time, it has evolved into a logical, practical solution for contemporary design and construction. And it's "to die for!"

★★★★★★   American Tile Supply   972/243-2377

2839 Merrell Rd.   Mon-Fri 8-5; Sat 9-2
Dallas, TX 75229
www.americantilesupply.com

This manufacturer/distributor is open to the public and it's a goodie. When they have a tent or parking lot sale, expect prices to take a downward spiral. If you are looking for top-quality slate, granite, or limestone at exceptional savings, then consider their Natural Stone Division and, for sure, take them for "granite." Prices started at 59 cents a square foot, hot-diggety-dog! All current sizes and prices included delivery (and sure to make even a stone cutter crack up!) Their huge distribution center at 2244 Luna Road in Carrollton (972/620-1866) is impressive in itself and occasionally, they, too, will open up to the public. Keep your eyes peeled for newspaper announcements. For more than 35 years, American Tile has been a top dog in providing flooring to builders, architects, designers, contractors and now the public. They are one of the largest tile and natural stone distributors in the United States, beside being associated with the Acme Building Brand companies. (Hello, Troy!) Enjoy a second outlet open on a regular basis in Richland Hills, 7412 Baker Blvd., 817/589-1252. Don't be confused and shop the other American Tile locations as they are retail showrooms.

★★★   Apex Carpets   972/986-9161

Mon-Fri 9-6; Sat 9-3

119 Plymouth Park
Irving, TX 75061

Carpets, carpets, carpets are now the only product that this Apex sells. It's carpet, though, at the highest peak. Save up to 70 percent at this former Pennell Carpet location with more than 45 years in the business, so they can lay it on thick. No longer selling tile, laminates or wood floors, they started selling carpet years ago and have gone back to their roots. Installation prices, a fair and square $3 a square yard. All major brands of carpet represented, with in-home or office appointments as easy as picking up the phone and dialing the number above.

★★★★★★   At Your Service   817/831-3113

Mon-Fri 8-6; Sat 9-1

4400 Airport Freeway
Haltom City, TX 76117
www.ayselectronics.com

If you want to be floored, At Your Service is where to do be or not to be, that is the answer! Don't question their intent. They want to save you money — on a lot of things. Located in an old building one block east of Beach Street on the service road of Hwy. 121, these guys, former Highland Appliance employees, will lay down the red carpet. Word of mouth has made them one of the fastest growing carpet retailers in Tarrant County. It's your one stop shop that says it all in their name. The showroom is now located in the middle of Tile Row where there are at least five major tile distributors that you can ogle over. They represent all the major manufacturers like **AMERICAN MARAZZI**, **DALTILE**, **INTERCERAMIC**, **MASTER TILE**, **MOHAWK** and **SHAW** for starters. They represent solid performers with substantial warranties. But, over and beyond that, they only use one reputable installer who has ten crews out there and you deal with the installers direct. Why is that important? Because other carpet dealers often mark up the installation, too. But not at At Your Service. They'll never bamboozle you with a flimflam song and dance, promise you the moon and deliver something else. Joe Lucas and Terry Ray are right in the thick of things, plush carpet and all, delivering what is referred to as service. Good service! That's what they mean when they say "At Your Service." Don't forget to ask about their electronics division for televisions! All kinds of electronics. Remember, they got their feet wet at the old Highland Appliances Superstores, now defunct.

★★★★★   Aura International   214/746-2872

1501 Turtle Creek Blvd.
Dallas, TX 75207
www.aura-rugs.com

When a showroom with such Aura announces they are opening their doors to the public and selling their carpet to the public at wholesale prices, don't you know we leave a trail of dust in our tracks. Look at the who, the where, and the what they are selling and if you want carpet or area rugs, need I say more?

★★★★★   Bargain Carpets   214/948-9449

Mon-Sat 9-5

200 N. Lancaster Ave.
Oak Cliff, TX 75203

Bargain Carpets is more than just their name, and cheap rugs are more than just their email address. It's really the crux and core of their carpet business and their way of life. This Oak Cliff bastion of bargains is still one of the best places to digest buys on carpets. After all, if it's your name, why play any other game? Over 40,000 yards of closeout carpet acquired through bankrupt-cies and liquidations, as well as mill overruns, irregulars and discontinues starting as low as $2.99, but that's where the story begins. It ends with you hiring your own installer. If you want an installer, they will recommend several good contractors and you will be billed separately for installation. Carpet and nothing but carpet, baby. Ralph Cole was known for years as the "King of Karpets" there's no denying his turf was carved out indelibly for his family to continue in the tra-dition that he established. Call if you need help getting there. On Lancaster, near 8th Street in South Dallas, Mapsco 55-A. Special orders welcomed, but nothing special in the way of ambi-ence. They keep their overhead low, way low, and pass the savings directly on to you without any frills just to thrill.

★★★★   Big Bob's New & Used Carpet   972/283-6600

638 E. Hwy. 67
Duncanville, TX 75137   Mon-Fri 9-6; Sat 9-5
www.bigbobscarpet.com

This is really a roller-coaster ride deciding are they or aren't they a bigger, better bargain? Or, instead, are they just big, bad bargains? Big Bob (founded by David Elyachar) is certainly one bad (of course, you know bad can be good, right?) dude, who's got carpeting on the brain starting at $3.99 a square yard. Of course, it's used, but clean and serviceable just the same. Then for new, watch the price escalate upward, ever so slowly, to as high as $27 a square yard for brand, spank-ing new. Expect to shell out $1.75 for a four-pound pad; a six-pound pad will bring the grand total to $2.75 a square yard. When all is said and done, Big Bob may not be such a big, big bargain after all. It's your call. Interested in a franchise with a little humor thrown in? Read more about all the opportunities on their website. Big Bob's is really growing strong, and its founder has been awarded many laurels for his enterprising philosophy in an otherwise staid business of selling car-pet. But it's not just carpet they sell. They've got vinyl, tile and laminate. If it's for the floor, Big Bob's gotcha covered. Stand and deliver also in North Richland Hills at 7245 Grapevine Hwy., 817/788-8447.

◆◆◆◆◆   Boule Wood Floors   972/317-1819; 214/908-6251

Dallas, TX   By Appt. Only

Don't get discouraged if you have to leave a message. Ronnie Boule is not one to stay put for long. But being down and out is how he stays busy (Being out on his hands and knees is how he keeps his overhead down....literally to the ground.) They have color charts for you to choose from, but, before you put the chart before the horse, you'll want to check out his many local references. After three or four, you'll know you're dealing with one solid craftsman. Taking pride in their quality performance, Boule'Wood Floors does installation, repairs, sanding and refinishing with a dust-controlled sanding system. A-choo! Stand up if it's hardwood floors or else. Though Boule installs all types of hardwood flooring, he prefers red oak above all others. Plank size can vary, from two and one quarter to as wide as five-inches. For the popular hand-scraped, distressed look, expect to pay about $1.50 more per square foot because it is so labor intensive. Ronnie will come out for the initial consultation and measurements; his wife delivers the bid. What a team! They are the best to lay down a hard bargain.

★★★★   Brumbaugh's Carpet Mill Outlet   817/244-8034

7714 Highway 80 W   Mon-Sat 10-6
Fort Worth, TX 76116-6416

As you mosey on down to Fort Worth, before you hit Cherry on Camp Bowie (Highway 80 W), you can't miss Brumbaugh's Carpet Mill Outlet. They have separate but equally appealing furniture and carpet divisions, but in Brumbaugh's case, the twains do meet. (Just the phones do not. Furniture has their own phone # 817/244-9377 — see write-up under the Furniture Chapter.)

★★★★★★   Budget Decorators, The   469/293-SHOP (7467)

                                                              By Appt. Only

Lewisville, TX 75067
www.thebudgetdecorators.com

There's nothing like it so far in the Metroplex, but if you like Design on a Dime, you'll love the Budget Decorators™. It takes one to know one. Since I'm great at launching new businesses, let me introduce you to my latest — and maybe my greatest. Called The Budget Decorators ™, it's my answer to being glued to Home and Garden Network. I love to play decorator. I know who some of the good ones who charge $200 an hour; and I know some of the good ones who charge $65 an hour. Who would you prefer? Ok, so now we're on the same wave length. If you are interior design challenged, you will love the Budget Decorators. We even intend to sponsor a total room EXTREME MAKEOVER later on in the year. Designers, afterall, have been sneaking around the "underground" for years and yet charge clients ten times what they find because nobody would believe how cheap it was. In fact, that's who we're marketing to. We'll pass the savings on when we find it on the cheap. Window treatments, upholstery, working with fabrics are are specialty, but we do it all. Meet The Budget Decorators (and the Lone Arranger) at our BD headquarters or at your home or office. An appointment is still necessary. Call the number above and we'll get you connected. Our Budget Decorators come with plenty of experience and charge half the usual and customary designer rates. Then, once you've laid out your plan of action, they shop at "underground" approved resources. Wholesale or less, staying within your budget, I guarantee it. We shop at only the best who charge you the least — and then pass on their low prices to you. The look may be one of opulence; the price tag will be more pauper-like. From chandeliers for $95 to floral arrangements right out of the lobbies of the Mansion Hotel for under $200, painting inside and out, faux painting to murals, to complete kitchen or bath remodels that will save you thousands, you'll can count (the savings) on us. We'll share our secrets, teach you a few design tricks, and hope you'll recommend us to your neighbors in the process. Nobody can beat our prices. The Budget Decorators ™ are on our website. You're but one click away for your design makeovers. From commercial lobbies for businesses, corporate offices, waiting rooms for doctors, lawyers or any professional who wants to make an impression for less; but mostly for home owners in need of a face lift, a room rearrange, a total house makeover, a room addition, or a new home from scratch. Here we come, ready or not. We've combined the talents of several designers who have the eye for color, scale, fabrics, room arrangements, how-to-mix and match and the Lone Arranger who will come out and just re-arrange with what you have already have to create a whole different look. Reality does have to come into play, however. They can't redo an entire room complete with 10 pieces of furniture, art work, accessories, florals, new carpet, wallpaper, faux painting, window treatments, an Oriental rug for under $1,000. We can do some of it, but let's get real! Expect to pay a small (considering the competition) hourly wage and then, let's go shopping!

★★★★★   Carpet Exchange   972/385-3545

4901 Alpha Rd.   Mon-Thurs 9-7; Fri-Sat 9-6; Sun Noon-5
Dallas, TX 75244
www.carpetexchangetexas.com

Like Texas, they boast that they're big. Realllllllllly big! But one of the concerns,
when shopping a discount store, was an absence of customer service. Not at Carpet
Exchange. They pride themselves on bend-over-backwards service and bent-over-
backwards prices. Then when you leave, you're apt to hear, "Y'all come back real soon, ya hear?"
Now that's Texas-style service. Love it or leave it, Texans are just plain proud to boast they're the
biggest and the best and in this case, they're not just whistlin'Dixie. Yee-haw! Choose from all the
big names in carpet, tile, vinyl, wood floor coverings, area rugs and laminates. Nary a brand is left
unturned. Their 96,000-square-foot showroom will leave you huffing and puffing. Their prices are
so good, they'll "floor you," but it's during sales that you'll be able to discern even greater discounts. Installation and padding are always extra so consider that when doing your comparative
shopping. They claim they will beat any price and ship anywhere, but remember, this is upscale
carpet and prices are not expected to be dirt cheap. Shop over 100,000 square yards of carpet in
stock, alongside vinyl, tile and wood. And if you're looking for area rugs, they have over one
thousand laying around. Ninety-days same as cash.

★★★★   Carpet Mill Outlet   817/481-3551

401 N. Kimball   Mon-Fri 9-6; Sat 9-3
Southlake, TX 76092

Southlake is one of the only mini-cities to boast a former mayor and his honor's furniture store.
But Southlake is also home to a 15,000-square-foot white metal building that holds the title of
Numero Uno Carpet One dealer in the country. Choose your comfort level and then line-up the
players: **CORONET**, **MOHAWK**, **QUEEN**, **SHAW** and **TUFTEX** where you can being your odyssey of walking on air including **SUTTON**'s new couture line (just like in the fashion business.)
Prices are quoted just the way you like them, with or without padding, installation, furniture
moved or not, so you are able to compare apples to apples. Hardwood flooring started at $6.25 a
square yard, installed for 3/8-inch wood. They do carry quarter-inch thickness, too, but they don't
recommend it. Vinyl flooring started at $6.99 a square yard without installation. Remember to get
a separate quote for that which will include embossing or removal of old flooring. In laminates,
choose from some of the best by **MANNINGTON**, **SHAW** and **WILSONART**, or perhaps you prefer it the hard way with hardwood floors by **BRUCE**, **HARTCO** or others. Their motto, "Large
enough to compete, but small enough to care."

★★★★★   Carpet Mills of America   972/267-8854

19129 Preston Road   Mon-Fri 10-7; Sat 10-6; Sun 12-4
Dallas, TX 75252
www.carpetmillsofamerica.com

Talk about being in an expansion mode! Carpet Mills of America is now part of a 40-store master
plan with stores throughout Texas and Phoenix, AZ. In any state, though, if the state of your flooring is in need of an uplifting experience, consider starting here. From berbers to trackless, tract
home carpeting to those in million-dollar estates, expect this carpet magnate to have you seeing
green if you choose any of their carpets. Of course, they also carry laminates, wood, tile and vinyl.
In business since 1989, *D Magazine* named them the best. **PERGO** named them the "Retailer of
the Year" in 1999, which speaks volumes for their credibility. Check directory for locations
throughout the Metroplex: Garland, three in Plano, three in Dallas, Rockwall, Carrollton, Allen,

Lewisville, two in Arlington, N. Richland Hills, Southlake, Fort Worth, Watauga. Also Houston, Austin, Arizona and Florida showrooms add up to a strong regional presence. This Dallas-based merchant is flying high and landing on square on the groun with both feet. If their website is any indication of their net worth, they are priceless. Of all the underground resources for saving money on flooring, they are the biggest and, often times, one of the best. Don't overlook them just because of their size. Power buying helps when negotiating with the mills and the manufacturers for the best prices.

★★★★   **Carpet Town Discount Center**   **972/438-4056**

3309 E. John Carpenter Fwy.   Mon-Sat 8-5
Irving, TX 75062

Nothing much new to uncover here this year. In fact, I'd say they were in kind of a rut, but in this case, shopping here could keep you out of the hole. If you want to replace your carpet from the ravages of time, kids, pets or people, this is a place for some heavy-duty overhauling. Premium padding, though (that's the six-pound kind), was $2 a square foot and, considering prices elsewhere, a steal. Commercial-quality carpeting (the kind that can stand up to a real workout) was priced at $7.95 a square yard, while residential carpet came installed with padding for around $9.95. They maintain their own installation crew, and that is very, very good. Paint the town red, roll out the red carpet, and red is the color of my true love's hair. They're not much to look at from the outside, but you're not buying an exterior, right? Here's where to put your foot down on high prices.

★★★★★   **CC Carpet Warehouse Store**   **214/631-0704**

7600 AMbassador Row   Mon-Fri 9-6; Sat 9-4
Dallas, TX 75247
www.cccarpet.com

I C that CC's carries **BRUCE**, **DUPONT**, **MOHAWK** and **PERGO** and that's just for starters. Stayed tuned to the latest specials. For example, laminate flooring with a 10-year wear/stain warranty first-quality was in stock at their warehouse store on Ambassador Row for 99 cents a square foot. Select flooring was especially priced at $3.99 a square foot with installation included on a limited quantity of flooring. Wow! If you want a laminate floor, though, floor prep was not included. Anyway, if you're dreaming about BRUCE hardwood floors, there was a limited supply at $4.49 a square foot and that included installation. Yikes! Now hear this: Three rooms of stained-protected carpet (up to 300 square feet) with pad and installation, selected styles and colors, was a flat $329 and that is good, very, very good. But, when we went in to collect on the advertised special, none was available. Should you choose to C what's available at their other stores (Mesquite, Bedford, Lewisville, North Dallas/Farmers Branch) and locations in Austin, you may find a C of possibilities.

★★★   **Ceramic & Marble Tile Outlet**   **214/951-9525**

909 Regal Row   Mon-Thurs 8-7; Fri-Sat 8-5; Sun 10-3
Dallas, TX 75247

Part of the Seconds and Surplus complex, these guys are the ones to dote on when it comes to laying tile. They carry grades four and five; in fact, lots of grade fives were available which is the same as being able to scratch a quarter on the floor and not leave a mark, but the ridges on the quarter will be smoothed out. Put another way, this tile is good — real good. The thin settings will cost about $5.11 a bag for do-it-yourselfers; add $3.25/square foot for professional installation.

They also stand and deliver on what they sell. Also at 5200 Gus Thomasson, 972/681-1300 and in Denton at 216 W. University at Elm, 940/243-9000.

◆◆◆◆◆◆ **Clanton's Tile & Etc.**   **214/341-0070**

9675 Wendell Rd.   Mon-Fri 8-5; Sat 9-1
Dallas, TX 75243
www.clantontile.com

 When you need cosmetic surgery, you don't turn to a plumber, do you? (Well, I guess if your plumbing needed a face-lift, you might. Then again, I guess that's a job done by a urologist.) It's better to shop a specialist, no doubt about it. And if you want a countertop done right, you go to Clanton's. He's a tile doctor, for sure, for tile countertops or tile floors, marble, granite or slate. Don't let just anybody tile away the hours unless they know what they're doing. What you forego in the way of discounts with Clanton, you make up for in superb service and exacting installation. What a nightmare if the crew who lays your bathroom floor has been hired off the street claiming, "Will tile for food!" Expect perfection here because the store is headed by its very own certified tile consultant. And, if you want to try your hand at it yourself, all you need to set the project in motion is the setting materials. Thin set, at $5.50 a bag, will cover approximately 70 square feet. Grout, about $15 and up, is available in lots of different colors. Just north of LBJ off Skillman, it's either in your hands or theirs. Most major tile manufacturers are represented including: AMERICAN MARAZZI, AMERICAN OLEAN, AMERICAN TILE, CEPAC TILE, CERAMIC TILE INTERNATIONAL, DAL-TILE and one of my personal favorites, VILLEROY & BOCH. But it's the installation component that gets our highest rating for quality service.

◆◆◆◆◆◆ **DFW Coating Concepts**   **972/488-2227**

11252 Goodnight Lane, Suite 800   By Appt. Only
Dallas, TX 75229
www.coat-it.com

 You know the old adage that appearance is everything! Well, let's face it and put your best floor first. AT DFW Coating Concepts, they do it all when it comes to coating your floors, interior or exterior applications including the garage. A lot cheaper than tile, but it can look just like tile with the use of scoring the concrete. Just look at the Kaleidoscope of Homes in the Colony or the new Angelica Theater in Plano. Then call Closets by Design to organize your garage (see in the Home Improvement Chapter). Call them if you want to stay ahead of the crowd. You'll be on the cutting edge of the coating business. Love the look of Soho? Well, let them create a hip contemporary backdrop that will be a look that will remain chic for years. Either residential or industrial applications are available from DFW Coating Concepts as they are the folks who specialize in floor coatings, concrete staining and woodcare. Look at the variety of examples on line and see what their coats of many colors look like up close and personal. Now, woodn't it be loverly if they also did wood floors? Well as luck would have it, they provide several services related to woodcare. Power Washing — to clean and remove mildew and stains staining — and then add waterproofing to protect and add color to enhance the natural beauty of wood fences, decks and decorative treatments. Magically, here's the coat of many colors and their name's not even Joseph. *Call toll-free: 800/301-3905*

★★★★★   **Dungan's Floors/Blinds & More**   **972/562-9444**

2306 Virginia Parkway   Tues-Fri 8:30-5:30; Sat 10-4
McKinney, TX 75070
www.dungansfloors.com

Explain the phenomenon how a husband and wife can stay happily married for more than 20 years, raise a family and corner the McKinney market for window and floor coverings, too? Surely they could make a fortune selling their secrets. With the McKinney corridor booming, they probably can't keep up with the demand. I can say I knew them when. They're one of the originators of custom tile on both floors and countertops. Let them install **ARMSTRONG**, **BRUCE**, **MANNINGTON**, **PHILADELPHIA** and **SALEM** carpet and hardwoods. Choose adobe, brick, ceramic tile, hardwoods or laminates. Then, there's the newest stain-resistant fibers and custom ceramic tiles. They maintain their own installation crews and head honcho husband, Lou Jenkins, is a master craftsman himself. Lennie's the decorator and together they make quite a team. FREE estimates are provided. **BRUCE** hardwood flooring started at $6 a square foot, including installation. Decorator service is provided free of charge since they provide unbiased and objective advice without trying to sell you merchandise. Amen, brother Dungan.

★★★★★★   **Floor & Decor Outlets of America**   **972/243-9230**

2350 Alberta Drive   Mon-Sat 9-9; Sun 11-6
Dallas, TX 75229
www.flooranddecoroutlets.com

 Start off with their talking website. If that doesn't take your breath away, try stepping foot inside their 75,000 square foot superstore. Maybe it's something in the water? This new era in flooring convenes at the intersection of LBJ and 35E, featuring more than 1.5 million square feet of inventory — hard surface floors and related decorative items at prices significantly below retail. For example, opening week they featured: slate for $1.99/square foot and 12" x 12" Absolute Black Granite for $5.99/square foot and Terra Cotta Porcelain tile for 99¢ a square foot. Compared to Lowe's and Home Depot, you'll see immediately why they made it into the 100 BEST. Visit their website and read up on wood and learn a thing or two. "How-to-Install" classes are held every Saturday. Select, buy and take home flooring on the same day as you buy and always at discounted prices. You will find more than just flooring. They carry every imaginable tool you'd need to do-the-job yourself: wet saws, moldings, transition strips — everything's all in one place. How convenient for Weekend Warriors.

★★★★★★   **Ged's Carpet Tile & Carpet Outlet**   **817/275-7631**

2985 S. Hwy. 360   Mon-Sat 10-7; Fri 10-5; Fri 10-5
Grand Prairie, TX 75052

 Ged's my kind of guy. If he wasn't so gracious about serving the Metroplex, you'd think his next assignment would be to carpet the runways at DFW Airport, maybe the new American Airlines Center, and if things really got going, maybe a shot at carpeting Mark Cuban's house? Now we're talking big. Anyway, even the rich and famous are prudent shoppers and this guy can really deliver the buys. Some of the brands highlighted included **COLUMBUS**, **MOHAWK** and **SHAW INDUSTRIES**, but don't expect to be nickel-and-dimed to death. No hidden charges, period. Prices, at first, appear to be a bit higher, but since everything's included in the price, including moving of furniture and the removal of your old carpeting, it adds up to a sensational deal. Furthermore, all prices include the better six-pound grade (not four pound) of padding. Check directory for other locations in Tarrant County. Then, if you need prices slashed to the bare floors, shop their outlet store on Highway 360 and Mayfield in Grand Prairie (above), where they still roll out the royal treatment even though you're only looking for the cheapest price on first-quality mill closeouts in carpet, ceramic tile, vinyl, laminates, or wood. See, you get the whole nine yards, without sacrificing the quality. The money you save may be your own! Note, they close at 5 on Fridays and on Sundays they put their feet up and rest. Prices start as low as $1.69 per square foot for carpet and that includes padding and installation. Installation, though, has a minimum charge of $150 (typically runs around 45 cents a square foot for installation). All's said and done right at Ged's. Visit their discount store also at 2633 S. Cooper in Arlington, 817/275-7631.

◆◆◆◆◆◆◆ **J.M.P. Tile Co.**   **214/762-7107**

Plano, TX 75023   By Appt. Only

Don't expect instant gratification. This company takes days to return messages, but if you want an installer for ceramic tile or hardwood floors, their prices are a throwback to the '80s. Besides, he's an expert fourth-generation floor installer who's been on his hands and knees almost since birth. (Instead of a breach birth, he probably came into this world as a beech birth!) This master craftsman has been installing tile, marble, granite, hardwood (hard surfaces, in other words), so don't even think about asking him to install carpets. His price for installation is $3.25 a square foot for ceramic tile and $2.74 a square foot for hardwood floors (I paid $2.25 in 1985). Book three to four weeks in advance. This guy's as busy as a bee.

★★★★★★ **LumberLiquidators.com**   **972/323-5077**

1620 N. I-35   Mon-Fri 9-6; Sat 10-3
Carrollton, TX 75006
www.LumberLiquidators.com

You can save some money at this franchised national Home and Garden TV advertiser. In fact, their guarantee is: "If you find a lower price on a comparable product, they will beat the competitor's written or adver- tised price on the same or comparable product." (But you must provide written documentation of the product's specifications and pricing.) If you are looking for hardwood flooring and are considering oak, exotics or pre-finished, then start the ball rolling at 99¢ a square foot. They also carry, in-stock, the HUSKY brand of pre-finished woods with a 50-year warranty and exotic woods like maple, oak and cherry for $2.95 a square foot. Super deals showcased on their website included: Natural Exotics from $1.99 square foot; 3¼-inch wide plank Red Oak flooring, $2.99 square foot; beautiful clear Bolivian Rosewood 2¼-inch for $2.75 square foot; 2¼-inch Bloodwood with a 50-year finish for $4.85/square foot. They also carry Butcher Block and Bamboo. The dura-wood Bamboo with a 25-year warranty, pre-finished, 3/8-inch was $2.89/square foot. Worldwide shipping and samples are available. Now open in Fort Worth at 2165 E. Loop 820 North, 817/589-2400. ***Call toll-free: 877/Mill-Dir***

★★★★ **Massey Distributors**   **972/394-7617**

911 N. Mill St.   Mon-Sat 9-5 (By Appt.Only)
Lewisville, TX 75067

Being on the run, in this case, means Massey is on the move. With 15 mobile showrooms on the road at any given time, someone, somewhere is being shown the carpeted side of life. With no overhead costs except gas and a truck, they can save you about 40 percent on all kinds of flooring options: carpet, vinyl, laminates, wood and ceramic tile. Everything that is available at their local showroom is available through their mobile units at no additional charge. This is convenience at the zenith with distributor-direct prices at the very least. Nothing down, no interest and 90-days financing with approved credit; what more do you want? Let them bring the store to you. Then you can really put your foot down on high prices and sink down into some of the plushest of luxury carpet. If you're lucky, a same-day appointment is possible. They are also a distributor of **HOWARD MILLER** Miller clocks. Clocks and carpet. What a grand time for singing — be it a grandfather model, marine, mantle clock or just one that'll wake-you-up going tick-tock, tick-tock, it's time to get up! Buy it right and keep track of both time and money. How's that for saving the day?

★★★★★   Nadine Floor Company   972/424-2525

1105 E. Parker Rd. @ Ave. K   Mon-Sat 9-7:30; Sun 12-6
Plano, TX 75074
www.nadinefloors.com

How can you not consider a company that will meet or beat any written estimate you bring in the door on anything that has to do with floors. Nadine has stood the test of time with not only great prices, but **FREE** estimates, name brands, a newly remodeled showroom, and any kind of floor covering known to mankind: tile, wood, laminate, carpet, area rugs, marble, stone, whatever. And yes, if you need matching countertops or shower tiles, they do that, too. The last time in, we were floored with the prices on cash and carry. For example, 99¢ (retail $3.99) for 18 x 18-inch porcelain tile, $1.79/sq. ft. installed with ½" padding, furniture moved included, instead of $2.39; and $5.99/square foot for real hardwood floors installed with a 15-year warranty. Then, they threw in a free $299 5 x 8 area rug of your choice if you bought a granite countertop slab which included the slab and the labor for the tear-off. Now, how about that? No relation to Steven King's Nadine but you can still drive a hard bargain here. Brands included: **ANDERSON HARDWOOD**, **BRUCE**, **HERITAGE COLLECTION**, **MANNINGTON**, **MASTER TILE**, **MOHAWK**, **PERGO**, **ROBBINS**, **SHAW**, **WILSONART** and **WITEX** just to lay on a few. Whether it's ceramic, natural stone (slate, marble, granite or Travertine), **ANSOCRUSH RESISTER** or **DUPONT STAINMASTER**, they have all of the latest and greatest. And since they'll beat any written price, you know what that means without me telling you. And they can smell a rat a mile away, so don't pull any cheesy tricks on having a friend write you an estimate that is ridiculously low only to bring that one into Nadine for a price match or better. Let's keep everybody honest.

North Texas Bomanite   972/484-8465

11107 Morrison   Mon-Fri 6 AM-7 PM
Dallas, TX 75229
www.bomanite.com

Cool. Complete. Concrete. **BOMANITE** is the name and the product that you can bank on. For more than four decades, the Bomanite Corporation has offered a variety of exceptional, high-quality concrete paving and flooring products. So, like we say in the biz, if you want the best and you want concrete, see what **BOMANITE** looks like by visiting their corporate offices, right off Stemmons and Walnut Hill, between Ables and Shady Trail. It's what I would call, "amazing floors." Yes, it's one amazing floor surface. Choose from countless textures and designs. But it's far more than just imprinted concrete. Transform your back patio or your inside floor surfaces into a unique and dramatic presentation. Be it commercial or residential, inside or out, you've got the right ingredients. Try it. You'll love it for your garage or patio. Even inside surfaces can be transformed into a dramatic flooring presentation. Learn more on their website. They have a network of over 250 specially trained and licensed contractors in more than 70 countries worldwide, so they aren't just some local yokels out to pave their way to riches. But once you've put their product down, you will be able to see how the road to riches looks from the unique prospective of an "aboveground" shopper even though you're a true-blue "underground shopper" looking to save some green. *Call toll-free: 800/492-2524*

★★★★   Oriental Rug Gallery of Texas   214/387-8787

8250 Gaylord Parkway, #1   Mon-Sat 10-6; Thurs 10-8; Sun 1-6
Frisco, TX 75034
www.rugstudio.com

Hundreds of Oriental rugs are waiting for you at this brand-new northern outpost. The Oriental Rug Gallery of **TEXAS** is laid out in its new digs, brimming with all the right stuff — the right size, the right pattern, the right colors....at the right price. This Gallery has been a significant supplier of Oriental rugs for almost 70 years. Not quite an octogenarian, but, no doubt, they'll make it to 80 with their buying power for every kind of hand-tufted rugs, handmade rugs, all wool rugs, all kinds of round and unusual-shaped rugs, and all at prices less than taking a first-class carpet ride. Rugs here began under $100 and escalated to several thousand. Rugs can be a fabulous wall-endowment for the arts, too. Hang it and see what I mean. Change a dull and lack-luster room into a showplace with a gorgeous rug. At "The Studio" within the Oriental Rug Gallery, learn about the art of Oriental rug-making, explore the various countries in the Oriental rug-making world, and find out what you should know before purchasing one. The staff will also help with decorating ideas. If you prefer to shop at home, visit their website. Full refunds are given within 30 days of purchase. *Call toll-free: 866/618-8787*

★★★★★★   Persepolis Oriental Rugs   214/599-9966

3926 Oak Lawn   Mon-Sat 9:30-6; Sun Noon-5
Dallas, TX 75219

 If you're interested in a floor show across from Park Place Mercedes, this may be the opening act in Uptown circles. This direct importer cuts out the middle man and delivers prices on Oriental rugs at particularly worldly-less prices. Talk about a Turkish delight....more than 7,000 of them are laying around at prices guaranteed to be the lowest. It's a difficult price-checking challenge even for someone armed with some sophistication. But instead of looking under a microscope at each and every thread, let's start with their selection which is awesome. Master-crafted rugs from China, India, Pakistan and Persia (Iran) can take you around the world without having to lift a foot. Another plus is their professional rug cleaning and repair. (Note: thus far, they have lived up to their promise of being able to fix anything.) Expect to be sans (without) a rug for 7 to 10 days while they're cleaning it. Other showrooms at 4100 Oak Lawn (where their office is located) and 19129 Preston Rd. in North Dallas, 972/732-8400. A website should be in the works soon. It's important to teach an uneducated shopper on how to best shop for an Persian rug. Are you listening Mr. Persepolis?

★★★   Rems & Rugs Carpet Outlet   214/630-8005

8888 Governors Row   Mon-Fri 9-5
Dallas, TX 75207

How can you shop if they're closed on the weekends. Sorry, Charlie, this is not convenient for the working woman. What if you wanted to shop, but work across town and have 30 minutes for lunch? Sure couldn't fit it in in a half hour and drive cross town, too. Well, enough ragging about Rems. I was just thinking out loud. Then I was thinking, if Rems stands for remnants, does rugs stand for ruglets? (That's a joke, folks.) In the scheme of things, it probably doesn't matter, unless you are looking for ringlets to add to your area rug. Actually Rems & Rugs is really a carpet store, wall to wall, or a roomful. Besides, when you can save up to 50 percent, who's counting square yards? Take any of the remnants and make your own area rug, carpet a dorm room, a spare bed-room, the garage, a workout area or any other smaller than normal-size carpet area. Leave it to this eager beaver located at the intersection of Governors Row and Profit. Shows you where their motive lies! But hours are not convenient to the worker bees. And who doesn't these days?

★★★★★   Royal Rug Gallery   214/696-6669

10759 Preston Rd.   Mon-Sat 9:30-6; Sun 12-5
Dallas, TX 75230

Wholesalers since 1955, they have decided to open to the public and see what deals they can have you ride out on. Enjoy the magic of it all. Showing at their retail location were over 5,000 genuine Persian rugs in all shapes and sizes including Antique and Masterpieces. Don't expect a $1.99 ride, that's for sure. But pay the same prices as the dealers pay. That's right, pay less. How much less" Well, that's up for grabs. Most of our research team felt confident these were the real McCoys. Experience counts when they also offer cleaning, repair and appraisals. Surely, they know which knot is not! If you're a dealer, call them at the World Trade Center, 214/696-8275. Watch this space. They may be expanding as we speak. But when it comes to being the area rug gallery of choice, they get our vote. The royal review is and it could be in the 100 BEST but since we heard rumors that the founder, after 48 years, may be calling it quits, we recommend you call first before wasting any gas on the drive over.

★★★★   Rug City   972/488-0101

11111 Harry Hines   Mon-Fri 9-6; Sat 10-6; Sun Noon-5
Dallas, TX 75229

Hit the streets. Harry Hines is the strip that's fit for most shopper's needs. If money is a consider-ation, walk on the wild side, just north of Walnut Hill and land at Rug City on the northwest cor-ner, at the light, at Southwell. There you'll see a thousand or more area rugs, and they're expecting you to take advantage of their sensational prices and walk all over them. Though they don't cus-tom make area rugs, they can alter them. The selection is far beyond your imagination. Take a trip around the world and bring back a rug from the USA or Belgium, China, Egypt, Russia, Saudi Arabia, Turkey and countries whose names had too many letters to type. Expect all of the rugs, though, to be machine made with inexpensive price tags. Rug City actually manufactures many of the rugs they sell, as well as being direct importers, so they're in a position to provide "Persian-to-Persian" prices. But mind you, this is their retail store. Their outlet store is next to Front Desk and they're down the street on Harry Hines. Here, too, they claim to match any competitors price. Delivery is free.

★★★★★★   Rug Expo, Inc.   214/956-9988

10333 Harry Hines Blvd.   Mon-Fri 9-6; Sat 10-6
Dallas, TX 75490

The guys at the Expo have it down to a science. Keep it lean and mean and you'll be the one that makes all the green. Forget that red carpet ride; take any one of these area rugs and you'll be floored, regardless of color, pattern, motif or size. They are all at the best prices with thousands to choose from, so why not? General Manager Moh Yasin, Retail Manager, Gaith Momani and the guys would like for you to walk all over them because they've got the best selection at the best prices on area rugs in the Metroplex, no pulling the rug from under you. Others pale by comparison. Though there are plenty of area rug stores in the big city, none has the selection or the prices that the Rug Expo outlet has. Next door to Front Desk, x marks the spot where area shoppers meet if their feet demands an area rug. No need to fret over whether these are real Orientals or not, they look the part and that's what counts. Who can really tell the difference anyway? When Jim Carey was making a movie that required the biggest area rug in the world, guess who they called? That's right. Now Rug Expo holds the record for manufacturing the "Largest Area Rug in America." Though Carey obviously wasn't interested in the price, just the size, at least now you know who holds the record. For me, what is as important is the three S's: selection, savings and lastly size. Most entry ways don't require a 100 x 100 foot rug anyway. So when you tire of the Safari look, you can go north to Tuscany and switch to a whole new decor. There's another Rug Expo (but it's also a retail sister.) Consider them for the decorator touch as well as the magic touch. Hey, at least they won't take you for a ride! Website is under construction, so they say.

★★★★★★ Rugmakers Gallery 972/458-9000

13655 Welch Rd.
Farmers Branch, TX 75244
www.rugmakersgallery.com

Mon-Fri 8-5; Sat 10-3

The name at least gives you an inkling as to what's inside this manufacturer's showroom but, unless you've been there and bought there, you haven't a clue as to the drama that is lying around waiting to be picked up and relocated to your home or office. In other words, you haven't seen nothin'yet! This custom rugmaker has anywhere from 200-300 rugs on display from $40-$800 in sizes 4x6, 5x7 or 6x9 feet. From a fabulous rendition of a children's nursery rhyme, to a drop-dead dramatic contemporary, to more traditional rugs, it's time you laid one on that speaks of good taste and smart looks. Remember, these are all showroom samples and are not only one-of-a-kind, but priced accordingly. Furthermore, these are custom area rugs and nobody in the Metroplex holds a candle to Bob Blevins'craftsmanship, creativity and customer service. Ask for Theresa or Sharon, if Bob's not around, and you'll be treated like the queen of hearts. Decorators come and go with customer fabric swatches. Yes, they can match fabric to something for the floor. Then, after they buy the perfect area rug, they resell it at twice the price to their clients. Shop yourself and save on every fiber. Some are even beautiful enough to be considered worthy as a wall-hanging, too. And now, an expanded full service carpet resource is available for your shopping pleasure.

★★★★★★ S & H Carpet Distributors 214/638-3311

8717 Directors Row
Dallas, TX 75247
www.shdistributing.com

Mon-Fri 8-5:30; Sat 9-3

Not as well known as green stamps, but when it comes to carpet or any other flooring option, it sure takes the licking out of paying full price! S & H Carpet Distributors is an icon in the carpet industry. John Stacy, its founder, started as a distributor selling direct from the mills to carpet retailers. Soon, he discovered the public wanted to get in on the act of buying "wholesale." After all, it sure beats paying retail. John Stacy's prices will save you anywhere from 50 to 70 percent off retail. Today, S & H Carpet Distributors is one of the largest carpet dealers in town. The lowest prices and customer service are both considered priorities by the Stacy family. Compare name brands to name brands. Save hundreds, even thousands on each and every job. Almost 45,000 square feet of warehouse, they guarantee to have the lowest prices anywhere. My personal favorite is **HARRIS-TARKETT** hardwood floors with installation by "Cowboy!" as that is what I chose for my home. To find S & H, exit Mockingbird off Highway 183. Stay on the service road going south from Mockingbird. Turn right on Profit and right again on Directors Row. It's the second building on the left. Shop also in North

Richland Hills, 817/581-7777, open Mon-Fri 9-6 and Sat 9-3 and more locations coming soon. Also Temple and Houston. *Call toll-free: 800/880-1717*

★★★★   Texas Discount Carpets   972/484-8051

11265 Goodnight Lane, Suite 1012   Mon-Fri 10-6; Sat 10-3 (By Appt. Only)
Dallas, TX 75229

Talk about a clandestine rendezvous with your carpet destiny. When calling this company, ask to speak to Pete or Mindy and don't be scared off if you simply get a cell phone recording. Leave your name and number. They really are wholesalers (you know the kind) and don't particularly go out of their way to accommodate a retail customer, especially those of a bargain-shopping kind. But if you tell them the Diva (that's me) sent you (or the underground shopper), they'll gladly pay homage to you by opening their showroom/warehouse doors. Hours are by appointment only. CABINCRAFT, SHAW and other brands are waiting for you to point and cart off the warehouse floor. Off Stemmons, two blocks west on Walnut Hill, prices ranged from 99¢ a yard & up. A luxury 63-ounce carpet was going for $16 a square yard; a 55-ounce carpet was less, $14 a square yard; and all 30-ounce carpeting and builders'grades came in stain-resistant, the only way to fly. FREE delivery, installation, repairs and restretching available. Keep it a secret, between us. OK?

★★   Tim Hogan's Carpet Outlet of Dalton, GA   817/831-4167

5724 Airport Freeway   Mon-Fri 9-7; Sat 9-5; Sun Noon-5
Haltom City, TX 76117

If these boots were made for walking and the sales personnel were made for talking, my feet would be hurting; unfortunately, that wasn't the case here. Their mouths didn't move a muscle. When we walked in, nobody even said hello so their mouths hardly had a workout. OK, so they were busy. That's no excuse for not even saying hello, much less make eye contact. Instead our eyes were peeled on the many brands available. MONSANTO Wear-Dated carpet was just one of the many product brands they represented at a fairly decent price. We did find their in-home service shopping a breeze and their other locations easy to get to in Grapevine, 817/481-8950 and Rhome, 817/385-5540. As we say, when in Rome, do as the Romans do. Never pay retail. It works. But these folks not only didn't say "hello," they didn't say "goodbye," either. There's always next year.

★★   True Discount Carpets   972/276-0348

1403 S. Jupiter Rd.   Mon-Fri 9-9; Sat 9-5
Garland, TX 75042

No need to plead the fifth....it's all black and white. And blue, beige, rose, or any color on the rainbow's palette. Honesty is the best policy, and we honestly were astonished with the 100,000 yards of carpeting available. Good thing it was cushy; we were not up to putting up with any rough wear and tear on our psyches. We saw CORONET carpet with padding and installation for just $10.49 a square yard; upgrade to a 4½-pound pad that was a half-inch thick for just 50¢ more. This carpet included Scotchguarding ® and remember, it won't shed. Brands including MOHAWK and SHAW were priced in true discount fashion, about 20 percent off. Well, not deep enough to send you through the roof or even to the stars, but discounted enough to take you to Jupiter in Garland. I still find square-foot pricing difficult to get used to. Across from E-Systems, how many rooms do you think you could carpet if the sky's the limit?

★★★★★   **Ultimate Edge, Inc.**   **972/564-9409**

PO Box 2405   By Appt. Only
Forney, TX 75126-2405
www.ultimateedgeconcrete.com

If you don't want to do-it-yourself (stain the concrete, that is), here is where to achieve the Ultimate Edge. Don't expect it to come cheap, but it's certainly affordable. Whether it's for a remodeling project or new construction, the possibilities are infinite for color and texture. For beauty, low maintenance and uniqueness, you can't beat an acid-stained floor. It's also a great choice for countertops in your kitchen. Floors, multiple colors or a diamond pattern will cost $5 a square foot. Stain, scoring and finish (one color) is only $3.75 a square foot; and stain only (one color and finish) is only $2.75 a square foot. Over 80 colors are waiting to be picked. Make your in-house/in-office appointment is now!

★★★   **Vac-Mobile, The**   **972/247-5838**

12895 Josey Lane, Suite 122   Mon-Fri 8:30-6; Sat 9-5
Farmers Branch Shopping Center Farmers Branch, TX 75234

There was the Smutzmobile (my old jalopy), then the Oldsmobile, and now the Vac-Mobile. Two were cars, and one is a seller of vacuum cleaners. Which one is the vacuum cleaner store? Okay, you got it. Although these are not the original owners, they have been making a clean sweep of it since taking over from a second-generation vacuum cleaning repair family. If you've got a vacuum cleaner that is not sucking up to you, then bring it in and consider it fixed. Their hands-on approach to vacuum repair is legendary. But they also sell used (and some new) vacuums cheap. These folks have been doing this for over 40 or 50 years in this one location. Buy used commercial vacs for less than new residential models. All the best brands are available for sale including; **ELECTROLUX**, **KIRBY** and **RAINBOW**. Suck up to Kirk, the owner, and he'll pass on a terrific deal on a **DIRT DEVIL**, **EUREKA**, **HOOVER**, **PANASONIC**, **RAINBOW**, **SANYO** or **SHARP**. Pick up a used model for as low as $39. Trade-ins are welcome. Tucked away at the southwest corner of Valley View and Josey in the Farmers Branch Shopping Center.

VacDepot.com   **888/822-8863**

Fort Worth, TX 76140   24/7
 www.vacdepot.com   ⌂ *Top Online Store!*

Gotcha, you dirt bag, you! Suck it up. This Fort Worth online dynasty has you sucking up with everything you've ever needed or wanted if the subject is vacuum cleaners. Bags, belts, filters, attachments, tools, cleaners and shampoos, items for central vacs and more. Lindhaus R4-10 Bags (six packs), retail $120, their price $99.99. They also operate www.vacdepot.com, as well as other online sites. They have been going strong for the past 30 years. They are one of the few internet floor care companies with a full staff devoted to online sales. They even answer and return phone calls, as well as respond to emails. No retail store to drain their overhead. Their website gives factory facts and customer's first-hand observations, as well as comments about the products themselves. You can only buy closeouts by calling their toll-free number during office hours (Monday-Friday, 9:30-5 CST) to check availability and any restrictions. They do not sell refurbished items. For bags, go online to their bag store at www.dirtbags.com. *Call toll-free: 888/822-8863*

★★★★ **Verona Marble Co.**   **214/381-8405**

4904 Olson Drive   Mon-Fri 8-5; By Appt. Only
Dallas, TX 75227

Marvel over exquisite marble, granite, slab remnants and porcelain tiles in all colors and shades without traveling to Verona. Supplying some of the Metroplex's finest interior designers, if you would like to create the designer look similar to those featured in *Architectural Digest*, then here's where to scoop up the slabs. Close-outs in various sizes, starting at just $1.90 a square foot, should elevate any home from rags to riches. This factory outlet is everything it should be, if you're wanting an impressive floor covering. Since these are all closeouts, huge quantities in any one style, color or size are hard to arrange. But if you're not as picky, you can marbleize your entry for a much lower price. Pick your project area and make sure it's small. All tile is imported directly from Italy, so by eliminating the mean-ole middleman, you can reap the savings. Plus, if you try and lay it yourself, they sell all the supplies. Let's hope none of it will lean like the Tower of Pisa. Hours are by appointment only; don't just show up and expect to be welcomed with the open arms of Verona. Weekend hours would be convenient.

S&H Carpet Distributing
See writeup on page 163

Cars & Parts

◆◆◆◆◆◆ **A-1 United Transmissions**   **972/278-9807**

2201 W. Kingsley   Mon-Fri 8-6; Sat 9-Noon
Garland, TX 75041

Family-owned and operated since 1976, the Easleys have the staying power when it comes to restoring your auto power. If yours has a transmission, and you aren't accused of any transgressions, they will willingly tackle the problem. Dealing in both **AMERICAN** and foreign models (no, not those that make a living posing on the runways), mechanics assigned to your car are all ASE-certified. They have access to the latest computerized diagnostic equipment, so no stone goes unturned. Bring it on in, take them on a **FREE** road test and evaluation and then hear the news, the good and the bad. At least you're in experienced hands. They even know the difference between a muffler problem and a transmission problem when, inadvertently, we asked about fixing our catalytic converter. In fact, they even recommended a few muffler shops in the area who could fix it. If you bring the problem in, Mike can usually tell you what's wrong after driving the car for a few minutes. At least, there's no trial-and-error waste of time here. They are a leading transmission company serving the entire Metroplex. I guess that's why they are called A-1. Family owned and operated since 1976, they've got plenty of years under their belt. They offer a variety of services that include repairs, overhauls and rebuilts with FREE road tests, FREE diagnoses and FREE estimates.

★★★★★★ **Ancira Motorhomes**   **940/320-4098**

5201 I-35 N   Mon-Sat 8-7; Sun Noon-5
Denton, TX 76207
www.ancira.com

There are mergers and acquisitions in every category, and in the RV World, they're no exception. Ancira Motorhomes bought out RV World of **TEXAS** and is now making their presence known in the **RV** world. When we visited, stock was low as they had only changed hands a week before. Give them a few months to get fully stocked, up and running, and then you'll see what power buying is all about. Find out more on the Ancira website and even shop for an RV online. What fun being a backseat driver in the front seat of my computer! Ancira is a 29-year-old family of dealerships (and the largest in Texas). If history repeats itself, they'll have a large and impressive selection of new and used Motorhomes, including diesel, class A, class C, fifth wheels and more. Ancira Motors was the first auto dealer online in Texas and has been a top sales leader in Southwest Texas, with one of the largest inventories of vehicles to choose from. I'm talking thousands! Shop online to see what's available. New or pre-owned, expect this RV dealership to be impressive. And when you see me hitting the road with "Bargains Across America," you'll know who's behind me all the way. *Call toll-free: 800/411-8533*

★★★★   **Atomic & Import Auto Salvage**   **214/371-6020**

8835 S. Central Expressway   Mon-Sun 8-6:15
Dallas, TX 75216

Looking for carburetors in all the wrong places? What about a missing tooth for a PORSCHE? An engine for your EDSEL? Well, try searching here for the cheapest link. If you bring in your old transmission, for example, to buy a new one (or reserve one with a $10 deposit until you can), they will make the exchange for about $96.95 on an automatic front wheel drive tranny or $69.96 on a standard. Even though they don't handle antique parts, they were willing to hunt one down through their hotline. And if all else fails and you want your car to go to hell, they do provide car crushing. Note their change in hours. There's no rest for the weary.

★★★★★   **Auto Buyers Assistance**   **214/361-0090**

14001 Dallas Pkwy., Suite 1200   Mon-Fri 8:30-5
Dallas, TX 75240
www.autobuyersassistance.com

Looks like Ronnie Shipper is no longer running on empty. He's gassed up and ready to roll off the lots of car dealers everywhere. Want a car, new or used, at the guaranteed lowest price? Start with Auto Buyers Assistance online or on the phone, and this **FREE** service will connect you to over 15,000 dealers ready to wheel and deal. It's pretty simple: Log online and fill out a questionnaire as to where you'd like to get your car (three area codes), what your time frame is and, of course, the make and model you're looking for. When you submit the Purchase/Lease Form, your information goes to the Internet department of appropriate car dealers. If you're a member of **AARP**, AAA and certain credit unions, you already have access to this service. You can get one low price on any new vehicle from participating dealers just by picking up the phone and getting it through the Auto Buyers Assistance Program. Domestic and foreign car seekers looking for cars, trucks, vans or SUVs are handled with equal opportunity assistance. Try it and let us know what you think! *Call toll-free: 800/361-4106*

◆◆◆◆◆◆   **Auto Critic**   **972/386-8388**

1919 Lansdown Dr.   Mon-Sat 8-5; also By Appt.
Carrollton, TX 75010
www.usedcarinspections.com

Don't drive off the lot with a lemon. Make your first call to Auto Critics (Dallas or Fort Worth offices), the largest inspection service of pre-owned cars in the U.S. They've been written about in publications from Time to USA Today, mentioned on "Good Morning America" to NBC's "Money Talk. They'll come to you at your home or office, seller's home or car lot with their 150-point diagnostic checklist to examine that vehicle from top to bottom. Let the experts review the body, frame, electrical and all the major systems. Auto Critic provides a comprehensive, unbiased written report by one of their certified ASE mechanics. They even take it out for a spin to ascertain any performance or operational problems. Then they compare the odometer reading to the way the car actually handles. Next is the most important credential of Auto Critic's service: They have no vested interest in finding anything wrong with your vehicle, as there are never any referrals to mechanics, even if asked. Same day or next day appointments available. In Fort Worth, call 817/460-8388. *Call toll-free: 800/765-1857*

★★★★   Auto Zone   **972/221-1433**

1106 W. Main   Mon-Sat 8 AM-11 PM; Sun 9 AM-10 PM
Lewisville, TX 75067
www.autozone.com

Since 1979, this national chain has opened over 3,000 stores, so for sure, this zone is a much bigger zone than a one horse town store in Lewisville. In fact, since they bought out Dallas-based
CHIEF AUTO PARTS, they are blowin'and goin'straight to the top. New this year, how about
their "Loan-a-Tool" FREE Program. Such a deal! Still, auto parts are their everyday low price
bread-and-butter mainstay and all stores offer free testing of batteries, starters, alternators, voltage
regulators and control modules. You can even bring in your used engine oil to the stores for recycling. All purchases, whether online or in store, can be returned to any location. If your battery's
kaput, have it recharged in 30 minutes....for nada. More than 60 different specialty tools are available to check out the one that will help get the job done for those who want to do-it themselves.

◆◆◆◆◆◆   Autoglass Plus   **972/ 817/222-2323 ext. 201**

1925 E. Belt Line, #513   By Reservation Only
Carrollton, TX 75006
www.autoglassplus.net

     It doesn't matter how it happened, they don't care. All that matters is, if the window
to your car, truck or van has been shattered, these are the folks to replace it. Autoglass Plus is the company to call for the least amount of effort or money on your
part. Windshield replacement, door glass, side glass, back glass, your name doesn't even have to
be **BILL BLASS** (or is it Glass) to get your glass replaced. Whether it be at your home or office,
they'll replace the glass and even clean up the mess caused by the mishap. AutoGlass Plus uses
quality replacement parts and sealants to make sure they get the job done right, and their **FREE**
mobile service usually is **JOHNNY**-on-the-spot, within an hour. In most cases, there is no cost to
utilize their service. They do all of the paperwork and receive payment directly from your insurance company for auto glass replacement or repair. Just give them a call to schedule a time and
after they finish, they'll leave you with a written lifetime guarantee. What's not to like about
them? *Call toll-free: 800/518-GLAS*

◆◆◆◆◆◆   Bergman's Paint & Body   **972/247-0925**

2316 Havenhurst   Mon-Fri 8-6; Sat By Appt. Only
Farmers Branch, TX 75234

     Thirty-plus years in the business gives Phil a solid foundation for his six-diamond
rating. Known around town as the Picasso of paint for your cars, trucks, vans or
SUVs, no appointment is necessary, just come on in. But make sure you've made
arrangements for another form of transportation. It could take two-three weeks from start to finish.
Then again, the word "body" also appears in Bergman's name and that spells dents, dings and all
things related to your car's exterior. If you need color matching, replacement of auto glass, frame
or body straightening, fiberglass or plastic repair, here comes the plastic surgeon, without a scal-
pel! Even if you don't have insurance, your vehicle will come through the operation like a champ
without a significant loss to your budget. Whether foreign or **AMERICAN**-born, they can handle
all the imperfections with aplomb. Though you can see them from Stemmons Freeway, it's wise to
call for directions. Every job is priced upon request. FREE estimates on repairs and paint. If Phil's
away, speak with Dalton and tell him the Diva made you do it.

★★★★★★ **CarQuest Auto Parts**   **972/790-4775**

115 S. Belt Line Rd.   Mon-Fri 8-6; Sat 8-3
Irving, TX 75060
www.carquest.com

Your quest for car parts is over. Today, there are over 4,000 stores in North America to connect you to — whatever you need for a moving vehicle. Since 1974, this chain has been the strongest and yet the cheapest link to car parts. As a proud sponsor of the Special Olympics, they deserve your patronage. If something goes bing-bong-gone before its time; simply return it to the store with your receipt within the warranty period and they will exchange the part for free, no questions asked. It's that simple. (The only catch is that you have to bring it back to the exact store you purchased it from as long as you're within a 50-mile radius. If you're farther away, you can bring it to any store, with purchases over $200 needing special approval.) Most parts are available at CarQuest at a fraction of what a dealer would charge you. Everything's computerized, so be patient on the phone or in line. They also can access, just as extensively, remanufactured, rebuilt and new parts for any car, truck, van or SUV. Check directory for the location nearest you. *Call toll-free: 800/492-7278*

◆◆◆◆◆◆ **Christian Brothers Automotive**   **972/691-3700**

1713 Justin Road   Mon-Fri 7-6 (Appt.s accepted)
Flower Mound, TX 75028
www.christianbrothersauto.com

Based on the principles of integrity and adherence to a code of sound moral values, this franchise chain of automotive repair shops has multiple locations around town and lucky for me, there's one up close and personal in Flower Mound. Individual locations are organized into one marketing entity that even have their own radio show on Legends 779 KAAM each Sunday with Jack Bishop and Gary Dodson. Here are two knowledgeable car buffs who answer your questions about the pings and the dings your car has been making lately. The Christian Brothers Auto Care shops are a pretty powerful chain with beautiful garages springing up all over the Metroplex. And what a boom to car owners who don't know the difference between a front wheel and an front alignment. What a pity I have to entrust my trusty shopping mobile to someone else whenever it goes on the blink. Thank goodness, I can trust Christian Brothers Automotive. You can't go wrong. It's your conduit to ASE certified mechanics with a flawless record at the BBB. Whatever's your problem, whether psychological (like is it temperamental?) or suffering from physical abuse, these car doctors can fix it. From wheel alignment to air-conditioning, radiators to transmissions, tires to oil changes, batteries to brakes. Nothing but the latest computer-supported diagnostic and testing equipment is used in their work-ups. Are you in shock over high prices over shocks? Need a new muffler or a brake job? Alignments for most cars run $69.95 (including an oil and filter change) and $24.95 for a lube job (or $19.95 with an online coupon using AMALIE 5W30, name-brand filter, lube and top off fluids). Other locations include: 19020 Midway Road, Carrollton, 972/380-2886; 3790 West Eldorado Parkway, McKinney, 972/542-1900; 9299 Lebanon Rd., Frisco , 972/668-9425; 2059 W. State Highway 114, Grapevine, 817/410-7200; 7780 Rufe Snow, North Richland Hills, 817/485-8900; 718 W. Sublett Rd., Arlington, 817/419-2700; 3213 Naaman School Rd., Garland, 972/575-9000 and 5800 Ave. K, Plano, 972/424-4044. Remember the commandment that thou shalt always take good care of your car(s), and entrust them to only those who promise to do their duty according to the ethical Christian principles, regardless of your religious affiliations. Download special coupons online.

◆◆◆◆ City Garage

475 N. Valley Pkwy.
Lewisville, TX 75067
www.city-garage.com

972/434-4340
Mon-Fri 7-7; Sat 8-5; Sun 9-4

Members of AAA can now show their cards and save some money at any location of City Garage. Two dozen garages in our fair city, and they are still going and towing! They offer free towing if you're within a 10-mile radius, if you allow them to work on your car. If you sign up online, they'll even e-mail maintenance reminders, weekly specials and valuable coupons and discounts. City Garage has FREE pick-up and delivery with an offer for a FREE 30-point inspection. They offer A/C service, belts and hose service, computerized alignment, brake and tire service, electrical service, scheduled maintenance services, oil changes and transmission services. Sunday hours are 9 to 4 (except for the downtown location, which is closed on Sundays). Online coupons, just click and print. 18 locations in the Metroplex.

★★★ Classic BMW Clearance Center

300 N. Central
Richardson, TX 75080
www.classicbmw.com

972/918-1100
Mon-Sat 7:30-5:30

It's full name is Classic BMW Clearance & Trade-in Center (The Clearance Center is actually two blocks east at 415 Greenville Ave.) so if you want a Beemer, here's the place to wheel and deal. No, not a **BEANIE BABY** but a Beemer, Baby. Maybe you'd like to collect them as a hobby? If so, you'll want to pay as low as they'll go. Current deals included a 2001 325 SIT Silver/Gray at $20,736 and a 2000 528I Gray/Black at $28,238. See, it's just like buying a moderately-priced car, but you're getting a **BMW** instead. And that's something to write home about and make your old high school buddies jealous. Looking for one priced even lower? Then how about a '95 BMW 325iS for $15,500 with 24,000 miles? That should do. Maybe buy two. Take advantage of service specials, too, including a wash and vac package of six car washes and vacuum service for $59.95 or get the complete detailing package for $125 (regularly $150). You gotta keep the machine clean, you know, or the car attendant at The Mansion will park yours incognito. How embarrassing. This is the only Clearance and Trade-in Center for new or pre-owned BMWs in **TEXAS**, so check 'em out. Find deals online for service and maintenance as well as monthly BMW car highlights.

◆◆ Comedy Defensive Driving

1701 N. Greenville Ave. Suite 300
Richardson, TX 75081
www.comedydefensivedriving.com

214/333-3674
By Reservation Only

If you want to stay awake while taking a defensive driving course, there are only three ways to make that happen. Coffee. More coffee with a few No-Doz. Or the Comedy Defensive Driving School, in person or online. Taking the course online or via a video from Blockbusters is the easiest way out ($39 a class). Want a good laugh? Go to school instead. Let's face it, you've been a bad girl or boy and the traffic cops caught you. Really, this is no laughing matter! Call the number above to find out the location nearest you. Classes in Arlington, Carrollton, Dallas, Denton, DeSoto, Fort Worth, Garland, Irving, Lewisville, Mesquite, Plano, N. Richland Hills, Tyler/Longview and White Settlement. Now get this. Are you interested in buying a franchise? Send a note to richard@comedydefensivedriving.com and find out what you need to know. The website itself is very informative. Call 877/826-6339 for information on discount specials. For example, if you bring your spouse or partner when you sign-up, they offer a cut rate. ***Call toll-free: 888/596-1911***

cwfreewarrantyquote.com   No Phone Listed

Dallas, TX   24/7

www.cwfreewarrantyquote.com   🖰 *Top Online Store!*

Save 40 to 60 percent on extended car warranties. You betcha! Remember, the minute you drive off the lot, the problem is all yours. Unless, of course, you've bought an extended warranty. But DON'T let them sell you a warranty at the time you're buying the car. It's one of the most expensive and profitable add-ons they can sell you. Save money and get that warranty after the fact. Run home and go online. You'll see the difference immediately. Isn't it the truth? Don't car troubles happen at the worst possible times? When you least expect it or when you can least afford it. Protect yourself with a quality extended warranty for your car, truck, van or SUV. Semi's and school buses are not their bailiwick. But with a regular vehicle, don't let a huge repair bill hit you unprotected. These warranties will cover most vehicles with less than 150,000 miles. You will save hundreds of dollars over the dealers' warranties, trust me. Expect prompt, toll-free claims and the plan also includes 24-Hour Roadside Assistance, a car rental benefit, a trip interruption benefit, extended towing benefits — what do you have to lose? Get a free quote online and make a note call for a fast, FREE quote!

★★★   CycleSmart   972/712-0712

6427 Main St.   Tues-Fri 10-6; Sat 10-4
Frisco, TX 75034

Are you **CYCLE** dumb? If you are, get some lessons from CycleSmart, where motorcycles and other bikes of the same persuasion are taken on consignment. You'll be buying a used bike, but saving some money in the process. Bring your bike down for a closer inspection and see the full spectrum of name brands like **BMW, HARLEY-DAVIDSON, HONDA, KAWASAKI, MOTO GUZZI, SUZUKI, YAMAHA** and others. With street and touring bikes (as opposed to dirt or ATVs), this company can propel you to greater heights at lower prices. So, if your bike is taking up space in your garage, or you want to trade it in so you can trade up, get going, you Wheelie Dan, you. New and used parts and accessories, too, are either in-stock or special-ordered. Bob Sutton's one of the men on the scene; the other is a full-time seasoned mechanic/racer. Between the two of them, they will show you the *Blue Book* value of your bike. You must be willing to sell it below the Blue Book price, or they will recommend you sell it in one of the trader magazines. On average, they negotiate 10 percent for themselves for their efforts. On the way out, we noticed a '99 **HARLEY-DAVIDSON** Sportster for $9,995 and we almost weakened. But we thought twice. Driving to the Zodiac Room at Neiman's to do a speech for Les Femmes du Mond in my wig on a motorcycle would have created a serious driving hazard, don't you think?

★★★★★   Dallas Can! Academy (Downtown)   214/824-4226

2601 Live Oak   Every Sat Morning; Special Auctions Last Sat/Monthly
Dallas, TX 75204
www.dallascan.org

If Dallas Can!, so can Fort Worth (817/444-5437). Every Saturday, auctions are conducted to raise money to help "at-risk" students, ages 16-21, achieve a high school education and become a productive member of society. (A special auction is held the last Saturday of the month.) Your donations help create this sale and your purchases put money in their coffers and tax credits in your pocket. Sales include regular and antique cars, boats, RVs, motorcycles, riding lawn mowers, large box cars, golf carts and various other equipment. Dallas auctions open at 8 AM and start at 9 AM and are held at the location above. Fort Worth auctions open at noon and start at 1 PM. Each auction is open to the public and requires a $200 cash deposit and a current driver's license. The Academy has three locations, all of which are located on or near a Dallas Area Rapid Transit system route. The other locations, beside Fort Worth, include Dallas Can! Academy (Oak Cliff), 325 W. 12th Street, Suite LL, Dallas, Texas 75208, 214/ 943-2244 and Dallas Can! Academy Families For Learning, 325 W. 12th St., Dallas, Texas 75208, 214/943-6073.

◆◆◆◆◆ Dent Doctor   972/434-2254

808 E. Hwy. 121
Lewisville, TX 75057
www.dentdoctorusa.com

Mon-Fri 9-6; Sat 9-2

Since 1986, The Dent Doctor has been like a chiropractor for my car. On call and ready to take care of those dings and dents, they were the pioneers of this industry by introducing painless dent repairs! Just quick repairs including hail damage is their specialty. Dents and door dings, without painting done in one day (though appointments are necessary.) And now, they have a truck accessory store with bed rails, bed mats, bumpers, hitches, tool boxes, running boards, vent shades, and they can spray a bedliner protection coating like **PERM-TECH** to keep your truck looking really cool. If you're interested in a franchise, call them at their 800#. If not, check directory for other Dent Doctors in your area. *Call toll-free: 800/946-3368*

Direct Service Contracts   800/324-3559

7641 E. Gray Road, Suite A-2
Scottsdale, AZ 85260

24/7

www.directservicecontracts.com ⌕ *Top Online Store!*

Don't buy extended warranties, if you're inclined to do so, on site. Wait and think it over first. Then buy online and save up to 60 percent. This is a place where you can save that much, all online, by answering a few questions and then clicking for a free quote. Direct warranties are available for new, near-new or used vehicles and the amount you save will probably equal at least a few payments a year. Since 1975, this company has been selling service contracts, as well as handling administrative claims. They also have been involved in the automobile liability insurance business and their volume speaks for itself; they've sold over $100,000,000 in service contracts. Furthermore, customers had to see REAL savings up to 60 percent, or it wouldn't click. Their ability to offer immediate coverage, with a small down payment, and provide zero financing over 10 months, on the balance of the contract is a real win-win for everyone concerned. Try it!

★★★★★★ Discount Tire Co.   817/571-2341

3233 Harwood Rd.
Bedford, TX 76021
www.discounttire.com

Mon-Fri 8:30-6; Sat 8:30-5

 America's largest independent tire company with over 450 locations in 16 states is a fact. But what they don't tell you is that they're also the best. Customers sing their praises and so do we. While their wheels go 'round and 'round, their "fix your flat FREE" policy is just one reason customers are so loyal. You'll save 25 to 40 percent on all tires. The lineup of makes and models of tires include: **ARIZONIAN, BF GOODRICH, CENTENNIAL, CONTINENTAL, DUNLOP, GENERAL, GOODYEAR** and **YOKOHAMA**. Custom wheels from **AMERICAN EAGLE, FITTIPALDI, ROH** and many others are available, too. Special orders, no problem. Their free fix flats policy still boggles our mind. Every year, Discount Tires is voted the best when it comes to new tires. Used tires, too, are part of their inventory, some as low as $5.

Ninety days same as cash. Check directory for one of the 20 locations in the Metroplex. Search online for inventory and sign up for their FREE tire newsletter.

Fred's Foreign Car Service   214/350-6787
5915 Peeler St.   Mon-Thu 7:30-6; Fri 7:30-5
Dallas, TX 75235
www.dwfnetmall.com/freds

 If your car's started to sputter in another language, it's time to take it to Fred. Although the website was not working during our research time, he was. Busy as usual, working on some fine European mobile machines such as **BMW, FERRARI, JAGUAR, MERCEDES, PORSCHE, RANGE ROVER** and **VOLVO**, he can afford to discriminate and refuses to work on American-made vehicles. Hey, this is America! Here's some assurances: At Fred's, they will not remove and replace items until they determine the problem. They want to find the cause of the problem and fix it, instead of treating symptoms at your expense. Ultimately, that will save you money. Though not cheap by any stretch of the imagination, they're right the first time under the hood. Regardless of the repair, Fred takes it upon himself to treat each and every car as a patient, and he'll fix it, no matter what. It's like an ER room for your precious children, only these come with four wheels and a horn. Calling all foreign bodies!

◆◆◆◆   Holloways   214/823-5888
4221 Ross Ave.   Mon-Fri 9-3; Sat 10-2
Dallas, TX 75204-5199

Don't want to be ripped off if your car or boat has a rip in the seat? Then don't. Don't even shed alligator tears just for a little tea and sympathy because here's your remedy. Ask for Ronnie, as he's the expert. He'll come to your location, if it's not too far (and Carrollton was OK from his shop on Ross). Or, you can bring the car or boat to him. No charge for estimates and they're very accommodating about setting an appointment around your schedule. They can really sew it up right. Reupholstering seats for a bass boat would cost approximately $24 a yard for Naugahyde and $28 a yard for Argonaut, a marine canvas. Each of the captains chairs would be about $150 in labor and take about three yards a seat. So for two bass fishing seats and two captains chairs, a rough estimate would be about $300 in materials and $500 in labor. Whoever said fishing was a cheap sport hasn't been fishing or maintaining a boat lately! Sorry to deflate your spirits but that's the way it is. The price would go up more if you chose a more expensive fabric or if the seats needed reconstruction with new plywood. But if ever there was an easier guy to work with, we haven't found him. He prefers to leave the shop by 3 PM. to avoid that downtown rush, but he's definitely flexible, especially if he comes to your location. Sew, what are you waiting for? Don't forget, he also works on car upholstery and he's good, very very good.

★★★★★★   Hub Cap Annie   972/669-9898
11648 N. Central Expressway, #B   Mon-Fri 9-6:30; Sat 9-4
Dallas, TX 75243-3840
www.hubcapannie.com

 Laurie had a better idea when it came to Hub Cap Annie. She suggested if you can't find a hub cap that matches the other three, why not buy two that are similar? Put two on one side and two on the other. No one will ever know the difference, since you can't look at both sides of the car at the same time, now can you? Boy, what a brilliant idea and something most folks have not ever considered. A set of four rims started as low as $30 but can go as high as $70, depending on the vehicle. They also carry rims starting around $10 to $15 each. Chances are, nobody beats their prices. On their web-site, you can enter the make, model and special information on wheel covers or hubcaps that you're looking for and if they've got it, you'll get it. So if your hubcaps are looking like Orphan Annie's, here you can choose from lots and lots of used wheel covers and hubcaps, including some original equipment that might even be considered an heirloom. Go north on Central, exit Royal Lane and stay on the service road. It's one mile down the road and your absolute best source for hubba-hubba hubcaps. Didn't meet Annie, but Jerry sure was helpful.

★★★   Lewisville Auto Auction   972/434-2020

1836 Midway   Mon-Fri 9-4:30; Closed Wed (dealers day)
Lewisville, TX 75056

You don't need a brother-in-law in the business to get it for you wholesale. Now, you, too, can shop for cars just like the dealers do....only they shop on Wednesdays and you don't! Unless you know what you're doing, you buy the car "as is," but they do allow you to drive the car around the lot giving you a hint of things to come. You can also bring your mechanic (or a service like AutoCritic). If you like it, they will call the car's owner (if it's on consignment) and if they like your offer, the car's yours. Though there weren't many cars we deemed acceptable, you never know what will be coming in next. Most seemed like jalopies, but you will have the "pick of the lot." Other cars come from area banks, credit unions and dealerships whose cars have been repos-sessed, but who cares from whence they came? Both foreign and domestic models, from 1980 and up, were spotted. During their occasional live auctions, registration fee was $10. Otherwise, you can shop the other days at your leisure. When buying any mechanical apparatus, be as thorough as you can because we always say, "Buyers Beware!"

◆◆◆◆◆   Line-X   817/268-4045

1501-B W. Hurst Blvd.   Mon-Fri 8-5; Sat 9-4 (extended hours By Appt.)
Hurst, TX 76053

www.linexfortworth.com

If you're a truck lover, line up here. At Line-X, they specialize in spray elastomers, polyurethanes and polyureas. Now that may not mean much to the average truck owner, but these folks know their bed liners. They've conducted many years of actual field testing and each location has its own specialized equipment, combined with the right kinds of materials and product knowledge to produce this sprayable elastomeric coating for your truck. How does $419 for a Ford F150 with a short bed sound? Line-X is the recognized leader in this industry. They were the first to implement a successful high temperature/high pressure elastomeric bedliner. They were the first to go nation-wide with a spray-on truck bedliner and protective coating franchise. You will also read about them in most major truck publications like *Motor Trend* and *Trucking*. In fact, the more you read about them, the more you recognize how important they've been to the trucking business. They've even been featured on Sixty Minutes II, as they were the first to apply a non-skid pure polyurea onboard a U.S. Navy Submarine. Line-X is sprayed on truck bedliners and was rated No. 1 in cus-tomer satisfaction.

★★★★★★ McClain's RV Superstores

I-35 E., Exit 460   Mon-Fri 9-7; Sat 9-5
Lake Dallas, TX 76205
www.mcclainsrv.com

 Did you know that car dealers have to post the MSRP price (manufacturer's suggested retail price), but RV dealers do not? Yet, McClain's always posts the price to show you they don't inflate their prices and then take a mark-down. These folks sell them for less! No doubt, this is the easy way to hitting the road, Jack, and don't ya come back 'til you're ready to trade-er in. Save thousands of dollars on the best brands in recreational vehicles. They will also make you a trade-in offer good for seven days that you can't refuse. Customers of McClain's can take advantage of their "Customer Care Program" which includes emergency roadside assistance and appointments for service in other areas. As part of your first year's service, they offer FREE trip routing and maps delivered to your door, FREE jump starts and FREE tire changes, fuel delivery and lock-out service with every RV purchased from them. After that first year, it'll cost you around $150 to maintain this kind of yearly service plan. There are three locations to check out, Lake Dallas above, Fort Worth and Oklahoma City. *Call toll-free: 800/ 497-3586*

★★★★★ Motor Home Specialist   **817/790-7771**

5611 S. I-35W @ Exit 26   Mon-Fri 9-6; Sat 9-5
Alvarado, TX 76009
www.MotorHomeSpecialist.com

Just south of Fort Worth on I-35W, take exit 26, because just like **FORD**, these folks have a better idea. With low interest rates, baby boomers considering retirement and the need for low-cost housing, shoppers are flocking to these pre-owned motor homes as the most economical way to hit the road. Wanderlusts can shop for over $3 million worth of them only 20 miles south of the Metroplex. Family-owned and operated, only late-model motor homes are available. Prices are great. All their motor homes are kept in climate controlled storage for your viewing comfort. See what's online....from a 1997 **WINNEBAGO** Luxor for $89,000 to a 2000 Navigator 43'Double Slide with only 18,000 miles for $210,000. Give it a look-see. Then pay cash for 1998-2002 Class "A" gas or diesel **ALLEGRO, BOUNDER, MONACO, NEWMAR, SOUTHWIND, PACE ARROW, WINNEBAGO** and others. You can consign yours to sell, store or trade. Just understand, They are "NOT an RV park." They store or consign RVs only. For example, a 1999 TRADEWINDS was $95,000, a 2001 AMERICAN EAGLE 40'Double Slide with only 22,000 miles was $185,000. *Call toll-free: 800/335-6054*

★★ National Tire & Battery (NTB)   **972/387-7966**

14107 Inwood   Mon-Fri 7:30-8; Sat 8-6; Sun 10-5
Farmers Branch, TX 75244
www.ntb.com

This **SEARS**-owned tire and battery chain used to be called National Tire Warehouse, but now it's **NTB**, National Tire & Battery. But even a name change doesn't mean you can forget from whence they came. Offering good prices on tires, even custom wheels, including **AMERICAN RACING, MONTEGI, PRIME, TSW, Z RACING** and more, we got a quote by phone and even a recommendation. They offer a price match guarantee and that's a very good thing. Offering a full range of motion, you'll find tires by **BF GOODRICH, BRIDGESTONE, PIRELLI, UNIROYAL, YOKOHAMA**, plus their own NTB house brand. They will rotate and fix your flats for free (if you buy the $9 lifetime package). A set of four **BF GOODRICH** tires would run anywhere from $51 to $89 per tire. Check your newspaper for current sale prices, as the deals fluctuate as often as the tires rotate. Senior citizens can expect a five percent discount along with other amenities. Other repair work such as alignments, brakes and **DIEHARD** batteries (guess who owns them?) are also available. Check directory for multiple locations throughout the Metroplex.

◆◆◆◆◆   **PDR Linx**   **972/410-1616**
15610 Midway   By Appt. Only
Addison, TX 75001
www.pdrlinx.com

When it rains cats and dogs and hail stones are as big as golf balls, it's time to call in the troops at PDR Technicians. Certified Painless Dent Repair Technicians, that is, can enter the fray and transform those dents with a smooth operation. Stop the bleeding and call on one of the seven convenient locations. Enjoy the luxury of a free rental car, if yours is out of commission, with same day service (in most cases). And, yes, most insurance carriers cover these services. These guys have been getting the dents out for lucky Metroplex cars for the past 13 years. Given that they offer a lifetime warranty, why not call for an immediate, on-the-spot quote? They are even the preferred performers by the insurance industry for the repair of small dents and hail damage. Now I finally realized that PDR stands for Painless Dent Professionals. And since they've created an alliance with Paintless Dent Professionals throughout the country, you can say they've gone national.

★   **Pep Boys**   **972/242-3136**
1455 W. Trinity Mills   Mon-Fri 8-8; Sat 8-7; Sun 9-6
Carrollton, TX 75006
www.pepboys.com

Let's be Frank. I'm not the biggest fan of Manny, Moe or Jack. Any time I've taken my car to their shop, their technicians act more like the Three Stooges. More nonchalant than most in a service department and less competent in their technical agility. That's what I think. However, they do have some redeeming graces. If you have their Pep Boys CarOne Card, you'll get 90 days same as cash on all purchases, including services over $150. It also includes emergency roadside assistance, including jump starts, towing (up to 25 miles), tire changes (with your inflated spare), fluid replacement (but fluids are not covered) and lock-out service. They sell name-brand tires like **BRIDGESTONE**, **GOODYEAR** and **MICHELIN**, as well as all the major brands of air, oil and fuel filters, spark plugs, headlights and waxes. Many locations also have HERTZ car rentals on site. The cashier lines are still bumper-to-bumper at any of their 24 Metroplex locations. Claiming only ASE-certified techs, utilizing state-of-the-art computer diagnostic equipment and practically 'round the clock service is available from routine maintenance to major repairs, give them a try. Their Pet Boys' Express Service, with no appointment needed for battery, headlights or wiper blades replacement. ***Call toll-free: 800/737-2697***

★★★★★   **Radiator Express Warehouse**   **800/252-1313**
320 South Belt Line Rd., #112   Mon-Fri 7-5:30; Sat 9-4
Irving, TX 75060
www.radiator.com

They've got Ste-e-a-m heat! Calm down and express yourself. Don't fume and get hot under the collar, or hood. If you're steaming mad about a radiator that just doesn't seem to hold water, then make a U-turn to the Radiator Express Warehouse. With over 20 years in the business, over

20,000 radiators and AC condensers in stock, this is the place to radiate. Then have it shipped directly to you or to your mechanic to install. All new radiators come with a lifetime warranty. Brands include **AC DELCO**, **MODINE**, **VALEO**, **VISTEON** and more. Their low price guarantee means that not only will they meet a lower price but they will beat it by 10 percent and you'll have up to 30 days after your purchase to take them up on this offer. How about the right fit and quality? If there's a problem, they'll replace your radiator for as long as you own the vehicle. FREE overnight delivery when you order online. Now do you know why we consider them primo, primo? *Call toll-free: 800/RADIATOR*

★★★★★ Randall Noe Auto Group   214/869-4886

1608 W. Moore Ave   Mon-Fri 8-7; Sat 8-6 (Sales); Mon-Fri 7:30-6; Sat 8-1 (Service)
Terrell, TX 75160-2308
www.randallnoe.com

Go online and view the Deal of the Day, if you don't want to drive to Terrell. No one's going to stop you from driving east for the deals that are easy to stop for at the intersections of Business Highway 80 and Highway 205. But if you can hop online, it's safer and quicker. Put your research to good use. For Randall Noe, deals are nothing new since he's been wheeling and dealing for a long time. You can search their inventory without leaving home or pounding the pavement just to find that perfect make and model. They also have a location in Kaufman at 825 E. Fair Street. By keeping out of the big cities, Randall Noe has created one of the most successful car dealerships in the Metroplex. In 2001, they were the No. 2 **DODGE-CHRYSLER-JEEP** dealer in the world. His store in Kaufman sells **CHEVROLETS**, **PONTIACS** and **OLDSMOBILES**. But it's his online shop that I find most appealing in my "spare" time. They focus on low prices and quality service, and their building, land and dealership are all paid for so that they can keep car prices down. They will beat any deal. Period! Additional hours for parts, Monday-Friday 7:30 to 6, Saturday 8 to 1, and the body shop is open Monday-Friday 7:30 to 6, but closed on Saturday. If you're looking to buy online, ask for Craig Baker, the Internet manager at the number above.

◆◆◆◆◆◆ Repairs Unlimited   972/436-0320

124 N. Mill   Mon-Fri 7:30-6; Sat 7:30-Noon
Lewisville, TX 75057-3936

 Want to pamper your **PORSCHE**, massage your **MERCEDES**, caress your **CHEVROLET** or jumpstart your **JAGUAR**? Then take thee to these repair magicians who can handle your repairs in a Jiffy. After more than 21 years at the same location, they've got the nuts and bolts of the repair business down pat. They do preventative maintenance, computer diagnostics, tune-ups, alignments, brakes, shocks, struts, emission repairs, heating and A/C service. All are ASE certified mechanics and all work is guaranteed by this family-owned and operated service center. Be sure to tell them the Diva (Josh's mother and Bob's wife) sent you. We've been there enough times to have our radar detector on speed-dial.

★★★ Richardson Motor Sports   972/231-4833

408 S. Central Expressway   Mon-Fri 8:30-6; Sat 8:30-5
Richardson, TX 75080-6125
www.richardsonmotorsports.com

V-rooom! V-rooom! Ah, the sound of the motorcycle is magic to a biker's ear. Interested in a motor sport? Then Richardson may be your manna for motorbikes, cycles, dirt bikes, ATVs (all-terrain vehicles). I have "spoken" highly of them since 1987 when the revolution began and never tire of cycling their praises. Over and over again, this is an expensive hobby, so you'll want to extract the most bang for your buck. Let's do a four-Wheelie: Brands include **BIG BEAR, GRIZ-ZLIES, KODIAK** and **YAMAHA**. They are also an authorized dealer for **POLARIS, SEA DOO** and **YAMAHA**, which tells you they also offer personal watercraft and sport boats, too. But it's what's not new that should covet your attention as it's where the buys are. Check out their large inventory of used equipment to see what I mean. *Call toll-free: 888/529-0112*

◆◆◆◆   Self Sell Auto Sales   972/219-1803

1035 S. Mill St.   Mon-Fri 8:30-6; Sat 8:30-6
Lewisville, TX 75067

FORD may have had a better idea, but Self Sell may have an even better one when it comes to selling your **FORD**. For a flat fee of $50 a month to keep your car on their lot, why risk having some pervert coming to your house at all hours of the night just to take a look? Take the risk, as well as the hassle, out of selling your car yourself. Let Self Sell sell it for you. Figure how much you want for it; then add on their fee for the negotiations and all the other elements to make that sale happen. They usually charge a minimum of $300 for themselves. They offer buyers a warranty on cars. Choose from a variety of cars with several financing options if you're the buyer. But consider trading in your car, too. They will even pay you what you want for your car, if you trade it in, as long as it's reasonable. Expect your car to sell in 30 days, the average selling time. For your monthly fee, they show it, handle all negotiations, advertise it in the local papers, offer multiple in-house financing options. But here's the reality check; If they think your car's unsuitable to sell, they tell you right up front!

★★★   Southwest Ford   817/596-5700

3001 Fort Worth Hwy.   Mon-Fri 9-7; Sat 9-6
Weatherford, TX 76087
www.southwestford.com

Whether you're shopping for cars or not, you've got to hear this. Head to Weatherford, where the living and shopping is easy. Look for the blue and gray building, home to Southwest Ford. Exit 414 from I-20, then go past the first red light. (Look for it about half a mile on your right.) New cars, of course, but they also have used cars and rentals. That's a new one. In case you need wheels for a special occasion, trip or family event, here's a place to rent one. Or maybe you want to haul some stuff and need a truck? Or maybe you just need a temporary replacement due to an accident or service/body work? Special rates available for daily, weekly, or weekend rentals. Used cars are listed on their web page and separated by price. Take a look at their website to view the current inventory before you make the long drive. They also have cornered the market on **TOYOTAS, JEEPS** and **EAGLES**. Stop at the first light to take a look at Southwest **TOYOTA JEEP EAGLE**, too. Looks like they've taken Weatherford by storm! And check out their website for current specials. Know before you go how much dough you're going to sow.

SUV Supply

Dallas, TX   24/7
www.suvsupply.com   🖱 *Top Online Store!*

If you've got a truck, a car or an SUV and are looking for a **HUSKY LINER**, have they got a deal for you. Find floor liners, cargo liners, floor mats, mud guards, contractors racks, tailgates, ladder racks, sunshades, dash systems and many other automotive products to keep your vehicle looking new and cool. Looking for an attractive flo-thru tailgate with a new black powder-coated or bright-dipped anodized aluminum finish that won't rust or corrode if scratched and available in a fifth-wheel style or straight-style? Here's your supplier. In fact, there isn't much for that fifth-wheeler that you can't find under the banner of this one-stop SUV Supply. Expect many to be easy-on and easy-off mounting, like an original tailgate on new truck models. Or maybe you prefer new OEM style rotary latches? Pick your model and shop away: **CHEVY, DODGE, FORD, GMC** brands available. I couldn't find a decent supplier with great prices, so I had to resort to the internet. If I've missed a great one, let me have it! For another good online source for liners online, go to www.ajusa.com. FREE shipping, discount prices and no tax. Neat, eh? *Call toll-free: 877/891-7665*

★★★★★★ Texas Cars Direct   972/243-3400

Mon-Fri 10-6

2718 Forest Lane
Dallas, TX 75234
www.texascarsdirect.com

It's official. Finally, Texas Mustang Sales has changed their name to better describe who and what they are. At last, since I've had to tell listeners for years that Pete does not sell Mustangs. But if a **JAGUAR** is on your list of dream cars, why not consider a late-model pre-owned car and drive off their warehouse lot as evidence of living the good life at the best prices in town. Since 1981, Pete and the guys have been at your service. Located on Forest Lane in an industrial showroom/warehouse, this is the way to buy cars. There are no salesmen to follow you around while you're looking. View the numbers in the ID number column, which are the last four digits of the Vehicle Identification Number (VIN). Once you have the VIN #, you can log on to www.carfax.com and get the lowdown on that car's history. With the VIN #, you'll also be able to secure bank financing on site, by fax, phone, or now online. Bumper-to-bumper extended warranties on most vehicles up to 100,000 miles are available. Trade-ins are welcome. Besides JAGUAR, see late model **MERCEDES, LAND ROVERS, CADILLACS** and **LINCOLNS**. They are local to the Dallas area but can ship nationwide. For shipping, contact Glenn Poe at 800/240-2101, or e-mail him at glenn@lonestarautotransport.com for more information. They are probably the largest dealer of used JAGS in the country. For Pete's sake, keep him the busiest dealer in town (I bet the JAG dealers in town hate him as much as we love him.)

★★★★★ Tire Factory Outlet   817/735-8061

Mon-Fri 8-6; Sat 8:30-3

3021 Alta Mere
Fort Worth, TX 76116
www.google.com

Where have all the online coupons gone? Gone to pasture, I presume. For over 25 years, Tarrant County drivers have supported the concept of saving money and shopping at this tire outlet. Since 1975, although they've been long-standing discounters, they've never sacrificed quality of service. They have a flawless record of service and performance. They offer a full line of competitively priced **BF GOODRICH, MICHELIN** and **UNIROYAL** passenger, performance and light truck brand tires. When you buy a tire from them, the price includes **FREE** mounting. They also offer alignments, front end service, shocks/struts, wheel balancing, oil changes, air conditioning repair, batteries, tune-ups and more, including state inspections. Other locations at 1901 West Berry, Fort Worth, 817/924-9191; 3300 Mansfield Hwy., Forrest Hill, 817/534-4964; 6516 McCart Ave. Fort Worth, 817/292-0957; 1441 N. Plaza Drive, Granbury, 817/579-1210; plus other cities throughout Texas like San Marcos, Seguin, Lockhart, Graham and Tyler.

★★★★ Vehicles-in-Motion

972/242-BIKE
Mon-Fri 9-5

1000 W. Crosby, Suite 100
Carrollton, TX 75006
www.v-i-m.com

For the true Biker Babe who coos over a good deal, here is where to go to rev one up on a **HAR-LEY**, **HONDA**, **KAWASAKI**, **SUZUKI**, **YAMAHA** and more. Hundreds of them go on the auction block: repossessed motorcycles, all-terrain bikes, personal watercraft and more. Bid for a bargain and cruise out on a **NIGHTHAWK**, **REBEL**, **VIRAGO** or **VULCAN**. Take a tour on a **GOLD-WING**, **VALKYRIES** or **VOYAGER**. Public inspections are the day before the sale. Call or check their website for times. Public buyers (non-dealers) must give a $500 cash deposit plus $25 bidder's fee. Cash deposits are refundable, if no purchase is made. Also, there's a $25 buyer's fee for dealers to bid, as well. Payment is due in full on the day of the sale. You don't think you can just ride off into the sunset and get away with a new bike without robbing Peter to pay Paul, do you? Arrangements and assistance for overseas containerization and travel are available upon request. Trip the bike's fantastic and watch them roll out of there: sport bikes, dirt bikes, ATV's, snowmobiles, golf carts and more. Call or go online for times and dates. Dealers must register online or call the toll-free 800 number above. There are closing fees based on the percentage of the sale. Review the website so you are familiar with all the rules and be sure you're up on all the necessary regulations for sales tax and use permit if you are a dealer. Then, hit the road, Jack. *Call toll-free: 800/292-7376*

warrantybynet.com

393 Mantoloking Road
Brick, NJ 08723

24/7

www.warrantybynet.com 🖱 *Top Online Store!*

Get a **FREE** quote online at the most well-known warranty service company for cars, trucks, SUVs and motorcycles (and more). Available in all states but California, they've been in business since 1994 and are backed by Heritage Warranty Mutual Insurance, RRG, Inc., and their Re-insurer is American Re-Insurance Company which is rated **A+**. They have a good record with the Better Business Bureau and their contract is available for review online before you even sign up. Vehicles with up to 79,999 miles through 105,000 miles are even coverable. This company is probably the best-known extended warranty dealer on the web because they currently provide warranty services for Kelly Blue Book and Auto Trader. So, why not you, too? With an extended warranty, enjoy more than peace of mind and ongoing owner satisfaction. With a variety of plans to safeguard your most valuable assets, from cars and other motor vehicles to computers, electronics, appliances and more. Don't be left out in the cold when the appliance you bought goes kaput. With an extended warranty, you will be able to get it up and running in no time and little or no cost to you. What about that large screen TV? Camcorder? Expensive **HASSELBLAD** camera? Cell phone? See what I mean? Get thee to a warranty! And now offering a FREE credit report, auto financing and a record summary, all online. *Call toll-free: 877/239-8363*

China & Crystal

Cooking.com

800/663-8810 (ORDERS)
2859 Ocean Park Blvd., Suite 310   24/7
Santa Monica, CA

www.cooking.com   ⌁ *Top Online Store!*

Not always the lowest price, but always a discounted price and the best selection when the cooks are looking to cook up a storm, they call this site "dy-no-mite!" You'll have a blast shopping for the best selection of china and flatware, whether for gift-giving or personal use (and you know how I am when it comes to prices). The brands are so Epicurean. Serve on the following: BIA CORDON BLEU, BORMIOLI, CHANTAL, CORELLE, DUROBOS, EMILE HENRY, HENCKELS, JK ADAMS, JOYCE CHEN, LE CREUSET, PFALTZGRAFF, SNOW RIVER, HOMER LAUGHLIN CO., TREE SPIRIT and others. Anything you need for your table top and cooktop, is here from Asian tableware to Wooden Salad Bowls and everything in between. Coffee and tea, accessories, dessert dishes, specialty plates, dinnerware, drinkware, flatware, glasses, pasta bowls, serving pieces, specialty serveware and even software to create your own dinner invitations. Expect to fulfill everything on your menu. No ingredient is missing. It's one of the best sites for everything you would need to be the Complete Gourmet. Dinner is served, mum. And mum's the word here. *Call toll-free: 877/999-2433*

★★★★   Dansk Factory Outlet

972/678-2905
820 West Stacy Rd, Ste 400   Mon-Sat 10-9; Sun 12-6
Allen, TX 75013
www.dansk.com

Two popular plate/glass names pop up at the Allen Premium Outlet Center and now we can enjoy saving and saying grace, whichever's your pleasure. Amen! Save the day with DANSK and LENOX's factory outlets with seconds, overstocks, discontinued patterns and limited editions of these two long-time favorites. Make me a match. Many matched sets, or mix 'n match, as both brands blend together effortlessly. More than 40 years ago, an engineer and his wife traveled to Copenhagen, Denmark and fell in love with a hand-forged fork, spoon and knife with teakwood handles that were named the winner of a design competition. That combination of teak and forged steel became the foundation for the successful launch of the DANSK company line. The rest is history. DANSK was born out of the combination of elegance and simplicity, rather than a revolutionary look in the '50s. LENOX is even older. Since 1889, they have been manufacturing china, crystal, serving pieces, flatware, gift items, wedding gifts, collectibles and more. Expect to save 20 to 50 percent at the outlet with an occasional price that will crack you up — up to 80-90 percent off any cracked piece that will still perform its original function. Both lines are coveted by brides-to-be on their Registries, so the least you can do is indulge them for less. Or if there's no bride in site, treat yourself to their wonderful pastel, delicate and elegant table dressing. At least you're not paying full price for filling your plate-full. Get stuffed without having to put your budget on a diet.

★★★★★   Dishes from the Past   817/737-6390

3701 Lovell Ave.
Fort Worth, TX 76107
www.dishesfromthepast.com

Mon-Sat 10-5

Looking for the perfect "Dish Fulfillment?" Then call on Dishes from the Past — the menu for a perfect repast. Feast on an entire collection displayed in their 6,000-square-foot store, if you're looking to buy china or crystal. This company not only replaces broken or missing pieces, they offer a bridal registry, and a table is already set up for mixing and matching the different patterns, or designing wall arrangements. What a novel idea. Owners Jennifer Marcell and Ida May Fleet know the difference between a gravy boat and a tureen, from **SPOKE** to **WEDGWOOD**, and every blue-plate special in between. If they don't have the piece you are looking for, they put out an APB (All Points Bulletin) for the lost or missing parts and add your request to their database. Then, when they locate it, they will call you for pick-up. These kinds of pick-ups are safe and secure. You needn't worry you're walking on the wild side. C'est la vie. If you want to complete a set and one plate is missing, then the detectives here will initiate the hunt. *Call toll-free: 800/ 984-8801*

LuxuryCrystal.com   949/470-4558

24461 Ridge Route Dr.
Laguna Hills, CA 92653
www.LuxuryCrystal.com   *Top Online Store!*

24/7

Saving 27 percent on the **BACCARAT** crystal may not send shockwaves through Hollywood (because they already know about this Laguna Hills discounter), but the rest of the world is still in the Dark Ages. So ping when the zing in your heart rings with the news about this site for saving on the entire **BACCARAT** line. Yes, every last item is discounted: vases, the famous animals, desk accessories, decorative items, jewelry, lighting, stem & barware, tableware, figurines, bowls — I'm mean every last item in their collection is discounted 27 percent. Everything's current and legit. No replicas, ever. Other discounters may have discontinued items or items strickly that are closeouts or irregulars. But not at Luxury Crystal. And no, the "Diva" line and I are not related I'm sorry to report. Everything comes in its original boxes, serial numbers (where applicable), etc. and warranties. To get an even lower price of a 3-5 percent savings is to pay by Wire Transfer. And of course, they will meet or beat any legitimate offers. With the high quality of **BACCARAT** comes the high prices. For example, a **BACCARAT** "Diane" vase, 9 7/8 inches high retails for $795.00/their price $580.00. That's a savings of $215.00. even though that reflects only a 27 percent discount. It does add up. The "Diva" vase, 19 1/2 inches long retails for $2,495.00 but here it's $1,821.00 . Your savings equaled $674.00 and that's not chopped liver. This vase lays on its side, is very contemporary and most usual — just like me. I did succumb to the **BACCARAT** gold cabachon ring for $156.00 and my husband saved $59. He was happy I saved him so much money.

★★★★ **Mikasa Factory Store**   **972/881-0019**

6100 Ave. K, Suite 100   Mon-Wed 10-6; Thurs-Sat 10-9; Sun Noon-6
Plano, TX 75074
www.mikasa.com

It's hip to be square and square dishes are in, just ask any savvy shopper who's been to Mikasa's Factory Store lately. In fact, they offered six new styles in square dishes alone. Dish it out and enjoy the savings. Step right up, ladies and gentlemen, and head to the back for even bigger, better bargains. If you dawdle, you'll lose out on those deals as they'll expire before you've even worked up a sweat. Strike fast if you want to gratify your every wishful gift giving. The same patterns you see in department and specialty stores are at their factory store for 30 percent off and more. Registries are even available online. It's a cinch to shop with ease and in an extravagant environment, though if truth be known, they're discounting every step of the way. Test the "ping" at Grapevine Mills, Tanger Outlet Center in Terrell, Prime Outlets in Gainesville and in Hillsboro. During clearance sales, it's possible to retrieve placemats for 99 cents from the pile that once retailed for $3.49, stemware for $2.99 instead of $11, casual fine china service for four for $39.99 instead of $290 and bone china service for four for $79.99 instead of $460. It pays to wait it out — until the sales begin. *Call toll-free: 800/833-4681*

◆◆◆ **Norma Baker Antiques**   **817/335-1152**

3311 W. 7th St.   Mon-Sat 10-5
Fort Worth, TX 76107

Dress to impress....your table, that is. If your flatware is looking a little flat and your crystal just doesn't have that ping, head to Norma Baker, the lady with a lot of "glass". Shine up any meal with new flatware, or just replace all those missing in action. Top it off with some eye-catching antiques such as a dining room suite and then invite the entire neighborhood in for tea. Accrue an entire tea set by filling in all those missing cups so all you need are the crumpets. If you can't find what you're looking for, Norma Baker will start the search for a small finder's fee. Take advantage of **FREE** wedding gift-wrap and the bridal registry when it comes time to bestow a gift upon the most happy couples. Prices, though, are not their priority. Service is. *Call toll-free: 800/742-1107*

★★★★★ **Oneida Factory Store**   **254/582-7449**

104 Interstate Highway 35, N.E. Suite 122   Mon-Sat 10-8; Sun 11-6
Hillsboro, TX 76645
www.oneida.com

Interesting facts about **ONEIDA**. First, they are the largest manufacturer of stainless steel and silver-plated flatware in the world. Secondly, they started in Oneida, New York during the 1840s when a religious group of "Perfectionists" started making, among other things, flatware. They became an official company in the 1880s. Oh my, how the silver spoon has grown! At their outlet stores, expect discounts of 25 to 75 percent on every last item. Serves you right if you bought ONEIDA somewhere else. Shame, shame on you. So what if it's last season's merchandise, discontinued lines or some seconds in silverware, flatware and crystal. Bet you can't tell! Make a "to do" list when it comes time to entertain, buy a wedding or shower gift, a baby gift, congratulate the grad, whatever, because you will look like a most generous fella when the recipient unwraps something with the name **ONEIDA**. Their Denton location has closed, so besides the Hillsboro location, you can visit the Allen Premium Outlets closer to home or the Tanger Factory Outlet Center in San Marcos. Want more good news? They accept orders by phone. Oh me, **ONEIDA**!

★★★★★   **Oriental Outlet**   **214/638-8382**
2250 Monitor   Mon-Fri 10-6
Dallas, TX 75207

Confucius say, "Wise man who save money for rainy day, find reason to shop here." Nothing is written in the wind saying just because it's at a sizeable discount, it can't be in sync with the latest style trends. See the Orient express itself in 20,000 square feet of warehouse. That means, there's a huge opportunity to snare something from authentic Chinese craft and gift items — cloisonnÈ and silk screens. The popular four-panel screens, for example, were tagged $65. Although there's often a language barrier, the walls of China came tumbling down when we saw the prices on figurines, antique porcelain, wood-crafted items, furniture, jade and more. Now, want to ship it anywhere in the country as a gift? No problem, they can do it. Yes, again and again, those who speak the language of savings don't have to speak Mandarin, they only have to have the desire to save a fortune, Cookie. Some items are even manufactured in their own factories. And if you're looking for a planter or urn with a Far Eastern bent, bet on any one of the thousands here. Their showroom phone number at the World Trade Center is 214/630-3369, but again, not speaking Chinese creates a serious communication schism. If you'd like to see beyond the wailing wall, here's where to shop off the Orient express-way.

PlaceSettings, Inc.   **704/847-6773**
901-L Sam Newell Rd.   Mon-Fri 10-5 (EST) Customer Service
Matthews, NC 28105

www.placesettings.com   🖱 *Top Online Store!*

Please, don't expect to have a discussion over dinner on the weekends or on any holiday as they are closed. Still, you can shop 24/7 for whatever's on your shopping list if the subject is a place setting. If you buy a five-piece place setting from select groupings, they will throw in a **FREE** soup bowl or you can buy it for half price. These kinds of offers are common place on their front page, including sets by **WEDGWOOD** and **SPODE**. The lineup of brands is stellar: **BELLEK**, **GORHAM**, **LENOX**, **ONEIDA**, **PICARD**, **WATERFORD** and **WEDGWOOD**. Choose china, flatware, crystal, gifts and specialty items and never look back. One favorite, the "Beaded Majesty" dinnerware set by **LENOX** in bone china was regally banded in 14K gold. It's tailored and elegant with gold and blue accents. And to make it more appetizing, FREE shipping was available.

Replacements, Inc.   **336/697-3000**
1089 Knox Road   24/7
Greensboro, NC 27420

www.replacements.com   🖱 *Top Online Store!*

To see it with my own eyes confirmed my original premise....Replacements, Inc. is irreplaceable. It should be listed as one of the "Greatest Wonders of the **WORLD**." Founded in 1981 by Bob Page, Replacements, Inc. (located in Greensboro, NC) houses the world's largest selection of old and new china, crystal, silver and collectibles. Over nine million pieces in 175,000 patterns, some over 100 years old, are just part of the story. They add items (new and old) to their website daily. You, too, can replace broken or missing pieces to your china, crystal or silver set, or add to your collectible collection. Every item is carefully inspected and entered into their computerized inventory system. Shopping online makes life easy, but, if you're ever in the area, be sure to visit their beautiful 12,000 square-foot showroom, it's worth a trip to Greensboro just to see the "Museum" which contains Bob Page's 2,000 rare pieces of china, crystal, silver, collectible plates and figurines. A free tour of their warehouse (behind their glass and chrome showroom) is also conducted every half hour. You can register online to begin receiving FREE inventory availability and price lists via e-mail, FAX, or mail for your pattern(s)! Oh, I almost forgot to mention you can bring your dog to the shop, employees do and there were quite a few curled up by their master's computers or shopping in the showroom on the day of our visit. So besides my returning success of The Underground Shopper this year, we are expanding and barking about it every step of the way. *Call toll-free: 800/737-5223*

★★★★ Southwest Gold & Silver Exchange   817/735-1451

5722 Locke Ave.
Fort Worth, TX 76107

Mon-Fri 10-6:30; Sat 10-2

The rush is on! This pan handler's going to town with sterling deals on well-known sterling merchandise. So, why be up the creek without a paddle? If you're looking for just a piece here and there to complete a set, here's where you can make a perfect match. In fact, if you've got a sterling piece you want appraised, there's no charge for appraisals. Southwest Gold & Silver is a sterling example of specialization in one niche of the market, and they've become noted for their prices and service. If you're looking for flatware and serving pieces, "The Pewter Principle has taught us to look for discounts on only the better brands: **GORHAM, LUNT, REED & BARTON, TOWLE** and **WALLACE**, for starters. For individual estate items, you can complete your set or just settle for an exquisite serving piece, platter or tray. In fact, most things here are "Tray Chic!" For coin collectors, just for old dimes'sake, they buy and sell rare coins, gold and silver (domestic and foreign) and lots of other little silver things. Try their 90-day layaway program, and other kindly incentives, makes shopping here a most happy feeling. *Call toll-free: 817/735-4696*

★★★★★★ Waterford/Wedgwood Outlet   972/678-7000

820 West Stacy Road
Allen, TX 75013
www.premiumoutlets.com

Mon-Sat 10-9; Sun 11-6

 If the name **WATERFORD** strikes a note of elegance, you're right on the money. **WATERFORD** designs, manufactures and markets an extensive collection of crystal, stemware and gifts and nothing speaks of status and prestige more than **WATERFORD**. It's in the same class as **MERCEDES** and **BULUGA** caviar. In fact, I have seen a **WATERFORD** ashtray in a car once and thought it was the most extravant accessory I'd ever seen. Then when my daughter-in-law returned from Russia recently, she told me the caviar she brought back was worth $1,400. Now, what plate will she serve it on? Only **WEDGWOOD**, I hope. See, one hand washes the other. Their worldwide reputation is well-founded....being one of the most prestigious tabletop and gift products one can buy. Recently, they branched into the "Marquis" by **WATERFORD** with the addition of **WATERFORD** Fine China, Flatware, Holiday Heirlooms and Table and Bed Linens. So, whether you're looking for a gift, for your own entertaining pleasure, or to add to your home decorating scheme, **WATERFORD** transcends the moment. Paired with its accompanying china, it adds even more muscle to their fine china presentation. Entertain like the rich and famous with a combined history of over 600 years, the **WATERFORD WEDGWOOD** Company, one of the leading luxury lifestyle groups, includes the **WATERFORD** Crystal brand, **WEDGWOOD** brand, **WC DESIGNS, ROSENTHAL** (my personal pick for china) and **ALL-CLAD**. Clap for **ALL-CLAD** — a great cookware line. So, when it comes to outfitting your china cabinet or your wedding/shower/anniversary/baby gift registry of "things you need to buy this year," unless you have a crack in your belfry, see you at the outlet!

Computers & Online

★★★★ **311 Computer (formerly Tran Computer) 214/660-0900**

12243 E. Northwest Highway
Dallas, TX 75228
www.311computers.com

Mon-Sat 9:30-6

Recommended by a faithful fan, Tran (now called 311 Computer), has been co-owned for the past 13 years by Dim Du. According to him, "They can ACTUALLY do what is known as "board-level repairs" on computers and monitors." They specialize in refurbished **HEWLETT PACKARD** and other brands of laser printers priced at a fraction of what one would cost new. Tom Tran is the service manager and has all the certificates to prove his net worth. Phu Tran has also come along as the sales manager and former founder and president of Tran Computers. He, too, is also MSCE, MCP+, MCP, A+ certified and Computer Technology certified, in case you're interested. Nhan Nguyen is their printer and monitor repair specialist. Though they are a small, locally-owned sales and service company in computers, laptops and printers in the Dallas/Fort Worth area, by joining with 311, they make a formidable presence in the computer business. Online sales are also available without leaving home.

◆◆◆ **Advanced Electronic Sales & Services 972/418-7505**

2305 Belt Line Rd., Suite 100
Carrollton, TX 75006

By Appt. Only

Since 1987, this company has been running circles around computers, networks, upgrades, accessories, printers, software, supplies, technical services and consulting. In other words, they are your back door into your front page. Since they are an authorized repair center for most brand name printers, why not consider their preventative maintenance program that schedules routine cleaning and maintenance. If truth be known, most computers and printers are just too dirty....even if they aren't talking to each other. Extend the life of your printer and see if you aren't seeing things in a much cleaner way.

★★★★ **Altex Electronics 972/267-8882**

3215 Belmeade
Carrollton, TX 75006
www.altex.com

Mon-Fri 8-6:30; Sat 10-4

Everything from A-Z is part and parcel of the Altex Electronics inventory. From A/V cables to Zip drives and everything in between, including CD-R and DVD drives, batteries and hand carts, motherboards and mouse pads, power supplies and network switches, whatever turns you or your computer on, are all waiting for a quick pick-me-up. Services include in-house and on-site technical and upgrade services, custom cable manufacturing, and on-site cable installation, to name a few. They've been in business since 1980; if you want to keep up with changing technology, take advantage of their lease plans. Altex works with Deutsche Financial Services and can provide in-house leasing, as well as repairs. If you carry your problem in, rates are $45 an hour; on site, it's a $60 per hour charge with a $55 trip fee. Appointments available within 24 hours. Be sure to ask for their free catalogs. Check directory for the Altex nearest you. There are seven stores in the state, including a new one in Waco; based in San Antonio to keep it all in Texas. *Call toll-free: 800/531-5369*

Chilitech   866/463-9888

9818 Country Cork   24/7
Dallas, TX 75218

www.ChiliTech.com   🖱 *Top Online Store!*

Half the price of AOL, $9.95 a month (with a 12-month contract), welcome to unlimited dial-up access from this family-owned and operated business. If you're not happy with their service, notify them within the first 30 days, and they'll refund your monthly amount. The only catch is that you pay only $9.95 a month if you pay the full year's amount up front; otherwise, you'll be paying $15.95 if you want to pay monthly. After the introductory rate for the first year, rates go up to $12.95, but that price again is offered if paid up front (total $155.40). For $4 more, sign up for ChiliTech Red and surf the net five times faster over a regular phone line. There's a 100 percent money-back guarantee after the first 30 days if not completely satisfied. The Red Hot Rewards program gives you a free month for every person you refer who signs up for a year and points are given for referrals, as well as prizes for those generating the most points over a specified period of time. Sample prizes? Computers, digital cameras, DVDs, MP3 Players....now, talk about some spicy incentives!

★★★★★   Clone Computer Corp.   972/934-2200

14839 Inwood Rd.   Mon-Fri 9-6
Addison, TX 75244
www.clonecomputer.com

You don't have to be a geneticist or a forensic whiz to understand what this company does to make a buck. That's right. Since 1978, they have been cloning. But nothing clandestine, mind you. After all, when you do it right the first time, you want to do it again and again. At CLONE, you simply start with the best computer and build from there. Keeping up with the Jones's is similar to keeping up with the latest technology: it's no small feat. Take the leap of faith and get 30-40 percent off published MICROSOFT manuals and training kits. Expect to see brand names, too, including HANDSPRING, NETBURST, PENTIUM, VISOR, XEROX and more, including their own personal brand, CLONE. Remember years ago, I had a mail order catalog called FACSIMILE? Little did I know then that a Fax would evolve and can you imagine had I registered that name as a trademark, how rich I might be today? Well, no sour grapes here. Cloning may indeed be the future of saving money on computers in the Information Age. They even have a special Customer Service number: 972/934-2208. To put it simply, they build quality computer peripherals and systems and save you money, honey. From books to cables, memory and software, printers and modems, storage and computer notebooks....you know, all that techno geeky stuff. A 15" LCD Flat Panel Display by DAEWOO was on sale for $345. Laptops started at a tad over $1,000 and went up from there. A two-year parts and labor extended warranty, including shipping, was an extra add-on for $275. Whew! All service is done on-site. We condone it, so clone it! *Call toll-free: 800/388-6636*

★★★★★   **CompUSA**   **972/233-4510**

15250 Dallas Pkwy.   Mon-Sat 9-9; Sun 11-6
Dallas, TX 75248
www.compusa.com

This year redirects this giant away from their emphasis on PCs. In fact, president Larry Mondry indicated in a story in the Dallas Morning News that PCs were just a "loss leader." Their Plano store on North Central near Collin Creek will be a test store showcasing different electronics. From security to audiovisual and appliance control, a home owner can run their whole house (but not their household) from their office chair. From digital cameras to web cams, telephones to MP3 players, wireless phones to video games, you'll find more than just computers here. CompUSA sells a wide selection of digital cameras from the amateur to the professional, and they sell all the supporting memory for the cams. Video game systems, surround sound speaker systems, cordless and wireless phones....you can choose from many pre-built packages or build one yourself at a HUGE savings. This store's for you! They also have one of the best translations from a bricks and mortar store to a webstore. Check out their ten locations in the Metroplex with a new store that just opened in Frisco. *Call toll-free: 800/COMPUSA*

★★★★   **Computek Systems**   **214/503-6500**

10420 Plano Rd., Suite 115   Mon-Fri 9-6:30; Sat 11-4
Dallas, TX 75238
www.zdsparts.com

Off 635 at the Plano/Miller intersection, see what computes at this company's service center hub. They are the ones to call for service and repairs. If you're interested in purchasing a new or pre-owned computers or any of the peripherals, turn to their online store at zdsparts.com. Specializing in ZENITH DATA SYSTEMS since 1990, they carry a large selection of parts for new and older ZDS as well as support ZDS and HEATHKIT computers. Order parts by email, fax, telephone or online. Whatever you're looking for — adapters to batteries, boards to cables, drivers to LCDs, keyboards, manuals, memory, mice, modems, power supplies and even laptops. Many choices in older or new software, garden and home software, even karaoke (....most in the $5-$10 range.) Keyboards started at $10 up to $45 with everything in between. Laptops started at $80. Titles galore: business, children's, cooking, education, games, internet, shareware, space, travel, utilities and so much more for PCs and MAC computers. Shop early, especially for consignment properties. Merchandise moves quickly!

◆◆◆   **Computer Recycle Center**   **817/267-9700 Euless**

201 Ector St.   Mon-Fri 9-6
Euless, TX 76039
www.recycles.com

I'm always a little suspect of a computer company whose website looks me in the face with a blank stare. Soon, they say, their order forms will be working again — just a temporary glitch. Well, we shall see. Certainly if you've found this computer pipeline for both new and refurbished computers, you are well acquainted with the dramatic savings. Unfortunately, most of the information on their website is on recycling in general and the forms for selling your old computer and software, but nothing about retail pricing. If you are selling computers older than a PENTIUM II, the Recycle Center requires that you sell more than one unit. The EPA stipulates that old computers cannot be thrown away. Repeat. DON'T throw your old computer in the garbage can. Computers and their components contain aluminum, plastics, glass, cathode ray tubes (CSR's), liquid crystal displays (LCD's), solder, lead and other materials that are not environmentally friendly.

You can drop them off at their Fort Worth facility (Singer Metal Company) at 3141 S. Main St. (817/929-9995) or arrange for a pick up of unwanted computers and parts. For computers not on pallets or ones that cannot be picked up at a loading dock or fork lift, there is a $30/per hour fee to palletize the equipment and a $20/hour per person. Call for a quote. Nationwide pick up can be arranged through the company, but the customer pays the shipping on scrap computers and parts. Because of rising costs, a $2 fee for stripped systems and an $8 fee for monitors is assessed. Looks like they've gotten out of the sales of refurbished equipment — so it's up to you to sell or dispose of your old equipment these days. Remember, don't toss your loss. Recycle. *Call toll-free: 817/282-1622*

★★★★ Computer Surplus   972/438-2767

2105 N. O'Connor   Mon-Sat 10-8; Sun 12-6
Dallas, TX 75061

Well, what kind of computer store can't get it together to offer a website? Got me. Then, they moved without telling me. It's a good thing at the last minute, when their website wasn't working, I called and discovered they don't have a website, they were no longer on the Airport Freeway and the changed zip codes, too. So much for over and out-let, Roger. But at Computer Surplus, you can still jump in without taking a big byte out of your budget. Computer Surplus has Pentium PCs for $249 complete with a one-year warranty. Each system comes complete with Microsoft Windows, Keyboard, Mouse, 56K Modem, 14" Monitor SVGA, Speakers and Sound Card, CD ROM, and no rebate hassles. Without a contract, what else is there to buy? Nada. I'd say you've got yourself the start of something big. But don't think only used computers and parts. They also carry new and fix any brand under the sun, even those that are brand-less. Click on accessories, software, CD's and floppys because they are part and parcel of their inventory repertoire. Also, you can pick up ERIC-SSON mobile phones plus COMPAQ, DELL, GATEWAY, HEWLETT-PACKARD, TOSHIBA computers and accessories.

★★★★★★ Computers Worth, Inc.   972/412-4947

1901 Miller Rd.   Mon-Fri 9-5:30
Rowlett, TX 75088
www.computersworth.com

 What is the best computer resource for software doing in Rowlett? Well, it doesn't matter 'cause this is an online supersite, no ifs, ands or bytes about it. Get acquainted, bargain shopper. Say hello to the great buys via excess inventory that they buy as surplus or liquidation and never pay full price for software, hardware or accessories again. This is it as far as CD-ROMs go. Look at some of the best software and applications in the business: ACT, ADOBE, BORLAND, COREL, LOTUS, WINDOWS and more. Software is available for Mac, WINDOWS '95, '98, NT and ME. Software titles start at just $3.99 like the popular, "You Don't Know Jack/ Sports" and "You Don't Know Jack/ Movies." Save money and get "Your Wedding Consulting Software" for just $15.99 or, if you're looking to remodel your house, do it with "Floor Plan Suite 4.0" for just $24.99. Their website is extensive and easy to shop. No need to leave home to enhance your computer's worth. Shop online or visit them in Rowlett in their garage or during "First Saturday" sales. (See First Saturday write-up.) $4 million in sales for this year ain't some small potatoes. Do not Ctrl, Alt, Delete! *Call toll-free: 800/838-7884*

◆◆◆◆ Computize

13657 N.Glenville Drive
Richardson, TX 75081
www.computize.com

972/437-3100
Mon-Fri 9-6

This company came on the scene in Houston in 1983, just when the revolution was beginning to surface. Since that time, they have been leaders in selling over 90,000 IT products. The company sells top tier products from A to Z, **ACER** to **ZEBRA** and that's just the first course. The main course includes computers to printers, plotters to monitors. Financing and leasing options are available as well as service, repair, extended warranties, networking and onsite IT support. If you're the government or an educational institution, special prices will be given priority but online shopping seems to be the direction they're headed so you might as well hop aboard. Their experienced and knowledgeable staff can provide you with pre-sales consultation, design, implementation and project management. Perhaps most importantly, they offer support services such as troubleshooting or improving your productivity. The huge deal they were working on when we were there was an **IBM** x Series 440 Demo that included the rack server, processor, loads of RAM, drive and full warranty for $9,999. For the tamer pocketbooks — what about an HP Personal LaserJet at a piddly price or an IBM II R32 Think Pad for $1,158.20. Add in all the extras like service and repair and it all computizes to a company worth patronizing. *Call toll-free: 800/289-7939*

★★★★ Cyber Exchange

360 East FM 3040, Suite 850
Lewisville, TX 75067
www.cyberexchangecomputers.com

972/316-3030
Mon-Thurs 10-8; Fri 10-5; Sat Noon-6

A new website may be a template as I've seen it elsewhere but it's sure easy on the eyes and easy to buy. If you want to hop aboard the gravy train, you'll see some terrific deals online and a pleasant welcome when you show up in person. Seeing as they're next door to a Sonic, at least you won't go away hungry. Buy, sell or trade pre-owned software and hardware is one way to take the byte out of your cyberbudget. Get a good deal, digest the helpful service and do it their way with repairs, upgrades and networking services. For in-house Pc upgrades and service, expect to shell out $99 plus parts. This national franchise is making lots of headway as folks fed up with certain games, video titles or how-to applications can trade in, up or away for a percentage of the original price. Then, you earn credits toward the purchase of something else. Hundreds of both new and recycled titles for both the PC and the Mac, including hard-to-find software for older computers and the **APPLE**. All the software has been checked for viruses and guaranteed not to be defective. (You, on the other hand, have not). They have lots of variations on the theme of getting you and your business off the ground, from leasing to upgrading, and they're convenient to the Vista Ridge community in Lewisville. Prices depend on supply and demand. If the title is still in demand, chances are the discount will be miniscule, if at all. Items that are a dime a dozen — may be a dime a dozen. Get it? I bought a great home design software program that is now getting plenty of use by The Budget Decorators (see write-up elsewhere).

Dallas Memory International

11520 N. Central Expy., Suite 100
Dallas, TX 75243
www.dallasmemory.com   🖱 *Top Online Store!*

214-221-2244
Mon-Fri 9-6

My son says, "Mom, these guys have the best prices on computers" and he buys all of his stuff online from them since he's moved to the West Coast. You may need a translator if you don't understand half of what they're selling. Computer buffs will get it; novices won't. They have Cases, CD/CDRW, Computers, Controllers, DVD/DVD-R, Hard Drives, Input/ Output, Memory, Microprocessors, Modems, Monitors ,Motherboards, Storage and Video Cards. Check out their website. Here is an example of a best-selling memory product. (Hold On!) DDR PC2100 512mb 2.0 (DDR266) Apacer Unbuffered Non-ECC CAS 2.0 all for $94! Brand names DDR SDRAM, crucial (in lower case) technologies, **MICRON**, **SAMSUNG**, and gigram (also in lower case). Be sure and check out their rather lengthy list of policies and procedures. Prices are final as you'll be stuck with a 20 percent restocking charge if you decide you don't like something. (Defective merchandise is another story.) Packages are shipped FED EX and a signature is required on all shipments....no exceptions! No refunds on shipping and handling. *Call toll-free: 800/965-2447*

◆◆◆   Dell Direct   972/712-5844
2601 Preston Rd.   Mon-Sat 10-9; Sun 12-6
Frisco, TX 75034
www.dell4me.com/mall

Looks like Michael Dell has jumped into the retailing ring and is following in the **GATEWAY** footsteps — sort of. Though you can't buy it at the mall in their kiosk, you can order it online. Welcome to Big D....Big **DELL**. Now deal with **DELL** direct by seeing, touching and ultimately buying what you see and touch at the kiosk, then buy it online. For home notebooks, choose an Inspiron 2600 Notebook with Intel Celeron Processor, 1.20 GHz, 14.1 XGA TFT Display, **FREE** upgrade from 128 MB to 256 MB PC 133 Shared SDRAM. Prefer a desktop? No problem, they start as low as $749 or monthly payments, a measly $23/month. I'm exhausted even before I've opened the box. Be sure to input all of their other mall locations into your database: Parks at Arlington, Town East in Mesquite. Then find **DELL DIRECT** at Stonebriar Centre in **FRISCO** (above), Ridgmar Mall in Fort Worth, Town East Mall in Mesquite, The Galleria in Dallas and DFW International Airport (Terminal C, Gate 7.) No farmers at this Dell? But for the real deals, go to www.delloutlet. *Call toll-free: 800/433-7841*

Dell Outlet   512/338-4400
Austin, TX 78701   24/7
www.delloutlet.com   🖱 *Top Online Store!*

Leave it to **DELL** to quell any rumors that they can't meet or beat any other sellers of DELL computers. If they talk to Michael, I'm sure anything's possible. At their own online repository, there's nothing but quality refurbished systems for sale plus desk tops, notebooks, monitors, peripherals, laptops, laser printers — all refurbished to DELL's exacting standards. If it's a new computer, it comes with a 21-day total satisfaction policy. Every once in a while, a computer does get returned but not very often. A few come back because of technical glitches. When they do, they are completely dismantled, taken apart and rebuilt to original factory specifications, then retested to ensure the same high standards are adhered to — in other words, as good as new. They even use brand new boxes for packaging! Shop online for special deals, online financing, high-speed internet access information, and read all about recycling. During the summer, you could save up to another $500 on select refurbished models. Now, Michael doesn't need the money himself but if he can help save you some, the fetter off he feels. You know charity begins at home. Sign up for their email deals for outlet shoppers only if you want to be in the know at all times. It's worth it. They are the factory, after all. Prices are better at Resource Concepts (now called Recycled Computers International) but the selection here can't be beat. *Call toll-free: 800/426-5150*

◆◆◆◆◆   **Doctor PC**   **972/235-3772**

209 W. Main St.   Mon-Fri 9-6; Sat 10-6
Richardson, TX 75081

If your computer is experiencing those "senior moments," it's time to call the doctor. Located at the southwest corner of Belt Line (Main St.) and Central, if you're suffering from a slipped disc or your hard drive has gone soft, this Doctor of PCs can be your conduit to wellness. Maybe it just needs a good cleaning? Or there's not enough memory to hold all your thoughts? They've got a remedy for most any Pc problem you're experiencing. Labor pains not included as labor prices are not per hour but run instead a flat rate of $85 to fix-er-uppers (plus parts, of course!) Expect to bring your baby home in a day or so. No house calls. You bring your computer in for the Doctor to execute the prescription. Business is booming. The place is booming with computers that all need a little TLC. Insurance is not accepted, but emergencies are. Unless you want to travel to Mexico and speak Spanish, don't log on to www.doctorpc.com. It's not our Doctor.

★★★★★★   **Electronic Discount Sales**   **817/548-1992**

908 E. Pioneer Pkwy.   Mon-Sat 10-7; Sun Noon-5
Arlington, TX 76010
www.electronicdiscountsales.com

   No, laptops here are not kitties purring in your lap, but rather the brands that will keep you feline fine. The brands are anywhere from **ACER** to **ZENITH** and hundreds of others in between. Even phones, accessories, surround sound and car stereos are available here at sensational prices. Service and repairs, too. Look for special reconditioned and used items not only in-store but also posted on eBay. Then, if you'd rather shop online at their site, go forth and ye shall prosper. The items represented online are but a fraction of the inventory that's in store. But they select certain items because of "price," "hard-to-find parts" and "Super Buys" that they deem worthy of distributing around the world. They have very lofty goals, but those more down-to-earth can also visit their stores. How can they sell so low while others are selling it at twice the price? Their philosophy is based on "turns." In other words, how fast can they turn (sell) the item so they can invest the money into more great deals? Not that many products for sale on line so it's probably a good bet to visit in person. Over 50,000 square feet of computer stuff. Found a HP Laserjet II Printer for $69.99 and I was a happy computer. Others with me jumped for joy over the non-computer stuff like the **MERLIN** daggers, $19.99, the 5X Makeup Mirror, $12.95, the ALICE COOPER boxer shorts, $3.99 and wound up buying an old Mac system for her toddler for only $39.99. Visit also in Irving at 4070 N. Belt Line, 972/570-7393.

★★★   **Electronics Boutique**   **972/783-6416**

501 S. Plano Rd.   Mon-Sat 10-9; Sun Noon-6
Richardson, TX 75081
www.ebgames.com

There's a boutique for clothes, a boutique for home furnishings, and now an Electronics Boutique....with bargains to boot. Play the game correctly and you'll wind up a winner. Here you'll find video and software titles looming wall to wall: **PLAYSTATION, PS2, XBOX, GAMECUBE, GAME BOY, GAME BOY ADVANCED, NINTENDO 64** and **DREAMCAST**, as well as PC and Mac computers. Save big on preowned titles like Playstation's Technu, Tony Hawk Pro Skater, Metal Gear or Final Fantasy 8 for only $14.99. For that same price, get Nintendo 64, A Bugs Life, Battle Tanx and Asteroid Hyper or Dreamcast Aero Wings and Evolution. Need the whole system? Get a used Nintendo 64 for just $54.99 or a used Game Boy for $49.99. Even pre-owned Playstation 2 titles were available from just $17.99 (and that's a real steal!) If you're playing on your computer, bring the games to life with new Sound Blasters, Micropoint ll Mice (mouses?), GeoForce3 graphics controllers and more. And, if you've never heard of any of these, welcome to the club. Sixteen locations in the Metroplex making them the world's leading specialty retailer of video games or so they claim.

Everyones Internet   800/504-SURF

2600 Southwest Freeway, Suite 500   24/7
Houston, TX 77098

www.ev1.net   *Top Online Store!*

 Why would you pay more than $10 a month for dial up local internet access for a Dallas number? Well, it could be because you don't feel good unless you're paying a lot of money for the service. But at Everyones Internet, you will not have to sign a contract, not have to pre-pay for the year (but pay monthly), and pay only $10 a month to have FREE unlimited e-mail accounts, FREE 300 megabytes of web space for your own web site, never get a busy signal, have unlimited access and usage, FREE 24-hour tech support and software and 56K or ISDN lines for the same low price. And this service should be everyone's. Honorable and above reproach, they also provide excellent communication regarding a number of relevant issues such as viruses- where else? On the internet, of course. We're not talking the flu virus.

★★★★★   First Saturday   214/720-9054

2632 Ross Ave.   Fri 6 PM- Sat 2 PM
Dallas, TX 75201
www.firstsaturdaysale.com

Expect a recording to give you the poop for scooping up some of the best buys for your computer dollar. On the First Saturday of the month, expect the parking lots at Ross Ave. and Routh St. to swell to a combination shoppers'bazaar and flea market, full of hams (the radio kind) and the balance overflowing with cyber-geeks. It's a place where 250 or more merchants show up regularly and set up temporary booths a la garage sale style at two distinct locations, selling a plethora of computer, radio and electronic supplies. On the north lot, it's more a garage sale than a serious vendor operation, run by former State Senator John Leedom, who owns the Wholesale Electronics Building. Spartan surroundings, no electricity, just a bunch of enthusiastic guys out to make a buck. Parking across the street, $5. And this year, there's a Snack Shack to help you make it through the night! Their corporate offices are in Carrollton; contact Elaine Franz or Robert Scoggins, 3723 Standridge Drive, Carrollton, TX 75007 972/492-1740.

★★★★★   GameStop (Software, Etc.)   817/860-1134

780 Road to Six Flags East #246   Mon-Sat 10-9; Sun 11-6
Arlington, TX 76011
www.gamestop.com

Consign your old software and hardware for up to 30 days at GameStop and reap a 60/40 split with you retaining the bigger half. Just agree to their simple terms (which is the only thing on their website), deliver the merchandise in good working condition, and they'll handle the rest. Over 30,000 different software products on consignment. This is THE place to get your software for home and office, interactive learning and non-learning games, accessories, video games and video systems, both new and preowned. You won't miss out on all the latest and greatest either. All computer and computer items, you'll be happy to learn, are new. You'll find best-sellers and bargains, and some best-selling bargains. If you are someone who covets Game Boy Dreamcast, NINTENDO, PLAY-

STATION and **PS2**, you'll find GameStop to be your heavenly conduit. Find software like *Easy Family Tree*, Cad packages, virus scanners, games and screen savers for a fraction of their retail cost. If you're a dummy, read any one of their "how to" books and learn the ropes. If you're cyber-challenged, they should come in handy. Most software is priced in the $7 range, but would cost $35-$40 new. Their 3,500 square foot facility is filled to the brim with software and more, complete with a fast check-out and point-and-find sales personnel. More than 30 locations to play games at, so connecting to one is as easy as one-two, button my shoe.

HalfPriceLaptop.com   972/998-2422

PO Box 2702   24/7
Frisco, TX 75034

www.halfpricelaptop.com   ⌐🖰 *Top Online Store!*

 Talk about a perfect name for describing the guts of this company's marketing mission. Laptops are half price. Simple, isn't it? No confusion here. Half price laptops are those that are coming off leases from various corporate accounts to trade in, trade up, trade off and you are the benefactor. Pick your favorite: **COMPAQ**, **DELL**, **HP**, **IBM** or **TOSHIBA** for starters. If you are a corporate or educational account, expect even additional discounts. For an unbelievable low of $309, you can be in the lap of luxury with an IBM Thinkpad. Don't even think twice, everything here is half price. A business plan of five (5) laptops could get your entire office up and running for around $2,500 including carrying cases for each and every laptop ordered. No argument here. It's the best deal money can buy. If you are interested in ordering laptops from them at great wholesale prices and think you can sell at least 10 laptops a month, consider being a reseller of laptops and buying them at even lower prices. Email or call them for more information. What about starting your own business for less than $3,000? Besides a welcome relief to high price laptops for the consumer and small business owner, it's not a bad deal as a business, either.

★   Hardin Computers   817/478-2775

5769 Southwest Green Oaks Blvd.   Mon-Fri 9-6; Sat 10-4
Arlington, TX 76017

The Rosedale location has closed, so you have the one and only Green Oaks location to connect to a big Mac. Unfortunately, there wasn't a preowned model on hand, nor was there much to choose from in the new department. They will order whatever you want and that's about it. They were pretty lethargic on our visit leading us to believe they were hanging on just to stay awake. But you CAN have it your way, as long as it's a Mac. Though the American Heart Association recommends cutting out the fat in your diet, we didn't see much to reduce the fat in your budget so it might be best to shop where it's not so lean. This was their parent retail location, so why would you bother anyway? Located at I-20 and Green Oaks in Arlington, maybe you just need to wait for their special sauces. What, a computer store without a website? How blasphemous!

★★★★★   ICS Computers   972/509-8000

2301 Central Expressway   Mon-Fri 9-6; Sat 10-6
Plano, TX 75075
www.imscomp.com

And the shelves came a-tumbling down. With over 50,000 name-brand products (and services) on their shelves, it's no wonder there's an occasional fall-out. But in general, ICS Computers sells hardware to software, supplies to setting up a network, technical training to launching a professional website. Need help? These are the guys to call. If the chips are down, like they were when I went to their website, don't give up. Their server could be the problem. Once I was able to connect, I headed right for the clearance merchandise and wound up buying a port replicator for my **IBM** THINKPAD for $80 and a MICROSOFT Office Word 2000 training video for $86. Now, I need to find the time to view it so I can learn it. Then, I contemplated the **TOSHIBA** Protege Ultra Thin Notebook computer ($1,200), but thought twice because there was a **CANON** Multipass with printer, fax, scanner and copying capabilities for $81. Seeing is believing. Located between Parker and Park Boulevard in Plano, connect to this computer company and you'll be able to purge your files, surge to greater heights, network to your office, or call upon them to make an on-site service call. Whether you want to jump aboard a DSL or ISDN line to ensure you're connecting at rapid-fire speed, you don't want to fall behind for you'll wind up lost in left field. But their Carrollton store (972/416-4000) was a different story. The IMS was to computers what Motrin is to PMS: a quick fix for when you're in pain. The Carrollton location has a substantial service center and state-of-the-art repair facility. Although their rates are steep, they're so good that they can probably solve the problem in half the time it takes others. Labor rates were $65 an hour with priority service at $95 an hour. They offer flat rates for monitor repairs at $49 for a 14", $59 for a 15" and $85 for a 17". But they can also provide solutions for networking, video conferencing and streaming, too. If you're looking for a deal on motherboards and CPU's, then pick up an Intel Celeron-2 700 for $159 or an **AMD** Duron 900 for $215. Don't overlook the CPUs, monitors, video cards, motherboards, printers, input devices, back ups, memory, hard drives, modems, cases, controllers, accessories and more. Start with the shell if you'd like to build your own system, then add name brand parts that are top-notch at the lowest prices, guaranteed. They even design web pages. No stone is left unturned when the subject is computers and all that they can be. Now shop like you mean it! Third location is in Lewisville at MacArthur and 3040.

★★★★★　**Micro Center**   **972/664-8500**

13929 N. Central Expressway   Mon-Sat 10-9; Sun 11-6
Dallas, TX 75243
www.microcenter.com

In 1979, Micro Center was just a micro-mini store in Columbus, Ohio, but, today, they're one of the largest computer retail companies in the United States. First, they sold books, magazines and one **DYNABYTE** computer. So much for selling computers. Today, it's a whole other story, as they are a whole other company. Departments were created for accessories and peripherals, classrooms were added (computer training is available with class sizes averaging 8-10 students with approximately 150 different classes available), curriculum was developed to educate customers. Then they added racks and racks of software (one of the largest selections in the country), then a furniture department and, finally, walk-in, technical support was established in-store. To further meet customers'needs and demands, all stores now offer a Digital Imaging Department. There are more than 700 product categories and sub-categories and nearly 36,000 products. Next to the Loew's Theater at Spring Valley and Central, there's only one Micro Center in town. *Call toll-free: 800/267-3434*

NEXTInternational.com   972/481-1113

3214 Belt Line Rd., #446   Mon-Fri 9-6:30; Sat 10-2
Farmers Branch, TX 75234

www.neqx.com   🖱 *Top Online Store!*

 Next on your list of places to shop should be this mail order/website company who can sell computer components for your PC, software and hardware set-ups and installation and configuration — for less. Now that that's done, it's time to install and configure, connect set-up, LAN-WAN set-up, administration, web design and development. Plus, they now offer on-site service for troubleshooting, upgrades, servers, workstations and PC design. You can indulge yourself with some of the best names at "Wholesale Prices." Pick from a variety of motherboards, hard drives, monitors, printers, video cards and more. But if something goes down, the service call price goes up. Try $75 an hour and a trip fee of $45. But, when your network has failed you, and the book is due, what else can you do? They serve the entire Metroplex, so everyone can get in on the act during their special sales that change monthly. You'll really rack up the savings from one month to the NEXT! *Call toll-free: 800/730-6398*

◆◆   PC House Call   972/234-0655

14001 Goldmark Drive, Suite 101   Mon-Fri 8-5:30; Sat 10-2
Dallas, TX 75240
www.pc-housecall.com

Don't worry if you don't have Medicare yet. You won't need it if the doctor is in. At least this one still makes House Calls. If your PC is experiencing a breakdown or any other mechanical ailment, you've turned to the perfect provider. Relax and take a load off. They can handle all the trouble-shooting, network integration, DSL installations, upgrades, system setups and data transfers and recovery, as well as phone support that any PC would ever need. Trip fees are $29 in their service area of Dallas to Frisco and Bethel to Wylie, then billed in half hour increments thereafter. Now, that's a deal! But it will cost $69 in extended service areas like Lake Dallas, Lewisville, Cockrell Hill, Irving and Lucas. Sorry, Flower Mound and Grand Prairie. If the doctor is in, emergency services will add an additional $30 to the trip fee and double the labor costs. Now, that's a real labor pain! Try to get your PC to cooperate and not have a nervous breakdown after hours. Drop-off service for in-House Calls are also available at $79 per hour. The cost of PC health care doesn't come cheap; but usually your business life depends on it. Too, what if you lost all your e-mails? You'd feel naked. So pay up, sucker, and hope your computer stays in shape!

Price Watch

Dallas, TX   24/7
www.pricewatch.com   🖱 *Top Online Store!*

 One of the best and fastest search engines to price check for computer or electronics online is www.pricewatch.com So, use it or lose it! Since 1995, when you land on the engine, type in what you're looking for and let the computer do all the searching. Watch it go. In a minute, it will have done all of the necessary comparison shopping. They search the universe of options for what you're looking for and then reveal the lowest price site. Miracles never cease to amaze me. You won't be disappointed. My son swears by it and he's usually never wrong. Excellent technical articles archived and guaranteed, the lowest prices, superb service, what more can you ask for? The **ROLEX** of price watches is this search engine.

★★★★★★   **Recycled Computers International 972/245-5050**

2940 Eisenhower, #130   Mon-Fri 9-6; Sat 9-3
Carrollton, TX 75007
www.outletcomputer.com

 Waste not. Want not. If you thought you couldn't afford the industry leaders (**COM-PAQ**, **DELL**, **HEWLETT-PACKARD**, **IBM**, **MICRON**, **TOSHIBA** and others), think again! Resource Concepts has a new name, new owners from Mississippi, but still sells computers and all the extras at "as low as they go" prices. They move factory-refurbished and excess inventory from major manufacturers at a substantial savings to the public. They also sell returns. They offer end-of-product cycle and demonstration models, as well as special deals and bulk-packaged products that are new, too. Now, should you worry if the computer's been refurbished? Nope. Expect them to be stringently checked and tested to exceed industry standards. All computers come with a one-year or three-year warranties. Truckloads of products arrive daily at their 150,000 square foot recycling warehouse and showroom facility. Save on servers, systems, notebooks, accessories and so much more! If you liked IKE (Eisenhower), you'll love Recycled Computers. *Call toll-free: 800/588-9468*

◆◆◆◆◆◆   **RescueTech**   **972/417-1234**

3941 Legacy Drive   By Appt. Only
Plano, TX 75023
www.rescuetech.net

 Call before 3 if your computers go down at 2:30 and they are there, same day service. What miracle workers they are. Ah, a name from my past is now back where he belongs....fixing our computers when the hard drives go soft and the network card goes into cardiac arrest. In no time, Chad Maisel or one of his Rescue-Techs have everything up and running smooth as silk. Read about their turn-key operation, from buying the right equipment to making sure it's running like a charm on his website above. And though you can't expect expert help to come cheap ($80/hour for on-site technical help and in 15 minute increments thereafter), all of the Tech's are A +Plus, **NOVELL**, NT, 2000 certified and provide quality service in all areas of computing. From networking to setting up a server, cabling to website design, these are the pros in the know. Servicing most of the Metroplex (within reason), Carrollton, Prosper, Duncanville, Mesquite and Irving, Plano, Frisco, Lewisville, Flower Mound — well, all I can tell you is they are like an umbilical cord to my office. I can't live without them. Try 'em for trouble shooting, on-site network and computer service, voice/data cabling, custom workstations/servers, windows 200/NT/XP 9X/Novell and same to next day service. These guys are good. Real good. And fast. Don't let their hourly rates deter you. They have always fixed things in a matter of minutes or at most, less than an hour.

Department Stores/Off Price & Buying Services

★★★ **Big Lots (formerly MacFrugals)**   **972/484-4821**

2865 Valley View Lane
Farmers Branch, TX 75234
www.biglots.com

Mon-Sat 9-9; Sun 10-7

The big Mac has finally been consumed by Big Lots; not to worry, it's still a whopper any way you slice it. When you see the word c.l.o.s.e.o.u.t., grab yourself a big one, from gourmet smoked salmon for $9.99 (compared to $19.99) to a **SALTON** Coffee, Cappuccino and Espresso maker for $29 (instead of $59.99). Just ask Pamela Anderson. She and her fiancÈ added their names to the wedding registries at Big Lots and Auto Zone. Well, that was short-lived as she's now thinking of going back to Tommy. Just be on the alert when shopping there, as much of the reconditioned electronic and housewares merchandise is co-mingled with new products. Prices on reconditioned products are usually the lowest. Motorized toy cars were $9.99 (compared to $29.99). All merchandise was priced 15 to 35 percent below most discount retailers and up to 70 percent below traditional retailers. Check directory for the location nearest you. *Call toll-free: 800/269-9571*

★★★★ **Burke's Outlet**   **972/487-7556**

1402-B W. Walnut Street
Garland, TX 75040
www.burkesoutlet.com

Mon-Sun 9-9

One day, traveling to Babe's Chicken in Garland, I happened upon the Burke's Outlet. I veered off into the parking lot, pulled up to a close-in parking place, and walk eagerly into this newcomer who has been as quiet as a mouse. It's like a poor mans Kohl's, a mini version of a one-stop department store with most everything for less. You'll find this Florida treasure-trove of surprises all over Texas: Allen (Allen Premium Outlet Center), Arlington, Carrollton (Woodlake Square, 3056 Josey Lane), Cleburne, Corsicana, Gainesville, Garland, Hillsboro, Mesquite (3636 Gus Thomasson Rd.), Mt. Pleasant, Palestine and other cities outside of the North Texas environs. Headquartered in Bradenton, FL, they operate over 130 retail stores in 11 states. In each, you'll find brand name apparel and accessories for the entire family at up to 70 percent off department store prices. Go, Divas, Go! *Call toll-free: 800/683-8039*

★★★★   **Burlington Coat Factory**   **817/571-2666**

1201 W. Airport Frwy.   Mon-Sat 10-9; Sun 11-6
Euless, TX 76040
www.coat.com

One of the few off-price powerhouses that offers an opportunity to shop online as well as onsite, **BURLINGTON COAT FACTORY** is anything but just coats. Women's, Men's, Children's, Coats, Shoes, Linens and Home Fashions, Baby Furniture and Accessories, Fragrances and Luggage. Couldn't resist leaping over to the "Cheetah" ensemble for my bath. Transforming a plain vanilla guest bath with jungle effects was the cat's meow. What's next? Their **MARTHA STEWART**-clone niche, the **CHRISTOPHER LOWELL** Collection. This HGTV decorator has his own collection of bed and bath ensembles at Burlington with detailed decorating recommendations for bringing the entire grouping into one coordinated look. Hop onto this bargain train and save 20 to 60 percent. See also Luxury Linens and Baby Depot Departments within most stores. Hop aboard the online train and save even more in time and money. Check directory for the location nearest you. And remember, some stores offer Fine Jewelry, some (not all) offer shoes, some The Baby Depot (with an accompanying baby registry) and some offer a separate Luxury Linen department in the same shopping center. But all locations feature an extensive selection of first-quality ladies'designer dresses, suits, sportswear and accessories; top-name men's suits and sportswear; and famous-label clothes for children of all ages. Another feature that has been lost by other off-price stores is the "hard to fit" customer, from petite to plus, short to big and tall. They will even special-order merchandise from manufacturers to meet special sizing needs. Within the majority of Burlington Coat Factories is their Baby Depot and Luxury Linens Department. Savings of up to 60 percent off there, too. Check directory for locations nearest you. For online shopping, go to www.dcfdirect.com. What fun. What savings.

★★★★★★   **Costco**   **972/244-0000**

3800 N. Central Expressway   Mon-Fri 10-8:30; Sat 9:30-6; Sun 10-6
Plano, TX 75074
www.costco.com

Happy days are here again. Costco, the creator of the warehouse club concept, has settled into the Metroplex and life is good. It's electrifying what a few well-priced gourmet food baskets and name-brand appliances will do. With six locations (Arlington, Southlake, Fort Worth, East and West Plano and now Lewisville), it's time you joined the club and get with the program. To describe Costco as cost-effective is like describing Mount Kilimanjaro as a molehill. They are the pinnacle in wholesale warehouse shopping, one-stop shopping for the family that has (or wants) everything; ditto for small businesses. The line-up includes appliances (both large and small), electronics, cameras, audio/video equipment, automotive accessories, digital cameras, video games and systems, furniture, wine cellars, gift baskets, houseplants, desk accessories, golf clubs, pens, sports memorabilia, hardware, outdoor furniture, pet supplies, barbecue grills, plumbing supplies, sauna and spas....whew, I'm exhausted just talking about them. Let's face it, Costco has everything. Oh, did I forget to tell you that you can book a vacation package at Costco's, too? And what about one-hour photos? Then, take a whiff of the food court? The bakery? Fresh meat and produce? Ah, hear the good deals in hearing aids. Fill-er up at their own gas station? Get your eyes examined, fill a prescription, order a sandwich, fix a flat, if it sounds too good to be true, don't even think it isn't 'cause it is. All under one roof true. Membership categories vary: The Gold Star is $45, which means you must have a business, be a non-profit organization, government agency, farmer or rancher; An Executive Gold Star and Executive Gold Star Business is $100 and will provide an additional two percent savings on most of your purchases, plus some added savings with affiliated businesses dealing with auto sales, travel packages, long distance services, mortgage and financial services, etc. Think of them as the upscale Sam's Club because they also have items you'd never see at Sam's, such as **LLADROS** and **WATERFORD** crystal. But see the China & Crystal Chapter to compare prices before you buy it here. ***Call toll-free: 800/774-2678***

★★★★★ **Depot 42**   **940/648-3344**

1429 West FM 407   Mon-Sat 9-6
Justin, TX 76247

Closeout carnivores will feel right at home at Depot 42, a 25,000-square-foot monster for food and housewares. Expect gadgets galore with popular grocery-store names like **RUBBERMAID** — how can you not buy a ton of stuff for the kitchen here? Or what about a coffee maker by **MELITO**? Stir around the pots and pans, cookware, stainless steel mixing bowls, storage containers, school supplies, stereos, luggage, purses, knives, tools....well, this is a closeout place and most anything goes. If you see it today, you better buy it today, or else you'll be sorry tomorrow. One day it might be **SEIKO** watches, or a sports watch, even a kid's watch, you just never know but what I do know is everything's at wholesale prices or less. You'll be astonished at the assortment of pottery to glassware, handbags to T-shirts, vases to **VASELINE**. What? Now you're telling me there are sundries? What about food? Okay, they've got some of that, too. Maybe it's a box of cereal with Christmas characters. Well, who eats the box anyway? Then again, Christmas cereal made for December to be eaten in May? No May to December recommendations here. (I wouldn't touch it with a ten-foot spoon!) But when you're Wright, you're right! (owner's name is Mr. Wright.) He's always had the right stuff. Formerly the Justin Outlet, new name, same game.

★★★★★ **Dillard's Clearance Center**   **817/649-0782**

3000 E. Pioneer Pkwy.   Mon-Sat 10-7; Sun Noon-6
Arlington, TX 76010
www.dillards.com

Spice things up at Dillard's Clearance Center with merchandise gleaned from area Dillard's stores that didn't make the grade. Take your wardrobe from "blah" to "ahh" with discounts on designer labels including **ANNE KLEIN**, **CAROLE LITTLE**, **CHRISTIAN DIOR**, **DOCKERS**, **ELLEN TRACY**, **KASPER**, **LITTLE ME**, **LIZ CLAIBORNE**, **LEVI'S**, **PERRY ELLIS**, **POLO BY RALPH LAUREN**, **TOMMY HILFIGER** and more. The list is endless and so are the savings, with up to 75 percent off. How about occasional sales that offer another 30 percent off the lowest marked price? Sounds like a bargain to me! Being at The Festival Marketplace is it's only drawback as this mall leaves much to be desired. Well, it's close to perfect but not quite.

★★★★★★ **DirectBuy**   **972/203-8881**

610 US Highway 80 E   Mon-Fri 1-9; Sat-Sun 10-6
Sunnyvale, TX 75182-9260
www.directbuy.net

 Well, here's the only shopping experience that will literally resurrect you wholeheart-edly, body and soul. The only members-only club worth joining. Join the club and buy it all....wholesale. That's right. This membership showplace will cost for the privilege of really buying wholesale for everything....and that means everything except for a husband (and match.com or eharmony.com are recommended for them!) You can take the savings to the bank with one of the largest private buying organizations in the country. Direct Buy's their name and brand name savings is their game. One step inside their remodeled gigantic showroom in Sunnyvale and you'll get the picture. Even artwork is available at wholesale prices without getting framed, though much of the artwork is framed so it's just about perfect for wrapping it up and letting it all hang out. The membership may sound a bit steep at first, so they have arranged for some very interesting payment plans making it so affordable, you won't be able to resist. Trust me, you will recoup the savings generally with your first purchase. (They make money strictly on your membership fees and that is how they can provide the resources direct to you.) That way, there's no middlemen and no mark-ups. Period. End of discussion. You are buying strictly wholesale. The Dallas Direct Buy Club is probably the primo club of the over 100 locations in 30 states and Canada. With membership, you get privileges such as being able to buy direct from the manufacturer at the same prices as a store — without the markup. No kidding. You'll have access to literally hundreds of manufacturers for furnishing your entire house, bedroom, living room, dining room, baby and youth furniture and more. In fact, they can provide just about everything from the floor up. Yes, floor coverings, kitchen and bath cabinets and fixtures, wall units, patio furniture, office furniture, lighting fixtures, exercise and sporting goods, bedding and mattresses, appliances and electronics, jewelry and giftware. And to top it off, artwork and window treatments. What don't they sell? Well, reread what they do sell above and you'll find out there's not much they don't sell. Folks, it's the only credible buying service we've found in the country with confirmation of their good-standing from the Better Business Bureau. So have at it! A total kitchen remodel was priced by one member at a Home Center for $20,000 and through Direct Buy, the couple got it for $6,000 — the identical cabinets and all! Visit also in Fort Worth at 2533 E. Loop 820 North, Bldg. 13, Fort Worth, TX 76118. To get to the Sunnyvale headquarters, exit Collins Rd. off Hwy. 80 E and stay on the feeder road 1.3 miles on the right. You can't miss it. Watch for their billboards and you're almost there. Meet your brother-in-law in the business who can really get it for your wholesale (without the guilt!)

★★★★ **Dollar Tree Store**   817/461-6899
2212 S. Fielder Rd.   Mon-Sat 9-9; Sun 11-7
Arlington, TX 76013
www.dollartree.com

If only it grew on trees. Well, even if money doesn't, the stuff here is ripe for the pickings. This national chain is rooted in good old-fashioned greed. A buck's a buck, and let your buck stop here. Closeouts, overruns and re-packagings from major and generic manufacturers of housewares, seasonal goods, candy/food, toys, health/beauty care items, gifts, party goods, stationery, books, accessories. Like a modern-day version of the 5 & 10, expect to see general merchandise in a variety of categories. Since they operate almost 2,000 stores around the country, they are big and they're getting bigger. By the way, they also operate stores under different names such as: Dollar Tree, Dollar Bill$Æ, Only $1.00, ONLY $ONEÆ and Dollar Express. Check directory for the store nearest you. Some are small, some are big, some are fair, others are fabulous.

★★★★★ **JCPenney Outlet Store**   972/874-0578
3000 Grapevine Mills Pkwy.   Mon-Sat 10-9:30; Sun 11-7
Grapevine, TX 76051
www.jcpenney.com

A "penney" for your thoughts? At their outlet, expect to get more than you bargained for and more than just a penny or two off. We're talking the real deal! A real outlet with really big savings. Often times, they're running a sale with an additional percentage off, and discounts of 75 percent off the original price is commonplace. That's when it's time to call out the troops. Strike up the band. Load up the truck. Reward yourself with closeouts, discontinueds, returns or overruns from their retail stores or catalog. The usual savings? At least 40 to 60 percent off. Just look what your pennies will buy: family apparel, athletic apparel, family shoes, athletic shoes, petites, misses, and tall women's fashions, home furnishings, home accessories, electronics and even big and tall men's apparel. The warehouse environment presents the merchandise without any distractions of fancy displays or colorful vignettes. Plain and simple. Shop and go. Even if you're not a full-fledged Penney's shopper, give it a look-see and you might be persuaded to join the Penney Brigade — where every dollar earned is several dollars saved.

★★★★   Kohl's   972/939-2887

4120 Old Denton Rd.   Mon-Fri 8 AM-10 PM; Sun 10-8
Carrollton, TX 75010
www.kohls.com

This Kohl won't burn you on high prices nor will they make an ash out of you, either. Fan(s) flock to this neighborhood discount department store concept while department store's flames are flickering in regional malls across the country. It doesn't take a brain trust to see why Kohl's is making its way across America. There's always a sale going on, somewhere, somehow. It's usually across an entire category, but when they're on, they're really on and generous across the board. Founded in 1962 in Milwaukee, Wisconsin, they carry all of the popular brands that a value-oriented family would want: everything from **ADIDAS** to **VANITY FAIR**. Their inventory, besides clothing for the entire family, will sometimes burn a hole in your pocket so beware. Fill up your arms (sorry folks, no shopping carts) with shoes, housewares, home decor, jewelry, toys, cards and more. They offer their own credit card and there's always a great sale going on. Twenty percent is their usual discount, but enjoy great savings during frequent sales and their "FINAL" clearances are the best when you can sometimes at the end-of-the-season. Merchandise is then marked for next to nothing (up to 80 percent off). At the beginning of the summer, they had a rack with junior knit long-sleeved shirts and sweaters, retailing $15 to $38 in name brands like MUDD, for $1.99. Check directory for store nearest you. *Call toll-free: 800/837-1500*

★★★★★★   Marshalls   972/248-8494

7609 Campbell Rd.   Mon-Sat 9:30-9:30; Sun 11-7
Dallas, TX 75248
www.MarshallsOnline.com

 Let me introduce you to the Marshall's plan and its sibling, TJMaxx. No doubt, it's soon to overtake the world of discount shopping. Going strong for more years that I want to remember, they now own the **CAROLE LITTLE** label and its plus-size division, CL II. Smart move, Bernie. Broadening its opportunity to be consistent by having this particular label in their off-price stores, expect them to be big source for both the **CAROLE LITTLE** clothing line as well as their shoes. This **BOSTON**-based giant is spear-headed by an old friend, Bernie Cammarato, who helped orchestrate TJ's buy out by his old alma mater, Marshall's. Always save 20 to 60 percent and more when there's a sale going on. Currently, they're expanding their gift department, bed and bath world, housewares and Women's World for plus sizes since TJ decided to exit that niche market. The expanded Women's Department in sizes 14-28 is welcomed since TJMaxx has virtually left the "real" women's world to their older sister. Big girls are not crying any more. When TJ left, **MARSHALLS** picked up the slack. And slacks it is, alongside dresses and sportswear, suits and lingerie. Desirable name-brand fashions for men, sportswear for women, children's apparel and lingerie, plus shoes and accessories, gourmet food items, jewelry, housewares, bed & bath items, swimwear, hosiery, the works! Check directory for the location nearest you. *Call toll-free: 800/MARSHALL*

★★   Mervyn's   **972/270-8800**

1201 Centerville Rd.   Mon-Sat 9 AM-10 PM; Sun 9-9
Garland, TX 75041
www.mervyns.com

Founded in 1949, this California-based chain offers popular name brands for about 20 percent off with a California-dreaming attitude. Similar in feel to Kohl's, their "target" audience is a neighborhood family wanting to get a few things to wear to the office for casual Fridays (which is all but disappearing on the corporate scene) or maybe something new to wear to school. Owned by the Target Corporation, expect to see brands that hit the bullseye: ARROW, CHEETAH, DOCKERS, FIELDCREST, GLORIA VANDERBILT, HIGH SIERRA, JEEP, JOCKEY, KEDS, KITCHENAID, LEVI'S, MARTEX, NEW BALANCE, NIKE, OLGA, OSTER, SAMSONITE, TIMEX, UNION BAY, VILLAGER and more. The trouble with the store, though, is that it's boring. No oomph. Nothing vibrant. All khaki and cream and nothing to dream about. Certainly not like Target, which has energy, electricity, drama in their merchandising mix. However, it does provide a valuable service to the community. What it that? Keeping North Hills Mall alive since there's no other reason to shop there (except for the new theater in the round that is attracting some attention.) Enough said. Go online for all their store specials, a nice feature to entice you to leave the comfort of your home and drive to the nearest store. Speaking of stores, since there's always something on sale, you might want to sing, "California, Hear I Come!" before you check out the location nearest you.

★★★★★★   Neiman's Last Call   **972/724-4900**

3000 Grapevine Mills Parkway   Mon-Sat 10-9:30; Sun 11-8
Grapevine, TX 76051
www.millscorp.com/grapevine

 Attention Fashionistas! It was just a matter of time before needless markups would make it worth your while. The opening of Neiman Marcus's Clearance Store is the reason to season your wardrobe with buys up to 80 percent off. Opened since the spring of 2002, this approximately 32,000 square feet of outlet bliss joins their other TEXAS location in Austin plus eight other locations around the country. No doubt, home-based fans of Neiman's have embraced them with baited bargain breath. Apparel and accessories abound, marked down 40 to 80 percent from their 32 regular stores, NM Direct, and one of their sister stores, Bergdorf Goodman. Now we're talkin'! What you see is the past season's merchandise, but how different is last season's DONNA KARAN black skirt from this season's? Nobody will ever know how low you would go just to bring home an outfit or two from NM. When asked where you shop, at last, you can say Neiman's (unless you're like me and brag how little you've spent!) Last Call is on the mall's east side, near Rainforest Cafe. Say hello to our favorite son. (and my son's favorite, too.)

★★★★★★   Nordstrom Rack   **972/267-1414**

1701 D-1 Preston Road   Mon-Sat 9:30-9:30; Sun 12-6
Plano, TX 75093
www.nordstrom.com

 You can shop their retail stores at the Dallas Galleria, North East Mall in Hurst, or Stonebriar Centre in Frisco, or you can be smart and go to the Nordstrom Rack instead. How many neighbors, friends and family have told you, you better shop The Rack, Mac or don't ya come back no more, no more, no more, no more! How many even knew it existed? To spark your interest, let me inform you of the thousands and thousands of ladies'shoes at 30 to 75 percent off retail? And those discounts carry over into the fashion departments for men, women and children, too, at similar discounts. Current merchandise, no less. Since my daughter-in-law is a Nordstrom employee, I wonder if this write-up would be considered "insider shopping." Over a 100 years old, this store was founded by John W. Nordstrom but it's the employees who have built a business on the principles of quality, value, selection and service. They win awards to that effect and are world renowned for their bend-over-backwards, personalized service. As one of the nation's leading fashion retailers, offering a wide variety of fine quality apparel, shoes and accessories for men, women and children at stores across the country, the Rack is just a miniature version for the shop-worn. How can you say NO to ABS BY ALLEN SCHWARTZ, DKNY, ELIE TAHARI, BCBG MAX AZIA, KATE SPADE, LAUREN BY RALPH LAUREN, LIZ CLAIBORNE, LUCKY BRAND....aren't you impressed yet?

★ Off Rodeo Drive

972/724-7860

3000 Grapevine Mills Pkwy.
Grapevine, TX 76051
www.bernini.com

Mon-Sat 10-10; Sun 11-8

Find it in Neighborhood 2 at Grapevine Mills but never look a gift horse in the mouth. The salesmen are standing with arms folded waiting to pounce on you when they see the whites of YOUR eyes and the green of your money. Honestly, I've never seen anybody shopping there. Rodeo Drive, now really? The fact is, you'd probably never see a cowboy dressed to ride the bulls in a fine Italian Bernini suit. As a matter of fact, **BERNINI** makes couturier apparel and, yet, supposedly opens an outlet store smack-dab in the middle of the biggest mall in Texas? Dubious at best. But beautiful men's clothing at its best. Shop on Rodeo Drive and you'll drop a bundle. Shop Off Rodeo Drive, and you'll drop a bundle — not much difference except the preponderance of Rolls Royces. Savings, well, very little. There's more than 50 Off Rodeo Drive stores around the country, with claims of savings up to 70 percent off designer fashions for menswear, dress shirts, dress pants and accessories like belts and cuff links or so the story goes. And their website relates to their retail/regular stores. It's all Italian — clothes, shoes, fragrances displayed in a beautiful 30,000 square foot emporium with sentries standing in as salesmen guarding the high-priced merchandise. Didn't get a dollar from me or anybody else I've walked through the store with including the crew of the TV Show "Extra!" Well, you win some, you lose some.

Overstock.com

801/947-3100

6322 South 3000 East, Suite 100
Salt Lake City, UT 84121
www.overstock.com   🖱 *Top Online Store!*

When it comes to writing RAVE reviews about a shopping site, this is one name that stands head and shoulders above the rest. Founded by wunderkind Patrick Byrnes, this is one of the dot.com success stories of the century. It doesn't get better than savings up to 70 percent everyday, seven days a week, 365 days a year with a guarantee that they will refund the difference if you ever find the same item for less anywhere on the web. A 100 percent, 240 thread-count down comforter that retailed for $199 was $69.96 — that's 65 percent off the bat. You've got bats in your belfry if you need more convincing that there's not much the department or specialty store has that Overstock doesn't have — at a fraction of the price. right there. The endless stream of categories and products will boggle your mind. Search by brand or by product. A few brands to brag about include ADIDAS, AMERICAN TOURISTER, ANNE KLEIN, AVIA, BETTY CROCKER, BRAUN, BVLGARI, CANON, CASIO, COMPAQ, CONAIR, CUISINART,

DKNY, DISNEY, ESPRIT, EUREKA, FARBERWARE, FILA, FOSSIL, G.E., GORHAM, GUND, HAMILTON BEACH, HASBRO, HOOVER, HUMMEL, KODAK, KRUPS, LENOX, LLADRO, MIKASA, MILTON BRADLEY, NASCAR, NIKON, NOKIA, ONEIDA, OSTER, POLAROID, RCA, REVEREWARE, RICOH, ROLLERBLADE, ROWENTA, ROYAL VELVET, SAMSONITE, SEGA, SERENGETI, SMITH & HAWKEN, SONY, SUNBEAM, TRAVELPRO, UNIDEN, WALLACE, WATERFORD, WEDGWOOD, XEROX, YAMAHA, ZENITH — yep, from A to Z, they can keep you shopping for a lifetime. Well-organized, flawless shipping (each item comes in a sturdy box, well wrapped, and within days for only $2.95), easy to communicate with, and every category under the sun: bed and bath, decorative accessories, furniture, kitchen, lighting, rugs, window treatments, small appliances, cookware, crystal and china, gourmet, health and beauty aids, tabletop, costume and fine jewelry, sporting goods and gear, luggage and handbags, collectibles, baby items, crafts, dolls, games & puzzles, toys — once you've made your first purchase, you'll be hooked! *Call toll-free: 800/989-0135*

★★★★★   Real Deal Outlet   903/567-6619

1503 N. Hwy. 19   Mon-Sat 9:30-5:30 & First Monday
Canton, TX 75103
www.realdeal.homeappliances.com

Looking for the real deal? Well, here's where it's at when there's nothing happening at First Monday. If you're fed up with the spin cycle of paying retail, consider drying out with scratch and dent appliances with names like **KITCHENAID, ROPER** and **WHIRLPOOL.** Deals move in and out faster than a speeding bullet. And if it isn't appliances, another day it could be leather goods like purses, gloves, motorcycle chaps, purses, gloves, coats, vests, totes and fanny packs. Had enough of leather, already, then see what's up in the replica department. I timed out with the antique clocks for $18-$59 that sure looked a lot more expensive. You know those intricate Victorian-carved clocks that are perfect on a mantle? Well, no need to kill time, then why not burn the candle at both ends. Dream on with the "Dreamers Candles" in over 71 fragrances for $12.50. Whatever they can get their hands on at a deal, they wheel and deal and pass the savings on. A big scratch and dent collection of dining room tables, chairs, coffee table sets of the budget variety though you can order more from the myriad of catalogs at a good price were also available. The **SAUDER WOODWORKING** products won hands down with a huge selection of computer desks, entertainment centers, chests, armoires and more. This is the same brand that you'd see at Office Depot and Office Max. Inexpensive knock-down furniture that will generally require assembly was also available but you have to be handy with a screw driver and you must not drink and drive a nail at the same time. You'll love the prices. Too, if you're remodeling a kitchen and expect to purchase three or more major appliances, don't be bashful and ask for a "builders'discount." It won't hurt to ask. You might even save some more money. And isn't that the "real deal" when all is said and done?

★★★   Ross Dress For Less   972/247-1228

3046 Forest Lane   Mon-Sat 9:30-9;:30 Sun Noon-7
Dallas, TX 75234
www.rossstores.com

There's always something new at Ross, or at least that's what I hear hundreds of times a day from their TV commercials. This national chain is a multi-billion-dollar company with the flow of merchandise so erratic, you wonder where it comes and goes faster than a New York bullet? It's either a feast or famine; some days there's a lot of great, trendy and classic styles; other times you might have to settle for a lime green sweater that's more slime than lime or a powder blue pair of jeans that's unraveling at the seams. That's the way it is. At times, we did hit paydirt and found great deals on **MIKASA** vases and crystalware, picture frames and photo albums that, in a pinch, saved the day when a gift was called for at the last minute. Some items are closeouts, some seconds and some slightly damaged, but all priced to sell fast. Check directory or online for the store nearest you. *Call toll-free: 800/289-7677*

★★★★★ **Sam's Wholesale Club**   **972/436-6684**
751 W. Main St.   Mon-Fri 10-8:30; Sat 9:30-8:30; Sun 10-6
Lewisville, TX 75067
www.samsclub.com

You don't need me to tell you about Sam's. (Uncle) Sam needs you! Even with a Super Wal-Mart nearby, you might find the prices compatible with the club though occasionally, I've found some prices at Super Wal-Mart to be less than at Sam's. Just in case you need an introduction, this is Wal-Mart's division for wholesale shopping. You'll need to be a member and get a card to get in the doors. You will be buying in bulk. They've added more services such as a photo-developing desk, an eyeglass counter, mobile phone service, travel, DirecTV and satellite TV and more. Load up on TVs and TV dinners, bargains in best-selling books and blue jeans, food and furniture, office supplies and equipment, faxes and floor care, carpet and Christmas wrap. Personal membership was $35/year and included two cards. The business membership was $30/year and included a spouse's card. You must have two forms of positive proof you've got a business. Then there's the Advantage Plus and Business Plus memberships, $100/year; this premium program included additional discounts from unrelated services like auto buying, auto servicing, boat buying, dental services (does that mean they offer root canals?), insurance, internet service plans, it's just doesn't quit. Check directory for other 14 locations throughout the Metroplex, most located next to a Wal-Mart. When shopping for a new car, pull out your Sam's Club Membership and there's a chance they'll negotiate. They did when we tried it. *Call toll-free: 888/733-7267*

★★★★★★ **Sears Outlet Store**   **972/418-2293**
2724 Realty Road   Mon-Fri 10-7; Sat 9-7; Sun 12-5
Carrollton, TX 75006
www.sears.com

 In August, they finally made their move....but not far from their location at Belt Line and Josey. Just head down Belt Line to Marsh Lane; one block north of Belt Line is Realty Road. Here is where living the good life at a great price is close to my own trademark, "Living the Good Life at Half the Price." Can't fault them for copying me. It is a great expression that tells it all. There is a definite synergism between the two of us. They are one of the biggest in their business; we're the biggest in ours. And if truth be known, we both offer some of the best prices in the Metroplex. For example, washers (as low as $371.99), dryers ($239.99), side-by-side refrigerators ($699.99), top-mount refrigerators ($399.99) and electric ranges ($399.99). Keep this posted when you're ready to take the plunge. They not only carry their own private label **KENMORE**, but also **AMANA**, **FRIGIDAIRE**, **GENERAL ELECTRIC**, **MAYTAG** and **WHIRLPOOL**. Indeed, they're the best source for **KENMORE** appliances and other brand names, plus big-screen TVs. In fact, that is where they shine. When their sale is on for big screen TVs, you better be first in line because at half price, they sell out quickly. Shop often, as the merchandise moves in and out as stealthily as an agile quarterback during a Cowboy game. Visit also in Grand Prairie at 2985 S. Hwy. 360, 972/988-3036.

★★★★ Stein Mart

817/735-4533
Mon-Sat 10-9; Sun Noon-6

6385 Camp Bowie
Fort Worth, TX 76116
www.steinmart.com

No relation to Goldstein, this Stein is still golden for discriminating shoppers. Designer and well-known brand apparel for men, women and children, it's the real McCoy. And it's where the Diva and Tammy Faye shop when together in Charlotte, North Carolina. The boutique ladies hover over their selective turf with all these upscale favorites. Guys can don luxury fiber sport coats, classic khakis and designer shirts and the all-important golf sportswear bearing golf hero's names. Stein-Mart also caters to Petites' and Women's Sizes and offers a Big & Tall men's department. Shoes for both, and more accessories and gifty housewares, gourmet food stuff, bed and bath items; it's like a mini Saks 5th. But it's the jewelry department that sends my heart a-flutter. Love it. Clasp it. Dangle it. Hang it. Wear it. Buy it. Look for 15 percent off coupons in your Sunday papers (they used to be 20 percent off) and are usually good for two of something. That means, if you find something you love — or it's already on sale, you can save even more. Many locations including Hurst, Arlington, Dallas, Irving, Lewisville, Fort Worth, Frisco, Plano. Remember, it only looks expensive. No online shopping yet, too bad. Just wait, especially if you can't get enough of designer stuff at 30-50 percent off. *Call toll-free: 888/SteinMar*

★★★★ Syms

214/902-9600
Mon-Fri 10-9; Sat 10-8; Sun Noon-5:30

4770 W. Mockingbird Lane
Dallas, TX 75209
www.symsclothing.com

Go online and print off a coupon worth an additional 10 percent off. Then go shopping at Syms. 5 STARS for the Italian men's clothes starting at just $99 for sports coats and $59 for dress pants represents one of the best men's values in the Metroplex. Save on young men's wardrobes of blazers, $59 and dress pants, $29. Remember, they retail for almost 40 percent more elsewhere. That's why you need to get an education, says Marcy Syms. "An educated consumer is their best customer." Syms selection is complete, just like in a department store, without the full price tags. Save 25 to 40 percent on merchandise that goes lower and lower as the days pass by. Names to consider include ADOLFO, BALLY, CALVIN KLEIN, COLE-HAAN, DKNY, DOLCE & GABBANA, GEOFFREY BEANE, GIANNI VERSACE, GIVENCHY, JONES NY, LIZ CLAIBORNE, OLEG CASSINI, PERRY ELLIS, REEBOK, STANLEY BLACKER, RALPH LAUREN, VALENTINO and others that could fill the pages of GQ Magazine. The men's department, though, remains their forte and occupies 60 percent of the store's merchandise in sizes 36S-54XL. They get 5 STARS; the women's I've never been a big fan of their ladies wear so they get a 4 STAR. Another location in the Mid Cities, in Hurst on the Airport Freeway (Highway 183) just west of Precinct Line Rd., near Abuelo's Mexican Restaurant.

★★★★★★ TJ Maxx

972/437-1842
Mon-Sat 9:30-9:30; Sun 11-6

12 Richardson Heights
Richardson, TX 75080
www.tjmaxx.com

Here we go again. To think I knew them when. Back in 1973, I was sitting on the floor with the yet unknown founder of TJ Maxx, who was then with Marshall's. Today, the same gentleman is the head honcho and founder of the biggest off-price retailer in the nation. It started out as small potatoes in Massachusetts and now it's stuffed with cheese and bacon bits — mashing prices to what has become the standard in the industry. Shoppers can expect 20 to 60 percent off everyday and during sale time, prices hit rock bottom. Since the opening of their first stores in Worcester and Auburn, MA in 1977, they have grown to be the nation's largest off-price retailer with over 660 stores in 47 states. TJ Maxx sells brand-name and designer fashions for the entire family and home accessories at up to 60 percent less than department and specialty stores bargains. See Sue at the checkout counter checking out CARTERS, KEDS, KENNETH COLE, LEVI'S, LIZ CLAIBORNE, MUDD, 9 WEST, SKETCHERS and XOXO. I invite you to smell the latest fragrances, try on a pair of shoes, find a matching handbag, discover some fabulous new kitchen towels, bath towels, accessories for the kitchen and bath, picture frames and sneak out the door with some imported olives and Italian crackers. Check directory for additional locations. They sure smell good like the best of them should. *Call toll-free: 800/2-TJ-MAX*

★★★★★★ Tuesday Morning

972/991-2996

14631 Inwood Rd.
Dallas, TX 75247
www.tuesdaymorning.com

Major Sales Throughout the Year

Not just another day of the week, when their doors open, run for your life(style.) Expect closeouts on a laundry list of everything that has gift potential at prices 50 to 80 percent less. Closeouts and excess inventory from manufacturers, department and specialty stores, Trade Mart samples, mail order catalogs, even failed dot.com sites are now fair game for this store. "Closed for restocking" is a customary sign in their windows and there, you have the beginnings of this almost 30-year-old veteran of the bargain biz. Go online to find the dates they're open and their seasonal hours. They are ranked the biggest closeout gift chain in the country. Satisfaction is guaranteed or your money back — for any reason. Some regular brands include AMERICAN TOURISTER, BILL BLASS, CIAO, CUISINART, FARBERWARE, LARK, LEGO, LIMOGES, MADAME ALEXANDER, MARTEX, MURANO, PIERRE CARDIN, REVERE, ROYAL DOULTON, SABATIER, SAMSONITE, WEDGWOOD and more. If you are looking for name-brand gifts, there isn't a close-out in the world that won't eventually land at a TM shelf somewhere. More than 300 stores nationwide. Do you really think LAUREN BACALL pulls up in a limo? It's one thing to have her Persian eat out of Baccarat crystal and another thing for her to be shopping at a Tuesday Morning when she could probably buy the entire store. I need to ask her the next time I bump into her — even if it's not on a Tuesday morning.

Electronics, TVs & Satellite Dishes

★★★★★★ **At Your Service Flooring Discounters** 817/831-3113

4400 Airport Freeway
Haltom City, TX 76117
www.ayselectronics.com

Mon-Fri 8-6; Sat 9-1

 If you want to be floored, At Your Service Flooring Discounters is the source to do it. But if you want to be floored and not just buy flooring from At Your Service, think electronics, satellites and TVs. That's right, this is their side business, (literally to the side of their ever expanding flooring business) located in an old building one block east of Beach Street on the service road of Hwy. 121 (Airport Freeway). You don't think they'd throw their more than 20 years experience working with the former Highland Appliance electronics and appliance stores away, do you? No sir. They not only lay down the red carpet, they will provide you with the best prices on name brand electronics like **PANASONIC**, **PIONEER** and **SONY**. Both **DISH NETWORK** and **DIRECTTV** satellites, equipment for your media room, appliances, and now the latest Noom system for HDTV. Word of mouth has made them one of the fastest growing one-stop carpet and electronic retailers in Tarrant County. At Your Service are straight shooters. They'll never bamboozle you with a flimflam song and dance, promising the moon and delivering something else. Joe Lucas and Terry Ray are men who stand up for the best service in everything they do, from representing the best products to providing the best follow-up on installation and service. You're in good hands at At Your Service.(AYE)

★★★★ **Audio Concepts** 214/360-9520

11661 Preston Rd.
Dallas, TX 75230
www.dalaudioconcepts.com

Tues-Thurs 10-7; Fri-Sat 10-6

To recreate the sounds of music of a 40-member orchestra, you'll want the very best equipment. For more than 15 years, Audio Concepts, at the southwest corner of Preston and Forest has been the place to be seen (and heard). For as little as $1,500 to as much as $50,000, you can create the level you're looking for in sound and TV reproduction. They sell, service and set up every system they sell with Free delivery anywhere in the Dallas/North Texas area. Sit down and put your feet up in one of their multi-media rooms and let them show you the difference. They carry the best and if you can't hear the difference, you might want a lesson in Audio Conceptology 101. Some of the brands they carry include: **ARCAM, AUDIO RESEARCH, AYRE, BENZ, GRADO, KOETSU, LINN, NAD, NAIM, REGA, ROTEL, THETA** and **WILSON BEACH**. Check inventory often as items change.

★★★★ Best Buy

972/239-9980
Mon-Sat 10-9; Sun 11-6

4255 LBJ Frwy.
Dallas, TX 75244
www.bestbuy.com

If you haven't shopped Best Buy, you probably haven't bought a computer, TV, camera, camcorder, piece of audio or video equipment, phone system, cell phone, home appliance, keyboard, CD, video game or office equipment lately. They are the big box player for everything that relates to Electronics & TVs — and then some. Everything you've ever needed or wanted that would add a little learning, fun or entertainment to your life is somewhere down their aisles. From PCs to software, VCRs to DVDs, car stereos to home theaters, big screens to movies, boom boxes to cell phones — along with a vast array of music CDs and now, you can buy it all online. Looking for a desktop, notebook, monitor or printer? What about a handheld computer? Need more memory? What about a digital camera, a portable MP3 player, a modem, a keyboard — maybe even sign up for internet services. For audio products, they carry audio systems, components, compact systems, speakers, TVs, VCRs, DVD players, camcorders and media furniture. Check directory for location nearest you! *Call toll-free: 888/BEST-BUY*

★★★★★ CAM Audio

972/271-0006
Mon-Fri 8:30-5:30

2210 Executive Drive
Garland, TX 75041
www.camaudio.com

If I've said it once, I've said it again and again — I make a tape of it. Save my voice, save my money thanks to CAM Audio. Here's their library of supplies: Audio, Video, Sound Supplies, Duplication and Packaging Services. Click "Para Informacion" if you prefer to learn about them in Espanol. Order in bulk and save big bucks. Video tapes with your name customized on the labels (FREE). Now do you see why they have 5 stars? And listen to this — no charge for freight shipping, if necessary. Located near Jupiter and Miller Road, CAM is a distributor of 3M audio products. Over the years, they've expanded to other audio, video and sound amplification products such as tapes, albums, storage units, video cameras, decks, monitors and blank videotapes. If you're looking for the best in sound equipment, including microphones, speakers, mixers and amps, CAM is the man! Tune-in to such brand names as **AMPLI VOX, ASTOUND, BOSE, BRAVO, BRETFORD, BUHL, DA-LITE, DOLBY, DRAPER, EIKI, ELECTRO-VOICE, ELMO, GEM, HAMILTON, JVC, LUXOR, MARANTZ, MAXWELL, MOTOROLA, OTARI, PANASONIC, PELICAN, SANYO, SHARP, SHURE, SONY, TDK, TEAC, TECHNICS, TELEX, ULTIMATE SUPPORT** and **VIDEONICS**. *Call toll-free: 800/527-3458*

★★★ Circuit City

817/738-1796
Mon-Sat 10-9; Sun 11-6

4820 W. I-20
Fort Worth, TX 76132
www.circuitcity.com

At last, they took my irritation about their restocking fees to heart. And now, take note: There is a 30-day full exchange or refund policy as standard operating procedure. Yea, team! No restocking fees. Period. End of discussion. The number of days, though, to return a **PC** is 14 days. If you are returning it, be sure to include all packaging and the box. And on CDs that have been opened, only exact exchanges are possible, and only in the case of a defect. What is nice, though, is that online purchases may be returned or exchanged at your nearest store; you don't have to mail it back. You can even shop online and pick "Express in Store" whereby you can pick up the item at your closest store. Pay with a credit card, and you can pick up the item immediately or within 14 days. This store offers some of the best buys (pardon the expression) audio, video, TVs, computers, car accessories, office equipment, cameras, phones, musical equipment, movies, games, gift cards, but watch out for buying those extended service warranties. They do car audio installations, but not on home appliances. Check weekly ads for sales and be sure to print out rebates online. *Call toll-free: 800/284-4886*

★★★★   Conn's   214/361-2798

11250 North Central Expressway   Mon-Sat 10-9; Sun 11-6
Dallas, TX 75243
www.conns.com

This regional category killer based in Beaumont, TX (appliances and electronics are their strengths) was a favorite of The Underground Shopper in Houston and San Antonio and has finally made its way onto the Metroplex shopping scene. Currently, they have 44 locations in the Southwest (Houston, San Antonio, Austin, Beaumont and the Gold Triangle in Texas and in Lake Charles, Lafayette, New Iberia and Baton Rouge, Louisiana.) With three locations in the Dallas area and more to come, I bet you can not believe there was even room for another store offering major appliances, small appliances, bedding, **BERKLINE** recliners, vacuums, lawnmowers, DVDs, computers, digital cameras, camcorders, **BOSE** sound systems, cordless phones, large screen TVs, turkey friers, karaoke machines, remote controlled cars and "Early Bird Specials" like a red or blue electric scooter for $119.99. Opening just in the nick of time for the holidays, no down payment, no payments, no interest for 12 months when they first opened on select **GE**, **FRIGIDAIRE** or **MAYTAG** appliances and select big screen TVs. Tune in to their other locations in Richardson at 1300 East Belt Line Road, 972/690-5034 and their newest in Lewisville at 2422 South Stemmons, 972/315-5080. *Call toll-free: 877/472-5422*

★★★★★   Ed Kellum & Son   214/526-1717

4533 Cole Ave.   Mon-Sat 9-6; Thurs 9-8
Dallas, TX 75205
www.edkellum.com

They've been leaders in the electronics, TVs and appliance business for 50 years; yet, a plain vanilla website? Go figure. Well, don't hold that against them. Since 1948 they've been busy doing other things like installing built-in kitchen appliances and the new Dolby Digital home theater rooms (with High Definition 52-inch big screen for $2,599). For any size TV, for that matter, Ed Kellum can deliver. From a nine-inch to 80-inch, they can make you see straight. Buy everything that makes your house come alive! From VCRs, DVD players, DSS dishes and receivers and camcorders to video cabinets, stands, remotes, tapes, cables and batteries. The line-up of brands is celestial: **CANON, DENON, ELITE, FUJI, GO-VIDEO, INTEGRA, JBL, JVC, M & K, MAGNAVOX, MB QUART, MIRAGE, MITSUBISHI, MONSTER CABLE, NILES, OMNI MOUNT, ONKYO, PANASONIC, PETRA, POLK, QUASAR, RCA, SONY, TOSHIBA, UNIDEN** and others. Then if you want to indulge in some electrifying personal hair styling, walk across the street to SoZo Hair Salon. Jody and Ron are the proprietors and offer comparable artistry to Ed Kellum's kitchen vignettes.

★★★★★★ **Fry's Electronics** **214-342-5900**

12710 Executive Drive
Dallas, TX 75238
www.outpost.com

Mon-Fri 8 AM-9 PM; Sat 9-9; Sun 9-7

 What a difference a year makes. Their newest location in Irving is the best Fry's — worth a look to try and ultimately to buy. Land a big one at any of their locations. Last year, they were at the bottom of my list, but this year, they captured a front position as noted by their 100 BEST destination. In their new location, above, they have set the bar much higher than at their other stores. You can bet your last dollar that at this location, you'll score a royal flush; although both have great prices, this location actually has great service, too. Both, of course, guarantee the lowest price by matching any competitor's price. But it's the service in Irving that will set them apart. They have really toed the line at this store; the lines moved along effortlessly, the staff were knowledgeable about the products, and there didn't appear to be any refurbished products hanging around without proper notice. Second location is in Irving, at 2788 Market Place Blvd., 214/242-4918 and a third in Plano at 700 E. Plano Parkway, 214/291-6000. They Fry-d the competition this year! *Call toll-free: 877-OUTPOST*

★★★★★ **Hawk Electronics** **972/316-3388**

2403 Stemmons Frwy., Suite 110
Lewisville, TX 75067
www.hawkelectronics.com

Mon-Sat 9-7

Soar like an eagle, but shop like a Hawk if an electronic product is on your shopping list. From wireless/cellular communications to DISH Satellite TV Systems, Personal Electronics to TVs and Home Theater Packages, Hawk flies with the best. They also custom install Car Audio & Security systems along with the latest Mobile Navigation or Mobile Video systems. There are multiple locations in the Metroplex, with the newest location being in Plano at 3801 W. George Bush Highway, Suite 132. Check their website for the location nearest you. For an expanded venue, shop their Home Theater and Personal Electronics departments from all the leading manufacturers: BOSE, HARMON-KARDON, PANASONIC, PIONEER, SONY, TIVO, UBL and more. The Meridian Platinum GPS system was $248.87, rather than $349.95, and a Sony CD/MP3 player was $88.87, rather than $129.95. Twelve months interest FREE! You don't see prices like this too often. Corporate offices in Fort Worth, so give a round of applause to this Texas endangered species — a 5-star home town favorite.

★★★★★★ **Hillcrest High Fidelity** **972/392-7636**

13400 Preston Rd.
Dallas, TX 75240
www.hillcresthifi.com

Mon-Fri 10-7; Sat 10-6;

 Hillcrest High Fidelity has been the cream of the crop in sound systems since 1947, so it doesn't surprise me that they'd be ripe for a takeover. Sure enough, they were bought by the Tweeter chain. With two locations and over 50 years experience, former owners Michael Gallant and Tom Kissell still maintain a hands-on approach to keeping customers in tune. Experts in home entertainment, custom design and a "we'll match prices" philosophy that guarantees your complete satisfaction, how can you lose? Tune-r in, Tweety Bird, for the finest in audio and video equipment. They call it high-end affordability. See the likes of ANTHEM by SONIC FRONTIERS, AUTOQUEST CABLES, B&W, KIMBER KAIBLE, KLIPSCH, KRELL, LEXICON, MARANTZ, MCINTOSH, NAKAMICHI, PARADIGM, PIONEER ELITE, ROCKUSTICS, ROTEL, SONY ES, TRIBUTARIES, VELODYNE and YAMAHA, for starters. Visit their Plano location at 3309 Dallas Pkwy. (at Parker Road) or call them at 972/473-2248. They are still maintaining their autonomy from the Tweeter chain.

★★★★　Home Theater Store　　　　　972/404-9500

13330 Preston Rd.　　　　　　　　　　　　　　Mon-Sat 10-8; Sun Noon-6
Dallas, TX 75240
www.hometheaterstore.com

Just north of LBJ, you can tune in to almost any high-tech, high-end, high-priced piece of electronic wizardry, but when there's a warehouse clearance, there's no better place to tune in to than right here. Watch newspapers for sales and then run, baby, run. Is it any wonder they were named one of the 10 BEST Custom Installers by *Audio Video Magazine* in both 2001 and 2002. I'll vote for them year 'round just in case they need my vote. Choose from hundreds of big screens, tube TVs, VCRs, A/V Receivers, Speakers, DVD players and more. From **SONY** portable stereos, as low as $39, to **MITSUBISHI** rack systems, brand-new in the box, starting as low as $199, you can calibrate the savings to be big on many products across the board. Tune in to audio and video systems from "Cinema Series" by **TOSHIBA**, "Elite" by **PIONEER**, **MITSUBISHI**, **SHARP**, "Triniton" by SONY and "XF" by **PANASONIC** were some of the brand highlights here. You'll also find a wide variety of speakers by **BOSE**, **PARADIGM** and **POLK AUDIO**, as well as media furniture by **CONTOUR**, **DRAPER** and **LEXINGTON** to name a few. They offer the "Guaranteed Low Prices" but who doesn't in this day and age?

★★★★★★　Radio Shack Outlet Store　　　817/654-0337

900 Terminal Rd.　　　　　　　　　　　　　　Mon-Sat 9-8; Sun Noon-6
Fort Worth, TX 76106
www.radioshack.com

Listen to this return policy: anything over $20 has a seven-day return policy; but anything under $20, that's it. It's a final sale and sold as-is! Some items come with a warranty and some warranties are voided for various reasons, so ask before you buy, and be sure to plug it in and kick the tires before your seven day return is up. Once the eighth day arrives, there's no turning back. This is Radio Shack's outlet and merely contains a portion of their regular store's inventory. At their retail stores, they do offer a full 30-day return policy, warranties and repairs and Radio Shack, by the way, will also repair any make and model of electronics, no matter where you bought it! How's that for service? Their outlet, though, is a fully stocked store that includes scratched and dented (mostly the boxes), seconds, imperfects, discontinued and over-produced items where savings of 50 percent can be realized. Located near the Fort Worth Stock-yards, bring those tourists to Fort Worth and visit both. Lots of fun and lots of frugality on TVs, computers, CD players, car stereos, mobile phones, scanners and more. At Christmas time, it's a mad house, so shop early. In the off season, you can often see goodies marked 50 to 80 percent off retail, particularly batteries. So stock up for those stocking stuffers now. ***Call toll-free: 800/223-8344***

★★★★　Robert Kent TV & Appliance/Repairs　817/923-1973

4944 James Ave.　　　　　　　　　　　　　　Mon-Fri 8:30-6:30; Sat 9-6
Fort Worth, TX 76115

From appliances to electronics, these folks are a mainstay in the Fort Worth metro area. No relation to Clark Kent, they are, nevertheless, the Superman of appliances and electronics. Expect to be electrified by the selection of TVs and VCRs, washers, dryers, refrigerators, stoves, microwaves, dishwashers — they sell them, service them, warranty them, and know about them. Now, all they need is for you to buy them! They'll even service them whether you buy it from them or not. Since 1953, Robert Kent has been turning hot and cold and on and off all the major players: **CARRIER**, **GE**, **KITCHENAID**, **MAYTAG**, **RCA**, **WHIRLPOOL** and **ZENITH** as well as offering bedding and furniture to complete the home scene. They charge $20 to check your TV to see what's wrong plus repairs. If they can't fix it, they carry new TVs, so you're never very far from "American Idol" or Fox News.

★★★★★   Tweeter   214/373-0600

9100 N. Central Expressway @ Park Ln.   Mon-Sat10-9 Sun Noon-6
Dallas, TX 75225
www.tweeter.com

Looks like Tweeter dee is Tweeter dumb if you don't know about this powerhouse. With eight metro stores including the Hillcrest Hi-Fidelity two-store specialty chain that was acquired this year, this is the only nationwide high-end specialty home entertainment chain generating an electrifying almost $1 billion in sales. Known as the Tweeter Home Entertainment Group, their stores under their banner is known industry-wide for the expertise of its sales professionals and for superior customer service. After all, they were named the "Consumer Electronics Retailer of the Year" by Audio-Video International every year since 1979 and was named one of the î100 Fastest Growing Companiesî by Fortune Magazine in 2002. You're sure to find something pleasing to your ear if your taste is one of high fidelity. High-end audio and video equipment at the best prices is how to tune in to their retail marketing strategy. Since they have the buying power, they take advantage of that clout and pass on the savings to the public. Audio, video and a lot of other high-tech toys for sophisticated boys in the areas of Home Audio, Home Video, Portable, Digital Imaging, as well as Car Audio and Video. Delivery, set up and instruction are all part of their service package. On-staff audio and video specialists are able to work along side your other contractors when building a house, for example, or adding a media room with a designer, builder or architect....from blueprint to installation ensuring the perfect fit. Among the brands carried: **ALPINE**, **ACOUSTICS**, **NAD**, **PHASE TECH**, **VELODYNE** and **YAMAHA**. Check directory for multiple area locations at the Galleria, Frisco, Lewisville, Mesquite and Southlake. Up to 70 percent off just by going online at the Tweeter site for mobile electronics and speakers. Mix the quality and warranty of a top notch manufacturer with Tweeter's world-renowned service and policies and that is what I'd call a whopper stopper. Check directory for other locations including Hillcrest HiFi (see write-up elsewhere in this chapter.)

◆◆◆◆◆   U-Edit   972/690-3348

1002 N. Central Expwy., Suite 689   Mon-Thurs 9-8; Fri 9-6; Sat 10-4
Richardson, TX 75080
www.u-edit-video.com

Make a U-turn if U miss U-Edit, because they are one of the few little editing booths you can utilize for your video projects without committing to a Steven Spielberg production. U-see what you can duplicate at U-Edit. Video services include editing, dubbing, titles, sound recording and special effects. Got a favorite French film you want to convert? What if your husband was a famous movie star in the '60s and his biggie with Racquel Welch only came on Beta? Take it to U-Edit and have it transferred, so you can show all your friends that your husband REALLY WAS A MOVIE STAR. What a hunk! Had I not seen it with my own eyes, I could still be a doubting Diva. How about a new twist on photo albums? Place up to 75 pictures on video for $75. That includes five-second viewing with music. Change any video to include your own narration for just $20 an hour. The equipment and the expertise is all here, and if you don't bring your own tape, they can sell you one. Visit other locations in Los Colinas at 5910 MacArthur behind Starbucks (972/910-8180) or Lewisville, 413 Round Grove Rd., #103, 972/459-0086 next to Calloways Nursery.

★★★★★★ **Ultimate Electronics**　　　　**972/316-3373**
321 W. 84th Ave.　　　　　　　　　　　　　Mon-Sat 10-9; Sun 11-7
Lewisville, TX 75057
www.ultimateelectronics.com

 Score one brownie point for this retailer who offered season tickets to the Dallas Cowboys to shoppers who came to their grand opening. Then, in no time flat, they had 10 locations and who would have guessed shoppers would covet a bigger, biggest and possible bestest electronics store? With 33 years behind them, this Denver-based retailer became the largest retail store entry since Kohl's Department Stores rolled into town. Selection is extensive and the prices, well, they offer the lowest price guarantee or they'll pay you 110 percent....what more could you want? Offering all the best brands on some of the most elite electronic models, you can't go wrong here. There were phones for $19.95, camcorders for $198.95 and DVD players for $99 — HITACHI, JVC, MITSUBISHI, PANASONIC, PIONEER ELITE, RCA, SAMSUNG, SONY ES and YAMAHA. Cameras by CANON and OLYMPUS, CD and DVD Players, VCRs, camcorders, portable and cell phones, even computers, in-car audio systems, audio equipment for the home, satellite dishes and, of course, large screen TVs. Check directory for multiple locations. But when they clean out their warehouse, that's when you should sprint over to 1432 Wainwright Way, off Frankford and Eisenhower in Carrollton or call 972/512-1155. Watch newspapers for blow-out sales.

Entertainment

◆◆◆◆ Air Jump Moonwalks   817/453-5867 (JUMP)

1610 Chretien Point Drive

Mon-Fri 8:30-5:30; By Appt. Only

Mansfield, TX 76063

www.airjump.com

Want to have a blast jumping, Jack? This is where it's at. Looking to jump for joy at your next birthday bash? What about an active activity for the company picnic? A festival? Actually any special event will do. Put into place the Air Jump Moonwalk. Everything sets up in perfect condition (all new equipment) and delivered for **FREE**, you could be bouncing around in no time. These folks also plan party packages for special events such as sports promotions, trade shows, carnivals, fund-raisers, neighborhood block parties or company picnics. In fact, have a field day! Serving the DFW Metroplex (Arlington, Dallas, Mansfield and Fort Worth) and Austin, San Antonio and Houston areas since 1996. You'll find that they are extremely professional, deliver on time, set up properly and pride themselves on customer satisfaction and safety. *Call toll-free: 866/494-5867*

◆◆◆◆◆ ArtCentre of Plano   972/423-7809

1039 E. 15th St

Tues-Sat 10-6

Plano, TX 75074-6221

www.artcentreofplano.org

The ArtCentre of Plano, Inc., formerly known as the Cultural Arts Council of Plano, Inc. (CACOP), was founded in 1981 as a private non-profit organization to promote the growth and development of emerging community arts groups. After many surveys, they realized there was a need for a much larger and more centralized community arts facility. To that end, the powers that be purchased the old Harrington Furniture Store, a 100-year old landmark at 1039 E. 15th Street in historic downtown Plano. It is now a showplace for the downtown area. In 1992, the warehouse annexed to the furniture store was completely renovated and now sits proudly as the ArtCentre Theatre, a 160-seat proscenium auditorium, home to the Plano Repertory Theatre. It's a great place to hold a wedding or reception if you're looking for a convenient and well-appointed catering kitchen, a wedding planner on staff, spacious gallery interiors and a landscaped and fenced outside courtyard. (Remember all those photographs!) To get to the Art Centre, go north on US-75. Take exit #29 towards 15th Street. Turn right onto E. 15th/FM 544. Turn to the right slightly onto E. 15th. You're there.

★★   Be-Bop Jukeboxes & Gameroom Goodies 972/724-1791

11411 Stemmons, Suite 133   Tues-Sat 10-4
Dallas, TX 75229-2120
www.2nd-sight.com/bebop

Be-Bop a loo ba, be my baby. Sound familiar? Return to the days of yesteryear when rec rooms meant jitterbugging and playing "Spin the Bottle," jiving to Elvis and wearing the ring around your neck proclaiming "Off Limits, I'm Taken!" Add a '50s-type checkered floor and who could ask for anything more? Well, how about a place to buy all the memorabilia? Capture the look in your home with a jukebox, either a collectible or a reproduction with CD player, or add other fun games to your hours of recreation. Sales, repairs or rentals of a number of gameroom-related items including pinball and video games, foosball and air hockey tables, pool tables, 3N-1 and 1-N1 game tables, neon signs, pool table accessories and more. If they don't stock a particular game or gameroom item, they can find it. Prices appeared competitive, but on the high side for neon signs and advertising novelties. Don't expect to get away cheap. Although some jukeboxes were under $1,000, most were not. One that was selling for $40,000 was outfitted to accommodate CDs. You can also rent items for parties. Hop over to Be-Bop just north of **ROYAL**.

◆◆◆◆◆   Behavioral Sensibilities/Manners by BREN 214/342-9412

Dallas, TX   By Reservation Only
www.BehavioralSensibilities.com

What do you get when you take a "classic model" who has lived in Paris for years, been raised on **GIVENCHY** who taught her the genteel rudiments of the finer things in life? Let me introduce you to Bren. Have her teach you what she has learned about manners teaching them to others, from children to CEO's. Everyone can learn a thing or two about communication, dressing the part, discovering the art of behavioral sensibilities is what Bren calls it. Try it. You'll love her programs. They are not only educational but entertaining since she is a trained actress and has been on the Improv circuit in New York. Some of her programs are cutting edge, some just down-to-earth and basic. Serious information, though, regardless of her humorous and impactful manner of delivery. For Executives: from the young to the seasoned, what are the differences? How can competitors at work be helpful to one another instead of doing battle for positions? How to be a better mentor and refine your methods of communication. Since luncheon and dinner meetings are often where deals are solidified, learn the many nuances to business dining as the pitfalls and pratfalls are revealed. Remember, there's always room for improvement. Then, what about Wardrobe and Imaging Programs? Both men and women executives, from soccer moms to society moms can learn the ropes for dressing for success without excess. How to improve your presentations — from the way you put yourself together to what you say is equally important to the ultimate selling package. A necklace with a sweater, a revealing neckline, stockings with open-toed shoes, too much jewelry or make-up, an ill-fitting hair piece, dirty shoes — they all say something about you and your interest in the ultimate job. Learn to stand out for all the right reasons. Brin calls it "Accessible Sophistication" and it's what is lacking in the marketplace today. From teaching manners that children have long forgotten to illustrating mock interviews for those entering or reentering the job market, you'll learn a thing or two that may make the difference between getting the job or not. And for a riveting program, don't overlook her program about better treatment of the elderly. It just may make a difference in your life for a change. Call Brin, the "Lady of the Manners!" Learn the **ART** of The Simplicity of Politeness and Good Manners and let Bren "polish the rogue within." *Call toll-free: 888/323- 876*

★★★★   **Brass Register, The**   **972/231-1386**

610 James Drive   Mon-Sat 9-5:30
Richardson, TX 75080
www.brassregister.com

Hop online to see a few of the highlights of the store, but don't expect to shop on their website yet. Just see the photos which should pique your interest, and I bet you'll want to make a pit stop fast. In fact, I'll wager a COKE from the old COKE machines where the little bottles were priced at a nickel. Ah, those were the days. Whether it's a diner counter from an old-fashioner cafe complete with the counter stools or a jukebox from the good old days, you will want to turn back the clocks and rock around The Brass Register. Well, if it's that mini-diner that turns you on your heels, you better grab it 'cause I have my eye on it, too. Whether you're looking to buy something out of your memory bank or rent a jukebox for that next sock hop, this is the place to register. They've expanded their inventory to include GO-PED motorized scooters so that now you can really "go-go." Start the engines and go, man, go. The Brass Register can ring up many nostalgic items — from soda fountains to antique cash registers, juke boxes to taxi stands but for a really fun ride, consider their motorized scooters including the fun quad riders. It is not recommended for Central Expressway commutes, but, in order to try one out, you will have to motor in a car, better yet a truck, to their store, off Central Expressway, between Belt Line and Spring Valley.

◆◆◆◆◆◆   **Carbon Copies**   **972/644-6660**

9801 Cross Creek Court   By Reservation Only
Richardson, TX 75080
www.carboncopiescelebs.com

 Dying to meet a celebrity and impress every one at the party? The fund-raiser? The club meeting? The convention? Or just out to dinner? Can you imagine the photo-op you can create with a Liz Taylor lookalike on your arm? Well, say hello to Janie Minick, the spitting image of Liz Taylor. Today, she has expanded her celebrity passion to include others of the same ilk. Now, she represents all of the best, both local and national. Having a Carbon Copy show up for around $250 an hour, depending on what is involved. Create a stir. Turn heads. Make heads roll just to get attention up close and personal. What about Selena? Imagine her at an Hispanic event. Janie Minick, a seasoned performer herself, found that her resemblance to Liz Taylor was her ticket to stardom. Bring a celeb lookalike to a party and you'll hear about it for years. See for yourself — as a great luncheon or after-dinner speaker, fund-raiser, corporate headliner, whatever, invite a celeb lookalike and make that event go down in history.

◆◆◆◆   **Cathy's Clowns, Etc.**   **817/481-6298**

Southlake, TX 76092   By Appt. Only
www.partypop.com

Looking for the perfect accompaniment to your child's birthday party? Forget the pizza parlor. Been there and done that. Instead, call this licensed agency, a division of Hetzer Theatrical. They have Batman look-alikes, Lion Kings, petting zoos and rides, a singing Pocahontas, purple dinosaurs, live performing pigs, Han Solo and Hercules, face painting....what more could you ask for? Well, if that's not enough, go to their website www.partypop.com and don't be a party pooper any more. There are hundreds of other ideas in the Dallas/Fort Worth area for individual acts for hire.

◆◆◆◆　　**Celebration Station**　　　　　　　　　　　**972/279-7888**

4040 Towne Crossing　　　　　　　Sun-Thurs Noon-9; Fri Noon-Midnight; Sat 10-Midnight
Mesquite, TX 75150
www.celebrationstation.com

Let's party! If you're in the Mesquite, Garland, 635-East corridor, here's a numero uno place to go. (Locations throughout Texas, Louisiana and even North Carolina.) Bring the kids, bring the entire family, and y'all have a real good time! Kids are not the only ones who will be screamin'with excitement as they navigate the bumper boats. With year 'round indoor and outdoor activities, plus all the food you love to nosh on with all the drinks to sip on, do not waste a minute. Waste not because during the summer, you can ride unlimited Go-Karts and Bumper Boats from 9 PM until closing for just $12.99. However, you must meet the height requirement (and I just made it) of at least 56-inches tall. New this year, paintball. That's right. They now offer paintball. Listen to this deal: Buy 500 paintballs for $25 and get your rental equipment for only $5 (save up to $17.) But this special is only good Monday through Friday 2-7 PM when there's a lull in activities. Love miniature golf? Batting cages? During their Labor Day promotion, golf was only $3.99. Then, for a really cool incentive, ice cream cones were a quarter. Don't forget to inquire about their packaged deals where all you need is a minimum of six to get the special pricing.

◆◆◆◆◆　　**Dallas Arboretum, The**　　　　　　　　**214/515-6500**

8525 Garland Rd.　　　　　　　　　　　　　　　　　　　　　　　Daily 10-6
Dallas, TX 75218
www.dallasarboretum.org

How do I love thee? Let me count the ways — first by going to the world-renowned arboretum where Dallas blooms all year long. There's always something to see. Fountains, sculptures, two historic mansions and more. See the Trammel Crow Visitor Education Pavilion, a $20 million complex that is the centerpiece for horticulture, gardening and environmental science education for children and adults. This congregation of small buildings was designed by the world renowned architectural firm in San Antonio of Lake/Flato. Each building was designed so that it never overshadows the most important element in the Arboretum — the beautiful gardens. Bridging the gap between the outdoors and the indoors is just one aspect of this 40,000 square foot pavilion. Within the pavilion, other benefactors'donations such as the Wyatt-World Education Center, provided by the widow of Will Caruth and the Cecil and Ida Green Foundation, will serve as an outdoor area to be used as a garden laboratory. Then, the Meadows Orientation Theater will be used to introduce visitors to the Arboretum with a high-definition film highlighting the Arboretum's events, programs and spectacular floor displays. What a beautiful welcoming act. For beautiful buds and interesting landscape designs, the Arboretum has more than 66 superbly landscaped acres of flowers, gardens and beautiful grounds. Rosine Hall is a 5,000-square-foot exhibit hall perfect to accommodate large groups for workshops, lectures, social dinners and receptions. Their spacious doors open to the patio and arbor areas, and has a flexible design to respond to accommodate a large party. You'll see lots of photographers and wedding planners in tow everywhere. Located on the shores of White Rock Lake, it's a great morning or afternoon outing anytime. The gardens and facilities are available for rent — a blooming backdrop for a wedding, reunion or any occasion celebration. Bring your camera and smile. It doesn't get any more colorful than here.

◆◆◆◆◆ Dallas Film Commission   214/571-1000

325 North St. Paul, Suite 700   Varies by event
Dallas, TX 75201
www.visitdallas.com/film/FILMtalent.php

One of the most useful websites for you to scour is the one put out by the Dallas Film Commission
(the official production professionals' organization). There are lots of avenues to take but you'll
want to hook up with the credible and reliable sources who won't rip you off. This website is one
that will direct you to the right course of action. Who are the casting directors to call? Where are
the acting schools and publications for actors? Who are the acting groups that help train and market professional actors? Where to buy the Dallas Actors Handbook for Dallas, the complete guide
to who to go-see for a list of people and companies who employ actors, or who have services or
products for actors (over 800 listings). Okay, I won't keep you in suspense any longer. Here's how
to get a copy for $12.95. Either order online at dalekassel@dallasactor.com, log on to dallasac-
tor.com or mail a check to DAHB, PO Box 38495, Dallas, TX 75238.

◆◆◆◆ Dallas Powerhouse of Dance   972/960-2484

12300 Inwood Rd., #124   By Reservation Only
Dallas, TX 75244
www.dallaspowerhouse.com

Don't let boredom stop you from trying to be creative for their a next birthday party — for anyone.
Here's one for all ages that they will really kick up their heels. Dallas Power House of Dance
offers fun and exciting birthday parties for all ages (though tailored to fit the musical selections
that would be age appropriate.) Pick out your favorite music, from line-dancing to swing, jitterbug
to rock, then call in the troops. A party from the Dallas Powerhouse of Dance includes 45 minutes
of dance instruction with an instructor and 45 minutes for enjoying the cake and opening the presents. The instructor will help you set up for the party, assist with cake and present opening, and
clean up afterwards. Can you see this as the perfect party for a teenager or just as exciting as an
80th birthday celebration? For $180, it's not a bad price to pay for a memorable event. Full pay-
ment is due at the time of scheduling your dance party. It's your party and I'll cry if I want to. Dick
Clark, eat your heart out!

◆◆◆◆◆◆ Eisemann Center   972/744-4600 (General)

2351 Performance Drive   By Reservation Only
Richardson, TX 75082
www.eisemanncenter.com

 If you haven't heard the sounds of Music at the Metroplex's newest contribution to
the arts, you're not just rockin' the boat .... you're missin' the boat, too. This entertainment venue offers the full spectrum of events without having to get all dolled up
and go downtown. Instead, get all dolled up and stay in Richardson, off Central Expressway and
Renner Road. This spectacular setting for the sites and sounds of music, dance, comedy, lectures
and other theatrical events is the next best thing since sliced bread. And what a bargain, too. From
the comedy My Cousin's Wedding to the Manhattan Transfer, it's just a great way to enjoy the
theatre without costing an arm and a leg. But expect your arms to get a workout with the many
rounds of applause. Tickets are available by downloading the order form, calling the ticket office
above or stopping by the Center's Ticket Office Mon-Sat 10-6. And during select performances,
enjoy the Prelude Cafe inside which is brought to you by the Renaissance Dallas/Richardson Hotel
for only $12 per person (definitely a lot cheaper than the buffet at the Music Hall at Fair Park.)
Call toll-free: 972/744/4650

◆◆◆◆◆   **Emler Swim School, Inc. (Corp.)**   **817/275-SWIM**

2201 Lavern St.
Arlington, TX 76013
www.emlerswim.com

Book the perfect birthday party at Emler Swim School! Relax while the kids have fun in their heated indoor pool with a lifeguard on duty. A private room is provided and at Emler you can have as many as 20 guests at no additional cost. Call 972/599-7946 for best times. Other locations in Colleyville 817/481-SWIM (7946) and Plano, 972/599-SWIM (7946). Jan Emler, the founder, is still active in guiding the company. As one of the most respected swim schools nationally, Emler Swim School began with 12 students in an Arlington backyard pool and has grown to almost 10,000 swim students a year. Over a quarter of a century of teaching almost 100,000 children the love and safety of the water is a comely achievement. Learn to swim as young as six months to as old as 100. Parents love the waterbaby classes of games, songs and loving swimming techniques. All levels of instruction are available. Do jump in with both feet and enjoy.

◆◆◆   **Frisco Horse Park**   **972/355-8000**
                                                   By Reservation Only
13100 Hwy. 121
Frisco, TX 75034
www.friscohorsepark.net

Miles of trails situated on 2,300 acres just east of Stonebriar Center, giddy-up and ride into the sunset. Better yet, trot at your own pace aboard a pony or just pet the pets if your child's too young to ride. Here's the place to customize a birthday party with what every child dreams of — riding their own pony. The Bandana Birthday Party includes two hours, 15 kids, and adults are **FREE**. You'll get two ponies with western styled saddle but you'll lead 'em to water, though you can't make them drink. Each child will receive a bucket of food to feed the animals in the petting zoo plus helium-filled balloons and checkered tablecloths for decoration. As they say, they provide the West, you bring the rest. Other party options are available, depending on size of party and budget. The children's parties escalate all the way up to a company picnic. They even offer a romantic interlude where they'll escort a couple to an old barn, supply the blanket, food, champagne, bottled water and a radio and pick them up in one hour. What a great place to propose. Anyway, for corporate parties, they charge $5 per person for entry to the ranch; $10 per person for the hayride; $20 per person for the horseback ride; $15 per person for a BBQ Plate plus four hours of volleyball, horseshoes, tug-oí-war and paddle boats. Adding a 20-minute hayride to your party will only cost you an additional $50. If you would like to have a hayride at your off-site event, they'll bring a tractor-pulled wagon for your hayride at a cost of $250 per hour and $100 for each additional hour. My favorite, though, is the horse-drawn wagon hayride at $450 for an hour and a half and $100 for each additional hour. There's tons more to do, including a weenie roast and campfire. Log on to their website for all the details.

◆◆◆◆   **Fun Fest**   **972/620-7700**
                         Sun-Thurs 11 AM-Midnight; Fri-Sat 10 AM-2 AM
3805 Belt Line Rd.
Addison, TX 75234

What a fest for sore eyes! This huge place is full of fun for the entire family! Racing, pool tables, virtual reality games, 30 bowling lanes, darts, laser tag and a huge penny arcade (OK, so it's not pennies anymore). Pizza Hut Express, Ginger's Grill and a full bar make this a fun place for everyone. Their arcade machines use the party card system instead of coins or tokens; everything else is "pay as you go." No charge at the door, ever. Located behind Joe's Crab Shack, they have several different party plans to choose from for all age groups. They range from $78 up to $148.95 and more. Call for details as there's no website. Boo Hoo! That's a gutter ball, for sure.

◆◆◆   Gymboree Play and Music   214/341-2386

3261 Independence Pkwy.   By Reservation Only
Plano, TX 75075
www.gymboree.com

Celebrate your child's birthday at Gymboree Play and Music — it's some kind of fun! You'll have the bright bubbles, colorful parachute, specialty-built play equipment and rhythmic songs for a private, custom party. Your group (children and adults) can party, play, laugh and sing along with an experienced teacher as host leading the band. Gymboree Play and Music is the worldwide leader in age-appropriate Parent/Child classes for newborns through age 4. Reserve your party time now! Other Gymborees in Dallas, Frisco, Lewisville and Grapevine.

★★★★   Half Price Tickets (Tickemasters)   214/696-4253

4849 Greenville Ave   Tues-Sat Noon-3 (that evening): Matinees Sat 10-1; Sun 11-1
Dallas, TX 75206
www.ticketmaster.com

Yes, it's true. On the day of most performances, if there are seats unsold, they'd rather fill up every seat so the performers do not play to an empty house. Call and see what's available. Then run to get in line. Limited tickets but you never know until you ask. Enjoy the sites and sounds of local theater and perhaps sit next to someone who's paid full price. Then laugh all the way home. Same enjoyment. Half the price. Now, impress a friend and ask him or her out. What a cheap date? Don't expect advance seating, however. Only the day of the show are those tickets available. Offered through Ticketmaster, you don't have to be rich to see a hit show. Why not support the arts with left-over tickets, eh? Call ahead to see what's available. You must show up in person; no clones or replacement parts, please. First come, first served on a very limited basis.

★★★★★   Just Jump'n   972/485-5006

2021 Copper Street   By Reservation Only
Garland, TX 75042
www.justjumpn.com

Do you think this belongs in the back yard chapter? Or the Toys Chapter? Probably yes, but it wound up here because it's all of the above: Kids....Toys....Fun. Enjoy a full day's rental of these inflatable bounceable house rentals, slippy slides, circus clowns, Jurassic Park or Princess Palace. It's worth every penny for the joy it brings to both little girls and boys. At Hannah's 4th birthday party, about a dozen kids were occupied for several hours inside these bounceable whatever you want to call them....houses of fun that keep them out of the sun. When all things are said and done, you can't beat it — as low as $49. FREE Delivery! FREE Setup! Lowest Prices! Call the number above and have a ball. Many different styles to choose from with same day service. Don't overlook the weekday specials, especially during the summer when any day will do for a birthday bash.

◆◆◆◆◆   **Kids Metroplex**   **972/401-2090**

11496 Luna Road   Hours Vary
Dallas, TX 75234
www.kidsmetroplex.com/theculart.html

For a one stop "what's available" for your budding actor or actress who wants to take center stage, why not let them learn the ropes of being a star? This website is the perfect resource for all of the artistic and cultural classes available in the Metroplex. There's a wealth of world class cultural and arts programs and facilities, many of them offering special enrichment programs for children and youth and many of them Free. For example, there's the Greater Dallas Youth Orchestra, the Children's Chorus of Greater Dallas, the Anita Martinez Ballet Folklorica for Hispanic youth, summer camps at the Amon Carter Museum or the Arlington Museum of Art Saturday programs and summer camps. What about kids who'd like to pursue a particular craft? There's the Crafts Guild of Dallas-Kid Stuff. Then, at the Capers for Kids website, you'll find classes for drama, art and theater for kids of all ages. The Kinderplatz! Fort Worth is another wealth of activities for art, music, movement, creative play and school readiness for pre-schoolers. What about the guide to summer camps for kids in the Metroplex? And the list goes on. There's so much to do, you'll wish you were a kid again.

◆◆◆◆◆   **Little Gym, The**   **214/515-0800; 888/228-2878**

410 Hillside Village   Hours Vary
Dallas, TX 75214-2447
www.thelittlegym.com

Tumble with the best of them. You can see it in their eyes the first time they run into your arms after class. The new found look of glorious, sparkling confidence. Confidence that will build a foundation to succeed in whatever they may try today that will last for the rest of their lives. For over 25 years, The Little Gym has provided that foundation in a non-competitive motor skill development program, such as gymnastics, sports skills and karate, all taught in a fun, safe and nurturing environment. The Little Gym encourages children to develop at their own pace, building the self-esteem they need for fulfilling a successful life. Look for brightly-lit, colorful, fun places, full of smiling faces. Each franchise varies but most are approximately 4,000 square feet and located in convenient strip malls. Check locations also in Arlington, Fort Worth; and Carrollton, Colleyville, Plano, Richardson. *Call toll-free: 888/228-2878*

◆◆◆◆◆   **Magination Studioz**   **972/612-2110**

2983 W. 15th St.   Wed-Fri 12-6; Sat-Sun.for scheduled parties
Prairie Creek Shopping Village Plano, TX 75075
www.magination-studioz.com

Want it memorable? Exciting? Stress free? Want your child to feel like a star? Want the kidz to say, "this waz the best party, ever?" "Come groove with us!" All inclusive partiez provide exclusive use of studio and staff. Stage, muzic, costumez, makeup, craftz and groovy staff, that'z 'MAGINATION STUDIOZ'. Expect a two-hour gig for twelve ages 3-12, cost, $275. The package includes: balloons, beverages, party coordinator, refreshment servers, exclusive use of studio, choice of theme and wardrobe, face painting, makeup, invitations, thank you notes, music, use of music activity props, all craft materials, protective smocks, tableware, professional staff and bubbles. What, they didn't invite Lawrence Welk? For more than twelve kids, 13-20, there's a $15.00 per child surcharge. For over 20, it goes down to $12.75 per head. But what a swell party it is! Their website is sooooooo groooovy!

◆◆◆◆   **Paint 'N Party**   **972/612-9312**

3295 Independence Parkway   Tues-Fri 10-6; Sat 10-5; Sun 1-5
Plano, TX 75075

At the southwest corner of Parker and Independence, consider Paint 'n Party if you don't want to crack up planning your next party. Pick out a ceramic piece to paint; the lowest price is $8.95. There are hundreds of items to choose from in this price range. Want to fire it? Then, expect to shell out $10 and up. But there is no "painting fee" as others stores are apt to charge. All you pay is the price of the ceramic piece and, even if you don't finish in one sitting, you can come back at no additional charge for a month to finish. This family Art Studio provides hours of fun with memories for a lifetime. Kids have a lock-in on Friday nights, and there are no exceptions. What a great idea for wholesome activities for the entire family. During the summer, they open up on Mondays from 10-2.

◆◆◆◆◆   **Parties Portable**   **817/467-3087**

PO Box 150001   By Appt. Only, 24-Hour service
Arlington, TX 76015
www.parties-portable.com;

Taking talent on the road is what these portable entertainers do best. Add some life to the party and put the details in their hands. It doesn't matter where or when, or even what the occasion is, Lico Reyes will provide it all. Weddings, bar mitzvahs, showers, birthdays, it's your party and you'll cry if you want to. Along for the ride are professional DJs, sound systems, spectacular light shows, music from the '40s to the '90s, karaoke, magicians, dancers, comedians, clowns, bands and emcees, celebrity look-alikes and even a carnival dunk tank. Packages start at $90 per hour, with a three-hour minimum. Services can be conducted in English, Spanish or Vietnamese. They will go anywhere you need them; previous parties have even taken them to the Bahamas and Mexico. Add video taping to their list of services this year. One of the most fun things to do is invite one of the celebrity look-alikes to join you. Imagine your guests' reactions when they think Elvis, Marilyn Monroe, Selena, Michael Jackson, Liz Taylor, Cher, Bill Clinton, Al Gore or Ricky Martin is on the invitation list. Yes, you can ask them for an autograph.

Party Pop

5200 Kanan Road, Suite 225   24/7
Agoura Hills, CA 91301

www.partypop.com   🖱 *Top Online Store!*

This is your online liaison to finding an entertainer outside the box. Forget Chuck-e-Cheeses as the only fun thing to do for your child's birthday party. Wait, even grown-ups could find one of their entertainers to highlight their 50th, their 60th, whatever special yearly event. Bring a magician, a hypnotist, a psychic to your next event and see how the party pops rather than poops. Go online and see for yourself the hundreds of area entertainers who'd rather perform than ever attend a party again — unless they're the featured event. Got a big budget and dream of hiring the Dixie Chicks? You can find out how here. Looking for a blue grass band? Or won't settle for any other band than Emerald City? What about a murder mystery? Plenty of production companies listed but only with their phone numbers and not their specialty. Great website for contact and party tips. *Call toll-free: 800/950-8238*

◆◆◆◆◆   **Pecos River Brass**   **972/219-0202**

560 East Church Street   By Reservation Only
Lewisville, TX 75057
www.pecosriverbrass.com/band

Ready to swing? How about a 19-piece big band that has you up and dancing within minutes of playing a few measures? I mean I dare you to sit still. It just can't be done. No, not a 40's nostalgia band or a 50's rock and roll band. This is a contemporary 21st century upbeat, up tempo, big band sound. Well, their version of "Embraceable You" and "I Only Have Eyes for You" should do it in a New York minute. And if you are looking to book a corporate party or wedding reception where people want to dance, this is the band to consider based on talent, price and presence. Check their website to hear where they're playing next. Their repertoire is extensive — over 1,400 arrangements ranging from classic swing to modern jazz. They even have some of the same arrangements that were first introduced by Count Basie, Woody Herman, Stan Kenton, Les Elgart and Buddy Rich. Call 972/446-1147 or mobile 214/629-0080, to book the band. And not only will they give readers of the Underground Shopper a break on a CD but on a big band price as well. If you're not up to "big," then consider there little three-piece combo — which is also a wonderful sound without taking a big bite out of your entertainment budget.

◆◆◆   **Perfect Image Mikey B's**   **972/527-5507**

14221 Dallas Parkway, Suite 1500   By Appt. Only
Dallas, TX 75254
www.planodj.com

Party, party burning bright. Well, if that's what you're trying to create, try slipping a note to Mikey B. Mike Bergenholtz, and his party crew can customize any kind of party: wedding, bar/bat mitzvah, corporate event, birthday, anniversary, pool party, school dances, or theme party. Add DJ or karaoke services, and expect the tab to escalate to around $800 for four hours on a Saturday, less on Fridays ($650). Put on your blue suede shoes and maybe "Elvis" will show up (for $225) but you know how temperamental he is! Don't expect him to linger, though, as he'll only stay the required 50 minutes. Perfect Image can create picture buttons for $240/hour and you get a CD with all the pics on it. What a party! Video and photography services, entertainment such as a comedian, DJ, Clowns, Magicians, Hypnotists, Fortune Tellers, Look-A-Likes and my favorite — A Butt Skeetcher!!!! Activities can include face painting, temporary tattoos, karaoke with lights and music videos. But remember, everything has a price!

◆◆   **Pines, The**   **214/522-6533**

1124 Commerce Drive   By Appt. Only
Richardson, TX 75081
www.thepines.org

The Pines offers fun and entertainment for the entire family. First it's a camp on 4,500 acres of rolling hills overlooking Lake Lewisville. But secondly, it's also a premiere party site for anyone living in the DFW area. They sponsor corporate parties, daily horseback rides, kids' birthday parties, a petting zoo, trail rides, old-fashioned barbecues and company picnics. If you are into horseback riding, saddle up at River Riding Stables which offers daily horseback riding tours throughout the lovely countryside. The actual campsite, though, is at 300 White Pine Rd. in Big Sandy, TX 75755, 903/845-5834. City Slickers revolt. You'll be glad that you did!

◆◆◆◆◆ Safari Kids Glamour Party   972/473-3336

5960 W. Parker Rd., Suite 240   By Reservation Only (Fri-Sat 6:30-8:30; Sun 5-7 PM)
Plano, TX 75093
www.safarikidsplano.com

What a neat idea but you have to remember that you're inside a full retail children's clothing store. Beware. Wander through the jungle decor and see what's in store without big tall racks or room dividers to block your view. Strollers are welcome complete with a great kids' area of toys and a VCR. Lots of specialty store labels, but discounted only during sales. BABY LULU, FLAPDOO-DLES, FLOWERS BY ZOE, MARSHA, MICHAEL SIMON, MULBERRIBUSH, UN DEUX TROIS, WES & WILLY and others are eagerly awaiting adoption. Although the store is open for shopping during the week, the "Glamour Party" is limited to weekends, Fri-Sat from 6:30-8:30 and Sun 5-7 PM. Located at the southeast corner of Parker Road and the Tollway.

◆◆◆◆◆◆ Slim's Discount University

PO Box 5094   24/7
Abilene, TX 79608
www.slimsdiscountuniversity.com

 Formerly Steve's Discount University, they have now matriculated to Slim's (I supposed because they've gotten older and heavier) and now can include a website in their ever-growing curricula vitae. President Clovis Seamthrottle still can't spell, so if English 101 is right up there as an essential requirement of your college education, you might not want to boast a degree from here. New photos and a book manuscript are in the works, alongside the calendar and video. In the meantime, you don't have to really think too hard about enrolling. It's a fun ride, although it'll probably take you a few semesters of laughing out loud before you even think of graduate school. "After all, education is all in the minds" of the beholders. I have been awarded an honorary degree and I've filed mine under Half Price Honors. For those who place a college degree dear to their hearts and for resume purposes, this may be a happy medium! But are they stopping with just an online presence? No siree. Now, they are opening a retail store in Denton, where they first began. As soon as I know of its address, I'll post it on our website. David Young and partner, Jim Hobdy, have great expansion plans. Today a store, tomorrow an entire campus where shoppers can get one big laugh until graduation.

◆◆ SpeedZone   972/247-7223 (RACE)

11130 Malibu Drive   Sun-Thurs 11-11; Fri-Sat 11 AM-1 AM
I-35 @ Walnut Hill Dallas, TX 75229
www.speedzone.com

The bright colors you see to the west of Stemmons at Walnut Hill are the SpeedZone tracks. No mistake about it, you can race your hearts out throughout the twists and turns from the slick track to drag racing. Height requirements are the only prerequisites for racing on all the tracks except the Grand Prix cars. For that, you must have a valid driver's license. You can also spend hours at the Electric Alley video simulators and video games. Then have a bite to eat and play some golf on either of the two racing-themed miniature courses. If you haven't been there lately, you haven't been there in a while. Keep a sharp eye out. NASCAR superstars are often spotted enjoying the thrills in between the spills. Whether you're planning for a party of 10 or 2,000, they can offer you a thrill a minute. Party packages are designed to fit almost anyone's budget. That means parties for birthdays, schools, fund-raisers, bar mitzvahs, reunions, award banquets, bachelor parties and more with unlimited entertainment options. Regardless of your age, height or skill level, enjoy a full-service cafe and attentive staff. Wanna Save 10 percent?

◆◆◆◆◆   Tarantula Train, The   817/251-0066

707 S. Main St.   By Reservation Only
Grapevine, TX 76051
www.tarantulatrain.com

Ride a little train that is going down the track and return to the good old days of leisurely transport. The beautifully restored Tarantula Train choo-choos its way from downtown Grapevine to the Stockyards and back each day. Step into the golden age of steam and ride this rejuvenated remnant of Texas history. Daily round trips depart the 8th Street Station at noon and return at 1; Sundays 3-4. Adult fare is $11 for a roundtrip, seniors ride for $10 and kids under 12 for $8. Also, there is a longer ride from Grapevine to the Stockyards Wed-Sat 10-11:15, returning 2-3:15; Sun 1-2:15, returning 4:45. Cost is $22 for adults, $20 for seniors and children over 12, and $11 for children 2-12. For reservations, call the Grapevine Station. (The Stockyards Station is at 140 East Exchange Ave. in Fort Worth, but the number above is who to call for reservations one hour before train departure time.) *Call toll-free: 800/457-6338*

◆◆◆   Texas Queen Riverboat   972/771-0039

I-30 at Dalrock   Reservations Only: Office Hours Mon-Fri 10-5
Lake Ray Hubbard Rockwall, TX 75087
www.texasqueenriverboat.com

You can either jump in the lake — or take a ride on one. The latter is Texas Queen's specialty. But with the new owners, it was more like a sinking ship. What was once dining on fine food and dancing under the stars on a jazz cruise, or a myriad of other kinds of music — the Blues, Country and Western, Reggae, South-of-the-Border — whatever floated your boat. But on our last visit, it was a bummer — an expensive one at that. It cost $125 for two for starters; then, we stood in the August heat for over an hour waiting to board. Ok, now we're starving but had to listen to jazz for another hour or so until the food was served and then, the food was cold (and it wasn't supposed to be.) To make matters worse, we couldn't set sail because of strong winds. Certainly it's not their fault but what an expensive dinner cruise it was that didn't even cruise. This riverboat is also available for private parties, cruises, personalized murder mysteries, weddings — whatever floats your boat as long as you don't have to take out a note to gloat what a fine party it was! Cruises are available Wednesday-Thursday from 7:30-9:30 for $48 (October-April 7-9); Friday & Saturday Evenings, 7-10 PM, $57; Sunday Evenings, 7:30-9:30 PM, $48. For groups, prices can vary depending on the particular meal selected, the type of entertainment and whether you want a two- or three-hour cruise. On the other hand, I have held one of our "Shoppers Choice Awards on the boat which was a blast even though it didn't leave the dock either. You can enjoy the company if nothing else.

◆◆◆◆◆◆   TITAS Organization   214/528-5576 (Box Office)

3101 N. Fitzhugh, Suite 301   By Reservation Only
Dallas, TX 75204
www.titas.org

Making a half dozen visits to McFarland's Auditorium was a feat that was nothing but a treat — a rare treat for provocative theatre and entertainment. If you, too, want a evening out that will jolt you from your seat, take a look at this not-for-profit cultural/educational venue that does nothing but uplift audiences everywhere. After achieving great success with dance presentations, TITAS expanded over the years in bringing top-notch talent to the masses at affordable prices. Tickets as low as $10-$55 for single tickets and less if you buy them by the season. And after 21 of them, Executive Director Charles Santos has presented many seasons (going on this 22nd) of eclectic and riveting performances which Dallas can really be proud and the upcoming season 2005 is no exception. Some of the highlights include Dance Cuba, Ralph Lemon, Less Ballets Jazz de Montreal in the dance arena, Laurie Anderson, Paul Dresher and Celebrating the Blues in the music venue and a special command performance of the International Ballet. All of the performances are at SMU's McFarland Auditorium, a wonderful theater for sites and sounds. Two of the performances left me on cloud nine: "Sweet Honey on the Rock" was the African-American women's a cappella ensemble that brought the audience to its feet and Momix — the performance of an intricate interweaving of acrobatics/ gymnastics/and dance that made this season something that spoke to every inch of our senses — but you had to see it to believe it. And you thought Cirque de Soleil was something to behold? Get on their mailing list of TITAS and don't miss a single performance of the upcoming season. You'll be sorry if you do. Your TITAS subscription will get you discounts on tickets to many other Dallas area arts events such as The Dallas Symphony, The Dallas Opera, Water Tower Theater, Dallas Theater Center, Dallas Summer Musicals, Dallas Wind Symphony, Dallas Black Dance Theatre, Dallas Children's Theater, Texas Ballet Theater, The MAC, Theater Three, Turtle Creek Chorale and more. Details will be included in your season ticket package. Now, here is another reason to join the group. *Call toll-free: 214/528-6112*

◆◆◆◆◆ **Weisfeld Center**　　　　　　　　　　　**214/752-8989**

　　　　　　　　　　　　　　　　　　　　　　　　　　By Reservation Only

1508 Cadize St. @ Browder
Dallas, TX 75201
www.weisfeldcenter.com

Looking for a most unique place to host your next event? Consider this downtown monument, a magnificently-restored, 800-seat multipurpose venue, at the south end of downtown Dallas'central business district. I know, I know. You hate to go downtown. But this is the place with the majestic silver dome, visible from Highways 30 and 35 and it really tops off any occasion with aplomb. Though originally the former First Church of Christ Scientist Building built in 1910, it had been badly neglected, but has now been completely restored. It has been home to national touring company productions from Broadway and really fills a void in the Metroplex for the performing arts community. It can be rented for weddings and other events such as corporate functions and my weight-loss group's Christmas party. There's a huge dining and social hall on the first floor with a catering kitchen, full bar, lobby and rear foyer with half bath that can double as a bride's lounge. Depending on the temperature outside, there's also an outdoor patio area. With 800 parking spaces, there's a spot for enough guests to do your next party proud.

◆◆◆◆◆ **Young Actors Studio**　　　　　　　　**972/401-2090**

　　　　　　　　　　　　　　　　　　　　　　　　　　　　See below

11496 Luna Rd., Suite G
Dallas, TX 75234
www.youngactors.org

This non-profit program is specifically designed for children for all the right reasons: to enhance creativity, develop self-esteem and for them to learn to express themselves through comedy, drama and improvisation. In other words, if you've got a ham in your family, let them learn the ropes while you can learn not to be a backstage Mother. Offering monthly acting classes for children ages 4-19, they meet once a week on Saturdays; and then for teens only on MONDAY Evenings from 7-9 PM. If your children aspire to be in the movies (or TV commercials,) being a student at the YAS (Young Actors Studio) could be the springboard to success. Since 1986, they have been the "guiding light" to many youngsters'roles on TV, from soap operas to an ongoing series. Does "ER," "Family Matters," "NYPD Blue," "Guiding Light," "Buffy: Vampire Slayer," "Walker, Texas Ranger" or "Touched by an Angel" sound familiar? Well, parts were filled by students from YAS. Lane Turney, one of YAS students, landed a role in the latest "Spy Kids 3D" and another student, Megan Rosser, had a part in the ABC's reality series called "Switched." Want to know who the SAG (Screen Actors Guild) franchised agents are? (You don't want to hook up with someone who doesn't have the proper credentials.) OK, then log on to their website. Want your child in a commercial for 7-11? Or to work at 6 Flags during the summer? Here's one place where being at the right place at the right time will pay off. Lights! Camera! Action!

Eyewear

★★★ 20/20 Eyecare Center   972/596-2250

4721 W. Park Blvd.   Mon, Wed, Thurs, Sat 9:15-6 (Closed Tues, Fri)
Plano, TX 75093

Expect to shell out $59 for an exam for glasses and $104 for an exam for contact lenses. Most of the prescriptions can be delivered in-house and within a hour, so once again, speed is next to seeing straight. Not only does 20/20 offer one-hour service, their one-hour service is often only 30 or 45 minutes! Designer frames like **ARMANI**, **FISHER-PRICE** (for kids), **GUESS?**, **JORDACHE**, **LIZ CLAIBORNE**, **NINA RICCI** and **VOGUE** are part of Bonnie Noyer's claim to frame. For more than 10 years, she has been discounting frames for less than the average and Dr. Haislip has been providing eye exams in 15 to 20 minutes. Don't worry. It just takes minutes to see straight these days. But expect to pay for the privilege. Oh, I see.

◆◆◆◆◆◆ Carter Eye Center   214/696-2020

7502 Greenville, Suite 700   By Appt. Only
Dallas, TX 75231
www.cartereyecenter.com

When they proudly proclaim LASIK eye procedures starting at $495 per eye to achieve 20/20 or it's free, don't you know I blink! Then I think — what am I waiting for! Talk about a deal. When have you heard of a doctor EVER offering a money-back guarantee if you're not satisfied? Probably not in this lifetime. But at the Carter Eye Center, they want ALL patients to focus on success. And they are so confident in their abilities that they can be bold. First of all, all of Dr. Carter's LASIK procedures are preformed with the state-of-the-art IntraLASIK, the bladeless LASEK CrystalensÆ tool and CK that will reduce or eliminate your dependence on reading glasses. Ah ha. No more, "Where are my glasses, dear?" Plus, listen to this! He offers interest FREE payment plans. Now, it just got even better — everybody has the opportunity to have it done. It's affordable and just think of how much you'll save since you'll not be buying glasses any more? I can't even imagine my life without them, can you? I think, though, I'll just fake it 'cause those rhinestone glasses I wear are so adorable everybody wants to buy them. For $30, why not? Anyway, they're just for looks, remember? Imagine not being dependent on glasses anymore? Another star is worn at Carter's Eye Center. Dr. Carter does Divas. After all, he did Preston Pearson, my friend, and Troy Aiken that I followed in the same chair that he sat on when he had a show on KRLD. When I find a deal, I not only kick up my heels but want to squeal....look at me now! Dr. Carter is the Mark Cuban of eyewear. While Cuban specializes in High Definition TV, Dr. Harvey Carter specializes in High Definition Vision. Their 20/20 program or it's FREE is an exclusive program ONLY to Carter Eye Center. You've got nothing to lose. Now, for Dr. Carter's expertise: He was the first to offer the CrystalensÆ, and the first in the country to perform the procedure after FDA approval. What kind of surgery is it? Well, it's surgery that allows you to have good vision for reading, intermediate and distance all without glasses or corrective lenses. Yes, you can see near, the computer, and a far. Wow! Being first counts for something. Dr. Carter is a household name and a pioneer in LASIK and cataract surgery. Thousands of patients throughout the Metroplex (and Texas) now look better, see better, are really better because of his skill and artistry. Carter Eye Center is like one-stop shopping for eyecare surgery: LASIK, CrystalensÆ, Conductive Keratoplasty, Glaucoma Management, Diabetic Retinopathy Treatment, Comprehensive Eye Exams and even skin care treatments of the eye and face. Whichever is right for you, they can provide it all (even if I don't understand them all.) One of the most experienced doctors in the field, over 10,000 LASIK patients are walking around today with perfect vision thanks to Carter Eye Center. Tens of thousands can thank him for seeing clearly since he removed their cataracts. Ah, didn't they write a song about him, "I Can See clearly?" *Call toll-free: 888/361-4520*

★   Contact Lens Center, The   214/739-2020

6921 Snider Plaza   By Appt. Only
Dallas, TX 75205

Be a good pupil and center your sights on this location; a packaged plan is ripe for sore eyes. Just down the street from SMU, prices have remained stable. A contact lens exam and four boxes of regular disposables by **ACUVUE**, the kind you can dispose of every day, will cost $219. Forget buying them by the box, as it looks like you have to go for broke these days. What's the deal? Don't they want to just sell the lenses without a packaged deal? What if you don't want an exam? How many exams does it take to buy one pair of contact lenses? H-m-m-m! For an exam and three boxes of FRESH LOOK colors, expect to see a $230 receipt. By appointment only. If you can see your way clear, you might find another source a whole lot cheaper that doesn't want to wrap it all up with a bow. Last year, we priced 4 boxes of **ACUVUE** disposables for $89. If that be the case, than that would make the eye exam of $219 a pretty expensive exam wouldn't you say? Other locations to peek into if you can afford it: at Belt Line between Josey and Denton Drive in Carrollton and off North Central Expressway in Richardson between Belt Line and Arapaho. Ah, now I see it. Now you won't. It appears prices are clearly better elsewhere. But expect to be treated royally.

★   Discount Optical   972/620-9242

2880 LBJ Frwy., Suite 155   Mon-Fri 9-6; Sat 9-5
Dallas, TX 75234

If you can wade through the accent, you might be able to discern the rules of the road at Discount Optical. First, you must have a current prescription (12 months or less). If not, forget it. But if you do have the proper credentials, then you can shop here and save some moola on either contacts or glasses. Every little bit helps. FRESH LOOK colors were $89 for two boxes and **BAUSCH & LOMB** clear disposables were $49 for two boxes. Clearly, good prices. Designer frames vary in price, as do the specifics of the lenses....it's all in the choosing. For thinner lenses (those with a mild to moderate prescription) expect an additional $20 surcharge. In fact, the rule of thumb is the higher the RX, the higher the price, up to $40 for the additional extras. Glasses started as low as single-vision frames for $29.95 and bifocals for $49.94. And those are cheap for the lowest grade and simplest lenses. It was difficult communicating, though, since the personnel were neither fluent in English or pointing. Even then, it appeared to be a difficult task making our choices known.

Besides, pointing has never been an accurate way of relating our eyewear needs. Maybe a Berlitz course in English would be beneficial. On the other side, prices are so-so but a starting point.

★★★★★★ **EyeLane**　　　　　　　　　　**972/233-4113**

2288 Valley View Mall
Dallas, TX 75240
www.eyelane.com

Mon-Sat 10-9; Sun 12-6

 Do you see my point? Seven days a week, Dr. George Orm III, OD is available to set the record straight. At least you'll be able to read the fine print. From monthly specials to the guaranteed lowest prices on name brand and designer frames and contacts, you won't be left in the dark, I promise. Exit the second floor level at Dillard's and you're there. An exquisite showroom glistens with eyewear in their own specially-designed and lit alcoves. Have your prescription with you, pick a pair or two, and have them made right before your eyes. It's an eye-opening experience. Brands in glasses include 9 WEST, CALVIN KLEIN, CE TRUES, DKNY, DONNA KARAN, NAUTICA, NEO STYLE and my new best friend, VALENTINO. Wait 'til you see my rhinestone VALENTINO'S. They really are knock-outs! If you book an appointment from 2 to 4 PM, Monday through Friday, at the Valley View location only, you will also receive a half price deal (and yes, that's for BOTH eyes). How's that for a Diva Deal that is an eye-opener?

★★★★★★ **Fashion Discount Optical**　　**214/526-6006**

3430 Oak Lawn
Dallas, TX 75219

Mon-Fri 9-5:30; Sat 10-4

 When it comes to seeing the bottom line, Mark Schanbaum is the man to see. Born into the business (his family founded ROYAL OPTICAL), his own Fashion Discount Optical in Oak Lawn can complete your high-fashion eyewear wardrobe with most brand-name frames without making you feel you're getting framed in the process. Now, for the big bang theory of bargain shopping: Save 50 percent on them all with almost instant gratification. Delivery time is generally one to two days, while more difficult prescriptions are delivered within a week. Frames start at $49, but the average is $89. Seeing is believing: CHAPS/POLO, ESCADA, GUCCI, KENNETH COLE, OLEG CASINI and many more that can not be divulged. At least 100 different designers can be ordered at huge savings. Do you have to read between the lines? This is one of the best discounters in town, with generations of experience and service beyond compare. Visit at the corner of Oak Lawn and Lemmon. See if you can get a parking spot on the first go around? If at first you don't succeed, try, try, try again. Practice makes perfect!

◆◆◆◆◆ **Key-Whitman Laser Center**　　**214/220-EYES (3937)**

2801 Lemmon Ave.
Dallas, TX 75204-2356
www.keywhitman.com

By Appt. Only

The shoppers called Dr. Jeffrey Whitman the key to unlocking their dependence on eyeglasses. Well, the "eyes" have it at one of the Key-Whitman Laser Centers in Dallas, Plano or Arlington where they have been doing the eye thing for over 40 years. Dr. Jeffrey Whitman, himself, is the developer of Cool Touch LASIK and has probably trained, demonstrated or performed the procedure with just that piece of equipment thousands of times. He is definitely one of the leaders in state-of-the-art vision options with the full range of progressive ophthalmic and image enhancing services. But who'd ever think to call him for eyelid rejuvenation or skin resurfacing? BOTOX?

Laser Hair Removal? Safe touch cataract surgery? Problematic eye conditions? Many of these are life-altering conditions so you certainly wouldn't want just any old Doc using you as a guinea pig. For cataract surgery, for example, they use the "no stitch" and "no shot" method that provides a much safer surgical procedure with reduced complications of inflammation and swelling. And now the latest advancement: CRYSTALENS so you'll never need cataract surgery and can see near, intermediate and at far ranges (Hey, they are calling me now so I have to go.) There's a Key-Whitman Laser Centers in Arlington at 1000 N. Davis, Suite H, 817/460-2272 and in Plano at 3801 W 15th St., Ste. 200, 972/769-2020. See you there. *Call toll-free: 800/442-5330*

★★★ LensCrafters   **972/991-9940**

13331 Preston Rd.   Mon-Sat 10-9; Sun Noon-6
Dallas, TX 75240
www.lenscrafters.com

With a dozen mall locations in the Metroplex, you can't go far without running into a LensCrafters. After all, they were one of the leaders (though not the first) in the one-stop eyewear business, bringing the eye doctor, frames, lenses and the lens-making lab all under one roof. They are also now the largest. Specials will make you dizzy, but don't expect to buy contacts here. Contacts are only available from the independent eye doctor next door. A recent promotion was for five days Free of the FOCUS Dailies, with the purchase of the new daily disposable contact lens, you get an $80 mail-in rebate. But you have to purchase eight boxes. So be it. Also, non-prescription sunglasses were all 50 percent off. Glory be! Signing up for other promos and coupons on their website is another incentive to keep in touch. Six months same as cash with the purchase of at least two pair of prescription glasses made the medicine easier to swallow but then again, what if you only want one? Check directory for one of their multitude of locations throughout the Metroplex.

★★★★★★ Luck Optical   **817/738-3191**

7108 Camp Bowie Blvd.   Mon-Fri 9:7; Sat 8:30-5:30
Fort Worth, TX 76116
www.luckoptical.com

 Luck be a lady in glasses. If you are looking, maybe luck is finally in your corner. Anyone who's been in the same business for over 60 years certainly has longevity in their genes. Think of it like having a relative in the eye business. If Luck would have it, they treat you like one of the family here. Maybe you are. But if not, exam rates for children's (12 & under) are only $38 and $43 for adults. Contact lens exams are $79 and broken down as follows: $44 for the exam, $15 for the fitting and $20 for the follow-up. Prices haven't changed in years, believe it or not. There are six doctors on staff, no appointment is necessary. Just walk right in and sit yourself down. Since their earliest beginnings in downtown Fort Worth, shoppers have been lucky, thanks to Dr. L.H. Luck. In fact, he was the first in the area to come up with "glasses in one hour" when he decided to add an in-house lab to his practice. (Lenscrafters made the concept a household word.) Offering the latest technology and a guarantee to beat the competition by 10 percent, including prices on eyeglasses, exams, and contact lenses, it all adds up to a value-enhanced experience when shopping for eyewear and the shoppers'choice in Tarrant County. *Call toll-free: 800/613-8117*

★★★★★ **Lux Eyewear for Less**   **972/686-0595**

1020 W. Centerville Rd.   Mon-Fri 9-6; Sat 9-5
Garland, TX 75041
www.luckoptical.com

Luxurious, they're not. Cheap they are. This cheap sibling store to Luck Optical offers a slightly different twist to selling eyewear. Just call it plain and simple. Flat prices appear to be their marketing strategy with single vision eyeglasses at $41. Now isn't that easy? Lined bifocals were $66 with any frame; no-line bifocals, $109 with any frame. For a thinner polycarbonate lens, expect to lay out around $77 with a turn-around time between five and seven working days. Single vision lenses are the fastest to get out from start to finish. See clearly with two pairs of single-vision glasses or two pairs of flat bifocals starting at $44.95 from their SMARTBUY line of frames. Or, two pairs of no-line bifocals, with clear plastic lenses, for $102.95. A pair, a spare and all frames from their SMARTBUY selection. Well, this is your lucky day! Bring in your current prescription and you'll be seeing the light at the end of the tunnel in no time. They can do some repairs on eyeglasses but most are sent out, so you might be better off seeking help elsewhere in an emergency. Check directory for the other locations nearest you in Burleson, Grand Prairie and Fort Worth.

★★★ **Optical Clinic**   **214/521-5775**

4309 N. Central Expwy.   Mon-Fri 8:30-5:30; Sat 8-1:00
Dallas, TX 75205

See them at many neighborhood corners, on highways, in self-standing buildings, they're everywhere. This home-grown native chain may indeed be your cheapest link. Then again, they may not suit your particular needs at all. But they must be doing something right, as their phones, year after year, stay busy forever. No joke. We tried months and months apart. Maybe they just keep them off the hook during business hours. Nevertheless, don't be too busy to take a peepers at some of their optical plans. For example, $109 will get you an exam for contacts, glasses and sunglasses; or one pair of regular daily wear, clear-view contact lenses; or clear single-vision glasses with lightweight "Herculite" lenses up to a certain correction; or frames from a certain collection (same with the non-prescription sunglasses); and a 30-day unlimited checkup opportunity. But if you snooze you lose. Special deals may not last forever.

★★★★★ **Optical Dispensary**   **972/285-8941**

3914 Hwy. 80 East   Mon-Fri 8:30-5:30; Sat 8:30-1 (Walk-ins on Sat)
Mesquite, TX 75149

Now hear this — so you'll be able to see your way clear. For $88, here's what you get: an exam for contacts and eyeglasses, one pair of clear daily wear contact lenses and a pair of glasses from a select group. Talk about a site for sore eyes! Of course, you may not find the frames they are offering to your liking, but, at this price, you may forgo beauty in place of the least! Check out their special — there's always one going on. This is the second year in a row that the special included the exam for contacts, the contact lenses and a pair of glasses. This dispensary can save you up to 50 percent on frames and more on contacts. Another day, single-vision lenses were $29 with $10 tacked on for an eye exam. Such a deal! Almost too good to be true, but it was. Bifocals, as low as $44. How do they do it? By eliminating expensive overhead, designer and brand-name frames. Somehow, most frames all look alike when it comes down to it. Forgo all the trappings and get to the root of seeing straight. Saving money may be the most important bottom line anyway. Same-day service has an upcharge and walk-ins are taken on Saturdays, but only the first 20 patients with appointments are booked every 20 minutes. Dawdlers, big mouths and shufflers need not apply.

★★★★ Optical Mart   972/669-9648

804 Plano   Mon-Fri 10-6; Sat 10-5 (Closed for lunch 1-2 PM)
Richardson, TX 75080

At the northeast corner of Plano and Belt Line, this guy has been in the biz so many years he's
stopped counting. No contacts. No eye exams. But glasses, glasses and more glasses. Consider
them smart and you cheap. You be the judge. Take the savings to heart at the Optical Mart and
perhaps adopt their philosophy in this day and age. Why pay for designer names? You got something against keeping costs within seeing-eye range? Here, the styles are staggering but the most
recognizable name was **Lauren Bacall**. I don't think she's a coveted designer name, do you?
(Well, she supposedly shops at Tuesday Morning, so we know she has some redeeming qualities.)
Nevertheless, without the designer names, they can bring in the frames and sell 'em cheap. It's that
simple. With designer names, you have to pay a royalty and therein lies the upcharge. (Of course,
I'll be changing my tune when I start to license my own line of Diva glasses, but until then, you
might want to just forgo that extra cost.) Over 400 styles and colors to choose from with single-
vision glasses priced at only $28.95 (same as last year's and the same as the year before). Truer
words were never spoken. Can you believe holding the line on prices for years and years? It's true.
Want some extras? Add another $12 if you want the scratch-coating protection and another $12
for UV protection. Or if you want both, they'll make you a deal....$20. If you want only one extra
feature, he recommends the UV protection. (I'm just telling you what he said.) Designer frames
cost anywhere from $10 to $100. If you have a strong prescription, those ultra-thin lenses will run
about $89.95. Don't be fooled by in-house labs, as that is what really runs up your cost in this
man's humble opinion. No in-house lab; these glasses are sent out and ready in about three to five
working days. Extras do add up, so consider seriously if you really need them. Lightweight or
oversized lenses do not cost more. Bring in a current prescription and away you go. Located across
from Richardson Square Mall, there are multiple locations throughout the Metroplex. Check directory for the one nearest you.

★★ Pearle Vision   972/239-8585

5549 LBJ Frwy.   Mon & Thurs 9-7; Tues, Wed 9-6:30; Fri 9-6; Sat 9-5:30
Dallas, TX 75240
www.pearlevision.com

"Nobody cares for eyes more than Pearle" is as good a jingle as I've heard, but for saving money
on eyewear, well, that's another story. Dr. Stanley Pearle founded his namesake back in 1961 and
I must admit, he does make an eloquent spokesperson. Distinguished. Smooth. Grandfatherly. If
you agree with his mission, you will be seeing clearer in no time. His contribution to the eyewear
industry is definitely the "one-stop shop." Thank you, Dr. Pearle! We love it. No wonder they
became an overnight success! Provide convenient locations, expanded hours, competitive prices
and a better selection of frames, and the consumers will come. And so they did. Locations all over
the Metroplex (and the country) confirm their acceptance. Go online and print out money-saving
coupons or check the daily paper's inserts for deals. Check directory for location nearest you.

★★★★★ Reading Glasses To Go   972/392-3111

5411 Belt Line Rd.   Mon-Sat 10-6
Dallas, TX 75240
www.readingglasses.com

Jeepers Creepers, where did you get those Peepers? If you're smart, you probably bought them at
Reading Glasses to Go. Have a pair (or two) tucked into the glove compartment, your purse, brief-
case or by your bedside and read the fine print without it costing an arm and a leg. Spend as little

as possible and still see straight is the whole purpose, right? Choose from a selection of inexpensive, yet fashionable specs to take with you wherever you want to go. What a selection! Although they are non-prescription glasses, they do come in varying strengths of magnification. They are so reasonable, you'll want to buy a few. Bifocals, no liners, sun readers, half frames, full frames, folding frames, accessories and more. As low as $18 each or two for $29, how can you go wrong? Full frame budget metal frames with spring hinges were priced two pair for $36. When you're ready "to go." they have four Metro locations: (Prestonwood above,) University Park, 214/368-4444, Plano 972/423-6284 and Grapevine, 817/424-2495). *Call toll-free: 800/238-0904*

★★★★★ Royal Optical Outlet   214/630-5791

1334 Inwood Road   Mon-Wed 9-6; Wed, Fri, Sat 9-5
Dallas, TX 75247

Boy, I can see the writing on the wall. This bastion of bargain eyewear has it both ways — retail and their outlet stores. We recommend the outlet route for the direct route to travel. Located at the Inwood Outlet Center, Royal Optical's the king of the road when it comes to setting the gold standard for savings. At their retail stores, you can often see right through to the savings. For example, when we last looked, most eyeglasses were 40 percent off; the second pair was 50 percent off. Choose from their most popular frames, lens styles and options. And if you're good, they'll throw in a complimentary **RENU** starter kit. Honoring most of the Vision Plans, including AARP, Aetna and PacifCare, you can bet that at the retail level, you are buying retail but at discounted prices. And as Martha would say, "and that's a very good thing." However, by detouring to one of their outlets, you'll be able to save even more. How does 50 percent off every frame, every lens, on every option sound? Contact lenses were as low as $17.95. Try out an $80 price tag for an exam and contacts or glasses. Visit the other outlet location at the Southwest Center Mall, 972/296-1141.

★★★★ Southwest Vision Center   817/281-3386

7728 Mid Cities Blvd.   Mon, Wed, Thurs-Fri 9-5; Tues 11-7; Sat 9-3
North Richland Hills, TX 76180

Now only closed on Sundays, this might be the place to make your brown eyes blue. Disposable packages included eye exam for glasses and contacts, as well as two boxes of the clear contacts, for $139. For colored contacts and the exam, expect the price to be $189. (At the Contact Lens Center, they would cost $219 for four boxes which by now is looking at not such a bad price.) Or mix and match — for the same price. Get one box of the colored contacts and one box of the clear. Great. At the time of our visit, there was a huge selection of designer frames at 50 percent off; while others were only 20 percent off. In contacts, for that $189, you can pick two pairs of **DURASOFT** colored contacts, or, for the same price, you can get a pair of clear and a pair of colored. But these **DURASOFT** contacts come in many more colors. Between great prices, they have lots of "gimmies" such as little gifts with promotions. Plus, they have more than 1,000 frames in stock at prices that have not risen much at all, even while the rest of the world continues to spiral out of control. Appointments book up to a week in advance but Saturdays are strictly walk-ins from 9-2:30. For a Mid-Cities shopper, this is a convenient place to see a myriad of options.

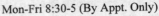

◆◆◆◆◆◆ **Tylock Eye Care & Laser Center**   **972/258-6400**

3100 N Macarthur Blvd.
Irving, TX 75062
www.tylock.com

Mon-Fri 8:30-5 (By Appt. Only)

Once you're attended one of Dr. Tylock's most informative Free seminar on Tuesday evenings at 6, and you recognize you're a perfect candidate for the LASIK or any of the other eye-correcting laser procedures that he specializes in, the only other ingredient to help make your decision is a $200 certificate to be applied to the surgery. How's that for a bargain? Do you want to know more? Then ask for a FREE CD explaining the process and everything you would need to or want to know about LASIK. After all, the world of opthalmological is changing by the minute with so many new techniques and scientific breakthroughs that you'll want to know everything that is available for your particular eye correction. See? There's lots to know and Dr. Tylock is in the know. Over one million have crossed over to affect a change in their eyesight — be it myopia, hyperopia or astigmatism. (Hey, that's me.) Well, a few years ago, I wasn't a candidate. Now I am. So, if you're one of them, too, join me and let's go together? Though misery is supposed to love company, they tell me this procedure is far from being miserable. So, let's just hold hands and sing "See for Two." If you want one of the best facilities with one of the pioneers in eye surgery, with over 20 years in practice, he has contributed to many in the glassless society. Too, Dr. Tylock built one of the country's first Excimer lasers designed specifically for the LASIK procedure. Tell him thanks because he was instrumental in having this procedure approved by the FDA and now, whether you're an athlete or radio personality, you have been quick to jump on the bandwagon. In fact, Dr. Tylock has performed over 43,000 refractive surgeries including over 32,000 LASIK procedures making him one of the most prolific and experienced in the field. Of course, if it's good enough for his family, his staff, other optometrists and ophthalmologists and physicians, it's good enough for Divas and her following. Now, don't blink until he tells you to. Dr. Gary Tylock is a board-certified ophthalmologist and eye surgeon. Only 1 percent of laser vision centers worldwide has the **INTRALASE** Laser, the advanced, state-of-the-art technology and the Tylock Eye Care Center is one of them. Their website is jammed-packed with information — to help you become an educated consumer before making your surgical decision. You can see clearly the best of the best.

Fabrics & Upholstery

★★★ **ABC Textiles**　　　　　　　　　　　　　　**214/357-8700**

2623 Perth St.　　　　　　　　　　　　　　　　　　　Mon-Fri 8-3:45
Dallas, TX 75220

Do you need help with your ABC's? If so, consider saving a stitch in time because it should save you money as well. This is an old "Confusion" saying, but if you want to dive into an ocean of fabrics priced from a low of $1/yard, take your chances and swim to the wholesale fabric district. Off Harry Hines, between Walnut Hill and Royal, new fabrics are knee-deep at this reef where there's a heap of bargains waiting to be reeled in. Dressmakers unite. Get a great deal on gabardine, wool, gingham, velveteen, sateen, crepe de chine, challis, silk, cotton, toile, batik, denim, linen, so many you could patchwork a quilt across the Metroplex. Find many moderate-to-better dress fabrics, overruns from local manufacturers, piled high. You will have a field day, but no longer on Saturdays! And note, they close like banks — earlier than most. Great prices on solids and prints for sewing projects from apparel to crafts, quilts to curtains. Remnants were out the door for $1/yard. Off the bolt, try $1.50 to $3/yard. Upholstery and drapery fabric begin at $2 up to $6. Add the trims to the mix and, alphabetically speaking, it's all you need to know to pass the first grade in Fabric Buying 101.

All Brands

20415 Highland Road　　　　　　　　　　　　　　Mon-Fri 8-5:30; Sat 9-4
Baton Rouge, LA 70817

www.allbrands.com　 *Top Online Store!*

One of the most useful websites for you to scour is the one put out by the Dallas Film Commission (the official production professionals' organization). There are lots of avenues to take but you want to hook up with the credible and the reliable sources who won't rip you off. This website is one that will direct you to the right course of action. Who are the casting directors to call, where are the acting schools and publications, who are the acting groups that help train and market professional actors, even where to buy the Dallas Actors Handbook for Dallas, the complete guide to who to go-see for a list of people and companies who employ actors, or who have services or products for actors (over 800 listings). Okay, I won't keep you in suspense any longer. Here's how to get a copy for $12.95. Either order online at dalekassel@dallasactor.com, log on to dallasactor.com or mail a check to DAHB, PO Box 38495, Dallas, TX 75238. *Call toll-free: 866/255-2726*

★★★   Allied Fabrics   214/741-4431

163 Parkhouse St.   Mon-Fri 8-4
Dallas, TX 75207

If you have a notion to get into a sewing project, here's a place to make an ally. Otherwise, you may lose the war on high prices. Located near I-35 E and Continental, you will see wholesale prices on notions and that means buttons, ribbons, elastics, rick rack, zippers, braids and hang tags. What's a hang tag? That's a tag that, if you were a dressmaker, you'd want to put on a garment to identify the "SIZE." Still, no fabrics, but if you need something they don't have, it could be ordered directly from the mill. No weekend hours, but savings up to 50 percent are possible. It doesn't hurt to ask. Looking for rattails? Eyelets? Maybe you never knew who to ask? Secure those final touches on your sewing or craft project and don't say we didn't find the cheapest link.

Benno's Button & Trimmings   214/352-0534

5611 W. Lovers Ln   Mon-Fri 9:30-5:30; Sat. 10-5:30
Dallas, TX 75209

Benno's has buttons. But at last look, no website. Too bad as it would be a boom to button seekers. If you're looking for buttons, this is the only store of its kind that has asked me to "button" my lips. When readers ask, "Button, button, whose got the button?" how can I suggest they go to Wal-Mart for a pewter hand-made button or one made of glass or crystal for that evening suit? Me, I love the funky ones. This store is a jewel, a treasure, a one-of-a-kind emporium of buttons, trims, beading, feathers, boas, notions and such that surely you'll find something to "suit you." I did for several outfits. They also carried lots of ribbons and trims for hair, wrapping a gift, or trimming a pillow. From crystal bangles to feathers, and everything in between to customize a purse, a lamp shade, a vase, it's all under one little gemstore on the north side of Lovers Lane near Inwood and the Tollway. One doesn't go to Benno's to quibble about a dollar off here and there. One goes to Benno's because it's the only specialty button store in the Metroplex.

★★★★★   Boca Bargoons   972/423-8700

1805 N. Central Expressway   Mon-Sat 10-6
Plano, TX 75057
www.bocabargoons.com

Florida's largest fabric company (we listed them in our Tampa, Orlando and Atlanta books) has finally made its way west (as all smart men, young and old, eventually do.) Take the Collins Street exit off I-30 and go north approximately half a mile. Upholstery and drapery fabrics from around the world are offered at a fraction of their original cost, making them the fastest-growing decorative fabric chain in the country. Log on to their website. Get up close and personal with high end designer names that are often seen in *Architectural Digest* and other chi-chi shelter magazines. Expect to decorate your world and look like the rich folks at bigger, better bargoon prices. Choose the A-to-Z selection of brocades, chenilles, cottons, damasks, prints, sheers and tapestries. The huge 15,000-square-foot phenomenon opened its doors with savings of 75 percent off. For example, tapestries that retailed for $100 would normally be at BB for $49/yard. Then take another 75 percent off and you'd pay $12. Now isn't that something?! Buy fabrics at a fraction of wholesale. And then there was two. Sew it up in Plano, too, at 1805 N. Central Expressway, 972/423-8700.

★★★   Calico Corners   214/349-6829

12370 Inwood Rd.   Mon-Sat 10-6; Thurs 10-7; Sun 1-5
Dallas, TX 75244
www.calicocorners.com

Fabrics, furniture and inspiration are what lies ahead at this corner. You'll find "seamingly" end-less bolts of fabric of all makes and styles discounted about 20 percent. Both drapery and uphol-stery fabric awaits your inspection. But now they've blossomed into four Metroplex locations (Dallas, Southlake, Fort Worth and Plano) and have branched into custom furniture as well. Bud-ding with ideas with a bouquet of over 2,500 fabrics makes for an easy make-over from start to finish. Upholstered furniture, meticulously crafted, renders an entirely new look. You'll save 30 to 50 percent on remnants and discontinued fabrics, but what's "sew" appealing is they allow you to take home an entire bolt for two days to examine the colors and textures in the room with your other pieces of furniture, lighting, etc. In addition to fabrics and trims, they have custom bedding from crib to king size, including shams, bed skirts, comforters, window treatments with hundreds of frame choices all made to order. Sew up a storm at their three other locations in Plano, South-lake and Fort Worth. Check directory for the one nearest you. *Call toll-free: 800/213-6366*

◆◆   Come and Sew   972/539-1948

                                                                By Reservation Only
Flower Mound, TX 75028

Remember how much fun you had threading that bobbin in Home Economics classes? Well, you might enjoy picking up that needle again — just where you left off. Kathy Arnold has been teach-ing out of her home/studio for 11 years. For beginners, Kathy, a professional seamstress, ensures first that you understand your sewing machine and what it's capable of doing. It's a basic skills class that lasts 12 weeks meeting once a week (Wednesday nights from 7-9 PM or Thursday morn-ings from 9:30 to 11:30). Cost is $85, which includes the book, fabric and all supplies including the machine, so you don't have to haul yours around. She teaches one of the few sewing classes around. Kids'classes are also available for quilting and crafting, including an occasional class for children with ADD, dyslexia, etc. She is involved in speaking, fundraising and coordinating dona-tions of supplies and projects for the volunteers. This woman takes her talent to the highest level. So Come and Sew with her and see what materializes.

★★★★   Current Fabrics   214/353-2766

2655 Perth St.   Mon-Fri 9:30-4:30; Sat 9-2:30
Dallas, TX 75220

The tides have changed and the current is flowing with discounted fabric from this warehouse. Au Current keeps up with the current fabric trends and anything you want in fabric, they can deliver at 50 percent off and more. All first-quality fabrics (but it's always a good idea to inspect all fabric before purchasing) for garments, formals, crafts, home decor, including upholstery, and drapery fabrics. Why pay retail when you can save on the most recent, up-to-date styles at closeout prices? Head to the current fabric district on Perth Street and see what's current on the horizon. If you'd rather not buy last year's dogs, you can bark when you see the selection of whites in the eye-lets. From cotton prints, plaids, florals, geometrics all the way to the delicacy of bridal toile, taffeta and lace, you might find out it's now cheaper to say, "I do" than to say, "you didn't!" Buy it by the bolt and your buy gets an even deeper discount. But to land on Perth, you don't have to fly Quantas Airlines. It's just off Stemmons, between the Royal Lane and Walnut Hill exits, off Harry Hines. Sew and sew tells me there's more than 15,000 yards to wander through. From dressmaking to upholstery, you can even fabric the front yard, if that's your pleasure.

★★★★★   **Cutting Corners**   **972/233-1741**
13720 Midway Rd., Suite 200   Mon-Sat 9:30-5:30; Thurs 9:30-8; Sun Noon-5
Farmers Branch, TX 75244
www.cuttingcorners.com

With millions of yards of experience, the McClintock family, headed by patriarch
Mac McClintock, has branched out into a forest of locations besides Dallas and Fort
Worth — they're now in Houston, Austin, Scottsdale, Oklahoma City, New Orleans
and Denver. Cutting Corners has been in a family way for more than 20 years and in their two
organized showrooms (Dallas and Fort Worth), it sure makes shopping for bargains a breeze. At
the corner of Midway, between Alpha and Spring Valley, you do not need a bolt of lightning to get
fired up about how they don't cut corners, just prices. This quality mill outlet is a fixture in the
Metroplex. They also have their own line of window fixtures, called "Iron Designs," in your
choice of metallic finishes at really great prices: adjustable rod, $4.99; extendable brackets, $2.99;
ball finials, $5.99; clip rings, $5.99. Fab new fabrics found hanging around: pleated "Fortuni" silk,
$7.99/yard; bronze-colored sheers, $11.99/yard; print and solid chenilles, $12.99/yard; and that
old stand-by, chintz, $5.99/yard. You don't want to pass this shopping experience up!

★★★★★★   **De La Rosa Upholstery & Mfg**   **817/581-2851**
5600 Rufe Snow Drive   Mon-Fri 8:30-5:30; Sat 8:30-4
Fort Worth, TX 76180

At last, we've found a Fort Worth re-upholsterer with a showroom in North Richland Hills who can whip up custom furniture, restyle your old, make cornice boards,
head boards and, yes, cover your walls with fabric. They have tons of sample books
to choose your fabric. With your own fabric (theirs start at $20 a yard and up), labor is $475 (that's
fabulous, ladies and gentlemen), a loveseat is $425 and a wing back chair is $225. There is no
charge for pick up and delivery. Turn around time is two-three weeks. They manufacture custom
furniture. Take them a picture and they'll duplicate it: ottomans, sofas, chairs, loveseats, benches,
vanity pull up chairs, parsons chairs, you will not be sorry!

★★★★★   **EmbroidMe**   **972/318-3434**
1425 FM 407, Suite 400 A   Mon-Fri 10-6; Sat. 10-4
Lewisville, TX 75077
www.embroidme.com

If you're looking to stand out in the crowd, put your name on a shirt and be proud. That way folks
will know you without questioning who you are, who you support or who you work for. If your
team is suffering an identity crisis, this is one way to build a name for yourself. When you want to
monogram a set of guest towels or add your company logo to 10,000 baseball caps, here's the
place to have them embroidered or screen-printed. Choose from lots of promotional items and get
your business circulated on polo shirts, your team name on a uniform, your shop's trademark on a
shopping bag, or your restaurant's menu on an apron. Choose from denim shirts, promotional
items, advertising specialty items and gifts, baby items; it's all available in this one-stop promotional shop. Set up fee is $10 to get started. Hats were as low as $4 but will run as much as $9 with
logo and embroidery. T-Shirts, for a Hanes 50/50 heavy-weight in black or red using the same
logo, would cost about the same with a nine to 12 day turnaround. Here's a great graduation gift
before they leave for college .... monogram their towels (so they are easier to retrieve from dorm
mates who like to steal!) Eight other franchised locations in the Metro area, check directory assistance for the one nearest you.

★★★   Fabracadabra   214/357-3555

5535 W. Lovers Lane   Mon-Fri 9:30-5:30; Sat 10-4
Dallas, TX 75209

Hocus pocus and presto—you'll even have money left over after you leave this shop. Even in the
Park Cities, money doesn't grow on trees. Still, you can magically transform your plain and boring
yard with yards from **FABRICUT**, **P. KAUFMAN**, **ROBERT ALLEN**, **WAVERLY**, and still maintain your integrity in the "underground shopping" philosophy. Now moved from their original
location, they still can transform your rooms from top to toppers before your budget bottoms out.
Depending on the deal they cut from the manufacturer, you can save 20 to 30 percent, but more
like 40 to 50 percent. For interior decorative purposes, count on them doing all the transformation
a room might need except the paint and carpentry work. Custom made window coverings include
draperies, curtains, cornices, window shades, etc., but don't expect them to come cheap.

★★★★   Fabric By The Pound   972/287-5447

110 West Elm   Wed-Fri Noon-5; Sat 10-3
Seagoville, TX 75159-3718
www.fabricbythepound.com

If crafting is your notion, then get all your ingredients off the menu here (or at their other walk-in
location at 203 N. Kaufman Street in Seagoville, 972/287-5447). Looking to braid a rug, make a
crochet rag rug, crochet a rag basket, a quilt, a toothbrush rug, or other fabric rug? Then get your
fabric at Fabric By The Pound. So, what will you find here? Warehouse prices on mill end strips,
textile remnants, lace, craft patterns and an assortment of trims for curtains, draperies and upholstery. Get all the accessories you need with **P**, Q and S-size crochet hooks, fabric holders, patterns
and more. Not sure where to start? How about their **FREE** classes? Call in advance, since space is
limited to six participants per class. Expect to pay for one to six-inch strips, $2.50-$3.50/pound;
wider strips, $4.50/pound. Many of their crafters have won ribbons at the Texas State Fair. For
ready-made items, expect to pay the piper. Order by phone, online or through their walk-in stores
in Seagoville.

★★   Fabric Factory   972/720-1400

12330 Inwood Rd.   Mon-Sat 10-6; Thurs 10-7; Sun Noon-5
Dallas, TX 75244

Sorry, this gorgeous facade at the intersection of Inwood and Forest sells gorgeous fabrics but....at
the lowest prices in town? I don't think so! Over 3,000 bolts of high-end fabrics at an occasional
discount does not solve the mystery at Scotland Yard. I hate to be a Knit Picker, but if you are in
the market for drapery and upholstery fabric, go ahead — make their day. First-quality, you bet.
Fine as wine, I'll toast to that. But at a savings? No way, Jose. You might liken them to "Operation
Fabric Storm," 'cause they can sure whip up a flurry of activity in their workroom. Not only window treatments, but custom furniture, too. Pick your fabric. Add a trim? Maybe a tassel? A knob
nail? A bow? Maybe a custom slipcover for those dining room chairs will do the trick. Fabrics just
for children's rooms tell you these folks mean business for any room in the house. But, again,
many retailers "buy direct from the mills" and pass the savings onto the customer. Looks like
something was lost in the translation here!

★★★★★★   **Fabric Source, The**   **972/267-3400**

2385 Midway Rd.   Mon-Fri 9:30-5; Sat 9:30-5
Carrollton, TX 75093
www.thefabricsourcecarrollton.com

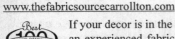

If your decor is in the Pitts, then why not let David Pitts transform it all. David Pitts, an experienced fabric retailer with decades of experience, has you covered. From one end of the house to the other, this is THE place to buy fabric and have it made into something wonderful, useful, functional, beautiful. Top to bottom and everything in-between, you can have it all for less. How much less? How does 40-60 percent off sound? From ottomans and pillows that are drop dead gorgeous, to upholstery furniture made from scratch to your own furniture reupholstered, to custom draperies, lamps, well, think fabric and think The Fabric Source. The place was buzzing with decorators and shoppers alike on the day of our visit, all clamoring for the designer's attention. If you don't know the difference between a pleat and a puddle, or a crushed matte to a moirÈ, then here are the experts to set the record straight. Meet at The Fabric Source and let them start the instructional process. Bring in a picture, look through their design books of completed works, and you will be impressed. It's time you look for a redo rather than a make-do and transform that favorite chair or sofa into something contemporary — or pick a vanity chair and see what materializes. But though you'll be the benefactor of their budgetary constraints, they never sacrifice the quality of their workmanship in the process. It's their craftsmanship that sets them apart from the crowd. If you can think it, they can make it. If you can't think it, they offer design specialists like Lazette Lee, Carrie Cain or Lela Yarborough (her custom lamps are the talk of the country club!). Each of them are just dying to get their hands on a project and take it from blah to beautiful. Then meet Jim. He's the pillow man. (Once he was considered the finest upholster for antique cars in the Southwest). Today, he's in to custom pillows. And bedding. You should see the results of his labor. Make him show you his photos (no, not his etchings). But I must tell you it's the collaboration of fabric, trims, prices, and the workmanship that sets them apart from the crowd and makes them THE source to contend with. So why bother shopping around? It's all under one roof. And if it's just fabrics you want, have at it here. With their expansion completed, it only means more fabric, more savings, more opportunities to blanket your household with fabrific new cover-ups. Within 7,000 square feet, you can surely transform one piece of furniture and enhance your lifestyle with the whole nine yards. Wander through the aisles of good buys. Hundreds and hundreds of bolts of gorgeous fabrics with prices averaging $9.99-$24.99/yard. Great buys on vanity chairs that were $289 but seen elsewhere for comparable quality around $600 and ottomans at $299, well once you see one, you'll want two. Trust me. Cut a piece of glass and it becomes an elegant coffee table. Forget the glass and it's now the place for your feet, or extra seating, displays, magazines or whatever, who knows? See why their ottomans win beauty prizes. Then, what about a custom painted lamp and lamp shade for the baby's room or a boudoir lamp that matches the fabric on your dressing table skirt, that coordinates with the vanity chair and fits in beautifully with your bedroom decor. See, I've captured your imagination already. One block north of Keller Springs on the west side, you can get it all sewn up and that's the nuts and bolts of this story. This is a one-stop source for the 3 R's: restoration, rejuvenation and reupholstery. Now read my lips. Shop the Fabric Source and write the final chapter on the book of love. Expect to wait a reasonable length of time for the finished product, but good things are worth waiting for, right?

★★★★★ **Fabric Yard**   **972/774-1740**

15317 Midway   Mon-Sat 9:30-5:30; Sun 12-5
Dallas, TX 75001-4250

"The Planet of the Drapes" is heating up in this North Dallas corridor. This newcomer recently opened its doors offering some of the most beautiful fabrics in town. We bolted out of our complacency and thought we'd roll up our sleeves and dig in. Thousands of yards of upholstery and drapery fabrics at up to 75 percent off were laying around neat as a pin in this 9,000-square-foot showroom. Star-struck names stuck out, including **BARROW**, **BLOOMCRAFT**, **KRAVET**, **SCHUMACHER** and **WAVERLY** creating their own red carpet. No washed up has-beens, just big bins filled with hundreds of bolts at deeply discounted prices. No need to call in the officials or ask for autographs, though some of their prices were indeed a steal. Uncovering the wealth of opportunities here makes the Fabric Yard a big plus in the decorating genre. Though you won't need a "hoe" to get it "hoesale," fabric is priced dirt cheap.

★★★★★★ **Golden D'Or Fabric Outlet**   **214/351-6651**

10795 Harry Hines Blvd.   Mon-Sat 9-4:30
Dallas, TX 75220
www.goldendor.com

This is remnant heaven. If you've got the notion to get your wardrobe in motion, or your house the recipient of an "Extreme Makeover," the buck(s) should stop here. They've got the Midas touch when it comes to all the popular fabrications for dressmaking, drapery and upholstery. They handle every type of printed fabric with closeouts being their middle name. Their online store means you can order from home or office and not have to hem or haw with finding a parking place. Shop where other fabric stores and garment manufacturers'shop. There's not much left to consider since they occupy over a 200,000 square foot warehouse, with over six million yards in stock. Wow! Everything we saw was priced 30-70 percent off. Sew, start your star search for fabrics here — as low as $1.99 to $4.99/yard; drapery fabric, $4.50/yard, designer fabric (brocades, bridal, velvets, sequins, satins, rayons,) $2.50 to $12 a yard and remnants .... oh, there I go again, another senior moment. Choose brocades, sequins, metallic mesh, nets, knits, embroidered lace, peachskin, microfiber, denim/stretch denim, double knit, silk chiffon prints, beaded trims, bugle beads, bone and shell, feather and fur trims, eyelash, crepe, woolens, cotton prints and solids, spandex, swimwear, actionwear, prints, stretch lame, satin, lame, tulle, netting, taffeta, silks, dupioni, organza, chiffon, brocades, shantung, embroidered/beaded laces and trims, bridal accessories, velvets- silk, rayon, and cotton, chenille, tapestries, faux fur, felt — well, has your buck stopped yet? *Call toll-free: 800/527-9547*

★★★★ **Interior Alternative, The**   **214/637-8800**

Inwood Outlet Center   Mon-Sat 10-5; Thurs 10-6; Sun Noon-5
1305 Inwood Rd. Dallas, TX 75247

If you have lots of interior motifs, and one of your favorites is **WAVERLY/SCHUMAKER**, then here's the best-kept secret. It's out now, on the streets, for folks with a cheap streak. Here's the outlet for powerhouse Waverly/Schumacher, but let this be a fair warning: On Saturdays the place looks like a tornado struck by mid-afternoon. Service is almost non-existent and it's not nearly as appetizing as their beautiful ads. Now, that's the bad news. The good news is, it's not always that way. Some days are quiet and serene and there's enough Waverly to wave the flag in all-American bargains. So there. Now you have the full picture. If you want to make a detour from paying full price, here's where Waverly/Schumacher disposes of their overruns, closeouts, discontinueds and irregulars. At least you can applaud the final curtain. Making it like the last chapter of a good book, there are savings on their popular fabric and readymade comforter sets as well. Choose chintz, damasks or tapestries, velvets and moires. Choose matching wallpaper, trimmings and accessories. And it does spell savings. In store, there's also a sewing center for small projects like toppers or pillows. In the Inwood Trade Center, there's lots of activity to make a day of it.

★★   Kay's Fabric Center   972/234-5111

518 W. Arapaho   Mon-Sat 10-6; Thurs 10-7; Sun 12-5
Richardson, TX 75080

If you see Kay's on the www.SewDallas.org website, you can lop another 10 percent off their often discounted prices. Every once in a while, they will be running a 20 percent off sale. This 33-year old veteran of the foreign fabrics imports a lot of the unusual fabrics including a devoted collection of bridal fabrics that are to "Die for." This large designer and specialty fabrics shop is where the brides go for their bridal and special occasion materials, including veiling, appliques and other accessories. Year 'round, they maintain a large selection of silk, linen and wool in stock. Sew, what are you waiting for? Look for them on the north side of Arapaho, tucked behind Arby's for a variety of imported and unique fabrics for fashion sewers and quilters. Both are tendered with TLC. Open seven days, the only thing they lack is a website. *Call toll-free: 800/637-6917*

★★★★★   Keeton Supply Co.   817/268-2931; 817/332-7888

912 E. Vickery Blvd.   Mon-Fri 8-5; Sat 8-Noon
Fort Worth, TX 76104
www.keetonsupply.com

For the industrious sort, here's the place to stock up on upholstery supplies. After all, the company started in 1898 and may just be one of the longest-running enterprises in the Metroplex. Zip your lip, button-up and keep Keeton on your supply list for Dacron, padding, welt cord, burlap threads, staples, tools. Furniture legs, swivel seats, pillow forms, cording, zippers, webbing, cane and all the tools you'll need for the job (cutters, hammers, button makers, staple guns, stretchers, upholstery needles, spray guns and supplies). They carry a variety of veritable vinyl (especially for marine, auto and furniture use) to velvet and everything in between. Foam? You bet, in various widths and shapes for chairs, sofas, ottomans, whatever. Stock fluctuates, so check back often. They will even special order if what you need is not in stock. The current owners have been running the place for the past 20 years, giving credence to the fact that longevity is in their genes. Note the new toll-free numbers both in the Metroplex and nationwide. Ask for Dale and tell him the Diva sent you. *Call toll-free: 800/792-7888*

★★★★★★   Leo Moses Silks & Interiors   800/383-7105

1135 Dragon @ Howell   Mon-Fri 9-4:30; Occasional Saturdays
Dallas, TX 75207-4207
www.leomoses.com

Best 100 SHOPPING DESTINATIONS   Finally, after years of taking up residence on Perth Street, around the corner and at the end of the street, Leo Moses, otherwise known as Silks Unlimited, moved south to the Design District to be closer to the action. These guys sell silks. Silks for the finer things in life like dressmaking or home interiors. A 44-inch silk was selling at Kay's for $30; here for $12.95. If you like the Curtain Exchange, you'll LOVE Leo Moses because it's better material and less costly. Want silk lamp shades? Pillows? Bedding? Table toppers? You are The Material Girl, aren't you? Roll after roll, you'll be closer to heaven than a silk worm. Remember, this is the same company, founded in 1954 by a Lithuanian immigrant, that soon became an icon in the fabric business of old. Today, they are making their moves and their word (and their fabric) is golden. This father and son duo will weave their way into you home and heart with their fabrics. *Call toll-free: 214/654-0156*

★★★★★★   **M & M Upholstery**   **214/391-4085**
8337 Lake June Rd.   Mon-Fri 8-5
Dallas, TX 75217

Bring your imagination when you shop here because the sky's the limit. This company has been around since 1857, and, today, the third generation is in charge of the family business. For years, decorators brought or sent their client's upholstery jobs to this location, but the secret is now out of the bag. The name is M & M, and they don't melt in your hands, but in your heart. Today, they sell both to the trade and the public. They shower you with the three R's: restoration, rebuilding, restyling. Bring your own fabric, as they do not carry any. They will tell you how much fabric to buy for a particular job. For example, a sofa with a skirt takes between 18 and 20 yards of fabric, and labor is $475. One of their unique fabrications is mixing and matching different fabrics like solid cushions with printed arm rolls and floral skirts. The proof is in the end product.

★   **Miracle Fabric**   **972/579-7451**
1720 E. Irving Blvd.   Mon-Sat 9-5
Irving, TX 75060

The number you'll call is their main switchboard. From there, they'll direct you to either retail or wholesale and never the twains do meet. Rats! What we like, as underground shoppers, is to ultimately "buy retail at wholesale prices." But you've got to have a resale/tax number to buy wholesale here or you're stuck with paying retail next door at their outlet. But it's not at wholesale prices. Double rats. So, by the grace of God, go I. Since Haber is the company, you might save a few dollars on dressmaking fabrics, but bargains are few and far between. Bridal fabrics, fake fur, fleece, dress fabrics, trims and poly-cottons, if you have a notion to sew, they may be a miracle, but it's a stretch. Sew, what else is there? Patterns. Retail priced. Why bother? It's a miracle they haven't decided to bite the bullet and start discounting and join the rest of the congregation. We continue to pray!

★★★★★★   **Mire' Less**   **214/824-1453**
3720 Canton, Suite 100
Dallas, TX 75226
www.mireless.com

Deep in the heart of Deep Ellum is one of the best kept secrets in the Metroplex. Now that the cat's out of the bag, you will be purring over the perfection that is delivered from this 25-year old upholstery workroom. If you see a piece of furniture that has been hand-crafted from scratch on their showroom floor, grab it because it is a one-of-a-kind. Jesse knows his stuff. You can have others duplicated or bring in your own pictures and let the crew pursue it. They can do almost anything that has to do with furniture and upholstering. After all, they've been doing it for more than a quarter of a century and have finally opened a showroom to the public. But it's the creativity, craftsmanship and customer service that sets this upholstery workroom apart from the crowd. Think of it as the 3 C's when it comes to custom-built furniture. A contemporary patchwork charcoal gray 90"W x 40"D x 31"H sofa would cost $950, plus fabric. But remember, this sofa looks like a $2,500-$6,000 (or more) model from a specialty showroom. They also have the matching chair (48"W x 40" x 30"H) for $495 and ottoman (19-30"W x 35"H x 17.5H) for $275. Gorgeous and affordable, what a combination. Whether it's for your home or office, boat or car, plane or train, restaurant or wherever, if fabric is involved, they can do it for less. Window treatments, too. It doesn't get better than this.

★★★★★ Old West Stitches 817/558-8828

3101 A. North Main St.
Cleburne, TX 76033

Tues-Fri 9-5

Gay Lynn Thompson is some sort of sew-and-sew. Once you've seen her work, you'll know that if you need anything monogrammed, even something that has not been thought of before, she can do it. The Cleburne Fire Fighters look so-o-o-o good in uniform, partly because of their great navy-and-red monogrammed polo shirts. Don't you want your staff to look as good (even if they're not as buff?) Put initials on almost anything. Her $10 special gets you two places on a shirt—the cuff and the pocket, for example, and is the start of giving you that polished look. Great for adding to any of your previously-worn designer clothes for climbing the corporate ladder. Add your initials to a set of towels or a set of sheets and, believe me, you'll dry off and sleep like a king and queen. This is the place to take anything you want personalized. And, while you're there, don't overlook everything western that Gay has in the front of her shop. She has the largest selection of western-motif wallpaper borders that I've ever seen. In fact, that's where I bought the leopard borders for my guest bathroom. Now, all I need is someone to hang it, keeping the spots all in a row.

★★★★ Pete's Upholstery Shop 817/274-2431

2620 W. Pioneer Pkwy.
Arlington, TX 76013

Mon-Fri 8-4:30

For completely reupholstering a deep-seated couch, chair, loveseat or anything that could use a good makeover, for Pete's sake, consider Bill Yeager. He's the perfect craftsman for a face-lift or an uplift. Pick your fabric from his repertoire and consider it done. He's been doctoring furniture with fabric since 1963 and considers word-of-mouth his best source of advertising. Repeat business is really how his business has grown exponentially. Expect to pay $425 for labor plus fabric (about 15 yards) and tax to reupholster a sofa; a wingback chair, $250. Fabrics were pricey, starting at $25 and up. If you buy the fabric from him and live in Arlington, then pick-up and delivery is free. If you buy the fabric elsewhere, expect to pay $50 for roundtrip pick-up and delivery. Once he's gotten it all together, expect to be sitting on your throne in about two weeks. Wow! That's fast. Yes, his fabric is a little more, but when you are good—very, very good—you can command it. And, too, you'll be sitting pretty in no time and that counts for something!

★★★★★★ Silk Trading Co., The 214/741-7455

1617 Hi Line Drive, Suite 700
Decorative Center Dallas, TX 75207
www.silktrading.com

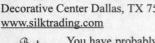

You have probably lusted after their luscious drapery treatments and fabrics at least a dozen times through the windows of their Decorative Center showroom. But like most of us, were too intimidated to step inside. No wonder? They're in the heart of where the designers shop and their showroom is so chi-chi, who'd think there would be something that would be within reach? Well, you're not just dreaming anymore. The Silk Trading Company is one of the most creative fabric and household decorating fashion accessory you can consider for a full-scale overhaul to your home. But most of their fabric inventory was meant for window or furniture dressing and therein lies the myriad of custom possibilities. For your windows, have at it — either custom or readymade, it's your choice. For furniture, they do it all. Pick your frame and your fabric and have at it. For bedding, watch for a ready-made section soon but custom work is right at their fingertips. Exit Oak Lawn off Stemmons. Turn right to first light which is Hi Line. Turn Left to the Decorative Center which will on your right. Take second right onto Slocum, then an immediate right after turning onto Slocum into the Decorative Center. *Call toll-free: 800/854-0396*

★★★★   Super Textiles Fabric Outlet   214/353-2770

2667 Perth St.   Mon-Fri 9-5; Sat 8-2
Dallas, TX 75220

Super Steve makes Super Textiles worth shopping just for his comedic delivery, if nothing else. He's hilarious and maybe has a second career in the wings. You never know; Letterman and Leno can't last forever. Ask him a basic question like, "Do you have any jacquards or denim?" and you'll wind up with a five-minute comedy routine. Just ask. You'll see. But you're here because you want to buy some fabric, right? This Perth Street warehouse showcases fabric from apparel manufacturers in town and, when it lands here, prices are cut accordingly. If he doesn't have what you're looking for, he'll send you to one of his sworn enemies up and down the street. Bring your credit cards, he admonished, all of them. You'll bolt out eventually with better womenswear over-cuts, closeouts, discontinueds or last season's castaways. Prices on challis, prints, jacquards, poly-cotton, interlock and denim (at a low $3/yard) were all discounted to the bare thread. While stock was great and prices low, this year the reception was definitely sterling. Now they've earned those gold stars. Warning: If you're not careful, not only will you buy fabric, you might buy Steve's recruitment pitch and wind up changing jobs.

★★★   Upholstery Place, The   972/271-6669

2406 S. Jupiter Rd., Suite 2   Mon-Fri 9-5
Garland, TX 75041
www.upholsteryplace.com

Looking to cover up a multitude of sins? That spot on the sofa? That worn arm on the recliner? Need some colorful pillows to puff up your decor? What about an ottoman to rest your weary feet? Teresa Garner is the seam-ingly master sewer who can custom craft it all in no time. As a matter of fact, she prides herself in being able to deliver the transformation in three to four weeks (not months or years). So why not get the ball rolling and reupholster that favorite old chair or trea-sured sofa? Prices, well, they're a whole lot better than buying new. Whether a slipcover or a com-plete make-over, you can expect savings in the neighborhood of 20 to 40 percent. And like an old-fashioned doctor who makes house calls, they will, too. Don't expect a wide variety of fabrics to choose from, though, as the fabric selection is limited.

Flea Markets & Bazaars

Vikon Village

★★★ **First Monday Trade Days**   **817/421-1778**

303 Palo Pinto (Santa Fe Dr. & Fort Worth Hwy.)   Fri-Sun 7 AM-Dusk
Weatherford, TX 76086
www.firstmonday.com

Weatherford is where it's happening the weekend before the first Monday of each month. It's a city that treasures its western traditions and heritage. But Saturdays, whether you're back in the saddle or not, are still the best days to shop. For over a century, vendors have been unpacking it up on Fridays, and packing it up on Sundays. When they sell out, they're out and ready to call it a wrap. You can buy anything here, including animals, so why bark up another tree? If you've been laid off or have retired early, think second careers. Lots of new-found money has been generated by wheeling and dealing at a flea market. In November, reservations are in order if you would like to rent a space, and it needs to be made the first week of the month prior to the month you want to open shop. Call 817/598-4215 for reservations, or fight City Hall, 303 Palo Pinto St. in Weatherford. Payments mailed should be addressed: First Monday Reservations, PO Box 255, Weatherford, TX 76086. Ask about their "Intent to Reserve" policy for ensuring the same place every time. To set up a food booth, it costs $150 for a hookup for wagons and $5 per day for electricity. A maximum of 10 spaces can be reserved by an individual/group/company, etc., and walk-up customers are accepted for $15 per day as long as space is available. For shoppers, there's still no charge to get in, but there's still a lack of free parking. Close-in parking will cost you $3 and up.

★★★★★★ **First Monday Trade Days**   **903/567-6556**

290 East Tyler   Thurs-Sun preceeding 1st Mon/month: Sunrise to Sunset
Canton, TX 75103
www.firstmonday.com

No other day of the month is as important as the first Monday in Canton, Texas. If you're a shopper who loves to walk the beat, this is the beat to Beat it! First Monday Trade Days in Canton is the largest outdoor flea market in the world. Born in 1873 as Canton's Court Days when the town's folks started selling their wares by "horse trading," today it's home to thousands of dealers who sell both new and used items, arts and crafts, antiques and collectibles, computers and electronics, food stuff to musical instruments and everything in between. Admission is Free; parking is not ($3-$4, typically). Hundreds of acres of shopping at this world-renowned event. Most of it is outdoors, but they do have climate-controlled buildings for "sensitive merchandise" and spoiled shoppers. If you are interested in being a vendor, prices start at $50 for a 12-by-20-foot open air lot and runs about $150 for a space in the trade center or arbor — obviously, the cooler, the higher the rent. (Check out our Travel Chapter for some neat Bed and Breakfasts to stay nearby.)

★★★★★★   Old Mill Mktplace, The Village, The Mountain

903/567-5445

542 Highway 64 East   Weekend prior to First Monday 8 AM-Dusk
Canton, TX 75103
www.oldmillmarketplace.com

Going to build a mountain! Welcome to the wacky world of First Monday, where "The Mountain," the "Old Mill Marketplace" and "First Monday" are all lying in wait for the onslaught of 20,000,000 bargain hunters. The Old Mill Marketplace has over 800 shops; they joined First Monday in 1994 as just another First Monday attraction. Each First Monday weekend, some 200,000 folks descend upon this sleepy East Texas town come rain or shine. Shoppers are shopping, umbrellas and all, dragging shopping carts, luggage on wheels and wheel barrels. There, you'll be able to shop for unique gifts, bargains and antiques. The 800 shops are all located within the "Old Mill Marketplace," "The Village" and "The Mountain." "The Mountain" is the pioneering town with shops with a western motif, cowboy shoot-outs, a petting zoo, artists and live local entertainment with a FREE "Saturday Night Live" musical showcase. Bed and breakfasts are even located on "The Mountain." Now, we're off to "The Village" for a flavor of the "Texas Hill Country." And don't forget to stay late on Saturday for their "Chinese Quarter Auction" held every Saturday during market in the Village Food Court. Doors open at 6:30 PM. Go online for discount parking coupons, gift certificates and other information about their seven pavilions, shuttle busses, benefits and more.

★★★   Second Monday Trade Days   940/872-1680

Business Hwy. 287 & Hwy 81 (Pelham Rd.)   Fri-Sun 7 AM-Dusk
Bowie, TX 76230
www.morgan.net/~a2ndmonday

This is not the town where David Bowie was born, but rather where shoppers converge on the rodeo grounds on East Wise Street in Bowie, Texas, the second Monday of each month. (Bowie is north of DFW and south of Wichita Falls off 287.) Get a whiff of fresh country air and put the airs of a citified corporate exec behind you. Mosey in and out of the antique shops around the Wise County Courthouse Square, where about 350 vendors set up shop on Saturdays before the second Monday of the month. Just north of DFW and south of Wichita Falls off Highway 287, expect 452 lots on five acres brimming with lots of stuff, some notable, others better left behind. See a wide variety of items, from clothing, cell phone accessories and antiques to animals and more. You'll find a plethora of prices and products, from TVs to livestock, handbags to cantaloupes. And food, well, you gotta eat, don't ya? Better be an early bird if you want to gather the most moss without building up a sweat. If you want to get into the act as a vendor, booths go for $20 for the weekend plus $4 for electricity. From Dallas, Fort Worth Metroplex area: Take Hwy. 287 north to Bowie, take first exit, go approximately one mile, turn right onto Pelham Road next to Rodeo Arena....you can't miss it.

★★★★★   **Third Monday Trade Days/McKinney   972/562-5466**

4550 W. University, Hwy. 380 `   Fri-Sun 9-5
McKinney, TX 75069
www.tmtd.com

Find it all, from Mr. Brown, who sells reconditioned vacuums, to Fred and his tools for sale. What began more than 100 years ago when judges rode the circuit from county seat to county seat, to today where it is the hub of contemporary horse trading, welcome to Third Monday. Head north on the Saturday and Sunday before the third Monday of the month. Treasure-hunt your way up Highway 75 to Highway 380 and go west for two miles to the historic Buckner Community where, since 1966, McKinney's Third Monday Trade Days have been a major happening. More than 300 vendors swell on the weekends scattered across the 30 acres. Open-air space rentals are $35 for the first lot and $25 for each additional lot. Western paraphernalia, hats, blankets, saddles and spurs to antiques, videos, **HARLEY** collectibles, toys, sporting goods and more. One of the nicest features this year is delivery to your car. FREE parking on Friday; $3 on Saturdays and Sundays. Restrictions are laudable: No alcoholic beverages, tobacco or pets allowed. One of the few marketplaces where area dog breeders have booths to sell registered pedigreed puppies. RV spaces and hookups available, if needed, and there are special rates at some nearby motels. Call 972/547-4500.

★★★★★   **Traders Village**   **972/647-2331**

2602 Mayfield Rd.   Sat-Sun 7 AM-6 PM
Grand Prairie, TX 75052
www.tradersvillage.com

Since Traders Village opened in Grand Prairie in 1973 and then in Houston in 1989, millions of people have browsed, shopped, haggled and picked through the bric-a-brac and all the other stuff in the world somebody somewhere wants to sell sometime to someone. In those years, shoppers have landed quite a few deals and an occasional steal. From the days of the Trading Post in the Old West until now, it has been one gigantic step for the bargain shopping kind. The atmosphere's like the State Fair though sometimes like **BARNUM AND BAILEY**, too. From paper clips to bulldozers, on any given weekend you can find it at Traders Village. There's an RV Park, kiddy rides and games, ATM machines, stroller and wheelchair rentals, snack stands, restaurants and all types of special amenities. Both new and used items are sold. The variety spices it up to pandemonium: birds, toys, furniture, electronics, produce, sunglasses, ear piercing, luggage, clothes, T-shirts, cosmetics, tools, sporting goods, garage sale items, shoes etc. Weekly events include such diverse fare as square dances, tractor shows, country music presentations and dog shows. A paradise, a paradox, parsimony at its best. (Hey, that's a good word for a change. It means extreme or excessive frugality.)

★★★★★★   **Vikon Village Flea Market**   **972/278-7414**

2918 South Jupiter   Sat-Sun 10-7
Garland, TX 75041
www.vikonvillage.net

 One reason to intersect Kingsley and Jupiter is to land at Vikon Village. A close-in garage sale all under one roof makes for easy shopping bliss. Entering middle age hasn't been easy for them, but being 33 years old with 200 plus devoted vendors makes the transition easier to accept. Go to the office and pick up your coupons for special Diva Deals. Direct your attention to those vendor specials first and then fill in the blanks with the others. Just two blocks north of LBJ, this indoor flea market is not as old as the hills, it just seems that way. In fact, if my memory serves me correctly, it was the first flea market I ever shopped when I moved to Dallas. For a devoted shopper who was always on the lookout for a deal, this was Nirvana. Finding it all under one roof was something new to the shopping scene back then — like traveling to one garage sale after another without having to get in and out of the car. Now that they've installed air-conditioning, new owners (Jay's the man who has made it all come back to life) has added some of his Midas touches so Vikon will be returning to its eminent position of a top-notch bargain shopping destination location. Watch this juggernaut to show its many strengths and return to prominence and already the improvements are laudable. From sporting goods to computers, bicycles to cameras, rare coins to gifts, and swords, man, do they have swords? Their prices are slashed, too, cutting your budget to the quick. Then move down the aisles and eye everything else from sewing machines, dinnerware, area rugs, jewelry, baby buntings, furniture, and lo and behold, even a TV repairman. Stock up on feed, grain and farm supplies, then mosey on over to the pool supplies. Jump in. Dive in. It's a sink-or-swim world. Somewhere in this maze, you will be introduced to trash and treasures and a lot of kitsch, some kaboodle and everything in between. And if you're lucky, you'll be the winner of the new Hyundai Accent car. Enjoy the music, food booths with home style cooking, a restaurant and special events such as a motorcycle show (with radio coverage and live music) that benefits St. Jude's Hospital. What's not to love about that? Lastly, some of my long-lasting favorites — Budget CD & Nadine's Indian Jewelry to name a few have stood the test of time on their own accord, with their individual 5-star store ratings. And when you find the outlet for the manufacturers of those herbal neck rolls, matching slippers & more, please let me know their name. I need to order some more. *Call toll-free: 972/278-7377*

Vikon Village

See writeup previous page

Food Stuff

★★★ **Andre Imported Foods**   972/644-7644

1478 W. Spring Valley Road   Mon-Sat 9-9
Richardson, TX 75080

If you are ready to depart the mundane and devour the exotic, Andre Fassihi should be your numero uno food specialty guide. With products from more that 100 countries, there is enough here to more than whet your appetite. In fact, there's enough to satiate your palate for life! At the intersection of Spring Valley and Coit, look for this melting pot of Greek food products. There's also food stuff from Iran and other countries in the Middle East and Europe. What will impress you, though, is the wealth of knowledge the staff maintains about each and every item. Want a recipe in a flash? Whip up a feast in no time. Ready-made baklava was delicious at $6.99. Looking for coffee stronger than Juan Valdez from Columbia? Then try the Greek coffee at $8.99/pound. Grape leaves for making dolmas (stuffed with seasoned rice) were $2.29/pound. Tarama (Greek caviar) was $3.49 for 8 ounces and orzo was 99 cents. But it's the olives and feta cheese that left with us for a last-minute hors d'oeuvres. Y-mmmm!

★★★★★ **Bagel Chain, The**   214/350-2245

5555 W. Lovers Lane   Mon-Fri 6:30-3; Sat 7-3; Sun 7-2
Dallas, TX 75209

Okay, I love bagels. But you don't have to be Jewish to love bagels these days. The whole world loves them, thanks to folks like **LENDERS** and **SARA LEE**. But there's nothing like bagels baked fresh in the oven and served hot with a cream cheese spread oozing off the sides. Bagels vary in flavors, and cost $3.48 for half a dozen and $5.40 a dozen. All the flavored "schmears" are here, too, from lox to veggie. But it's their sandwiches that are considered world-class. Owned by Herschel Rayford, their chicken salad has been considered the best in Texas. (I'll let you know after I taste it, as I am the award-winning chicken salad taster.) But after I saw the turkey, roast beef and the corned beef and sauerkraut piled high for a Rueben, I am reserving judgment for any awards just yet. Our team will be reviewing bagel factories throughout the Metroplex this year on our radio show and in our magazine, so stay tuned to the results. In the meantime, try this chain and tell me what you think. And what about the bagels? Our shopper again says she votes them the best!

PS Bailey's Berry Patch   903/564-6228

905 Crawford Rd.   Tues-Fri Dawn - 2 PM; Sat & Sun Dawn - 4 PM (Seasonal Picking)
Sadler, TX 76264
www.txberry.com

If life is just a bowl of cherries, this patch is the place to get out of the pits. If you love fresh berries (and they don't get any fresher than right from the patch!), starting mid June and extending through July and sometimes into August, you can pick 'em and eat all you want for ffreeree; then keep picking and take home more for just $10 a gallon. (This is a lot of berries — so expect to freeze.) Go north on Preston Rd. (Hwy. 289) until it dead-ends into Hwy. 56. Go west on Hwy. 56 approximately nine miles to Hwy. 901. Go north on Hwy. 901 for about six miles to Crawford Rd. and then west on Crawford a third of a mile. The farm is on the north side of Crawford Rd. Expect to be on the road from LBJ and Preston about an hour. But, you will not be disappointed. It's the berries! Bailey's has three varieties of blueberries and four of blackberries. You'll also find delectable homemade jams. MAYHAW jelly and jam also a treat for the palate. Get on their mailing list so they can keep you "current!"

★★★ Best Cellars   214/252-9463

3205 Knox St. @ Cole   Mon-Thurs 10-9; Fri-Sat 10-10; Sun Noon-6
Dallas, TX 75205
www.bestcellars.com

With the success of New York Best Cellars, wine writer and entrepreneur, Joshua Wesson, uncorked his wine wisdom on the Dallas scene in Highland Park at the end of September, 2002. It's their first store to feature a wine bar that served a selection of BC's wines by the glass every night. Sit back, relax and enjoy the people-watching. On Saturdays, between 2-4, they frequently host local chefs for free wine and food pairings. And each evening, they offer a free taste of a featured wine in the store. Wines are pre-selected by a New York tasting panel with daily tastings, classes under the name "Best Cellars University" and Saturdays are special event days pairing food and wine. Not a bad gig, if you can imbibe without falling flat on your face. Elle magazine called this winery "revolutionary" while others have described them as "taking wine shopping to a higher plane, and having a really smart staff." I think they'll all wet, but somebody's got to do it and if they're not the worst, they might as well be — the best!

★★ Big Town Farmers Market

U.S. 80 at Big Town Blvd.   Mon-Sun 8-7
Mesquite, TX 75149

Let's have a hoe-down in the old town tonight by starting sunny-side-up. Want the tomato scoop? How about this farmer's market where fresh fruits and seasonal vegetables are given top shelf? Both indoor (covered barn) and outside stalls are home to farmers who come here to roost. Did you hear about the guy who died "post-hummusly" eating chick peas? (That's a joke, folks!) Well, join in the fun when vendors show up early to swap stories and talk crop shop. See shoppers lined up with open arms. From bedding plants to lush hanging baskets, just produce your money and you'll take home some honey, honey and other delicious wares. Prices aren't particularly cheaper, but the selection is richer and most inviting. Don't expect to call them: A phone doesn't exist.

★★★★ **BJ's Restaurant & Brewery**   **972/459-9700**

2609 S. Stemmons (I- 35 and SH 121)   Sun-Fri 11-11; (open 'til midnight on Sat)
Lewisville, TX 75067
www.bjsbrewhouse.com

Have you dined at the new hot spot in Lewisville and now on Belt Line in Addison? No? Why not? This chain is no California Dreamer. Instead, they have entered the Metroplex with a menu as large as the California coastline. And since we're landlocked, the food is its draw. One meal and you're hooked. Their Addison location opened shortly after Lewisville at 4901 Belt Line and now, there's even twice the potential of gracious casual dining AND homebrewed beer. The beer is brewed right there in Addison. The garden fresh specialty salads are great: the Santa Fe, the "Not exactly a Cobb, Cobb," the honey-crisp chicken salad, and the Italian chopped salad, well, they were crisp, different and delicious. Leave room for dessert and their Famous Pizookie — a fresh baked cookie topped with vanilla-bean ice cream served in its own deep dish. When you choose chocolate chunk or white chocolate macadamia nut cookie in the deep dish, a portion of its proceeds goes to fight Cystic Fibrosis. It's their charitable contribution — as well as a decadent ending to your otherwise healthy start.

★★★★ **Blue Fish, The**   **214/824-FISH (3474)**

3519 Greenville Ave.   Lunch 11:30-2 ; Dinner 5-11
Dallas, TX 75206

When it comes time to start fishing for compliments, jump into The Blue Fish for lunch or dinner. If you want an inexpensive taste of Japanese fare, here is where it's good enough to eat and cheap enough to defeat the high cost of eating out. During the week, lunch is two for one for sushi. Tuesday, it's $1 draft beer nights and Thursday, it's the $1 hot sake night! Larger groups that must be seated together will not be seated until your entire party has arrived — don't even ask. Even if you come in with 25 Kabuki girls and 10 Geishas, until everyone arrives, forget it. Also a second location at 18149 Dallas Parkway, Suite 100, (SW corner of Frankford & Tollway), Dallas 75287, 972/250-FISH. Anybody that provides a two-fer for lunch gets my vote, even if I prefer my sushi cooked.

Bruno di Nola Classic Cheesecake   **972/539-3429**

Flower Mound, TX 75022   By Reservation Only

   Bruno da Noli? Or is it Bruno di Nola? Either way, it all goes
                            down the same pipe. The di Nola Classic Cheesecakes ranks
                            right up there with the Mona Lisa (and if you think about it,
that's probably why she is smiling.) Bruno whips up the finest ingredients into all of his cheesecakes from a recipe handed-down for generations. Made in the Old World Style, this no-crust cheesecake melts in your mouth with no aftertaste. Five tantalizing tastes include: Classic Lemon Zest, light and refreshing with just enough tang to make you semi-pucker; Chocolate Almond, a kiss of almond to cap off the rich and creamy chocolate base; Mango, the perfect tropical dream cake for lunch or an afternoon tea; Pumpkin, well, what's better at the holidays than this? And lastly, Spice, an ample apple pie substitute, without the apples. Order for gift-giving or in-home parties, weddings, luncheons, afternoon teas, elegant dinner parties, or even a midnight snack. Every cake is made with love and can be hand-delivered by Bruno himself. Or available at the following specialty food shops: FM Specialty Foods, 1001 Cross Timbers in Flower Mound, TJ's Seafood Market at the southwest corner of Preston and Forest in Dallas and Kuby's Sausage House at 6601 Snider Plaza in Dallas. If you are a restaurant or store and would like to carry the creamiest and cheesiest cakes this side of the Atlantic, give Bruno a call at the number above. And

this cheesecake chef has one other cheesecake up his sleeve and it's his low fat/low carb cheesecake. Tasting is believing. Remove the calories. Remove the fat. Keep the flavors, the texture and the taste. Trust me, you won't stop with just a bite! He has mastered the art of the cheesecake and has chosen to reign supreme with his one and only specialty. Order one for tonight and freeze several to have on hand. Puree some fruit and top them off with a glace of raspberries, strawberries, peaches, apricots, whatever you want. You're one swirl away from heaven. Prices include delivery. But it's the low fat, low carb cheesecake that has folks drooling and keeping with their commitment to a low fat regime. Find these at the specialty stores above or direct from the cheesecake maker himself.

★★★★★★   Buck n' Loons Cafe   817/466-2825

3517 S. Cooper Street   Mon-Thurs 11-11; Fri-Sat 11 AM- Midnight; Sun 11 AM-10 PM
Arlington, TX 76015

Want to duck the buck and have some luck at your next burger bash? Then, work up an appetite and head to Buck n'Loons, a unique, fun, one-of-kind dining experience. Here is the best burger Arlington has ever seen which includes your choice of handmade potato chips (or fries,) soup or salad of only home-town greens. Add American cheese, cheddar, the apple wood-smoked bacon and cheese, the Swiss cheese, the Swiss and sauteed mushrooms, the Monterey Jack cheese and green chilis, homemade chili and American cheese for the Texas special or cheddar cheese, sauteed onions and barbecue sauce. Dress up that plain burger and make it sing! Then, what about a Frito burger with chili queso and Fritos? Or the spicy model, with American cheese and jalapenos, the midnight burger with 1000 island dressing, bacon bits and Swiss cheese, or one with blue cheese and bacon. Double or triple-size your order if your stomach is as big as your mouth. The next section on the menu describes their backyard sandwiches, triple deckers, chicken cordon bleu, BLT's, their fried chicken sandwiches, the different kinds of melts and more. I guarantee they will melt in your mouth — and your hands, your shirt, sometimes your lap if you're not careful. (It's definitely worth every drip.)

★★★   Candy in Bloom   214/363-2399

728 Preston Forest Shopping Center   Mon-Fri 10:30-5:30; Sat 10-2
Dallas, TX 75230
www.candyinbloom.com

Yummy in the tummy. Candy is dandy, but what good is it if it lies in state? Forget flowers. Soothe my savage taste buds and send me something to satisfy my sweet tooth (that was before my surgery). This company puts it all together, ties it with a bow and sends it post haste. Even if the recipient's on a diet, they can create a masterfully decadent low-cal, low-fat, sugar-free basket. Tsk-tsk. Cookies, chocolates, hard candies, if you're craving something sweet, or consider these baskets as an alternative to traditional gifts for: House Warmings, Corporate Congratulations, Kiss and Make-up, Weddings, Get Well Quickie Basket — really you can create any occasion that you want to make memorable to send a basket. All can be wrapped up in any price range and customized to a theme (football, hearts, angels, whatever). Order by phone or online, it's sublime or spend as much as $150 and get a humdinger. For internet orders, allow seven days for processing. Same day local service (by phone) available. They have a Phoenix store, too. Pre-made designs are available in the store for pick-up and go. Local and nationwide shipping available — but no chocolate in the summertime. Can't imagine why? ***Call toll-free: 800/37-CANDY***

★★★★★★ **Carrabba's Italian Grill**   **972/732-7752**

17548 Dallas Parkway @ Trinity Mills   Call ahead for reservations
Dallas, TX 75287
www.carrabbas.com

 Mama Mia! Why wasn't I born Italian. I sure do love the food. But not all Italian food is created equal. Carrabba's has the ambience, the recipes, the wait staff and chefs to consistently deliver a quality meal that's also a deal. It's the best buy for the buck in casual/chic dining in the Metroplex. Forget the restaurant of the moment. Carrabba's should be a staple in your dining-out routine. It's on my list, whether it's personal or for business, I didn't choose to hold my "Dining with the Diva" seminars here because I didn't like the food or the atmosphere, friends. Carrabba's has its own special elegance but it's like going home to Mama's where an embrace is waiting for you the minute you walk through the door (which by the way is always opened for you by one of their personnel.) Warm and demonstrative, it's definitely not some stuffy joint reserved for the high and mighty. The food is fresh, piping hot, imaginative and delicious. Johnny Carrabbas and Damian Mandola are its founders in Houston and are famous as the hosts of the PBS cooking show "Cucina Amore." True to their Italian culinary heritage as well as their Texas spirit, their show, like their books, appeal to home chefs and novices alike. Watch them in action as they cook up a storm with recipes and techniques from their Sicilian family with some Texas schtick thrown in! How about the Mezzaluna, a half moon ravioli stuffed with chicken, ricotta and spinach in a tomato cream sauce. Oy, vey! The house salad is as good as the Caesar salad but is often my personal choice for it's crispness and delicate dressing. You can't go wrong on anything on their menu including the specialty drinks and after-dinner coffees. Even their wood-fired pizza's a home run. Check our website for First Tuesday and "Dining with the Diva" where at 6:30 on the first Tuesday of the month, we dine on a fabulous feast for $15 (including a dessert sampler) and meet with one of the 100 BEST merchants to learn more about their particular specialty. Space is limited so reservations are necessary by calling our office 469/293-7467. Log onto our website, www.underground-shopper.com and click on the button that says Dining with the Diva for information on the latest speakers. Ciao, Y'all! Chow down at their other locations in Grapevine, Preston Center and Plano and more around the bend.

◆◆◆◆ **Catering by Distinctive Designs**   **214/351-4263**

14715 Dallas Parkway   By Appt. Only
Dallas, TX 75254

Allan Ruben whips up a mighty creative spread when you call on his company for a catered affair. Want grounds for a celebration? Since 1988, they've been doing up Kiddish luncheons in the synagogue, bar and bat mitzvahs, wedding receptions, shabbat dinners, Shiva trays (when someone has died and you want to send a food tray over to the family in mourning), holiday take-out trays, bridal luncheons, weddings, and more. You guessed it. He has specialized in Jewish catering since he began, but I often get asked to recommend somebody good who knows the difference between a matzo ball and a malted milk ball. Looking for someone to do lunch? They do lunch plus Shabbat dinners, bridal luncheons, the whole megillah! (that means, the works!) And if you want something like pork and beans a la orange because your not in to Jewish food, he can handle it all with aplomb (or is it plum?)

Celebrate Cakes   972/271-4396

4310 Saturn Rd.   Mon-Fri 10-6; Sat 10-3
Garland, TX 75041
www.celebratecakes.com

 If there's an occasion that calls for a cake, celebrate here. Delicious custom cakes are their modus operandi. Whether it's a bridal cake or the supplies to do it all yourself, expect flavors such as amaretto, champagne, Italian cream, raspberry, traditional vanilla, carrot, lemon and white chocolate to be their bread and butter. Wedding cakes started at $2.25 per serving, plus toppers. See their huge selection of cake toppers, cake pans and templates to make your own creations, including a full line of colorings. From cake-decorating classes to a party-in-a-box, Jack, delivery is free within the Metroplex. Check for their bridal open houses where complimentary taste testing is available for prospective brides and grooms. Try before you buy is their motto. Accessories included handmade invitations, thank-you notes and programs by CREATION STATION. Custom-made veils and tiaras are supplied by VEILED IN BEAUTY. A one-quarter sheet cake, serving up to 24 and hand-decorated, runs $36; add $10 onto that for a photo cake (my personal favorite.) Additional classes offered included: beginning, intermediate and advanced cake decorating, cost $40 (plus supplies) meeting two hours a week for four weeks. The wedding cake class is on Saturday, all day, and runs $50, plus supplies.

Central Market   214/234-7000

5750 E. Lovers Lane   Mon-Sun 8 AM-10 PM
Dallas, TX 75206-2921
www.centralmarket.com

 This specialty foods emporium is brought to you by San Antonio's H.E. Butt market scion, and there's nothing quite like it. As close as you'll get to Zabar's in New York City, this Texas kingpin houses everything new and notable, fresh and flavorful. From prep-less produce to their chef-prepared meals, they will save you time, but you'll pay for it. Dearly. Unique departments include: produce, seafood, wine & beer, healthy living, specialty foods, bulk foods, bakery, deli and cheese, a fabulous cafe on the run, a full catering department, a cooking school, a floral and gift basket department, well, if there's anything left you might need, chances are they're getting ready to launch it soon. When the subject turns to varieties, I'm referring to a massive selection of often over-whelming proportions. Find fresh fruit, fresh pasteurized homogenized milk and the highest quality imported chocolate and nuts. Visit in Plano at 320 Coit Rd., 469/241-8300 and in Fort Worth at 4651 West Freeway, 817/987-4700.

◆◆◆◆◆ Chef du Jour Catering   972/245-9033

1440 South Broadway Street   By Reservation Only
Carrollton, TX 75006

What happened to Larry Goldstein who used to own Bagelstein's? They ask me all the time presumably because we have the same last name, and his wife's name is Susan. So, I tracked him down to his Carrollton kitchen and found out first hand what's he's been up to since his retirement. Remember, his wife is the bagel lady Susan Goldstein and I'm the bargain lady, Sue Goldstein. Now, back to Larry. Not wanting to rest on his laurels, Larry has plenty of shabbat dinners and Kiddish luncheons on his calendar along with all those Sunday brunches that want his deft touch. And besides, since his daughter's wedding that was described as one of the most lavish weddings ever in the Metroplex, he probably needs the work to pay for it. So be it. He's one of the pro's in the catering business and he's back doing what he does best. Now you know who the Chef of the

Day Catering is. It's Larry Goldstein. Another number to reach him at is 972/323-9399. Bon Appetit!

★★★★   Chef's Gallery at Art Institute of Dallas   214/373-0548

8080 Park Lane   Tues-Thurs 11:30-2:30 (Lunch); 6-8 (Dinner)
Dallas, TX 75231
www.aid.artinstitutes.edu

I don't recommend dining in a laboratory unless it's the dining lab at the Art Institute of Dallas. This is where the chefs-in-training get hands-on experience preparing gourmet meals for the public on Tuesday through Thursday. Lunch is from 11:30 to 2:30 and dinner from 6 to 8 (when school is in session, only). Call the number above for information. The last reservations for lunch are at 1:30; and the last reservation for dinner is 7:15. There are multiple opportunities for training in the arts, be it visual, media, culinary, fashion, photography, etc. Specifically, though, in the Culinary Arts, those in the program receive an Associate of Applied Science degree and this school is fast becoming one of the better places to learn the art of cooking. The Art Institute of Dallas offers training by some of the finest chefs and restaurant experts in the country to introduce newcomers to the art of cooking as a career. It's a 21-month program that includes everything from basic cooking skills to international cuisine. Lunches and dinners are well worth the wait!

★★★★★★   Coffee & Tea Outlet   214/353-0328

2324 Shorecrest Drive   Mon-Fri 8-5:30; Sat 9-12
Dallas, TX 75235
www.cavallinicoffee.com

 This subsidiary of Globex America comes by their stars naturally. They are considered one of the finest wholesalers of coffees, teas and beanery scenery including all the equipment to rent or buy in the Metroplex. Satisfying about 95 percent of the gourmet 4 and 5-star restaurants and hotels in town with their own special blends, I met Bonnie and Jerry Itzig when I had a special ambrosia-combination tea created when I owned The Argyle Spa. We offered both leaded and unleaded blends of coffee and teas that patrons always raved about. But in those days, you had to have a restaurant or retail establishment to get your coffees and teas wholesale. Today, you can shop where the restaurants shop and at the same wholesale prices. Wholesale! Read my lips. See the green beans. See the green beans roasted into deeper and darker colors. See the hundreds of flavors that are hand-blended into the coffees and teas and then sip and save. Wholesale prices throughout, from an individual pound of Java to a spot of tea, there's none finer in the Metroplex. Experience the CAVALLINI Coffee and once you've tried it, there's no going back. They are heads and shoulders above Starbucks — which I thought was a tough competitor. But now that I can make my own frappaccinos and coffee lattes, there is no comparison. Their showroom/outlet is in the front of their art-deco building, and the aroma will envelop you the minute you walk in. CAVALLINI Coffee and Teas is the name of their own coffee line and though you may not have heard of it yet, it is grounds for divorce if you don't sip and save at their outlet showroom. If you have a coffee shop or restaurant, have a company that you'd like to have a special blend for the break room, or you just have gourmet tastebuds for the finer things in life, this is where you'll find the lowest prices on espresso machines, drink mixes, electric shakers, if it was meant to accompany tea or coffee, here's where you'll find — "COFFEE, TEA and ME!" I'm a sucker for an espresso or cappuccino kaluha coconut chocolate whatever. I'll drink to that! Oh, don't forget to check out "Teaology." The first ever "on the go" healthy iced tea available that you can carry in your purse to add to a glass of cold water (even without having to steep or boil in water.) Only 15 calories/4 carbs per serving and oh, so rich in antioxidants. Ideal to take with you when traveling or to the office, and delicious, too. Up to 10-15 times the levels of antioxidants as one cup of traditionally brewed tea is available in one Teaology wallet (the equivalent of carrying six 16 oz. bottles of tea in your pocket.) The Hawthorne Berry Sage Green Tea alone has 649 mg. of antioxidants. Live the good and healthy life, at last, at half the price. Enjoy all of the tea and coffee accoutrements including the fabulous imported biscotti's and other gourmet dunkin'donut-like dessert cookies. Exit east on Regal Row off Stemmons; then left at Harry Hines and right on Shorecrest. You're there. Enjoy!

Collin Street Bakery   903/872-8411

401 W. 7th Ave.   Mon-Thurs 8-4:30; Sat 7-6; Sun Noon-6
Corsicana, TX 75110
www.collinstreetbakery.com

 Don't call me a fruitcake, but folks are nuts about the Collin Street Bakery. Ever wondered what was in that DeLuxe fruit cake that has been sent to millions of recipients around the world? Here goes: pecans, cherries, corn syrup, sugar, flour, pineapple, raisins, eggs, invert sugar, honey, water, high fructose corn syrup, corn syrup solids, orange peel and so forth....yum. After more than 100 years in business, they only sell their cakes directly from where they're made, yet they have created an empire without having sold one single cake in another bakery or grocery store. You can buy it at their factory bakery in Corsicana, or order by phone, by mail, online. At their bakery, they offer shoppers a lounge and restrooms. The original recipe came via Germany to Texas in the mid 1800's. They also sell cookies, pies, breads, brittle, muffins, pastries and honey. Be smart and order early for Christmas, since they sell approximately 85 percent of their cakes during this holiday. They also offer a deep dish pecan pie, tea breads and a cookie medley. Shipping is available. ***Call toll-free: 800/282-7400***

★★★   Cooper Street Farmer's Market   817/276-8810

1606 S. Cooper St.   Mon-Sat 9-7; Sun 9-6
Arlington, TX 76013

Getting down to their roots, the Cooper Street Farmer's Market doesn't carry any exotic fruits or vegetables. Instead, they're just selling your everyday varieties of fresh fruits and vegetables, opting out of selling those varieties that they could neither pronounce or spell. In the height of the season (April through October), they're selling perky peaches, plump plums, perfectly contoured melons, mouth-watering watermelons and others ripe from the farms to market from South Texas, California and Florida. Expect prices to be juicier than the grocery stores, meaning you get more squeeze per bite. Then again, comparing apples and oranges may not matter much. Just touch and go — from tomatoes to potatoes, and then watch your peas and Q's (squash). Somehow, coming straight from the farm to you just tastes better, don't you agree? Depending on the season, anything that can be local....is. Tomatoes, squash, cucumbers, okra, beans, cherries, in season is the reason they taste so good. They're open year 'round since they sell Texas pecans and citrus, too. Take a bite out of your budget and enjoy the squeeze.

★★★★   Country Meat Markets   817/457-9781

6899 E. Lancaster Ave   Tues-Fri 9-7; Sat 9-6; Sun & Mon (Phone Orders Only)
Fort Worth, TX 76112

Steak your claim to this meat market and see if you've hit paydirt. Head to the counter where you can pick out your steaks, chops, bacon, chicken and take it home with you just like the good ol'days when you bought your meat fresh from the butcher. If you'd like to purchase meat in bulk where it's sold by the hanging weight (the meat's weight, not yours), then set an appointment and see what "meaterializes." Prices start around $250 and go up depending on the quantity ordered. Figure around $40 a month for about six months if you serve a hearty meal at least once a day and occasional leftovers for lunch. All meat is cut and wrapped on the premises to your specifications. They used to sell to restaurants primarily but have now opened their counters to the public. You might find them a real meaty deal. And for sure, it gives new meaning to hanging out at the meat market!

★★★★★   Cupboard Natural Foods & Cafe   940/387-5386

200 W. Congress   Mon-Sat 9-9; Sun 11-6
Denton, TX 76205
www.cupboardnaturalfoods.com

Denton can be mighty proud of its universities, its horse farms, and the Cupboard Natural Foods & Cafe. Right from the pages of home-grown treasures is this combination health food restaurant/ market and recycling center. The cafe itself has been voted, by the Denton Record-Chronicle, the best veggie fare/health food restaurant for six years in the running. This creatively-ensconced favorite of the academic community is a treasure to those who are organically-inclined. Eat in or take out, the food's as fresh as Mother Nature. Organic. Natural. Whole Grain. Antibiotic-, hormone- and steroid-free meats, dairy and vegetarian choices fit for a king. Items include: salads, burritos, wraps, rollups, smoothies, power drinks ($2.75 to $3.75) and desserts that are as decadent as nature allows. The "Burrito Meal" for $4.95 was fabulous with black beans and brown rice and all the fillings, plus your choice of a mild or spicy sauce, chips and a Blue Sky natural soda. Then there's the selection of imported, specialty and micro-brewed beers and wines. We love it! And it's good for you, too.

★★   Curly's   817/763-8700

4017 Camp Bowie Blvd.   Sun-Sat 10:30 AM-10:30 PM
Fort Worth, TX 76107

What mental genius came up with combining a fabulous frozen custard with a HEBREW NATIONAL HOT DOG and FRITO pie? What an ecumenical concoction. Even if you haven't tried it, you still might want to buy it. Perhaps Curly and Moses got together and thunk this up themselves. No, I don't mean they've combined hot dogs and custard together in one recipe, but rather they serve the two individually at the same restaurant. Two greats sometimes add up to something indescribable. Let me know what you think. But remember, to stop when you feel you've had it up to....here! Located at the intersection of Camp Bowie and Crestline in Fort Worth, it's reminiscent of the old-fashioned ice cream stand, except that it's not ice cream. Instead, it's frozen custard, a Midwestern import that is soft, smooth and creamy with more butterfat than ice cream. (Well, Dr. Cooper, you can't always be perfect!) Curly's scoops up a large cup with your choice of "mix-ins" (50 cents each) for $2.45. More and more custard shops are cropping up in the Metroplex. Another beaut in Fort Worth is Milwaukee Joe's Gourmet Ice Cream, 6387 Camp Bowie Blvd., 817/377-1927, offering frozen custard in addition to their homemade hard ice cream; and another new one is Wooley's in Northeast Fort Worth which was recently opened by two twenty-something upstarts from the Midwest. I sense a trend in the making. Curly's, Wooley's, who or what's next? Too rich for my blood.

★★★★★   **Dallas Farmers Market**   **214/939-2808**

1010 S. Pearl Expwy.   Mon-Sun 7-6
Dallas, TX 75201
www.dallasfarmersmarket.org

With the addition of cooking classes and facility rentals, I wonder when couples will be asking to take their wedding vows amongst the eggplants? This downtown legend is alive and well and stays heads of lettuces above the fray. One flew over the coconut nests of baskets full of fruits, vegetables, meats, cheeses, plants, and who knows what else will ensure a real "Food Awakening." See more than seven varieties of pecans, in the shell, out of the shell, cracked, salted, unsalted, hot, cold, well, nuts if I remember them all. Come Christmas, the trees line up like an army gearing up for battle. Have them your way, flocked or unflocked. Add in gift baskets and fruit baskets. From Daniel's Gourmet Coffees to Paula Lambert's famed **MOZZARELLA COMPANY**, very few palates are ignored. Open 363 days (closed Christmas and New Year's Day), this farm-to-you source is the reality trip to bountiful!

★★★★★★   **Dallas Food Depot**   **214/942-3201**

909 S. Tyler   Mon-Fri 9-7; Sat 9-6; Sun 10-4
Dallas, TX 75208-6254

 This is and will remain the only controversial listing in the entire book. I rarely talk politics or religion (unless it's a good Jewish joke) but with Dallas Food Depot, the discussions have reached a fervent pitch at cocktail parties everywhere. Should you or shouldn't you shop for gourmet foods at half price at a place like this? As we say, if you can't stand the heat, then get out of the kitchen. Same with the Dallas Food Depot. If you can't tolerate the surroundings, then forget shopping here. No, this isn't an Oak Cliff outpost for Whole Foods or Central Market. But if you want great foodstuff at fantastic prices, then this place will satiate your appetite and leave room for dessert. Wander through the aisles grabbing deals on everything from **SMITHFIELD** hams to **JOHNSONVILLE** bratwurst. It's perfectly okay to eat. Trust me. You'll find frozen food, grocery items, health and beauty aids and general merchandise on the shelves and usually in tip-top shape. The cheesecake may be from The Cheesecake Factory, the lobster tails may be going to a Surf and Turf restaurant. The fajita meat is the best you'll ever taste and the tiramisu is in a class all by itself. Then add up the savings on the large bottles of jumbo olives, artichoke hearts, capers, gourmet pickles, whatever and you'll see why folks in North Dallas make this a monthly trek.

★★★★★   **Dallas Tortilla & Tamale Factory**   **214/821-8854**

1418 Greenville Ave.   Mon-Fri 7:30-6; Sat-Sun 7:30-3
Dallas, TX 75206
www.dallastortilla.com

They don't call me Guacamole Goldie for nothing. With five area locations, all you need to eat your way into oblivion is to add in a few tortillas from here. Since 1950, this family has been making fresh tortillas, tamales, chips, tostados and taco shells for both Dallas and Fort Worth. Corn tortillas go for $1/package or $15 for a 20-count case. Flour tortillas are $1.25/pkg. or $22.50 for an 18-count case. Pork, beef and chicken tamales cost $5.75/dozen. Other offerings include Mexican style BBQ, $5.50/pound; beef tongue, Mexican style, $5.75/pound; chicharrones (fried pork skins), $5.95/pound; Menudo, $5.75 for a half gallon and Lugua for $5.95/pound. If you are looking to throw a real Mexican bash, get it all from here. Located at the corner of Greenville and Bryan at the address above. But shop at their main location at 309 N. Marsalis in Dallas, 214/943-7681; 9545 Lake June Rd. in Dallas, 214/398-5453; in Lewisville, 310 S. Mill Street, 972/436-

4333 or in Lancaster, 370 W. Pleasant Run Rd., 972/275-0445. For out-of-state shipping and catering information, call 214/583-698. Hasta la vista, baby. ***Call toll-free: 800/583-6981***

◆◆◆◆◆   Deli News   972/733-3354

17062 Preston Rd. , #100   Mon-Fri 7 AM-8 PM; Sat-Sun 7-4 (Summer); Sat only 7-6 (Winter)
Dallas, TX 75248
www.deli-news-dallas.com

Stop "rushin'" all over town looking for a decent deli. Set your sites on one of the best of both the old world and the new. So new? Here, you can have your cake and eat it, too. Order in. Order out. Cater it all and have it for any meal — lunch or dinner or a combination of both, the menu is large enough to pacify even a Krushchev appetite. This Russian deli is just like in the old country, authentic with all the traditional deli items, plus the Russian mix of ethnicity — everything from herring a-washed in sour cream or cream sauce to blintzes as big as Broadway. My son is married to a Russian diva so who better to discern the quality of a Russian deli? There is more to Russian dining than borscht. Combine the best of New York deli's with a hint of Russia and you have TRADITION! Traditional Russian/European cuisine where the secret family recipes have been resurrected in their catering services since 1987. As they like to say, "They put the "essen" (means eating in Yiddish) back in "Delicatessen!" Homemade knishes and homemade kasha give us our fill of potatoes and noodles. Choose from their sandwich board and add a choice of cole slaw, potato salad or chips on freshly made rye, wheat or egg bread, bagel or Kaiser roll — just like back in the old country (of Detroit where I grew up.) Of course, there's the fish platter with smoked fish flown in from New York and hand sliced (yes, there's a difference in taste when you hand slice it.) My favorite on Sunday mornings is still the sable (smoked fish.) Their breakfast and brunch items are varied and take up almost two pages of their total menu. A NOVA BENEDICT is my husband's favorite: 3 poached eggs, Nova salmon on a fresh Bialy roll smothered with home-made hollandaise sauce. Give me the DELI-NEWS Supreme with corned beef, pastrami, salami and baby Swiss. For $8.99, it's four meals for me. And how many places in the Metroplex serve calf's liver smothered in sautÈed onions, mashed potatoes and fresh steamed veggies or chicken fricassee with meatballs? Now that's a new one on me. My mom made a mean chicken fricassee but never served it with meatballs. But since you only live once and you can substitute most anything, I'd leave off the meatballs and ask for some noodle kugel. Oh, maybe I should order a potato pancake. There are so many decisions to make, I'm already overwhelmed. Come to think of it, just bring anything from the menu. I'm not picky. It's all good.

Diet Gourmet   972/934-0900

4887 Alpha Rd., Suite 285   Mon-Thurs 9-4; Fri 7-7; Sat 10-4
Dallas, TX 75244
www.dietgourmet.com

 Since 1989, Diet Gourmet has been the "weigh-to-go." As the most successful diet gourmet service in Texas, they make staying on a healthy, fresh and delicious regime a cinch with their food plan. DG does all the cooking, planning and shopping. You do all the eating with one meal to 21 prepared by a master chef who has it down pat when it comes to low-fat, low-sodium, high-energy, calorie-controlled lunches and dinners. New this year, they'll ship anywhere in Texas for just $20 (up to 25 lbs.) Okay, prices may average just over $100 per week but remember, that's for all your food, delivery, no muss, no fuss and a lot cheaper than a personal chef. For locations to purchase their fabulous food, deliveries are now made to The Sunflower Shoppe, 5817 Curzon, Fort Worth, TX 76107, Monday & Friday 10:30-7, 817/738-9051; in Colleyville at the Healthy Approach Market, 5100 State Hwy. 121, Colleyville, TX 76034, Monday & Friday 9-9, 817/399-9100; and in Lewisville at Abundant Health Food Store, 1130 A

West Main St., Lewisville, TX 75067, Monday & Friday 10- 6, 972/221-1210 and in FRISCO at Natural Health Market, 4971 Preston Rd., Monday & Friday 10-8:30, 972/668-7088. Go online to salivate and read their menus and a la carte items. Bet you're drooling!

★★★ Dolly Madison/Wonder Hostess   972/399-0770

584 S. Belt Line   Mon-Sat 8-6; Sun 11-5
Irving, TX 76060

Ah, the wonders of shopping this day-old outlet. Good grief, Charlie Brown, when we run of out "ZINGERS," what shall we do? Well, shopping here is one of the solutions to buying all of the unsold DOLLY MADISON sweets and HOSTESS/WONDER bakery treats on the cheap. DOLLY MADISON/WONDER and HOSTESS BRANDS all belong to the same parent company, but there are different outlets for them. The DOLLY MADISON cake store (outlet) is at 4226 E. Belknap in Haltom City (817/834-6182); a WONDER BREAD/HOSTESS Cake Store is at 4120 W. Ledbetter Dr. in Dallas (972/263-8313) and a WONDER/HOSTESS Store is at 6280 McCart Ave in Fort Worth (817/294-9916). What a great place to feed the neighborhood gang, the soccer team, the Brownie troop with dozens of cupcakes and goodies. Check directory for more DOLLY MADISON and WONDER/HOSTESS stores. Don't forget to ask for the 10 percent off if you're a senior citizen (save more dough, sister!) And for anyone younger, they also offer free cards they call the "Snacking Card" at the DOLLY stores and the "Sweet Treat" card at WONDER/HOSTESS.

◆◆◆◆◆ Dream Cafe   972/503-7326

5100 Belt Line Rd, Suite 208   Mon-Sun 7 AM-10 PM
Addison, TX 75240-7326
www.thedreamcafe.com

Is it any wonder kids voted this a must eat? Dream on, brother. It wins every night as one of their favorite restaurants, especially on Mondays when it's kid's night out. Let them take a pony ride or pet the zoo pets from 6 to 8:30 PM. Or what about a Mickey pancake (a whole wheat buttermilk pancake with butter?) Now we're cookin'! You won't have to tempt them for lunch or dinner either. Served from 11 AM 'til bedtime, the choices are plentiful, from bow tie pasta to organic black beans and rice, with jack cheese, sour cream and corn chips. Note the chicken fingers are grilled and not fried, yet come with fries and steamed broccoli. Add in a glass of chocolate milk or a vanilla coke. Grown-ups love the "little" portion menu where they can order something "lite" or they can fill-er up with a Thai noodle salad, a Caesar wrap, a Routh St. Club (with smoked turkey, Swiss cheese, avocado, sprouts and tomatoes.) If you're starving, then have at it. Dine at their original location, 2800 Routh St. in the Quadrangle in Dallas, 214/954-0486, too, but please leave room for dessert.

★ Drinks By the Case   972/401-0043

5609 Alpha   Mon-Fri 9:30-5; Sat 10:30-3
Dallas, TX 75244

Case opened. Now shut the door on your insatiable thirst and quench any thoughts of getting a deal on your sodas and bottled water here. Ah, what convenience! Just call and place your order for COKE, PEPSI, MOUNTAIN DEW, DR PEPPER, etc. and have a case of a 24-pack delivered to your front door, home or office, for $8.60. No, they don't deliver to beaches or parks. But if my math is correct, that's $2.15 a six-pack or over $4 for a 12-pack. And other than the convenience, that's not a particularly stellar savings. They are always on special somewhere — elsewhere — Walgreen's, Target, wherever for $5 for two 12 pack so the delivery may not be worth it to you.

To others, though, it may be an easy fix. Regular pack at even Tom Thumb was $6.68 — so their price is no big deal. Then again, the price for gas and someone's time is worth a lot these days. OZARKA bottled water was $10.60 a case (24-16 oz. bottles). If you want to be the "Life of the Pantry," check directory for other locations. Or, get in your car and go get 'em elsewhere for less.

Drinks Fantastic   214/363-5286
Dallas, TX   By Reservation
www.drinksfantastic.com

 How many cappuccino's does it take to turn on the party? Well, if your answer is one or a thousand, my answer is the same. Call Drinks Fantastic. One formal espresso, cappuccino or latte service comes complete with server and all. The barista arrives in full tux or tails, will grind freshly-roasted beans and serve each cup to order. Only filtered water is used so you can expect the finest cup of coffee this side of Starbucks. Too, there will be an assortment of syrups to kick it up a notch or two: **GHIRARDELLI** Chocolate Hazelnut or Amaretto with a full gourmet coffee service makes for a most happy party goer. Since I'm not an alcohol lover, specialty coffees are really my cup of tea. But for those who do imbibe, here is where to turn to for parties fantastic. They have been creating specialty drinks for over 20 years and they're not drunk yet. In fact, they call themselves Liquid Caterers offering drinks for both adults and kids at the same time. simultaneously. (But kids' drinks are strictly virgin versions.) They offer over 100 different flavors of frozen drinks so don't expect plain Jane Margaritas like the other drink makers. They pride themselves on the variety that can be whipped up by their mixologists. Besides, they're so much fun. Drink a frosted latte with coconut morsels marinated in pineapple with an oversized straw so you can actually capture the entire flavor. Mike Miller's the man to light the drinks fantastic. It's the perfect party condiment at bar mitzvahs, weddings, corporate conventions and meetings when a festive event is planned and something special is required. I'll drink to that!

★★★★★   Entenmann's/Oroweat Bakery   972/231-3487
1419 E. Spring Valley   Mon-Fri 9-7 Sat 9-5, SUn 11-5
Richardson, TX 75080

So, what's your favorite **ENTENMANN'S**? Doesn't matter 'cause you can find most (if not all) varieties of your favorites at this one and only remaining **ENTENMANN'S/OROWEAT** Bakery Thrift store in the Metroplex. (Their former location at 3068 Forest Lane is now a **MRS. BAIRD'S** Thrift.) Now owned by the Best Food Baking Company, their no-fat coffee cakes are still on my replace weekly shopping list. **MRS. BAIRD'S** moving into the **ENTENMANN'S** market, so enjoy the one and only while it's still around. Items arrive fresh daily and are discounted as time goes on. Whole grain and specialty breads, cinnamon, fruit and nut coffee cakes, cookies, buns, rolls, etc. are all discounted and absolutely de-lish! Calling all gluttons! Eat your heart out without having an attack of the guilties when you check out. Save up to 50 percent on products right-from-the-ovens to maybe a day or so old. I love hippie bakers — they are our favorite "Flour Children!" But remember, rich foods are like destiny....they, too, shape our ends. *Call toll-free: 800/356-3314*

★★★   **Fairview Farms Marketplace**   **972/422-2500**
3314 N. Central Expressway   Mon-Fri 9-5 (Office)
Plano, TX 75074
www.fairview-farms.com

Smack dab on the service road of US 75-Exit 30 at Parker Road sits Fairview Farms, one of the premier party facilities, farmers market and western-style marketplace all rolled into one. This unique development comes complete with party barn, restaurants, shops, petting zoo and hand-writing clinic (no not that kind of handwriting analysis but rather a class that provides therapy in fine motor and pre-handwriting development for pre-schoolers and Kindergarten readiness.) The Corral Barn is an 82,000-square-foot facility with AC/heat for up to 350 guests. It's used for wed-dings, special occasions and corporate functions with catering available or you can provide your own. They also offer breakfasts, snacks, box lunches, buffets, BBQ's, cookouts; choose your plea-sure. Prices began per person with buffets starting at $8.95 up to $14.95, depending on your taste request. All day rentals were hardly a drop in the bucket, $1,500. Their outdoor gazebo, available for additional seating, is particularly important if you have an overflow during a wedding recep-tion. Alcohol is available by the glass, keg or five-gallon container. For more information call 972/ 633-9779. The Farmers Market is open April-October, Tuesday-Sunday, 10-7 with fresh-from-the-farm fruits and vegetables. Amigos Imports (972/578-8936) is open Tuesday-Sunday 10-6 and closed Mondays.

★★★★   **Farmers Market**   **817/838-8781**
5507 E. Belknap   Mon-Sat 8-5:30.
Fort Worth, TX 76117

After 27 years in business, Fort Worth's Farmers Market is a hand full of fruits and vegetables, including some exotics that you may not see everywhere. In-season papayas, pineapples, guavas and plantains make the world go around at this original Fort Worth's Farmers Market. Wait with baited breath for the Sweet Vidalia or 1015 Onions....they're worth crying over. They're also great for making your own Bloomin'Onion, just like those at Chili's. Melons are ripe and waiting for your special touch. You don't even have to get up at the crack of dawn to beat the farmers unload-ing their trucks. But an occasional scuffle will ensue if you and someone else grab the same quart of three-inch strawberries. Stand your ground. You got there first. Although not as large as the Dallas Farmers Market by a long shot, they are big enough to deliver the variety, but not so large as to let a bad apple spoil the apple cart. They're open all year long as they maintain a healthy wholesale business, too. And talk about being stable — they've been in the same location for 30 years and are two blocks east of 28th on Belknap. Although they sell as much Texas produce as they can get their hands on, they do supplement from other states and countries.

★★★★★   **Fiesta Mart**   **214/944-3300**
611 W. Jefferson Blvd.   Mon-Sun 7-11
Oak Cliff, TX 75208
www.fiestamart.com

Since 1972, this Houston-area institution has grown to include Dallas/Fort Worth and Austin. Tagged the fastest growing minority business in the U.S., it makes perfect sense to have a store that caters to the Hispanic population. (Fort Worth is 52 percent Hispanic, si?) This grocer boasts a 50,000-square-foot grocery store with an entertainment flair offering the highest quality meat, groceries, fresh produce, seafood, a world class delicatessen, beer and fine wine, as well as a vari-ety of international and specialty foods and products. The menu of Hispanic favorites include everything from camellias to mangoes, shitake mushrooms to radicchio. Services beyond the typical grocery store amenities include paying your utilities, purchasing license tags, buying concert and sporting event tickets, and the usual money orders, lottery tickets and more. At various locations, you'll see fresh seafood departments, a fresh deli, Taquerias and Salchichonerias (Mexican-Style Hot Deli), an in-store bakery that provides fresh baked goods daily and an International and Specialty Foods area which offers products from around the globe. Check directory for 14 locations including Dallas, Fort Worth, Arlington, Garland, Irving, Plano and Forest Hills. It's a wonderful resource for the galloping gourmand as well, regardless of ethnic preferences.

Flavors From Afar   214/696-2327

6705 Snider Plaza
Dallas, TX 75205
www.flavorsfromafar.com

 You don't have to be a traveling troubadour to hop to it with stores like Flavors From Afar. It's simply divine whether you're a diva or not. Making ordinary moments extraordinary, why not taste the finer things in life from perfect pastas and pesto to sensational sauces and specialty rice from around the world. Some you've never even heard of, so it's a adventure in expanding your customary and usual palate. Take Olive Oils and Balsamic Vinegars direct from Italy, for example. You're but one liter away from Tripoli. Start somethin'in the kitchen and see how your family will join in the fun and the festivities. From all the tools of the trade to get you cooking to the decorative tabletop accessories to set the mood. Then, all you need to do is fill up your shopping cart, whether in person or online. If your cup running over, it's time you moved to a gift basket that would take the load off. Send an abundant Gift Baskets overflowing with ingredients from any country or theme you would like. You pick out your own elements and voila, they'll ship it out, to you or wherever you want your gift basket to go. I've got my eyes and my taste buds locked on the Chocolate Habanero Fudge Sauce that can be used to top off my low fat, sugarfree ice cream, or encircle a Bruno di Nola Cheesecake. What great patio fare to put some of the Fudge Sauce in a bowl to dip fresh strawberries, or drizzle over cake, brownies or biscotti. Are you drooling yet? Then join their Meal-of-the-Month Club. Six months of great meals at your fingertips. They supply the international ingredients; you supply the staples — that includes the menu, shopping list, and recipes — even what to do with left-overs. Get involved and get a taste of the flavors of life. Order a catalog via email or by calling the number above. Thank Nancy and Gary Krabill for this imaginative addition to the gourmet scene. Flat $2 delivery fee within 50 mile radius of Dallas or shipping by UPS ground.

★★★★★   Gene's Fruit Stand & Patio   972/247-7301

2508 Forest Lane   Mon-Sat 9-6; Sun 9-5
Dallas, TX 75234

Since it ain't broke, Gene's won't fix it. And why? Because for more than 30 years, they have been doing it right in front of everyone's eyes. Their very visible LJB/Forest Lane open-air emporium is laden with hanging baskets and trellises, gazebos, bird baths, fountains, willow lawn furniture, concrete benches and tables; it could be your back yard's best friend. But as fresh as the day is long, don't overlook from whence they came — fruits, herbs and vegetables, all plums when it comes to quality. Seven days a week, you can pick from the shelled peas brought in from East Texas or squeeze the succulent squash when the season beckons. Just don't expect to squeeze the CHARMIN or the delicate Swedish Ivy or Airplane plants. See some of the biggest pots in the city hanging from the eaves or swinging from their swings; either way you'll be in the "Garden of Eatin."

★★★★★★ **Georgia's Farmers Market**   **972/516-4765**

916 E. 15th St.   Mon-Sat 10-6; Sun 10-5 (March-Dec)
Plano, TX 75074

 Open 10 months out of the year, if you've got Georgia on your mind, turn in here. Perhaps you'll meet up (or beet up) with its founder, Georgia Machala Massey, who was literally born into the Farmer's Market business. What began as a downtown family enterprise with her father and brothers at age seven has evolved into a budding establishment in Plano as well. The Machala family is still rooted in the downtown Dallas Farmers Market, operating a stand in the No. 2 shed, but in 1997 some of Georgia's brothers followed her to Plano to continue in the family tradition. Everything that Georgia sells is a peach. Just try eating one of those plump seedless grapes. Bet you can't eat just one! But with grape prices so high, looks like you might have to forego even a cheap glass of wine (or start stomping your own in your back yard). Nevertheless, you're not getting "graped." You can hardly believe that this bastion of produce was once home to a body shop, complete with roll-up doors. Today, it is an open-air marketplace, reminiscent of those in Europe. All the produce is from farmers, including home-grown specialty items, with quality not found in grocery stores. They also carry 139 varieties of nuts, salsas, trail mix, home-mades breads and preserves, pickles, salad dressings and WATKINS products. Exit 15th Street off Central Expressway. Turn right and go approximately half a mile, across the street from City Park.

★★★★★★ **GNS Foods**   **817/469-7420**

2109 E. Division St.   Mon-Fri 9-5; Sat 10-3 (Dec Only)
Arlington, TX 76011-7817
www.greatnuts.com

 You're nuts to pay retail for....nuts. And you won't here. You'll go ape over all the varieties that are actually prepared in their back factory that are not just your plain vanilla cashews. The possibilities for gift-giving are endless. Imagine sending a wheel of nuts, almonds, cashews, pistachios and others of your choosing at holiday time. They'll crack up over your thoughtfulness, but, better yet, it will be love at first bite. Their outlet store fronts their manufacturing and distribution site where the aroma of pina colada pecans, as well as eight other flavors, permeates the air. Talk about being addictive. Bet you can't eat just one! For additional treats for the sweet tooth, have you ever tried dried mango? Well, I'm hooked — I can do a fab fandango and a terrific tango after each piece. Healthy treats, without having to be wealthy, are just part of their delicious deli of candy and nuts, priced to go for less dough. Although their address is on East Division, they are west of Highway 360 which is considered east Arlington. Go figure! But very easy to find. They are a delicious outlet and website which you will confirm with one visit or order.

Goodie Basket, The   **817/377-4222**

4319 B Camp Bowie Blvd.   Tues-Fri 10-6; Sat 10-4; Closed Sun-Mon
Fort Worth, TX 76107
www.yourgoodiebasket.com

If you don't make it to Camp Bowie during business hours, you might like to shop in your jammies online. Put that in your basket and save 10 percent off your first purchase. A gift for any occasion, from weddings, birthdays, get well soon, Mothers'Day, any day is reason to celebrate. New baby in town? Kid finally graduated? Reward your secretary, celebrate anniversaries, thank Dad, well, you get the message. Just don't forget those special days when a colorful and delicious reminder would make their day. Baskets start as low as $30, but, at that price, it looks like you're a cheapskate. Their scrumptious chocolate truffles, white chocolate raspberries, exotic and flavored coffees and gourmet cookies are all arranged by a member of their assembly line team rather than what I would call a creative team, but, still and all, Epicurean treats delight everybody. Delivery and shipping anywhere in the Metroplex and beyond. So, be a goodie, goodie, and order one Goodie Basket ASAP. *Call toll-free: 800/580-GIFT*

★★★★   Goody-Goody Liquor Store   972/701-8475

14851 Inwood Rd.   Mon-Sat 10-9
Addison, TX 75247
www.goodygoody.com

Didn't I read that there was a Goody-Goody store opening in Lake Dallas? I thought taking over a Buckeye Liquor store at 102 N. Stemmons (940/321-4723) was a very goody-goody thing, but nowhere is it listed. Be sure to check it out before you cross over the bridge as you may be disappointed. It is supposed to be completely remodeled, with an enlarged wine cellar, beer section and cooler, so do you think the prices may have enlarged, too? The same low prices that made Siegel's begin running 40 to 60 percent off sales continues at Goody-Goody. Here, they're about as competitive as it gets: Andre Champagne was still $2.95, right up to the **DOM PERIGNON** for $115. Prices are on the rocks, best on moderate liquors, but still pretty good on top-shelf brands as well. By the bottle or by the case, Goody-Goody is a formidable liquor store. Check directory or online for their six locations: 2937 Greenville Avenue, 10301 Harry Hines Blvd., 7124 Greenville Ave., 5285 Highway 121, The Colony and 1950 FM 407, Highland Village. Cheers!

★★★   Grapevine Farmers Market   817/410-3185

701 S. Main St.   Wed 3-7 to sellout; Sat 8 AM to sellout
Grapevine, TX 76051

This Grapevine moves in very healthy circles and wraps its tentacles around the heart of the community. Located near the train station and the blacksmith in their now-permanent pavilion, look for the crowds standing in line for the freshest, most sought-after items. With its historic overtones, the look of Main Street, its gazebo and antique stores, add this small Farmers Market to the charm of a downtown revival. About 15 farmers roll up their sleeves and roll in their carts usually twice a week toward the end of May to entice you with their fresh produce. Presenting a seasonal exchange of earthy tales and mouth-watering peaches, plums, tomatoes and corn, the season starts the weekend after Main Street Days in late May and runs through November when the frost hits the pumpkins and gourds. This is another nostalgic contribution to shopping in small towns and its merchants who have a unique and personal hands-on approach to selling one-on-one. "Cheese Whiz," what's next? They're members of the Central Texas Farmers Market co-op, which requires sellers to only offer produce grown within a 150 mile radius of the Metroplex. *Call toll-free: 800/ 457-6338*

Greenberg Smoked Turkeys   903/595-0725

221 McMurray, PO Box 4818   Mon-Fri 8:30-5
Tyler, TX 75712
www.gobblegobble.com

 Five stars for the web site name, four stars for the taste, three stars for the price equals a four in my book. This seasoned company works seven days a week when the season dictates, but returns to normal the other times of the year. If you're looking to get smoked, think GREENBERG SMOKED TURKEYS in East Texas (Tyler, to be exact) for they have all the right stuff. Glowing reviews from *The New York Times* and *Connoisseur Magazine* confirm our savory tastebuds. No catalog, no toll free number and no credit cards. Expect your turkey to cost $3.50 per pound, plus shipping and handling. Order by phone, fax or mail. You can order a turkey any time during the year. Current birds are weighing in at 6 to 15 pounds. You can send them a check for the bird and then they will bill you separately for shipping and handling. Order early for the holidays to assure your weight choice of bird. (Too bad you can't order your weight for the holidays yourself!) Delivery takes one to five days depending on final destination. Shipping and handling charges vary, from about $6 into the D/FW area to about $10 into New York or California. In business for more than 63 years, these turkeys are still smokin'! Download order form from the computer and delivery is guaranteed within the continental USA.

Herby's Soda Fountain   972/548-7632

210 N. Tennesee   Mon-Fri 11-5; Sat 11-6; Sun 12-5
McKinney, TX 75069

Enjoy an old-fashioned '50s party at Herby's Soda Fountain in Downtown McKinney. Return to those "Happy Days" days or is it, "Back to the Future" Parts 1,2 and 3? Get with the program and look for the authentic soda fountain and juke box hideout katty (or is it kitty)-corner from the McKinney Public Library. Never mind, just book it for a party for kids of all ages. Step back in time with delicious burgers, fries, sandwiches, chicken or steak, whatever's your pleasure. Don't forget dessert, darling. If you really want to blow the diet, you can always make room for sundaes, shakes and malts made the "old-fashioned" way. Grab yourself a booth, kick back and let the music rip. Open seven days, there's no excuse not to get into the mood. And a one. And a two!

★★   Homebrew Headquarters   972/234-4411

300 N. Coit Rd., Suite 134   Mon, Wed, Fri-Sat 10-6; Thurs 10-7; Sun 1-5
Richardson, TX 75080
www.homebrewhq.com

At the intersection of Coit and Belt Line in Richardson, expect a brew-ha-ha to get going for around $100 complete. Their Arlington location has gone under, but no word if they were cited with a DWI. Beer-brewing kits started at $49.95, but you'll still need to have a large metal pot, ingredients and about two cases of bottles. So stop whining! The fruits of *your* labor can also be made into wine for about the same price. Then distill, my darling! Grab a loaf of bread, a jug of watermelon wine and thou art on thy way to enjoying the fermented fruits, flowers and vegetables of thine labors. Beer and wine-making supplies are all here for you to produce your own stash. All the ingredients and tools of the trade, juices and additives are available for thine own eyes to be true (but don't uncork them before their time). Toast this location, as it is their one and only. If you can read a recipe and boil water, you can pretty much make beer that will be cheaper and might even be tastier than those you've been imbibing at the microbreweries around town. ***Call toll-free: 800/966-4144***

IWA-International Wine Accessories   214/349-6097

10246 Miller Rd.   Mon-Fri 9-6; Sat 10-4
Dallas, TX 75238

www.iwawine.com   🖱 *Top Online Store!*

IWA stands for International Wine Accessories and if you're dedicated to the red, white and brewer, this may be the perfect liaison to fine wine accessories. If you are a wine connoisseur, this local mail order company, formed in 1983 by Robert S. Orenstein, an ex-corporate tax specialist who just happened to love wine more than he loved doing taxes, is for you. He wanted to obtain quality, wine-related items that he couldn't find elsewhere. So, in 1999, he went online with wine accessories and never looked back. He already had 17 years experience in the traditional bricks-and-mortar catalog business, so establishing a web-shopping portal was not much different. He already had a highly-trained and knowledgeable customer service department that could handle the questions. Secondly, he already had a purchasing department that was prepared to maintain stock and lastly, he already had a warehouse the size of a football field. Shopping direct, from home or office, by phone or by mail, by fax or web — well, have it your way. Trade and wholesale programs are open to volume purchasers such as wineries, retail establishments, wine stores, hotels and restaurants, but the public can sip and save because these importers and their prices are highly competitive. For gift-giving, they'll even be able to private label your company's name and logo on a bottle of wine. Although they specialize in wine cellars and racking systems, they also carry all the wine accoutrements: corkscrews, bottle stoppers, stemware, preservation systems, cooling units, decanters, wine luggage, wine-themed art, books, videos, furniture and cigars and their accessories. Described as "The Horchow Finale of Wine," the closeout section features beautiful items from previous catalogs, samples, one-of-a-kinds, overstocks, blemishes/imperfections and canceled orders, all at prices 10 to 50 percent below original cost. See antique bottles, glassware, crystal, decanters, room dividers, sculpture, tables, rotisserie grills, even dining room tables — all themed with the fruit of the vine. Espresso machines were a little steep, $999-$1,500, but remember, these are the finest commercial/home models. (If you buy one, it may wind up as "grounds" for divorce!) Name brands like **RIEDEL**, **SCREWPULL**, **SPIEGELAU** and **VACU-VIN** were available and some specials and closeouts would make us dizzy with anticipation — they were up to 50 percent off. The oak serving tray, filled with your own collection of wine corks for under $20, was a winning house-warming gift and a deluxe Italian waiter's corkscrew for under $18 (no, the Italian waiter didn't come with it.) A double-blade cigar cutter was under $5, and 25 bottle notes for under $15 were gift-wrapped and given in celebration of a male friend's promotion at work. But finally, we toasted our good fortune and called it a day. *Call toll-free: 800/527-4072*

Krispy Kreme Doughnuts   817/461-2600

2600 S. Cooper St.   Mon-Sat.5:30 AM.-Midnight; Sun 5:30 AM-11 PM
Arlington, TX 76015
www.krispykreme.com

 The first line of this store's write-up use to read, "I have yet to eat a Krispy Kreme, but I am certainly alone." Well, that no longer is true 'cause I've met Jan Michael and had the pleasure of "scarfing" down a pumpkin-spiced "sugar-free" Krispy Kreme. There are 24 varieties of these world-famous donuts but the glazed is their original secret recipe and guaranteed to melt in your mouth. These melt-in-your-mouth pastries win all kinds of awards, win every poll, and no doubt would be rated No. 1 by *Consumer Reports*. A dozen glazed will cost $5.19. For a dozen assorted, $5.69. From lemon filled to chocolate mousse, some folks think of them as Nirvana. Keep posted to our website, www.undergroundshopper.com and watch for the light to go on when we let you know when the first low carb/low fat donut comes down the conveyor belt. I'll be first in line. Six area locations: Grapevine, Arlington, Dallas, Fort Worth, Plano and Frisco and it's no wonder they are hot. Now they are popping up in supermarkets and are nearing how many locations now?? For sure, though, they did announce there would be a KK to meet the demands of the low carb/low fat constituency. Start collecting their memorabilia in the store, too, from T-shirts to bibs, boxer shorts to the trucks that deliver KK ingredients coast to coast.

◆◆◆◆◆◆   **La Duni Latin Cafe & Bakery**   **214/520-7300**

4620 McKinney Ave.   See website or call for hours
Dallas, TX 75205   McKinney Location Closed Mondays
www.laduni.com

 There are plenty of new restaurants in the Metroplex. They open. They close. Some are good. Some aren't. Some leave no impression; others leave an indelible impression. La Duni is one that is etched into my brain forever. It was the finest meal I've ever eaten in the city where chefs vie for the top spots in culinary circles as desperately as movie stars covet an Academy Award. Named one of the best new restaurants in America and Top 5 in Dallas, it's no wonder. No reservations. Closed on Monday. Okay, there is one negative. (How can I eat at La Duni on a Monday when they're closed? Closing is not a good thing. Wait--I can now go to their new Highland Park location at 4264 Oak Lawn on Mondays!) They are the only four-star restaurant I know with entrees under $10. So, here's one plus. They're affordable. Blending European traditional fare with a Latin American soul is how they describe their mixes of flavors, aromas, colors, textures, forms and recipes of both cultures. Though a prix fixe menu is available on special evenings like Valentine's Day, the $49.50 for two is worth every penny. It included salad, appetizer, choice of three entrees and desserts to share. Looking for wine? The list is extensive and exclusively South American. And also affordable. Bet you didn't know that the owners of La Duni were the same folks who originated ZuZu's. Try it. It will become one of your favorites, too. The blends of unusual taste combinations are one of the reasons their dishes are hard to beat. The mixing of colors and hot and cold, sweet and sour, fruity and otherwise, well, they are unusual but tasty, no doubt about it. And where else would you leave you car in a parking lot and have your car hand-washed and detailed while you're having lunch. What great just desserts. Worth every penny to drive off after I cleaned my plate in a clean car, too.

★★★★   **La Spiga Bakery Italian Bakery**   **972/934-8730**

4203 Lindbergh   Mon-Fri 7-3; Sat 8-2
Addison, TX 75001

There's no loafing off at this company. They're up at the crack of dawn, baking breads as fast as they can. Do you think Mrs. Baird started this way? Since 1994, Donato Milano and Carolyn Nelson have been whipping up breads and pastries and selling them to many of the major hotels and restaurants in town. When the public got a whiff of their focaccia, their famous Italian Milano bread, and their menu of other breads like Calamata Olive, Jalapeno Cheese and Rye, they were forced to sell them to the public. Today, there are 20 different breads baked daily. At lunchtime, you can devour a humdinger of a sandwich on homemade bread: Ham, tuna, turkey, veggie, etc. Or for a hot lunch, try their lasagna, penne or cheese tortellini. Soups are tomato basil, cream of mushroom and roasted garlic potato. Oh, did I forget dessert? How about their eclairs? Or their biscotti cookies, which are notorious as a dunkers'delight. Most entrees are $3 to $10; expect a 10 percent surcharge for delivery. Catering orders are accepted with 24-hours advance notice. I never knew I was so Italian in my taste buds.

◆◆◆◆◆◆   **Lifestyle Gourmet**   **214/692-1500**

13628 Gamma Road   By Reservation Only (Mon-Fri 9-5 Customer Support)
Dallas, TX 75244
www.lifestylegourmet.com

 If you're too busy to cook and not too busy to drive through a fast-food restaurant, here's an answer to your prayers. One call to Lifestyle Gourmet and you will have a fresh, healthy and yet gourmet meal delivered to your front door at home or office. If you're watching your weight (creep up) and you'd like to make it go in the opposite direction, you can opt to stop dieting and choose instead, healthy, balanced meals delivered by Lifestyle Gourmet. Enjoy the variety of options: Dinners only, two meals and two snacks, three meals and two snacks. Rest assured that Lifestyle Gourmet follows all of the sound conservative nutritional guidelines so you're in good hands. Expect to order in four week increments with automatic renewals unless otherwise notified. Order by phone or online. From apple-braised pork medallions, couscous and broccoli to balsamic glazed catfish with steamed spinach. Oh, you don't like spinach? Well, what about Cajun Catfish with roasted green beans, or beef fajitas, or Citrus-glazed salmon with wild rice pilaf? See, the menus are so varied and I just touched a few entrees. So much to eat, so much to lose. Without ordering in a few pizzas, you'll find how affordable these folks are as well as nutritious. Fresh food prepared and delivered daily. Nothing is frozen. Fresh, baby, strictly fresh.

◆◆◆◆   **Margarita Masters**   **972/641-7926**

PO Box 540502   By Reservation
Grand Prairie, TX 75054

When was the last time you hit Margaritaville? If you're due, then take time to chill out with a frozen drink machine that you can rent for your next party. Their service, their attention to detail and reliability, not to mention their prices, are reason enough for party planners, both professional and amateur, to seek them out. For a rental fee of $95, you get free delivery and set up, 50 plastic nine-ounce cups, salt and straws. For the average size drink, this should serve 71 drinks, give or take a few. Add $15 per Margarita mix and three liters of tequila per package of mix, and you're in business. If in doubt, call Carl, the friendly Margarita man. He's the bartender-on-call. You'll need about a week's notice to reserve the machine. Salud!

◆◆◆◆◆◆   **Marsala Restaurant**   **972/988-1101**

1618 Hwy. 360 North   Lunch; Dinner (Reservations Recommended)
Grand Prairie, TX 75050-2436
www.marsalarestaurant.com

   Five minutes from DFW Airport, The Ballpark at Arlington, Six Flags and the Antique Sampler Mall, this restaurant is perfectly situated to capture all underground shoppers looking for a time out. Pull up to this unobtrusive front, step inside an elegant environment that is anything but formal or stuffy and be greeted by the Maitre D/owner, Jacob. He will take you by the hand and see to it that every morsel of your dining experience is perfect to the last bite. Not only is the food fabulous (French/Italian/Continental is how best to describe it) but so it the ambience and service. Superb is an understatement. Even at lunch, the wait staff is dressed in tuxedos; at dinner, there's a wonderful and personable classical guitarist who takes special requests, and, ladies, expect a red rose to grace your table any time you're seated at a Marsala table. Order carpaccio as an appetizer and the pork chops as your main dish and you're as close to heaven as a restaurant experience will allow. There's no doubt about it. Many media personalities have ducked in for....OK, it was duck. Me, I'm a chicken kind of gal. There are so many divine chicken dishes to choose from, I am often overwhelmed as to which one to choose. Cluck, Cluck!

★★★★   **Mary's Sweets**   **972/221-7707**

1114 W. Main   Mon-Fri 10-6; Sat 10-5
Lewisville, TX 75067

The eyes of **TEXAS** are upon Mary Jennings, the purveyor of Mary's Sweets at the Main Street Shopping Center. This native Texan has her shop knee-deep in chocolates. For more than 16 years, Mary has never been contrary regarding Texas chocolate gift-giving. She is regularly called upon because of her Texas-specialty gifts that are shipped worldwide. Everybody loves something from Texas and Mary's the gal to deliver. From a chocolate boot to a cowboy hat, the state of Texas to an armadillo, who can resist gloating with an extra layer of white chocolate? When you want to nibble on just one as a treat for staying on your diet all week, or you want a half pound with almonds or pecans, go for it. It's only $5.99. Though it's certain to bring lots of smiles, expect it also to add about five pounds. For holidays, Mary always adds red and white color bits to her chocolate treats and, of course, business picks up substantially as the weather cools. Texas hospitality and real good sweets makes Mary a home-town favorite. Do not visit on an empty stomach or if you suffer from the chocoholism (unless this dish out a 12-step program for chocolate over-indulgers.)

◆◆◆   **Mattito's Tex Mex**   **214/526-8181**

3011 Routh Street   Open Daily Around 11 AM (Hours flexible)
Dallas, TX 75201
www.mattitos.com

Jeffrey Frankel continues to make food his master and Mattito's is no exception. From his earlier career with yogurt to his partnership with Matt Martinez, he has carved out a career starting right out of college. Today he's the head honcho at this little hideaway, winner of numerous awards and featured in a variety of publications. Mattito's offers plentiful platillos with special dips that really brings out the glutton in me. His new location is in hiding, yet intriguing. Grotto-like, the perfect "underground" environment, it's cozy and charming and the food's good, too. Having a party? They offer party rooms and banquet facilities for that special occasion. The private rooms can accommodate 20-250 hungry hands, so if you're looking to book a rehearsal dinner, brunch, or a bar and bat mitzvah, go ahead. Their "Especialidades of the House" includes a grilled fried steak. Yes, in a Mexican restaurant, this hand-made buttermilk battered steak is delicious served with country style cream gravy, salsa fries and Texas toast. Not for me, but there's somebody out there who will not doubt order two.

★★★★★   **Meat Works**   **972/418-7373**

2760 Trinity Mills   Mon-Fri 9-7; Sat 8-6
Carrollton, TX 75006-2196

I hate to say that this family-owned meat market business is a dying breed, but there are not too many butcher shops waiting to be handed down from one generation to the next. But here, they have kept it all in the family. Strike while the iron is hot! Check out their counter-full of USDA top quality T-bones, filets, ground chuck, pot roasts, pork chops, chicken, lamp chops, bacon, pork roasts....well, it's a meat market, what did you expect? By the steak or by the freezer full, this is a full-service market that caters to whatever cut you want, however you want it. But don't think they leave seafood, tuna steaks, mahi mahi, or ahi to somebody else, because they don't. They are always fishin' for compliments and between the quality and the prices, you can really reel in the deals.

★★★★★★ **Metro-Webb Foods**   **817/274-9994**

1411 W. Randol Mill Rd.   Mon-Fri 8-6; Sat 9-3
Arlington, TX 76012

 Since 1939, this tucked-away little secret food source has been a Tarrant County treasure. When it comes to food, glorious food, gluttons are often found hovering around all days of the week because of their wholesale foods and groceries. This salvage operation buys closeouts from area food distributors and then sells them wholesale to the public. Everything's delicious, from pre-made foods like lasagna to hamburger patties. Add in sauces, salad dressings, desserts — just about anything for the pampered purveyor of foodstuff. This is no Whole Foods. They are well-known and sought-after for their pre-cooked chicken fajita meat which is all white meat chicken. But wait 'til you taste their cobblers. It's the berries! For moms who pack lunches, remember those LUNCHABLES? Well, wait 'til you've bought them retail at a convenience store and then compare the prices here. You'll barf! So, shop Metro-Foods and protect yourself from getting ill. Ken has been holding down the fort for more than 20 years and sell quality restaurant food at wholesale prices. (Dallas Food Depot is their Dallas counterpart.) He has not jumped aboard the information highway and prefers to stand grounded in a old-fashioned, neighborhood depot and keep it simple. Real simple. The deals, though, are not hard to discern. You'll love them.

★★★ **Milk And Honey Kosher Market**   **972/404-0704**

6959 Arapaho, #116   Sun - Fri 10-4:30; Sat Closed
Dallas, TX 75248

When you're the only kosher market in town, you can gloat. And Milk and Honey is it — the only stand-alone kosher market we've found. Although there are other kosher departments within certain grocery stores, it's the only one that stands alone with kosher meat products, a CHOLOC Israel dairy, and a large selection of Israeli products at the most competitive prices around. Kosher confirms that the ingredients meet with particular dietary needs. So what exactly is kosher food? Well, let me tell you what it is not. It is not food that has been "blessed" by a rabbi nor is food that came about for hygienic reasons. Keeping kosher, or following "kashrut," means adhering to the volumes of Jewish law regarding the suitability of foods to be eaten. Some of the major principles when keeping a kosher kitchen, for example: **1)** eating only meat that comes from cloven-footed animals who chew their cud; **2)** Meat and dairy products are not to be mixed in a meal or in food preparation; **3)** Utensils used for their preparation must be kept separate, as well; **4)** Only fish with fins and scales may be eaten; **5)** No shellfish is allowed; **6)** Fruits and vegetables are allowed, except for certain rules regarding grape products and grape derivatives; **7)** Certain foods, such as eggs, honey, fish, grains, fruits and vegetables are neutral, or "pareve," and can be eaten with meat or dairy. If you're looking for a place to shop that keeps kosher, here it is. Ah, the good ole land of "Milk and Honey." To me, it's a commitment that for those who do, I commend them wholeheartedly. Me, I'm too lazy and hope God will turn the other cheek. Besides, I couldn't give up having my no-fat sour cream on my baked potato when enjoying an occasional steak. (That's a lame excuse, I know, but at least I'm honest!)

Mozzarella Company   **214/741-4072**

2944 Elm St.   Mon-Fri 9-5; Sat 9-3
Dallas, TX 75226
www.mozzco.com

 So glad crackers became popular after being a "wafer" awhile because I found it a necessary foundation for the Mozzarella Company. Founder Paula

Lambert's brain child since 1982, cheeses made in her downtown factory in Dallas, are now shipped internationally, and, no wonder, they're the best. She produces 250,000 pounds of cheese a year as well as 30 other products. From the Academy Awards to Presidents, her acclaimed fresh mozzarella and mascarpone tortas have been savored even by royalty. To learn the basics, order online *The Cheese Lovers Cookbook and Guide* for $35, which not only has hundreds of recipes but various types of cheeses and how to maintain their freshness. These award-winning cheeses are handmade daily from fresh milk. For special occasions, order some party platters. Or for gifts, their baskets are swell. My favorite gift is the "Cheese of the Month," where they'll send one of their cheeses each month for a year's worth of indulgence for $450 — twelve months of heaven on earth. Just give them the start date and they'll take it from there. The recipient will get a different selection of gourmet cheese every month for a year. When you're in the area, stop into their factory for some to sample. Among the cheeses are: Italian (fresh mozzarella, mascarpone and scamorza) and much more. Low or no-salt cheese is available by request. And now, serving up cheeses at a kiosk inside Grapevine Mills. "What a friend we have in cheeses! " *Call toll-free: 800/798-2954*

★★★   Mrs. Baird's Thrift Store   972/247-2392

3068 Forest Lane @ Webb Chapel   Mon-Sat 9-5
Farmers Branch, TX 75234

Boy, oh boy, the Dough Boys will have a field day at this hometown favorite thrift store. Save some bread even on dinner rolls — after all, you knead it! Shop a day or so later for **MRS. BAIRD'S** fresh from the oven rolls. Pop 'em in the freezer and the next day, they'll be fresh as new. Save yourself some dough in the process. It's just a matter of hours' lag time. From split-tops to dinner rolls, load up for your next dinner party (they all taste the same in the end) and it looks like you're the perfect "Roll Model." Check directory for other locations including McKinney, Plano, Richardson, Sherman and Garland. The sun may set in the west but the dough rises at this thrift store.

★★   Omaha Steaks   214/368-7597

10854 Preston Rd.   Mon-Sat 10-6; Sun Noon-5
Dallas, TX 75230
www.omahasteaks.com

"One of life's affordable indulgences," is steak. So if you're mad at cows, give it up. If not, stake your claim to a great steak for at least one more time — your last thrill of the grill! Meat-eaters have been ordering a piece of the beef from Omaha Steaks since World War I. Corn-fed, Midwestern beef is considered the best (just ask me, I'm a Midwesterner who prefers it over Texas beef). Do not make an issue out of it, however. So, where's the beef? Locations in Dallas, Lewisville and Plano, that's where. But wait 'til coupons shave 50 percent off the price. Occasional discounts like these are when you load up. Beef, sauces, seasonings, kosher foods, poultry, seafood, veal, pork, lamb and desserts. There are even some cookbooks to start you on your way. Shop online or in their stores (some of the items found online can also be found in their stores while others cannot). Meat is flash frozen which is how they can maintain their freshness. But always dig out the coupons or flyers for bonus gifts (like a pair of kitchen sheers or clock radio with purchase) or special discounts. It'll make Dr. Atkins proud! I'm not a personal fan of their meat. I've tasted better. *Call toll-free: 800/228-9055*

★★★★★★ Patricia's Coffee & Tea Diner   972/485-8533

612 W. State Street   Mon-Sat 11-3; Closed Sun
Garland, TX 75040

Patricia's Coffee and Tea Diner located smack dab in the middle of old downtown Garland is a must when you start to salivate anytime from 11-3ish (though they have stayed open until 5 when folks were still on their second piece of coconut cream pie.) Talk about home baked goods, plus sandwiches and other stuff — all home made and down right delicious. Just don't expect anything fried. Period. She doesn't even have the tools to do so which is no big loss to anybody looking for healthier fare. Her potato leek or broccoli cheese soup is the best, her chicken salad club was as good as it gets, her desserts (well we had a sampler of coconut cream, chocolate cream, chocolate cake and a fresh blackberry cobbler with homemade crusts and freshly whipped cream....well what can you say that hasn't been said before. But for the pieces de resistance was her pickles and if she doesn't package them for sale, she's a pickle. We still can say "olive you." These garlic sweet pickles are the best I have ever eaten. Not too sweet, not too hot, but just enough of a kick to make you come back for more. And more. You will not be able to stop with just one. Betcha! Betcha! If it weren't for my reduced stomach pouch capacity, I bet I could have finished the jar in one sitting — they were that good. Patty's Pickles is to pick a perfect pickle. Try 'em, and if they're not hot enough, ask her to kick it up a notch on her next batch. Patty Prepared a Pair of Perfect Pickles. Enjoy.

★★★★ Pendery's   817/332-3871

304 E. Belknap   Mon-Fri 8:30-5:30; Sat 9-5
Fort Worth, TX 76102
www.penderys.com

Remember, if it's chili today, it'll be hot tomorrow. This adage may be as old as the hills but so is Pendery's. Since 1870, they've been spicing up the town with their custom-blended chili powders and spices via their beautifully-crafted catalog, and now they're online. In the 1800s, they shipped via stagecoach; now they use the Internet. Why pay for the fancy bottles when all you really want are the spices themselves? From generation to generation, the Pendery family has produced an innovative and vast collection of spices. Whether you cook with them, or ingest them for medicinal purposes, start with the first family of spices, right there in Cowtown, where the West began! Their expanded inventory now includes candy, fruits, nuts, sauces, teas, jams and jellies, plus things that you can't eat like utensils, flowers, plates, jewelry, peppermills, posters, spice containers and racks, lights, cookbooks and more. The only caveat in shopping their catalog or online is when you finish shopping, you're hungry for more! Start with the discontinued items for the best buys and then go from there. ***Call toll-free: 800/533-1870***

★★★★ Peter Piper Pizza   817/860-7233

1511 New York Ave.   Sun-Thurs 11 AM-10 PM; Fri-Sat 11 AM-11 PM
Arlington, TX 76010
www.peterpiperpizza.com

Man, you can't kick a guy when he's at work seven days a week, morning, noon and nighttime, too, 'cause he's always rolling in the dough. Try Peter Piper Pizza for a perfectly pleasant place that sells pizza. Looking for an inexpensive place to hold your next party? Their package includes: pizza, soft drinks, soft-serve dessert, a balloon bouquet, party hats, a gift for the birthday child, party invitations, tokens for the entire party and a hostess. With one call, let them take care of it all. And let's hold down the noise like at that "other" pizza party place in town where it's a madhouse. Instead, keep your party here to a dull roar. Call them now before you have to rob Peter to pay

Paul. You might as way pay it to the Piper, instead. Also, party in Dallas: 729 W. Jefferson, 214/
943-6582; 951 W. Centerville Rd., Garland, 972/279-0200; 9480 Webb Chapel Rd., Dallas, 214/
366-2600 and in Fort Worth at 221 NE 28th St., 817/625-5151. Chow! Or is it Ciao? Peter Piper
Pizza, based in Scottsdale, AZ, currently has 95 franchises which are run by 15 different franchisees. Do you want to be one of them? Check it out. Their concept is very interesting.

★★★★★★ PF1 Seafood & Grill   972/682-6288

3820 Towne Crossing Blvd.   Mon-Fri (Lunch) 11-2:30; 4:30-10:30 (Dinner); Sat-Sun 11am-10:30pm
Mesquite, TX 75150

If you are a glutton for punishment, this is where the pedal hits the medal. Winner of
the Grand Prix of the all-you-can-eat steak and seafood buffets, it's almost too good
to be true but try it, you'll like it. Lunch is a meaty $7.99; dinners are $14.99. I dare
you to find a better meal deal anywhere. Saturday and Sunday brunch is an all day affair (from 11
AM-10:30 PM) for $14.99. The buffet table is brimming with peel and eat shrimp, cocktail and
fried shrimp, calamari, oysters, scallops, sea bass, catfish, crab legs, New York strip steaks and a
sushi bar, salad bar and dessert bar. Whew! Oh, did I forget the hibachi grill where they stir fry
scallops, shrimp, beef, chicken, vegetables into one big wok and roll out this extravaganza? This is
their one and only location, so far, but expect the success to spawn more if the crowds reflect its
acceptance. Don't expect the strip steaks or the crab legs at lunch, though, just everything else. But
you won't miss it with all the other stuff piled a mile high. Look for PF2, I bet!

★★ Rainbo Bakery Stores   972/686-2330

2914 Centerville Rd.   Mon-Fri 9-7; Sat 9-6
Dallas, TX 75228

Somewhere over the Rainbo Bakery Stores, you'll find there's some unfulfilled dough waiting to
be kneaded. Yeast I forget to remind you, they flunked Spelling 101. You can take advantage of
day-old baked goods and save yourself plenty of wear and tear on your budget. Day-old or otherwise, sure tastes the same to me once you've popped them in and out of the freezer, or warmed
them in the oven. The prices you save may be your own. EARTH GRAIN is how they answer the
phone (or is it Earth Green with a Southern accent?) Large hamburger buns were two packs for
$1.89 and five packs of hot dog buns for $2.99. Hot dog! Yes, they still carry donuts, but keeping
up with their daily specials is harder than keeping up with the Jones's. Well, now that you know
how the other half lives, do as the Roman's do, and do it. It's cheaper. Check directory for other
area Rainbo Bakery Stores, but don't expect a cordial greeting by phone. All we wanted to know
was the cross street that intersects Centerville; their attitude was as plain as day. "LOOK it up
yourself, babe!"

★★★★ Red Coleman's Liquors   214/363-0201

7560 Greenville Ave.   Mon-Sat 10-9
Dallas, TX 75231
www.redcoleman.com

With 10 locations, you'd think the Metroplex would be drunk with rapture by now. Given that Red
Coleman has been supplying the area with spirits since 1946, it's still nice that they've kept it all in
the family. That way, they can keep "Beer Pressure" under control. Imagine staying sober and sol-
vent all these years between their 10 liquor stores and 20 convenience stores. You'll see red, white,
and probably blush since they're always on the lookout for a closeout on wines. On a regular basis,
you can sip a brew or two for as much as 50 percent off or more. Make sure to try their French
Bordeaux and Burgundy selections — tres bien! With their expanded inventories of beer, wine,

spirits, micro brews and lots of hard-to-find cigars, there's not much they've missed whether you're a novice or a connoisseur. Pick-up and delivery also available. This location is between Meadow and Walnut Hill on Greenville. You may not want to miss any of them since they carry all the Gold Medal Winning wines determined by the Dallas Morning News.

★★   Rocky Mountain Chocolate Factory   972/724-6868

Grapevine Mills   Mon-Sat 10-9:30; Sun 11-7
3000 Grapevine Mills Pkwy. Grapevine, TX 76051
www.rmcfusa.com

Give me Rocky Mountain or give me death. Forget GODIVA! Just, Go, Diva, go — to the Rocky Mountain Chocolate Factory. In 1981, they opened their first little chocolate shop in Durango, Colorado. Today, ROCKY MOUNTAIN CHOCOLATE FACTORY offers a taste of the Rockies in more than 200 locations throughout the United States, Canada and Asia. Originally located in a tiny 800-square foot space above a bakery, the company's 53,000-square-foot office and manufacturing facility now produces over two million pounds of candy each year. Get boxed chocolates as well as dessert sauces, candy bars and instant cocoa mixes, too. A three-pound box of assorted chocolates was $42.90; a 1.6 pound box will set you back $16.95. Sugar-free goodies could be snared for $11.95 for eight ounces or three 3-ounce bars were $7.50. They have non-chocolate items just in case your sweet tooth prefers a peanut, cashew or macadamia nut brittle. Check directory for other metro locations at the Allen Premium Outlets, the Gainesville Prime Outlets and a location in Fort Worth. Call 817/338-1966 for information. *Call toll-free: 800/496-0361*

★★★★   Russell Stover Candies   972/563-8227

Mon-Sat 9-6; Sun Noon-5

200 Apache Trail Terrell, TX 75160
www.russellstover.com

Since 1923, RUSSELL STOVER has been finger-lickin'good. So, when traveling to the Tanger Outlet Center, don't bypass one of the best little chocolate houses in Texas. Besides, they're the biggest candymaker in the USA. It just so happens that their Southwest distribution center has a little outlet store that is open to public chocoholics. Take the FM 148 exit in Terrell (Off I-20 and 80) to get to the Metrocrest Industrial Park; or order a catalog from their toll-free number above. Selection at their outlet store includes over 30 varieties of their candies which are marketed to grocery and drug stores mostly. They also offered some that are sugar-free and they were as good as the leaded varieties: Toffee, Truffles, Caramel, Peanut Butter Cups and their famous Pecan Delights. Today's demand even includes low carb choices for all those on the low carb bandwagon (Mint Patties, Toffee Squares, Peanut Butter Cups and Truffle Cups.) free gift wrapping makes this a gift shop must stop. You can find RUSSELL STOVER candies and pay retail at Albertson's, Walgreen's, Hallmark, Kroger's and elsewhere; or you can go underground and get your fix for less at the outlet. *Call toll-free: 800/477-8683*

★★★★★   Save-A-Lot

372 E. Pipeline Rd.   Mon-Sat 9-9; Sun 9-7
Hurst, TX 76053-5831

Hopefully, by the time the book hits the streets, the doors to this replacement for Grocery Outlet will be settled in and open for business. This Minnesota powerhouse wholesaler has come to town and have taken all of the GO locations for themselves. This particular store is located in one of those funky dying shopette centers that includes a Polynesian, Latino and an African grocery outpost, but if it's anything like Grocery Outlet, we've got a winner on our hands. Acquiring the former Yes!Less and then the Grocery Outlet stores, this company may have the staying power to compete with the powerful grocery chains like Wal-Mart, CostCo, etc. At least I'm rooting for them. They entered the Texas market in 1994 when they acquired the Texas T chain. Smaller than the standard supermarkets and limited in product selection but then, the price is right! They may be a new guy in town, but they are no newcomer to the supermarket business. They have almost 1,500 grocery stores already with about 850 operated by licensees including those stores in Texas. Since they were the wholesale biggie that competed favorably with the Fleming folks from Lewisville, they, too, have longtime relationships with most of the national brand-food manufacturers. Secondly, they had enough clout to buy all 17 Grocery Outlets in one fell swoop. Now that that's done, expect food prices to continue to be rock-bottom with their buying power. This full-service store offers canned and boxed goods alongside meats, produce, frozen foods and paper goods, pet food and supplies, health and beauty aids, well, it's a grocery store....only cheaper. Many of the products are recognizable name brands — others are off brands like you'd see at stores like Big Lots. They limited their selection to the top 1,250 items and restrict their size to about 14,000-16,000 square feet. Savings may been 30-50 percent off on many items — and often times more. We shall see since they just made their moves in the Metroplex as we were on our way to the printers. They were remodeling so we couldn't see first hand of their progress. What do you think? Read all about when they open in the magazine, on the web and on radio. If they are even close to Grocery Outlet's prices, here's where underground shoppers need to do the bulk of their grocery store buying. Expect to see brands like **BORDEN, BREYERS, DEL MONTE, HUNT, DRYERS, GREEN GIANT, JUICY JUICE, MRS. BAIRD'S, QUAKER, SARA LEE NEW YORK CHEESECAKE** or **TOMBSTONE** Pepperoni Pizza. But if you want to keep on the straight and narrow, I hope to see **HEALTHY CHOICE** and **WEIGHT WATCHERS**, too. Health food items should be cheaper as well alongside laundry and cleaning supplies, sundries, drug store items and more. At every turn, look for a bargain waiting. Look high but pay low.

◆◆◆◆◆ Spice of Life Catering   214/343-2598

101 Medallion Center   Mon-Fri 9-5; By Appt. Only for Weddings
Dallas, TX 75214

Sue and Jeff Kollinger have quite a reputation as one of the few mother-son teams in the catering world. After all, the way to every man's heart is through his stomach and the Kollinger's approach is to first feed them and then they'll be a client for life. Full-service catering for any occasion, from a romantic dinner for two to a blow-out event for one thousand. Having their own kitchens and three full-time chefs, their repertoire runs the gamut from soup to nuts. They cook everything from scratch and deliver it with a full regalia of wait staff, bartenders, china, serving pieces, whatever it takes, they'll take good care of you. Want something ethnic like a Mexican or Chinese buffet? Or an elaborate sit-down French buffet? Their client list of law firms alone would wonder if they Spice of Life on a retainer? They do many corporate and charitable accounts on a regular basis but are also in demand for bar and bat mitzvahs, christenings, confirmations, birthday parties, 50th wedding anniversary bashes .... if it's a special occasion, isn't food the Spice of Life?

★★★★★★ Spirits Liqueur Store   214/748-2459

2825 Canton @ Malcolm X   Mon-Sat 10-9
Dallas, TX 75226
www.spirits.com

Now it's time to sip the savings in any number of spirited liquid pleasures from a wholesaler in downtown Dallas. Deep in the heart of Deep Ellum, this 15,000-

square-foot warehouse is open to the public and was voted best liquor store in several different publications — but we named them first! More than 8,000 different items from A to Z (Absolut vodka to **ZIEGENBOCK** beer) can be found standing or sitting or laying horizontal on their warehouse shelves. Other spirits are at your fingertips in this expansive warehouse where you don't even have to be a little tipsy to get great service. Celebrate with champagne from **DOM PERIGNON** or a less expensive, though notable, **VUEVE CIQUOT BRUT YELLOW** (this French champagne is from one of the world's most respected champagne houses, founded in 1772.) Toast any special occasion with sparkling wines such as **MARTINI & ROSSI**'s "Asti Spumanti," the No. 1 premium imported sparkling wine from the heart of Italy and a gold medal winner at the New England Wine Festival of "Opera" — a real zinger! Heaven knows, when you're ready to get into the spirit of things, or are planning a party, start here. Great prices, great selection, lousy location. Except now that downtown is happening, it's probably a great location for some. From domestic to imported, from France to Oregon, from Germany to Texas, there's something for everyone. Remember, you don't have to sacrifice quality to sip the savings. Just don't get "snookered!" (or is more polite to say smashed? Looped? Soused?) In polite circles, friends don't let friends drive drunk. So I'm asking you to look out for your friends, just in case.

◆◆◆◆   Suze   214/350-6135

4345 West NW Hwy, #270   Tues-Sat 5:30-10:30
Dallas, TX 75220

Okay, so I'm drawn to a restaurant because of its name. And this one comes from the original owner, Susie Priore, who ultimately sold out to the chef Gilbert Garza but he kept the name in place. Glad to say it's one of the best little bistros this side of the Mediterranean. It is open for dinner only. The reason I'm a devotee is that I've followed this chef from the Riviera, to Mediterraneo and Toscana until he finally landed this gig at Suze. He has won many accolades such as the 10th Annual American Institute of Wine & Food Caesar Salad Competition, but men or women do not live by Caesar salads alone. Meals are feasts for the eyes as well as the stomach and it's described as Southern French-Northern Italian. So be(an) it! Lots of interesting garnishes and herbs sprinkled on to traditional dishes give a hint of differential treatment. Most appealing was the champagne butter sauce that graced its presence. The prices are moderate, the presentation superb, and the atmosphere European. Leave room for dessert, though I could only ogle the chocolate soufflÈ cake. I promised to be good. But I can dream, can't I?

★★★★★   Taylor Farms (Fresh Express Dallas) 214/421-1947

2500 S. Good Latimer Expwy.   Mon-Fri 5-4; Sat 5-11
Dallas, TX 75215
www.taylorfarms.com

Although the name has changed from Fresh Express to Taylor Farms, who doesn't like the freshest fruits or the best vegetables (lettuce, spinach, cabbage, broccoli, carrots, potatoes, tomatoes, onions) for commercial use by restaurants? I do! I do! But at such low prices, lettuce explain further. Prices fluctuate with the seasons, the droughts, the heat waves and such, but as we speak, a five-pound bag of fruit salad (cantaloupe, honeydew melon and grapes) was $11.55 and a five-pound bag of an assorted fruit tray was $12.50. Want to throw a party and have them do up the veggie trays so all you have to do is whip up a dip? Easy does it, $7.50. Price lists change, but calling in advance for your orders, hasn't. Why chop 'til you drop? Let these folks do it for you. They know their stuff and will suggest what fruits or what produce is in season, what looks good, what IS good. Note the addition of a website this year and the early morning hours. Some folks really do get up at the crack of dawn and you can meet some of them here. It's their packaged salad blends that we buy in quantity — you know, the ones you see in grocery stores and restaurants (Caesar, Cole slaw, garden salads, Italian, French and American blends) are on their package salad menu. I buy them for my neighborhood and then divvy up when I get home. It's nice to know my sub-division is eating healthier these days, not that I'm on a mission. I just like to share a fresh approach to the Homeowners Association (and you know how I feel about Homeowners Association!) *Call toll-free: 800/248-9288*

★★★★ Texas Pecan Co.   972/241-7878

2850 Satsuma   Mon-Fri 8:30-5
Dallas, TX 75229

Are you nuts? Are you paying retail prices for pecan halves or pecan pieces? Why? You can buy them here for as low as $5.50 for the haves or pieces, $2,95 for honey-roasted peanuts, $4.95 for pistachios in the shell, and that's just the beginning to the nuts and bolts of saving money in or out of the shell. You'll crack up with the selection: almonds, Spanish peanuts, walnuts, filberts, Brazil nuts, pumpkin and sunflower seeds, pine nuts, trail mixes and roasted/salted nut mixes. Off Stemmons between Forest and Royal, whether for cooking, for baking, for the candlestick maker as a gift, or just for yourself, you're nuts if you don't shop here. You can't even compare the quality and freshness of their nuts to those you buy in the grocery stores. Hours extend during the holidays to Saturdays in November and December, the peak baking and cooking season. Orders by phone are accepted.

◆◆◆ Tony's Wine Warehouse & Bistro   214/520-WINE

2904 Oak Lawn   Mon-Thurs 10-2; 6-10; Fri & Sat 6-11 PM
Dallas, TX 75206

How many bottles of wine on the wall, how many bottles of wine? If one of them falls, how many are bottles are left? Well, at Tony's, we're talking more than 2,000 bottles off the wall and stocked at their warehouse/bistro. Imbibe and indulge yourself with excellent French-Italian cuisine at the Bistro; then, choose a bottle of wine from the store, have it opened and brought to your table; each bottle is extremely affordable that way. Their warehouse is home to literally thousands of options with informative wine tasting seminars that cost $35/per person with a minimum of 25 participants. Reservations are taken three to four months in advance. Open wine tastings are held monthly on the weekend. The open Jazz Dinner costs $55 per person and includes a five-course meal in addition to tasting a dozen wines. Between Cedar Springs and Congress, lunch is served from 11-2:30, and dinner 6-10. Bid adieu to pretentious dining; this one wins the Tony. Reviews run the gamut, from arrogant pompous French with so-so food and to overpriced wine to witty and excellent service, wonderful food and incredible wines. So, what's your take?

★★★★★★ Top Line Warehouse Store   972/262-5326

433 E. Church St.   Mon-Sat 9:30-6
Grand Prairie, TX 75050

 Top shelf and premium brands line the aisles of this warehouse. A little of this and a little of that, all well-organized and priced low. That's how Bud Bobbitt started his company 25 years ago and it's how he continues to maintain the "Top of the Lines" today. We reeled in good deals on pet food and supplies like **NATURE'S RECIPE** — a five-pound bag was $1.99 and a 40-pound bag was $12.95. **WALTHAM** eight-pound bags were $8 and **IAMS** canned food was a mere 89 cents a can. From pet supplies to paper goods, groceries, office supplies (paper, pens, binders), trash bags and paint to occasional supplies of large and small appliances and furniture, it's all here at big savings. Simply find your way to the corner of Church and

5th Streets, but don't forget to look across the street to their other store, Top Line Select which specializes in clothing, fabrics, toys and books. This location is at 208 N.E. 5th St. and is open Tues-Sat 10 to 5. Top shelf. Top dog. Top Line.

★★★★★   Vending Nut Co.   817/737-3071

2222 Montgomery St.   Mon-Fri 8:30-5; Sat 9-Noon
Fort Worth, TX 76107

Open to the public since 1968, this company has been shelling out the nuts, both retail and wholesale, roasted or raw, alongside dried fruits and seeds, bulk or pre-packaged, have it your way. From hotel and bar nuts to gift packs and Christmas gifts, you can expect prices to reflect direct vending machines with the absence of the middle man. Pecan halves were $5.50/pound; black walnuts (not seen often around this neck of the woods), $7.50/pound and sliced almonds for $4.25/pound. This is a wholesale warehouse environment that sells to the public in their company store. But you're nuts if you ignore the opportunity to shell out less for these nuts. Filament up on roasted cashews, Hawaiian macadamias, Southern pecans, almonds and pine nuts as well as gift containers of candy and nuts. Then mix up some trail mix with grated coconut, pumpkin or sunflower seeds, or if you'd rather have it already mixed, buy it ready made. Well, what do you think?

Whole Foods Market   817/461-9362

801 E. Lamar Blvd.   Daily 8 AM-9 PM
Arlington, TX 76011
www.wholefoods.com

I remember them when, as a consultant to Lake Austin Resort, we used to order in their freshly-baked whole grain breads and each guest lived for each and every little morsel. (When you are dieting, you're apt to relish crumbs.) That was back in 1980. Today Whole Foods is the largest natural food store chain in the world with six locations in the Metroplex (Arlington, Richardson, Plano, and three in Dallas: 1) Highland Park, 2) Greenville Ave., 3) Preston Road; 4) Coit Rd. That adds up to seven. What gives? Find every product you need to live the good life — but hardly for less. Spend more because it's displayed in elegant surroundings. Spend more because some of the products are unusual, rare, organic? Spend more just 'cause. From the bakery to the wine cellar and everything in between, including body care, cheese, coffee, groceries, meats, produce, seafood and stuff for your pet in between seminars, bottled and exotic waters and chair massages. Again, don't plan on saving money! Everything's more expensive at Whole Foods. Just enjoy the experience. See exotic food products. From produce to meats, seafood, dairy, canned and boxed goods, dairy, frozen foods and more, it's tempting to buy it all. The Arlington store generally has cooking classes on "Cooking for One" (Singles Sunday), "Lunch Box Ideas," "Tofu 101," etc. They have a Kid's Celebration in anticipation of the beginning of school and also a community project where a percentage of all proceeds go to the Women's Shelter in Arlington. Check directory for location nearest you. It's a toss up which specialty food store gets my vote as the best. I really can't decide because they both have its special niches. Which is yours? Tell us your foodie favorite or beware of botulism story on our Shop Talk button on our website. Spill the beans. It'll feel good to get it off your chest!

★★★★   Wonder Bread Thrift   817/534-3152

5609 Wichita Ave.   Mon-Sat 8-6; Sun 11-5
Fort Worth, TX 76119

I WONDER where the HOSTESS went? If she's smart, she went to this thrift store. Be the HOSTESS with the mostest when you buy your day-old WONDER BREAD from here for the leastest!

After all, isn't it the staff of life? So what if it's a day late or fancy-less? Saving money is what it's all about. Chomp into hot dog or hamburger buns in the eight count, each pack was 69 cents or two for $1.35. Sandwich bread (small loaf) went home three for $1.45 or two for $1.35 for the large loaf. TWINKIES flew out the door for 99 cents. I'm loading up the trunk now for that rainy day. Remember, pop 'em in the freezer and they're as good as new. DING DONG Wednesdays and Saturdays are bargain days, when prices are slashed even more. Though promoted as day-old, some are right from the ovens. My nose sure doesn't know the difference. Check directory for multiple locations.

★★★★★★   **World Food Imports**   **972/480-9911**

13434 Floyd Circle   Mon-Sun 10-8
Dallas, TX 75243

Best **100** SHOPPING DESTINATIONS   If you're a galloping gourmet, and want to command attention at your next soiree, here's a warehouse full of worldly food imports that are waiting to be digested. One Israeli gourmet cook revels in their international foods and imported cheeses. Step into this warehouse environ and get a whiff of delicious foods from around the world not often seen at your typical grocery store. They also have restaurant-quality meats with prices that are hard to beat. (Hey, I'm a poet — and I don't know it!) And some of their breads were like Long Fellows. Once you've found them, you'll make a mad dash on a regular basis, especially if you're a gourmet cook (and unless you hear otherwise, you don't have to be a "Naked Chef" to shop here!) Of course if you are, please alert our photographer so we can be there for a photo op. It'll put World Food Imports on the map.

Funerals & Caskets

◆◆◆◆◆ **Blend Wolfe Funeral Home**   **972/774-9925**

7810 Spring Valley   Mon-Fri 9-5; Sat-Sun (By Appt. Only) Answered 24/7
Dallas, TX 75254
www.blendwolfe.com

If you are Jewish, chances are you'll want a funeral home that would be well-versed in Jewish customs. But you don't have to be Jewish to enjoy the professional services at this full-service funeral parlor with affordable prices. Remember my old saying, "You don't have to be cheap to love a bargain!" Well, the same goes for anyone who is non-Jewish. Everybody loves a deal and here is a full-service funeral parlor that offers not only a bargain but can provide anything that any religion would require when performing the last rites. They offer rosaries and crucifixes and can handle all of the necessary elements for a cremation, even though Jewish people do not believe in cremation. They'll even provide a motorcycle escort (minimum of two), if requested, to the cemetery. But up until this year, there has been no other place to hold a Jewish funeral except at Sparkman/Hillcrest. At last, Sharon and Stephen Wolf Blend have opened such a facility steeped in procedures appropriate to Jewish traditions. The first of its kind in the Metroplex, and the second in the state, expect them to master every detail. Since this is a full-service funeral parlor, they can take care of connecting you right to the burial plot. If you let them order the plot for you, they can save you considerable sums of money....as much as half price. Wow. Their small sanctuary can accommodate as many as 25. They offer packaged plans when you purchase a casket from them for as low as $3,185. That would be for the minimum of services but it does include everything you'd need. For approximately $5,200, you'll have a complete Jewish funeral — the works.

★★★★★ **Budget Casket (The Funeral Store)**   **817/654-9438**

5430 E. Lancaster   Mon-Fri 9-6; Sat 10-2
Fort Worth, TX 76112
www.budgetcasket.com

Direct from dawn to dust, you might as well celebrate with the ultimate in "underground" shopping. At Texas'largest casket warehouse, you'll die over the selection. Well, let's hope not....but lighten up, this may be your last chance to beat the other couples. At least here, "The Price is Right!" Choose from over 300 caskets at Budget Caskets with prices dirt cheap (as low as $275!) The selection is staggering: wood, metal, copper, bronze, cremation urns and shipping boxes. They claim to beat anybody's price or they'll give you the headstone FREE! Other locations include 5430 E. Lancaster in Fort Worth, (817/654-9438) and Bedford at 3508 Harwood Rd., #218 (817/267-5590) and Houston, should you choose to draw your last breath on Loop 610.

Celestis Inc.   713/522-7282

2444 Times Blvd. Suite 260   24/7
Houston, TX 77005

www.celestis.com   🖰 *Top Online Store!*

Looking for an eternal ride into space? Then consider this celestial option, whether you prefer an earth orbit ($5,300) or a lunar orbit ($12,500). The possibilities are infinite. You can have your ashes (from one to seven grams) sent into space with services held right at the launch site and a video made as a keepsake. Earth to capsule, earth to capsule, come in. One gram of cremated remains in Earth's orbit costs $995, a small price to pay for a dignified memorial take-off, wouldn't you say? If you'd like an upgrade, it'll cost $5,300. Here's what you'll get: seven grams of cremated remains into Earth's orbit, your flight capsule with an imprinted personal message, an invitation to the launch event, a personalized video, a dedicated virtual memorial on their website, a contribution to the Celestis Foundation and a guarantee that the event will be performed. They also offer payment plans — for you before hand, or for those after-the-fact! *Call toll-free: 800/ 672-4811*

LifeGem Created Diamonds   866/543-3436

836 Arlington Heights Road #311
Elk Grove Village, IL 60007

www.lifegem.com   🖰 *Top Online Store!*

Forget this ashes to ashes stuff. Instead get with the program and turn those ashes into a diamond piece of jewelry ranging in price from $2,000 up. Let your love one wear it around their neck forever....celebrating your life once you have departed. And since diamonds are a girl's best friend, you might as well leave her with a "ring around her collar!" No kidding, this is the latest in creating lasting memories. Why not? Why rot? (Sorry, I didn't mean to be disrespectful, but I couldn't resist!) Keep your loved one with you forever. Even a pet can be recreated as a recycled piece of jewelry. No stone is left unturned. Grief support is offered online. This website will answer all of your questions and then some. Life is but a gem when all is said and done. *Call toll-free: 866/ 543-3436*

◆◆◆◆◆◆   Mid-Cities Funeral Home   817/838-3370

5706 Airport Freeway   By Appt. Only
Haltom City, TX 76117-6005

En route to Mid-Cities is City Mattress where you can lay out when you're still alive but be in heaven on one of their custom latex mattresses. However, further down the street, Mid-Cities Funeral Home & Cremation Services can lay you out en route to heaven and save you 40 to 60 percent off the competitors'prices in the area. They also accept pre-arrangements from any funeral home and can bury you in any cemetery (a relief if you've already bought your plot). Off Highway 121 between Haltom Road and Carson, this is a family-owned funeral home that offers dignified funerals without all the extra costs that are never really necessary or appreciated. Let's face it — when all is said and done, do you think you'd know the difference whether you're laid to rest in a casket made of wood, metal, bronze or inlayed with ivory? Tsk! Tsk! If you think about it, even an old trunk will do, if you could fit. (Then again, most of us are way too big for a trunk, unless it was originally intended for an elephant. Tusk! Tusk!) Direct cremation started at $675 and a funeral with graveside services with a 20-gauge casket was $1,995. Not bad, eh? It makes fiscal sense, when it comes to having your body depart in the physical sense. Why pay for the afterlife? If you're good, you know where you'll end up anyway! And if you're bad, even in a gold-plated casket, it won't matter where you're going!

◆◆◆◆◆   New Hope   972/226-2111

500 E. Hwy. 80   By Appt. Only
Sunnyvale, TX 75182
www.newhopefh.net

Why pay more....for less? That's a serious question in life, but what about in death? Don't think me disrespectful in talking about the bottom line at the end of the road. If you want a full service funeral with all the bells and whistles, that's your prerogative. But in my honor, please don't spend more than you have to. Furthermore, do not sacrifice the quality and compassion that this family-owned business brings to the table (or wherever you want your last rites). The owners are proud lifelong residents of Mesquite, from the Little Red School House to graduating from Mesquite High School. Just go to the endorsement letters on their website to highlight that not only do they provide hope, but faith and charity, too. That's the benefit of shopping a "mom and pop" funeral establishment rather than with the big boys like Sparkman/Hillcrest (though the person who actually manages the funeral parlor comes to the business with years of experience with the big boys. A."Hutch" Hutchinson has been a licensed Funeral Director for 34 years. He was the Managing Funeral Director for Restland Funeral Home in Dallas from 1992 to 1998 and was the recipient of the "Funeral Director of the Year" by the North Texas Funeral Directors Association in 1999.) But if you're a shopper, who wants to shop 'til you drop and yet, you'll still want to review their price comparisons. And if saving money is the last bequest you make, make it count. Their new and modern facilities are impressive and reflective of your needs in your time of sorrow as well as those of the dearly departed. They are considered from the very beginning of the shopping process to beyond the services rendered. So, what can I say except to extend my condolences. "New Hope" means going back to the good old days, the way things were before corporations took over the funeral home business, back when decisions were made to benefit the community, not Wall Street. See for yourself why New Hope gives you just that. Meet Mr. and Mrs. Jay Vandiver, proprietors, who are proud to give you Hope.

Furniture & Home Accessories

Cantoni Outlet

★★★★★★ **5th Avenue Dinettes & More** 972/241-5565

14000 Stemmons Frwy.
Farmers Branch, TX 75234

Mon-Fri 10:30-7; Sat 10-6; Sun 2-5

Man does not live by food alone. Man needs a table to eat on. Man needs one that will look great but cost little. Man needs durability and name brands. Man needs to shop at 5th Ave. Dinettes. Man, oh man, when it comes to satisfying all of the above, there's no better street to travel to than 5th Avenue. You buy your clothes at 7th Avenue, now sit down and enjoy them at your casual dinette set at 5th Avenue. Only the best names, like **CHROMCRAFT**, can be found, so shimmy up to hundreds of choices including all the popular and funky bar stools. I bought a pair of chrome and purple leather ones for $100 apiece. Such a conversation seat! Then, when it comes to playing games, they also have a large selection of game tables. OK, poker-face, you can let down your guard. Everything here is a winner. The combination of service, selection, styles and savings is like being dealt a "Royal Flush!" Going north, exit Valley View and stay on the service road. Just don't expect them to answer the phones very often. They are always busy with customers. Katie did as Katie does! Be sure to tell her the Diva told you to take a seat (but be sure to pay for it!)

★★★★★ **Adams Furniture** 940/648-3145

PO Box 37
Justin, TX 76247
www.adamsfurniture.biz

Mon-Sat 9-6; Thurs 9-7

Stroll down Memory Lane, especially if you're a fan of small-town prices on uptown furniture. Adams Furniture in Justin is just the place to make you homesick. Some of the brands they were brandishing included **BENCHCRAFT**, **BROYHILL**, **CHANDLER**, **KATHY IRELAND HOME**, **LANE** and others of equal distinction. A $99 **ISABELLA** metal headboard was perfect for a guest room; $499 for a nine-piece Farm Dining set with a table, six chairs and bench (with a **RALPH LAUREN**-like look at a fraction of the price) done in a natural stain and white was perfect for casual dining. FREE delivery available close by. They are well-known for what is referred to as the "Texas Western" collections. It's no wonder they've been getting rave reviews for years, especially on furniture made by Texas artisans and craftsmen. You're a Texan now and you'd better look the part. Take 114 west (out of Southlake) to 156 (after Texas Motor Speedway) and head north for four miles. Their new website is just down-home friendly, as well.

★★★ AFFORDIT Furniture   940/566-3222

1802 Alice   Mon-Sat 9-7; Sun 1-5
Denton, TX 76201

Muy Buenos, Amigos. Though they've closed their Watauga store, their focus is still the college-bound bargain shopping student and what a bargain behemoth they are. If you can't afford much but you need to buy it all, this is where to go. Affordit Furniture is on the right track to outfitting your first home away from home. Enjoy real furniture for unreal prices. Students love it here. This family-owned enterprise has settled into their bigger location across the street from their original university digs. Hop aboard a futon bunk bed, complete with twin mattress and regular mattress, for under $300. A kitchen dinette for $118? Yes sir. Great starter shop for students, second homes, RVers and folks who like to keep their budgets lean, mean and green.

★★★★★★ American Backyard   972/422-9222

3300 N. Central Expressway   Mon-Sat 10-9; Sun 11-6
Plano, TX 75074
www.americanbackyard.com

 Make the circuit but land up here if you are looking for anything at the guaranteed lowest price for your backyard. It's just that simple. Located next to Circuit City at Parker and 75, this newcomer will become the standard operating procedure for the great outdoors (although they do carry wicker furniture that could be used in the great indoors, too.) An incredible selection of casual furniture sets the stage for entertaining as an extension of your indoor dining. From aluminum and cast aluminum patio sets to outdoor wicker, wood and cast iron sets will set the scene to MARTHA STEWART standards. But what good is outdoor entertaining without the grill, the gas logs and all of the accessories? Add in all of the brand names that are considered the best in the industry: BIG GREEN EGG, BROILMASTER, FIRE MAGIC (The Ultimate Barbecue), TEC and WEBER and it spells substantive dining all year long. Add CFI cushions, OLYMPIA Lights, TREASURE GARDEN umbrellas, PIAGES (architectural-looking table bases) and Ancient Mosaic Table Tops that you have to see to appreciate plus a swingin'selection of hammocks. What more could you want to set the world on fire? Well, maybe a few gas logs. That's coming to their online shopping site soon. Be patient. Surely they will be available when you most need to warm the cockles of your heart. Here you can outfit your backyard the All American way—at the guaranteed lowest price. If you see it within two months at a lower price, they will gladly refund the difference. All products come with industry warranties and only the best names in furniture are represented. Some of them include: HOMECREST, LANE VENTURE, (EDDIE BAUER), LLOYD FLANDERS, MEADOWCRAFT, TROPITONE, WOODARD, WINSTON....well, what's more AMERICAN than the best names at the best prices! *Call toll-free: 800/ 677-4090*

★★★★ American Furniture Warehouse   972/866-6600

4554 McEwen Rd.   Mon-Sat 10-9; Sun 10-6:30
Dallas, TX 75244

Times have forced the closing of their Grand Prairie location, but they're still open for business in North Dallas, deep in the heart of the Furniture Capital of North Texas. Down the street from **BASSETT** Direct, they are still selling inexpensive furniture the all-American way: cheap. Even if you weren't born in the USA, you can still sing the praises of this warehouse merchant who promises good prices and makes good on that promise. Circumnavigate the globe in search of that elusive bargain, or turn your car around and head for this bastion of bargains. At least you don't have to travel to North Carolina. The brands are stellar, but I wonder how they feel about still selling **ASHLEY** when the Ashley Direct stores are just down the street. Turn the other cheek and instead concentrate on **CLAYBROOK, MAYO, PIONEER, SOUTHERN TRADITIONAL** and others too numerous to list. If looks could kill, these are all "killer" looks. Dinette sets were under $100 or just over $1,000. It's either high end or bottom of the barrel. Keeping their overhead low by paying warehouse prices is one way to contain costs and pass the savings onto you. Right on. That's certainly the all American way. Financing can be arranged through Norwest with 90 days same as cash. Try 'em, you'll like 'em.

★★★★★★ American Leather Outlet Center   972/296-9599

4501 Mountain Creek Parkway   Tues-Fri 10-6; Sat 10-3
Dallas, TX 75236
www.americanleather.com

 You'll fall in love with this manufacturer's outlet for leather furniture. After all, all Americans love a bargain. And after all, they are the private label manufacturer for such national chains as Crate and Barrel, Design Within Reach, Retrospect and Room and Board. The demand for leather has never been greater 'cause we want what we want. President Bob Duncan should know. Since 1992, **AMERICAN LEATHER** has been manufacturing high-end leather furniture, generating a multi-million dollar success story with a solid foundation both in product design and construction with high integrity and a chic designer look. Sink into the seats of high-end leather sofas, chairs, recliners, loveseats and ottomans at 50 to 70 percent off. What you see is what you can buy with only showroom samples available for sale: sofas, chairs, recliners, headboards and benches which were all available during our undercover shopping trip in traditional, contemporary, transitional and European styling. Closed on Monday, but open enough hours to do enough shopping to outfit all of your leather furniture needs. *Call toll-free: 888/254-9758*

★★★ Arabella's   972/562-0607

114 E. Louisiana   Mon-Sat 10-5:30
McKinney, TX 75069
www.arabellas.com

There's an nostalgic air about Arabella's in Historic Downtown McKinney. It's like a return to shopping for clothing and furnishings during a weekend retreat to the Hamptons, the Cape or the Hill Country....only in north Texas. Offering a complete interior design service with hundreds of faded cabbage rose fabrics, for example, if you're smitten with the craze of mixing florals and stripes on the same chair, well, you've come to the right shoppe. Breeze through the new painted furniture, oversized finials, braided rugs, silk flowers, candles, topiaries....the **TRACY PORTER** iron ribbon drawer pulls for $8 were tugging at our purse strings. (Note: They are open on Mondays, but many stores on the Square are not.) Although we got through to their website's front page, nothing else was operative. Try again and let me know if that cocoa-colored vase is still available. It certainly cried out to "Buy me, Buy me, please!"

★★ Armoire Store, The   214/696-2684
Mon-Sat 10-6

10745 Preston Rd.
Dallas, TX 75230
www.armoirestore.com

What was once just an afterthought as a second job for Pete Markwardt in 1992, is now his passion....and business is booming. Store managers in Dallas are the design team of Jamie Ray and Ryan Elmore, and, boy, are they shaking up the town of San Miguel de Allende in Mexico! They travel there on buying trips on a regular basis since that's where most of their armoires come from. Choose from hundreds of high-quality wood armoires such as French, country French, art deco, **CHIPPENDALE** pine, Louis XVI, even Queen Anne — their artistic reformations are imaginative and functional. From wine racks to computer stations, bookshelves to a unique pantry, armoires can take on a whole new meaning. Expect prices to range from $899 to $3,599, but they can be configured to meet your specifications from their own in-house cabinet shop. Chic, for sure, cheap not. *Call toll-free: 800/5-FURNIS*

NR Art is Art Consignment Studio   214/821-2940
Thurs, Fri-Sat 11-6; Sun 12-5

1801 Greenville Ave.
Dallas, TX 75206

Art is **ART** is as simple as simple is. At the last minute, we heard about this new, custom-designed contemporary and gently-recycled furniture and accessories store. Rumor has it is is like none other. Look at where they're located! Lower, lower Greenville to bring out the artsy audience clamoring for something unique and not the same ole, same ole. Well, here it is. Mother and daughter have joined forces to create this anomaly. It was discovered too late for an onsite-visit but word has it that it's a must stop on your home accessories menu.

◆◆◆◆◆◆ Artistic Additions   817/236-8314
By Appt. Only

Eagle Mountain Lake
Dallas, TX

 Looking for artistic additions in all the wrong places? Then stop in the name of love and call Sherry Abendschan for custom murals, faux finishes and hand-painted furniture. Don't brush her off! She and her imagination will turn heads. Call for a free consultation and let her transform a room or just a piece of new or existing furniture with her brush strokes of genius. She's moved to the lake to catch her breath and await the birth of her first child, so painting will be resumed in the fall. She began her career as an art teacher in Flower Mound and had so many requests from the parents of her students to paint furniture and walls, she decided to leave teaching to devote herself full-time to her artistic pursuits. You can see some of her talent in the murals at Plano Memorial Hospital, where her sister is a neonatal nurse. Paint thee to Tuscany and never wish for more.

◆◆◆◆ Artistic/Design Resource   214/742-1996
Mon-Fri 8:30-5

1308 Dragon St.
Dallas, TX 75207

Add remodeling to their name, too, even though they don't do weekends, this studio can help slay the dragons of full-price designs. Tucked away in the heart of the Design District, eliminate the middleman and let Casey be your guide to her 6,000-square-foot warehouse. She's usually there Monday, Tuesday and Wednesday mornings, and the rest of the time, she's out of town on building projects. Worm your way into her good graces because she will help you eliminate the middleman and work through almost any interior design project (layout, construction, draperies or interior finish, for example). Everything except the roofer, the plumber and the electrician. (For those, check out our expanded chapter in HOME IMPROVEMENT.) From the foundation up, getting the job done efficiently and effectively is her expertise. Selling wholesale services such as dry wall and painting, draperies with both fabric and labor at 30 percent less, 65 percent off wood blinds and 20 percent off interior design, carpeting and remodeling, this is really a one-stop trip to a bountiful transformation. Watch the workers, right in front of your eyes, create a project from scratch. Browse through their sample books, if you're plumb out of ideas. From Neo-Classic to contemporary, Gothic to Oriental, all they need is your nod of approval to go ahead. Not being open weekends hurts the working masses who are tied up at their own workplace during the week. But, then again, working 9 to 5 sounds like a song to me!

★★★   Ashley Furniture Clearance Outlet   972/590-1360

1850 Westpark Drive   Thurs-Sat
Grand Prairie, TX 75050-1924
www.ashleyfurniture.com

This whole new concept in furniture buying is hardly new to this city or to the Levitz family, its owners. Similar in its reincarnation, Ashley has made its presence known in a big way. Competing with the Bassett and ROOMS-TO-GO outlets and retail direct dynasties, they haven't paid as much attention to their outlet, we're sorry to report. But chances are, they will eventually. At the moment, ASHLEY is the largest furniture manufacturing company in the country now selling its brand of furniture direct to the public. Owned and operated by the Levitz family with multiple Metroplex stores, they continue to open store after store at an astounding clip. Last we saw, they just broke ground and the drywall was up across from Grapevine Mills on 2499. Watch them pop up at a furious pace in all the right places but expect the sales pitch to be equally fast and furious. Don't worry about putting your feet up — they are anxious to get you in and out of the store. But expect the furniture to be relaxed enough for you to enjoy putting your feet up for years to come. Problem is, just when you're starting to get tired of the furniture, the FREE financing finally kicks in and now you don't like the furniture anymore. Still, you've got to pay the piper. Remember, nothing is really FREE in this world. Ashley itself is headquartered worldwide in Arcadia, Wisconsin founded in 1945 as an output of the creativity of Carlyle Weingerger. Furniture fans have found Ashley to be in the moderate range of stylish things with direct pricing the kicker while others can't resist their financing plans. But it's the outlet that got our goat this year. Not Baaaaa-d! Check out the Clearance Outlet off Hwy. 360 and Ave. K behind their corporate offices. Unfortunately, it was almost an afterthought and strictly a disposal unit for what hasn't sold, has been returned, has been discontinued or damaged en route. Still, if you're looking for a sizeable savings, you can be endowed with something suite-able here. But watch out, Charlie, read the "fine" print on the FREE financing. A minimum purchase of $1,999 is required with 24 equal payments and if the terms of the contract are not met, interest is charged from the date of delivery. Expect, too, to pay sales tax and delivery charges when you buy as well be assessed with the "Elite Protection Plan." So buyers beware, there are some serious qualifiers before your dreams can come true.

★★★★★★ Bar Stools Plus, Inc.   817/589-7055 (Metro)

2220 A-Delante Ave.   Mon-Fri 9-5; Sat 9-3
Fort Worth, TX 76118
www.barstools-plus.com

 Hit the road, Jack. In fact, on your way to Gravel Furs, you'll be driving right by Ann and Jack's Bar Stools Plus, so why not pull in, if you're in the market. This is the manufacturer's outlet for bar stools and table. Great for the game room, the breakfast bar, or the plain old bar. Saunter up to the bar and choose either a wood or metal base, 24 or 30-inches, and then cover the seat with your choice of hundreds of fabric, vinyl or Naugahyde options; unless, of course, you'd rather be barbaric and sit on pins and needles instead! They have a huge assortment of stools in metals, woods, with or without swivels, with or without backs. Stools are available in 24 and 30-inch heights, or they can be totally custom built to your specifications. Because they are manufactured on site, there's an eight to ten day turnaround time. You'll find the '50s style tables and stools to bring back the rock 'n'roll times of yesteryear, alongside restaurant-type stools, kitchen stools, stools, stools and more stools. (No longer #2, they were voted to the top of the heap this year!) *Call toll-free: 800/817-8665*

★★★★★★ Bassett Furniture Direct Outlet   972/503-0330

4205 McEwen   Mon-Sat 10-9; Sun Noon-6
Dallas, TX 75234
www.bassettdfw.com

 Next door to their North Dallas (Farmers Branch) showroom above, you could be fishing at the Bass-ett outlet quicker than you can land a big one. But their outlet won't remain in tact (since much of their inventory wasn't even Bassett). They are closing in a few months for remodeling and a Capel Rug Outlet will be taking its place. All Bassett Outlet inventory, however, will relocate to the back of their mainline store. You'll still be shopping direct at this manufacturer made easier by the room vignette set-ups. But don't expect to get the kind of prices you've come to expect from the outlet. It's less. But not that much. There are six Bassett Direct locations in the Metroplex (Arlington, Garland, Lewisville, Mesquite, North Richland Hills and Plano) and now their outlet store in the back of this store only. Each Bassett Direct comes complete with their own Design Center and a specialized line called "Simply Yours." From casual to formal, home offices to entryways, entertainment centers, media rooms, armoires, you can even design your own sofa. Financing and delivery available. Delivery costs $59.99 for the DFW Metroplex — more for outlying areas. Check directory for a location nearest you.

Bean Bag Chair Factory   877/251-4406

Chicago, IL   24/7
www.beanbagchairfactory.com   🖰 *Top Online Store!*

If you want Pottery Barn quality bean bags at factory direct prices, you've entered the cream of the bean bags. It's the only bean bag chair that comes with a ten-year warranty that is made in the USA. Their denim bags are as cool and comfortable as slipping into a pair of LEVI'S. The top-of-the-line soft 100 percent brushed cotton in a 14 oz. weight can even be ordered with a waterproof inner bag, if you desire. FREE shipping and embroidery on every bag makes for a delightful place to plop. Another one of their trademarked designs is called the "Peaceful Blob" ™ bean bag chair. Only quality materials are use and if you have love in mind, why not consider their love seat in a myriad of colors. Enjoy these bean bags even more because they are now filled with a super-mix fill. It's really more comfortable, less noisy, less smelling and lasts longer than virgin polystyrene beads or recycled polystyrene. Get your bean bag embroidered, personalize in 2" high letters, an ultra leather look, designer colors, with removable and washable covers.

★★★★★ Bedrooms to Go — 972/481-9131

13990 N. Stemmons
Farmers Branch, TX 75234
www.bedroomstogo.com

Mon-Fri 10:30-7; Sat 10-6; Sun 1-5

Take 10,000 square feet and put them on N. Stemmons, exit Valwood, and it spells success. If it's bedrooms you're looking for, you can have your pick from some of the better known brands this side of the loop. And you will be looped-de-do when you see HOME ELEGANCE, VAUGHN BASSETT and WEBB bedroom ensembles. Where else can you shop for the entire suite all under one roof? Get everything to match or you can mix and match, it's your choice. Save across the board during their grand opening extravaganza, 40 percent on everything; then when things settle down and folks start to recognize that this is where they shop for everything you need for a bedroom, their everyday discounts will be 35 percent everyday. Expect these discounts to be maintained as they will be one of the volume discount dealers of bedrooms in the Metroplex. Ah, beddy beddy good buys and to all a good night.

★★★★★★ Bins & Cupboards — 214/741-2321

130 Howell St
Dallas, TX 75207

Mon-Sat 10-5

 How(ell) this newcomer came into being is anybody's guess. But never you mind. If you want to know the story of how Old Mother Hubbard went to her cupboard only to find it not only bare, but too expensive, then you'll love the casual furniture and accessories offered here. If you're looking for a cupboard for your kitchen, dinette, bedroom, game room, media room, living room or any other room that you need to store whatever, here is a place that now invites the public in to shop. From simple armoires under $400 to more elaborate glass and wood storage cupboards at $800, isn't it about time you moved your belongings from under the bed or up from the floor to a place your "stuff" can call home? Looking for casual dining, how does a steel-leg round table with four fabric chairs sound for $499.99? Or more formal dining tables and chairs for $539.99 to $589.97. Sit a while. Buy a lot. Located in the Industrial/ Irving Boulevard antique area, have at it! They own the custom furniture place across the street called Zapata Handmade Furniture which is also a site to delight. Since it's manufacturer direct, you've got a double whammy to "Howell" about!

★★★★★★ BOCA Leather Gallery — 972/776-0011

13465 Inwood Rd.
Dallas, TX 75244
www.bocatannery.com

Mon-Sat 10-8; Sun 12-6

 If you're looking for the finest in leather furniture, expect to pay wholesale prices at this tannery, on the northwest corner of Inwood Rd. at Galleria Rd. Stop playing "hide and seek" and cushion the blow of high prices while sinking down on the best. They are perhaps the only fully integrated leather furniture supplier in the country, with more styles, more colors and even lower prices than anybody else. Expect a five-year warranty on workmanship and defect-free materials. Save 40 to 70 percent off suggested manufacturer's retail price. Corporate offices are in Buenos Aries, Argentina and Dallas, Texas. Choose from the highest grade of full-grain cowhide. From classic designs to contemporary, hand-crafted pieces by artisans and small manufacturers made one at a time, will have you sitting pretty in no time. (Well, maybe not. Delivery times vary considerably.) Available in 50 styles, 200 different colors, and 30 types of leather, choose from their extensive collection and discover the stylish and beautifully-crafted fine leather furniture custom-built just for you! Check directory for locations before you go as locations flow to and fro. When they close one, another pops up elsewhere. Their north Dallas location is now in the former location of predecessor Leather! Leather but claiming no relation. At the helm of Boca, is Guiora Kaplan and if a problem arises, he has certainly risen to the occasion and gotten one frustrated customer their order. So, we're proud to report success in the matter.

★★★★★★ Bombay Co. Outlet, The   817/485-3151

6039 Precinct Line Road, Bldg. C   Mon-Sat 10-9; Sun 11-6
Fort Worth, TX 76180
www.bombayco.com

 Settled onto Highway 26 near Kohl's, you don't have to travel to India to enjoy the riches of this manufacturer. No! But you will need a long memory if you want to remember the depth of their product line. Beds, bedroom furniture, bedside tables, cabinets, coat racks and caddies, coffee tables and much more. What I'm saying, in a nutshell, is that this **TANDY**-owned company is the place for gifts for you, your home and for others homes, lock, stock and barrel. The season's "flops" can be found discounted up to 50 percent off. They not only feature classic and traditional styles, but they coordinate with matching accessories and wall decor. Although their look represents reproductions, they're also manufacturers themselves and sell direct via their over 400 retail stores in malls across America. Other outlet locations in Texas include Allen Premium Outlets, Hillsboro Outlet Center and San Marcos Outlet Center. Shop online 24/7, if you get the urge after hours. Outlet prices are also available on their website. Yippee! *Call toll-free: 800/829-7789*

★★★ Bova Contemporary Furniture & Leather 817/261-9977

2160 N. Collins   Mon-Fri 10-7;Sat 10-6; Sun 1-5
Arlington, TX 76011
www.bovafurniture.com

Considering that they sell leather furniture and their name is characteristic of a cow, do you think it's coincidental? Well, where else but in Texas would the ex's run all over kingdom come looking for contemporary furniture? Even if you're not an Aggie, this is no joke. There are but a few players on the block of contemporary furnishings and Bova is one of them. And this Arlington location is it. With three months, no interest financing, the least you can do is sit down, put your feet up and buy yourself some "piece" of mind. Their biggest sellers are recliners and no wonder; they offer them in your choice of four grades of leather, from the least expensive on up. For under $900, you, too, could enjoy a cow-a-bunga experience. If you're feeling really groovy, these lines are really Smooooooth Operators. The Unisomi chaise lounge — the kind of almost horizontal wavy "S" shaped 70-inch chaise — in fabric or leather started at $699. But we fell for the really cool and hip "Lisa" recliner in a crazy lime green (you can pick your own color) with metal round legs for $999 and a great glass table, with super sleek Monza chairs, at a special price of $1,000 for the table and four chairs. I'm sold! And when they're running a sale, run even faster.

★★★★★ Brumbaugh's Leather Gallery   817/244-9377

11651 US Hwy. 80 W (Camp Bowie West & I-30)   Mon-Sat 9-6
Aledo, TX 76008

What do you mean, "Whoa Doggies?" Well, if you're in Braumbaugh country, it's just another way of saying, "Mercy, Mercy!" See, this is where folks who know something about saving money on furniture, carpet, lighting, and all things western like to shop. Located at 11651 Camp Bowie West & I-30, you're "plum crazy" if you don't shop at Brumbaugh's! They're a peach. Isn't it time you "moseyed" on down to Aledo, where the living is easy and the shopping is, too. From top to bottom, Larry Braumbaugh has got you covered. If it's carpet and other floor covering, you'll be floored, from area rugs to the complete repertoire of carpet. From a casual throw rug to an opulent hand-knotted piece de resistance carpet for the living room, at Brumbaugh's the designs are virtually unlimited. The sky's your limit. What's even nicer is that you have a wealth of opportunities to shop for floor coverings that fit all the necessary criteria: room size, color scheme, and furniture placement, as well as your design style and budget. Lots and lots of namebrand furniture — just don't fence yourself in. Visit their Carpet Outlet at 7714 Camp Bowie W.

★★★★★★ Budget Decorators, The   469/293-SHOP (7467)

Lewisville, TX 75067   By Appt. Only
www.thebudgetdecorators.com

 There's nothing like it so far in the Metroplex, but if you like Design on a Dime, you'll love the Budget Decorators™. It takes one to know one. Since I'm great at launching new businesses, let me introduce you to my latest — and maybe my greatest. Called The Budget Decorators ™, it's my answer to being glued to Home and Garden Network. I love to play decorator. I know who some of the good ones who charge $200 an hour; and I know some of the good ones who charge $65 an hour. Who would you prefer? Ok, so now we're on the same wave length. If you are interior design challenged, you will love the Budget Decorators. We even intend to sponsor a total room EXTREME MAKEOVER later on in the year. Designers, afterall, have been sneaking around the "underground" for years and yet charge clients ten times what they find because nobody would believe how cheap it was. In fact, that's who we're marketing to. We'll pass the savings on when we find it on the cheap. Window treatments, upholstery, working with fabrics are are specialty, but we do it all. Meet The Budget Decorators (and the Lone Arranger) at our BD headquarters or at your home or office. An appointment is still necessary. Call the number above and we'll get you connected. Our Budget Decorators come with plenty of experience and charge half the usual and customary designer rates. Then, once you've laid out your plan of action, they shop at "underground" approved resources. Wholesale or less, staying within your budget, I guarantee it. We shop at only the best who charge you the least — and then pass on their low prices to you. The look may be one of opulence; the price tag will be more pauper-like. From chandeliers for $95 to floral arrangements right out of the lobbies of the Mansion Hotel for under $200, painting inside and out, faux painting to murals, to complete kitchen or bath remodels that will save you thousands, you'll can count (the savings) on us. We'll share our secrets, teach you a few design tricks, and hope you'll recommend us to your neighbors in the process. Nobody can beat our prices. The Budget Decorators ™ are on our website. You're but one click away for your design makeovers. From commercial lobbies for businesses, corporate offices, waiting rooms for doctors, lawyers or any professional who wants to make an impression for less; but mostly for home owners in need of a face lift, a room rearrange, a total house makeover, a room addition, or a new home from scratch. Here we come, ready or not. We've combined the talents of several designers who have the eye for color, scale, fabrics, room arrangements, how-to-mix and match and the Lone Arranger who will come out and just re-arrange with what you have already have to create a whole different look. Reality does have to come into play, however. They can't redo an entire room complete with 10 pieces of furniture, art work, accessories, florals, new carpet, wallpaper, faux painting, window treatments, an Oriental rug for under $1,000. We can do some of it, but let's get real! Expect to pay a small (considering the competition) hourly wage and then, let's go shopping!

★★★   By Consignment Only   972/867-1592

2757 W. 15th St. @ Independence   Mon-Sat 10-5; Sun Noon-5
Plano, TX 75075

Talk about flexibility. No price is firm so practice saying, "How much?" Then act surprised and repeat to yourself, "How much?" Then act disappointed. Then act REALLY devastated! Then start to snivel and lastly....grovel. They are more than willing to work with you on price, as nothing was set in stone. In the dining room department, there was a medium wood top table with green finished bottom and four chairs for $497.50; the matching china hutch was the same price but if you buy both pieces, well, "Let's make a deal!" Instead of $995 for both how about taking $100 to $150 off? This particular dining room suite originally came from CHARTER FURNITURE and the table alone was originally over $1,000. Most of the furniture is used, no new samples, plus collectibles, china, glassware, art memorabilia, antiques, unique gift items, silver home accessories and estate jewelry....all By Consignment Only. Find them cloistered in the Cloister Square Shopping Center at the northeast corner of Independence and 15th Street. Everything's strictly castaways, but no WILSON soccer balls were seen. Delivery available for $35.

★★★★★★   Cantoni Outlet   972/720-0052

4245 Simonton (off Midway)   Mon 11-7, Wed-Fri 11-7; Sat 10-6; Sun 12-5 (Closed Tues)
Farmers Branch, TX 75244
www.cantonioutlet.com

 If you are looking for the haute items that are hot in contemporary furnishings, you are talking Cantoni. No one else in the country even comes close to what Michael Wilkov founded in 1984. I never thought in my lifetime I'd be able to write about a Cantoni Outlet and now, look what I've found on the street that soon will be called the Miracle Mile for Outlet Shopping. (See Gabbert's, Infinity Leather, Bassett and Furniture Warehouse as side-kicks.) Take LBJ and go north on Midway to Simonton. Ask for John, Dear, Dear John but don't write him off. He's the outlet manager and can lead you to the 50 off the lowest price area if all you want is a quick pick-me-up. If you want to redo your entire house, here is where to start for a drop dead sectional, a four-post bed and matching bedroom pieces, miscellaneous chairs, mirrors, lamps, picture frames, what has been returned, discontinued, repossessed, nicked or whatever reason is given as to why it didn't sell at full price. Let's make a deal and start the descent to at least 40 percent and then it goes lower and lower until it reaches the 50 off bottom line. What the outlet lacks in ambience and hours opened is made up for in product selection and savings. Another success story from a classic entrepreneur whose knowledge of contemporary design and shoot-from-the-hip business savvy has built a national specialty store showplace that has the furniture industry talking from Houston to California, Atlanta and now across from their distribution center, their first outlet. From conversational pieces and dramatic furniture and accents to lighting and floor coverings, this Dallas-based design hub is where shoppers look for the latest designer trends. They are the Picassos to set your design palate from blah to wow! If you are rolling in the dough and want to know where to go if you'd plenty of cash....then head to their mainline store at 4800 Alpha Rd in Dallas, 972/934-9191. Then again, if you've won the $200 million plus lottery, you may not want to let the cat out of the bag. Send your decorator instead!

★★★★★★   **Cargo Factory Outlet**   **817/294-5717**

5000 S. Hulen Street, Suite 100   Mon-Sat 10-8; Sun Noon-5
Fort Worth, TX 76011
www.cargofurniture.com

Wow, what a difference a year makes. CargoKids is moving on up. No Jefferson hill-
billies need shop here. Just those looking to jazz up their kids'rooms with the cutest
cargo on board. One outlet south of the Hulen Mall, take it or leave it! If you leave it,
you'll be sorry. If you take it, your bill of lading will say, F.O.B./ Fort Worth because the furniture's coming from CargoKids overstocks, discontinueds, floor models and scratch and dent that
have finally made its way to its final remains of the day. Keep that in mind when you see 50 percent savings since this is the outlet to Cargo Furniture, a Fort Worth-based designer, retailer and
wholesaler of casual lifestyle furniture, including children's furniture and accessories. With their
CargoKids division, you'll see fun, affordable, stylish, and safe furniture and decorative items for
your child's room. Furniture designed with safety in mind and made specifically for kids. Their
specialty is bunkbeds, so when the kiddos are screaming for nothing but bunkbeds, here's the outlet to jump to. Twin and Full-sized beds, Daybeds and all their companion furniture pieces, too,
plus perfectly coordinated bedding, lamps, rugs, wall art and other decorative doodads. Founded in
1981, it is owned by Tandycrafts and is well-known in most circles for its common-sense approach
to living the good life....and now, at half the price. Its look combines the best of Shaker, Country
French and **MISSION** designs. Their unique four-in-one approach bedroom system includes models for sleep, study, storage and safety. Ready for study and a good nights sleep? Then, here's your
ticket to not counting sheep!

★★★   **Carlson Furniture**   **817/831-6116**

2819 E. Belknap St.   Tues-Fri 8:30-5:30; Sat 8:30-5
Fort Worth, TX 76111

This is a mixed bag. Some new, some old, probably something borrowed, and a few things blue.
How they got their merchandise is anybody's guess. Probably by gathering closeouts from stores
and from discards from individuals. You never know what will turn up on any given day. But one
thing's for sure — it's a mish-mosh. From dinettes to appliances, brand-new bunk beds by **ASH-
LEY** for $239 to a used bunk bed with twin top and futon bottom for $169 (new, $300). Mix and
match dressers, chests, headboards, desks, tables, you might just get it all together and have an
eclectic ensemble. Anyway, who said everything's got to match? Delivery fee remained the same
from last year, $20-$35. Now, that's a deal. But if you don't want to buy anything, what good is a
deal on delivery?

★★★★★★   **Changing Places**   **214/570-0077**

101 S. Coit Rd., #82   Mon-Sat 10-6; Thurs 10-8; Sun 12-6
Dal-Rich Shopping Village Richardson, TX 75080
www.changingplaces.net

If you're a fan of "Trading Spaces," you'll love Changing Places. Louis
and Susie Ring are its founders, established long before the popular TV
show but what a resource to creating a complete makeover on a shoe-
string. Trade in your old and buy something that's new — to you. Actually, this consignment shop
also has some things that are new, too, that could work very nicely into your second-hand decorative scheme. I promise not to tell. Consign your gently worn furnishings that you've fallen out of
love with; then use the monies collected to buy someone else's previously-loved items. This is the
"coil" boom of the 21st century. With so many sofas to choose from, you'll get dizzy trying to see

which one gets your lap. Stay home and curl up in your new recliner, sofa or love seat; or maybe the perfect entertainment center to house that big screen TV that has been sitting on the floor with nary an appropriate perch; then turn on that torchiere that lets you see the light. The business of consigning castaways, even if they didn't win an Oscar, is always busting at the seams. Changing Places, from their house to yours, is a business whose time has come. Dirt-cheap prices throughout their showroom with merchandise moving in and out daily. You better buy when you see it because chances are, if you don't, it will be tagged S.O.L.D tomorrow. You snooze, you lose.

★★★★★★   Charter Furniture Clearance   972/484-1101

13550 Stemmons   Tues-Fri 10-8; Sat 10-5
Farmers Branch, TX 75234-5766
www.charterfurniture.net

 Looking for a low-cost source for designer furniture? Then try charting your course to this outlet who has been furnishing the Metroplex since 1983. If you're a fan of **PENNSYLVANIA HOUSE**, you'll love the fact that it's the only place where you can buy it for less. Expect to see in-store galleries at their retail stores (15101 Midway in Addison and 8100 Bedford Euless Rd. in North Richland Hills). Then see what's available at their distribution and clearance center without the gallery setting. The sign across Stemmons is bigger and bolder, at last. It's time to stop and see, drool and buy unique designer accents and accessories as well as: **ALAN WHITE, ALEXVALE, BERNHARDT, HOOKER, KLAUSSNER, LANE, NATUZZI, PALLISER, PULASKI, RIVERSIDE, ROWE, SEALY, SOUTHERN, UNIVERSAL** and more. Once you've been to their Clearance Center, you'll be a confirmed Charter shopper. Internet specials, too, will make you a believer in low-cost designer furnishings. Closed Sun and Mon.

Circa Interior Design Showroom   214/630-5185

1311 Inwood Rd.   Mon-Sat 10-5:30; Sun Noon-5
Dallas, TX 75247
www.circadesignshowroom.com

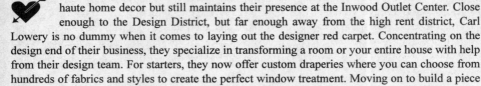 Circa has gone full circle, from consignment and bargains to off-the-chart, high-end haute home decor but still maintains their presence at the Inwood Outlet Center. Close enough to the Design District, but far enough away from the high rent district, Carl Lowery is no dummy when it comes to laying out the designer red carpet. Concentrating on the design end of their business, they specialize in transforming a room or your entire house with help from their design team. For starters, they now offer custom draperies where you can choose from hundreds of fabrics and styles to create the perfect window treatment. Moving on to build a piece of furniture with a custom approach that will fit into the new designing scheme of things. From one-of-a-kind sofas, chairs and more, the only thing you'll forgo is blah. Instead, create mystery, romance, drama, real conversation pieces that only your imagination (and budget) will allow. Located next to Crate & Barrel Outlet, expect to ogle designer names seen only at the finest retail stores but you'll pay for it. You can apply for a credit application online or in their stores. Visit also in Fort Worth at 3000 S. Hulen at Bellaire, Suite 180, Fort Worth 76109, 817/738-1116.

★★★★★★ Closeout Corner   214/951-7474

1325 Inwood Rd.   Mon-Sat 10-5; Sun 12-5
Dallas, TX 75247
www.closeoutcornerdecor.com

 Say "Good Bye" to the shop that proceeded them (Oncor Floral) and say Hello to the "Great Buys" at Closeout Corner at the Inwood Outlet Center. How much more appropriate to locate your closeout emporium tucked away in the corner two blocks west on Inwood off Stemmons, and call it Closeout Corner. But first, stop into 7th Ave for ladies' designer clothes from 4-34 if you don't have a thing to wear to a dinner party you're hosting so you can then go around the corner to Closeout Corner. If you want THE home decor counterpart, walk the aisles of closeouts for home accessories, accents, seasonal decor and furniture. Some are complete showroom relocations. Not only are these high-end accents that are seen in all the decorating magazines, but the prices are equally appealing — 40-80 percent off retail. If ever you feel faint, just fan yourself, take a deep breath and move on to the next shelf. There's always something that will revive you and bring you to your senses. The prices are unreal. Though they're new to the underground shopping scene, if you support their first effort, you might find a Closeout in every Corner of the Metroplex. The Brothmans maintain this as a family outpost when they're not at mother Flora's jewelry showroom at the World Trade Center. Say hello to sons David, Michael and Craig, mom, Flora, and Dad, Steve. Ok, so they're keeping it all in the family, but if truth be know, son David Brothman is the commander-in-chief.

★★★★ Consignment Collection   972/788-4444

12300 Inwood Rd., Suite 116A   Mon-Sat 10-6
Dallas, TX 75244

Whether you need to get a tolltag (on one side) or a taco (on the other,) there's always room for more shopping. Look for the large 4,000-square-foot beige stucco building with the blue awning that sells furniture and accessories on consignment across from the Jesuit High School football field. More than 5,000 items are displayed throughout the spacious showroom space with 200 to 300 new items added daily. Now the best part....the average price of a sofa was $295. For an eclectic mix of furniture, antiques, gifts, accessories and more, it's like scrounging around your grandma's attic! Whether you're buying or selling (they split it with you 55/45 percent), you'll wind up a winner. This showroom houses furniture and antiques wall-to-wall, but some of them needed collagen injections. What you see is what you get — sofas, chairs, dishes, dolls, tables and lots of home accessories and bric-a-brac, all priced accordingly. No delivery, but a referral to delivery services will be offered.

★★★★ Consignment Corner   972/490-8801

130 Spring Creek Village   Mon-Fri 10-6; Sat 10-5
Dallas, TX 75248-5720

She loves me, she loves me not. If you're at that place in your life that you're ready to throw in the old and start with something new, even if the new is old, consider making a clean sweep of it and turn to Consignment Corner at the NW Corner of Coit & Beltline. Offering upscale consignment furniture and antiques, you can have your fill. Brimming with bedroom suites, sofas, chairs, tables, armoires, art deco, accent pieces and more that you will adore (there I go again, with another little ditty,) you might as well go for broke! But before you bring down the house, bring in a picture of your items; after a review, if they are accepted, a contract will be drawn up granting you a 55/45 split. If you're a traditionalist at heart and don't like to rock the boat, here is where the consignments could go. But they don't let them linger too long without finding them a new home. They don't mind being a foster parent for a while, but they're not willing to commit to an adoption on a permanent basis. So, if you don't want them to be considered orphans, you better hope they sell. In the far north Dallas corridor, you can corner the market on home furnishings from bigger, better days. New orders bring new energy to this corner shop with an eclectic mix of upscale and down-home furnishings. Everybody is a potential candidate, whether you're a buyer or seller.

★★★★★ Consignment Galleries   214/357-3925

5627 W. Lovers Lane   Mon-Sat 10-5:30
Dallas, TX 75209

Hang on to this one. A wrought-iron chandelier with eight candlestick bulbs and measuring approximately 24 inches in diameter was $125 and perfect for a rustic dining room or casual dinette. Located between Inwood and the Tollway on the north side of the street, how does saving 75 percent on Highland Park estate items sound? No names are included, but the quality of the furnishings speaks for itself. Expect most to be from the proximity of the Park Cities, such as an exquisite Queen Anne dining room table with pads, eight chairs and two leaves by SUMTER for only $1,295. Add in the matching china cabinet for another $1,295 and, well, "Dinner is served, Mum." From traditional to antiques and the accessories to fill in the blanks (area rugs, china, sterling, wicker, lamps, crystal, mirrors, paintings, objects d'art, copper and bronze figures, and all kinds of collectibles,) why not outfit your home from the million dollar mansions you drive by at Christmas time? Gee whiz, oh what a relief it is not to pay full price. Once it arrives on your doorstep, who would ever guess its origins? Consigned pieces are split 55/45 with the consignor (you) coming out on top. This isn't your typical consignment furniture store, though, as prices are much higher to begin with since they've come from such blue blood lineage. And don't look for a website; they did away with it this year. Owner Kathy Robinson is still at the helm.

★★★ Consignment Solution, The   214/827-8022

1904 Skillman   Mon-Fri 11-7; Sat 10-6; Sun 12-5
Dallas, TX 75206

From moderate to better and sometimes the best, expect this 10,000 square foot consignment shop to be an amalgam of opportunities. For sellers wanting to sell their home furnishings and accessories, you'll reap a 60/40 split in favor of the seller. A medium-stained wooden rectangular dining room set with two leaves and six chairs was $1,800. Okay, so it wasn't a steal, but it wasn't overpriced for what you were buying, believe me. Just price a dining room suite and six chairs retail. I have seen some whose chairs alone are $1,800 a piece! A small maple set with six chairs was $500, some as low as $400. We flipped over the queen-size sleigh bed for $600, but couldn't decide between it and the cherry four-poster for $950. Framed art work, lamps, coffee and end tables, desks, chairs, sofas were just part and parcel of options to choose from in their huge showroom. From Victorian to traditional, ordinary to extraordinary (like their vintage 50s dinette set), this store's very impressive on the consignment scene. Monday is pick-up day. The only negative, the constant answering machine. There's never been a live person who has said, "Hello!"

★★★★ Consignment Store, The & Outlet   972/991-6268

5290 Belt Line Rd., Suite 122   Mon-Sat 10-6; Sun Noon-5
Dallas, TX 75240
www.dallasconsign.com

If Dean hadn't called us Sweetie so many times, he might have endeared us more to the store. Then we learned that Dean Coffey was their resident in-house designer, so we forgave him. We think the world of designers who can help us put together the look of the rich and famous — especially at a used furniture store. And this one is a good place to start. Since 1986, Maryanne O'Neal has been considered the matriarch of consignment stores and was first on the block to get the ball rolling before it became fashionable. Today, it's a whopping 15,000 square feet showplace with a series of vignettes that will no doubt make you drool. They also have a year 'round Christmas table where gingerbread houses stand ready for delivery even during July. Just don't expect all of their merchandise to be inexpensive. Some are new, others are antiques and some are pre-owned, but though they are all given equal billing, the prices escalate accordingly. This store is very seriously traditional. Once your household furniture is accepted, there's a 60-day contract with a 50/50 split issued. Pickup and delivery extra, $45, and can be arranged around your schedule.

★★★★★   Cort Clearance Center   972/445-2678

250 W. Airport Freeway (exit O'Connor)   Mon-Fri 9-6; Sat 10-5
Irving, TX 75062
www.cortfurniture.com

After one visit for residential, office or model home furniture, you'll want to Cort them for a permanent live-in relationship. As America's only national furniture rental company, imagine the savings on brand-name furniture for your home or office that lies in wait at their two rental clearance centers. The one in Irving, though, is the one to covet. You will be unduly impressed with the substantial savings on previously-rented furniture. Ask for Jeremiah, the manager at the time of our last visit, and you'll be in excellent hands. For more than 20 years, they've been "corting" home and office customers who want to nurse their budgets. The reason we suggest the Irving store above over the other one is because it's the source of much of their design studio's model home furniture returns. It's right out of homes beautiful and the prices are next to nothing. Support the other Cort Clearance Center in Dallas, on Inwood Rd. near the Galleria, but it doesn't hold a candle to the one in Irving. Bet you didn't know that they outfit many national home builders'model homes. When a subdivision closes down their models, guess where the furniture and accessories go? That's right. To the Cort Clearance Centers and in greater abundance to their Irving Store. *Call toll-free: 888/669-CORT*

★★★★★★   Crown Furniture   817/551-7988

760 N. Beach St   Tues-Sat 10-6
Fort Worth, TX 76111-5943
TxCrownFurniture.com

Give me a 130-page catalog online to entice me into a store and I'm there, mark my word. "X" marks the spot where Merchandise Exchange has closed its door and relocated with a new configuration to Beach Street. From an original amalgam of office furniture with executive or steno chairs for $5, they have gone upscale to moderate and better furniture and home furnishings. Clocks, lamps, pictures, armoires, game tables curio cabinets, shelving, bar stools, Bakers racks, futons, sofas and love seats, recliners, daybeds, water beds, youth bedroom sets, it an assortment by category on their website catalog for your viewing (and shopping) pleasure. It's pretty self-explanatory and straight-forward. The only thing you don't know until you call them, is the price. So until I hear it with my own ears, I can only say it "appears" to be more than just promising. Based on the way they priced merchandise at their previous incarnation, I can only speculate that the prices here will be equally appealing....and stripped to the bare bones. Acting in good faith, I'm going to go ahead and give them the highest rating. Please let me know if I've gone out on a limb and blue it! Believe me, variety is the spice of life: bedroom, living room, dining room, game room, home office, home accents, youth bedrooms, office furniture, lighting and more. One stand-out were the Adirondack and log beds and yard furniture. They were begging to come home with me. Practically walking distance to At Your Service, if you need flooring and electronics to accompany your new furniture, what a dynamite combination. Plus, they're only an exit south of City Mattress off Hwy. 121 going south to Fort Worth. So now you can get your mattress, too. Worth the drive to put a Crown into your palace. It should be a mote point as this point.

★★★★★   Custom Oak Furniture Mfg.   972/267-2727

2385 Midway Rd., Suite 100   Mon-Sat 9-6; Sun 12-5
Carrollton, TX 75006-2572

Settled into their new digs, this furniture maker has expanded to greater proportions. Not only does he custom craft armoires and other entertaining pieces for your home and office, he is bringing in antiques and other furniture items for your shopping pleasure. But his forte is still custom cabinetry for those built-ins, be it a unit for that large screen TV or a drop-in sink for an antique washstand. Here's the closest thing to the unfinished symphony for the do-it-yourselfer who doesn't want to do it. Let Dusty Taji whittle away the hours building that perfect piece. And if you can't part with a few hundred dollars for his artisanship, his wife has a room that she calls her own to sell fashion jewelry, purses and knick-knacks. Surely a funky purse for $19.95 can fit into a squeezed budget. Whether it's a bookshelf or an armoire, you have your choice — finished or not. If you take it upon yourself to add your elbow grease, you'll save about 30 percent. During specials, the prices are shaved even more. Since this is the showroom to their factory so to speak, you could have them carve out a final creation that is priced direct from maker. It's an option to consider with plenty to choose from: in-stock bookcases, tables, chairs, wall units and more, some already finished to perfection with the Midas touch. Pick your finish, your color, your stain and call it a day. Then wait a few weeks for the end product to be delivered. Original and imaginative projects are a challenge and, as a matter of fact, encouraged. They prefer to start from scratch and will save you some scratch. A hope chest could be made from beginning to end in four weeks, instead of the usual six or seven for one ordered from a store at twice the price. Well, it was tempting. No website yet, but they're working on it. Next door to Fabric Source.

★★★★★★   Custom Woodcrafting   214/695-3612

216 Creekside Drive   By Appt. Only
Plano, TX 75094
www.customwoodcrafting.com

On the cusp of Murphy, you can start singing, "Unstained Melody" as prices of bunk beds started as low as $180 for some of the most popular pieces. What kid wouldn't go ape over sleeping in their own bunk bed? Regardless of their age, stop monkeying around — just face it, that's what they want and you might as well get them the best, for less. Bunk beds are especially important in rooms shared by siblings; or just as popular for sleepovers. All of the beds made here are super sturdy, durable and classic in their styling, some more intricately carved than others. Large storage drawers underneath have room to hold all sorts of treasures — from bedding to books, clothes to cash. Then, if a bunk bed is not in the works, how about a trundle bed for space saving and versatility? Every piece of furniture here is hand-crafted (no assembly-line construction) and in nothing but solid wood with your choice of 20 different color stains. If you think you've outgrown a bunk bed, think again. They even make a more sophisticated bed perfect for college kids that they call the loft bed. They are terrific complete with large storage drawers for an entire wardrobe befitting anyone from freshman to graduate student. Too, select the perfect mattress and bunk board to complete the picture including the trundle, if needed. Their website was just in the beginning stages but should be up and in full pictorial splendor by pub date.

Danish Inspirations   972/490-9141

4630 Alpha Rd   Mon-Fri 10-7; Sat 10-6; Sun 12-5
Dallas, TX 76244
www.danishinspirations.com

I love Danish! Any kind of Danish, but I'm probably partial to apricot. If you want a taste of Danish, I'd say head to this Danish for Inspiration. Located west of the Galleria in Dallas at the corner of Alpha and Welch, you'd expect the name to give you a clue as to what's in store. Well, it doesn't. Danish Inspirations is anything but Danish. Most of the furniture is Italian — go figure! What is inside is very contemporary furniture by **JESPER**, **NATUZZI** and **NOTIO**. Leather to weather the storm of economic woes and a breathtaking Travertine marble dining room table, for example, for $1,299 with metal and fabric chairs for $299 each. I flipped over the "Negretti Premella" chair with wooden arms and another appetizing entree was a sleek, streamlined occasional chair for a not-so-cheap $1,869. But life is short and comfort shouldn't be ignored. Financing is available with nothing down, no interest for six months on purchases over $1,000. Put that final touch on your room's decor. Their collection of hand-blown glass from Denmark can add just the right dramatic touch.

★★★★★★ De La Garza Furniture Services   972/864-1933

2901 National Drive   Mon-Fri 9:30-5
Garland, TX 75041

These true artists speak to the spirit of ingenuity. Custom furniture is this family's claim to fame. Since 1960, they've been providing **FREE** on-site estimates. Don't ask for them over the phone! Located just off Kingsley, between Jupiter and **SHILOH**, De La Garza will create a piece of furniture from the ground up. Stay put — they pick up and deliver for FREE, and will be happy to bring a large selection of fabrics to your home or office for your pick of the lot. Re-dress your favorite chair or sofa. Now, what about a face-lift for furniture that's made of wood? Refinishing is another specialty at this house of De La Garza. The lost art of refinishing, along with carpeting, is on their menu of services with a turnaround time of about two or three weeks, for both upholstery and refinishing. Speed does not supercede quality. The "Black Forest Cuckoo Clocks" can also be special ordered, all sizes and models, at very good prices, along with carpet at $1 above cost. These guys aren't kidding. They mean business.

★★★★ Decorator's Reserve   972/620-8999

13970 Stemmons Frwy.   Mon-Thu 10-7; Fri, Sat 10-8; Sun Noon-6
Farmers Branch, TX 75234

Bargains for millionaires couldn't cut it in the Big Apple, but they're still reserving the bargains for their two stores — Orlando and Dallas. They changed their name that they used successfully in Orlando (Liquidation Station) in deference to the Dallas shopper, I suppose. You know how touchy some of the hoi-polloi are when a truck with a name such as Liquidation pulls up onto their cobblestone circular driveway. What will the neighbors think? Unbeknownst to them, being a bargain shopper is a badge of honor in this city. You're not cheap....you're smart! This store is definitely a fun foray into some of the latest and greatest replicas — from artwork to furniture, lighting to wall decor. Oh la la. The carved wood and painted statues, bronze mermaids, and lions and tigers and bears....oh, my!

◆◆◆◆◆   **Dragon Street Storage**   **214/752-7777**

1980 Dragon Street   By Appt. Only
Dallas, TX 75207

Great service .... if you're looking to have a van and one man deliver something of value. Stop scrambling to fit that armoire or that marble dining room table into your SUV. Not many delivery companies will deliver a small load without sending out a full crew and a big truck with minimum hours. At Dragon Street Storage, one man-one van, $36. Larger loads that would require a two-man crew, $68/hour. From a single lamp to an entire household, this is the company that treats each item with fine kid gloves. For bigger moves, go to All My Sons, my all time favorite moving company.

Durango Trading Co.   **972/716-9898**

420 Spanish Village   Mon-Sat 10-7; Sun Noon-6
Dallas, TX 75248
www.durangotrading.com

 Visit **DURANGO**, without crossing any state lines, and stake your claim on any one of the pieces from the Southwest's largest collection of unique Southwestern/Mexican furniture and accessories at direct-from-the-border prices. Their 10,000-square-foot hacienda showplace at Arapaho and Coit is some kind of "Pow Wow!" With two locations in Dallas, (the other being in Preston Center, 6116 Luther Lane, southwest corner of Preston and Northwest Highway), experience hand-crafted wood furniture from Mexican artisans, decorative folk art and accessories, armoires and entertainment centers, dining room tables and chairs, hand-painted masks, stone and hand-forged iron, terra cotta, Pueblo clay pottery — it's in, it's chic, but it's not cheap. But then again, see what they're getting for this stuff in Telluride? In Aspen? Choose mesquite, cedar or pine, or pick your finish as custom work is also accepted. With further expansion, there are lots of new Mediterranean and Moroccan-styled furniture and accessories now sharing the spotlight. Lots of skins cover many of their sofas and chairs, and if by chance you get lost shopping in Texas, how about a map of Texas embroidered on a throw pillow? The white tiger chair was a roaring hit with a Leo friend who accompanied us on our shopping safari — until he saw the price tag of $1,800. He roared, "Outrageous! It's a jungle in here." He dug the hanging mound of antlers for a chandelier, but thought about taking it in a standing floor lamp model, instead. He did. Lots of furniture in leather, fabric, animal skins, glass, wood, metal and more. The animal skins are actually cowhide that are dyed to look like tiger, zebra, leopard. (No endangered species to worry about.) Furniture arrives from Mexico as well as India, South America and Europe. Recently, they established their own exclusive line of "Durango" furniture. You can take different frames and then choose leather or fabric options that meet your specifications; or custom design your own furniture. Expect to also see traditional furniture with a twist — funky upholstery and copper head accents, for example. Outside delivery available, but it costs. Think The Arrangement, less pricey and more creative.

★★★★★★   **Ethan Allen Outlet Store (Ethan's Alley)**   **817/595-0490**

633 Northeast Loop 820   Mon-Sat 10-6; Thurs 10-8; Sun 1-5
Hurst, TX 76053-5210
www.ethanallen.com

 Behind closed doors lies an outlet right out of the story books. Ethan Allen has finally jumped off the deep end and is now rewriting the book on bargains. Ethan's Alley as their outlet is called sits in the back of their Hurst store. There you'll find closeouts, last-years models, discontinued lines, overstocks or what hasn't sold in their retail stores. Ethan's Alley stocks furniture and accessories, even custom draperies and pillows that may have been returned after being made especially for a customer. Savings start at 30-50 percent and more depending on how long the merchandise has been sitting on the floor. After all, it is Ethan Allen. Don't expect design help. Then again, read about The Budget Decorator (see write-up elsewhere in this chapter 'cause this is one of their favorite haunts.) Although their outlet merchandise is congregated in the Alley, the twains never meet at their full retail Mothership. To find out what's "in" at the "outlet," you head to the back. Ethan Allen's philosophy is one of creating both an exquisite home setting and a place where you'll love to come home to, either a homey retreat or just a plain escape. Since Ethan Allen is both a manufacturer and a retailer, they're in the perfect position to maintain the integrity of each of their designs and, by virtue of them being the manufacturer, sell them direct and eliminate the middleman. Imagine, then, how great their outlet store is. No room of your house is ignored: bedroom, living room, dining room, office, media room, even a kid's room, now that they've launched a kid's specialty line. Want to "buy" the book? Well, there's also a place online that you can. Their gorgeous Ethan Allen Product Catalog is $12.95 and includes their casegoods and upholstered furniture, as well as fabric and accessories. ***Call toll-free: 888/324-3571***

★★★ Family Furniture Warehouse 817/498-8005

5230 Denton Hwy. Mon-Fri 10-8; Sat 10-7; Sun Noon-6
Haltom City, TX 76117

It's all in the family, and now that they've got their family tree rooted on firma terra (they were formerly Discount Furniture Warehouse,) you can plant yourself on sofas for as low as $319, wrought-iron coffee and end tables for as low as $199 (with over 30 different styles to choose from) and commissioned- sales personnel who will wiggle their way behind every move you make. Yuck! Expect high-pressure sales pitches, which is not the most endearing way to lure a bargain shopper into a sale. Nevertheless, be strong and say, "No thanks, I'm just looking, honey!" They do sell plenty of popular brands like **AMERICAN DREW**, **ASHLEY**, **BASSETT** (both of whom have direct outlet stores in town), **BENCHCRAFT**, **CARLETON**, **COVINGTON**, **KEMP**, **LANE**, **LEA**, **MAYO**, **PULASKI**, **SIMMONS** and **SOUTHWEST**. Take the I-820 Loop to US 377/ Denton Highway (Exit 19). Look for a two-story building sitting on four acres with 13,000 square feet of selling space. Some appliances like washers, dryers and gas ranges (but no refrigerators), mattresses (Fort Worth's own **GOLDEN** or **RESTONIC**), and yes, plenty of chairs for your seating options. Expect the sales force to repeat their name to you several times should you leave without buying. When and if you return, be sure to ask for Kerry as he's expecting the commission.

★★★★★ Freed's Home Furnishings Clearance Ctr 972/233-6871

4355 Lyndon B Johnson Fwy. @ Midway Mon-Sat 10-9; Sun 12-6
Dallas, TX 75244-5808

If I've passed it once, I've passed it a hundred, no thousands of times and though I can sing their jingle, I haven't stepped foot inside a Freed's since the infamous family feud. And that was at least ten years ago. Now that things have settled down and Howard Freed has taken the helm of this decades'old home furnishings business, what a difference a decade makes. What a boon to North Texas discount home shopping without sacrificing style, selection or service. Every inch is to "ooh and ahh — " now the size of two football fields. Imagine that? But score a touchtouch by going to the back where their clearance center is beckoning you with bargains. Ever square foot provides for decorative know-how — a most inviting backdrop for the proverbial extreme make over. (Watch our website for EXTREME PRIZES.) From the media room furniture to house that large screen TV to the chairs that provide sound controls all the way to the intricately- carved bedroom suites, there isn't a room left unadorned. Talk about their house dressing for less! Lofty looks at down-to-earth prices makes for the perfect combination for the home shopper aficionado. Step foot inside a Nirvana of excellence where the matching circular duo staircases lead the way to the second floor, complete with grand piano playing. More bedrooms suites, a special theatre section complete with movie posters and neon lights, a complete leather department as big as most leather specialty stores, more dining room ensembles, more "movement" furniture which includes chairs and sofas that move (recliners) that literally are lined from floor to ceiling in their own special cubbies. Take a walk down the wild side for that Home, Chic, Home. Not cheap. Not expensive. Oozing with quality for the look that you'd only find in those high-end shelter magazines. The difference, though, the price. Wind through the myriad of room vignettes that put Gabbert's or Robb & Stuckey to shame but it's really the price tags that give them our applause. Solid values day in and day out and then their clearance center offers 25-75 percent off. Stock added daily and many one-of-a-kinds. Their bedding alone makes for a visual Academy Award. Visit their colossal store-front where budget furnishings sit side by side with the best, the economical side by side with the elegant all wrapped up with a designer touch that speaks to every one's home instincts. Is it any wonder why their tent sales bring out the hordes of hungry eyes? (I eyed it and I bought it!) Slow moving items from their main showroom floors are moved to their back Clearance Center but so what? Do I need to say more? That's where there is more action than in any action movie you've seen recently. Then, if it hasn't moved out their clearance outlet door, it cycles back to the tent sale. And you ain't seen nothing like it in Dallas. It's where "you can afford your dreams." No website? Don't go to www.freeds.com or www.freedsfurniture.com as neither one is theirs.

Furniture By Design   817/556-0150

3101 North Main   Mon-Fri 9-5; Sat 9-12
Cleburne, TX 76033
www.furniturebydesignmfg.com

Furniture by Design is a custom furniture, upholstery and home accents showplace that is — to put it bluntly — to die for! No kidding. From it's "underground" location to it's "aboveground" haute designs, you only have to see it, touch it, or sit on it to know that it's la creme de la creme. Yet, prices are factory-direct. Relocate the merchandise to Robb and Stuckey and the prices would escalate upward two or three times. Owner/creator Lisa Cornish does not want to be known as a "discount" resource, though, as it might conjure up cheap prices. But I'm here to tell you that dollar for dollar, you are getting MORE than your money's worth. Prices were very reasonable for custom work and so, in spite of her reluctance to be associated with "underground," she is an epitome of service, selection and value. Custom furniture made literally from the ground floor up — starting with hand-crafted frames that are made right there in the back of their country showroom to the fabric that you pick right off the bolts. Want a child's chair that is every bit as detailed as a grown-up counterpart? Want chairs that are so comfortable that even with a petite frame and short legs, you'll fit? Ask the Channel 8 "Good Morning Texas" crew how they liked their monogrammed stockings. So, listen to the Diva. They are worth the drive. End of discussion. Then walk across the way to the other "finds" in the complex and you'll be glad you drove to Cleburne.

★★   Furniture Castle   972/527-3102

111 W. Spring Creek Parkway   Mon-Sat 10-7; Sun 12-6
Plano, TX 75023-4614

If you like to live like a Prince on a Pauper's paycheck, then consider shopping at this castle for furnishing most of the rooms on the other side of the moat. It's a perfect match as long as royalty is not part of your lineage. Just don't expect much in the way of a royal treatment, because it was quite the opposite on our visit. We were ignored for the most part; then, the hard sell came into play. Either approach was unappealing and we wanted to cross back over the drawbridge and ride off into the sunset. Budget to moderate lines such as **ASHLEY**, **STANDARD** and **SIMMONS** mattresses, no big deal; other lines like **ASPEN**, **CATNAPPER**, **CLASSIC**, **HICKORY HILL**, **JACKSON**, **KATHY IRELAND** and **MILLENNIUM** are popular, but not something I'd run across town for. It's just another furniture store with "castle in the sky" dreams of striking it rich. If a store is worth something, they usually have a website, if for nothing else than to introduce customers to their store information. Hello 21st century.

★★★★★★ **Furniture Consignment**   817/571-5618

501 N. Main, #107   Tues-Sat 10-5
Euless, TX 76039

 This 5,200 square foot home furnishings, antiques and collectibles is one of the mid-cities'secret hideaway tucked away in the Cici's Shopping Center. Their name was Furniture Consignment Plus but that was when they carried appliances. They don't have room any more for any more appliances so the plus has gone. Still, it's worth a trip to Euless because everything else is still all priced for less and here is where you'll find antiques, home furnishings, collectibles at ridiculously low prices. Why? 'Cause this is a consignment store and it's somebody else's estate castoffs. So, skip the pizza and devour the deals of **PRECIOUS MOMENTS** and **HUMMELS**, for example. They are priced lo-cal and no crust, too. Shipments arrive daily with an ever changing supply of new stuff that's old. Moderate furniture lines reflect their devotion to serving the Haverty's customer. For example, there was a striped/floral sofa in excellent condition that would cost $1,200 new for $499. Saw a round oak class-foot table with four chairs for $299. Expect kitchen tables to fly out the door the minute they arrive on the floor, though there seems to be plenty to choose from. One particularly noteworthy table was a contemporary black base/glass top design with four black upholstered chairs for $499, and, I say, "Black is Back!" Bring in what you're not enjoying any more and split with this company 50/50. The owner was more than accommodating in answering the myriad of questions. We think this store holds great promise to the Mid-Cities and Irving set.

★★★ **Furniture in the Raw**   972/270-4469; 972/270-4660

1118 W. Centerville Rd.   Mon & Fri 10-8; Tues, Thurs, Sat 10-6; Sun 1-5
Garland, TX 75041-5903
www.furnitureintheraw.com

When you're the biggest, does it mean you're the bestest? You might as well start here to get a benchmark on prices since they are the biggest. On Mondays, there are free staining classes that start at 7 PM which are always a popular draw. Too, look for sidewalk sales. They certainly bring in the crowds, especially when there are over 15 styles of armoires waiting for your finishing touches. The selection is stellar, but prices are high, starting at $319. Familiar with any of these unfinished manufacturers? **ABLE PRODUCTS**, **AMYX INDUSTRIES**, **ARCHBOLD FURNITURE**, **DONIE CHAIR COMPANY** mortise and tenon construction, sturdy posts with all natural materials and environmentally-friendly finishes, in case you were interested in this little piece of history,) **EAGLE INDUSTRIES**, **KENTWOOD**, **HARDWOOD INDUSTRIES**, **NADEAU IMPORTS**, **OZARK CEDAR FURNITURE**, **SANTA FE RUSTICO**, **POWELL** and **WHITEWOOD**. Unfinished pieces included furniture for the living room, bedroom, dining room, kitchen and office including tables, chairs and more. Delivery in the Metroplex started at $45 and up.

★★   Furniture Warehouse   972/991-3800

4263 Simonton Rd.   Mon-Sat 10-7
Dallas, TX 75244

Furniture, Furniture, Furniture Warehouse. With five Metro area stores, three in Dallas, one in Garland and another in Arlington at I-20 and Cooper, you won't see the referee waving his arms signaling you to come in, but, you will admit, it sure was an effective commercial, even if you couldn't stand the messenger! Anybody who has the fortitude to wave us down over and over again deserves at least some respect. At least on the clearance items. If you're just getting started, if it's your first apartment, or your budget squeaks, this is where you can exercise your least expensive interior motives. Sofa and loveseat sets began as low as $199 and actually came with a one-year warranty. Five locations in the Metroplex — just don't confuse the one on Midway with these clowns. The Midway store is a wrought-iron source. Additional locations at 10850 Harry Hines in Dallas, 214/366-0202; 5900 W. Davis in Dallas, 214/333-9597; 2918 S. Jupiter in Garland, 972/271-9009; and 1704 Greenville (at Ross) in Dallas, 214/515-0785.

★★★★★★   Gabbert's Furniture Outlet   972/385-9666

4207 Simonton Rd.   Mon-Fri 11-7; Sat 10-6; Sun 12-5
Dallas, TX 75244

 Don't believe it. Gabbert's Furniture Outlet is no longer Dallas's best kept secret. Lots of shoppers now know where to shop their 52,000 square foot outlet store near their Dallas mainline store at LBJ and Midway. Now settled into their expanded showplace, you can choose from more than 4,000 items, hundreds of one-of-a-kinds, open seven days a week, with truckloads, really, at 40-80 percent off manufacturer's suggested retail price. Two-three blocks north of their main showroom (corner of Simonton and Midway), you can enjoy the savings, the selection and the service and never feel compromised by your propensity for being chic yet cheap. Yes, the Diva had a hand is helping them launch their outlet many years ago and look at them now! A few years back, they were named the numero uno furniture retailer in the country by *House Beautiful.* So imagine what their outlet is like when some of the same items are marked 50 to 80 (sometimes 90) percent off. But don't think it's only what doesn't sell at their mainline store as they shop specifically for the outlet, too, with closeouts and samples from the trade marts. Shop for entire suites, bedding, lamps, odd pieces, mirrors and lots of miscellaneous objects. Oriental rugs, a great selection. Delivery is available seven days a week. And now at their Fort Worth store, 6301 Oakmont Blvd., one mile south of Hulen Mall, 817/346-5600, don't miss their Odds & Ends room. That is how the Dallas outlet got started with such a room. Now, they have a huge outlet that intersects Simonton and Midway Rd.

★★★★★   H & K Furniture   972/709-8989

303 E. Camp Wisdom Rd.   Mon-Sat 10-8; Wed 10-7; Sun Noon-6
Duncanville, TX 75116

Handsome, kid-proof and all prices negotiable. That's right. That's because sales personnel are not on commission. Isn't that special! The salesmen can negotiate with you even though they may not be a manager or the owner. For more than 13 years, their 43,000 square foot store in Duncanville has been home to furnishing every room in the house. Expect wisdom to rule on brands like ASH-LEY, MILLENNIUM, SEALY and UNIVERSAL. Rocking chairs for $49 and plant stands as low as $19 sealed their fate. Then we eyed a cafe table with two bars stools by ASHLEY for $149 and decided to toast our good fortune. Low prices, six months free layaway with 10 percent down, and now you can see why we're hooked on their good looks. Shop other locations at 11055-B Harry

Hines Blvd. in Dallas, 972/484-8986 and at I-35 and 635 at 11621 Reeder Rd. in Dallas, #200, 972/484-8986. Delivery available. And note, they close at 7 PM on Wednesdays (instead of 8).

★★★★ Haverty's Clearance Center   972/239-7174

4505 LBJ Freeway   Mon-Sat 10-9; Sun Noon-6
Dallas, TX 75244-5905
www.havertyfurniture.com

Well, it was only a matter of time before Haverty's got into the act by opening their own Clearance Store with all the other big name stores that have opened right around the corner (**BASSETT, ASHLEY, PRESTIGE, GABBERT'S, CANTONI**) before Haverty's would throw in their hat, too. Inside their North Dallas showroom, at Midway at 635, you can save up to 70 percent on one-of-a-kinds, overstocked and discontinued items as well as slightly damaged merchandise. Remember, that's just how Gabbert's began with their "odds 'n ends" room. The stuff moves fast, so you'll have to pay particular attention 'cause if you don't, you'll be left out in the cold. If you like Haverty's, you'll love their Clearance Center, although limited to inside their full retail store. All items are sold "as is," so stop belly-aching if the knob is missing or the drawers squeak when opened. All sales are final. Don't expect to bring it back if it doesn't fit. Come armed with a tape measure and your room's measurements. Delivery is available, but extra. Remember, not everything at this location is priced for the clearance area so tiptoe around the full retail priced merchandise and be on the alert. This 100-store chain packs a powerful punch in the furniture business by offering a low-price guarantee. But remember, low price is not "lowest" price. However, it's worth starting in their clearance area, a horse of a different color.

Hemispheres   972/424-3340

600 W. 15th St.   Mon-Sat 9-8
Plano, TX 75075
www.hemispheres-us.com

 Kin to Hobby Lobby, this 70,000 square foot juggernaut is a one-stop world class emporium. Dallas is the third city to have a Hemispheres. Expect to visit around-the-world imports for the home, garden, patio, bedroom, office, living and dining room set in vignettes too tempting to ignore. Oklahoma City residents, David and Barbara Green, planted the seeds over 20 years ago and are now making their expansion move, thanks to the power of Hobby Lobby. You will find this fine furnishings store both attractive and affordable and most of all, fun. The result of hours of dedication to detail, each product has a story steeped in history. Their buyers travel directly to remote villages and tucked-away markets to unearth accessories and furnishings that are unique to Hemispheres. One-of-a-kind treasures, such as hand-knotted rugs, Italian-designed armoires, luxurious bedding, and solid marble statuary and fountains provide a window to the exotic Old World luxury of merchants and royalty. A store just opened in Lewisville at 2325 S. Stemmons, Suite 400 A (972/315-7883) and I'm there!

★★★★ Home Concepts   214/761-1872

2900 Main St.   Tues-Sat 11-7; Sun 1-6
Dallas, TX 75226
www.homeconceptsdallas.com

A little birdie told me they were "cheep, cheep, cheap...." but I wanted you to know not to expect some fly-by-night operation. Perched in the heart of Deep Ellum, you can't miss them. There were over 30 different fun and funky CD holders, from towers to wall racks. Minimalist furniture and accessories are their modus operandi, with full-size eight-foot futons in black or white metal

frames priced at $159 (same as last year). There were hundreds and hundreds of futon covers rang-
ing from $39-$99, and choices included velvet, textures, prints and even matching throw pillows
starting at $9. An iron room divider with 30 glass votives was $149. They claim their futon frames
are imported from Europe but I don't speak any foreign languages. Though delivery is available,
most everything will fit into your car. Feeling groovy? Then conceptualize your new home furnishings from Home Concepts.

★★★★   Home on the Range   972/562-9877

110 E. Louisiana St.   Mon-Sat 10-5
McKinney, TX 75069

If you're back in the saddle again and ready to take a ride to McKinney, don't forget to return to
Home on the Range. Oh, give me a home where they specialize in hand-crafted rustic, western and
Southwestern furniture at prices that won't create a stampede. If you love the look of pencil post
beds and leather seating, consider the look here. How else do you think the West was won? The
range is massive. Whether it's fabric or skins, tables and chairs, cabinets and armoires, rugs and
pottery, you can incorporate the look without the mark of Zorro. Continue the war against high
prices. Isn't that how the West was won to begin with? Oh, give me a home, where the buffalo
roam and I will decorate it with western primitive all the way.

NR IKEA

Hwy. 121 and Dallas North Tollway   Opening Summer 2005
Frisco, TX
www.ikea.com

At last, I can stop holding my breath. Sometime this year, if the stars are all aligned in the right
direction, IKEA, the Swedish home furnishings juggernaut will be coming to Big D — with a
310,000-square-foot store. Frisco has been chosen as the designated destination. And you better be
prepared for the traffic jams. Lucky for this booming northern suburb, it will be IKEA's second in
Texas (after Houston,) and is part of the chainís aggressive expansion mission to open 50 new
North American stores in 10 years. Wow! They've bought 25 acres near Stonebriar Centre at the
northeast corner of the Dallas North Tollway and State Highway 121 and expect to be open in
early summer, 2005. Well known around the world, the store will feature 60 room settings, four
model homes and a 300-seat restaurant that will serve Swedish specialties. Ok, so you're not a big
fan of herring in sour cream or meat balls, I'm sure there will be other items more appealing. You
won't leave hungry, I guarantee it, especially if you're looking for chic cheap furniture and home
accessories. An economic development agreement with the city of Frisco calls for IKEA to spend
at least $40 million on the project which is some chunk of change. When they finally open, you
can bet the cream will rise to the top and they will be voted into the 100 BEST.

★★★★   Infinity Leather Clearance Store   972/387-7878

4263 Simonton   Mon-Thurs 10-8; Fri-Sat 10-6; Sun Noon-6
Farmers Branch, TX 75244
www.infinityleather.com

Best 100 SHOPPING DESTINATIONS   What started as a small, family-owned leather specialty store in 1994 has now mush-
roomed into quite the manna from heaven. That's, of course, if you have an affinity
for leather. If their website is any indication, you will be impressed. It's gorgeous,
just like their leather furniture. There's an infinite number of options to choose from now that
they've grown to such proportion. Wander 'round the 18,750 square foot arena at the corner of
Alpha and the Dallas Tollway for their mainline store and see which piece you can't resist. Then,

see what's "in" at the "out"let. Business is booming, despite the threat of mad cow disease. Even if the cow is sick, it doesn't mean there's anything sickly about their hides. Plus, it's still the preferred choice of coverings in many Metroplex households. Since Dr. Atkins' diet is so "in," so is the meaty choice of high-quality protein leather. Hide and go seek skins in a panoramic selection of styles. Choose from over thirty-five styles, available in over ninety different leathers in five different grades. Enjoy the comfort and luxury of the myriad of sofas, loveseats, sectionals, chairs, recliners, occasional chairs and tables. During one great fourth of July sale, they were offering any grade leather at one low price, which means prices were all a bit lower than their regular price on the lowest grade. Other locations in Plano at the NW corner of the Tollway and Parker, 972/781-2800; in North Richland Hills at 7927 Grapevine Hwy, 817/427-5850; and in Arlington, 629 W. Pioneer, 817/299-9141. Have a seat! And enjoy. Their recliners make you melt in the chair.

★★   Interior Store, The   972/403-7300

5964 Parker Rd.   Mon-Sat 10-6; Sun Noon-5
Plano, TX 75252

The furniture is interior-ly pleasing, but let's say the discounts were melting in the hot summer's sun. A "Province" dining table by **HOOKER** with six chairs was $2,699 (saw it at the website of ballarddesigns.com for $2,995), so I wouldn't consider this to be a substantial discount, would you? A matching hutch with side board was $2,199 (retail $2,495). So, show me the money! Savings are only enough to whisper about, but their outlet store in Carrollton at 3235 Skylane Dr., 75006-2558, 972/818-7777 could materialize into something great, if they would ever answer their phone. It stayed on "busy" for many, many tries over the course of our research. We suspect the merchandise will make more than just interesting fodder, but we'll have to let you know next year, if they ever answer. If there are any savings to be realized at their retail store, they're miniscule, perhaps ten percent. Nothing to write home about. Delivery, $50, and financing by Wells Fargo. And that's all, folks!

Iron Chinchilla   817/427-5992

711 Katy Road   Mon-Sat 8-5 (Generally unless traveling to art shows)
Keller, TX 76248
www.ironchinchilla.com

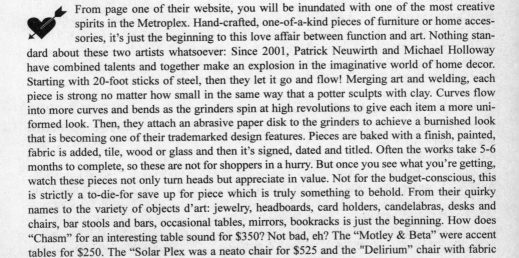

From page one of their website, you will be inundated with one of the most creative spirits in the Metroplex. Hand-crafted, one-of-a-kind pieces of furniture or home accessories, it's just the beginning to this love affair between function and art. Nothing standard about these two artists whatsoever: Since 2001, Patrick Neuwirth and Michael Holloway have combined talents and together make an explosion in the imaginative world of home decor. Starting with 20-foot sticks of steel, then they let it go and flow! Merging art and welding, each piece is strong no matter how small in the same way that a potter sculpts with clay. Curves flow into more curves and bends as the grinders spin at high revolutions to give each item a more uniformed look. Then, they attach an abrasive paper disk to the grinders to achieve a burnished look that is becoming one of their trademarked design features. Pieces are baked with a finish, painted, fabric is added, tile, wood or glass and then it's signed, dated and titled. Often the works take 5-6 months to complete, so these are not for shoppers in a hurry. But once you see what you're getting, watch these pieces not only turn heads but appreciate in value. Not for the budget-conscious, this is strictly a to-die-for save up for piece which is truly something to behold. From their quirky names to the variety of objects d'art: jewelry, headboards, card holders, candelabras, desks and chairs, bar stools and bars, occasional tables, mirrors, bookracks is just the beginning. How does "Chasm" for an interesting table sound for $350? Not bad, eh? The "Motley & Beta" were accent tables for $250. The "Solar Plex was a neato chair for $525 and the "Delirium" chair with fabric was $525. My favorites though were the "Manic & Delirium Bistro set for $1,500 and the "Wishbone for $525. See what tickles your fancy.

★★★★ Kirkland's   972/724-1426

Grapevine Mills Mall   Mon-Sat 10-9:30; Sun 11-8
Grapevine, TX 76051
www.kirklands.com

Kirkland's has been in business since 1966, operating 250 stores in 30 states, at last count. Founded by its current Chairman, Carl Kirkland, their first store was in Jackson, Tennessee, but look at them now. It's just a fun and addictive kind of shopping experience because you never know what will lie in state. Framed art, mirrors, candles, lamps, picture frames, accent rugs, garden accessories and artificial florals are their mainstay. The prices make you want to buy more and more. If it's inexpensive home decor accents you're after, think no further than Kirkland's. Their outlet at Grapevine Mills is a definite coup for area shoppers. Shop online, then run and see if the store has it on sale, or when it might be coming in. Expect to save up to 75 percent off and that is just the beginning of your love-love relationship with Kirkland's. One of their strong suits is table lamps — expressive monkey figures, textured art deco, elegant metals, but there's more, so much more. Design professionals can receive an additional 10 percent off. There are six Metroplex locations so check directory for the one nearest you. If you need the address to Grapevine Mills, you must not live in the Metroplex but I'll give it to you anyway — 3000 Grapevine Mills Parkway. *Call toll-free: 877/208-6668*

★★★★★ Kiss It Good Buy Furniture   817/481-9754

150 N. Main   Tues-Sat 10:30-6
Grapevine, TX 76051
www.kissitgoodbuy.net

I heard it on the Grapevine, and promised not to tell but you know me, I love to Kiss and Tell. Located in the heart of downtown Grapevine, across from Elliott's, this is the place to buy (or sell) antiques and gently-used furniture and accessories. When they see that they're weak in one department, they will fill in the gaps with market samples. Say hello to the Good Buys and start your journey by shopping smart on your way to consignment heaven. If you're wanting to redo your mini-mansion and trade in so you can trade up, this store's merchandise should fit the bill. From a cast-off mantel to an intricately adorned buffee to a beautiful rosewood armoire, such luxurious goldie oldies would fit comfortably into anyone's home decor scheme. Lots of accents should keep you busy running from cut glass to artwork. After many calls to the answering machine, we gave up any thoughts of talking to a live person. Perhaps their personnel is on consignment elsewhere. Still, I'll shop on Main Street 'cause it's a great place to take a walk down the avenue. There is plenty to see on the main drag — even if Grapefest is not underway.

PS Lam Lee Group, The (First Weekend)   972/462-8688

488 S. Royal   First Fri-Sat (of the month)
Coppell, TX 75019
www.lamleegroup.com

 This is one periodic sale that should not be missed. Mark your calendar and call All My Sons to help you move the mountains of marvelous merchandise from here to — there. The Lam Lee Group offers an extensive assortment of unique decorative accessories, accent furniture, gifts and home furnishings that I think that I shall never see an opportunity as unparalleled as thee. This 10,000 square-foot warehouse/showroom opens their doors to what would euphemistically be called a periodic sale of high-end designer furniture, decorative accessories and gift items. The only way you can participate is to circle your calendar the first of the month and flock to this lamb — The Lam Lee Group. If you want something out of the ordinary at a warehouse sale price, expect to find the cream of the crop here. Fifty head- and footboards will start your bedroom decorating redo from $500-$1,500. Forty plus armoires were waiting to be adopted. So what are you waiting for? The first of the month, that's what! Funky, fun, frou-frou and fabulous will best describe your journey through these superbly crafted showpieces. From a $1 music box that would be a playful addition to any little girl's room to a $50 vase that looks like it was plucked from the Ming garden to a most elegant etagere, you will be forever grateful that I revealed this secret weekend of shopping.

★★★★★★ Lost Empire Trading Co., The   214/742/1253

1202 N. Industrial   Tues-Sat 10-6; Sun Noon-6
Dallas, TX 75207
www.lostempireimports.com

 This mammoth undertaking has now settled into their new second location warehouse and showroom, close to the Design District, from their original slot at Farmer's Market. At the northeast corner of Industrial and Howell, exit Continental off Stemmons and go east, young man, if you want to partake in a shopping excursion worthy of a diversion. The prices here reflect how products from foreign lands can often beat the pants off products made in the USA. During sales, prices are slashed to as much as 75 percent off their original low prices. Their monthly giveaway of a Free armoire was sure the topic of conversation at my Fourth of July barbecue. These hand-crafted beauties were made of solid mahogany with hand-rubbed finishes. You can shop online or in person. Personal service included within their 26,000 square foot showroom makes for an around-the-world shopping spree from the Far East, Indonesia, India and parts unknown. Their original location is still operative at 1010 S. Pearl, Building #2, Farmers Market, corner of Marilla and S. Harwood, 214/752-9393, Tues-Fri 10-6; Sat and Sun 9-6. You won't need any frequent flier points to benefit from a trip to bountiful. Just show them your passport (The Underground Shopper book will do!)

★★★★ Main Street Rustic   817/481-6774

1900 S. Main St., Suite 102   Mon-Sat 10-8; Sun Noon-6
Grapevine, TX 76051
www.mainstreetrustic.com

You won't have to drive to Joshua to rope in a handmade rustic ensemble perfect for the lakehouse, the lodge, the ranch, the boy's bunkhouse or for your mountain retreat. Right on the main drag in Grapevine, you can rustle up some steals on custom-crafted examples one piece at a time. Skilled craftsmen replicate antique looks paying attention to the intricate details. What you have at the end of the process is a work of art in solid wood, kiln-dried and finished with natural wax which creates a beautiful sheen to the finish. No need to worry about upkeep. It says beautiful forever reeking of antiquity. Outfit your bedroom, dining room, living room with couches, chairs, occasional tables, home offices, bars and barstools, armoires and accompanying accessories with a rustic flair. Special orders take four-six weeks for delivery and all pieces are made of solid pine and hand-crafted iron. Over 25 years of selling furniture give this family seniority on the scene. Log online and print out a 10 percent coupon to apply to any purchase in the store.

★★★★★★   **Massoud Furniture Manufacturing   214/388-8655**

8351 Moberly Lane   Tues-Thurs 9-3:30
Balch Springs, TX 75227-2316
www.massoudfurniture.com

 Another find that is worth sharing — just remember who told you. This manufacturer has lots of extra stock....from cancelled orders to a series of dropped fabric that
you can choose from to go on any one of the couch or chair frames that they make.
Wow! Whoa! It's worth ponying up to (or down to) Balch Springs to get top-notch case goods
(furniture with fabric) at wholesale prices. Three days is all they're willing to allow you inside
their outlet doors since they stay busy selling other days to their retail furniture accounts (like all
the biggies in the Metroplex as well as parts unknown.)

Mathis Brothers   **405/943-3434**

3434 West Reno   24/7
Oklahoma City, OK 73107

www.mathisbrothers.com    *Top Online Store!*

 What's a nice Dallas-based shopping diva recommending a shopping destination in
Oklahoma City? Well, one visit to their website and you'll see. Save up to 60 percent
on most of the sought-after brands of furniture like ALEXANDER JULIAN, ASH-
LEY, ASPEN, BERNHARDT, BROYHILL, CENTURY, HENREDON, HOOKER, KLAUSSNER,
LA-Z-BOY, LANE, LEXINGTON, MARTHA STEWART, MILLENNIUM, NATUZZI,
PULASKI, RALPH LAUREN, RIDGEWAY, SLIGH, UNIVERSAL....who did I leave out? Since
the mid 1940s when this west Texas family moved to Oklahoma City to open their furniture store,
they now are entering the third generation of family management. You've got to see it to believe it.
They were named the #1 furniture store in America. One visit, and you'll see why. Moving into the
next millennium of shopping, jump onboard the shopping highway to their online virtual store. It's
a one-stop shop for nightgown shopping 24/7. It's hassle-FREE, stress-FREE and full-price Free.
You're but a few clicks away from outfitting your entire home from top to bottom. Maybe we
should get the busses ready for the trek? It sure is closer than North Carolina (by a thousand
miles.) Call if your group wants to go (469/293-SHOP) and we'll make it happen. *Call toll-free:*
800/329-3434

★★★★★   **MF Industries**   **817/795-2368**

2110 W. Division   Mon-Fri 9-5; Sat 10-2
Arlington, TX 76012
www.mfteakwood.com

Shop the warehouse way and get it wholesale. It can't get any clearer or easier than MF Industries.
Meet Michael, the world traveler, who is on a plane or in the jungles negotiating the best deals he
can find on teak products and furniture. Whether for indoors or the great outdoors, there is plenty
to choose from for both. Their designs epitomize fine craftsmanship and beauty that will last a lifetime. Teak is probably the most versatile hardwood used in furniture- making today, requiring little
or no care; so, choose the style and have yourself a field day. Their teak is harvested from plantations established by the Dutch in the Mid-19th century in Indonesia. The Indonesian government
allows a limited amount of teak to be harvested yearly, which ensures an equal amount of refores-
tation. All of their products, then, are created from sources that can be recycled—making them
ecologically and politically-correct. As a manufacturer, they hold the benchmark for bargains in
benches. Get them with backs, without backs, benches that fold or are extra large. If all else fails,

have yourself a seat—a love seat. Add coffee tables, end tables, big tables, small tables. Cover up with an umbrella or add planters, teacarts, swings, arbors or poolside bars—there's an endless array of choices. And don't forget the kids, because they make miniature versions of the grownup benches and chairs to size. Then, to make an even smaller statement, why not something for Barbie? Even she has her own line of teak and mahogany doll-size furniture. Shop online or in person. This year I carted off a fabulous hand-carved bistro table and four chairs with a horse motif for $299. Of course, as I've said, they are a horse of a different color.

★★★   Nayfa's Furniture   817/731-9828

6901 Camp Bowie   Mon, Wed, Fri-Sat 10-6; Tues, Thurs 10-8; Sun 1-5
Fort Worth, TX 76116
www.nayfasfurniture.com

No, this is not Ninfa's, but Nayfa's. Turn your appetite here toward the rustic-looking pine ladder-back chairs for $99, or a myriad of other unfinished items. Get your paint brushes and have a field day. Although you won't get the brush-off from any of their personnel, you might want to try your own hands at their unfinished business. Perfect for a children's bedroom transformation: start with a twin bed headboard, add some bookcases, a desk, an entertainment center for the TV, VCR and DVDs, and you can transfrom some young person into a pretty happy camper. Of course, if you have a green thumb, you'll be up to your elbows in stains and grains, paint and paint remover. If you're not proficient with the brush stroke, you may want to leave it to the pros, but the price goes up for their efforts. Exit I-30 going west and, when you get to the "Y" in the road with Office Max and Highway 80 on the right and Denny's and Camp Bowie on the left, choose Camp Bowie on the left. Go for a couple of blocks and it's on the left. You've got to love them for staying open seven days a week. Color them brave hearts.

★★★★★   Neal's Unfinished Furniture   972/596-1251

3100 Independance, #314   Mon-Sat 9:30-6; Sun Noon-5
Plano, TX 75075
www.nealsunffurn.com

Although they don't violate any obscenity laws by selling nakedness, you can buy nude furniture without looking over your shoulders (or any other part of your body). At the southwest corner of Trinity Mills and Marsh Lane, get ready to add some of your own personal touches because this location is their outlet store where prices get the axe even more. There isn't a room that is left out in left field without your artistic contribution. They have dining room tables (with or without leaves), pub tables, arm style tables, barstools (with or without backs), rocking chairs, coffee/lamp/sofa tables, entertainment centers, TV stands, oak bookcases, computer desks, writing desks, juvenile bedroom furniture, baby changing tables, chairs, child's rockers and horses, footstools, pine bookcases, toy boxes (with safety hinges), high chairs, vanity tables and stools and over 30 varieties of chairs. Of course, they will sell you all the tools of the trade to finish what they don't. Knock on wood, you may even have the rudiments of a second business. Painted furniture is not only hot, it's haute! And Neal's has the best prices in town. Visit also in Plano at Independence and Parker. Other locations in Houston and Austin. And now, shop online for a limited selection. Stay home. Stir those creative juices. And go with the flow.

★★★★★★   O'Neal Furniture   **817/337-0068**

1711 Keller Pkwy.   Mon-Sat 10-8; Sun Noon-5
Keller, TX 76248

 You've gotta have hope (chests), and for only $79 you can buy **FAITH** and Charity one, too. Hope chests by **LANE** are just one of the items on the showroom floor. Home, cheap, Home by these O'Neals could be your connection to the bargains (and you don't even have to be Irish to love 'em!) He and his family have spent their every waking hour making sure Fort Worth and nearby furniture shoppers have something to sit on, relax on, sleep on. They've been doing so since 1935, so they aren't going away anytime soon. In fact, they're going and growing. Specializing in traditional, colonial and country furniture designs, they don't ignore accessories, either. See art. See art on the wall. See furniture alongside the art on the wall with names like **AMERICAN DREW**, **DREXEL HERITAGE**, **FAIRFIELD**, **HFI**, **KIMBALL**, **LANE**, **RIVERSIDE**, **STANLEY**, **SUMTER CABINET** and others, at decidedly discounted prices. Any room in the house is fair stomping grounds. They stand (by) and deliver. Savings are substantial on sofas, dinettes, bedroom suites—this Homer is a home run!

★★   Oak Mill, The   **817/263-4097**

5531 S. Hulen   Mon-Fri 10-8; Sat 10-7; Sun Noon-6
Fort Worth, TX 76132
www.theoakmill.com

Four metro locations could make you nuts, but if you want to buy furniture for peanuts, try planting the seeds at the Oak Mill. You won't have to store up the acorns since there are plenty of locations in California, Nevada, Washington and Texas. Find a forest of oak furniture in many shapes, styles and budgets, but you'll be paying close to retail (and that's a no-no!) Bedroom, dining room, home office or media rooms can be acquired, though, at affordable prices if that's any consolation. Now, all you need to do is tie a yellow ribbon 'round the old Oak Mill....so you won't forget them. This chain has spread its roots to locations in North Richland Hills (807/428-0391); Addison (972/702-0330); and Plano (972/423-9111), too. Do you prefer your finished products in light or dark oak? It's your choice. From computer desks to curio cabinets, haul it off yourself to save some green; or pay as they go—delivery is extra. Although they guarantee the best prices, I dare you to compare! Beds started at $300 and went up from there. Up to five pieces, delivered and set up in Colleyville, expect to pay for the goods plus $60 for delivery. You may find this an interesting specialty store, but don't expect to save a trunk full of money, honey. Check directory for location nearest you. *Call toll-free: 866/625-6455*

★★★★   OF   **214/887-6363**

1810 Skillman St. @ Live Oak St   Mon-Sat 10-6; Sun Noon-5
Dallas, TX 75206-7952

OFfically, this unusual store name was an abbreviation for Objects Found, but for those in the know, it means you can find objects "for the home and garden," including flowers to bring the outdoors in. From the ground up, you can select from a myriad of products to make your home or office a grande statement "of" artistry and drama, to say the least (and it may cost you the least for the best quality). Carry the fresh flowers into your home as you make a grande entrance, a loving statement on a special occasion, or.... if you're late for dinner! Add in a mixture of architectural accents, bath products, candles and church candle stands and you can see that anything goes. We saw a dark distressed wooden dining room table for $795 (36" X 72") with matching chairs at $225 each. A beautiful couch for $1,800 was equally appealing with stunning fabric. End tables and interesting wine cabinets were interspersed throughout the displays with new shipments of pottery arriving daily. You never know from whence they came; or in other words, "OF" whence they came. Just be grateful their buyers have good taste and your household could be the recipient of original artwork, architectural accents, stained-glass crosses, jewelry and more. Then take in a whiff of fresh-cut flowers and smell the sweet smell OF success.

★★★★★★   Patio One   972-633-5522

1401 Summit Ave, Suite 3   Mon-Fri 9-5; Sat 10-6; Sun 1-6
Plano Dallas, TX 75074
www.fullrich.net

 Patio One is the first name that should pop up when the subject of patio furniture is raised. Why? Because they have been manufacturing outdoor furniture over a decade and are the supply chain to Alsto's, Pier One, Crate and Barrel to name drop a few. Headquartered in Jakarta, Indonesia, their brand is called **NYATOH**. See the collections displayed in their 3,000 square foot warehouse that is a little off the beaten path, but then nobody said it was going to be easy. They are not going to dish it out without a little effort on your part. Well, they may not do so on a silver platter, but they have most any other kind of server for your patio or casual dining spot. Remember teak is the all-weather wood that lasts a lifetime and here, you can get tables, chairs, benches, lounge chairs, chaises, rocking chairs, servers, for at least 50 percent off retail. And when it comes to umbrellas, al fresco dining was never this cool. Remember, keep the sun out of your eyes and the money in your pocket and shop here first. Also known as Fullrich Industries and now open seven days a week for your shopping pleasure.

★★★   Rooms To Go Clearance Center   972/623-3020

2725 S. Highway 360   Mon-Sat 10-8; Sun 12-6
Grand Prairie, TX 75052
www.roomstogo.com

No smart go-go girl would turn her nose up at this sleek, one-stop shop for outfitting almost any room in the house, including the often-overlooked kids'room. If you purchase all five pieces in an ensemble, you can whack off another 10-20 percent. Furniture, from their Rooms to Go stores throughout the Metroplex that doesn't sell, or is on the showroom floor too long, or has been discontinued, or in some way, shape or form is scratched or dented, moves to their Clearance Center in the sky. Lots of scratch, dented, bent or broken stuff but you can expect to save about 40 percent. An entire bedroom suite can be had for as low as $750, up to an average of $1,200. Another Clearance Center is in North Richland Hills across from North Hills Mall in the old Ware's store, off Holiday and Grapevine Highway. This mega retailer can now boast of being the biggest furniture retail chain in the country but not the bestest clearance store for living room, bedroom, dining room, bedding, recliners and more. Most appeared to have been retired from the war zone. You'll need to be a medic to transform many of the clearance items to an acceptable working condition. A bed without legs is not something to rest easy. But still, you've got to see the place. After all, Rooms to Go is not the faster growing furniture retailer for no good reason. Just don't expect much of what they sell to last more than a season. Buy with caution. See overstocks, discontinued, damaged, scratch and dent and brand new in the box items some from their regular stores and some specifically purchased for the clearance center. Thousands of items to choose, so if you're not picky, you can come home baring gifts. Delivery $69.99 for five pieces.

★★★★★   **RoomStore Clearance Store**   **214/358-7287**

3546 Forest Lane @ Marsh   Mon-Sat 10-8; Sun 12-6
Dallas, TX 75234
www.roomstore.com

Factory overstocks, discontinueds, showroom samples, one-of-a-kinds and some scratch 'n dents
all add up to one big furniture outlet from one of the giant discount furniture retailers. Add in a
catchy song, and it spells s.a.v.i.n.g.s. Odd mirrors for as low as $28, lamps starting at $18, cocktail and end tables beginning at $38—although most cost more. But for an inexpensive addition to
your home life, you could find a real steal on an odd headboard for $68 or an **ASHLEY** bunk bed
for $198. Save 40-50 percent on all shapes and sizes of dinette sets. A king-size **SEALY** mattress
set was $288 and 100 percent leather couches were $578, instead of over $1,000. Don't expect to
overpay; you'll get what you pay for. Moderate furniture at inexpensive prices....that's what
they're all about! Merchandise comes from their regular stores with savings up to 70 percent off.
Don't expect this store to be set up in vignettes but, rather, a hodge podge of anything goes. If it's
on the floor, it's for sale; delivery is available for $50 and financing is available if you want to buy
more than you can afford in one fell swoop. One store—and one store only—is home to all of their
clearance merchandise, so make a bee-line to this location and wade through the forest to stake
your claim. Don't be a sap, honey, there are ways to beat the other couples!

★★★★★   **Rosewood Fine Furniture**   **214/575-7888**

751 S. Central Expressway   Mon-Thurs 10-7; Sat-Sun 10-8; Sun 12-6
Richardson, TX 75080-7410
www.styleusagroup.com

Check location before you go as they were having a moving sale right as we went to press. Then,
once you've installed the Chinese to English translator, you'll be able to call them for their new
digs. If you're looking to shop for fine rosewood furniture like a six-piece sleigh bedroom set for
$1,990, here's the place to wrap your arms around. Want to save up to 70 percent? Then, this is the
place to express yourself Orientally. Founded in 1989 and headquartered in Dallas, they have manufactured and launched many interesting and innovative products such as the automatic sunlight
shield for automobiles, navigational equipment, a children's safety quilt and many other patented
items. The company takes advantage of their modern equipment and scientific drying processes to
insure precise moisture content in their rosewood furniture production. Combined with a blend of
skilled workers who carve, lay the mother of pearl and finish the furniture by hand, the end result
is furniture of the highest quality and beauty. All of their furniture comes with a lifetime warranty.
Exit Spring Valley and stay on the service road going north if you catch them before they move.

★★★★★★   **Rustic By Design, Inc.**   **817/517-2572**

1409 S. Broadway #E (Hwy. 174)   Mon-Sat 9-8
Joshua, TX 76058
www.rusticbydesign.net

Rustic conjures up visions of sugarplums and ski slopes. I can't explain it, but, if you
want to minimize cabin fever in custom furniture with the elan of **ASPEN**, Colorado,
here is the place to covet. It doesn't hurt that they are based in a town with my son's
name; or that the town's name has some reference to doing battle against high prices, either. Custom ranch-style furniture with flair is how best to describe their artistic contribution to your
home's design. They not only design it, they manufacture it, too. Nothing but the best and priced
factory-direct. Yes, they are the factory. Choose one of their existing designs or let them create
something from their imagination or yours. Custom upholstery and reupholstery, too. Wrought

iron furniture, wood furniture, some antiques with a "western" motif, as well as a town full of home decor items is located just minutes away from the Dallas/Fort Worth county lines. You know how we are? Us city folks that want to be country slickers? This may be just what the doctor ordered. (Are you reading this Dr. Sanders? Dr. Standefer? Dr. Martin? Dr. Provost? Dr. Smith? Dr. Titensor? Dr. Mary Jo?)The list is endless. Doctors and dentists and candlestick makers, oh my! Once you've found them, never let them go.

★★★★★　Sam's Furniture & Appliance　　　817/838-5555

5555 E. Belknap St.　　　　　　　　　　　　　　　　　　Mon-Fri 10-7; Sat 10-6
Haltom City, TX 76117
www.samsfurniture.com

Founded in 1946, Sam's Furniture and Appliances has come a long way, baby. From a small corner grocery store to an most interesting evolution, you've got to see what lies in wake. The sons of the founder, Sam Weisblatt, run the place now: Paul runs Sam's Video, and Herb is the president of Sam's Furniture and Appliances. What's interesting about their approach is their ability to offer several different ways for you to buy — the old-fashioned way and pay cash (although they do accept checks and credit cards,) or you can choose outside financing options for larger purchases, or you can try their unique "Lease-to-Own" program. They call it a five-star lease program for anybody who may not be credit-worthy but who has enough credit for a credit card. But it's their rates that are outstanding. Most "Rent-to-Own" stores'interest rates are outrageous. At Sam's, they pride themselves on personalized customer service and lower interest rates. Currently, they operate three locations in the Fort Worth area. Their main store is located at 5555 E. Belknap which is also home to their corporate offices. Right across the street is Sam's Annex, their Lease Return outlet, offering terrific values on their entire line of lease returned items. When an item is returned from a lease, it is restored and repaired, if necessary, and then sold in the Annex for a lot less. Same with the jewelry lease returns. Then there's their Grapevine Store and warehouse, located on Highway 26 in North Richland Hills. Choose your course of action, and consider that this Sam wants you!

★★★★★★　Scratch & Dent Store　　　　　972/564-1160

207 E. Hwy 80　　　　　　Sat 10-5; Sun 12-5; Closed on all major holidays.
Forney, TX 75126
www.wefurnish.com

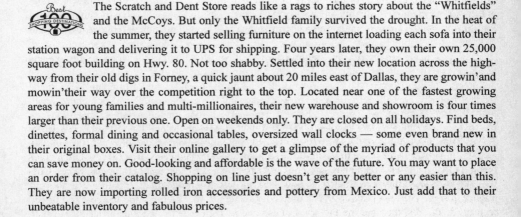

The Scratch and Dent Store reads like a rags to riches story about the "Whitfields" and the McCoys. But only the Whitfield family survived the drought. In the heat of the summer, they started selling furniture on the internet loading each sofa into their station wagon and delivering it to UPS for shipping. Four years later, they own their own 25,000 square foot building on Hwy. 80. Not too shabby. Settled into their new location across the highway from their old digs in Forney, a quick jaunt about 20 miles east of Dallas, they are growin'and mowin'their way over the competition right to the top. Located near one of the fastest growing areas for young families and multi-millionaires, their new warehouse and showroom is four times larger than their previous one. Open on weekends only. They are closed on all holidays. Find beds, dinettes, formal dining and occasional tables, oversized wall clocks — some even brand new in their original boxes. Visit their online gallery to get a glimpse of the myriad of products that you can save money on. Good-looking and affordable is the wave of the future. You may want to place an order from their catalog. Shopping on line just doesn't get any better or any easier than this. They are now importing rolled iron accessories and pottery from Mexico. Just add that to their unbeatable inventory and fabulous prices.

★★★★   **Second Home Furniture**   **214/222-4663**

1288 West Main Street, #132   Mon-Sat 10-6
Lewisville, TX 75067
www.secondhomefurniture.com

Taking over the old Tuesday Morning location (since they moved to bigger digs) could mean the start of something big Mondays thru Saturdays. This newest entry into the consignment furniture and accessories field promises a half price decorating haven. Stacy Van Cleve is the leader of the packed house where furniture is coming and going at a staccato-like pace. Another home-town favorite should add plenty of "a plumb" to residents who want to trade in their old/new for something new/old. There must be something in the water in Lewisville since there are several consignment shops opening back-to-back. Or more like it, there are more shoppers out there moving into the area who want beautiful furniture and decorative accessories on the cheap.

★★★★★   **Sell It Again, Sam!**   **214/340-6897**

10233 E. Northwest Hwy., Suite 401   Mon-Sat 10:30-6; Sun 1-5
Dallas, TX 75238

Love it, trade it, buy it! This eclectic paradise is seasoned with just the right stuff. If you're dancing through the aisles as fast as you can, you'll be able to see quite a potpourri. Let Sam "Sell It Again, Ma'am." Beside The Book Rack, this entrepreneur continues to amaze shoppers from miles around with her mix and match collections of individual and unique items. Over 20,000 square feet of surprises at every turn. Furniture, housewares, accessories and accents are what you'll find lying in wake. Garden furniture and furnishings, too, so not to worry, dig in — all at dirt cheap prices. For example, an oak bedroom set in great shape (full/queen size) with the headboard, footboard and rails was $49. The matching dresser and mirror were another $159 and two night stands were $39 each. A cream-colored dining room table with eight chairs, in brand new condition, was a steal at $500. One of the best prices on home furnishings, antiques, pottery and china in the Metroplex. Consignments are still a 50/50 split, but bring your own truck or arrange for your own delivery.

★★★★★★   **Shortell Bros. Intl.**   **214/748-4233**

122 Howell St.   Mon-Fri 8-5; Sat By Appt.
Dallas, TX 75207
www.shortell.com

In business for over seven years, they haven't gotten the itch yet, but what started as a hobby for Joseph Shortell has emerged into a full-fledged specialty store for handmade Mediterranean, Southwestern and Spanish-colonial style wooden furniture and accessories. Their clients include restaurants, hotels, interior designers, architects, landscape architects and retail stores. All custom work is done on the premises and artisans in Mexico and Central America contribute to the rest. Browse today, but buy in manana. Products include: handmade wooden furniture, wrought iron, pottery, hand-carved stone fountains, table bases, figurines, tile, marble and stone pavers, pewter, glazed and unglazed ceramics and lots of decorative accessories. They also offer stone pavers that can be used indoors and out and are available in a variety of beautiful colors and I might add, very reasonably priced. They're just waiting to be picked. Howell is located just south of where Irving and Market Center Boulevard come together. What a windfall at Shortell. Do your promise not to tell? ***Call toll-free: 800/628-0437***

★★★★★ Simple Things   817/332-1772
1540 S. University Drive,   Mon-Wed, Sat 10-6; Thurs-Fri 10-7; Sun 12-5
Fort Worth, TX 76107

It's very simple. No catalogs, no websites, just a simple notion that a quality product with true customer service is the best advertising around. But to find out first hand, you're gonna have to go in and see for yourself. Located at the University Park Village (just south of I-30), simply put, you choose the fabric and frame, then wait about 6 to 10 weeks, depending on which of their two lines you pick, and presto! In practically no time, you'll find incredibly soft, washable slip-covered sofas, deep sumptuous cushions, impressively-constructed and generously-sized frames. Handmade in North Carolina, to your specifications, by two of the largest, high-quality manufacturers (LEE and CISCO BROTHERS), this is slip-covered furniture, but don't let that fool you. Pick from thousands of fabrics, thousands of frames with a million variables and then pick your cushion fill. You'll be sitting pretty for as low as $1,299 up to a more elaborately-curved and rolled arm sofa covered in a gorgeous chenille with down fill for $4,000. Delivery is $25. Get one sofa with two slipcovers and you'll have two sofas for the price of one! The quality justifies the end price so don't let it deter you from letting this one slip by.

★★★★★ Simply Elegant   817/431-6582
241 S. Main   Mon-Sat 10-6; Sun 1-5
Keller, TX 76248
www.welovekeller.com

Add one more compelling reason to shop Main Street Keller — Simply Elegant. The corner of Olive and Main is home to the bright yellow 1920s themed house with a hostess with the mostess — Maria Sands. Welcome to the world of fantasy and fantastic furniture finds. Consignment of both traditional and contemporary name brand furniture and accessories that are literally crammed into every inch of potential space, top to bottom and in between. Maria learned the business from other consignment shops where she earned her stripes. Now it's her turn. Separating herself from the crowd, she's the one with a Saturdays-Only little girl's Tea Party. For $150, (and book well in advanced), you can schedule a little girl's tea party at 11, 1 or 3 every Saturday. For a minimum of nine children (and $15 for each additional child over nine), the party girls get to wear their own flapper dresses for the one and one half hours of partytime in their own separate tea room behind the main store. Ta Ta! Enjoy tea served with its own sterling silver tea service complete with croissant sandwiches and petit fours for dessert. Learn the Charleston as part of the party plan. And while the lil'girls are enjoying their tea party, big girls go shopping up front at the main eclectic consignment shop with a DREXEL dining room table and six chairs (table, $875 and chairs, $975), lots of drop leaf tables, a custom sofa, some antiques, a dining room suite with a table and six chairs, $595 or an oak pedestal table and six chairs, $475. Where can you eat on such luxury for less?

★★★★★★ Sweet Dreams Bedding Co.   817/790-8510
4125 S. I-35 W   Mon-Fri 9-5
Alvarado, TX 76009
www.sweetdreamsbedding.com

Besides carrying mattresses, frames and rails, sink down into sweet dreams in bedroom sets, leather sofas, wing chairs, rustic armoires and bookcase, French-like furniture, coffee/end tables, occasional tables, oak curios, misting fountains and accent furniture. What more could you ask for to ensure a good night's sleep, cheap. Well, mattresses, of course. But it's the furniture that makes this visit worthwhile. Newest products to be added to the mix include Grandfather clocks, mirrors and area rugs. Visit closer to town via the CDI Warehouse, 2810 Ave. E., Arlington, TX 76011, 817/608-0073; 888/236-5835. No need for soothing lullabies, this is all the comfort you'll need. Several 3-piece leather sets of excellent design and quality was a low of about $1,400 and a leather recliner was $290. Now where have you seen prices like that lately? Once you've decided what you want, they will be delivered in their own "marked trucks!"

Texas Longhorn-Horn Co.   936/326-4049

Rt. 5, Box 2630   24/7
Nacogdoches, TX 75961

www.txlonghorns.com   ⊖ *Top Online Store!*

I rarely get stumped. But when a caller asked for mounted cow horns, I did not know then what I know now. I now know about Texas Longhorn-Horn Company because I have been introduced to James Dawson via his sister, Sarah Dawson. I can now send any Metroplex shoppers to the above website or to the local flea markets, backed by a quarter-of-a-century of selling experience. James Dawson is his name (the brother) and longhorns are his game! Dealing in the various sizes of mounted cow horns and cow skulls, you can order via his website above or locally at Traders Village and Canton's First Monday. He's got a satisfaction guarantee and seven-day return policy. Some close-outs were even cut to the quick. For example, the imported BOWIE knives with 9-inch blades and leather sheaths were $8, plus $4.50 shipping and handling. With other items, expect them also to be affordable: fancy blowin'horns, cow skulls, bullwhips, mounted steer horns, authentic power horns, even genuine cowboy ropes were just part of this Texan's **LONG-HORN** inventory.

★★★★★   TF Howard Bedding Factory   972/775-3997

300 N. 8th Street, Suite 108   Mon-Fri 8-6; Sat 8-4 (online 24/7)
Midlothian, TX 76065
www.beddingfactory.com

Convert that spare bedroom into a home office, craft room or game room. Keep your kid's bed neat and out-of-sight, creating extra play space. Maximize space at the cabin, ranch or lake house. Add a beautiful place to sleep almost anywhere. Does that sound like some kind of pipe dream? Actually, no truer words were ever written. Then if you want to save up to 40 percent off retail on a wall bed system, and who wouldn't, one call to TF Howard is all it takes to make it happen. Meet mattress man, Fred Howard, the classic entrepreneur who finds a niche and then goes after filling it. Today, rather than making mattresses which he used to do, he is transforming spare rooms into useful rooms with custom wallbeds nationwide and that is no small feat. Speaking of feet, by having a bed that even a rank amateur can install, it is possible to raise the legs of the bed so that sufferers of the condition known as acid reflux can get relief from that heartburn that often keeps them awake — just by taking advantage of the wall bed's adjustable legs. Save money and transform any small space into a useful "other" space. Expect turnaround for custom wallbed systems to be three-four weeks. And with the savings on your wall bed, you'll have the money for a facelift. Go to their website and view their one-stop shopping site complete with one-minute video, catalog and gallery — that's if you want to be impressed and see the systems up close and personal. Order with ease. One click of the mouse or call toll free, it's that simple and soon you'll be sleeping pretty. You can select specific components and build a custom system right there on line. Then point and click and you're practically there. Create your entire wallbed system online; choose various options for size, function, color, design, and choice of wood. And if your mind goes blank, and you haven't an idea swimming around in your brain, their Design Consultants can help. Getting your money's worth is what this company provides routinely. Offering the best quality product at the best possible price is why these wall beds are being shipped all over the world. Yes, the world. If you don't believe me, ask Fred for some testimonials — from England, Germany, Japan, The Netherlands, South Africa and of course the USA because we all like buying the all-American way....factory direct! *Call toll-free: 800/987-2818*

★★★★★★   That Furniture Store on Greenville   214/821-8230

3723 Greenville Ave.   Mon-Sun 11-6
Dallas, TX 75206-5311

 What does Lower Greenville have that nobody else has? How about That Furniture Store on Greenville? Guess they came by their name naturally as fans were calling it that forever. Afterall, it is the furniture store on Greenville. Choose from dramatic armoires that are eight to ten feet tall, four-poster and sleigh beds and dining room suites all appearing hand-carved and elegant with that Old World charm. Located just three blocks south of Mockingbird, soon you'll be singing their praises, too. Play like a tourist once in a while and hobnob with the best of them while taking in a bite to eat at Terelli's. Shop for accents like candles and crosses, accessories, trunks, tables, entertainment centers and more. Lower Greenville is where the artsy-fartsy locals mingle with the visiting tourists who are hip, but don't want to appear SO hip that they miss the point. This 1920's neighborhood is filled with unique shops, restaurants and clubs. By the way, some of my favorites are Avant, 2716 Greenville, filled with great women's apparel and accessories that are all to die for (Say hello to Donna for me.) Josh's favorite is HD's. (Say hello to Henry from him.) Open seven days a week.

★★★★★   Tommy Snodgrass Discount Furniture   972/262-1507

505 E. Main St.   Mon-Sat 10-7; Sun 1-5
Grand Prairie, TX 75050

Don't expect your best friends to spill the beans. Typically, they've shopped here but give you the silent treatment when asked, "Where did you get that gorgeous art deco chair?" Since 1945, Snodgrass Furniture has been kept under wraps. The Budget Decorators were introduced to **TOMMY** recently and flipped. Now they're one of his biggest fans. They probably won't win any prizes for elegant surrounds, but they will win hands-down in service and prices. Remember, they're the ones pulling up to mansions in their unmarked trucks. If you don't want your neighbors knowing how cheap you are, call for their delivery in an unmarked truck and we'll keep it our little secret! Tick off the savings on clocks, from cuckoos to contemporary, traditional, curio, grandfather or anniversary. Choose from their stock or special order for the living room, bedroom, dining room, mattresses, lamps, recliners — if you haven't heard of the Snodgrass legendary layaway plan, where have you been hiding? Pay whatever down you want, pay whenever you can, how much you can, as often as you can. Combine old-fashioned, unpretentious surroundings with down-to-earth country charm and see first-hand why folks from miles away drive to Grand Prairie. By the way, ask Tommy to show you his collection of Dr Pepper memorabilia (the largest around.) And congratulate him for installing the touch tone phone (he fixed his rotary phone until it died and he had no choice). Say hello to my of my favorites.

★★★★   Unclaimed Freight Company & Liquidation Sales

817/568-0495
Mon-Sat 10-8; Sun 12-6

9320 South Fwy. (I-35W)
Fort Worth, TX 76140-4920

Hop aboard this Tarrant County freight company and tow the line at any of their four area locations. Choo-choo, baby, and don't look back as you ease on down the track. Parsons'chairs in an off-white linen-like fabric were $99.95 and in black, $89.95. A hi-leg **LANE** recliner with a fisherman's print was originally tagged at $1,194.95 but now marked $669.95. A **BERKLEY** recliner, on the other hand, was $349.95 rather than $694.95. Not sit on that for a while! This is unclaimed freight, furniture that is shipped via the trains but somehow gets damaged in transit. Where else can you find a five-drawer, light pine dresser for $429.95? Or an **ASHLEY** dinette set complete with a wrought-iron table and four padded chairs for $599.95? Lastly, we bumped into a modern, five-drawer dresser with silver hardware for $239.95 and that broke my stalemate. Visit also at 7003 S. Cooper in Arlington, 817/557-0007; 1841 W. Division in Arlington, 817/277-8441 and in Haltom City, 4850 N.E. Loop 820, 817/281-3394.

★★★★★★   Walker & Co.

214/744-3100
Mon-Fri 9-6; Sat 11-5

141 Glass St.
Dallas, TX 75207
www.importsfromabroad.com

Located in the Design District and affiliated with the award-winning designer, Susanne Walker, as president of the Premier Design Group, this company has opened its doors to the public, even if you're not a Tennessee Walker. Since 1995, the company has focused on outfitting model homes; however, those who saw Susanne's model home furnishings wanted to buy them. Her furniture line is a higher quality line of products for residential use at affordable prices. Shop for over 4,000 pieces of unfinished, stained, sprayed and handpainted exotic furniture and accessories from Indonesia and India. Their 18,000 square foot warehouse is brimming with the unusual and the dramatic and inventory is forever changing. Pieces are exquisitely hand-painted and handcrafted with a lot of attention paid to the myriad details that go into the making of much higher-priced furniture. A new fabulous SOHO line is in the works and will be arriving soon. No delivery or financing, so bring your checkbook and your own transport. Take the Oak Lawn exit off Stemmons and turn on Irving Blvd. Left to the first street called Glass.

★★★★   Weir's Clearance Center and More

214/528-0321
(Ask for Clearance Center)
Mon-Fri 10-5:30; Sat 10-6

4510 Buena Vista
Dallas, TX 75205
www.weirsfurniture.com/clearance

Just around the corner from their Knox Street Furniture Village at 3219 Knox Street, see what bargains are lurking for your discovery. And now, too, at their Plano location, located upstairs in their store at 5801 Preston Rd. (972/403-7878). No phone orders, holds or CODs, and a $50 delivery charge per stop within the Metroplex, but who cares if you're going to save substantial dinero? Many of the items, though, are "take with" so you might not even need to consider delivery. What you see is what you get in factory seconds, "as is" merchandise, clearance, odds and ends, mismatched, sanitized bedding, scratch and dent, handyman's specials, discontinueds, and some which are just plain and simple, value-priced. For example, a dining group crafted of hardwood solids and veneers in a heavily distressed walnut brown finish with black iron strap work was $299 for the table (instead of $699). Add an arm or side chair for $99 (instead of $179.) Set up and delivery will set you back a notch but check as it may not even be available, especially for the "handyman's specials." I just hate discrimination. You have to be perfect to get delivered, eh?

★★★★★   Woodbine Furniture   817/514-0372
8705 Davis Blvd.   Tues-Sat 10-5:30; Thurs 10-7; Sun Noon-5:30
North Richland Hills, TX 76180
www.woodbinefurniture.com

Shaker-up baby, let's rock and shop. Want that **RALPH LAUREN** look? Then look no more. Here's the source for Amish-made furniture crafted in small, individual wood- shops, built from scratch, one piece at a time. From country armoires to five-piece cherry wall-units, what makes this furniture so unique is that everything is crafted utilizing hand and medium-sized stationary tools. Choose from many different styles where seeing is believing. **COUNTRY, MISSION**, Queen Anne, and the sought-after Shaker styles abound or, if you prefer, custom work is available. Every room in the house can be accommodated: living room, bedroom, dining room, kitchen, play room, media room. There's more than 750 items in Woodbine's line. Most furniture is available in Oak, Cherry, Hickory and Walnut and available in 12 finishes. Delivery is available for $35; financing is with American General with six months, no interest. From the time you place your order, expect delivery in 8 to 12 weeks (remember, it's made by hand and by the Amish.) They're in no rush (or deal in cane, either.)

★★★★   Wooden Swing /Children's Furniture   972/386-6280
13617 Inwood Rd.   Mon-Fri 9-5; Thurs 9-7; Sat 10-6
Dallas, TX 75244
www.woodenswing.com

For the active tykes, get them the tree house in the August moon but let them enjoy their private space all year long. Thanks to this company, they can enjoy indoor and outdoor activities without missing a beat. Imagine keeping them up a tree without it costing a fortune? Just think what a pool costs? Sleep-a-way camp? A trip to Grandma's? For a fraction of the price, build them a vacation in your backyard to keep them looking up to the stars or looking forward to staying indoors for a sleep-over with their best friend. For example, keep them occupied with lots of space-saving bedroom suites, such as modular bedroom sets that grow as they grow right through their teen years and beyond. What kid wouldn't drool over his own set of bunk beds complete with a slide? Better yet a canopy bed? Maybe even captains beds and lots of imaginative twin beds? But remember, this furniture grows with your child well into their teen years, so you can count on its sturdiness and reliability. Learn more about their product line by logging on to their "swingin" website. Delivery available, though limited. Financing also available.

★   Your Furniture Connection   940/382-0690
733 Fort Worth Drive   Mon-Sat 9:30-6
Denton, TX 76201

Looks like they got out of the website business and decided it wasn't for them. Still, what you no longer see online is proudly displayed on their showroom floor on Fort Worth Drive in Denton. Their location may throw you off, but trust me, it's right there off Highway 377. Their July and January sales are legendary for the prices on all of their floor models, "scratch and dent" and such, but the rest of the time, well, see for yourself. When we asked about a full-sized bed, there were two choices: a solid wood spindle with headboard, footboard and rails for $799 and a metal one for $399. If you live in Denton Country, delivery was a steal at $25. Financing includes 90 days same as cash. Brand names from their past continue to reside close to their warehouse floor: **ASHLEY, HAMMARY, LA-Z BOY, MILLENNIUM, PULASKI, RIVERSIDE** and others—almost 40 different manufacturers. When we asked about last year's "Discounted" prices as we read in the Underground Shopper, the sales gal said emphatically, "WE ARE NOT DISCOUNTERS." So we suggest you listen and wait for their bi-annual sales. So be it! I guess being a discounter is verboten! Want to bet that I hear from them about their write-up this year? *Call toll-free: 800/ 658-8814*

Cantoni Outlet

See writeup on page 304

Gifts

Dallas Sample Sale

Abra-Cadabra
234 S. Main St.
Keller, TX 76248
ww.Abra-Cadabra-DÈcor.com.

817/337-3175
Mon-Sat 10-6; Closed Sun

 ♥ If you are a member of the "Two Old Broads who love to shop" club, then you will be right at home at this Keller jewel in the heart of historic downtown Keller. I can't think of another store like it in the Metroplex. From cards to inspirational, hand-made custom wall hangings, exquisite jeweled crosses to custom floral arrangements, tapestries to iron work for the patio or back yard, there's something to touch, admire, ogle or buy — you just can't help it. The store oozes with originality and stuff that is slam-dunk fabulous. Mostly one-of-a-kinds, from antiques to not-so-old home decor that your home will cry, more, more! Or what about yard art or ironwork for your patio? Bet you have never seen custom coasters with inspirational messages emblazoned or an entire room devoted to kitchen accessories and accents? The florals, the tapestries, the sculpture, the pottery, well, in every room of this restored historic house on Main Street in Keller is the place where heaven can be spent. You won't leave the store empty handed. Not from this lady who's name gives you a clue what else she sells. Proprietress Tari Fudge sells....you guess it! Hand-dipped chocolates — bless her heart, but I left without taking a bite. Everything else, though, I wanted to taste and none was priced out of the range of my fiscally-fit diet. Everything in her store is delicious. Log on to her website and then you, too, will become a believer.

★★★ Amber Room Gifts
1360 W. Campbell Rd., #113
Richardson, TX 75080
www.amberroomgifts.com

972/235-0086
Mon-Fri 11-7; Sat 10:30-6:30; Sun 1-5

Amber, amber burning bright, who's got the selection that is out of sight? The Amber Room does, no doubt about it. For unique, handmade amber jewelry imported from Poland (the country of origin for the charming owner,) one-of-a-kind gifts from around the world, decorative glass by the artist Blenko, Nemtol and others, Italian and French soaps and other bath delights, nobody does it better. If you like **GOEBAL** porcelain, **TRAPP & VOTIVO** candles, and the sought-after **LAMPE BERGER**, this is the place. Don't know what a Lampe Berger is? Well, first it's a beautiful ceramic bottle that comes in a variety of collectible designs. Second, it's like a candle whose scent lingers on and on while it cleanses, purifies and perfumes the room. Somehow through catalytic combustion (no flames are involved), the Lamp Berger eliminates odors, no kidding, including pesky fish smells and tobacco smoke while releasing a captivating aroma. However, we lit ours in one small office and almost were smelled to death. Make sure it goes in a room big enough to dissipate the powerful fumes. Over 150 designs and shapes with 36 fragrances. They even come unscented. Prices range from $49 to $109 (even up to thousands.) Visit also at Farmers Market downtown at 1010 Pearl St. in Dallas, 469/967-8898. It makes perfect scents.

★★★★   Another Time & Place   214/824-1875

2815 N. Henderson Ave.   Mon-Sat 10:30-6; Sun Noon-5
Dallas, TX 75206
www.anothertimeandplace.com

Stumbling across a treasure when you least expect it always makes for a perfect shopping excursion. That's just how we found this treasure. We wanted to pick up something to bestow upon those who were meeting us for a special business luncheon. Though I was "just looking," it didn't take long to ring up $100, although I was still "just looking." You can't help it. Everything is irresistible and affordable. Different. Unique. One-of-a-Kind. From jewelry to soaps, candles to clothing that you'll never see anywhere else. Though the shop is small and narrow, it's brimming literally floor to ceiling. Some of the glass candle holders were beckoning to go home with me, but, alas, I didn't have room on my ceilings to hang anything else. Cards to stocking stuffers, bet you can't buy just one! This couple, Mehmet Celilk and Lisa Raymer, have great taste and an eagle eye for bargains with a high-class look. Visit their second Another Time & Place at 7200 Bishop Road, Suite D6 in Plano, 972/398-0101. This store has all the right stuff for opening Another Time and Another Place. Watch them grow. There's even the possibility of buying it wholesale should you choose to resell their artifacts at during your Time & Place.

Basket Case, The   972/231-5100

700 University Village   Mon-Sat 10-6
Richardson, TX 75081
www.thebasketcaseonline.com

 More than 20 years in business and they're still a basket case. What did you expect? A Prozac-laden packaged plan? No, this company prepares baskets full of specialty items, thematically handpicked and put together in one basket for a personalized gift of simple but classic proportion. Celebrate the new baby, a birthday, wedding, anniversary, seasonal/holiday, or "just cause" — any occasion you can think of will give this company food for thought. Inventory changes but they always carry AROMATIQUE POTPOURRI, CAMILLE BECKMAN LOTIONS and TRAPP and YANKEE CANDLES. Expect baskets to start between $28-$35 for small, about $50 for the mediums and large baskets around $75. Make your former neighbors wish they were back in Texas with a delectable Texas basket that includes ADOBE HOUSE dips and chips, pralines and candies from LAMMES or better still, delectable treats from JARDINES. I'm salivating already and I haven't even moved. *Call toll-free: 866/231-5100*

★★★★   Beading Dreams   214/366-1112

5629 W. Lovers Lane   Sun-Mon 12-5; Tues-Sat 11-6
Dallas, TX 75209

Located between Inwood and the Tollway, this is where dreams begin and nightmares end. Ever wondered what to do with your spare time that's both creative and satisfying? Maybe even profitable? Be the next Diane Malouf (or is it Dian?) and start your own jewelry line that Neiman's has got to have. Bead down in a good night's chic by creating some of your own jewelry creations (although some ready-mades are also available). Beads are both precious and semi-precious like turquoise, citrine, peridot, coral, pearls plus glass and metals. Prices vary, but what price do you assign to your own imagination? It could be priceless, right? All supplies are available as well as classes, books and a knowledgable staff to guide you every bead at a time. Birthday parties for those 10 and over (minimum 12 children) start at $13 per person. What fun for the jet set's Diva's in Training (or Ditz's for short.) They couldn't have picked a better zip code to locate their business. So when Mama says, "Bead it!" you can head for here.

★★ Creative Gift Baskets & Balloons   972/633-9396

1717 E. Spring Creek Pkwy., #182   Mon-Sat 10-9; Sun Noon-6
Plano, TX 75074
www.creativegiftsofplano.com

We were hoping their new website would hold promise, but it was almost as flimsy as the old one. Besides, it's very confusing. What are we to do with only names of products (you have no idea what they are), no pictures, no prices? So, I guess, you wing it. All baskets here are custom-made with no pre-made baskets for purchase. So, if you want to start the ball rolling, prices start at $60 and the baskets take about an hour to assemble. Expect the outcome to be a creative gift basket and balloons, just as the name implies. But buying online, well, that's a whole other ballgame and no home runs were tallied this year. They still might be working on a new website as we speak. If you're tired of saying it with flowers, consider the alternatives: not sending anything, or going Creative. From balloons and gourmet gift baskets to something for the brides and grooms or what about a candlelight basket for their "First Anniversary?" Need to butter up the boss? Or a "Let's kiss and make up" basket? Hey, I've got a few of those on my list of things to do. Expect delivery charges to be extra from their storefront at the Plano Outlet Mall. *Call toll-free: 877/629-4994*

PS   Dallas Sample Sale   214/655-6181

2200 Stemmons Freeway   Fri Noon-6; Sat 10-6; Sun Noon-5
Dallas, TX 75207
www.dallasmarketcenter.com

Call the hotline for the sale time at Market Hall when they open these wholesale doors for their annual (no, bi-annual) sample sale. Shoppers anticipate this sale with baited bargain breath every year and now that's there are two of them, that means twice as often the opportunity to buy it wholesale. They huff. They puff. And now they're ready to blow the hall down just to get a glimpse of what's inside. In 2004, circle the weekend of November 5, 6, 7 for their Fall Sample Sale (2005, the dates have already been committed and they are November 4, 5, 6. Don't miss out on the best wholesale sample sale under the big roof. On Saturdays, we're usually broadcasting live from the show. (And I wanted to kill two birds with one stone. Since I always go to the sale and I always do my radio show on Saturdays, I might as well combine my two favorite activities!) Bring your checkbook. Most of the wholesale vendors prefer cash to credit. Watch newspapers, too, in case you haven't circled it on your calendar already. After one visit, you won't commit any further "Crimes of Passion"....oops, I mean "Fashion" as they always have plenty of apparel showrooms, gift and home decorative accents, and other vendors who choose to use this forum to clean out their showroom samples, at wholesale or below! Get with the program. You can shop where the retailers shop. Then again, you may even be a retailer who wants in on the action, too. The atmosphere's festive and the variety is the spice of the life of this show. This year, Richard Kollinger sold a $25,000 **CARTIER** watch for $10,000. Life is good. Life is better at half price.

★★★★★★   Distinctive Designs by Sherry   214/513-1745

2809 Justin Road, #11   By Appt. Only
Flower Mound, TX 75028-2450

 We had a hard time deciding where to put Sherry Taylor and the coterie of craftspersons who have joined forces with her in this almost-buried treasure. It takes more than a Geiger counter to find them behind the closed doors of this warehouse storage unit. Behind the Fina Gas Station, it's a "knock three times and see if they're even there" kind of place. But when the door opens, your mouth will drop as you see the assortment of unique accessories for your home or office. Indeed, this is how all great stores begin. They fit the bill to a T. No advertising. Only word of mouth will get you there. But on the third Saturday of each month, they open the doors to everyone and you will see the magnificent floral arrangements, the wholesale pewter gift items and the hand-made jewelry they create during their weeks off, only to sell out in one day. No kidding. Sherry is the ringleader with her elegant arrangements. Her imagination will leave yours lagging ten paces behind. She is a perpetual human creativity machine and wants to continue customizing unique floral arrangements — one arrangement at a time, all with natural flowers and unusual containers. Once you've found them, watch how word will spread even more!

★★★★★   Dr. Livingston Group   972/438-7272

1502 E. Irving Blvd   Mon-Fri 8-5
Irving, TX 75060

Here's an outlet that I presume will be one of your favorites. But finding it can be a challenge. Once inside, though, you'll find the trip a worthwhile adventure. If Dr Livingston could find his way around the world and even send gifts to those who remained at home. So why not buying one yourself? The stock varies, but jewelry is no longer a part of their plan. They are still closed on the weekends, but they're worth adding to your weekday menu of "must shop stores!" Assorted lamps, artifacts, antique reproductions, woodcarvings, baskets, home accessories, and collectibles line the shelves. They have it all — from market samples to closeouts, all below wholesale prices. Restaurants shop here as do retail stores for some of their decorative accents. Good things come to those who shop the outlet way. Haven't I always told you so? Exit Loop 12 and go three miles south of Texas Stadium at Irving Blvd. Go west three miles. Make a U-turn at E. 6th. See, I told you it would be a challenge.

★★★★★★   Er'go Candle Outlet Store   214/905-9050

9200 W. Carpenter Frwy. @ Regal Row   Mon-Sat 10-4
Dallas, TX 75247
www.ergocandle.com

 If it's Oprah's favorite, then count me in, too. Talk about the ultimate candle outlet. Sweeter scents were never created. Don't be a drip; find your way on the highway at the Regal Row exit and find closeouts, overstocks, incompletes, leftovers, poured in the wrong glass, private labels, whatever's your aromatic pleasure, you can become addicted. Take advantage of all of their mishaps and go with the glow. Er'go candles are considered the premium blend of affordability and essence, so imagine having to get your fix on a regular basis. For two years in a row, they have been voted the best candles and Oprah says it's the real thing - "a genuine aromatherapy candle." The Diva says, "It's scents-ible chic and cheap!" Their new and improve manufacturing site is spacious and clean. You can even see them producing and pouring right there on the premises. Jimmy Belasco is the gifted nose who knows how to make the best candles in the world. Now the Diva knows where to buy the best candles in the world at $5 and $10. Call for your buy 3 and get one free coupon waiting for you at the outlet IF you tell them the Diva sent you.

 For Goodness Sake! A Gift Shop   **214/691-9411**

NorthPark Center, Second Level   Mon-Sat 10-9; Sun 12-6
Dallas, TX 75225
www.forgoodnesssake.net

Upstairs and next to Lord & Taylor, the formerly Our Children's Store of Dallas is now For Goodness Sake. But nothing else has changed from its original mission of mercy and dedication to the charitable contributions it makes to the community. Every time you make a purchase, you make a difference. Thanks to this cooperative effort between the Dallas business community, non-profit organizations, community volunteers and others who are dedicated to providing relief to children in crisis, your purchases do double duty. One hundred percent of the proceeds from every sale goes to the 17 local agencies benefiting children in need. This is all accomplished with donations from major manufacturers, samples from wholesale showrooms and other contributions, freely given. Then proceeds of the sales are distributed to the children's charities. Located between Neiman's and Lord & Taylor on the second level, expect lots of housewares, china and crystal, gifts — both fun and expensive — whatever's donated is what you'll see. See the unusual and the unique; jewelry designer, Patricia Tschetter, even presented her newest collection in person at this location. Thousands of gift items — from cheap to costly—although most are $50 and under. Shopping for the holidays is a smash hit with holiday items, pet gifts, greeting cards, picture frames, specialty baskets and much more. And what a fine service it is.

Handmade & Co.   **972/480-9202**

1455 W. Campbell   Mon-Sat 10-6
Richardson, TX 75080

 Who can resist those fabulous LITTLE SOLES dolls with their gingham pinafores and their patent leather shoes? I absolutely go gaga over them! Gotta have at least one new one to add to my collection every year. (See, I was deprived of dolls as a child and I'm making up for it as a grown-up!) This company sells many things that are hand-made, although not everything is. Now that the cat is out of the bag, do you care? Located next to the Richardson Bike Mart, they're now putting together small gift baskets with items from throughout the store. Handmade-in-a basket couldn't be a more perfect gift to give to a person who has everything. For example, they have the JEEP COLLINS line of sterling, gold or brass bracelets, made in the Hill Country, and similar to JAMES AVERY in quality and price. If you like one, you'll like the other. For unique gifts and collectibles, this little shop also carries candle lines by ASPEN BAY, TRAPP, VILLAGE DAY and YANKEE plus all of the TY products. Maybe you're a collector of those SCARBOROUGH & CO. wooden houses? Or the VERA BRADLEY purses? Ever wonder where to buy monogrammed guest towels and napkins? See, I told you they've got everything, but inventory changes frequently, so shop often. And don't miss the clearance shelves. Of course, that's where I always head first.

★★★★★★   **Havelka Enterprises**   **817/222-1141**

4913 Airport Freeway
Fort Worth, TX 76117
www.havelka.com

 Ah, the sweet smell of success. Judy Havelka has single-handedly revolutionized the home fragrance business. Talk about a Garden of Eden for your home or office. Heavenly scents created with some of the most imaginative botanicals. Nothing beats a beautifully-scented room to put your mind at ease. Set the mood with fragrant pot-pourri and buy it direct at the manufacturer/maker of these extraordinary botanicals. Nobody has put this industry on notice. Judy Havelka has. Rooms without her are just plain boring. These handmade natural explosion of gragrance, color and texture are in a class (or glass) all by themselves. Choose potpourri, candles, room sprays, oils, botanicals and accessories that put them at the head of the glass. Over 40 fragrances spanning the full plethora of possibilities: aromatherapy, florals, citrus, fruits, spices and food odors that will make your salivate as well as luxuriate. Talk about getting down to earth, you should smell their natural earth aromas like a breath of fresh air. Expect to see these botanicals at specialty stores, hotels and spas, salons, furniture stores, galleries, wherever they want to create the ambience of luxury and relaxation. Buy direct at their factory outlet and save. Just get in line and don't you dare take cuts. Just make room for the Diva and all the Divas behind me.

★★★★★   **Horchow Finale**   **972/519-5406**

3400 Preston Rd.   Mon-Fri 10-7; Sat 10-6; Sun Noon-5
Plano, TX 75093
www.horchow.com

You may know the name **NEIMAN MARCUS** (or at best, Last Call), but do you know Horchow....Roger Horchow, the founder of the Horchow Collection (now owned by Neiman's) and the New York producer of Broadway revivals? Well, Roger's out and The Finale Shops are in. This step-child to the giant mail-order mogul's catalog sells the remains of the day. Chi-chi fashions for the home and closet are temptingly displayed on the gorgeous pages of their catalogs. Log on to their website, if you want to be on their mailing list. Then, when the catalogue arrives, dream on! And that's where the Finale Shop comes to the rescue. What doesn't move fast enough wends its way to The Finale Shop, at a fraction of the price. You can save 30 to 70 percent off the catalog's prices. And the merchandise is beautiful with meaningful bargains, giving us all a pause that refreshes. Second location is at 3046 Mockingbird Lane (at the northwest corner of Mockingbird and Central Expressway in Dallas), 214/750-0308. *Call toll-free: 800/456-7000*

★★★★   **International Market Place**   **469/867-8898**

1010 S. Pearl, Building #2   Tues-Fri 10-5; Sat-Sun 9-6
Dallas, TX 75201

Want to take the Concorde around the world and forgo jet lag? Then, slash the prices to current currency woes and here we goes....down to Farmers Market to buy, to buy. This little pinkie went to Market, Farmers Market and found a worldwide selection of unique gifts from around the globe. Expect prices to be low under the tin roof. See hand-carved furniture and wooden accents, hand-blown glass, Mexican pottery, figurines and collectibles, hand-painted ceramic pottery, wrought iron furniture, crafted tin, handmade silver jewelry, gourmet coffee, African carvings, mirrors, amber jewelry and the oft-asked-for **LAMPE BERGE** (don't expect to see it discounted (though it's better to light just one little Lampe Berger, than to stumble in the dark.) It's a fun

weekend excursion for the multitude of diversions. Plus, you're right smack in the middle of produce row (s). And that's how is goes!

★★★★   Mark & Larry's Stuff   214/747-8833

2614 Elm St.   Sun-Mon 12-5; Tues-Thurs 11-7; Fri-Sat 11-9
Dallas, TX 75226
www.mark-larry-stuff.com

It's all in the name....of fun. And that's exactly what Mark Sonna and Larry Groseclose have in
their Deep Ellum repository and their second location in downtown Dallas in the old Woolworth
Building at Elm and Stone (214/760-8833, Mon-Wed, 10-6; Thurs-Fri 10-8; Sun 1-5). When they
opened their doors in 1995, they became a roaring overnight success. Their huge eclectic inventory (3,000 items) includes inexpensive watches, dolls, purses, chairs, pet items, perfume, toys,
cards (largest card selections in the city with over 2,500 choices) and goat milk soap for $3.99.
They have emerged as the darlings of print media who always look for something quirky. Looking
for a Spin-o-matic ashtray that makes ashes disappear with the push of a button for $14.95? I
remember those. The rather unusual store hours attract a rather unusual crowd. Returns and
exchanges are permitted up to seven days after purchase with a receipt. All sales are final on jewelry, discounted merchandise, bath accessories, artist pieces, custom orders and seasonal items.
These two guys love retailing and it shows. They are both showmen and what a swell party it is!

★★★★★★   Mary Lou's Gifts & Collectibles   972/466-1460

1017 S. Broadway   Mon-Sat 10:30-5:30
Carrollton, TX 75006

 After 20 years, you can't help but want to skip to Mary Lou's. Her store's a Lou
Lou. It's fun. It's fabulous. And it's affordable. And I bet you can't leave with just
one! Located in downtown Historic Old Downtown Carrollton, across from the Carrollton Skin Spa, you can relax under the myriad of skincare treatments and then cross back over
the street after they've put your best face on. You won't get a facelift at Mary Lou's but you can
get a wardrobe and gift lift. Every compliment I get on my knockout sterling silver mosaic-tile
ring, I think of Mary Lou. After one stop, you will load up with some gorgeous outfits, ladies and
some unusual gift items all of which have been hand-picked by this veteran merchant. If you're in
to collectibles at great prices, start adding to your collections of ANNALEE, BYER'S CHOICE,
BOYD'S BEARS, FENTON ART GLASS, LIZZIE HIGH DOLLS, "TY" and others that are
coveted as a collectible for generations. She has exquisite taste and it shows in her store brimming
with boutique bargains in every nook and cranny. This secret stash is out of the bag and I bet
you'll want to come back for more. Mary Lou is one of those old-fashioned merchants who caters
to her clientel as if each one is her best friend. Talk about a change of pace. How refreshing a generation makes.

Near and Far   214/219-3839

3699 McKinney Ave. @ Blackburn   Mon-Wed 10-8; Thurs-Sat 10-9; Sun 12-6
Dallas, TX 75204
www.nearandfargifts.com

 West Village is hopping and Near and Far is one of the hip hoppin'reasons. Although
they've closed their Lovers Lane location, the other location at The Shops at Legacy
(5800 Legacy Drive in Plano, 214/473-8768) is coming in loud and clear. If you're
looking for an imaginative gift, and candles are one of your favorites, to give and to get, then consider traveling Near and Far. One of my personal favorites is the TRAPP candle for $22 that will

burn 100 hours in Orange Vanilla. Another is ER'GO, especially the Hawaiian Jasmine and the Pink Grapefruit. Former fashion editor for D Magazine, Jeanne Tave, has created her own candle line. Her company develops and manufactures scented candles and fragrances whose names play on the words true and faux. Her scented candles are called "Couture Candles" and she packages them in drawstring pouches made from recycled clothing. The fabric pouches reflect each season's fashionable looks. Also, she has created a fragrance line called "Soul Scents." You can find her stuff at Near and Far at 20 percent off. Website is a work in progress.

Noel Christmas Store   972/991-8481

12835 Preston Road, Suite 401   Mon-Sat 10-6; Sun 12-6 (Oct-Dec); Open Year 'round
Dallas, TX 75230-7200

 When the seasonal mania hits, there is no better store than The Christmas Store to find what you need, want, didn't need or didn't want —until you see it here, tucked away at the southwest corner of Preston and LBJ. The 5,000 square foot holiday decor store will impact you the minute you step foot inside. Decorator Charles Story has worked his talented fingers to the "cone" to create some of the most dramatic and awe-inspiring trees imaginable. The CADILLAC of trees, BARTHELMESS™, are the only trees you'll see because they are the best in the business. These German-made trees come with a 25-year guarantee and they're patented because of its "umbrella" tree construction. Since 1987, Peggy Chappell has dedicated herself to finding the most unusual, the most unique and the most sought-after ornaments, collectibles, decorations, lights and quality items that can be bought year 'round. My favorite collectibles are the SNOW VILLAGE ORNAMENTS, LEGENDARY BALLPARK SERIES and the NORTH POLE VILLAGE HOUSES. And lights — do they ever have lights! This is one item that is popular all-year long. Enjoy the Noel Christmas Store during the holidays and the other 364 days of the year. I even bought a wedding gift of a wedding ornament that was treasured by the young couple since it was the first ornament they got as a couple. I was touched by their appreciation. I also got a wonderful dental village for my dentist when he moved to his new offices. So, here's one Jewish girl who found happiness at the Noel Christmas Store.

★★★★★   PMG Factory Outlet   972/724-2111; 972/724-1623

4260 Justin Road (F.M. 407)   Mon-Fri 9-5; Sat 9-4
Highland Village, TX 75077
www.patchmagic.com

The magic to decorating begins at Patch Magic. Everything imaginable can be added to transform your home, your bedroom, your baby's room, your wardrobe. Since 1987, when the company was founded by Sukhminder Boparai to fill the niche in high-quality designer quilts and accessories, Patch Magic has realized the potential in creating an entire line built on their quilt manufacturing facility in India. Whether for baby bedding, kitchen accessories, children's and women's apparel, floor coverings and yes, even furniture and wrought iron. They have an outlet at their distribution facility west of Lewisville in Highland Village. With over 140 styles to choose from in patchwork or appliquÈs, they seem never to run out of design possibilities. If you ever wanted a coordinated look for a baby's room, this is the place to get covered from top to bottom. From nursery rhymes to golf, the great outdoors to seasonal motifs, add in coordinated accessories, floor coverings, apparel, hand-carved and hand-painted wooden furniture, the list is a patchwork of possibilities. Look for the parking lot on Justin Road (FM 407) just west of FM 2499 where you'll see a van that says "Big Sale." Across from the new Home Depot in Flower Mound. *Call toll-free: 888/ 728-2462*

★★★★   Trinity Candle Factory   972/262-4360

113 S. Center St.   Mon-Sat 11-6
Grand Prairie, TX 75050
www.trinitycandlefactory.com

When you least expect it, you often find it. In this case, we found the light in old downtown Grand Prairie (Highway180 and Center Street) not too far from our long-time favorite, Tommy Snodgrass. This factory-direct candle shop specializes in wicks for your homes. Great deals on them, as a matter of fact. For example, their 16 oz. jar candles were $12.99 (MRSP was $16.99), so every little wick helps. To conserve and contribute to the recycling effort, just bring your container back for a refill for $11.50. Then, mark your calendar for their daily sales: Tuesdays, two 16 oz. jars are priced at $22; Wednesdays, slice 15 percent off pillar candles; Thursdays, buy 12 votives and get three free. Here goes the scentsible list: Almond Bark, Apple, Peach, Fresh Baked Bread, Gardenia, Gingerbread, Hazelnut Latte, Heather, Irish Cream, Jasmine, Key Lime Pie, Lemon Chiffon, Lily of the Valley, Mango Mango, Oatmeal Raisin Cookie, Pear Glace, Blueberry Fields, Chocolate Fudge — no calories but it smells the part. Just one mile south of Lone Star Park, four miles from Six Flags over Texas and 4.5 from the Ballpark in Arlington on Highway 180 (Main Street). Across from Jack-in-the-Box. So food is very much in their equation. It makes scents, don't you agree? *Call toll-free: 877/631-1894*

★★   Welcome Home   254/582-9488

Prime Outlets of Hillsboro   Mon-Sat 10-8; Sun 11-6
104 NE I-35 (Exit 368) Hillsboro, TX 76645
www.outletbound.com

There's nothing like coming home and being greeted with a warm and genuine welcome. Well, this is a store that helps keep it cozy. Keep it homey, honey. Although this is not on my chosen few list, they must be doing something right with locations in almost every factory outlet mall in the country. (See the website above to read all about their locations.) On the plus side, they do have a commendable selection of crystal and silver accent pieces, **BEARLY BEARS** and **MANN** dolls (just don't take her across state lines). Throws and lace doilies, well, one out of two ain't bad. Set your table for your next dinner party and make it zing with coordinating napkin rings and candlesticks. Add an afghan to the sofa or recliner, and you're almost home. Also visit at the Allen Premium Outlets, Prime Outlets of Gainesville and Tanger Outlet Mall in Terrell. They've closed their Denton Factory Stores location so you're not welcomed there any more.

★   Wishing Well Collectors Plates   817/244-0340

8652 Spur 580   Tues-Thurs 10:30-6; Fri-Sat 10:30-5
Fort Worth, TX 76116

If a store's got an answering machine, well, why bother? I needed directions and I didn't need to make a production out of it. They do sell **Hummels** and discount them 15 percent (or so the rumor goes). Well, that may lure you in to the store but frankly, we're still waiting for a call back. If you are adventurous and like collecting collector plates, we wish you well. This may be just wishful thinking, however. Although it looks like you are going to have to pay the piper to pay hommage to these collectibles, you may find haggling an option. Beside **HUMMELS, LILLIPUT COTTAGES, SERAPHIM ANGELS, BOYDS** and **HARBOR LIGHTS**. Digging a little deeper, we discoverd that the **SERAPHIM ANGELS** are often refered to as "The Voice of God." Seraphims are supposedly the Angels closest to the throne of God. They speak to mankind for God because God's voice is too powerful for our human bodies to withstand. Seraphims exist off the love that God emanates. It is this fiery love that makes Seraphims impossible to look at, even by other divine beings, because of the intense light they give off. There is said to be four of these angelic beings. They are listed as the four holy beasts in the Book of Revelation and are also described as angels with four faces and six wings. It got me spooked, so I moved on to the Harbor Lights. Note they are closed Sunday and Monday and mostly are selling their wares as full price (MSRP).

Dallas Sample Sale

See writeup on page 337

Handbags & Luggage

★ **Airline Ventures @ Ballpark Inn**　　　　　**817/226-2525**

903 N. Collins, #101　　　　　　　　　　　　　　　Mon-Fri 9-5
Arlington, TX 76011-6081
www.avishop.com

Finally, they've stabilized and leveled off in the stores that are sought by traveling professionals like pilots and flight attendants. In addition to the Arlington store, a store at the DFW Airport-Terminal C (972/574-3607) is open Monday through Friday (9 to 5) and Saturday (10 to 2), and one other store is open in Fort Worth at the Flight Crew Gift Shop (817/967-5540). They sell at a discount to the traveling public, as well. And who should know what sells to those on the go better than a pilot and his flight-attendant wife? Specializing in carry-on luggage such as totes, duffels, cosmetic bags, rolling bags, garments bags, expandable suiters, overnighters and flight bags, you can carry them to kingdom come. Brands included: **BRIGGS & RILEY**, **SAMSONITE**, **TRAVEL-PRO** and more. They also are the official company for American Airlines'uniforms and logo items. Then again, do you want to board a **DELTA** or Southwest Airlines'flight in an AA T-shirt? A **BRIGGS & RILEY** deluxe tote that would retail for $119.99 was $114.95. How's that for a deal? Whoopee! A deluxe garment bag (46 by 24 by 4) that retailed for $399.99 was reduced to $295.59, a much better buy but nothing that would avoid a bumpy landing. A softside portfolio (8 by 13 by 19), retailing for $219.95, was $189.95 (back to being hum-drum). So, what's a beleaguered traveler to do but pack it in....elsewhere! *Call toll-free: 800/874-1204*

★★★ **Bag n' Baggage Outlet**　　　　　　　**214/355-3050**

11065 Petal St.　　　　　　　　　　　　Mon-Fri 9-5:30; Sat 10-4
Dallas, TX 75238
www.bagn-baggage.com

I remember the founding owners from years past, but my, oh my, how times have changed! The new owners took the bull by the horn and have grown to epic proportions to become one of the leading luggage retailers in the country with 80 stores to date in eight states. However, their outlet store at Grapevine Mills leaves us groping for more. Having a section devoted to 20 percent discounts and the rest at full price does not an outlet make. Often, repaired pieces are left unclaimed and wind up in the outlet. Online, look for monthly specials that might include a **FREE** duffel bag with purchase of a two-piece set or money-saving deals on flasks, valets and **PALM PILOT** cases. You can save with rebates, too. The complete lineup of brands sounds like the Red Book of Blue Bloods: **AT CROSS, ANDIAMO, DAKOTA, EAGLE CREEK, FOSSIL, FRENCH** (a personal favorite), **GHURKA, HARTMANN, HUGO BOSCA, JACK GEORGES, JANSPORT, KEN-**

NETH COLE, KIPLING, LODIS, PATHFINDER, RETRO 1951, SAMSONITE, SCULLY, TIM-
BERLAND, THE SAK, TRAVELPRO, TUMI and ZERO HALLIBURTON. Small leather goods
and writing instruments from MONTBLANC, WATERMAN and others. But wait until there's a
sale on before you set sails — at their outlet. The other 11 Metro locations are strictly mall, full
price retail stores.

★★   Cases Unlimited   214/343-3494

10757 Mapleridge Drive   Mon-Fri 9-5:30; Sat 10-6; Sun Noon-5
Dallas, TX 75238
www.casesunlimited.com

Case closed. This is a wholesale supplier of leather and vinyl attaches, briefcases, pens and accessories, so why travel the world to find a world of difference? Two blocks south of LBJ at the Plano
Rd. exit, you'll find AMERICAN TOURISTER, KLUGE and TRAVELWELL luggage promoted
at sizeable savings — but head to their closeout section for those that are really substantial. They
are also the Starwalk Party Rental Company specializing in birthday parties, carnivals, church
fundraisers and corporate events. They rent giant inflatable slides, obstacle courses, fun houses,
"Bounce Houses" (8'by 8'to 26',) castles, dragons, lions, ponies, clowns, sports games, carnival
games, dunk tanks, concession stands, even generators. On our last foray, we dug some funky,
hand-tooled saddle cases, rifle cases and handbags, but disregarded the SAMSONITE soft-side
carry-ons in three colors at $139.50, as the prices appeared too close to retail. Website tips for
repairs on cases were unlimited (and appreciated.) *Call toll-free: 800/536-3496*

★★★★★★   Choice Jewelry & Accessories   972/818-3133

17194 Preston Road, Suite 120   Mon-Fri 10-7; Sat 10-6; Sun 12-4
Dallas, TX 75248

 At the northeast corner of Preston and Campbell (in the Kroger Shopping Center,) it's your choice. But given your choice, would you opt for
the real designer purse or the "knock-off?" Let's call it like it is. Reality
shows are not so popular if we didn't want to covet the way it is in the "real world!" If it looks the
part at a fraction of the price, why not buy two or three? Some of these purses look so real, you'd
think they were, but when you see the prices, you'll know they're not. You pay for what you get
and these lookalikes do look the part. If you never want to leave home without your COACH,
DOONEY & BOURKE, FENDI, KATE SPADE, LOUIS VUITTON and PRADA, well, these will
do you just find. Even if it's an interpretation of a designer bag, the quality's superb and the prices
sensational. Mariam Kebere also carries some of the "real" bags; the only difference is the price
(compared to the specialty boutiques around town.) Don't leave home without one of her funky
bags with feathers and boas, faux fur, cigar box purses, exquisite evening bags that had Diva written all over them. I bought a black velvet clutch for $37 that was drop dead gorgeous with a pew-
ter-carved handle. Find costume jewelry, custom one-of-a-kind jewelry and other fashionable
accessories to accompany your new handbag. Mariam makes gorgeous jewelry on site to match
that special outfit. Just bring it in for inspiration. And her husband, Gene, gets his inspiration in his
back private hair salon where clients (some famous, some not) are coifed to the hilt with his artistry (he was Jose Eber's former partner.) Cut, Color, Perms. But no updo's for prom princesses.

★★★★★ Dixie's Fashion Accessories Outlet   817/649-1112

2500 E. Randol Mill Rd., #113   Mon-Fri 9-6; Sat 10-5
Arlington, TX 76011
www.dixiesoutlet.com

You'll whistle Dixie when you cross over to this side of the Mason-Dixie line. Scoring a home run is easy being so near the Ballpark at Arlington. You're but a hop, skip and a slide into home base for a grand slam. Here's a great little mom and pop source for handbags, totes, gift items, garden accessories, candles, candy and jewelry. Buy it all at a discount. Make note of the gift sets, bath products, leather accessories, sunglasses, key rings, Christian bracelets, oh Dixie, how we love Dixie's. *Call toll-free: 800/535-6825*

Fat Rat   972/931-3366

17811 Davenport Road, Suite 54   By Appt. Only or Online
Dallas, TX 75252
www.ishopwow.com   ⌐ *Top Online Store!*

First, the name Fat Rat. Margee King is Fat Rat, the mother of the rats, the mother of invention. Not some nasty rodent that you wished would live elsewhere, but her signature name for all of her custom furniture, purses, shoes and clothes that she manufactures. See Fat Cat's creations on her website. See Fat Rat's prices on their website. Everything Margie King manufactures is "Wow!" Quality with every stitch, at every dove tail joint, at every heel and handle, she uses only the finest fabrics and accoutrements in boa and ostrich feathers. Everything is one-of-a-kind. Want sandals to match every outfit? Want a purse to go with every outfit and every pair of shoes? That's what turns her creative juices on high gear. She's also one of the most sought-after decorators in town. Yes, she builds and decorates custom homes. She even builds houses. Call for an appointment to see her lines up close and personal if you'd rather not order online.

★★ J. Tiras Classic Handbags   214/956-8181

5600 W. Lovers Lane, Suite 122   Mon-Sat 10-6
Dallas, TX 75225
www.jtiras.com

These used to be copies of the best, so a knockoff of a **JUDITH LEIBER** was, indeed, something to write home about. Today, this Houston-based company has endured lawsuits brought about by some of the designers they've copied, and it looks like you're paying for their legal skirmishes. Even with copies, you can expect to tote a note with the prices here. Beautiful handbags and accessories. Online there is an occasional sale. Spending $60 to $80 for a slipper is not something most moms would find practical, yet cute, I admit. Some of their purses have been featured in In-Style and Woman's Day magazines which means even mass magazines have good taste. Frankly, some of their bags look like the same as those at Sam Moon's, just displayed in a more opulent setting. Based in Houston, Jeannie Tiras and her husband have taken their road show sales and established roots in both cities now and it sure means less schlepping for them. (Their Houston store is across from the Galleria, 5000 Westheimer which is the high rent district, for sure.) Their latest haircalf bags started as low as $164 up to $285. Not what I would call a steal. But initial bags were half price just as they are elsewhere since we are at the peak of its popularity and declining as we speak. Everyone else's initial bags are half price, too. The cuff band watches, of which there were many to choose from were at least $28 —but at Sam Moon's, they appeared to be $10.50. Too, see what Sam Moon is selling his initial purses for. Of course, the quality may be better at J. Tiras, but they sure looked the same to me. *Call toll-free: 800/460-1990*

★★★★★★   **Sam Moon Trading**   **972/484-3083**

11826 Harry Hines Blvd.   Mon-Sat 9-6:30
Dallas, TX 75234
www.sammoongroup.com

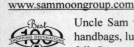 Uncle Sam wants you! Enlist his help if you want the premiere source for gifts, handbags, luggage and jewelry on the street of dreams, Harry Hines. In fact, this past fall, Sam went big time with his two grand slam openings. One's just across to the other side of Harry Hines and LBJ and another in Frisco at Hwy. 121 and Preston Road (2449 Preston.) He outgrows his "new" locations faster than the busses can find a parking place. HAGGAR Outlet has become their anchor tenant and none too soon since they wanted out of their Lemmon Ave. headquarters. Sam Moon's new center is a 125,000 square foot bargain-shopping emporium built in a u-shaped, easy to pull up to each front door shopping experience. Easy to shop. Easy to drop a bundle. Sam is also test marketing a home decor store there to add to the mix of building his own shopping empire besides becoming a significant real estate developer. He is the granddaddy of "underground shopping" and a legend in his own time. His sons, Sam and Daniel, are carrying on in the finest tradition. Watch this space. Watch them grow. watch for more copycat Sam Moon stores. Ask any woman where she buys her jewelry, handbags, scarves and more and if they are in the know, they'll say Sam Moon is where they go — to save the dough. Oh, did I forget to mention he's THE source for brief cases and attaches, picture frames, toys, backpacks, hair pieces and perfume, too. The Frisco location at Highway 121 and Preston Rd. (2449 Preston Rd., 214/297-4200) is open and has contributed to as much excitement as is generated by a Krispy Kreme opening. Only Sam Moon is low fat and low carb. The only days they close is on New Years Day, Independence Day, Thanksgiving Day and Christmas.

World Traveler   **800/314-2247 (BAGS)**

225 Larkin Drive   24/7
Wheeling, IL 60090
www.worldtraveler.com   ☞ *Top Online Store!*

 When it comes to luggage, there's nobody better than this former Grapevine Mills merchant. It's just that these days you'll have to travel to Chicago to shop them in person. I say, stay home and hop aboard the online train. Save tons of money if you're a travelin'man, and spend it on your destination, not your traveling companions. So if you have aspirations to be a world traveler, hop aboard their website for all your travel needs. Save 20 to 70 percent and still get complete manufacturer's warranties, great customer service, and the lowest price guarantee. Offering the largest selection of luggage I've ever seen and a 100 percent customer satisfaction guarantee, names that will go in the overhead compartment include: AMERICAN TOURISTER, ATLANTIC, BRIGGS & RILEY, DAKOTA, DELSEY, HARTMANN, JANSPORT, KENNETH COLE, LARK, RICARDO/BEVERLY HILLS, SAMSONITE, SKYWAY, TRAVELPRO, VENTURA and ZERO HALLIBURTON. On another purchase, we found a SAMSONITE "Aspire Expandable" 30-inch upright suiter that retailed for $280 but was $118 here. Expect to pay 40 percent off HARTMANN luggage and a SAMSONITE "Flite" 31-inch upright in five colors was $119. Another must-have was an ATLANTIC "Infinity II" carry-on suiter for $79.99. They will not be undersold; they will meet or beat competitors'prices. They want you to be completely satisfied! Being a bag lady from here is a compliment. *Call toll-free: 800/314-2247*

Health & Fitness

Prescription Assistance Services for Seniors
See writeup on page 478

★★★ Abundant Life Health Foods

972/221-1210
Mon-Sat 8:30-7

1130 W. Main
Lewisville, TX 75067

Looking for the staff of life? Then consider the staff at this family-owned, full-fledged grocery/ health food store that is 100 percent organic from the git-go. From the produce to the canned goods, this is farm-fresh from the ground floor up. Located in a strip shopette in Lewisville, between the bank and the Coffee Mill, they leave no stone (ground) unturned. From flours milled the old-fashioned way to vitamins, minerals and herbs, they can guide you along the path of nature's own. If there is a product that you would like to have and they don't carry it, they will find it for you. Closed on Sundays, still, they've been an open and caring resource for healthy alternatives in the neighborhood since 1975. The knowledgeable owner and other staff personnel take a real interest in your well-being and seem to know what nature had in mind as a remedy. Their growing stock responds to what ails you. And when you shop there, you'll experience the camaraderie that exists between health food addicts. Once you grab your cart and start down the aisle, you'll hear about someone's latest remedy for what may ail you. Or the greatest skin cream. Or the latest diet craze. It's like over the garden fence, only more expensive. Information-rich rather than prices-to-make-you-sick should be your reason for shopping at Abundant Life.

◆◆◆ Affirmed Medical Inc.

972/774-9777
Mon-Fri 8-5

13766 Beta Road
Dallas, TX 75244
www.cintas-corp.com

Got a boo-boo at work? Then get with the program. First aid supplies, kits, cabinets and van-delivered safety products are what you can expect from here, just don't Xpect to be able to leave a message before the answering machine cuts you off. Formerly Xpect First Aid Products, they still sell safety glasses, hearing aids and respiratory protection products. Whether your business is large or small, if employees' welfare is a consideration, then consider this company's services. Do employees have to lift heavy boxes or equipment? Well, don't let them scream out in pain. Make sure they're wearing some kind of back support. Get those here, too. And if you want someone designated as a First Aid specialist, call upon them to provide a CPR/first aid training class or the OSHA Compliance training program. I know, I know. You didn't know who to call. That's why you need me. And I love to feel needed. Bring in the emergency oxygen — I can't breathe. Be prepared. It's more than just the Boy Scout's motto. *Call toll-free: 800/878-7152*

★★★★ Arbrook Affordable Retirement Living 817/446-4792

1101 E. Arbrook Blvd.   By Appt. Only
Arlington, TX 76014
www.thecovenantgroup.com

If you'd rather pay less and receive fewer amenities upon retirement, this unique six-acre senior
housing complex might be just what the doctor ordered. Developed by the Covenant Group out of
Fort Worth, their niche may fit the bill. First off, you may be plain and simple and find it unnecessary for a lot of the bells and whistles. For example, in the monthly fee you pay, there are only two
meals daily and bi-monthly visits from a housekeeper rather than weekly. As long as there's
access to outside health care resources, this non-profit facility is for folks who do not need any
health-care assistance. Rates start at $895 to $1,845 for a two-bedroom unit. Remember, your
monthly rate includes meals. There's a neat barber shop, a general store, an exercise room and
walking trails just for residents. If you figure what it costs for a nursing home (about $3,500/
month) or at an assisted-living facility (around $3,000/month), you can see what a bargain this is.
They have seven floor plans with full kitchens, and, in addition to meals, the fees include transportation to shopping, banks, medical appointments, festivals and events. There are other complexes
around the Metroplex, so check them all out and see which place is perfect for your retirement
needs.

★★★ Blue Cottage Herb Farm   903/498-4234

8050 FM 4030   Mon-Fri 10-6
Kaufman, TX 75142
www.herbfarmacy.com

Go 35 miles southwest of Dallas to Kaufman and see how the other half lives out in the country.
Make a stop at Blue Cottage Herb Farm if you're seeking home-grown herbs for medicinal purposes. Purchase them by phone or in person, either way, you can ease the pain. Online sales may
be available soon, so stay tuned. See an herb farm in all it's greenery. Alongside the greens, they
have other natural products such as extracts, capsules, powders, oils, teas, vinegars, candles and
books for sale, workshops to improve spirit, mind and body that include Herbs & Health, Yoga &
Fitness, and Massage & Bodywork. They offer therapeutic and aromatherapy massages by
appointment, but there're only open during the week. Too bad. How many folks have the time during the week to take off to a retreat? Take Highway 175E, through Kaufman, about eight miles
past the Kaufman Exit. Turn left on FM 2860 and go about 2.5 miles to the stop sign at FM 1895.
Proceed through the intersection, there's a Methodist church on the left and Blue Cottage Herb
Farm on the right. If you've got a hankerin'for herbs, see for yourself during a tour of their greenhouses and a stop over in their herb shop to buy the dried and fresh herbs, including those that are
recommended for what ails you. Call ahead before you depart on your journey.

◆◆◆◆◆ Crazy Water Retirement Hotel   940/327-5000

401 N. Oak   Mon-Fri 8-5 (office hours)
Mineral Wells, TX 76067-4969

Crazy as a bed bug? It takes an acorn to grow into a nut, so count me in at the Crazy Water Retirement Hotel on Oak Street. Under new ownership, they've gone up on their single room ($50) so
now it costs $650, but reduced charges ($50) for a suite to $800/month. Still a deal! An all-inclu-
sive retirement environment consisting of 169 units on seven floors where the amenities are as
inclusive as needed. Here's a list of what you get for your monthly fee: van/errand service, all utilities, home-style cooking (three meals daily), evening/weekly dances, local telephone service,
maid service, a dorm-size fridge in your room, complimentary ice machines, Direct TV, plus

weekly field trips. There is a washer and dryer on each floor, a game room, a library, vending machines and planned activities. Want to cut costs even more? Then take in a roomie, and you can slash your outlay substantially — and then splurge on trips, dinners out, a new wardrobe and a weekly beauty shop appointment. Compare to other retirement living accommodations at $1,500 to $2,500-plus a month, you'll see why folks have been flocking to this Mineral Wells retirement residence for more than 35 years. *Call toll-free: 800/637-6078*

★★★★★★ Curves   972/219-2339

982 N. Garden Ridge Blvd.   (See hours in write-up)
Lewisville, TX 75077-2827

This national fitness and weight loss center for women has taken the country by storm. Talk about having a better idea! Founder, Gary Heavin, hit the nose on the bullseye. The reality is — most women hate to exercise. *Entrepreneur* magazine has referred to Curves as the fastest-growing franchise in America. Its success is owing to Heavin's marketing strategy which has been focusing on those women who most likely would avoid going to a health club....period! You know the kind. Like you and me. Expect to attend classes three times a week with a regimen of 30-minute workouts, in a sparsely decorated room of women who go around each routine's circuit with music that will surely get you moving and grooving. Their Quickfit circuit, with music alternates, of hydraulic resistance strength training machines and aerobic recovery stations has been carefully thought through. There's an instructor or a recording that will tell you to move every thirty-five seconds and check your heart rate every eight minutes. See me at a Curves during the following hours: Mon, Wed, Fri 6 AM-Noon; Tues & Thurs 8 AM-Noon; Sat 7:30 AM-10:30 AM; Mon-Thurs 4 PM-8 PM and Fri 4 PM-7 PM. Anybody in Lewisville, Flower Mound or Highland Village enjoys the location above; but believe me, there are countless others all over the Metroplex. Check directory assistance for the one nearest you. Success doesn't have to cost a bloody arm and leg.

◆◆◆ FM Specialty Foods   972/724-3388

1001 Cross Timbers, Suite 1060 (Main Street)   Mon-Thurs 8:30-6:30; Fri 9-6; Sat 8:30-12:30
Flower Mound, TX 75028
www.fmspecialtyfoods.com

Mary Hutt has hunted all over the world for the natural remedies to ease a broken heart (or any other body part and function) and foods to savor for folks who are challenged by allergies. Expect to see a selection of food products that are wheat-free, egg-free, lactose-free, foods for diabetics and vegetarians and of course, the craze, the low fat/low carb demand which is now the darling of the eating public. Then, too, if you need to stay sugar-free, well here's a feast rather than a famine. Shop direct from their website and don't leave home without placing your order for what's right for the fight for good health. In person, they are located next to the full-service compounding pharmacist and herbal pharmacy called Flower Mound Pharmacy. Between the two stops who are joined at the hip, it is your one-stop shop for what ails you. Alternative medicine and homeopathy is fast becoming more and more mainstream every day. Coupled with traditional medicine, who can look a gift horse in the mouth. These same remedies have been used for centuries in the Far East — just ask the Queen of England what she prefers? Most Europeans are never far away from their homeopathic and natural treatments and Americans are now just beginning to catch up. So if you want a more homespun source of alternative medical options, this is the place to congregate and perhaps say, "Amen, brother!" Too, they carry specialty foods like Bruno Di Nola's low fat/low carb cheesecake that I can make a meal on. Either way, it's sooooo good and it's low calorie, not too sweet, and frankly, delicious. Try it....you'll love it. Take several of their individual servings home and freeze them. Then when you're in the mood, defrost and devour. Do not eat directly from the freezer as it really takes a while for all the flavors to reach their peak — and that only comes when the chill is off.

★★★★★   Herb Mart   972/270-6521

1515 Town East Blvd.   Mon-Sat 10-7; Sun 12-6
Mesquite, TX 75105

Spice up your life the natural "whey" at the Herb Mart. Get the popular METABOLIFE, 60 capsules for $6.95, or get the MAA HUANG for $10.95. I almost fainted when they told me the price of METABOLIFE because the same bottle, strength and number of capsules was selling at Wal-Mart for $20. How could that be? Well, we shall see. Across from Town East Mall, savings of 50 percent on NATURE'S WAY is one of the reasons our blood coagulates when we see their prices. Their everyday low prices make living an alternative life style almost worth living. Choose your poison: EMERGEN-C, GREEN MAGNUM, METABOLIFE, PRO-GEST CREAM, RICE DREAM — then dream on. Oh wellness, for goodness sake, why not take the road less traveled because, soon, it probably will be more mainstream than mainstream. It might even be the recommended course of medical action because so many of the homeopathic and natural remedies actually work. Duh! And prices here are so much healthier than at GNC. All name brand products (herbs, vitamins and minerals) are discounted with store personnel knowledgeable about each's potential power. No chit chat like at your typical health food stores and that's the way we like it. (We're all Herb-an Cowboys at heart.) Across from Town East Mall, at the Market East Shopping Center, you'll see and feel the difference almost immediately.

★★★★★★   Linda's Penta Water By The Case   214/337-0107

Home Delivery Only   By Appt. Only
Dallas, TX

    Water, water everywhere and not a drop to drink? Then consider the
fact that this particular water, PENTA HYDRATE WATER, is superior
to other bottled waters. According to the lab that developed it (Bio-
Hydration Research Lab) in San Diego, CA, this patent-pending process (don't ask me to explain about smaller water clusters, but it has to do with physics and that's where I have to draw the line) makes this water a fairly pricey investment to hydrate your cells. But once you drink it, you'll see (and feel) the difference. Linda McCoy is a nutritional consultant and sells this water for A LOT LESS, plus a measly $5 for delivery anywhere in the Dallas area. How's that for service? This water is particularly recommended for the sick or elderly; but anyone interested in their health should consider themselves a candidate. It is a water coveted by athletes, and it's also used at the John Wayne Cancer Institute in California. I'll drink to that and I'll let you know if I'm clicking up my heels running through the airport as a result of my H2O-h-h-h! I'd rather switch than fight — the ravages of time. It also tastes wonderful. Like a smooth bottle of wine without the sedating effects. We're all drinking it at the office now that we can get it cheaper and delivered to the front door. If it's good enough for Gwyneth Paltow, (and she certain can afford to pay retail,) why not you, too! Hey, do you think she got PG as a result of the water?

◆◆◆◆◆   Marilyn A. Scholl   214/208-3528

5313 Strickland Ave.   By Appt. Only
The Colony, TX 75056

You've heard of the healing power of the laying on of the hands, haven't you? Good. Now you'll hear about the laying on of Marilyn's hands. Once this registered massage therapist (#42843) lays her hands on your body, you will see stars. I did. But fortunately, it's part of the therapeutic massage technique that ultimately will "kneed" those kinks right out of your — head, neck, legs, back, wherever you're hurting, she will rub you the right way. Then the next morning, after a bath of equal parts of salt and baking soda, you will feel better than you've felt in years. Has table will travel to your home or office for an on-site massage for $65 or at her studio for $50. Love me, love my knots. Marilyn worked her magic on my stiff neck and cramped shoulders and got rid of every last ache and pain in no time. You're in good hands. She comes with table, hand-made afghans that keep you all warm and toasty, your choice of fragrant or non-fragrant massage oil and a heated pad under you — your choice as to where you want to be warmed. Try her, you'll love her. "Kneed" her for Swedish, Trigger Point, Hot River Rocks or a chair massage that will send you into orbit!

◆◆◆◆◆ **Mark Horton, R.M.T.**   **817/423-5557**
3309 Winthrop, Suite 76   By Appt. Only
Fort Worth, TX 76116
www.askthemassagetherapist.com

Want a great massage at a great price? Nothing beats half price and that's what Mark Horton offers to first-time clients. So, for $25, you can hop aboard the heated massage table and float away. He specializes in repetitive use injuries like carpal tunnel, hammer toes, claw toes, fibromyalgia, shin splints, whiplash, chronic low back pain (Hey, I resemble that remark!), plantar fascitis, tendonitis, knee pain or sports injuries, so, if you suffer from any of the above, try getting relief with his stretch/massage techniques. This is the therapist you knead to work out those kinks. He has other state-of-the-art techniques that are his very own creation. Ask for those glasses that will lull you to sleep or stimulate your creative process. Call for an appointment at his new location and enjoy!

◆◆◆◆◆ **Natural Health Therapies**   **903/651-3300**
2508 Highway 82 East   By Appt. Only
Whitesboro, TX 76273
www.naturalhealthhealing.com

Want the best massage outside of the Metroplex? Well, you're meeting one of the best therapists locally, but he's now moved to the boonies to get away from it all. Take thee to Whitesboro where the living is easier and the shopping's sublime. Make an appointment with Natural Health Therapies and James Snow, D.C. Head north 90 miles, my friend, to Whitesboro if you want to meet Dr. Snow and his wonderful wife, Carolyn Jo. Both are RMTs, registered massage therapists, but if you want to learn more about natural remedies and homeopathy, then engage Doc in a homeopathic session where he can suggest various natural remedies that are all but magical. He even holds sessions by phone. The next time you're tense and can't sleep, instead of reaching for a Valium to relax, try dissolving a little chamomile under your tongue. Doc and his partner/wife, Carolyn Jo, are both fabulous therapists, provide any number of different kinds of therapeutic massages and, of course, Doc can do chiropractic adjustments as well. For $50, you get a full therapeutic hour. You might be a little sore the next day. Individual and couple massages work wonders for couples on a number of different levels. Whatever skill and power they possess in laying on of the hands, don't question it. It works. Now, even insurance companies are recognizing its therapeutic benefits. Try it....you'll like it. (Or LOVE it as the case may be.) Call for your appointment. They book up fast! Ask them about some of their natural hormone replacement therapies, their pillows, and the homeopathic kit for your medicine chest. I can't live without mine. *Call toll-free: 877/485-8350*

◆◆◆   Natural Silhouettes   817/263-0014

5260 S. Hulen St.   Tues-Fri 10-6; Sat 10-5
Fort Worth, TX 76132

Natural Silhouettes understands that the search for a prosthesis or specialty bra is not only a challenging task but an emotional one as well. The staff understands the dilemma and is both empathetic and professional in their approach. Not only are they certified in their respective clinical fields, but they also offer fashion expertise, understanding the myriad of options to have you looking and feeling your best. Let them be the support you need, from bra fitting to wig design, hats to medical make-up. Donna's Wigs is located just inside their shop for added convenience. You won't have to go through the hassle of shopping around when it's so important to get it right the first time. Make it a one-stop shop at this location or at their other stop at 1600 Central, Suite 157 in Bedford, located in the Respiratory Connection at the Oaks Shopping Center, 817/868-0118. It's natural to want to feel nurtured when you're vulnerable, and they look after you emotionally, as well as physically. Everything for the breast cancer patient and survivor is available, all under one roof.

◆◆◆◆◆   North Texas Institute of Massage   972/221-7717

1310 S. Stemmons Frwy   Mon-Sat 9-5; 8:30-8 (By Appt. Only)
Lewisville, TX 75067-6389
www.ntimassageschool.com

Given the hands-on approach to feeling good, is it any wonder that this is THE school to matriculate? So whether you're a student or a customer, getting a one-hour, full body massage by a student intern, close to graduation, at a price of $25 just can't be beat (unless, of course, you're a first-time client of experienced massage therapist Mark Horton); a two-hour massage will run $50. Now, where do I sign up? Their number is above, but don't run, walk slowly and let's not create a stampede. Remember, as soon as the students graduate, their prices go up when they hit the health club, spa, hotel or rehab center. What better way to relieve stress than the wondrous effects of a Swedish massage, in a private room, for so little? If you are interested in a Saturday appointment, call early in the week as they book up fast. Can't beat it! You can train to be a registered massage therapist, or reap the benefits of being a customer ready to engage in an hour of bliss. The North Texas Massage Institute has been registered with the Texas Department of Health since 1995. You'll enjoy two private massage rooms, one wet room and one private massage room with shower facilities. Log on to their terrific website where you can even tour the facilities. *Call toll-free: 972/219-0291*

◆◆◆◆   Relax the Back   469/633-0070

2693 Preston Rd., Building A, Suite 1090   Mon-Sat 10-7; Sun 12-5
Frisco, TX 75034
www.relaxtheback.com

 Do you swing low, then scream high, "Oh my aching back?" Then relax, my friend, and pick up where the pain will let up. Get back to basics at this store that offers the largest collection of massage chairs from the PHP 2027 to an i-JOY. Then turn over a new leaf and sleep without the creek (in your neck) on a **TEMPUR-PEDIC** Swedish mattress and pillow. Then stretch out on a **BACKSAVER** Power Ultra Recliner. If you've never watched a football game from one of these, you haven't really gotten into the spirit of "The Boys." From the seat in your car, to the seat at your desk, to the ultra good night sleep on a coil-less mattress, take a test seat and see why doctors have referred patients to this store for years. I hope you won't banish me to the corner for putting them in the "To Die Category" but there are no deals. However, slipping into one of their executive leather chairs for my desk made me a believer. The price you pay may save you a lifetime of chiropractic adjustments. So let's just say this is a business that won't break your budget but is worth every penny if you are suffering. From the very beginning, this company has specialized in working with your doctor, your therapist — be it a physical therapist or a massage therapist. If you are looking for healthy products for your home or office, you're back where your back belongs. And if you prefer to keep your derriere planted in an ergonomic chair and shop from your home or office, they offer a free catalog that will ease you into something that will support the cause. From lift chairs (if you are having trouble getting out of that chair) to massage chairs, if you'd rather do it yourself, this is the place that chairs the latest in technological advances. Ah-h. It feels so-o-o-o right! Visit also in Highland Park at 4256 Oak Lawn, 214/521-5999, open Mon-Sat 10-6; Sun 12-5 and their Fort Worth location on Camp Bowie. Don't expect the products to be discounted — but comfort should count for something, eh? *Call toll-free: 800/222-5728*

★★★　Scooter Store, The　　　　　　817/737-3900

4616 A SW Loop 820　　　　　　　　　　　　　　　　　　　　Mon-Fri 9-5:30
Fort Worth, TX 76109
www.scooterstore.com

This national franchise are real operators in the Metroplex with four locations including the one above. (Also, 8401 Anderson in Fort Worth, 817/274-4454; 8224 Bedford Euless Rd., in North Richland Hills, 817/514-9090 and in Dallas at 13374 Preston Rd., 972/980-0040.) There's always something going on to make your life easier and more liberating, emancipating you from the confines of restrictive mobility. Why not go up, up and away by getting out of that chair with one of those power lifting cushions? Or need help getting out of the tub? I know mine's so deep that I can use one of those railings onto my tub to help me keep my balance. So see, even the Diva can see how to add more power to her lift! Scooters, power chairs, lifts, ramps, walkers, transport chairs — all designed to help make your life more independent. Take advantage of knowledgeable sales personnel who'll help you with insurance filing, and products that are the ultimate in mobility. Join the upwardly mobile class and shop here. The SCOOTER Store is the country's leading provider of power mobility products so there's power in pricing as well. They've been helping people get around since 1991 and at times have been a lifesaver. Over 85,000 physicians have worked with The SCOOTER Store to prescribe just the right mobility equipment for patients; don't be shy. Ask your doctor for his recommendation for an apparatus and none too soon, The SCOOTER Store will pre-qualify you for a new scooter or power chair. Then if Medicare, for example, denies your claim, The SCOOTER Store allows you to keep your scooter or power chair at no cost. Some restrictions apply, so call for details. Very interesting. Call for your free mobility consultation and get moving. FREE no-pressure, no-obligation consultation. A Mobility Consultant will assess your mobility needs and then go from there to help you understand the options. Get on the road, Jack, in regaining your freedom and independence. Celebrate your own personal Fourth of July, Independence day. Oh, when I shopped the store, I did buy that bath rail for 25 percent less than retail — but at least, I didn't take a bath! *Call toll-free: 800/895-4336*

◆◆◆◆◆　Spectrum Proterties, LC　　　　　214/987-0943

10448 Stone Canyon, Suite 105 North　　　　　　　　　　　　By Appt. Only
Dallas, TX 75230
www.spectrumprop.com

After a scrumptious lunch at Meadowstone Place, I was hooked. When the time comes for setting down roots, slowing down, and having a ball in my golden years, this is the place for me. Choose from three equally appealing properties: Meadowstone Place, 10410 Stone Canyon Rd. in Dallas, 214/987-0943, Preston Place at 5000 Old Shepard Place in Plano, 972/931-1123 or Parc Place in

Bedford, 1301 Airport Freeway, 817/267-8614 or 817/283-6700 (both metro numbers.) Prices started as low as $1,180 but remember, that includes all of the amenities such as planned activities, transportation, a library room, a billiards room, an exercise room, even a spa that would be the envy of anybody's eye. Covered parking, a car wash, lighted tennis courts, a swimming pool, a computer lab, a business center, on-site banking, a putting green, Dale Carnegie Life Enrichment Classes, an evening concierge, a walking trail and covered parking, a health care liaison and health and wellness programs. They have fabulous chefs, beautiful appointments, landscaping and caring personnel of all ages. Add in the extras as you desire: gracious meals, a guest suite, housekeeping, an emergency response system, and a beauty salon. Mention the Diva when you sign a lease, and there might be a very special gift waiting for you!

◆◆◆◆◆ Texas Blue Stuff Pain Mgmt Center   817/467-6423

3509 McKamy Oaks Trail   By Appt.Only
Arlington, TX 76017
www.bluestuff.com

Bob and Nita Antcliff are the enterprising entrepreneurs who deliver the Super Blue Stuff through their local distributorship. If you want the miracle stuff, get the original miracle stuff and don't settle for some cheap imitation. I limped into last year's Home and Garden Show and hobbled past the Texas Blue Stuff's booth. They offered me a sample and I proceeded to put it right over my pantyhose since there was no time to apply it properly before my radio show. One application in front and behind my knee, and I became a believer. Within seconds, the pain was completely gone. It is a miracle on parts of you that are in pain. Once you've tried the lip balm, you'll likely get hooked on that product, too! *Call toll-free: 866/250-4131*

★★★★★★ Vitamin Shoppe, The   972/250-2365

5930 West Park Blvd., Suite 900   Mon-Sat 9-9; Sun 11-6
Plano, TX 75093
www.vitaminshoppe.com

 Though dwarfed by the number of GNC stores (last count, 5,300), my favorite Vitamin Shoppe (two P's and an E) has finally made it to the Metroplex. Soon, it will become your vitamin center of choice. I have ordered vitamins online from them for years, so I personally welcome this expansion into Texas. Now I can run to the store when I run out of my multi-vitamins — PROVIDE that without it first thing in the morning, I can't move! It's the best gel-cap multi-vitamin for me and without it, I'm dragging all day. As far as their vitamins go, you can expect discounts of 20-60 percent on name brands and private labels. Grand opening week in Lewisville netted a discount of 40 percent across the board. Knowledgeable managers and accommodating clerks made for a pleasant and healthy shopping experience. For the store nearest you, call the toll free number above. The line-up's pretty impressive: save on everything from A to Z — Acidophilus to Zone Bars. Over 25,000 items in more than 300 brands: COUNTRY LIFE, MET-RX, NATROL, NATURE'S PLUS, SOLARAY, SOLGAR, TWINLAB — all the best, for less, to live a long and healthy life. I'll drink to that! Get healthy savings in Denton, Northpark, FRISCO, Mesquite, Southlake, west Plano and at last, Lewisville. *Call toll-free: 800/370-8747*

★★★   Vitamin World   972/234-5030

607 S. Plano Rd.   Mon-Sat 10-9; Sun Noon-6
Richardson, TX 75081
www.vitaminworld.com

How can you go wrong with a return policy that allows you to return the product for up to one full year if you are not completely satisfied? Vitamin World's a kingpin in the world of vitamins and they also own their own private labels: NATURE'S BOUNTY and PURITAN'S PRIDE via their sister mail order business. Located at the Richardson Square Mall off the food court by Ross, if you've outgrown your size 14s, you might want to consider VW's weight control product called METABOSURGE (compares to METABOLIFE) which sells for $14.95 a bottle or CHITOSAN, a fat absorber. Something for everyone from vitamins and minerals to antioxidants, nutritional supplements, digestive aids, eye nutrients, nutritional oils, pain relief remedies, teas and even books, if you need help getting started on the road to good health. It's a Vitamin World after all! They also maintain a strong online and mail order business. However, most of the savings are on their private label vitamins, so, there's no basis of comparison. I don't consider them of the same quality as others, and this is where The Vitamin Shoppe's strength lies. Check directory assistance for multiple Metroplex locations.

★★★★★   Years to Your Health   972/579-7042

503 E. 2nd St.   Mon-Fri 10-6; Sat 10-5
Irving, TX 75060
www.yearstoyourhealth.com

Cheers to Years to your Health. They're alive and well, after almost 20 years. What's good for the goose is good for the gander. You will get an education because owner Lonnie Redd and her colleagues are very knowledgeable about vitamins, herbs, and other natural healing alternatives. Open your eyes to more than 500 botanicals at 30 to 40 percent less than traditional health food stores. Serve up one of the largest selections in the country of bulk herbs, pot-pourris, spices, teas and candles. Herbs are their spice of life and they carry powdered versions to capsules. They also have homeopathic aids, tinctures, essential oils and flower remedies, cosmetics and environmentally-safe products. A selection of quartz crystals and gemstones, tissue-cleansers, massage oils, astrological charts, flower essences, vibrational medicine, mysticism and herbs for health and spiritual use. You never know what may work. Tea blends are intriguing especially for those that induce sleep like their "Night-Time Tea" for $2.60/ounce. Check it all out! *Call toll-free: 800/ 860-7042*

Home Improvement

Discount Building Materials
(formerly Surplus Depot)

◆◆◆◆   **AAA Custom Windows**   **214/340-0078**

206 Abrams Forest Shopping Center   Mon-Fri 9-6; Sat 10-5
Dallas, TX 75243
www.aaacustomwindows.com

To get a clear view to the great outdoors, consider windows, French doors or security doors. See the world through the windows, French and security doors from AAA, the leader of the pack. Replacement windows have been their only business since 1981. They maintain a satisfactory relationship with the Better Business Bureau, both in Dallas and Fort Worth, and as a consumer, that's important to know. You don't want some rummy knocking on your door one day, claiming he can replace your windows if you provide him with a $2,500 down payment and vanishes the next. This company is proud of their excellent reputation and rightfully so. They provide excellent workmanship, dependability and professional integrity, those three important ingredients we hold so dear in our book. Not typical of those sleazy-knock-three-times and whisper low, here today and take your dough and skip installers. These guys pride themselves on being top craftsmen in their field. Expect word of mouth to be their best form of advertising, but now that I have found them, guess who has the biggest mouth to get the ball rolling? Watch for specials such as replacing your old hard-to-slide patio doors with insulated French doors and they'll deduct $100; or trade-in your old windows for new and they'll give you $50 for each window you replace. Now, do your windows still give you a pane?

★★★★★   **AAA Home Elevator**   **972/392-1949**

6532 LBJ Freeway   By Appt. Only
Dallas, TX 75240

What goes up, has to come down. And for what it's worth, I wished I had known about this company years ago. Not only personally, but for all of you who've asked me where to get an elevator cheaper. Well, I finally found it. When I lived in a three-story lakehouse, an electrical fire imploded two of the floors. When I took a look at my lifestyle, and the possibility that my dad might be moving in with me, I decided I needed to rebuild the house into a one-story model. It became increasingly difficult to navigate the steep stairs to the third floor. But there was one problem. The insurance company said I couldn't do it, as stipulated by the bank. At first, I thought, okay, I'll just put in an elevator. Well, that was before I did some price checking and decided that that was a bad idea. Instead, I decided to sell it "as is" and I have never looked back. Not until a call several weeks ago on the air. You know the kind, "Where can I get an elevator cheaper?" Well, I didn't know. So, to not go down in history as "stumping the Diva," I found it! AAA Home Elevator is the brainchild of Bob Lynch who has designed this affordable system that will no doubt soon be the #1 seller in the country. You may find this appealing in your multi-story situation, even an office where only employees (not the public) would go up and down. *Call toll-free: 800/803-1949*

★★★★   ABC Air Duct   214/341-0159 ; 972/404-8873

Dallas, TX   24/7
www.abcairduct.com

ABC Duct Control — oops, that song is for ABC Pest Control and though dirty ducts may be a pesky situation, these guys do air ducts, as well as carpet cleaning. Serving both the Dallas and Fort Worth areas, consider all those sleepless nights with itchy, watery eyes, sneezing, coughing, catching that runny nose....well, all the headachy symptoms that a good duct cleaning would eliminate. Their professional technicians are bonded and insured and will vacuum as well as brush those ducts to the bone, eliminating bacteria, smoke, dangerous chemicals, mold and dust. If it's not supposed to be there, "Out, damm mold, out!" If you're a senior citizen, expect a 10 percent discount. A recent current special when we shopped was $7.50/duct. If you wanted all vents that connected to the furnace cleaned, the price was $99. With that, a four-year warranty ($100 value) was thrown in for free on a nine-vent cleaning. Carpet cleaning prices panned out as follows: Two rooms, $45; three rooms, $55; four rooms, $65; five rooms, $75 or a whole house up to seven rooms, $120. As always, watch for the FINE PRINT. These are very good prices, but make sure they don't get you for "pre-spotting" or "moving furniture" or something else that you hadn't thought of, but they did!

◆◆◆◆◆◆   Accurate Foundation Repair, Inc.   972/623-2500

2125 W. Pioneer Parkway, D-1   By Appt. Only
Grand Prairie, TX 75051
www.accurate-foundation-repair.com

 It's all in their name. Accurate, as an adjective, means "free from Error," and that's how this company grew into one of the most respected foundation repair services in the Metroplex. Taking a hands-on approach, with state-of-the-art technology, Tom Laymon and his crew are to your home's foundation what a doctor is for your health. They fix what ails your foundation while keeping an independent eye and open mind to unearthing what caused the problem in the first place. You get your foundation repaired; they get paid a fair amount for an Accurate Foundation Repair. Uniformed personnel proceed with professional knowledge of the latest advances in the industry and take into account everything from plumbing leaks, initiating a watering program for maintaining a solid foundation and protecting your most expensive investment, your house. Foundation problems are serious. With the Underground Shopper's Seal of Approval, Accurate Foundation Repair is our preferred provider for foundation repair. They were nominated and voted the best.

★★★   Acme Brick   817/390-2409

2811 W. 7th St.   Mon-Fri 8-5; Sat 8-3
Fort Worth, TX 76101
www.acmebrick.com

Based in Fort Worth, this company is as solid as a ton of bricks. As the official brick of the Dallas Cowboys and the Kansas City Chiefs, I'd say it's a great line of defense. Their **ACME** king-size brick is a best seller. Look for **ACME**, **MANNINGTON** and **PAVESTONE** bricks and tiles. Expect factory-direct pricing and professional sales personnel to guide you down the path of least resistance. They're the source for creating a glass block window, a dividing wall, a skylight and they carry a full line of masonry accessories, ceramic tile, fireplace systems, even pool coping. Located in Dallas at 11261 Harry Hines Blvd., 972/241-1400, once you've shopped **ACME BRICK**, you'll see why this company's been paving the way into Metroplex homes since 1891. Since they're also connected to **AMERICAN TILE** (202 E. Felix in Fort Worth,817/924-2232), you can spruce up your entry way, your kitchen, bath....well, any room for that matter, with beautiful ceramic tile. They only carry the premium tile from **ENDICOTT**, Italian-glazed tile from **CERIM**, **TERRA NOVA** and their own **ACME QUARRY** Tile. Whatever shape, size or purpose for your bricks or tile, Acme has you covered. They also sell masonry and tile supplies like mortar, grout, sealer, tools, etc. *Call toll-free: 800/792-1234*

 ## Additions Plus   **972/633-3999**

PO Box 942161   By Appt. Only
Plano, TX 75094
www.additionsplusonline.com

With almost 30 years under their tool belt, this family-owned remodeling company does it all. Since 1984, they have provided residential, commercial, industrial and church remodeling and building from the ground floor up. Interior and exterior painting, custom cabinetry, and general contracting are their specialties. Online coupons can be printed right from your printer: $250 off five rooms painted; $250 off exterior painting; $500 off patio or garage conversion; $50 off installation of standard exterior doors; 10 percent off kitchen or bath remodeling; $1,000 off any room addition more than $45,000. Free estimates; three-year warranty on services; one-year warranty on stained and varnished exterior doors, carpentry, repairs and deck construction and 90-day warranty offered on stained surfaces. Ask for references, of course. We did. They usually use **KELLEY MOORE** paint, but that can vary. When getting a painting estimate, remember there are many different grades of paint. Do not get the cheapest grade as most likely it won't last a year. They will build cabinets in your garage that are solid wood, not laminates, for less than the franchised companies do with particle board. With no showroom, they keep their overhead expenses to a bare minimum and pass the savings to you instead.

 ## Affinity Designs, Inc.   **972/539-7380**

By Appt. Only
Lewisville, TX
www.affinitydesigns.com

If you have an affinity for nice things, then consider adding this company to your roster of services. If you need quality decorating or storage solutions that meet your standards of excellence and beauty, this firm builds custom shelf-systems and cabinetry, entertainment centers and accent furniture. "From Here to Affinity," everything will be in its place and there will be a place for everything. For all the stuff you buy that has no place to go, here's your answer to cleaning up the clutter. Of course, that is, if you have a "Mission for Organization!" Too, it's the affinity they have for the artistry that counts in everything they build that speaks for itself.

◆◆◆◆   **Air Conditioning Services**   **817/426-3366**

Mon-Fri 8-5 (By Appt. Only)

Fort Worth, TX 76097

Keeping their cool since 1985, you can expect both 24-hour emergency service and same day service, if either your heating or air-conditioner has gone on the blink. Then to get them working again, call on this company who bought all of a former company's client list (Climate Works) and proceeded to absorb those customers into their already growing base. But to their credit, ACS (and owner Jim Rattey) have been in business for almost 30 years, and although they're located in the White Settlement area, they have a Fort Worth mailing address. They deal in both heating and air-conditioning sales and service. For example, for $49.99, they will do what they call a "Spring Check Up" and go over your unit with a fine-tooth comb — from coil, filter, electrical, to the motor and even throw in one pound of freon (a $14 dollar value), if need be. Their service call may seem pricey at $58 — but that includes the first 30 minutes and $56 every half hour after that. You get what you pay for and for good service, expect to pay. Because they want to be the best, they have their own sheet metal shop in-house; at least the work is sure to be fast and done right. Carrying their own brand helps to improve the quality of air indoors with air cleaners, humidifiers and CO detectors. And yes, financing is available, if you're in a pinch. They also service all makes and models like **FRIGIDAIRE**, **LENNOX** and **TRANE**.

◆◆◆◆◆◆   **All My Sons Moving & Storage**   **214/219-8900**

9761 Clifford, #150   By Reservation Only
Dallas, TX 75220
www.allmysons.com

   You're out of luck if you intend to hand this company down to your
daughters. The sons are already committed to carrying on the family
business. These local titans have come down the pike with plenty of
experience plus they have one up on many of their competitors. They can move you locally or nationally. That means, whether you're moving across town, need to store your furniture until the house is built, or are having to get out of town — quick, All My Sons can get you going in a jiffy. Now that one listener who happened to be in the real estate/relocation business used All my Sons on her move to Houston, she was so pleased, she is using them exclusively as she moves companies into and out of the Houston area. Geographically desirable, they have both a Dallas and Fort Worth office to accommodate you. The company is family-owned and operated giving you a personal connection that means that Ron Clare takes his business seriously. Though they can move you across the street, cross town, cross the state line, even cross country, they are not so big that the president of the company is so far up the corporate ladder than he's not accessible to his customers. Visit him online and see one of the most advanced and comprehensive web sites for the industry. They provide quality service at a reasonable rate, not brain surgery. They offer storage, packing services, unpacking, placing and setting up in your new home, yes, they do it all. Same day/next day service, if you have to make a quick getaway, they can help you make your moves — be it locally, within 15 states and 60 counties nationwide. Relax and enjoy your move.

◆◆◆◆   **Amazing Buildings**   **972/287-4842**

By Appt. Only

Seagoville, TX 75159

How much is that doggie house in your backyard? Well, one thing's for sure. My doggie house is better than yours? (Tammy Faye Bakker.) Mine's bigger. Better. And has its own picket fence. But then how many folks do you know have built an English cottage for their mutts? A mini-mansion for their own canine retreat is hard to beat. If you want a condo or a contemporary spread that would fit into your backyard decor, here's the architect/builder who can do it up right. They build it all, from backyard storage sheds to an observatory tree house, a mother-in-law suite that's cheap to a room addition to keep your expansion plans to a manageable mortgage. Rodney Upchurch is the chairman of the boards! If he can build the bridge to the fitness center at the Anatole, or the locker room for the Mavericks (before the Cuban invasion), he must know a thing or two. Custom-built portable buildings, storage sheds, playhouses, cabins, decks, sheds and garages. An 8 X 10 building was $745; 8 X 16 was $995 and a 12 X 24 was $2,495.— compare that to an add-on room and you'll see how much you're saving. Make sure he buys what he needs from G & S Sales in Terrell to get you the best prices on building supplies. Well, he already knows that because that's where he buys ALL of his building supplies.

◆◆◆◆◆◆ Amazing Siding 817/329-8830

1705 West Northwest Highway   By Appt. Only (Mon 1-8; Tues-Fri 9-8; Sat 9-1)
Grapevine, TX 76051
www.amazingsiding.com

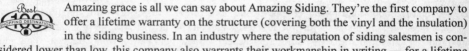 Amazing grace is all we can say about Amazing Siding. They're the first company to offer a lifetime warranty on the structure (covering both the vinyl and the insulation) in the siding business. In an industry where the reputation of siding salesmen is considered lower than low, this company also warrants their workmanship in writing — for a lifetime of the house (and yes, it's transferable to the next owner). Amazing! They also provide those efficient vinyl replacement windows with similar guarantees. Vinyl siding is available in a variety of styles, textures and colors. Select from many different clapboard widths in horizontal or vertical styles. Choose smooth or wood grain finishes along with a full line of accessories, including shutters, soffits, fascia and trim. Save 30-50 percent over Sears'prices. They have an impeccable rating with the BBB and though they are based in Grapevine, they service the entire Metroplex. In fact, they do the same Amazing Siding service coast-to-coast. And, lest you forget, installation labor is free. *Call toll-free: 800/4-SIDING*

★ American Marazzi Tile 972/728-7000

2250 LBJ Frwy., Suite 200   Mon-Fri 7:30-5; Sat.8-12
Dallas, TX 75234

Forget it! In spite of their most inviting showroom (actually three showrooms, Dallas, Plano and Fort Worth), these folks are not open to the public. You can look but not touch. Only contractors can buy from them. Sorry about that! But if you can maneuver your way into them selling to you, let me know. They refused us but why tickle our fancy and then instead of laughing all the way to the bank, we cried all the way home. What's the deal?

◆◆◆◆ American Porcelain Enamel Co. 214/634-2969

2737 S. Westmoreland Rd.   Mon-Fri 8-3
Dallas, TX 75233-1311

Rub-a-dub dub, this is the answer to saving money on your tub-a-tub tub. It's called resurfacing. Instead of replacing the entire tub, these folks go into your bathroom, shut the door, of course, and transform your tub from grungy to brand-new looking. A regular-sized bathtub can be resurfaced in a white or neutral shade for $220. If you want a custom tint, color it beautiful for another $35. Bargain! Bargain, burning bright. Expect the process to take approximately three to three and a half hours; then, you'll have to wait another 24 hours if you want to take a bath. (Can you wait 24 hours without stinking? Do you have another possibility — like another bathroom? Or, at best, a friend who will lend you some water?) They can also resurface sinks (including pedestals), refrigerators, kitchen appliances, tile and countertops. To resurface a laminated countertop, they sand and prep the surface, mask the surrounding areas and spray on the finish. It takes about a day and a half and would run between $300-$400, depending on the size. What a difference in price compared to adding an entirely new counter surface. Too, they will come out for a free estimate. Although their showroom is small, they do have some clawfoot tubs. Call before you head out the door, to make sure someone is there to help you.

◆◆◆◆◆◆ **American Service Center**   **972/681-2222**

4612 Buckner Blvd.   Mon-Fri 7-6; Sat 8-5
Dallas, TX 75227
www.americanservicecenter.com

 Open sesame! This company is a GENIE and LIFT MASTER authorized dealer and here you can get factory-direct, same-day service on garage doors. Other brands are available, too, like the AMARR 24-gauge steel garage doors that start as low as $299 installed. They offer several different sizes and qualities alongside the GENIE PRO SCREW DRIVE garage doors and openers. This garage door offers a direct drive for maximum lifting force, a one-piece solid-steel screw for added strength and security, fewer moving parts, a quieter operation and an automatic 120-watt lighting system. Protect your car(s), your garage contents and the security of your home with an enclosed garage. Free estimates for repairs. Whether it's garage doors and openers, residential or commercial installation, repair or replacement, this center can get you up and down in no time. And don't forget, they also offer the retractable DURASOL awnings. FREE consultations serving the entire Metroplex, but for service in Fort Worth, you need to call 817/436-3000.

◆◆◆◆◆ **Amersol, Inc.**   **214/503-9977**

9770 Skillman   By Appt. Only
Dallas, TX 75243
www.amersol.com

Looking for a parasol for your windows? Cover up with this unique window film that prevents fading, sun glare, hot and cold spots and, in fact, will cut the heat and block 99 percent of the harmful UV rays, while letting light in. There are varying shades of color and different degrees of UV and heat protection, so prices vary according to specific needs. An alternative to solar screens may be just what the doctor ordered. Since 1974, Amersol has been an established and reputable service company with a client list that reads like a "Who's Who" in the Metroplex. Consider the benefits again: energy savings, reduced fading of furnishings, prevention of heat build-up and the harsh glare associated with uncontrolled sunlight, protection from broken glass and flying fragments as the film holds broken glass in place. Their motto is clear, "To enjoy light your way, look our way." Call for your in-house or in-office estimate.

★★★ **Anchor Paint Co.**   **972/699-0151**

715 N. Central Expwy.   Mon-Fri 7-5; Sat 7-Noon
Richardson, TX 75080
www.anchorpaint.com

It's anchors away, my friend, if you plan on painting the town red with the paint from this company. In business since 1962, you can shop where the professional painters shop, but if you want a special color, expect a 50-gallon minimum. Flat, semi-gloss, oil-based glosses, latex enamel, undercoats, drywall sealer, water repellants, masonry sealer, primers, stains, varnish, stain killers and elastomeric coatings are available. Even specialty items like oil-based safety colors, hi-temp silicone, tar epoxy and communication tower paints can be found. But if you're a homeowner, I doubt if you're thinking about painting the towers of any TV station anytime soon. Special requirements for coatings can also be requested. Besides all this technical stuff, they carry a complete inventory of paint supplies for the do-it-yourselfer. Since this paint is made in their own Tulsa, Oklahoma factory and sold via their own outlets, you can moor the savings because they've eliminated the middleman. Make sure you stay cool, though. I don't want you suffering from "brush stroke!"

★★★★   Aqua Natural   972/329-7627

2127 Estes Park Drive   Mon-Sun 8-8 (Office hours); Mon-Fri 9-5 (Technician hours)
Allen, TX 75013
www.aquanatural.com

You may know where your children are, but do you know what's in your water? If you did, you'd might never be thirsty again. Call this company pronto. Formerly Aqua USA East Texas, they carry all kinds of reverse osmosis systems, under or on-top models at wholesale prices. For mere drops in the bucket, the same system that is used by public water companies, school districts and commercial buildings can be ordered for your home use, too. Take the worry out of drinking water by installing a filtration apparatus. For those households who are concerned about ecology, consider other environmentally-friendly products like biodegradable soap. Since laundry detergents are one of the worst chemicals we put back into the environment, you can eliminate that problem with just one of the products you buy from this company. Have them come to your home for water testing, servicing of equipment or have them customize a unit to meet your family's needs. The end result is that with a water filtration system, you will save time and money. You'll clean better, use less soap, keep your pipes clean; therefore, your pump doesn't have to work as hard. Too, it makes your water heater last longer. And the list goes on! So, if you want to make your "green" contribution to being earth-friendly, here's a good place to start.

★★   Architectural Manufacturing Inc.   214/704-9028

PO Box 154   By Appt. Only
Mesquite, TX 75114

If your brain is wrought with a lack of anything interesting or ornamental for your garden or patio, this company may offer just the right metal accessory to add that much needed drama. Then again, shoe-polish black new wrought iron is not your idea of substantive wrought iron to transform your drab backyard or patio. If you're looking for fairly expensive but inexpensive-looking wrought iron lighting, furniture, mailboxes, urns, statuary, fencing, fireplace accessories, candle holders and such, give these folks a call. Expect pricing for fences to be by the length and height. See them display their wares at various Home and Garden Shows rather than visit at a showroom which they describe as "of sorts" in Mesquite. See what "of sorts" is all about but to this day, I've not been able to shop at a post office box. From what we saw at the Home and Garden Show, you'll be dis-wrought with inexpensive wrought iron accessories that appeared sturdy enough to last a few blustery gusts of a Texas windstorm, but not to last a lifetime. Their products remind me of Wayne Newton's black shoe-polish hair color which makes me gag. So I moved on to the next booth and you might, too.

◆◆◆◆   ARI Sunrooms   972/458-3030

13617 Inwood Road   Mon-Fri 9-5; Sat 10-4
Dallas, TX 75244
www.ari-dallas.com

Looking to let the sun shine in? Consider, then, an airy sunroom as a worthwhile addition to your hearth and home. With 20 years experience, they would be happy to add a smile to your house and a room to grow. In-home assessments, including customized sunroom plans, are part of their repertoire, but they don't stop with just sunrooms. Complete home remodeling comes naturally on their list of possibilities, with one of the strongest warranties in the industry. Combining both intrinsically sound construction and artistic integrity, let the experts make your transformation dreams come true. From their maintenance-free sunrooms, to arbors, patio covers, windows, siding, screened-in porches, walls of windows and more, let them have at it. Their insulated windows are custom-built with a lifetime warranty on materials, how's that sound? Energy efficiency. Protection against the elements. Attractive styling, What more can you ask? And, best of all, you'll be protected from the heat and cold, and those bugs. Hate those bugs! *Call toll-free: 800/483-0085*

◆◆◆   Awning Works   817 or 972/329-4161

1803 Tarrant Lane, #200   Mon-Fri 8-5; Sat 8-11:30
Colleyville, TX 76034
www.awning-works.com

In my humble opinion, awnings are one of the most under-rated additions to your home's curb appeal and energy efficiency. This family-owned business in Colleyville, located just off Hwy. 26, can make a sizeable contribution that will not only improve your home's aesthetics but your utility bill as well. Utilizing the solar protection of the **DURASOL** retractable awnings, they're really easy to operate, are maintenance free and self-storing when not in use. These awnings protect your household contents from the sun's rays as well as enhance its overall ambience of your home and patio. In fact, they claim awnings will lower indoor temperatures by 10-15 degrees. Their work does not stop with awnings, though, as their name might suggest. They also do garage doors under their Door Works division. Choose from a number of garage doors, from steel, wood or copper. Call for a free consultation and estimate. Also another location at Clanton's Quality Awning Co., 214/388-5444 or 800/876-5926, www.clantonqualityawnings.com. Both locations service the Dallas/Fort Worth area with **DURASOL** AWNINGS (www.durasol.com). Financing available with approved credit.

◆◆◆◆◆   Baker Brothers Installations   972/438-3212

518 N. Britain   Mon-Fri 9-5; Sat. By Appt. Only.
Irving, TX 75061-7608
www.bakerbrothersinstall.com

Knowing Doug and his family is almost as good as having a brother-in-law in the business. After 34 years in business, pretty much at the same location (within two blocks), don't expect them to be going anywhere anytime soon. Acting as the "general contractor," they can build a sunroom, add a carport, replace your windows, add aluminum or vinyl siding or reroof using only the most reputable of products. All aluminum products carry a limited lifetime warranty, plus Baker Bros. provides a five-year workmanship warranty. Thermal double- pane replacement windows carry a lifetime warranty on workmanship and leaks. Now that puts some teeth into a warranty. Doug's the man! Now Baker's the company to bake you a deal. *Call toll-free: 800/203-6596*

★★★★★ **Bath-Tec**   **972/646-5279**
5142 Hwy. 34 W.   Mon-Fri 8-5
Ennis, TX 75119
www.bathtec.com

Since 1984, Bath-Tec has been manufacturing a complete line of luxury acrylic whirlpool bath-tubs, soaking tubs and shower bases for residential construction and the lodging industry, so they know how "NOT" to soak you. They offer factory-direct pricing plus quality and craftsmanship all rolled into one. Soak in an acrylic whirlpool bath, invite a friend into a two-person whirlpool, or wash off in an acrylic shower manufactured from durable, easy-to-clean, high-gloss, cast acrylic. Their shower bases have a slip resistant surface, built-in flange, raised dam to prevent water leak-age over the threshold and they're really easy to install. They come in a variety of sizes and colors with optional chrome or brass drains. Take 45 south towards Houston, to Highway 251 (the Ennis/Kaufman exit). At the stop sign, turn right and go to the third red light. Then turn right at the four-way stoplight. Follow that road over the reservoir approximately .8 of a mile to Bath-Tec. FREE delivery in the Dallas/Fort Worth area but they don't do the installation. For a plumber, check write-up under Devard's Plumbing elsewhere in this chapter. *Call toll-free: 800/526-3301*

◆◆◆◆◆◆◆ **BCS Foundation Repair**   **817/692-5040**
6412 Crawford Lane E.   Mon-Fri 8-5; By Appt. Only
Fort Worth, TX 76119
www.BCSfoundationrepair.com

Formerly Brown's Construction/Awning Co, it's now firmly planted in the ground of foundation repair with a lifetime transferable warranty. And this is no B©S. In business since 1970, thirty years later, they are still one of the leaders in the foundation repair business, operating from the same location in south Fort Worth. When Bob retired, his son-in-law, Corey Ingram, and Corey's partner, Craig Powers, took over. Although other compet-itors may promise a lifetime guarantee, read the fine print. They often have loopholes with no intention of being honorable. This is totally unacceptable to BCS. A business with integrity? You bet. The company has endured because of its core values: Honesty, Trust and Integrity. It believes that foundations should be fixed only one time, the right way. Foundation problems never fix themselves, so call a company that you can count on, a company that goes above and beyond the local ordinance requirements, that ensures that the job is done right the first time around. Taking on one repair job at a time, they've not wanted to spread themselves too thin and dilute their prom-ise of superb customer service. If you've noticed a shift in your foundation, call on a company that is already built on a solid foundation. *Call toll-free: 888/282-7822*

◆◆◆◆ **Berkey's**   **817/481-5869**
PO Box 1748   Mon-Fri 8-5; Sat. (Limited Appts.)
Grapevine, TX 76099

When your heating or air-conditioning is on the blink, you've got a problem. But when your plumbing goes out, too, you've got trouble in River City. Considering this company fixes it all with one call, I'd say you're safe in Grapevine. For $79, a serviceman will perform a complete precision tune-up, inspection and cleaning on your AC unit or your heating unit. Not a bad price for piece of mind. For a regular service call, it's only $49, but is waived if work is to be executed. Price quotes are by the job — not by the hour, so you know exactly how much it's going to cost, even if the tech is a slow-poke. Now we're talking, "Advantage consumer!" For a Saturday appointment, call the Monday before to prearrange.

◆◆◆◆◆   Better Shelf Co., The   972/578-1760

Plano, TX   By Appt. Only
www.bettershelf.com

Founded in 1977 by LEE and Pat Pfoutz, why break your back bending and reaching for that sautè
pan or that waffle maker somewhere in the back of your cabinet? If you had rollout shelves, life
without these back-breaking efforts would be possible. So, organize your cupboards, your cabinets, your drawers by letting them install their custom-made models, or do-it-yourself for less.
Regardless, each comes with a 90-day guarantee even with the Do-It-Yourself manual. If you
don't like it, send it back for a full refund. Featured on the Discovery Channel's, "Your New
House," after a decade of exposure, they still come out, measure and review the various options
that are open for discussion. A final and firm estimate, along with a confirmation date, is then
given. Then, it's back to the shop where they custom construct your rollout shelves made of ½"
plywood with wood veneer. Prices start at $54 for you basic rollout and go up to $325 for more
intricate designs. You can buy the "how-to" book online for $32.48; or just pop 'em an e-mail or
call for help and they'll walk you through your installation question. It helps protect your back and
put your pots and pans and other kitchen utensils within easy reach.

★★★★   Black & Decker/DeWalt Service Center 972/620-8655

1881 Valley View   Mon-Fri 8-5; Sat 9-1
Farmers Branch, TX 75234

Note, new location, you ole tool-timer you. Here, under one roof, the two most famous names in
tool history (BLACK & DECKER and DEWALT) have joined together, apparently in happy
"matromoney!" Actually, there are two other locations besides the Farmers Branch outlet (Fort
Worth, 817/831-3828 and Garland, 972/686-9302) but if it's tools you're after, consider the
source. New and refurbished tools are available on a daily basis. Warranties on new as well as
refurbished products are offered; be sure to register your power tools, outdoor power equipment,
accessories, home appliances and cleaning tools in the event of a recall. Here is the place for
authorized service repairs for either BLACK & DECKER or DEWALT. Don't be a slug, plug into
their service center and start those projects now. And don't forget the drills, jig saws, mowers and
hedgers with a two-year home-use warranty. Talk about a "power buy!" Located one and a half
blocks west of I-35, although they do have two others locations. See writeup above.

Blue Sky Specialities   972/406-1290

542 Briarcliff   By Appt. Only
Garland, TX 75043-5602
www.blueskyspec.com

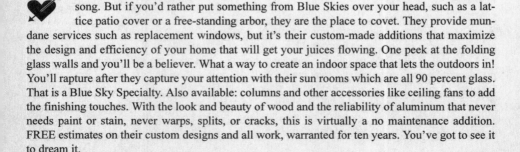

Blue Skies shining above, nothing but Blue Skies....well, that's if you're singing the
song. But if you'd rather put something from Blue Skies over your head, such as a lat-
tice patio cover or a free-standing arbor, they are the place to covet. They provide mundane services such as replacement windows, but it's their custom-made additions that maximize
the design and efficiency of your home that will get your juices flowing. One peek at the folding
glass walls and you'll be a believer. What a way to create an indoor space that lets the outdoors in!
You'll rapture after they capture your attention with their sun rooms which are all 90 percent glass.
That is a Blue Sky Specialty. Also available: columns and other accessories like ceiling fans to add
the finishing touches. With the look and beauty of wood and the reliability of aluminum that never
needs paint or stain, never warps, splits, or cracks, this is virtually a no maintenance addition.
FREE estimates on their custom designs and all work, warranted for ten years. You've got to see it
to dream it.

★★★   Bosch Factory Service Center   972/241-5385

2457 Walnut Ridge St.   Mon-Fri 8-5
Dallas, TX 75229

Grab when you see the "blue" and don't let go. Beside being the factory service center, you'll want to look for the blue color wrapped around the tool that means you should buy because it is the real **BOSCH** tool. Too, some items stashed in the front have been left unclaimed and they are even further discounted than those refurbished tools. Designed differently than most other tools with an easy-grip handle, they are a tool most folks can easily handle. A **BOSCH** drill 18V was $179 (new $249), or a 13V, with just as much torque, was $129. A **SKIL** saw was a drop in the bucket for $34. Rebuilt routers were about $100, jigsaws from $30-$100. Off Stemmons and Walnut Hill, go east on Walnut Hill and left at the second light, Abels. Turn left. Look for it at the corner of Abels and Walnut Ridge.

Boss Resurfacing   972/438-4658

1915 Peters Rd.   By Appt. Only
Irving, TX 75061
www.concretesolutions.com

Now, who is the Boss in YOUR family? If it's Bruce Springsteen, I guess this listing won't matter much. But if you're just a Boss fan, or an all-American family looking for an interesting surface to cover up a multitude of sins, this place should be high on your list. Located near Texas Stadium, call the number above and speak to Kim who'll set up an appointment. Learn the ropes. Resurface exterior or interior surfaces with stamped concrete and literally transform driveways, pool decks, walkways, kitchen floors, bathroom floors, living room floors, entry ways, etc. with a quick fix. A look this beautiful doesn't come cheap, but it does the trick. Fast. A ¼" to ½" layer of concrete can repair, restore and beautify your existing hard surface. Then, it can be stamped to resemble wood, slate, tile, terrazo — it's all quite amazing. Cost is between $6 and $7.50/square foot with a choice of 25 different colors. If you have an ugly garage floor, cover it with the Boss. If you have an ugly driveway, cover it with the Boss. Then, consider yourself the boss and go from there. This is one of the haute hard surfaces I predict for the 21st Century.

◆◆◆◆◆◆   Brennan Enterprises   817/860-0121; 972/660-3106

608 Grand Ave.   Mon-Fri 8-5
Arlington, TX 76010
www.brennancorp.com

Serving the entire state of **TEXAS**, this lone star provider has done many a projects for the rich and famous as well as those not so rich and not so famous. And the prices remain the same. Offering siding, windows, roofing and enclosures, including accessories such as gutters, shutters, solar screens and other relevant exterior building products, you can expect a fair price for an excellent product installed without a hitch. The **CERTAINTEED** vinyl windows are practically maintenance free. Over 50 years in the home improvement business, these are second-generation family-owned contractors. You want it done right the first time around, and you want it done by a reliable company. Dallas residents call 972/660-3106. Visit their showroom located near Cooper and Park Row in Arlington, if you need more convincing. They do it all: siding, windows, roofing and enclosures, including accessories such as gutters, shutters, solar screens and other relevant exterior building products that is sold all under one roof. FREE estimates, as well as no obligation home consultations and demonstrations are available. They say it all on their website, "The Most Innovative Products Installed by Award Winning Craftsmen at the Most Affordable, Value-Oriented Prices in the Nation." *Call toll-free: 888/503-0044*

◆◆◆   Buckets & Bows Maid Service Inc.   972/539-9270

3700 Forums Drive   By Reservation Only
Flower Mound, TX 75028
www.bucketsnbows.com

Buckets & Bows Maid Service Inc is a nationally-known franchised company that offers residential cleaning services with a variety of choices: weekly, bi-weekly, monthly, one time or occasional (move-in or move out). It's your choice whether you want the deluxe top-to-bottom thorough cleaning one time, or are you a harried mother or newly-married with little experience and can't seem to get organized? (Gift certificates are sold in four hour blocks at $30/hour — $120.) Whew! That's a steep clean sweep. This franchise serves Denton, Corinth, Argyle, The Colony, Frisco, McKinney, Allen, Flower Mound, Lewisville, Highland Village, Coppell, Carrollton and Plano. They will do Free in-home estimates, one maid per household (with same maid cleaning your house every week so you don't have to teach them the ropes.) They provide only trained and trusted professionals who have been pre-qualified. Their quality service is guaranteed, insured and bonded with carpet cleaning and office cleaning, too. A ball park figure to clean a 2,200 sq. ft. home would be about $75-80. Online coupons for $15 off general cleaning for first time new clients is available on their website. Now, get with the program and at least, come clean! This is pretty typical pricing of maid/cleaning services throughout the Metroplex so the only way to think cheaper, is to think a student could use the extra money during the summer, or an individual looking to get hired because she's cheaper. Those are hard to come by because if they're cheaper, they're already working for somebody else. What a difference a decade makes. I don't think there was anything like Maid Services ten years ago. And now there's a strange car parked in front of most people's houses during the week. Have feather duster, will travel! *Call toll-free: 888/258-5540*

★★★★★★   Budget Decorators, The   469/293-SHOP (7467)

Lewisville, TX 75067   By Appt. Only
www.thebudgetdecorators.com

 There's nothing like it so far in the Metroplex, but if you like Design on a Dime, you'll love the Budget Decorators™. It takes one to know one. Since I'm great at launching new businesses, let me introduce you to my latest — and maybe my greatest. Called The Budget Decorators ™, it's my answer to being glued to Home and Garden Network. I love to play decorator. I know who some of the good ones who charge $200 an hour; and I know some of the good ones who charge $65 an hour. Who would you prefer? Ok, so now we're on the same wave length. If you are interior design challenged, you will love the Budget Decorators. We even intend to sponsor a total room EXTREME MAKEOVER later on in the year. Designers, afterall, have been sneaking around the "underground" for years and yet charge clients ten times what they find because nobody would believe how cheap it was. In fact, that's who we're marketing to. We'll pass the savings on when we find it on the cheap. Window treatments, upholstery, working with fabrics are are specialty, but we do it all. Meet The Budget Decorators (and the Lone Arranger) at our BD headquarters or at your home or office. An appointment is still necessary. Call the number above and we'll get you connected. Our Budget Decorators come with plenty of experience and charge half the usual and customary designer rates. Then, once you've laid out your plan of action, they shop at "underground" approved resources. Wholesale or less, staying within your budget, I guarantee it. We shop at only the best who charge you the least — and then pass on their low prices to you. The look may be one of opulence; the price tag will be more pauper-like. From chandeliers for $95 to floral arrangements right out of the lobbies of the Mansion Hotel for under $200, painting inside and out, faux painting to murals, to complete kitchen or bath remodels that will save you thousands, you'll can count (the savings) on us. We'll share our secrets, teach you a few design tricks, and hope you'll recommend us to your neighbors in the process. Nobody can beat our prices. The Budget Decorators ™ are on our website. You're but one click away for your design makeovers. From commercial lobbies for businesses, corporate offices, waiting rooms for doctors, lawyers or any professional who wants to make an impression for less; but mostly for home owners in need of a face lift, a room rearrange, a total house make-over, a room addition, or a new home from scratch. Here we come, ready or not. We've combined the talents of several designers who have the eye for color, scale, fabrics, room arrangements, how-to-mix and match and the Lone Arranger who will come out and just re-arrange with what you have already have to create a whole different look. Reality does have to come into play, how-ever. They can't redo an entire room complete with 10 pieces of furniture, art work, accessories, florals, new carpet, wallpaper, faux painting, window treatments, an Oriental rug for under $1,000. We can do some of it, but let's get real! Expect to pay a small (considering the competition) hourly wage and then, let's go shopping!

★★★★★★   Builder's Surplus   817/831-3600

5832 E. Belknap   Mon-Fri 9-6; Sat 9-4
Haltom City, TX 76117

Too many cooks may spoil the broth, but there could never be too many cabinets in my kitchen. When you're ready to remodel, consider Builder's Surplus for cabinets by **CDI** (now called ARROWROOT) and **WESTERN**. The bulk of their inventory is of the higher-end caliber, although they do have a builder's grade of cabinet called **ARISTOCRAT** which is plenty serviceable, especially for a workroom, garage, etc. Bring in your measurements and they their computer will generate an entire layout for you, in color no less. This color rendition will show you exactly the coloring of your cabinets, appliances and walls, should you decide to paint them, too. What a "before" and "after" transformation. Of course, if they don't have what you're looking for, they will order it for you and still save you a ton of money. Other products abound for many home improvement projects: **ATRIUM** windows and doors, **H & R WIN-DOWS**, **STANLEY**, **WILSONART** and more. The prices will be 25-50 percent off and the service is impeccable! They're geographically desirable for Tarrant and the Mid-Cities home owner, but with prices this good, wherever you live, you can justify a trip here just because of the prices and the selection.

◆◆◆◆◆   Certa ProPainters   800/462-3782

672 Hawthorn Circle   By Appt. Only
Highland Village, TX 75077
www.gocerta.com

With seven area franchises to choose from, you've lucked out when it comes to interior and exte-rior painting, as well as light carpentry work and sheet rock repair. Certa (or am I thinking SERTA?) is the perfect painting company that promises not to sleep on the job. These painters offer fully guaranteed work, with a two-year written warranty. Read the fine print — peeling or blistering of paint is covered due to a defect in workmanship, but not the cost of paint, just the reapplication. If peeling and blistering is caused by defective paint, well, then, you've got a prob-lem with the paint company, not the painters. What they do is assure you of what they call "no trace" spotless painting, the use of the finest primers, finishes and paints....and all at a fair price. You can get an estimate just by filling in the dimensions and specifics of the area to be painted on their website. Groovy! How more simple does it get! Final payment is not made until you've given your approval. The brand of paint varies, but many of the contractors use **SHERWIN WILLIAMS**, which is considered one of the best in the business. Make sure you verify that you want the best grade, or close to it. You Go, Certa, Go! *Call toll-free: 800/462-3782*

★★★ Chambers Brick Sales Inc   817/332-9377

451 S. Main Street   Mon-Fri 8-5
Fort Worth, TX 76104-2402

Not too far from downtown Fort Worth is a showroom and brickyard with a selection large enough to cover an entire subdivision of your choice. Lay it on, thick. Choose from 25 different brick manufacturers — just imagine the variations on a brick theme. Delivery charges apply to any order under 2,500 bricks, but for $75, they will go all the way to Granbury or all the way up to Gainesville. Is there no end to their endurance? Prices go by the packaging. For example, 4,000 bricks will equate to so much per brick, but for a smaller order of 1,000 bricks, the price goes up to about 35-40 cents per brick. So what are you waiting for? To huff and puff and blow you house down, so you can build it back up, one brick at a time?

◆◆◆◆ Chimney Sweep, The   214/284-8107

Flower Mound, TX   By Appt. Only

Not just another Tom, Dick or **HARRY**, Tom Smith is THE Chimney Sweep to call if you need a pro to inspect or clean your chimney or fireplace system. He also does chimney caps, bird nest removal and mortar work, so you can make a clean sweep of his services. Just remember to leave a cappuccino on the mantle rather than a glass a milk so as to distinguish his visit from Santa Claus's.

◆◆◆◆◆◆ Christian Painters   817/795-5696; 972/965-8575

PO Box 531   By Appt. Only
Mansfield, TX 76063
www.ChristianPainters.com

 What's a nice Jewish girl calling on the talents of the Christian Paint- ers? Well, Michaelangelo wasn't Jewish, was he? But he was the best, right? He came bearing brushes and worked straight through until the job was complete and in the process, he created a masterpiece. So, if it's good enough for the Sistine Chapel, it's good enough for the Metroplex. Until a crew is hired for the North Dallas corridor, consider Christian Painters to concentrate on Tarrant County. Do as the Romans did and call in the troops —at the Christian Painters. No, they are not the wine sellers (CHRISTIAN BROTHERS'wine) but they are the ones to call when it comes to a spirits-ual paint job. They always clean up after themselves and go the extra mile. Polite. Courteous. Honest. They have shown up and provided meticulous workmanship in Southlake, Grapevine, Colleyville, Keller and North Richland Hills since 1999. As Members of the Southlake Chamber of Commerce, Christian Painters have a mission beyond the palette of your walls. Their line-up of services include interior and exterior painting, sheetrock repairs, special finishes and textures. See the results of their labors of love on their extensive website and for personal references, don't hesitate to call me. My faux painted guest bath walls now match a faux painted chest of drawers perfectly.

◆◆◆◆◆◆ **Clean Team** 972/417-6961

Carrollton, TX 75006 By Appt. Only

This team hits the spot, especially 'cause they do everything I don't want to! And, they do it right the first time around. From make-readies, if you're a landlord and want to clean up the mess from the previous tenants, to someone who is trying to sell a house that hasn't had a thorough cleaning in years. This is the team that means clean. Their motto, "They do dirt, cheap!" Both residential and commercial clean ups, they are not adverse to doing windows, one-time or on a regular basis during their routine cleaning regime. They also will clean carpets and floors — any flooring is fair game, stripping and waxing floors, too, makes for a clean sweep of things. Try 'em, you'll like 'em. For new customers who mention the Diva, a $10 discount for residential services and a $20 discount for commercial accounts sweetens the pot. They are superb on "make-readies" for apartment clean-ups, commercial offices, window-washing inside and out, hauling trash, just about any odd job that nobody else wants to do.

◆◆◆ **Closet & Storage Concepts** 972/509-9500

1845 Summit Avenue, Suite #406 Mon-Fri 9-5
Plano, TX 75074-8148
www.closetandstorageconcepts.com

Yes, they do closets. But it doesn't stop there. They will organize your pantry, home office, garage, laundry room and entertainment center as well — to pristine condition. Headquartered in New Jersey, their Dallas area franchiser is based in Plano. Since 1987, they have been organizing, manufacturing and installing custom closet and storage systems in homes and offices across the country. Call for a free in-home design consultation, and they will measure the closet or area in need of organization, show you previous projects that perhaps would give you an idea of what yours will look like upon completion, even perform a wardrobe analysis, if it's your clothes that need help. In a few days, they will return with a plan of action and go from there. A trained installer, an employee of the company, will deliver and install the cabinets (they do not use sub-contractors.) All work is covered by a lifetime warranty. They've got it all; built-in drawers, pull-out baskets for storage, jewelry drawers, belt and tie racks, shelf dividers and more. According to their website, they have installed over 40,000 closets throughout their franchised network. But remember, that includes their national network, and not all concentrated in the Metroplex. *Call toll-free: 888/THE-CLOS*

◆◆◆◆ **Closet Factory, The** 214/390-0606

2305 Belt Line Rd., #150 Mon-Sat 9-5 (By Appt. Only)
Carrollton, TX 75006
www.closetfactory.com

This franchise has been organizing closets, garages and offices for over 20 years and have repeatedly been named a top franchise opportunity by Entrepreneur Magazine. When you factor in all of your bargain purchases, no doubt you'll need a bigger and better way of organizing them. If your closet poles are bowing in the middle with all that weight and you can never find your favorite slacks, it's time to pull out all the stops and let them get your act together. Although you won't pay for installation, you will pay for custom workmanship. They offer a Free in-home planning session, which can last as long as an hour. Custom-built garage organizers and modular office spaces are also part of their repertoire. And if you think white is the only color choice, think again. With such added features as their SafeDrawer for storing valuables and The Jewel, a Lucite marvel for displaying jewelry, how can you resist? Closet Factory designs closets that will fit your home and your lifestyle but expect to pay the price to have everything at your fingertips. Call 817/740-0606 if you're in the Fort Worth area. ***Call toll-free: 800/260-0606***

◆◆◆◆◆◆   Closets by Design   972/361-0010/817-416-9250

4301-A Lindbergh Dr.   By Appt. Only
Addison, TX 75001
www.closetsbydesign.com

 And the winner is? With all the closet organizers in town, who is the fairest of them all? Closets By Design was founded in 1982 by European developer Rafael Feig who specialized in condominiums and large custom home developments. He understood how to utilize space and what homeowners wanted most — the proper use of space. He customized the closets not only to maximize space, but to add real value to the home, both in increased property value and the enhanced quality of life. The Greenup's (Brian and Lisa) are the driving force in the Dallas/Fort Worth area with a stable of talented artisans in their custom workroom warehouse behind their Addison showroom. Their products come with a lifetime guarantee. Go to my website, www.undergroundshopper.com and click on the button that says, "Before & After," to confirm their talent. My home office and my garage are testament enough to their craftsmanship. All of their installers are bonded and insured and more than anything else, talented and professional. And yes, they are radio-dispatched and arrive when they're suppose to be. What a novelty! And don't forget about their price guarantee. It's your insurance that nobody will beat their prices. Mention the Diva sent you, and they usually throw in a free gift or accessory. Take Midway, just north of Belt Line and turn right (east) on Lindbergh. Visit their showroom so you can see up close and personal their workmanship. Closets are now like rooms onto their own. Seeing is believing. And buying is usually the end result. ***Call toll-free: 800/BY DESIG***

★★★★★★   Concrete Design Center   972/436-8900

701 S. Stemmons, Suite 90   By Appt. Only
Lewisville, TX 75061
www.fritzpak.com

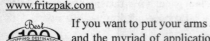 If you want to put your arms around the entire industry springing up around concrete and the myriad of applications, here is where to land. At the Lewisville Shopping Center, see the latest techniques and products that are used to enhance any existing concrete surface: concrete stain, stencil, stamp, overlay products, concrete countertop design essentials and a revolutionary vertical system for texturing walls, inside or out. Concrete Design Center. Achieve the look of a contemporary lifestyle with the stability and versatility of concrete. This company is also a distributor for the Fritz-Pak Corporation which manufactures and sells concrete admixtures that actually make better concrete and make construction practices easier and safer. The Fritz-Pak company was established in 1998, but the product line is the result of over forty years of experience in saving you money while improving concrete quality and performance. These powered admixtures are packaged in patented **FRITZ-PAK** water-soluble bags, small enough to be carried in the cabs of ready-mix trucks and, therefore, can be dosed anywhere. All bags are pre-measured to avoid mistakes and reduce wasted and lost products. Read all about it on the website of www.fritzpak.com, so you can see all of the applications.

★★★★   **Cooper Concrete Co**   **972/276-1167**

1100 N. 5th St.   By Appt. Only
Garland, TX 75040-5036
www.cooperconcrete.com

One of the most respected names in the business of concrete, this family-owned institution has
been laying it on since 1947. Though it started as a ready-mix supplier, today this company only
supplies the concrete — you supply the patio, driveway or slab, prepped and ready to go. If you
need help with the design or the preparation, they have recommended contractors that will use the
concrete from Cooper. Some of these recommended contractors are: Samples Concrete at 972/
276-0440 and Lone Star Concrete at 214/552-9233 — ask for Wes. There, you have it all with one
call. For sophisticated web users, you can shop for concrete online. Go ahead. Make their day!

★★★★   **Dallas Direct Kitchens**   **817/233-6930**

Fort Worth, TX   By Appt. Only
www.dallasdirectkitchens.com

Contact Patrick Greenlaw for a free proposal, for starters. That's if you can get him to return your
calls. We've left several, to no avail. If he does call you, then you're on your way to doing it — his
way. Bypass the middleman and buy direct from the factory. The ROBCO CABINET Factory for
furniture-finished cabinetry is specifically designed for your kitchen and bath. Save thousands of
dollars and buy where the contractors have been buying since 1979. Quality kitchens have been
installed throughout North American and Japan, and now those of us in the Metroplex can call on
them, too. European-styled frameless doors from alder to pine, red oak, hard maple, cherry and
more. At your private consultation, you will make decisions about the kind of wood, style, finish
and color you want. Oh, there are so many decisions to make before you sleep. Then, in a few
days, they will return with the drawings for your new kitchen from many different perspectives.
The project will then be priced and construction can begin. Expect to be cooking up a storm in six
to eight weeks, depending on the wood and finish chosen. Whether it's a contemporary or traditional design you want, you will enjoy solid wood cabinets with nothing but the finest Canadian
hardwood in your kitchen or bath. Now, if the cupboards are bare, you should be off to the Dallas
Food Depot and load up with gourmet condiments at half the price. If he'd ever call back, no doubt
he'd be elevated to the 100 BEST!

★★★★★   **Dallas North Builders Hardware**   **972/248-0645**

6709 Levelland   Mon-Fri 8-5
Dallas, TX 75252
www.dnbh.com

Looking for the cat's meow? Then take a look at the "wow" selection (over 230 different manufacturers'product lines represented) of decorative hardware and plumbing equipment at the best
prices in town. From traditional to contemporary, you will save at least 30 percent less on literally
thousands and thousands of decorative hardware that blows the competition to smithereens. For
doors, cabinets and bathroom hardware and accessories, there isn't a knob known to mankind that
you can't find here. Then, what about door locks that are both the look of tomorrow with the security needed today? But if you think that's it, what about all the groovy wash basins that sit majesti-
cally atop a hard surface? A piece of granite or marble? Or inside an antique washstand? They are
all the rage these days? GRAVITY GLASS, HECTAURAUS, STONE FOREST are some of the
high-tech and high-end lines that you won't see at your home centers. These are works of art. Add
in faucets, lavatories, sinks and water closets that you don't see inside the track model homes.
Instead, these are what you'd see at the "Parade of Homes" where the manufacturers are showcas-

ing nothing but the finest. Yes, there are gorgeous products beyond **KOHLER**. Have you ever seen **JADO** or **TOTO**? Looking for an unusual mirror, a decorative mailbox, a safe, **MR. STEAM** or a whirlpool or steeping bath? It's not just the ordinary — but the extraordinary. Then, what about a decorative pot rack over your kitchen island? Dallas North Builders is where to land for service, selection and savings. They install and deliver the products direct to the job. No wonder they are considered the "King" of the decorative hardware road. Paul King is head king with a talented group of king's helpers to make your shopping as easy as knocking on their front door. Transform your bath or kitchen with just a change in hardware; what a difference it'll make. Stay flush and rush to their showroom Monday-Friday in the Preston/Frankford area. One block east of Preston which is Davenport; then one block east of Davenport to 6709 Levelland. For a map, log on to their website above. Wife to another talented merchant, see Fat Rat under Furniture.

◆◆◆◆◆ Dallas Plumbing Company   214/340-6300
11055 Plano Rd.   Mon-Fri 8-5; Sat 9-Noon
Dallas, TX 75238
www.dallasplumbing.com

Whether it's coming in through the vents or out through the pipes, Dallas Plumbing & Air-Conditioning can keep you flush. Air-conditioning, heating, plumbing, hot water heaters, kitchen and bath installation and repair is their "plumb de force." All makes and models are serviced 24/7, including Emergency Service. This 110-year-old-company just celebrated their 100th Year Anniversary. Specials for this event included: a 40-gallon hot water heater, $209; a 50-gallon model was $229. Taking 25 percent off the manufacturer's suggested retail price for kitchen items may not float your boat, but, then again, every little drip helps. They recommend if your AC unit is 12 years or older, you can save 40 percent on your cooling bill with the new unit that uses Puron rather than Freon. Offering a Free evaluation on your system and a 10-year parts and labor warranty should provide you with some additional comfort. Water heaters are from A.O. SMITH as they have a limited 10-year parts and labor warranty. Their extensive parts department can usually fix you up the first time out with fixtures: faucets, lavatories, toilets, sinks, tubs, showers and whirlpools, well, what abut a steam room or a sauna? Now we're talking! Their labor warranty is one-year only on installation and repair.

◆◆◆◆ Decorative Paving Systems   817/988-5800
Euless, TX   By Appt. Only

If you have to ask, "Where is the yellow brick road," you're probably calling on the wrong company. It's probably the only paving option they haven't considered. But they most everything else: driveways, walkways, retaining walls, pool decks and patios. Price, of course, depends on the size of the area and materials to be used, but they do it all — for less. This one-stop shop doesn't even collect their final payment until you're completely satisfied. Ask them about a replacement retaining wall, and they'll gladly tell you what they do, from top to bottom. First, the old materials should be removed, proper ground preparation would be undertaken and materials would be placed 6" below the ground before the retaining wall could be (or should be) built. You don't want to retain a company that's doesn't know what a retaining wall is, do you? Over 16 years serving the Metroplex, you'll find them reliable and restorative to your home's health. Easy over, without egg on your face 'cause you know enough to call on the very best. And easy-does-it on your budget, too.

★★★★★★ **Denton County Surplus**   **940/365-2889**

301 S. Hwy 377   Mon-Fri 9-5; Sat 8-2
Denton, TX 76227

I wonder if they ever intend to answer their phones? We couldn't say for sure, as we called for many days in a row to no avail. Their answering machine was on all day; in-between, the lines were busy. At last, you can capitalize on someone else's lost arch, or French door. For $250, go price them new and see why Sue says, Buy, Buy! Entry doors, well, they were as low as $75, and one low, low price for a carport should get your motor running. Now in their expanded warehouse, you can conclude your weekend seek and search mission with something from here. My only complaint? Limited Saturday hours and the absence of Sunday hours? Some of us only have one day off and here you are closed! Always save 50 percent....on windows, doors, well, it's a surplus store and a whole lot more! Now those in Denton county can take advantage of a demolition derby or Denton County Surplus's buying power when it comes to closeouts. Quite a selection and something that could add the finishing touches on a myriad of projects — from room borders to framing. They also carry wallpaper, bathroom fixtures, some antique doors and windows; DCS has what it takes for a total room makeover. About 95 percent of the items are new, due to factory overstocks, store closures, or discontinued items, but prices are definitely from the Dark Ages. Lighten up, folks, and head to the intersection of 380 and 377, just outside the city limits of Denton.

◆◆◆◆◆◆ **Devard's Heat, Air, Electric & Plumbing**   **972/422-1505**

1000 14th Street, #387   Mon-Fri 8-5; Sat 8-1 (or By Appt.)
Plano, TX 75074
www.devards.com

Expect to pay a $69 check-up charge for their spring or fall check-up calls, but when there's a break-down in your air, heat, plumbing or electrical system, they prefer to quote by the job. Train yourself to call them for service on all **TRANE** heating and air-conditioning systems and units, although they service any make or model. Consider them, too, for any projects left incomplete on your "honey-do" list. Whether it's hanging that ceiling fan or creating a French drain in your yard, these folks are available for many of life's little problems. Regardless of your home or office needs, they can be your conduit to maintaining the good life on full power. Electrical services include lighting, wiring, remodeling, new construction, ceiling fans, new circuits, spas and pools, landscape and outdoors lighting, or anything that requires a circuit. Now offering plumbing services, as well. If you've got good credit, there are financing plans available with a 100 percent guaranteed satisfaction. Please, don't sweat the small stuff (as long as you're in the Plano/Dallas corridor!) They've been serving the area since 1968 and have that all-important clean record at the BBB. If you're out of their service area, you may have to beg.

◆◆◆◆◆◆ **DFW Pest Control**   **214/349-2847; 817/595-2847**

10875 Plano Rd., #105   Mon-Fri 7-7; Sat 7-2 (By Appt. Only)
Dallas, TX 75238
www.dfwpest.com

Do you hire a pest control company based on their jingle? Let's get real. Nobody likes to share their personal space with an ant. When there were uninvited guests living inside my cupboards, I finally had to call in the big guns. With their trend-setting, pest-ridding procedures, it's no wonder they're light years ahead of the competition. For one, they have the Mister Mosquito System — and it's the best. One push of a button sets it off for 30-45 seconds; wait 10 minutes....and your yard is mosquito and bug-free. I finally got to enjoy an after-dinner swim without being eaten alive. This system not only rids your home and yard of mosquitoes, it also does away with flies, bees, wasps, gnats, spiders, fleas, ticks and roaches. Dallas/Fort Worth Pest Control is the official pest company of the entire Dallas/Fort Worth Metroplex. I have jumped on the DFW Pest Control bandwagon and listen to the experts (and stop bugging them!) After 33 years, they're the oldest and the biggest independent pest company around that services both commercial and residential customers in both Dallas and Tarrant counties. For do-it-yourselfers, go to www.epestsupply.com to order professional supplies online — at a discount, of course.

◆◆◆◆◆◆ **DFW Re-Bath**   **214/352-2669**

1801 Royal Lane, Suite 700   Mon-Fri 8-5:30; Sat 10-1 (Preferably By Appt.)
Dallas, TX 75234
www.dfwrebath.com

 Unlike the popular re-glazing of tubs (where you have to continually repeat this process every few years,) this company patented a better idea, one that forms a vacuum custom seal with a material (high impact acrylic) that is the same as fighter pilots have in the windows of their jet planes — and priced at a fraction of the typical bath remodel. Suppose you have an **AMERICAN STANDARD** tub from the 1950s. Well, in their warehouse, they'll have a mold for it so you needn't replace it — just reface it and save about 50 percent of the cost and all of the mess. From ugly to magnifico in one day is just what lies ahead. It's practically indestructible. It comes with a lifetime warranty, so let's all "splish splash" while taking a bath, even if it's not Saturday night. Even if you have run out of rubber duckies, with their unique process, they can remove your current tub and convert it to a drive-in shower so those in a wheel chair can get in and out easily without getting soaked. Everything we priced was about 1/2 of what it would cost for similar remodels. Add in a grab bar, even a shower seat if you'd like to relax on a chair while taking in the raindrops overhead. From vanity tops to a complete remodeling job, from just a plain tub to one with the complete wall surround and shower base liners, without the cost, without the mess, clean up at Re-Bath. Only the best hardware is used by **MOEN** and **WOLVERINE**. *Call toll-free: 800/BATHTUB*

◆◆◆◆◆◆ **DFW Security**   **972/567-0418**

2913 Downing St.   By Appt. Only
Flower Mound, TX 75028

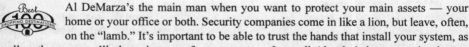 Al DeMarza's the main man when you want to protect your main assets — your home or your office or both. Security companies come in like a lion, but leave, often, on the "lamb." It's important to be able to trust the hands that install your system, as well as the man you'll phone in case of an emergency. Just call Al, who's been securing homes and offices for more than 27 years. Service and value is what he sells when it comes to securing yours. Here's a ballpark figure for a two-story, 2,800 square foot home (with 400 square feet upstairs); and a wireless system that has you covered all around, here's the deal: You'll be buying the system outright for about $499.99 installed and, then, your monthly monitoring will run about $12.95/month. No contract. No hidden costs. No fooling. The reason the monthly fees are so reasonable is because you buy the equipment outright, and over the long run, you'll save a lot of money without compromising your safety. Other companies "give" you the equipment, but recoup their "freebie" by having you sign lengthy contracts at much higher monthly fees. Al is serious about selling security and your safety at a fair price. Right on, Al! That's why he made it into the 100 BEST. Better safe than sorry, I say.

★★★★★★ Discount Building Materials (formerly Surplus Depot)

817/834-7575

220 S. Sylvania, #213   Mon-Fri 7-6; Sat 8-4
Fort Worth, TX 76111

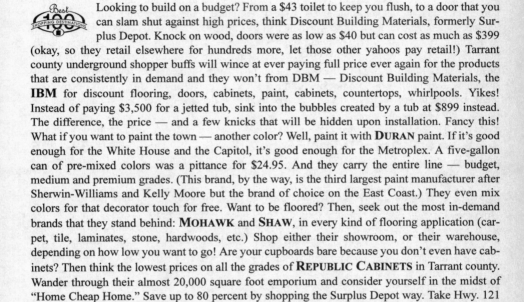

Looking to build on a budget? From a $43 toilet to keep you flush, to a door that you can slam shut against high prices, think Discount Building Materials, formerly Surplus Depot. Knock on wood, doors were as low as $40 but can cost as much as $399 (okay, so they retail elsewhere for hundreds more, let those other yahoos pay retail!) Tarrant county underground shopper buffs will wince at ever paying full price ever again for the products that are consistently in demand and they won't from DBM — Discount Building Materials, the **IBM** for discount flooring, doors, cabinets, paint, cabinets, countertops, whirlpools. Yikes! Instead of paying $3,500 for a jetted tub, sink into the bubbles created by a tub at $899 instead. The difference, the price — and a few knicks that will be hidden upon installation. Fancy this! What if you want to paint the town — another color? Well, paint it with **DURAN** paint. If it's good enough for the White House and the Capitol, it's good enough for the Metroplex. A five-gallon can of pre-mixed colors was a pittance for $24.95. And they carry the entire line — budget, medium and premium grades. (This brand, by the way, is the third largest paint manufacturer after Sherwin-Williams and Kelly Moore but the brand of choice on the East Coast.) They even mix colors for that decorator touch for free. Want to be floored? Then, seek out the most in-demand brands that they stand behind: **MOHAWK** and **SHAW**, in every kind of flooring application (carpet, tile, laminates, stone, hardwoods, etc.) Shop either their showroom, or their warehouse, depending on how low you want to go! Are your cupboards bare because you don't even have cabinets? Then think the lowest prices on all the grades of **REPUBLIC CABINETS** in Tarrant county. Wander through their almost 20,000 square foot emporium and consider yourself in the midst of "Home Cheap Home." Save up to 80 percent by shopping the Surplus Depot way. Take Hwy. 121 to Sylvania, head South to 4th St. and turn right. They're the second building on the right. Tell them the Diva sent you and they may even give you a FREE gift.

★★★★★ Discount Countertops   214/951-0313

4735 Almond Ave.   Mon-Fri 8-Noon and 1-5
Dallas, TX 75247
www.discountcountertops.com

Between Mockingbird and Irving Boulevard, look for a place to counter the revolution — Discount Countertops. A family-owned business since 1990, first off, counter any competitors'prices right off the bat, and consider getting your counters, custom or ready-made at a discounted price. Yes, sir. I'll drink to that! Whether it's for your kitchen, bar, bathroom, garage, craft room, computer workstation, even an entertainment center, these are the folks that can fabricate whatever you want to your specs .... and that's the truth! FREE estimates and measuring done in-house (your house or office), including additional remodeling finish-outs, where required. Don't expect to be enlightened by their website. It's nothing but their name. Try on countertops in laminate or solid surfaces only. What is a solid surface? Corian, for example, at a better price that those big box home centers. It's also a one-stop shop with installation available. Notice business hours are interrupted by lunch, and expect their answering machine to usually say, "Hello," and the message to be in halting English, since it is not their native tongue. Just be forewarned that though you'll save 30 percent over Home Expo's prices, you will wait weeks for an appointment just for the measurements. They're booked floor to ceiling, but especially in between. Of course, they're worth waiting for.

◆◆◆◆◆   **Discount Quality Roofing & Repair   972/446-9242**

1221 Cannes Court   By Appt. Only
Carrollton, TX 75006

Oh Hail, don't you just hate to start roof shopping after a major hailstorm? But, if you're a roofer, well, no doubt you're in hog heaven as visions of dollar signs dance over your head. Well, you must admit, it nice to be needed, like being at the right place at the right time. But if you're the homeowner, that means your house was at the wrong place at the wrong time. But man can't go without something over his head so when the first leak appears, it's time to head to Discount Quality Roofing, if you want a Free estimate and a whole host of references. Only the highest quality products are placed overhead with a 20-40 year manufacturer's warranty from such stellar manufacturers as **ELK** and **TAMKO**. Whatever kind of roof you're after, consider it a done deal, as they specialize in them all: wood, composition, shingles, tar and gravel and modified roofs of any combination of the above. So there. It's now all signed, then sealed and delivered. You don't want it to rain on your parade, do you?

◆◆◆◆◆◆   **Down Home Fence & Deck   972/253-1316**

Irving, TX 75038   By Appt. Only
www.downhomefence.com

If you're a fan of down-home cooking, bring on the folks that have been serving up down-home design and building experience since 1986. With reasonable prices, they can build you a custom wood fence or deck, a barn or an utility shed, an arbor, sealing of fences or decks, staining of fences or decks, and light remodeling. Expect them to know their stuff by utilizing spruce, cedar, redwood, white wood and the use of ONLY galvanized nails. That's important. Talk the talk so they don't walk the walk (all over you!) Act like you know that galvanized nails are the only nails to use. FREE estimates round out their down-home service. Although they're available 24-hours (if you need a temporary fence for security purposes, for example), most folks manage to call during usual business hours. Of course, they are insured and guarantee their work 100 percent. Their website shows off their workmanship so you can see first hand, these guys are in the groove and can stand on their own merits.

◆◆◆◆◆◆   **Drain Doctor   214/372-4637; 817/336-7448**

PO Box 36044   Mon-Sat 7 AM-8 PM; Sun & Holidays 8-6
Dallas, TX 75235
www.draindoctor.org

The name Charlie Sarao may not be familiar to you but that doesn't mean you don't know him....or love him. In my past life, I knew him as Mr. Rooter. Does that give you a clue? Today, he's known around the Metroplex as the Drain Doctor. And you guessed it. He cleans clogged drains. His phone number is one you'll never forget: 214/draindr. (214/373-4637) should be now committed to memory. His team of professionals are pros in the know when it comes to sewer and drain cleaning. It's a dirty job and somebody's got to do it. When you haven't, that's when it's time to call the doctor. He has been prescribing money-saving drain tips since 1973 and has not branched off into a million and one other plumbing-related services. Drains are it. He's not all wet, either, with his money-saving tips to keep those drains from backing up. Read his prescriptions on his website and learn the ropes such as 1. DO run cold water through your disposal during and after use; 2. DO pour hot water down the drain once a week. 3. DON'T pour grease down the drain. (Hey, after reading, "Drains for Dummies," I knew that that was the first rule of thumb. But do you know how many out there do not know that you should NOT put stringy foods such as celery, corn stalks, or banana peels in the disposal? Drain Doctor came after I put all three down the drain and turned on the disposal. No wonder my disposal went kaput! Then, what about coffee grounds? Tea bags? Eggshells? Should you or shouldn't you put them down the drain? Answers are on the draindoctor.org's website. But man does not clog up the drain to the disposal alone. There's also the drain to your washing machine. How many of us dump tons of non-biodegradable detergent into the machine and wonder why it gasps for fresh air? Or throw Paper Towels down the toilet? Or have enough hair in the shower to braid a foot-long ponytail? The Drain Doctor will then ask you about your sewer lines? Yes, these doctors get to the root of your problems. But I'll save that conversation to when they meet with you. After all, that's a pretty personal question to ask. Who do you want to sewer next? (I hope not me! I am staying out of trouble and the courtroom.) Look for the Drain Doctor's white with red lettered trucks out and about serving the entire Metroplex. Their radio dispatcher can even give you an estimate by phone. There are NEVER any hidden charges. These guys are up front and honorable. They could write the book, "Drain and Able." A tech can usually be dispatched within one-two hours; or a convenient appointment will be arranged. Yes, these doctors make house calls. They are upfront with their prices and down home in their demeanor. They're the best for the less and that's why they were voted as the only Drain Cleaning service in the book.

◆◆◆◆◆◆ Dunlap Construction Company   817/284-5111

7248 Glenview Drive   Mon-Fri 8-5
Richland Hills, TX 76118

 What a sport! Since 1974, they've been bouncing around the court of happy home-owners. Just about anything you need done to your home can be handled by the pro-fessionals here. With almost 30 years in the business, in the same location, just ask for references and you'll see a book full. Whatever needs building, they do it all (except arks, I'm told.) They leave those up to Noah. But the menu of possibilities is extensive: wood decks, flag-stone decks, arbors, cabanas, room additions, second story additions, kitchen remodeling, bath remodeling, siding, windows, garden rooms, spas and patio enclosures. FREE plans and estimates are provided. When you deal with a business owned by a family who can still show their faces at the local Chamber of Commerce luncheons and at the corner grocery store, you know they can hold their heads up and face the community where they have performed remodeling and building services satisfactorily for decades. Dunlap is a solid company that can do your home improvement project proud. Be sure to tell them the Diva made you do it! *Call toll-free: 888/284-5111*

E Sauna Steam

Dallas, TX   24/7

www.esaunasteam.com    *Top Online Store!*

Since 1963, AMEREC has led the way in the steam and sauna industry. If you're looking for cluck, cluck, pssst .... steam-m-m-m-m-m heat, then consider all the innovative products coming from this manufacturer. All the popular features such as "soft steam," "warm start," "automatic flush systems" and "removable elements" all come from the design team at **AMEREC**. Install units with easy-to-use bath digital controls with the highest quality woods. See rich colors and high performance in a spa-like environment, and it spells a sauna from here. Whether you want what is referred to as a "true sauna" (which is what most people have experienced in the past with heat emanating from an electric sauna heater) or the "infrared sauna," the newest version which uses less energy to operate at a lower temperature and preheats in less than half the time, they are the ones to deliver. They also deliver steam systems for the ultimate steam room plus all of the accessories for steam or sauna-taking. Ah-h-h, that's what I call living the supreme life. It's all done on the internet and it's all at a savings. If you need help with installation, well, check out our handymen that we recommend and you'll have the best of both worlds. FREE shipping with an online purchase; a small $8 handling fee. Too, want a tanning bed? If so, be my guest. I don't recommend them. But for other related websites, check out www.spawarehouse.com; www.aquapoolchemicals; and www.aquapoolwarehouse.com. The neat thing about these product kits for do-it-yourselfers, you can utilize your existing shower space to upgrade for steam. *Call toll-free: 866/367-7286*

★★★★ Economy Signs & Banner   214/341-5007

10833 Alder Circle   By Appt. Only
Dallas, TX 75238
www.economysign.com

Want to let others know who you are? Ever thought about a sign? Ever thought about a sign online? How's that for convenience! Economy Signs and Banners in Dallas was founded in 1984 in a garage and is now considered the fourth fastest growing privately-held company in the Metroplex for the year 2000 (by the Dallas Business Journal). Spear-headed by Nancy and Mark Sanders, Economy has worked hard to become a cornerstone sign supplier for many commercial firms in the Metroplex, particularly real estate firms, and they are the only signage company to have an office on site at DFW International Airport to service the aviation industry. If it's good enough to fly right, expect that you can buy right, also. Sign in here. Since they are a small, privately-owned company with 21 full-time employees and 11,000 square feet of production and office space, Economy can handle just about any job, big or small. So many merchants have asked about sign companies (yes, even merchants ask us where to go), that we decided to investigate sign companies, too. And why not? Companies that save you money are companies that we like to recommend whether it's for business or pleasure. Want an appointment? Just give them a call or send an email. Either way, they'll sign you in. Real estate companies have Economy's phone number on speed dial if that tells you anything.

Elliott's Hardware   214/634-9900

4901 Maple   Mon-Fri 8-6; Sat 9-5
Dallas, TX 75235
www.elliottshardware.com;

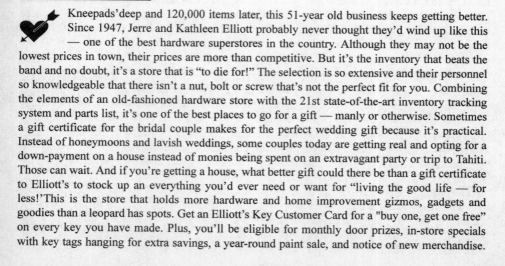 Kneepads'deep and 120,000 items later, this 51-year old business keeps getting better. Since 1947, Jerre and Kathleen Elliott probably never thought they'd wind up like this — one of the best hardware superstores in the country. Although they may not be the lowest prices in town, their prices are more than competitive. But it's the inventory that beats the band and no doubt, it's a store that is "to die for!" The selection is so extensive and their personnel so knowledgeable that there isn't a nut, bolt or screw that's not the perfect fit for you. Combining the elements of an old-fashioned hardware store with the 21st state-of-the-art inventory tracking system and parts list, it's one of the best places to go for a gift — manly or otherwise. Sometimes a gift certificate for the bridal couple makes for the perfect wedding gift because it's practical. Instead of honeymoons and lavish weddings, some couples today are getting real and opting for a down-payment on a house instead of monies being spent on an extravagant party or trip to Tahiti. Those can wait. And if you're getting a house, what better gift could there be than a gift certificate to Elliott's to stock up an everything you'd ever need or want for "living the good life — for less!'This is the store that holds more hardware and home improvement gizmos, gadgets and goodies than a leopard has spots. Get an Elliott's Key Customer Card for a "buy one, get one free" on every key you have made. Plus, you'll be eligible for monthly door prizes, in-store specials with key tags hanging for extra savings, a year-round paint sale, and notice of new merchandise.

What a refreshing change of pace. Located in Plano at 2049 Coit Rd. at West Park Blvd. and in Grapevine at 108 W. Northwest Hwy. at Main St., 817/424-1424. See ya!

◆◆◆ Everlasting Builders   214/328-7550

2325 Lakeland Drive
Dallas, TX 75228

By Appt. Only

Benjamin C. Nebe is the man, the everlasting man who is recognized as a MWBE general contractor, a tenant contractor and a paving contractor. In other words, he's your man to get a residential or commercial project designed and built. Whether it's to finish out a retail tenant space, fix a flat roof or install a new one, do interior or exterior painting, concrete or pavement work, he's the man. He and his able-bodied crew can do it all when the subject comes to remodeling. And if the number above doesn't connect you to the man, this one will: 214/616-5842. Mobile and out. He's been building his business since 1987 and has many projects to his credit, to his everlasting credit. His projects have come in under $100,000 up to one-half million, both residential and commercial, so he can pretty much do it all. And this Benjamin doesn't need to remain Private. (Get it, Private Benjamin?) I do have a weird sense of humor, don't I? ***Call toll-free: 214/319-7671***

Expo Design Center   972/934-2900

13900 Dallas Pkwy.
Dallas, TX 75240-4323
www.expo.com

Mon-Sat 10-8; Sun 11-6

We'd be remiss if we didn't include this whopper. Have it your way, but don't hold anything back. Even the kitchen sink can be thrown into the mix for home improvement addicts. Get your fix and don't even think about putting a nix on any home product or project. The Home Depot's Expo is your mainline, the height of luxury, where shopping for everything for your home is under one roof. If you are upgrading or starting from scratch, this place is mammoth. It's so big, it can be daunting. Here's the lineup: appliances, lamps, wallpaper and window coverings, kitchen cabinets, sinks, countertops, bathroom tubs and fixtures, flooring, tile and wood, outdoor patio choices from built-in grills to rolling ones. Many choices of in-stock, as well as special-order door and cabinet hardware and small appliances. What's even more appealing is the knowledgeable design staff and series of "How-To-Do-It" classes that make your project as easy as A-B-C. Expect Free delivery and hauling away of your old on select appliances. Lots of FREE offers and rebates, too. Check directory for multiple Expo Design Centers in Plano and North Richland Hills. And open wide (your wallets) and say, "Ah-h-h!"

◆◆◆◆◆◆ Extreme Floor Coatings   214/876-5239

Addison, TX
www.extremefloorcoatings.com

By Appt. Only

What do you do with a garage that has nothing but stains and blotches on the floors? Well, there are several options in the market, but none can compare to Extreme Floor Coatings for uniformity and selection. Then, when you compare the price over tile, you will not lament much longer. Hands down, this is the application of choice. Transform that garage into a room with a purpose, whether for cleanliness, orderliness and neatness sake for your car and your sanity; or transform the garage into something new like a playroom, workout room, daycare room, media room, craft room. Don't you deserve a break today? Just imagine how much room you'll have left now that everything's off the floor? Maybe, just maybe, you'll be able to park your car in its rightful spot — the garage. Now isn't that special!

◆◆◆◆◆◆   Fashion Glass & Mirror   972/223-8936

585 S. Beckley Ave.   Mon-Fri 7:30-4:30
Desoto, TX 75115
www.fashionglass.com

This company's a glass act. For over a quarter of a century, they have managed to stay clear of any "tarnishment" to their impeccable reputation. They're all trained professionals serving the Metroplex from three locations, including Desoto (above — the main branch), their north branch in Justin and a southwest branch in Arlington. With 35 fully-equipped trucks running their "gl-asses" around town, they not only provide the service, but they're fast, too. Glass appears magically from their stocked trucks with inventory from their gigantic 43,000-square-foot manufacturing plant. What do they sell? Well, let's start with custom mirrors, frameless shower doors, tub enclosures, special 1/2" thick frameless shower units, and mirrored bi-pass doors for starters. Add leaded glass, etched glass, insulated glass, glass tops for tables, and as you can now see perfectly clear, their specialty is glass. Ask no more questions. They're the ones to call. Since 1973, they will work within your budget, travel to any part of the Metroplex and provide a one-year limited warranty on any mirror, shower door or mirrored wardrobe door they install. So, if you're glass-conscious, Fashion Glass and Mirror is the one to call. And in this case, since they are the largest manufacturer of this type in the country, they also equate as the best! *Call toll-free: 800/289-8936*

Ferguson Bath & Kitchen Gallery   817/261-2561

2220 Duluth Drive   Mon-Fri 8-5
Arlington, TX 76013
www.ferginc.com

They're the nation's largest distributor of plumbing supplies, pipe, valves and fittings (PVC) and the third largest for heating and cooling supplies, so they must have all their little duckies in a row. Selling plumbing supplies since 1953, today there are 10 locations in the Metroplex area including Grapevine, Denton, Fort Worth, Dallas, Arlington, McKinney, Rowlett, Euless and Plano. So, look around, then turn around and head to Ferguson's. Tap into the faucets and fixtures for the bar, bidet, kitchen, lavatory, **ROMAN** tub, tubs and showers. Looking for sinks with pedestals, wall mounts, bar, kitchen, laundry or maybe just a new toilet, shower pan, tub or tub and shower combo unit, whirlpools, shower doors, one of the above or all of the above which are artfully displayed in their showroom? Any of these names ring a bell? ALSONS CORPORATION, AMEREC PRODUCTS, BALDWIN BRASS, DELTA FAUCET CO., DUPONT CORIAN SURFACES, ELKAY MANUFACTURING CO., GROHE AMERICA, INC., JACUZZI WHIRLPOOL BATH, JADO, KALLISTA, INC., KITCHENAID, KOHLER CO., KWC FAUCETS, MOEN INCORPORATED, NUTONE, ONDINE, PRICE PFISTER, PHYLRICH INTERNATIONAL, ROBERN, ROCHAILLE, SEA GULL, STEAMIST CO., ST THOMAS, WHIRLPOOL — well, don't settle for anybody less. Why don't you "Skip to their loo" and shop where the contractors do!

◆◆◆◆◆   Firehouse Movers   972/412-6033; 817/572-9797

Dallas, TX   By Appt. Only
www.firehousemovers.com

Have you ever seen a fireman who wasn't a hunk? Not me. When I'm laying there panting during a minor medical emergency that required a call to the fire department, I've always welcomed the distraction. Instead of any pain I might be experiencing, I was more interested in "batting my eyelashes." So, you might as well take advantage of their bulk in not only putting out fires but in moving you into a new place where you can maybe get the home fires burning. They pack 'em, they move 'em, they price 'em so you don't see red. (trucks, either.) Too, if you want boxes, they have 'em. At the helm is owner Brian Purcell. In 1997, they started with one truck and have grown to a fleet of four. Let them help you move from point A to point B and remove the wear and tear on your truck, your back, or your bank account. All employees undergo rigorous background and criminal checks. Three of their four trucks are fully enclosed 32 foot trailers that would hold approximately three rooms or the contents of a 1,500-1,800 square foot house. Another truck, a tad smaller, would hold approximately three rooms or the contents of a 1,400-1,800 square foot house. Their hourly rates are provided up front. No hidden charges. There is no additional charge because you live on the second floor or there's a walkway to get to your house. Expect the guys to charge $70/hour for two; $95/hour for three; $120 for four. The clock starts ticking the minute they arrive at YOUR house and ends when they leave YOUR house. The only other charge to consider is what they call a "trip charge." And that amount varies, depending on where you live, from $25-$60 depending on the location of the move.

★★★★★★   Fireplace Equipment Warehouse   972/783-6988

1002 N. Central Expressway, #111   Mon-Fri 9-7; Sat 10-6
Richardson, TX 75080-4616
www.fireplaceequipment.com

 At last, here's a newcomer that will get those home fires burning bright. What a coup! Tucked away on the side of Arapaho at Central Expressway, these guys have taken their 25 years of fireplace experience and decided to open up to the public with lots of great buys on fireplaces, screens, tools, firepits and the chimenaes. You can log on to their online site or visit their showroom. Just exit Arapaho from Central and go a few yards on the service road into the first opening into the strip center and go all around to the south side of the complex. They feature the full gamut of fireplace equipment such as glass doors, gas logs, free standing or attached screens, tool sets, fireplaces of all types, and every accessory you'd ever want or need to keep your world aflame: gas keys, covers, damper hooks, gift baskets, fire pits, and other types of fireplace-related items. Then, when the season changes, they stock up on firepits, barbecue grills and smokers, hammocks and other accoutrements for living the good life — for less—in the backyard. *Call toll-free: 800/871-8004*

★★★★★★   Fixtures of America   214/638-5990

2229 Valdina   Mon-Fri 8:30-5; Sat By Appt.
Dallas, TX 75247

 Get a mixture of fixtures at up to 75 percent off. Both new and used fixtures are perfect if you need extra shelving for the garage, your office, or the kids'room, for starters. Although prices vary between individual fixtures, depending on size, condition and where they acquired them, they know their stuff. For example, before they could show me some clothing rounders so we could display clothes for TV, we got the third degree. Do you want it to be stationary or moveable? What were those height requirements? Did we want one that was adjustable? Exit Wycliff off Stemmons and go west to Valdina. They buy and sell quality used fixtures, including a sizable selection of showcases. No one can outdo them on prices or selection. Thinking jewelry display cases. I have put several to good use in my bedroom and talk about those shoe racks. They really come in handy when I leave Vantage Shoe Warehouse during a 2- or 3-for-one sale! *Call toll-free: 800/527-1892*

★★★★ Four Seasons Sunrooms   972/231-1314

804 S. Central Expressway   By Appt. Only
Richardson, TX 75080-7413
www.fourseasonssunrooms.com

If you want to meet the largest sunroom manufacturer in the country, let me introduce you to Four Seasons. But being the biggest, doesn't always mean the best. Nevertheless, they are a quality volume buyer and seller of sunrooms and can therefore offer the consumer one heck of a decent deal. Buying power means, lower prices. This franchised company out of New York does have a showroom for you to visit in Richardson and references are available upon request. Take the Belt Line exit off George Bush and stay on the service road. Offering volume pricing does help keep costs down. Head to their online site to get all the particulars about their sunrooms. Very impressive and with the depth of information they impart online, you may go into sunroom overload. Look for their landmark conservatory visible from Central Expressway. *Call toll-free: 800/FOUR-SEA*

◆◆◆◆◆ Fresh Air   972/412-0005

1529 E. I-30, #104   Mon-Fri 9-5; Emergencies 24/7
Garland, TX 75043
www.freshairstore.com

What image conjures up in your mind when you dream of fresh air? Isn't this a great name for a great service and isn't it time you got your ducts in a row? No newcomer to the world of keeping your home in squeaky clean condition, they even have an aerobiologist on staff. They are masters at air duct cleaning. Out, damn, mold. They eliminate all the ills that you can't see or touch that may be causing you physical and or psychological problems: bacteria, pollen, smoke, mold, odors, dirt, even dangerous chemicals. Don't wait until it's too late. Make a date with these professionals and take the free mold test. (On your house, silly, not your hair piece!) If you or anyone in your family suffers from allergies or seasonal sneezes, this company's a breeze. Members in good standing with the Better Business Bureau, that tells you everything you need to know about their reliability and quality service since there are a million companies doing duct cleaning and they're not all up to snuff. With Fresh Air, they are more than just a breath of Fresh Air. They are one of the best that you can invest in for a whiff of a job well done as they are the air testing and mold identification laboratory. Yes, they can stop mold in its tracks. Prevention is the key.

★★★★★★ G & S Sales   1-972/563-3201; 1-972/563-7821

4304 Hwy. 80 W.   Mon-Fri 7:30-5:30; Sat 7:30-5
Terrell, TX 75160
www.gssales.biz

 Don't even think about it. Buying your home improvement supplies anywhere else but G & S Sales is like throwing money out the door. And yes, even on doors. Just think about it. Do you think you're getting the best deal you can get on that candy you buy at the movies? The same goes with running to your nearest home center. Except of the convenience factor, you're not getting the most of your home improvement dollar. If you don't shop at G & S, expect to be paying twice or three times the price elsewhere. Do you need your head examined? OK, I know there's a sucker born every day; but here's the place you can lick high prices away. Five acres under roof of everything including the kitchen sink. Carpet, cabinets, whirlpools, shingles, sinks, exterior shutters (painted, $2.99 a pair), tile, hardware, ceiling fans....well, they really do have almost anything you would need for that home improvement project. Tubs and commodes for $50, whirlpools for $325 — no, you're not dreaming. And they even offer delivery. Love the Doors? They you'll love the selection that sings out, "Buy Me!" A vast selection of doors, all kinds of doors, paint, flooring, plumbing supplies, windows, cabinets, lumber and more — seeing is believing. Their custom cabinet shop ensures that you can get your cabinets any way you want them; or any other piece of wood whittled into whatever you want, at factory-direct prices. You can even see them make it. Or, if you'd rather, buy a ready-made cabinet. Same with doors. Custom or otherwise. It's THE best place to buy home improvement supplies under one roof in the Metroplex. Delivery daily into Dallas or Fort Worth so if you're not pulling up in your own truck, don't worry, they deliver. Remember to dial a one before the number to connect to Terrell if you are calling from Dallas. If not, call toll-free at 800/926-9534. This is THE place for all your home improvement projects and they win hands down. Five acres under one roof — all at prices that put the competition to shame. Portable buildings? Truckloads of cedar lumber for decks, gazebos and fences BELOW wholesale. Looking for wainscoting? They've got it — not at $35 a foot (wholesale price) but at $12/foot. Now isn't that something! *Call toll-free: 800/926-9534*

◆◆◆◆   Garage Storage Cabinets   972/239-5850

Richardson, TX   By Appt. Only
www.garagestoragecabinets.com

Can't pull the old Jeep into the garage for fear of running over the baseball bats, the birdcages, cartons of the *Bachelor Book* and more? Then, get with the program and unclutter that mess. Whatever's the problem, if it is the garage, call these doctors of garage-ology for their free advice and estimates. Gladly, they will rush to the scene of the mess, and, gladly provide a five-year limited warranty on storage systems that include cabinets, hanging systems, shelves, bins and drawers, pegboards, workbenches and more. All construction is made of solid wood, not pressboard. So, press on to your new and improved garage and storage space. They use a modular system that is manufactured in Stillwater, Oklahoma and you will get a custom look and design without the custom prices. Units are not permanent fixtures, so when you go, they can go, too.

◆◆◆   Garage Tek   214/451-3400

10748 N. Stemmons Frwy.   By Appt. Only
Dallas, TX 75220
www.garagetek.com

If you are too embarrassed to be seen in your garage, let alone pull your car into it, here is a solution. Garage Tek is a national one-stop answer to getting that mess organized. Each add-on makes for easy access to any tool, any project, any bicycle, any storage area. If you can't find it instantly, you probably don't have a Garage Tek system. More industrial-looking than some of the others of the same ilk, it's a matter of preference which system you like the best. Maintenance-free, waterproof and weather-resistant, their patented system of getting your act together makes for a professional statement about how you cope living in this world of chaos. Keep all that seasonal yard equipment like rakes, lawn mowers, leaf blowers close to where you can grab them within a moment's notice. Get all that "stuff" off the floors. If you're lucky, they'll be running a special, such as offering a 28" x 12" cabinet free with your first purchase. Over 30 franchises across the country, including the one above in the Metroplex. *Call toll-free: 866/867-3965*

◆◆◆◆◆   **Get A Grip Resurfacing of Dallas**   **214/358-4003**

3319 Regent Drive   By Appt. Only
Dallas, TX 75229-5058
www.getagripresurfacing.com

David's the Goliath to call when you need to get a grip on many of your household improvements.
When push comes to shove, you just can't ignore those countertops that are peeling and grungy.
Let these folks do it all: resurface your countertops, tub, pedestal sink, vent hood, oven door
fronts, stove tops, showers and vanity tops. They can even resurface your kitchen appliances and
counter tops, should you choose to do a less-expensive make-over, rather than a complete overhaul
from top to bottom — starting from scratch. They use a modified gel coat substance, and, for special effects for countertops, can use a texturing spray to create a multi-color fleck effect. Estimates
can be done on-site by David's wife, Cindy, who is the Marketing Manager. Call her at 214/207-
6202 if you want an estimate.

◆◆◆◆◆   **Granite Garage Coatings**   **817/784-2759**

PO Box 170051   By Appt. Only
Arlington, TX 76003
www.granitegaragecoatings.com

Ver-r-r-y interesting. Tracy Davis is the owner of this remodeling company, having spent 13 years
doing the same kind of job in California. Today, he's got five years in Texas under his belt and if
he's good enough for Pudge Rodriquez, he's good enough for me. Complete garage design, epoxy/
poly floor coatings, cabinets and organizers are the specialty of this house. Take advantage of the
terrazo-like floor covering is that it not only looks gorgeous but eliminates all that concrete dust.
They offer another less expensive floor coating that is very popular and runs about $2.45/square
foot, and either type can be used for work out rooms. The cabinets are suspended from the ceiling
and are a melamine-type that creates a seal with one-inch adjustable shelves. So, if a new garage is
on your wish list, but the price is prohibitive, consider instead a garage makeover from here! *Call
toll-free: 866/453-0490*

★★★★★★   **Granite Transformation**   **972/423-7878**

6905 Ave K, #202   Mon-Fri 8-5; Sat By Appt. Only
Plano, TX 75074
www.granitetransformations.com

Like **FORD**, this worldwide company had a better idea. You've heard of cabinet
refacing? Bathtub refacing? Now comes countertop refacing without the mess of
demolishing your current counter surface. Wow! This worldly franchise has just
opened in Plano — a perfect time to counteract the high cost of granite replacement. Instead of
replacing, Granite Transformations'unique product line includes beautiful Mosaics, Cristallinoô
and Rocksolid Granitô slabs manufactured from the finest stones in the world that goes right on
top of your current surface. It doesn't get any easier. Look like you're rich with the elegance and
beauty of granite or glass mosaic countertops but this process instead creates the look of Italian
granite and glass mosaic without the high cost and difficult installation typical of the real en-
counter. These can be installed right on top of your existing countertops! Call now for your free in-
home or in-office estimate or stop by their showroom and see for yourself "the countertop that fits
on top" should now go to the top of your home makeover wish list. It's like plastic surgery for
your counters rather than for your face. But let's face it, if it looks as good at less money and less
mess, why mess with the mess? Talk about an extreme makeover. Use on kitchen countertops,
backsplashes and kickplates, as well as bathroom wall cladding, shower areas, vanity tops and

floor tiles. For commercial projects, use on reception areas, entry foyers, lobbies, restroom areas, bar tops, tables, boardroom tables and retail shops, as well as hotel and motel lobbies, guest rooms, investment properties, retirement villages, and entertainment facilities. Quick and easy installation results in a fast refurbishment turnaround and less disruption to you, your customers or your guests. At least now you won't mind being taken for granted!

◆◆◆◆◆ Gurkin Security Systems   940/498-1818

Lake Dallas, TX 75065   By Appt. Only
www.gurkinsecurity.com

No pickle when it comes to security, Tim Gurkin is the voice of authority. Katrina was away from her desk when we called, but this family-owned and operated security company comes with 14 years experience. Only $18 (plus tax) for monitoring, equipment comes with a lifetime warranty, and no contracts. How's that for security? Switch to their company and they'll throw in three months of monitoring free when you convert to a Gurkin Security System and three months FREE with an installation of one. FREE is always better than a low price guarantee since they already are a low-free operator. Web site not up and running yet, but they are, so protect your most valuable assets....you, your home, your office or all of the above. Security doesn't have to cost an arm and a leg and your first born but protecting it is what Gurkin promises.

◆◆◆◆ Handyman Complete   972/221-0273

Dallas, TX   By Appt. Only

If you're looking for someone reliable who will show up, fix it, leave it better than new and not have to return a second or third time, here's the guy to consider. Tony Barr, bar none, has 30 years of experience in handyman projects, from big to small: painting, minor electrical, minor plumbing, installation of ceiling fans, installation and repair of vinyl floors (squares not sheet), sheetrock and texture, trim carpentry, door repairs and bathtub tile repair. You know, all those little annoying projects that the big companies can't be bothered with and the smaller companies think are TOO small to even entertain. We're not lion about this Tony. He's good and provides free consultations but only by appointment, please.

◆◆◆◆◆◆ Handyman Matters   214/879-9962

Dallas, TX   By Appt. Only
www.HandymanMatters.com

 This national company with a local outlet is built on taking care of business — the business of fixing things in your house. From trim carpentry to having doors hung or repaired, replacing kitchen cabinets to installing a new appliance, adding a closet or shelf, installing a fence, caulking, brick work, installing a garage door, installing a bathroom fixture or a towel rack, laying any kind of hard flooring surface, in essence, most any kind of repair service even if you've already purchased the product. (See rest of the book for buying the products.) These North Dallas handymen guarantee their work for one year. What a great service to a harried homeowner. Who to call and will they show are two questions I get asked on a regular basis. So here's a national franchised company with local answers including a discount of 10 percent to seniors. (Hey, I resemble that remark!) Remember, this is not a referral network but instead they are employees of this company with local employment opportunities. They provide the service, ma'am and nothing but. No payment, by the way, until you are completely satisfied.

★★★★★   Harbor Freight Tools   972/231-1872

1704 E. Belt Line Rd.   Mon-Fri 8-6; Sat 8:30-5:30; Sun 10-4
Richardson, TX 75081
www.harborfreight.com

With two locations in the Metroplex, a catalog and website to lean on, ask any boy where they go for their toys, and if they don't answer Harbor Freight Tools, tug on them a bit. For the tools of the trade, this huge mail order company has an outlet in Richardson and another in Fort Worth at 5268 Trail Lake Drive, 817/370-1892. Hammer away with the guaranteed lowest prices. The menu of options includes almost any tool that relates to: automotive, hand tools, power tools, hardware, electrical, outdoor, air tools, lawn & garden, household items, tarps, even clothing and boots. Their physical outlets carry most of the same inventory that's in their catalog at the same hammered-down prices. Their slogan is "Best quality tools at the lowest prices guaranteed!" That says it all in a tool box, lock, stock and barrel. Remember everything comes with a lifetime warranty. Here are a few goodies we couldn't live without: a 9.6 V battery, $3.99; 5" 2 amp orbital sander, $39.99; a **DRILL MASTER** cordless drill, $14.99, and lastly an 18V cordless **VSR** Drill/Driver for $49.97, instead of $72.99. Now, none of these should grind you; nobody wants to nail you just sell you some great ad-vises. ***Call toll-free: 800/423-2567***

★★★★   Hard Rock Tool/Stone Tools Direct   214/350-8655

9990 Monroe Dr., #202   Mon-Fri 8-5
Dallas, TX 75220-1421
www.hardrocktool.com

Although no relation to the Hard Rock Cafe, they are related to selling about 2,000 items online, and more than that at their Monroe store above. If it has to do with fabrication, installation and restoration of marble, granite, limestone, tile and both natural and man-made stone, this is the place to go. They have tile cutters, sealers, diamond blades, diamond pads, cleaners, machines etc. We have no quibble over prices. They are the best, although this is a highly specialized category of tools. Go to **AMERICAN TILE** for the actual tile, then shop here for the do-it-yourself installation supplies. Since so many homes these days have tile floors, try some of their specialized cleaners like their **PRO SEALANT**. You can use the Pro Sealer on interior or exterior surfaces. Stone Tools Direct is a division of Hard Rock Tool Company above. Hard Rock has 20 trucks, serving customers in 32 states from coast to coast, and well-stocked warehouses in every time zone in the U.S. Very customer-oriented company makes it "hard" not to recommend them. ***Call toll-free: 877/ 461-0211***

★★★★★★   Holland Marble   972/247-1621

2148 Royal Lane, Suite 800   Mon-Fri 8-4:30; Sat. By Appt. Only
Dallas, TX 75229
www.hollandmarble.com

 Marble is just the rage these days. Everybody's gotta have what they've gotta have. Whether it's marble fountains, statues, busts, basins, table bases, vases, planters, fireplaces, moldings, columns or mosaic borders, mosaic medallions, mosaic tiles, to slab sizes of travertine, slate, marble, granite, onyx, limestone, Holland Marble is ready to install it in a kitchen or bathroom counter for....how does saving up to 70 percent sound? A variety of tiles (travertine, slate, marble, granite and tumbled stones) were as low as 99-cent a square foot. Holy marble! That's really taking it for granite. Their showroom/factory site is where they actually bring in the slabs and fabricate them right there, and on their website, they showcase their products. It's almost like being stoned with intoxicating decorating-overload. It's a wonder to behold.

Since 1984, it's no wonder Holland Marble is considered one of the leaders in natural stone fabrication.

◆◆◆◆◆◆ **Home Improvement Coordinators**   **972/691-9778**

2701 Cross Timbers   Mon-Fri 8-6
Flower Mound, TX 75028-2706
www.homeic.com

Home Improvement Coordinators started when a group of "Raise your hand if you waited all day for the plumber and he never showed up" folks got together to discuss these kinds of problems. What to do when the handyman didn't show or showed and did a lousy job, or said no job was too big or too small to do, but when push came to shove, the jobs were really too big or too small. To meet their stringent credentials, this company has taken the guess work out of, among other things, is the handyman any good or isn't he? Their business model, too, is a little different. In January, Home Improvement Coordinators was born. The founders of the company are homeowners themselves, so they know the elements that are necessary for a satisfactory relationship that must ensue between homeowner and contractor. And, too, they understand that if the contractor is good at his trade, he needs support in the marketing and advertising arena. Homeowners pay a small fee to the Coordinators for doing the necessary due diligence on the contractor and to REALLY make sure the contractor is reliable, responsible, respectable and has a repeat clientele. In other words, they make sure you're not his first customer or the first roof he's ever built. Then, they welcome you to their Home Improvement Design Center where you can get help with design aids and ideas, such as costing tools; too, they offer a private conference room, if you need to bring several people together on one job. The Home Improvement Coordinators makes all the arrangements for the project, helps you choose the right contractor for you and the job, and will follow the project all the way to completion. Read more on their website but say adios to any contractor who'll paint for food. All of their referrals are top notch and stay that way or there's no more referrals. They have to maintain their good rating or else they lose points and if lose a few points too often, they're off the list. End of discussion. Jeremy Andries is the Flower Mound HIC to call above.

◆◆◆◆◆◆ **Horn Brothers Roofing**   **888/328-6956**

12015 Shiloh Rd., Suite 130   By Appt. Only
Dallas, TX 75220
www.hornbros.com

Don't worry about horning in on their business. The Horn Brothers are already there since they joined this California-based roofing company way back when. They started in 1984. Now they have offices in the Metroplex via the Horn Brothers Roofing above. Their specialty? Selling and installing GERARD STONE COATED STEEL ROOFING. Why is that so important? It may be the best roofing system around for either residential or commercial use. What did Lone Star Park in Grand Prairie choose? What did Michael Holigan choose to feature on This New House TV show? For the combination of beauty and durability, you can't go wrong and that's why we toot their Horn!!! It comes with a lifetime warranty and your 100% complete satisfaction is guaranteed. Lots of references for you to check, if you still need some assurances. Don't bother calling them, though, for a problem with a flat roof. They don't handle those flatliners.

◆◆◆◆◆◆◆   **Hughes Window Cleaning Service   972/342-9999**

4300 Horizon No. Pkwy., #327   By Appt. Only
Dallas, TX 75287

At last, you don't have to answer yes when asked, "Do you do windows?" When these guys are in your neighborhood, let them do your dirty work. Expect a good price for window and gutter cleaning and keep those fingernails in tact. In fact, they offer a neighborly savings about 25 percent off the nearest competitors'pricing. The first 20 windows are $4.50; $3.50 for each window thereafter. They consider one unit/window (even if it's two windows stacked) to be only one window. Half moons, eyebrows, transoms and sidelights are what they consider odds and ends, and you get two for one pricing. Screens and screen tracks are included. If you want inside windows cleaned, too, they will price them as well. Gutter cleaning is priced at 60-90 cents per foot. This company's bonded and insured and the prices are good for all standard windows whether on the first or second story. They'll even leave an invoice, so you don't have to stay home to receive their services. Jason Hughes is the Hughes in charge.

◆◆◆◆◆◆   **J & M Glass Co./Thermal Windows   214/630-5885**

8808 Empress Row   Mon-Fri 8-5; Sat 9-1
Dallas, TX 75247
www.thermalwindowsdfw.com

Since 1979, Thermal Windows has been custom-making some of the highest quality, most energy-efficient window systems for residential and commercial construction in the Metroplex. However, since their Fort Worth location has closed, you have only the Empress Row factory to pick your window options. Choose to insulate your house or office with the windows that leave the competition in the wake. Few can match the performance, durability, security or ease of operation that is standard on all their window systems. Need storm doors, exterior doors or sliding patio doors (with beautiful and artistic glass options?) Window selections range from solid vinyl windows and storm windows to thermal barrier aluminum windows. Looking for a wood window or a patio door? No problem, they offer products by VETTER — a company that has been making wood windows for over 100 years. With a full fabrication facility and one of the most experienced in-house installation crews in the Southwest (they do their own installation and service work), give them a call and start saving today. FREE delivery within the Dallas-Fort Worth area (100 mile radius). If your A/C or heating bills are giving you a "pane in your pocketbook," consider the cost-saving advantages of thermal replacement windows. You won't believe how much you'll save, regardless of which utility company you've pick. *Call toll-free: 800/339-3697*

◆◆◆◆   **J.J.'s Window Service**   **972/479-1302**

811 Alpha Dr.   Mon-Fri 8-5 By Appt. Only
Richardson, TX 75081

Can't see a thing through the fog or film on your windows? Well, if there's a cloud hanging over your range of vision and you live in Richardson, Plano, Frisco, McKinney or Allen, you're in luck. That's where J.J comes into the picture (window). Serving this select geographic area for more than a decade, J.J. really knows their stuff. But what's a person to do in Grand Prairie? (Otherwise, they would have been a 5 diamond rated company.) Let them show you the world, without seeing it through fog-covered filters. Through thick and thin, let them do all the cutting up in the back of their warehouse. Then, all your windows and doors can be replaced with new glass, insulated glass, storm windows, solar screens, utility screens and patio doors. Double and triple-plated glass only, with a 10-year warranty. Make sure to ask, "How much?" They will not be undersold (they even give free estimates). But don't bother asking about front screen doors — they don't do them. The more windows you buy the better the price! Whether you've got small windows, odd-sized windows — no problem! They will gladly come to your home·FREE of charge and give you a price quote. Installation is always included in the final price. But since they are a small company, with big growing "panes," don't expect them to offer same-day service. And do not call them if you out of-their-target range.

★★★★★★ JEH/Eagle Supply/MSI   817/572-3260

Corporate Office   By Appt. Only
Mansfield, TX
www.smartroofs.com

 As we say in the biz, you don't have to be cheap to love a bargain, you have to be smart! Now, here's "p-roof" that supports that philosophy to a T. Tough as nails. A Metro roof system is one that can re-roof over your existing roof, only with steel. Hey, that's a better idea anyway. Steel will withstand rain, sleet, snow, hail, fire and wind. Isn't north Texas the tornado alley? Don't we have a hail storm more often than we'd like to reveal in the Chamber of Commerce's brochures? Oh yes, we have such a mild temperate climate all year long? Since when? Not since I've been in Texas (1972) have I experienced a mild season for more than a day or two. For a heavy-duty performance that really withstands the harshest of weather disasters, in the long run, this is the smartest and most economical way to go. FREE estimates are gladly given by their local distributor, Eagle Supply, above. At only 1.41 pounds/per square foot, it's also lightweight, yet delivers the strongest punch for your money. Besides, they offer a variety of stone-coated steel roofing in either Shake, Shingle, or Tile looks. From the graceful curves of MetroTile to the deep ribbed grain of MetroShake and the low-profile of MetroShingle, these panels create a weather-tight roof system that is as beautiful as it is functional. Protect your property once and for all. Now isn't that a better idea? *Call toll-free: 866/METRO-4U*

★★★★ Jetta Design Services   972/245-2922

1755 N. I-35   Mon-Fri 8-5; Sat 9-2
Carrollton, TX 75006
www.jettacorp.com

It's all in the name, but if I didn't elaborate, you'd never know whether this was a start-up airline or the pied piper of interior designers. Once I describe their products, you will be glued to the page. Stop by their factory/showroom on the service road going south on Stemmons, off Sandy Lake Rd. Ogle the three kitchens they've set up as sample vignettes so you can see the presentations. Expect prices to vary based on the three different grade options and finished edges. The most reasonable grade runs $35/square foot, but the next two grades upward would increase the prices 10 and 20 percent respectively — putting that last grade in the same price category as granite. The color options and durability are greater but with less maintenance. If you're looking for lasting beauty for a kitchen or bath, or both, this manufacturer makes premium whirlpool baths, acrylic baths, solid surface countertops, sinks, vanities and shower kits. Jetta-StoneÆ Solid Surface is a trade-marked solid surface material for both residential or commercial application. Beside use in countertops in a kitchen or bath, it's also applicable for creating furniture for the home and office. *Call toll-free: 800/839-5382*

★★★   Joe Wallis Co.   817/335-1295

Mon-Fri 8-4:30

401 Bryan Ave.
Fort Worth, TX 76104

This company's got a firm grip on lockers. You know, the kind you hung your jacket in when you were in elementary school or taped your favorite pin-up to when you were in the army? Anyway, if you need one, this is the place to buy them since they're the ones who make them. Joe Wallis has been a major supplier of lockers to schools for decades. Now, you, too, can expect that the lockers runneth over and are available for sale to the general public. Overruns and used lockers can be adopted and put to many good uses. Adapt them for any number of uses for your home or office. A used locker painted to fit into the scheme of things for a child's bedroom or your garage can be the perfect storage solution to any crowded condition. Used lockers start as low as $40, with delivery to the Mid-Cities another $50 (or haul it off yourself). Lots of new overruns for $90, but you must get them in a set of three. (That's a total of $270. See I learned my multiplication tables in the third grade.) If you need prices, simply fax Tim at 817/335-6404, and he will put together a list of prices and options to meet your needs. Just use your imagination. What a great place to store sporting goods, toys, lawn equipment, office supplies, even doggie treats. Almost anything. And if you're looking for heavy metal (storage cabinets or metal shelving, that is,) they can help out there, too.

◆◆◆◆   Kelly's Air-Conditioning and Heating   972/436-4340

24 Hour Service

151 Ridgeway Circle
Lewisville, TX 75067

Expect an answering service to take your call as Kelly's is always out on a call. If it's an emergency, they're Johnny-on-the-spot. If it can wait a day or two, they will set up a time convenient to all concerned to fix whatever's ailing your system. Heater giving you a headache? Air-conditioner's got its own aches and pains? Well, if you want a reliable, less expensive (lower overhead) and more responsive company to fix the problem, Todd Kelly is the man to call. His company's philosophy: They won't quit until the job is done and if it's minor, they're won't run up unnecessary or extraneous hours, just to charge you more money. Reasonable rates and keeping their service area limited to Carrollton, Lewisville, Farmers Branch, The Colony, Coppell, Double Oak, Copper Canyon, Flower Mound and surrounding areas is the way I know about them. If you've got a comparable company in your area, let me know; I sure would like to spread the word. Anyway, we love Kelly, even though we're not Irish. (At least he helps us save some green.) We wish they were big enough to service the entire Metroplex.

◆◆◆◆◆◆   Kemiko Concrete Stain   903/587-3708

Mon-Fri 9-5

PO Box 1109
Leonard, TX 75452
www.kemiko.com

Years ago, I started recommending **KEMIKO** concrete stain, and that was probably 30 years ago. Today, they are the "rage." Everybody has to have that permanent concrete stain that will not fade, chip or peel. Available in a multitude of colors and useable both indoors or out, they can now ship the product nationwide. The look is expensive, the process is not. The process works best in new construction since they only have to apply it directly onto the concrete. To get the product, call above; to find out who are some recommended applicators consider 1) Baker's Decorative Concrete (Tracy Baker at 972/642-1195) and 2) Aristocrete (Maria and Jack Holland, 214/914-8488) who will stain it after carpet or tile has been pulled up as well as new construction. If you want to tackle it yourself, keep it simple but the application process is a lot more complicated than it appears. So I couldn't try it myself (unless you pride yourself on being a **KEMIKO** kamikaze pilot!)

◆◆◆◆◆ King Air-Conditioning 972/494-1957

1406 Forest Lane
Garland, TX 75042

By Appt. Only

One of my friends called the King and said, "I saved $3,000 on a complete new unit that I had King A/C install." Believe her because she was the former operations manager for a Wall Street public company who was always looking to save money (or spend it wildly) as the case may be. The problem with them, though, is that they want you to order a complete unit that cost thousands OR you have to live in the Garland/Richardson or Mesquite. So if you live in Royce City or Flower Mound, you're geographically undesirable. No doubt, though, that their prices hold up under scrutiny. But for routine everyday calls, for heating and air, they prefer to stay closer to home. Their distance barometer is as far as 635 and 35. They carry the **TRANE** systems and the ballpark quote for a 13 SEER, five-ton heating and AC unit with a variable speed unit was about $7,000; for a two-speed unit, the cost was approximately $6,200. We compared the prices to several others, and the cost savings were more than a $1,000. See what I mean; the Queen of Lean only recommends those that mean savings.

◆◆◆◆◆◆ Kitchen Solvers 817/292-7909

4858 Ledgestone Court
Fort Worth, TX 76132
www.kitchensolvers.com

By Appt. Only

 Yes, the owner's name is Ron McNew, and, yes, he was born to restore your cabinets to a like-new condition. Suppose destiny was in his genetic DNA? Why replace when you can reface is a commonly used phrase in this industry, but not all cosmetic cabinet surgeons are alike. If you want a company whose finished product looks like they've cut corners, forget it. You certainly don't want the scars, the seams, the caulking, whatever, to show, do you? It should look as good as new. You want the best, for less. This is an open door policy to solve the problems in your kitchen and save you money at the same time. Listen to Mother Cupboard. Kitchen Solvers is considered to be the most experienced cabinet refacing franchise company in the country. Ron is the local installer who can save you both time and money. You have the option to choose which services best suit your remodeling needs. And with their national purchasing power, you will get the products at the best possible price. So there, your cupboards will no longer be bare. You'll even have enough money leftover after the remodeling job to buy some groceries. And if you need to save on groceries, head to Dallas Food Depot. *Call toll-free: 800/ 845-6779*

◆◆◆ Kleen Air Services 972/527-3207

1000 Jupiter Rd.,Suite 700
Plano, TX 75074
www.kleenairservices.com

24/7 (By Appt. Mon-Sat 8-6)

When I was gathering information for the first Underground Shopper in 1972, I thought my partner, Ann Light, and I were another **WOODARD** and Bernstein investigative reporting team, especially when we uncovered Joy Manufacturing Company. It thrills me to know that we found a real Attic Insulation company who offered blown-in attic insulation, as well as heating and AC service and duct cleaning for residential and commercial properties. Downloading their Internet coupon for $50 on services over $375 makes good sense. Their services are pretty sophisticated and you'll pay for it, but sometimes if you want the best, it's worth it. Duct cleaning ran $9.99/vent and $15/ return. They use the patented "Rotobrush" system to help eliminate pollutants, mold, mildew and dust mites. They utilize wool insulation fiberglass and it's called "ProWhite" which contractors have recommended to me in the past. But if you need convincing, give them a call. *Call toll-free: 800/789-1618*

◆◆◆◆◆   **Lasting Impressions**   **972/333-7249**

Dallas, TX   By Appt. Only
www.greatkitchens.net

You might say Les Darnell was born into the business of contracting and building. His dad was a homebuilder and contractor, so it was a natural career path. In 1980, after working in the commercial and residential masonry business as a superintendent, he and his wife LuAnn finally bit the bullet. Eventually, they honed in on kitchen and bathroom remodeling and additions. They maintain a hands-on approach to every step along the way. Some of the subs have worked for them since the early 80s. Whether you have architectural plans or just a hair-brained idea for making your kitchen or bath a dream come true, their references will attest to their perfection. See for yourself, online, a visual confirmation of their attention to detail, but expect to pay the piper. No need to cut corners when cutting corners can cost you in the long run. They can even bring on board a renowned area designer, should you need design assistance. If you want to remodel your current home and maintain its integrity, or completely transform it, they will take charge and you could wind up as a "Before and After" segment on the Home and Garden TV Network. If it's a kitchen or bath remodel, choose this couple to lead the way and stay flush. And remember, too many cooks, in this instance, do not spoil the broth. The more talent in the kitchen, the better.

◆◆◆◆◆   **Lee Air Services**   **972/436-2211**

Lewisville, TX   By Appt. Only 24 Hrs; 7 Days

If you're experiencing a hot spell or a cold spell, it should spell L-E-E Air Services, any way you cut it. They can handle it all, from heating installation and repair to air conditioning, hot water heater repair, ceiling fan installation and duct cleaning. They'll even do pre-exams to make sure you'll make it through the night. For check-ups, by appointment only. Offering a one-year guarantee on parts and labor, what do you have to lose (except maybe a leak or a disaster?) Specials such as tune-ups for $73.95 (save $35) or 20 percent off on condenser replacement, keep their prices, as well as their good service, competitive year 'round. Besides, their prices remained constant from last year. So be it. They service the Metro area. They carry TRANE systems. FREE of charge, a salesman will be happy to evaluate your replacement needs and give you a quote on a new heating and air conditioning system. And you know, you can't wreck a TRANE! *Call toll-free: 817/ 5337-179*

◆◆◆◆   **Lone Star Granite**   **972/429-0774**

114 Regency Drive   Mon-Fri 8-5
Wylie, TX 75098-7016

The closer you get to the country, the closer you get to good ole country service. Folks here are just the best and at Lone Star Granite, they are the salt of the earth. Just like the first treasure that I found in Wylie in 1972 (The Ladylike Shop and Mr. Storey), the folks here just get nicer and nicer. Seeing as they've chosen their name to be Lone Star, I don't see any reason why they should remain a lone star, do you? Everyone agreed, so now there are two stars to Lone Star Granite. Just east of Plano, this family-owned enterprise is really the fabricator (meaning they are the ones who cut it to fit), although, they do have some granite in stock. In fact, granite is all they work with.

Builders send granite slabs to fabricators (like Lonestar), and the granite is turned into those countertops that everyone covets in their kitchen or bath. Actually, they will cut the granite for any end use, but you decide, you measure, and you find the installer. That way, you can save some money. Sign up for their Builders Program and your project will cost less than if you chose Home Expo to do the job. Every little bit helps in the Lone Star state of mind. Don't shop during lunch time (11:30-1:30) as they are, you guessed it — out to lunch!

♦♦♦♦♦♦ **Lone Star Locksmith**   **972/724-7233**

PO Box 270248   By Appt. Only
Flower Mound, TX 75028

Knock knock! Who's there? I don't know cause I can't open the door. If this is your problem, then it's time to call in the Lone Star Locksmith for the taming of the screws. As a former security consultant, this guy gets down to the nuts, bolts and screws. Expect a house re-keyed for $45 and installation of a handle set on your front door about $55-$65. John Murphy, the Lone Star himself, recommends buying the actual fixture at Home Depot because he can't buy them any cheaper than you can. (Actually G & S Sales in Terrell has them even cheaper!) Serving the entire Dallas/Fort Worth area, this locksmith can handle any residential, commercial or automotive lock request and be Johnny-on-the-Spot, even in emergencies. What's even more appealing is that he'll go out of his way to recommend cheaper alternatives that are available. Most jobs are completed the same day or next. I'd say he deserves more than a Lone Star.

♦♦♦♦♦♦ **LoneStar Solar Screens**   **972/445-0856**

2334 Hinton Drive   By Appt. Only
Irving, TX 75061
www.lonestarsolarscreens.com

Who is the company that competitors like to clone? Lone Star Solar Screens, that's who. Lone Star Solar Screens has been serving the Dallas/Fort Worth Metroplex since 1991. They expanded into the Houston area in March 1997, so their 20,000-square-foot facility in Irving acts not only as their retail showroom for the Metroplex, but also as their main distribution center for all of Texas and Oklahoma. They are the statewide distributors of Twitchell **TEXTILENE**, the industry's highest quality solar screen material available. Texilene is made of the finest PVC coated woven polyester and custom gridwork is available, if requested. LoneStar Solar screens are the new light-colored screens that have been specifically designed by this company to better coordinate with most exterior brick colors while still having an amazingly clear view. They also have **BUFFALO** 80 and 90 percent screens, a darker color that still provides the opportunity to get a great view. Solar screens are one of the best ways to stop up to 90 percent of the sun's heat which ultimately means it's a great way to cut those utility bills!

★★ **Makita Factory Service Center**   **972/243-1150**

12801 Stemmons, #809   Mon-Fri 8-4:30
Farmers Branch, TX 75234
www.makita.com

This 48-Hours is not the movie, but the repair turn-around time when you bring in a **MAKITA** tool to be repaired. FREE estimates and FREE labor to schools. They carry a full line of **MAKITA** parts and accessories, should you choose to do-it-yourself. Expect to shave about 20-30 percent off the price of new tools when you buy the refurbished ones. This 80-year company is one of the most respected in the industry. Their only Metroplex location is on the service road of Stemmons, exit Valley View going south on the service road. Save money on the tools that are refurbished. For the casual home user or the heavy-duty contractor, you'll see circular saws, cordless drills, compressors, routers, rotary hammers, jig saws, reciprocating saws, grinders, miter saws and parts. You'll receive a seven-point safety certification and a 90-day warranty on all repairs. They also repair **B & D, BOSCH, DEWALT, MILWAUKEE, PORTER CABLE, SKIL** and other major brands. Go ahead, request their catalog.

◆◆◆◆◆   McFall Masonry   972/966-8833
Lewisville, TX 75077   By Appt. Only

Humpty-Dumpty had a big fall, but, fortunately, McFall Masonry was able to put him back together again. Since 1979, they've offered custom brick work, custom stone work, retaining walls, repairs, planters, brick and mortar cracks fixed, concrete, patios, walkways, add ons and more without making too big of a dent in your budget. Then again, after the fall, you'll be able to see your way clear to an increase in your home's bottom line appraisal.

◆◆◆◆   Modern Home Patio   214/349-0303
10550 Church Rd. @ LBJ & Plano Rd.   By Appt. Only
Dallas, TX 75238

If you want an attractive carport or patio cover, look to Modern Home/Patio Company for a free estimate. This family-owned and operated business got started when Bobby Sheridan, back in 1970, began installing carports and patio covers. When the company expanded in 1975 to their current address above, they added an experienced sales and installation crew. Stocking only quality materials that are maintenance free (from rain and sun, that is), they will last for decades. Their carports shelter your vehicle from the ever-changing Texas weather, beside being maintenance free. In fact, the carport should last a lot longer than your car, truck, RV or even your boat. Anchors away, my friend. References available. A two-car carport 20'wide by 16'long would run about $1,215. (But just price check how much repeated hail damage costs for that third car, that RV, that boat?) Get the message? Check with you city to see if carports are allowed and also permitted by your homeowners association. In our sub-division, they're not allowed. Although they're located in Garland, they will work the Metro area; if it's too far (like Colleyville), they will refer you to Baker Bros. (I always wanted to meet them and maybe even sing a song from atop the grand piano!)

◆◆◆   Moisture Shield   214/638-0502
2912 Barge Lane   Mon-Fri 8-5
Dallas, TX 75212
www.moistureshieldinc.com

If you're water retentive, you might want to consider Moisture Shield. Moisture Shield will rid your home of water ever seeping in. (Do you think they landed on Barge Lane for nothing?) Soggy problems can keep you knee deep in trouble, as well as debt. At Moisture Shield, they do all the preventative and remedial waterproofing work that you may need. Too, they also provide masonry restoration to stucco, repairs to concrete and brick, stone and wood, tuck pointing, and power washing and cleaning. Then, if you need to coat or seal your walls, your floors, your deck, whatever, they're the ones to call since they are the source that wears many coats. They do coatings, sealers/patching, paint striping/painting, dry walling, urethane, epoxy injections, and they work on sheet metal, too. They will meet you on the job site or in your office; it's all at your convenience.

After 14 years of waterproofing the Metroplex, you certainly can't consider them all wet. New this year, an informative website with references posted front and center. *Call toll-free: 800/766-3393*

★★★   Monarch Paint   972/436-2001

701 S. Stemmons   Mon-Fri 7-5; Sat 7:30-1
Lewisville, TX 75067
www.monarchpaint.com

If you have trouble finding the right paint color because it's "varnished," then try spreading your wings and shopping at Monarch Paint. In business since 1967, they migrated to Dallas in 1984 and have been painting the town in a multitude of colors since. All paints, by the way, are specially formulated for the rugged Southwest climate. They manufacture their own stains, varnishes, poly-coats, enamels and latex. See drop cloths, masking tape, painter caulk, brushes and rollers, you know, all the stuff you need to implement your favorite strokes. Catering more to the contractor and home builder, you are still welcome as a retail customer. Don't expect a wallpaper depart-ment, but the least expensive interior flat latex paint cost around $8.35/ gallon, with the highest grade running about $25/ gallon. Check directory for multiple area locations, online or through directory assistance.

Move for Free   .   877/532-3757

Dallas, TX   24-7
www.moveforfree.com   🖰 *Top Online Store!*

Operated by TEXAS licensed real estate agents, if you're going to move on, you might as well do it for "FREE." Well, almost. How do they do it? The apartments they move you to pay them to move you. Since they are licensed real estate agents, they are paid a generous real estate commis-sion each time they refer a customer to a MoveForFree.com property. But, don't expect them to pay for a large move, like from one Italian villa to another. All done online, it's really an efficient way to move from Apartment A to Apartment B. Once you've registered, you can search thou-sands of apartments, condos and townhomes through their online searchable database. When you see a place that meets your approval, you can schedule your FREE move and leave the rest to the professionals. If you don't want to take advantage of their generosity but still want to move into one of their recommended apartments, they will pay you a $100 cash voucher. Either way, it's bet-ter than nothing. And refer back to All My Sons Moving if you are wanting to move to an apart-ment other than the ones on THEIR list or move to a house. It's not free but they're the best.

★★★★   North American Stone Co., Inc   972/562-9992

3745 County Road 997   By Appt. Only
McKinney, TX 75071-0322
www.northamericanstone.com

Ver-r-r-y interesting. Don't worry about making any faux pas. But for other things faux, this com-pany may be the perfect replica, as they deal in a synthetic stone that resembles limestone. Address blocks ($35-$72), balusters, bandings, columns and pier caps, fireplace mantles and shelves, keystones, pool coping, quoins, spheres, surrounds, urns, wall coping and window sills. They also have a CD as their brochure and their catalog showcases over 500 cast stone designs, 85 designs of fireplace mantles varying in price from $650 to as much as $12,000. Custom orders are welcome, so designers love this place because they like to create special products for their special clients so they can charge special prices. This place offers expert design, installation and sealing, aftercare programs and architectural planning, if you need help yourself. Just ask. Relate to them via their website to get the ball rolling and, maybe, get going on the faux limestone project.

★★★★★★   Northern Tool & Equipment Co.   972/705-9545

584 W. I-30 @ Belt Line   Mon-Fri 8-7; Sat 8-6; Sun 10-5
Garland, TX 75043-5700
www.northerntool.com

 This Minnesota chain is perfect for sophisticated home improvement projects. Northern-ers find them particularly appealing as they fill in the gap between the Home Depots and and the Ace Hardwares. Their specialty is tools and equipment at some of the lowest prices in town, but they are tools of a different ilk. Mix and match a variety of machine screws, marine accessories, water pumps, go-carts, hunting gear, storage units and equipment for trailers and RVs. How about a titanium drill bit set that will ensure you drill faster for longer or a **NORTHSTAR** pressure washer for $399? Big boys shop for the big toys here. No tooling around. Northern's main product lines are generators, small engines, pressure washers and hand, air and power tools. But they also pride themselves on carrying hydraulics, pumps, trailer parts, seasonal equipment and more. Brands include **BOSCH**, **BRIGGS & STRATTON**, **CHANEL LOCK**, **COLEMAN**, **DEWALT**, **FULLER**, **HOMELITE**, **HONDA**, **INGERSOLL-RAND**, **NORTHSTAR**, **STANLEY**, **VISE GRIP**, **YARDMAN** and others. Their own private label brand is a money-saver, too. Visit their other locations in Grand Prairie at 2630 W. I-20, 972/602-8877 and Fort Worth at 8080 West Freeway, 817/367-2464. *Call toll-free: 800/533-5545*

★★★★★★   Open--Sesame   972/414-6900

10420 Plano Rd.   Mon-Fri 7:30-5; Sat 8-2 By Appt. Only
Dallas, TX 75238
www.open-

 Open--Sesame Surburban Door has two dashes in their name so don't forget when wanting to land on their website. If not, you will land on a site for witchcraft. So, please, add two hyphens (--) though you might wonder if the witches haven't already infiltrated your garage door if it goes up and down, at will. This company's the largest seller of garage doors, openers and remotes, as well as all aspects of repair, in the Metro area. But don't expect them to travel to Fort Worth. A service call in the Dallas area is a very reasonable $39, which is waived if work is ultimately done. The satisfied customer and vendor list are several miles long, so expect to sit a while and just read it. Their mailing address is PO Box 472251, Garland, Texas 75047-2251, 972/414-6900. Do not show up at the above address, though, because it is simply their offices. Their office phone number is 214/341-3667 and their fax is 214/348-7114. If you want to email them, do so at orders@open--sesame.com. All work is done on-site. Their warehouse is actually in Allen (972/414-6900) but it, too, closed to walk-in trade. They also sell garage door accessories, circuit boards, keypads, remote controls, door hardware and wall controllers just to list a few. Brands that they carry and/or repair include **ALLISTER**, **ALLSTAR**, **CARPER**, **CHAMBERLAIN**, **CRUSADER**, **GENIE**, **HEDDOLF**, **LIFTMASTER**, **LINEAR**, **MARTEC**, **OVERHEAD**, **SEARS** and more. FREE estimates for all! Open--Sesame!

★★★★   Orr Reed Wrecking Co.   214/428-7429

1903 Rock Island   Mon-Sat 9-4
Dallas, TX 75207

Yep, Nope, Yes Ma'am is their standard response, year after year. Nothing's changed from day one since we stumbled upon this booming graveyard of salvaged treasures. They might even be asleep at the wheel, at times, when you call. We're never quite sure. We do know, though, that they are alive and well. But since we're not looking for animation, what do you care as long as their salvaged finds are what you're looking for? Orr Reed Wrecking Co. still maintains one of the largest selections of used building materials in the Metroplex, but it's an ever-changing merry-go-round. If I tell you they have hundreds of pedestal sinks one week, they may have none the next. This is a designer's paradise if you're looking to re-do your castle on a pauper's budget. From doors to a/c units, ceiling fans to tubs, sinks, telephones, cabinets, columns and door handles to small electronic items and more....at drop-dead prices! They don't offer delivery but can recommend a few names, if you're in need. Orr you can "Reed" between the lines and demolish the notion that salvage is more than recovering old building materials, it's also recouping your losses when it comes to the high expense of home improvement and remodeling. They are one of the original resources who saw the writing on the wall when the idea of recycling came into vogue.

★★★   Overhead Door Co.   972/416-7100

1800 Vantage Drive   Mon-Fri 7-5; Sat 8-Noon
Carrollton, TX 75006
www.dallasdoors.com

Are you a fan of the Doors? If so, turn to the pros at the Overhead Door Company. They are hardly a newcomer when it comes to providing homeowners and businesses with doors, windows, security gates and other products for construction and maintenance projects. Since the early 1920s, this company's doors have been open. They have steel garage doors, garage door openers, entry and patio doors or vinyl windows, start by looking overhead! And that is just for homeowners. For commercial users, you can choose from entry and freezer doors, office walls, dock equipment, locksmith services, even restroom facilities. There's always a special going on. Their Carrollton location is the number to call (above); the Fort Worth residential showroom is located at 840 Southway Circle (817/921-3641), and their two commercial showrooms can be found at 2617 Andjon Drive in Dallas (214/350-4621) and 1039 E. Dallas Rd. in Grapevine (817/481-5502). The big draw here, in my opinion, is the selection of custom-designed Carriage Doors. If you want a one-of-a-kind garage door, here's where they'll push your buttons. Check out their website for more information! *Call toll-free: 800/974-3641*

★★★★★★   Pest Shop, The   972/519-0355

2231-B W. 15th St.   Mon-Fri 12:15-6; Sat 11-3; Morning Service Calls
Plano, TX 75075
www.pestshop.com

 If you have any desire to make a reservation at the Roach Motel, why don't you shop here first and get acquainted with the species. Not only is this shop a do-it-yourself pest control armory, but they are also home to the infamous Cockroach Hall of Fame Museum. Just because Michael Bohdan has a list of media appearances a mile long, doesn't mean he's not serious about controlling those darn little creatures. He's been seen on *The Today Show*, *Good Morning America*, and more, this year alone and he's appeared on *The View* and *Animal Planet*. You can now read all about him via his book, *WhatsBuggingYou'*, available online for $12.95. He also makes private appearances at parties. The Pest Shop is still the place to learn the ropes and gather the products that will do the job to eliminate those unwanted pest guests. He's got the answers, if you've got the problem. They also provide service if you'd rather not do-it-your-self. (If you want to do-it-yourself, why not collect them and sell them to the Fear Factor?) Trust these folks know a thing or two about bugs. And for those who'd rather not do harm to the environment, they also offer low impact and organic products to control pests. Save 50-60 percent if you do it....his way.

◆◆◆◆◆◆ Phillips Painting, Gutters & Roofing 972/867-9792

1631 Dorchester, Suite 156   By Appt. Only
Plano, TX 75075
www.phillipspainting.com

  Jason Phillips is your man with a stroke of genius. Almost a decade of experience, his reputation is well earned in the Plano and North Dallas area. From the time the free estimate is given to the time the work is completed, all their professional personnel will execute the job smoothly and without a glitch. They will ensure your complete satisfaction from start to finish. Furthermore, they use only full-strength paint. No diluting the paint to extract more coverage for less paint; nor do they use a second rate paint. They use only the best products period and Jason won't have it any other way. They pride themselves on their motto, "Workmanship beyond your expectations." A manager is always on the job for supervision and written guarantees are executed with every project. That means there is an expert overseeing the technicians who are actually doing each job, be it painting, gutters or roofing. Painting for walls, ceilings, trim, doors, cabinets, paneling, and necessary carpentry to finish off each and every paint job is standard operating procedure. A final customer walk-through with any touch-ups is the last step before a three-year warranty is issued. And that's just in the painting arena. They are our contractor of choice for gutters and roofing, too. Ah, GPR for your house (gutters, painting and roofing) — or is that CPR? Their service area is primarily Plano, Richardson, Dallas, Allen, Lucas, Garland, The Colony, Carrollton, McKinney and Irving so until further notice, if you live in Fort Worth, it will be raining on your parade without them. But watch this space for expansion!

◆◆◆◆◆◆ Power Jack Foundation   214/651-1805

5224-A Saunders Rd   By Appt. Only
Fort Worth, TX 76119
www.pjfr.com

 This has nothing to do with body building, but if your house is in need of a lift, consider this system a good way to pump it up. If you notice cracks on interior walls, doors or windows not fitting snuggly or pulling away, nails popping out of the gypsum board, cracks in your brick fireplace, cracks on the base of your concrete or water standing near your house after a rain storm — hello? Call for a free inspection. Foundation cracking can happen anytime. Power Jack uses the PolyLock Pier System to properly and safely repair your slab or pier and beam foundation. The price depends on the severity of the problem, size of the foundation, etc. Here they offer top quality repair services including water drainage corrections and tree evaluation, if its too close to the home. They guarantee the lowest price and by the way, shoppers voted them the best!

◆◆◆◆◆   Premier Foundation Repair   972/417-0823

3767 Forest Lane, #124-400   By Appt. Only
Dallas, TX 75244
www.premierfoundationrepair.com

Their full name is Premier Foundation Repair & Soil Stabilization, a mouthful. But as long as you recognize that if you're having a foundation problem, these folks are who to call — afterall, you may not recognize if your soil is stable or not. I wouldn't know, would you? When doing foundation repair research, you run into plenty of dunces and plenty of those whose expertise rivals one of a PhD. Here's one female who knows her stuff. Julie not only knows a thing or two about foundation repair, she is willing to share it all. She will come out for a free evaluation and estimate. Then she'll call Steve Sutherland on his cell at metro 817/253-4775 for his over 30 years of business expertise and his knowledge as the #1 soil stabilizer in North Texas. Signs of foundation problems include diagonal cracks in the brick, cracks in swimming pools, bowed walls, trees too close to a house, separation of window framing and cracks in the slab. They use the **TERRA FIRM** system that permanently changes the composition of the soil so that it does not retain too much water. The provide FREE inspection too! You won't go wrong utilizing their expertise. This woman knows her stuff and besides, don't women usually know how to sell foundations? *Call toll-free: 800/705-7370*

◆◆   ProStar Security   972/418-0600

3033 Kellway Drive, #128   By Appt. Only
Carrollton, TX 75006

Chuck Goforth is the man who can connect you to a standard security system, which includes one keypad, motion-detector and three opening sensors. Best of all, they are all free with a 36-month monitoring contract (about $25 per month). But you're locked in for three years. And that's way too long. The good part, though, since they use **ADT**, if you move or get transferred and you're contract is not up, you can take it with you. Still, three years is three years. Estimates are FREE. (no big deal!) ProStar is the nation's largest **ADT** authorized dealer. Too, they offer the "Protection One" system, which is what elderly citizens living alone might consider. It's the rapid, reliable monitoring system for about $1 a day with a 96 percent customer satisfaction rating in this area of more than 50,000 monitored customers. You will receive a FREE lifetime service program for the length of your monitoring contract and for one year, you'll get a FREE SafetyNet guarantee. Now I like that. *Call toll-free: 800/SMART-80*

◆◆◆◆   Protek Painting   972/658-7625

6021 Oldham Dr   By Appt. Only
McKinney, TX 75070

When I lived in Flower Mound, I was considered geographically undesirable. Now that our research team lived in Colleyville and Fort Worth, respectively, they heard that they were, too. Some of the companies that were recommended by shoppers this year would not go to Colleyville or to Fort Worth, but guess what? They do go to Flower Mound! This family-owned painting company not only runs the crews, but is out with paint brushes themselves. Interior painting and dry wall repair are just part of their menu of services. All painters are bonded and insured with jobs under a three-year warranty on labor and materials. Protek Painting also goes outside to paint. Exterior painting, small carpentry repairs, power washing, scrape and sand, oil prime, 45-year caulking, extensive masking and landscape protection, full strength top-of-the-line paint throughout and, yes, a complete clean-up on the way to their trucks. For interior paint jobs, they mask the floors, sand all the wood trim, clean all surfaces, caulk all joints, and provide a tip-top clean up when they're finished. FREE estimates gladly provided.

★★★★ Quality Surplus

940/497-3749
Mon-Fri 9-6; Sat 9-4

1004 S. Stemmons Frwy.
Lake Dallas, TX 75065

It's an open and shut case if your looking to unlock a new look for your home's interior, as well as exterior. Who knows what you'll find when walking through these doors....well, other than doors, that is? Styles may change, but metal and wooden entry doors, French doors and leaded glass doors keep this store grounded. Peek and peck your way through the large warehouse. Don't see what you're looking for? Then open up a catalog. Orders will be on your doorstep within a week or two, provided you pick them up since delivery is not available. Install it yourself; or you might be out the door on luck. They will recommend several handymen if you just can't get the job done alone. We welcomed the wealth of information and advice provided on installation, staining, painting and fixtures. Quality Surplus is a welcome addition that should be invited in to do any home improvement project. But doors are not the only opening remarks available. They do have them in both new and used varieties as well as flooring, cabinets, countertops, windows, door hardware and "cheaper than anyone else around!" Check it out. A leaded and beveled glass exterior door was $400 (compared to one twice that price at Home Depot.) Next door to Subway, enjoy a bite to eat, while Quality Surplus takes the bite out of your home improvement budget.

◆◆◆◆◆ Rent-A-Hubby

972/871-8696
Mon-Fri 8-5; By Appt.

PO Box 153308
Irving, TX 75015
www.rent-a-hubby-usa.com

Too bad we can't hire them to escort us to our high-school reunion. For the right hunk, it might be worth it. But this year, we called several times only to find the answering machine working overtime. Never could talk to anybody so we're going by their past performance. Maybe they were on vacation or on a high .... on a ladder doing a ceiling fan installation. Never mind, they're still around. Founder/owners Stephen and James Haley offer business opportunities by way of a franchise committed to "Serving the Women of America." Rent-A-Hubby specializes in residential and light commercial services to include plumbing, heating, air conditioning, electrical, Honey Do lists and general construction (for women). They claim to be honest, fair with a knowledgeable staff with no subcontractors. They are booked about two weeks ahead, so call fast! Hey, what about a Rent-A-Wife franchise to go along with it — following them around, picking up after them! The service has a two-hour minimum on job so know what you want done so you maximize the time spent. Making a list is best. Install ceiling fan, change locks for front door, hang picture, move the recliner to another room, install new hardware in my guest bathroom — see, I've already got my "honey-do" list started.

★★★ Rhino Steel Building Systems

888/320-7466
Mon-Fri 8-5

4305 I-35 N
Denton, TX 76207
www.rhinobldg.com

Like a charging bull, these Rhino Steel Building Systems offer pre-engineered steel buildings for farm, commercial and industrial or aircraft hangars. If you're looking for something to house your extra equipment, there is usually a special going on. For example, a spring fling included free color walls and trim along with an overhead door. And that special was available all spring long.

Can you imagine what the fall will bring? Their claims of offering the best value in price and quality and many options for square footage, floor plans, eaves, colors, skylights, ventilation and trim appears right on the mark. Of course, it doesn't hurt to shop when sale prices are in effect: for example, a 30' x 50' x 10' building was $6,244 and that included free color walls and trim and an 8' x 8' overhead door; 60' x 100' x 16' was $17,379 w/12' x 14' door. Now we're talking elephant sized (tsk, tsk!) Expect a four-five week delivery on all specials. Their office is a Rhino Building, too, so you can see up close and personal just what you're ordering. It's a super structure that should do you well. And talk about a savings over new construction! *Call toll-free: 888/320-7466*

◆◆◆◆ Service Magic, Inc.

14023 Denver West Pkway, Bldg. 64, Suite 200   24/7
Golden, CO 80401
www.servicemagic.com

This national company based in Golden, CO is your one-stop call for a recommendation for most household projects that is beyond the "honey-do" list. Consumers can use this free service when seeking a recommended repair service in a myriad of home improvement categories: additions & remodels, carpentry, fences, flooring, foundations, garages, handymen, roofing and gutters, siding — most anything that relates to a home improvement project around your home or office. Add in a library of recommended reading, the ability to refer a professional that you deem worthy. And if you think their match-making stops at contractors, think again, because they also refer you to real estate agents and lenders, too. *Call toll-free: 800/474-1596*

◆◆◆◆◆◆ Skillful Improvements/Restoration   972/279-0119

2143 Gus Thomasson, Building 1   Mon-Fri 8:30-4:30
Mesquite, TX 75150
www.skillfulimprovements.com

 What started out in 1976 when a group of student painters and carpenters at the Dallas Theological Seminary began painting and restoration work in hopes of getting by on a little more than peanut butter and jelly sandwiches, has turned into a saintly champagne and caviar business. The reality came to life in 1986 when Ray Dettmer, owner and a NARI-Certified Remodeler and his four lead carpenters, also certified, and the other employees who are IICRC certified in restoration work and cleaning went to work. An entire division of the company is dedicated strictly to insurance repairs for everything from water damage to fire and smoke clean up, drying out the structure and more. Another division is dedicated to cleaning air ducts. Skillful doesn't just vacuum your ducts, but rather runs the air through water, capturing the dirt and dust, then dumps the water into tanks on their trucks that prevent those dust bunnies and allergens from re-entering your home. For carpet cleaning, they also offer TEFLON stain resistance by 3M that comes with a one-year warranty. They are the best!

★★★★★★ Skylights-To-Go   214/498-5998 (Cell)

Arlington, TX   By Appt. Only
www.skylights-to-go.com

 There's no better gift than the "gift of light — natural light." And there's no better way to go than Skylights-to-Go! These tubular skylights offer a 25 year warranty and are a snap to install according to Bill Ellis, who installs them. I wouldn't do it myself, but they do have do-it-yourself-kits for those who would like to take on the challenge. The idea of their state-of-the-art tubular skylights originated from an idea as far back as ancient Egypt when they put reflective gold leaf on the inside of shafts cut into the huge stone structures they built. These shafts were from the outside leading into chamber rooms deep within. Thus, natural sunlight outside was channeled to the rooms below. The Romans also used similar variations on the more modern tubular skylights. See, there's no such thing as an original idea. Here they use all the latest energy-efficient engineering technology bringing healthy UV filtered natural light into your home or office. Since it's a sealed unit, it is extremely energy efficient with NO heating or cooling loss. And, by saving on electricity, you help save money and the environment. Plus the unit itself is inexpensive. Open up those dark closets, those hallways that seem closed in, well, just look around your house and see where you need to get out of the dark! It takes less than two hours, there's no painting, no dry-wall work, no major construction and no mess as with traditional sky-lights — all with a 25-year warranty. The 10' model (suitable for most home applications) is only $349. Installation by a professional installer is $99 — or you can do-it-yourself, big boy! Watch for specials when maybe Diva listeners will get **FREE** installation. (Wishful thinking, but possible.) Skylights-to-go is a member of the Better Business Bureau and of course, in good standing. *Call toll-free: 888/759-8646*

★★★★   Stone Carving Unlimited   214/742-4200

1415 Slocum Street   By Appt. Only
Dallas, TX 75207
www.stonecarvingunlimited.com

Sticks and stones may break YOUR bones but, at least, not your budget. Tom Robinson can cast your stone and if you can dream it, they can make it. Here's the company that quarries the stone, fabricates the objects and directly imports everything that is shown on their website. That means, the savings are rock-solid, though not cheap. Sticks and stones may break your budget, but stone and marble mantels, columns and capitols, windows and door surrounds, table bases, fountains, exterior architectural elements — well, it will make you dizzy (but, at least, you won't be accused of being stoned!) Create that mansion in the sky (even if the house didn't start out as such). Just don't tell a soul you got it for the lowest prices on earth. Since they are a custom fabricator of hand-carved natural stone, balustrades, archways, flooring, counter tops, urns, exterior stone cladding, pedestal sinks, counter top sink bowls, expect that they can make just about anything. With such a variety to choose from, you will never take them for granite — but marble and travertine are just the beginning of a solid introduction to their artistry. Their showroom/warehouse has a variety to choose from for immediate delivery. Since they are always running around doing installs, an appointment is necessary. When we can nail them down on a regular basis, it will be much easier to shop and raise their rating to the top.

★★★★★★   Stone Station Dallas Inc   972/488-8887

1377 Motor Street   Mon-Fri 8-5; Sat 9-1
Dallas, TX 75207
www.Stone-Station.com

 Stop motoring around all over town looking for granite countertops. Why bother? Here's your one-stop source and they'll come to you, make a template of your countertop needs, and you'll just pick out (not up) the slab. It's that simple. Expect to wait about four weeks from start to finish, but, when all is said and done, you will not only have a fab fabrication but save a ton of money by cutting out the middle man. So stop casting the first stone and pull up to this station first. Their retail counterpoint is the Stone Galleria, 3529 Preston Rd., Suite 6, Dallas 75034, 214/618-3420, www.Stone-Galleria.com, but it's their fabrication warehouse that you'll want to get to know. The money savings train doesn't stop at too many other stations, but it stops here for countertops.

★★★★★★ Surplus Building Materials   940/726-3598

S. I-35 @ Lone Oak Rd., exit 483   Tues-Fri 8-5; Sat 8-3:30; Closed Sun-Mon
Valley View, TX 76272

When you put over one million square feet of trim under one roof, you can expect a windfall. Add ceramic tile (over 100,000 square feet of choices) starting at a low of 69¢/square foot, and you can start saving at least 50 percent. Corner whirlpool tubs jarred our attention creating a real rush of excitement. Then, for windows, we were floored. Insulated windows 48 x 60-inch with screens were $65. They also had the top-selling vinyl windows with screens, alongside the aluminum and single panes, to ensure the bugs would not be enjoying the comforts of heat and air-conditioning. Then, the choice of mirrors was staggering and the French doors for $275, likewise. For do-it-yourselfers, perhaps the laminate floor coverings would be your project of choice from a low of 99¢-$1.59. Drive north of Denton and save more than a dollar or two. Get a different view of the world from Valley View where the living is easy, and the prices are even easier on the pocketbook. Looks like you'll have to travel for the best buys, so load up on each trip and enjoy the economy of scale just by going north, young man.

★★★★ Surplus Warehouse   972/287-5190

104 Simonds Rd.   Mon-Fri 8-:30 -5; Sat 8-1
PO Box 876 Seagoville, TX 75159

With the sound of a slow Southern drawl, you'll be escorted around this warehouse, but don't put the pressure on to rush. The keys to economic freedom may be just lying in wait. No ambush, though, as Seagoville is home to the federal pen. Don't worry, you won't be in any danger. Stay firm in your convict-ions of not paying high prices, and you will be singing "Jailhouse Rock" when you leave. They have it all: siding, paint, doors, hardware, cabinets, countertops, lighting and plumbing fixtures, shingles and more. Exit Simonds off 175, and, make sure, you head to the right warehouse. Most items are first-quality closeouts, although some have been slightly damaged but are still useable. Look for blowout sales! When you buy something, they tag it and separate it from the floor inventory until you can arrange for a pick-up.

★★★★★★ SW Canvas Products   817/624-9932

2418 Clinton Ave.   Mon-Fri 8-5; Sat By Appt. Only
Fort Worth, TX 76016

Family-owned since 1956, if it can be measured, it can be covered in canvas. Just ask me, and I'll be happy to tell you how I achieved a Highland Park look in the middle of Lewisville — just with awnings. Awnings, awnings burning bright, shelter me from the daytime light. But who to call when the sun comes shining through? SW Canvas, that's who. This family-owned business is up before sun-up and running with the founder's son, Carlos, performing their day-to-day duties. Whether you're a business or a residence, whether it's front, side or back windows that you want to dress up, why look anywhere else? This is the place that does it better and cheaper than anybody else. Make your appointment for a free estimate. They utilize the SUNBRELLA brand for awnings, canopies, tarps, tents, truck and boat covers. Price depends, of course, on size, but an average single window awning can run between $175 and $250, with discounts for quantity orders.

NV   Terra Shade (Permashade)   972/509-9242

2455 E. Hwy 121, Suite 101   Mon-Sat 10-5
Lewisville, TX 75057
www.terrashade.com

Whether it's Terra in the Shade you're after, consider **PERMASHADE** as the answer to what could
be referred to as "The Shining." Enjoy the great sun's glow — as long as it's not beating down on
you in an 100-degree scorcher. Or, if you're finally sitting out on your patio, the sun's shining, the
weather is mild, you're having neighbors over for a bite to eat, and, then, here it comes — the rain.
Head now to **TERRA SHADE**. Their showroom is in Lewisville, although their mailing address is
in Grapevine. **TERRA SHADE** is durable heavy-gauge virgin aluminum that's easy to maintain
with the realistic appearance of deep wood grain. Then, bring in **PERMASHADE**, the builder, who
uses this material for custom-designed patio covers, carports, room enclosures, patio rooms, carports — even concrete resurfacing and decorative concrete for driveways. So now, if you want
custom concrete in the standard simple gray, washed aggregate or a variety of colorfully stamped
concrete for your garage slab, driveway, sidewalks, and more, you've got it made. Watch for their
new Frisco showroom opening soon.

★★★★   Texas Safes (Liberty Safes)   972/579-8014

1431 N. Loop 12   Mon-Fri 10-5:30; Sat 10-3
Irving, TX 75061-5618
www.gunsafe.com

With over 200 safes in stock, how can you possibly feel insecure? No longer Pony Express, Liberty Safes has taken over, and all I can say is Oy-ge-vault! My one word of caution, though, since
you've got a safe, always keep any guns in there in a safe and locked position. Too, what about
keeping all those important documents such as your passport, stocks and bonds, life insurance policies and more in a safe and secure place? Free yourself from the tyranny of high prices, but you
get what you pay for. Get a full size gun safe as low as $495 and they also carry individual cases
for long guns and pistols. Delivery and installation is available. Look for CENTURIAN, **CHAM-
PION**, LIBERTY and SUN WELDING brands. Their other location is at one of my all-time favorite addresses: 614 Easy Street in Garland, 972/272-9788.

★★★★★★   Texas Stone & Tile Inc.   214/358-4698

2683 Lombardy Lane   By Appt. Only
PO Box 540755 Dallas, TX 75354-0755
www.texasstone.com

Today, many manufacturers, distributors, wholesalers and such are straddling the
fence between their traditional customer base of designers, decorators, contractors,
wholesalers and such — and YOU. Slowly but surely YOU are becoming more and
more appreciated. What was once closed-except-to-the-trade doors are opening more and more to
the public as a way to survive in tight economic times. Let's face it, business is business. This
company was once, too, open only to the trade selling top-quality natural stone, cast stone, brick,
ceramic, quarry and paver tiles to designers for exquisite flooring materials. Today, it's available
for all of us Material Girls. This company has flourished over the years based on repeat business,
so that should tell you something. The structure of the company, though, allows it to be multi-faceted, so they are capable of selling small to large projects, commercial to residential, decorators to
individual home owners. Expect marble, granite, limestone and other natural stone products to be
the material of choice and their installers know which works best and where based on the material

used. It's a very technical installation, so you should only consider hiring professionals, such as the ones here. From paving applications to conventional thin veneers, they are considered the leaders who have carved a fine reputation in stone (and the Better Business Bureau). To see elaborate finished projects, view their gallery online, but some of the pictures take three minutes to load, so be prepared to wait. Fabrications like natural stone countertops (for inside your house), can be installed in residential kitchens, bathrooms, etc. Granite countertops are all the rage, so check them out before you buy elsewhere. Same with brick, block and stone masonry for outdoor kitchens and terraced landscaped projects. They are the greatest. It's the same with the installation of ceramic, quarry and paver tile. Go to the experts and you'll get expert results. Direct pricing. Superb service. If it's good enough for the floors of the Hotel Crescent Court, it's good enough for me. Bet you didn't know they used Texas Stone for the Mary Kay building, too? Do you know what colors of granite they used? I do. They used Carmen Red and Absolute Black Z. For countertops, ask for Marty Gunderson. He's in charge of residential countertops. Many different types of stone are available through Texas Stone and Tile. At this time, only a granite catalog is available; however, catalogs for marble, limestone, and slate are coming. Don't ask for a sample sent to your mailbox. That's too heavy a request.

★★   Texas Tool Traders   972/278-0049

2414 S. Jupiter Rd.   Mon-Fri 7:30-5:30; Sat 8-Noon
Garland, TX 75041
www.texastooltraders.com

If you're a fan of "Trading Spaces," you love the Texas Tool Traders. Why, because if you ever decide to decorate your neighbor's house, you'll need all the tools of the trade to do the job. From painting to carpeting, Texas Tool Traders has five locations to answer your song quest, "If I Had a Hammer." In business since 1973, there are locations in Garland, Arlington, Lewisville, McKinney and Watauga. Buy those grown-up toys (for girls and boys) who can't live without the newest in hand and power tools. Watch to be able to shop online in the future. But, for now, they will take your order over the phone. *Call toll-free: 800/998-7001*

◆◆◆◆◆◆   Tile & Marble Installation   972/236-9100

1325 Whitlock Lane, Suite 309   Mon-Fri 7:30-4:30
Carrollton, TX 75006
www.ceramictileinstallations.com

 Surely you do not want just anybody laying around on the job. In this case, though, here's a company that lays it on without a hitch. It's their job, as a matter of fact, to install tile or marble for most any room or function. From a unique custom back splash in your kitchen to a matching mosaic border on the floor, you can stand on their workmanship for years to come. Looking for a new and improved seamless shower with marble seat and coordinating tile? I do. I do. What about a marble or granite countertop for the vanity? I do. I do. Or a custom fireplace surround? Like limestone or porcelain instead? What about slab granite countertops for your kitchen or bath? Here we go again. These guys specialize in tubs and showers, repairs and insurance work and are all insured and bonded themselves. FREE in-home estimates gladly given with specials on installation and labor going on most of the time. With over a decade of design experience in the tile, marble and granite industry, they have delivered thousands of unique, decorative and functional tile creations. Browse their online gallery without even leaving home for inspiration and validation. Then while they tile away the hours, you can appreciate their craftsmanship.

★★★★★ **Tile America**   **817/595-7900**

7337 Dogwood Park Drive   Mon-Fri 8-5; Sat 9-2
Richland Hills, TX 76118
www.tileamericainc.com

Tile America boasts the largest supply of in-stock tile in the Metroplex, with over three million square feet of tile available. No one manufacturer stands alone. They represent hundreds from all over the world, including Spain, Italy and Indonesia. Try dancing around the issue of their huge selection of wall and floor tiles as low as $.89 a square foot. They even offer their own brand of all-glazed tile, from an 8 by 8-inch square all the way up to 18 by 18-inch. Pay attention to their closeout sales — you'll be floored with even lower prices. Take Highway 121 south and exit Handley. Go over the freeway and you'll see it on your right as you enter the industrial park. And now that they have an outlet for their outlet, you've got two places to call home. Visit the Tile Depot for the basics, ma'am, just the basics at rock-bottom prices at 2200 Carson, Haltom City, TX 76117, 817/831-4702. *Call toll-free: 888/560-5700*

★★★★★★ **United Window Warehouse**   **817/640-3800**

1301 E. Corporate Dr., Suite F   By Appt. Only
Arlington, TX 76006
www.unitedweview.com

 Utilizing the TRACO manufactured windows and doors, this marketing company, out of Deerfield, Florida, offers replacement windows and doors at wholesale prices. No need to crack up, this is at savings of up to 50 percent. Call their locally-owned replacement windows and doors agent and they'll arrange for an installer to come out to your home or office to provide a free in-home estimate, FREE installation and 100 percent financing with zero down (with approved credit, of course). Imagine what your energy savings will be with just the new and improved window panes. Not only will it improve your home's curb appeal, sound will be tempered by up to 75 percent, heating and cooling costs will be reduced up to 59 percent, there will be reduced condensation, and even your home-owners policy may be reduced. Since 1943, this company has been making improvements to your home and office and can credit the Statue of Liberty, the Empire State Building, Bally's Hotel and Casino, and even the Hilton Hotels, on their ever-expanding list of references. Now, surely, you don't have as many windows as the Empire State Building, do you? So, when you think of that age-old question, "Do you do windows?" at last, you can be united in your response. United we call and united we stand, committed to the best — for less! A lifetime transferable warranty is also provided. *Call toll-free: 866/928-3719*

◆◆◆◆ **US Inspect**   **972/263-1007 (Metro)**

1601 East Lamar, Suite 210   By Appt. Only
Arlington, TX 76011

Looks like Affordable Inspections has just gone national and now has a new name. Across the country, this is one service that's a no-brainer when buying or selling a house. Call these folks when you need a house or termite inspection. They've been around since 1985, and their on-the-spot instant computer inspection is very impressive, as well as thorough. These are experts in their field who spend several hours going through your house with a fine-tooth comb. When they're finished, they deliver a computer printout of the inspection. Their service includes color digital photos of any problems for further clarification. Expect them to spend two-three hours on an inspection, depending on the age of the home, type, square footage, foundation type and any extras.

★★★★   Walnut Hill Paint Warehouse   972/484-5800

2720 Royal Lane, Suite 172   Mon-Fri 7-5:30; Sat 8:30-12:30
Dallas, TX 75229

If only the walls could talk. First, they'd tell us that Walnut Hill Paint Company is not on Walnut Hill. Instead, you have to head for Royal Lane. This full-service paint store carries many lines of name brand paints like BENJAMIN MOORE, JONES-BLAIR, MARTIN SENOUR, MOBILE, PITTSBURGH, PRATT & LAMBERT and RALPH LAUREN, at least for starters. I forgot to look for MARTHA STEWART, but surely they can get it. I understand there's a new color being formulated for her line called Jailhouse Gray. Do you suppose that's just a joke? Per gallon, how does $6.15 for flat paint sound? No strain on the pocketbook with stains like CABOT and OLYMPIC. Seal your fate, then make a date to paint the town red, white and blue. Enjoy the variety of mixing and matching. Stand elbow-to-elbow with professional painters and handymen getting the tools of their trade. Faux finishes are the rage and they've got what you need to create the look, phony or not. The selection is stellar for paints, stains and coatings, plus all the sundries you need to complete the task — from top to bottom and in between. They also carry metal effects and aerosols for touch-ups. Head just west of Denton Drive for the Royal treatment and you can paint the town green with the savings.

★   Windoor World   817/467-1777

3420 Dalworth   Mon-Fri 8-5; Sat 9-3
Arlington, TX 76013
www.windoor.com

Knock on any door and save some bucks. Windows, too. Vinyl, wood windows and patio doors are their stock in trade. Save some money, too. Not a whole lot, mind you, but enough to let you in on at least a 20 percent discount. Patio doors began as low as $499. HURD windows for new construction or replacement were up to 20 percent off. Note: I said "up to." That's not even worth repeating! But these are the windows that block 99.5 percent of the sun's harmful rays. GUARDIAN steel doors started at $299, solid mahogany doors were as low as $399 with 10-year warranties and ALCOA vinyl siding was priced upon request, but appeared retail. Same with skylights. Shop their online catalog at their website or in person at their factory showroom above. Check directory for additional locations.

◆◆◆◆◆   World of Windows (Father & Son)   214/637-2626

7108 Envoy Court   By Appt. Only
Dallas, TX 75247

Nothing beats the pane of shopping for windows more than hearing about the prices. Well, if you keep it all in the family you'll be relieved immediately. This father and son duo (also known as Father & Son Windows as well as World of Windows) guarantees the lowest price (comparing apples to windows) for simply the best. Hey, that would make a good slogan, don't you agree? Do not confused them with Windoor World (see writeup above). Make sure you note the distinction. Double-pane vinyl replacement windows, any size, $189.95 installed (that's for a basic wood replacement). That compares to a typical $600 job installed. To remove a metal framed window, add another $25 per window. Now, to get these low prices, the minimum order is eight windows which is usually not too difficult to honor. After all, you wouldn't want to have a few energy-efficient windows alongside those that would counter that efficiency, would you? Surely you'd want to outfit your whole house with these energy-efficient replacement windows; otherwise, you'd defeat the entire purpose of replacing them in the first place. Of course, this company is in good with the Better Business Bureau, and with us — the other BBB!

Discount Building Materials

See writeup on page 379

Housewares

★★★★ **Ace Mart Restaurant Supply**   **214/351-5444**

3128 Forest Lane   Mon-Fri 8:30-5:30; Sat 9-2
Dallas, TX 75234
www.acemart.com

Cook up a storm and set the world on fire with all the cooking gadgets, utensils and equipment at this one-stop kitsch emporium. Surely there's something from the oven that's worth serving for dinner that you didn't know you needed until you saw what's cooking here. At this warehouse, which has become so cook-friendly to all the gourmands galloping around the Metroplex, you will lose all of your will power to resist buying something. Browse through this spacious and airy warehouse/retail store offering every kind of new kitchen gadget and equipment. Select from any one of their 7,000 products. From their kitchen to yours, this is definitely your Ace in the hole. Their Forest Lane location is the only one open on Saturday, and they still maintain they are only open to cater to caters and chefs. Of course, you can receive a discount if you buy in dozens or in case lots. For example, the hand-held knife sharpener for under $10 is the best I've ever used. Whether it's the dinnerware or the commercial gas stoves (although not approved for home/residential use), "burn-er" the midnight oil and get cookin'! What really turned us on were the platters, but great for everyday use, right up to those special dinner parties. There's plenty more on Belt Line Road in Garland, Haltom City at 5600 Denton Highway (817/498-5900), and 1605 W. Pioneer Parkway in Arlington. The website's extensive and their catalog is available by phone or in-store. In this case, too many cooks won't spoil anything you whip up from here. *Call toll-free: 800/841-4747*

◆ **American and European Clock Repair**   **214/460-2861**

739 Woodlawn Ave.   Mon-Sat 9-5; By Appt.
Dallas, TX 75208

If your clock's missing a beat and the second hand doesn't make it through the night, this guy can probably get it going. Just about any clock can be repaired — whether old or new. Most repairs take about two weeks, although he can do them quicker, if your life depends on it. Though his main focus is clock repairs, there were a few assorted models for sale. You pay for his expertise and meticulous time....but expect him to be extremely high-strung and probably the type that sounds rushed all the time. If fact, he sounds breathless, although he continues to tick. Repairs on antique, mechanical and electric clocks, too. Pick-up and delivery is an option, especially if you're out of time. Call ahead. Time does stand still when you have an appointment. Each time we did call, though, it was forwarded to a voice message machine with no return calls to this day. So, his rating is reflected in his lack of response. Maybe he called a "time-out?"

★★ Case-Baldwin   972/434-8197; 972/221-6868

890 N. Mill St., Suite 113   Mon-Fri 8-5 (Closed Noon-1 PM)
Lewisville, TX 75067
www.yourjanitor.com

If you want to make a clean sweep, don't bother during 12 to 1. That's their lunch hour and no business is conducted, other than eating, that occurs then. Other times, though, if you've got a notion to clean up with janitorial supplies and equipment, you might find something to make it into the clean team supply bucket. You don't have to be a janitor or a professional cleaner, either. Who can't use trash can liners, towels, tissues, disinfectants, a good industrial mop, and a bucket that won't tip over with a gallon of water? Add soaps and detergents, carpet-care products and floor waxes, and you will wax ecstatic over the selection. They also repair vacuum cleaners and they decided a while back to open to the public. Manufacturers of supplies include CLOROX, EUREKA, FORT JAMES, GEORGIA-PACIFIC, NOBLES, PROCTOR & GAMBLE, PRO TEAM, RUBBERMAID and others. But let's back up a minute. Pay attention to what I said earlier. These guys do carpet cleaning, refinishing of floors and janitorial services. Now that's where my hearth lies. Over 1,000 items available with no minimum order restrictions and discounts when you order in bulk. And practically next door to my favorite wholesale source of little gifts Wigand's. So now there's two very good reasons to get your fill on Mill Street.

★★★★★★ Clockery, The   817/261-9335

2401 W. Pioneer Pkwy.   Mon-Sat 10-6
Arlington, TX 76013

 Fly like an eagle over to the Clockery before the bell tolls. What? Are you cuckoo? Don't shop anywhere else if it's a timepiece you're after. You've got to admire this Mom and Pop operation where Mom answers the phone and Pop does the TV commercials. From Highway 360, exit Pioneer Parkway and go west for 4 1/2 miles. Keep that little mouse climbing and earning his keep. After you pass Fielder, it's only another quarter of a mile on the north side of the street. Time doesn't stand still when it comes to their selection — it just doesn't quit. More than 1,500 different clocks are sold at this pioneer of discount clocks. My, doesn't time fly when you're shopping? Grandfather clocks alone practically rule the roost. Then, fill in the blanks with small clocks, mantle clocks, anniversary clocks, wall and floor clocks, every kind of clock is ticking away, time after time. They have one of the largest clock selections in Texas including the popular RIDGEWAY and SLIGH. An AWI-certified clock-maker is on site and all floor clocks are sold with a one-year manufacturer's warranty.

★★★ Cookworks   972/960-2665

5213 Alpha Rd.   Mon-Fri 10-9; Sat 10-6; Sun Noon-6
Dallas, TX 75244

Located right off the Tollway, you're but minutes away from taking a cook's tour of where a cook's work is never done. This company, based in Santa Fe, has many hands in the kitchen. Mike was our guide, and boy, was he knowledgeable about what works, what doesn't, what to buy and what really is more hype than ripe for reality. What a cook's tour! But when they have a sale, you better have worked up an appetite. Memorial Day weekend, for example, an Alley Sale began on Friday with discounts of 40 to 50 percent off on Friday and Saturday with an escalation up to 60 to 70 percent on Sunday and Monday. Located by the Tollway near CRATE & BARREL, cooking classes. This is where the cook works a little less with all the added help of great cookware, bakeware, gourmet cookbooks and more. Cookworks also produces its own line of tableware, gourmet foods and top-of-the-line kitchen equipment. If it's not **FARBERWARE** or **RUBBERMAID**, it doesn't count in my kitchen!

★★★★   Corningware/Corelle/Revere Factory Stores   972/874-0920

3000 Grapevine Mills Parkway #311   Mon-Sat 10-8; Sun 11-6
Grapevine, TX 76051
www.worldkitchen.com

Reduced to three area locations (Grapevine Mills, Tanger Factory Outlet in San Marcos and the Corning Factory Store in Katy, outside Houston), this powerhouse may be waning on the home front. Although we're not trying to be "Corning Dog" this popular cookware/bakeware has been a fixture in most kitchens for decades. Arf! Arf! A **CORNINGWARE** cookware set for $19.99 was just one of the reasons we shop the outlet store. Since savings averaged 30 to 60 percent off retail, you're apt to buy more cookware than you have shelf space, and then, complain you need a bigger kitchen! But while you're at it, why not take a stab at bigger savings with a Purchase Plus card that gives you a little extra punch? Get one punch for every $20 spent and after 20 punches, you'll get $20 off your next purchase. Glasses to cookware, pans to cutlery, with names like **BAKER'S SECRET, CHICAGO CUTLERY, CORRELLE, CORNING WARE, ECKO, FRENCH WHITE, OXO, PYREX** and **REVERE ELECTRICS**. Take a cut out of your budget, as well as the beef! *Call toll-free: 888/246-2737*

★★★★   CPAPC Restaurant Supply, Inc.   972/620-3030

3212 Belt Line Road, # 301   Mon-Fri 9:30-5
Carrollton, TX 75006

At the corner of Webb Chapel at Belt Line lies another restaurant supply secret stash waiting to be discovered. Located in a very unobtrusive strip shopping center, you'd pass it by if your eagle eyes were not looking for it. Run by Asians, you can wok and roll to your heart's content. If you like to cook Far Eastern dishes (Chinese, Japanese, Vietnamese and Thai, for example), you can start with the plates and buy them by the dozens. An elegantly decorated lacquered sushi serving tray was $33 and an elegant wooden sushi boat tray was $64. But remember to pay attention to the feng shui of the table. You don't want to get the plates out of alignment. Forget the Benihana routine of dicing and chopping. Get the same knives yourself with 8 x 2-inch blades from $11 and up. Have you ever chopped on a hard-rock maple cutting board? What about a bamboo steamer or a wire skimmer? Steel woks from Japan start as low as $9 for a small nine-inch model to one whose diameter is three feet. Me, I prefer the non-stick kind. Ask for a catalog and if you want to shop on Saturdays, you'll have to visit their Arlington location at 3447 Dalworth St., 817/640-8989 as they're open Mon-Fri 9:30-5 and Sat 10-3.

★★★   Crate & Barrel Outlet Store   214/634-2277

Inwood Outlet Center   Mon-Sat 10-5; Thurs 10-6 Sun Noon-5
1317 Inwood Rd. Dallas, TX 75247
www.crateandbarrel.com

Started in 1962 in an old elevator factory, Crate and Barrel is on a mission to provide the following P's: People, Product and Presentation. One visit to their stores, including their outlets, and you can see all three in action. The merchandise is part of the plan. too, as they seek out sleek and chic items in unusual and unique housewares. From artisans, designers and manufacturers from little known factories, you won't see the same products at C & B that you see in housewares departments or specialty stores anywhere else in the country. Their distinctive flair has separated them from the rest of the sheep, as kosher dishes are separated from non-kosher — and never the twains shall meet. As an aside, this company gives considerable sums to charities like Aids research and breast cancer-related causes. Now back to their outlet. Let your plate runneth over. The dinnerware and tabletop accessories are the objects of my affection for any of one's dish fulfillment. Since 80 percent of their stock is discontinued, strike while the bargains are hot; otherwise, you'll starve to death. Unfortunately, at the outlet, you'll save only a measly 20 percent, though specials net deeper cuts, it's only a measly amount. But you'll see only first quality!

◆◆◆◆◆◆   Dal-Tex Rental   972/285-1863

910 Belt Line Rd.   Mon-Sat 7:30-5;30
Mesquite, TX 75149

When our favorite Rent-All Centers flew the coop and all calls were routed to Dal-Tex, we thought we were out of luck when we wanted to rent tables ($5) or chairs (35 cents), let alone the Moonwalk ($95). But not to worry, they still rent it all. Pull out all the stops and let's have a party, a wedding, or any other celebration. Just make sure you have all the right equipment to do it up right. But don't expect this company to be all fun and games. They also rent serious stuff like medical equipment, power and hand tools, floor and carpet-care equipment, painting and plumbing equipment, camping and sporting equipment, automotive tools and more. What about machines to make cotton candy, or snow cones, hot dogs, popcorn and margaritas? Life is a party, you know and it'll cost you to sip a margarita — about $75/day, plus delivery charge based on where you live. Second location at 4504 Lakeview Parkway, Rowlett, TX 75088; 972/ 475-7773. (The Mesquite store is the larger and better equipped of their two stores.)

★★★★★   Dr. Livingston Group   972/438-7272

1502 E. Irving Blvd   Mon-Fri 8-5
Irving, TX 75060

Here's an outlet that really gets out there. Finding it can be a challenge but once inside these doors, you'll find the trip to be a worthwhile adventure. Dr Livingston, I presume, enjoyed finding his way around the world and sending gifts to those who remained stateside. How about buying one for yourself? This year, the stock still varies but jewelry is no longer a part of their plan. They are still closed on the weekends, but worth adding to your weekday menu of "must shop stores!" Assorted lamps, artifacts, antique reproductions, woodcarvings, baskets, home accessories, and collectibles line the shelves. They have it all — from market samples to closeouts, all below wholesale prices. Restaurants shop here as do retail stores for some of their decorative accents. Good things come to those who shop the outlet way. Haven't I always told you so? They'd be in the 100 BEST if they opened on the weekends.

★★★   Fort Worth Shaver & Appliance   817/335-9970

1900 Montgomery St.   Mon-Fri 8:30-5:30; Sat 9-3
Fort Worth, TX 76107

This is the official service center for **BRAUN**, **CUISINART** and **NORELCO**. So if you're looking for any of these brands, here is the Mother Load. Find coffee makers, toasters, ice cream makers, juicers, roasters — just about any small appliance that has been refurbished and left behind to die a slow death. But folks, they still work and have many years of service left before they turn in their time card. Prices will be 25 to 35 percent less than new. Just overlook the ugly box. What, did you expect them to do .... pack it with a Neiman's-like wrap? The good news is that they also carry some new appliances and new shavers and shaver parts (like new blades). Even if you can only shave a few bucks off small appliances, every little bit helps. Again, if they've been used before, all have been reconditioned but may still have a few minor nicks or bruises. Who cares? For starting off, or outfitting the kitchen of a boat, a lake house, a dorm room, this is a hit. Sorry, they had no espresso machines on our last visit. But if you're in the market for a **CUISINART**, you're headed in the right direction. A four-slicer toaster, big enough for a Lender's bagel was $59.99. An **OSTER** blender was under $20; even a foot soaking massager by **SUNBEAM** was a meager $15.99. Put your best foot forward, and don't get soaked. Here's a good place to get away from the daily grind.

★★★★★★ Greenbacks   214/352-0700

11722 Marsh Lane
Dallas, TX 75229-2600
www.greenbacks.com

 Not only will be you saving lots of greenbacks at the Greenbacks/All A Dollar store, but once you get a glimpse behind the scenes, you'll be proud to boast you're a Greenbacks'fan. Bringing together several successful retail concepts into one retail chain that is bursting at the seams, it's a very creative approach to the single price point format. Here, the emphasis is on name-brand merchandise, exceptional value, first quality, service and convenience. Is it a variety 5 & 10-type of store? Or is it a 7-11 type of store? Lastly, is it a discount store? Well, it's all of the above combined into one easy-to-shop neighborhood shop where everything is indeed priced at one dollar (or multiple thereof) or less. Merchandise comes from all over the country, even from around the world. The size is formidable, over 10,000 square feet of bargain bliss in what appears to look like an upscale environment. The line-up of product categories is mind-boggling: Cards & Party, Food & Candy, Snacks & Beverages, Housewares, Health & Beauty, Gifts, Toys, Books, Office & School Supplies, Hardware & Automotive and more. "Buck" the high cost of living and put more Greenbacks back into your purse instead of someone else's.

★★ Heritage House Clocks   972/934-3420

14450 Midway Rd.
Dallas, TX 75244

Mon-Fri 10-6; Sat 10-5

A gazillion clocks at very competitive prices (mostly expensive in our opinion) is how they've built their heritage of clocks. And, if price is no object, you'll find them appealing. Shop both locations timed perfectly. (The other's in Highland Park at 5419 W. Lovers Lane, 214/350-9119.) Strike at the stroke of midnight. This nationally-acclaimed clock house is no ding-a-ling. When time is on anyone's hands, think Heritage House. Time certainly doesn't stand still for owners Val and Glenda Marchesoni, who are in charging of keeping things tickin'. The world is their oyster with clocks from Europe, Canada, American-made, as well as many special editions you won't find anywhere else. From Italy to Ireland, Germany to Great Britain, **NEW ENGLAND** to Holland, there are literally thousands of clocks to choose from. Consider this shopping experience a time-intensive mission. Choose **ANSONIA**, **HARRINGTON HOUSE**, **HOWARD MILLER**, **NEW ENGLAND**, **SLIGH** and others, with nary a full-price tag in sight. Save 15 to 50 percent on a menagerie of clocks: Cuckoo, antique models, mantle clocks, grandfathers....after all, they've been in business since 1974, they must be able to keep time by now. Don't bypass the possibilities of an unusual gift, either. Their music boxes and porcelain accessories are popular collectibles with serious antique buffs, as well as newcomers, looking to sink their teeth into a new hobby. There's something for everyone, but time doesn't come cheap. *Call toll-free: 800/238-5201*

PS Kitchen Store, The   817/561-1200
4714 Little Rd.   Mon-Fri 10-6; Sat 9-6; Sun Noon-5
Arlington, TX 76017

If you want to see what's cookin'in the kitchen with Dinah, shore up your ideas and head to The Kitchen Store right off I-20 and Little Road. It's the place in Tarrant County to find what you need to whip whatever you're fixing into shape. Kitchen gadgets, cookware and small appliances such as mixers, blenders and toasters are all waiting in a row to relocate to your kitchen. Don't expect a discount, however, unless there's a sale going on. But if you need a gourmet utensil, at least you know where to shop. Ah, who pays retail these days even if it's a store that caters to the upper crust? This wonderful store crams more stuff into a small space than I do in my kitchen drawers, so it's not all wasted. Did you know I used to own a gourmet shop in Carefree, AZ? At the corner of Ho and Hum, so it's not like I don't love to shop at little gourmet shops. It's just that I don't want to pay full price.

★★★★★★ Pier 1 Clearance Store   972/255-9811
2350 N. Belt Line Rd.   Mon-Sat 10-9; Sun 11-7
Irving, TX 75062
www.pier1.com

When you can snare a $150 iron barstool for $5 because its leg was bent, then I say, "Right on!" However, don't expect too many to have splinters or be a cause for pause. Most are all first quality but have just remained on the retail store shelves too long. It's like being on a treasure hunt where the bounty is striking paydirt. Like gold, these values are rock-solid. If you like their retail stores, you'll go ape over their Clearance Store located in Irving, across from the Irving Mall. Let's stop monkeying around. First, case the joint, then load up with an armful and wait at the checkout counters with shoppers who have come from surrounding states. Since 1962, this Fort Worth-based charmer has let the deals out of their myriad baskets without ever having to call in the snakes. My, oh my, from love beads to hearts and flower pictures with frames, their store is one of many splendid things. Even with their enormous success, they are still generous with the savings and to the community. Who cares if the item was a floor model or a scratch or dent? It's the price that counts and the function your find will perform once it relocates to your house. Is it any wonder realtors love this Clearance Store?

★★★★★ Promenade Clocks   972/644-3979
1325 Promenade Center, #132   Mon-Fri 10-5:30; Sat 10-5
Richardson, TX 75080

There are bubbas and zaydies, but there's nothing quite as regal as a Grandfather....clock, that is. Though sexist in its intent, it's universal in its appeal. Since 1962, Promenade Clocks has been keeping time with the best of them. Located between the 24 Hour Fitness and a pizza parlor in Richardson, at any given time, Larry will save you a minimum of five to seven percent off other retailers. On our visit, there were over 85 models of the grandfather clock in stock with prices ranging from $999 to $18,000. FREE delivery is available. Save up to 60 percent off by making your big hand head straight on to Promenade Clocks, located off Coit Road between Arapaho and Belt Line. They will meet or beat any advertised price on most grand brands like HOWARD MILLER, RIDGEWAY, SEIKO, SETH THOMAS, SLIGH and more! Hurry up! Time's a-wasting.

★★★★★★ **Rush Restaurant Supply, Inc.**   **214/956-7874**

6000 Denton Drive   Mon-Fri 8-5
Dallas, TX 75235

 Rush to the best restaurant supplier in town. Outfit your kitchen with everyday kitchen wares; or buy for the time you're having a party and never can find a punch bowl, have a large enough coffee pot, serving platter or enough glasses. When do you ever have enough glasses? No, not those you wear to see the fine print. Rather, these are the glasses you drink from. Whatever's your pleasure, water, tea or me? I'll take iced tea, wine, champagne, beer, well you name the beverage, they've got the glasses for it. Here's the places that showcases enough wine glasses in every shape and size to fulfill all of your red and white requests. Too, if you're thinking about a specialty drink, you can't put those in any old glass or cup. You'll need specialty glasses for these as well: hurricane, poco Grande, Margarita, Irish coffee, champagne coupes, flutes and brandy snifters, I mean they've got glasses for any kind of libation. For $2 each, how can you go wrong? Buy a case and get an additional 15 percent off. Is it any wonder it's where I recommend caterers get their glassware (which includes you and me, babe.) Recommended as an acceptable vendor for the El Centro Restaurant Curriculum, you can't go wrong, even if you're not studying to be a chef. Enjoy! And that's not all, folks. They outfit restaurants, so if you're cooking for the family and are expected to be available 24/7, then you can get what you need to cook up a storm at a lightning good price.

★★★★★★ **TCB Liquidators**   **972/222-9494**

1000 W. Crosby @ I-35   Mon-Fri 8-6; Sat Noon-12
Carrollton, TX 75006-6935
www.tcbl.com

 This 65,000-square-foot Carrollton restaurant equipment warehouse holds all the products that have been liquidated from restaurants and clients all over the country. Products are both new and used, but the new is priced like it was used. Expect good pricing whether you have a commercial use for them or you're a wannabe chef-in-training. Always look for the best for the commercial kitchen and then buy it for your home kitchen, if applicable. At least, try. Move over Dean Fearing, there are lots of aspiring chefs hungry to take your place. TBC buys and sells new or used store fixtures, supermarket equipment, restaurant equipment, walk-in coolers and gondola shelving. For anyone who likes kitchen gadgets, there were lots here that would fit the bill: a 6-inch Pizza Dough Scraper was $1.35; a 10-inch Round Blade Pizza Turner was $1.95; and a great hamburger turner for the next barbecue was $3.69. Load up folks! And enjoy the sweet smell of success.

★★★★★★ **Tic Toc Clocks**   **214/321-9331**

8928 Garland Rd.   Mon-Fri 10-5; Sat 10-3
Dallas, TX 75218

Don't expect their website to be tictock.com; that's already registered to a Dallas Marketing and Promotions company. But they are trying to get going online so stay tuned and you will be the first to know when they go up. It's just a matter of time. With over 50 Grandfather clocks in stock, how can you ignore a favorite relative? For as low as $700 up to $5,000, you can add this octogenarian to your family tree. Save up to 50 percent. Expect all grandfather, mantel, wall and cuckoo clocks to sell for close to half price off. Consider buying an **AMERICAN HERITAGE, ANSONIA, BALDWIN, BLACK FOREST, DOLD**, or others. Hands down, this store will save you money on both new and antique clocks. And they are winning the race against time, every time.

◆◆◆◆◆◆ United Rent-All   972/492-0550

3749 N. Josey Lane   Mon 7:30-5; Tue-sSat 8-5
Carrollton, TX 75007
www.unitedrent-all.com

 Yes, at one time, you could take me to Margaritaville. But today, take me to United Rental, the home to Margaritas-R-Us. Since 1954, you can drink the different sizes of Margaritas, Bellinis, Cha-ladas, PiÒa-coladas, Long Island Iced Teas — just make sure you have a designated driver. Confirmed? Margarita Lovers take note: for Margaritas R US, call 972/690-1880, a separate number that will take you directly to their order desk. Rentals cost $95 with 17 different mixes with each mix making 80 drinks. For $45, they will deliver, set up and pick up, as long as you live close to Carrollton. Party items are everywhere; serious party items are their specialty. Need something to display your ice sculpture (an ice-carving display stand?) It's here for $25. The finest silver serving pieces, china, flatware, serving utensils, champagne fountains (up to $60), punchbowls and glassware, table cloths and other linens. For business meetings, they have office equipment that you only need occasionally like lecterns, easels, projectors, video cameras and players. Well, there isn't enough space to list their inventory but they've got everything you could possible want at some time or another for rent. I'll drink to that!

★★★★ Weatherly's Clock   817/294-1281

5041 Granbury Rd.   TuesSat 10-6
Fort Worth, TX 76133

You can weather any storm with battery alarm clocks starting at under $20, so load up. You know, the weather in north Texas can take a turn for the worse within a moment's notice. Paying attention to timepieces can mean everything from getting to the church or getting to work on time (unless it's to both and you're a minister). Better late than never won't cut it with the boss! If you're looking for a particular style of clock, this is the place to dial. Dial C for clocks, even if they don't have it in stock, they will special order. Time lines at Weatherly includes grandfather clocks, mantle clocks, cuckoo clocks and more. A new clock would look good hanging in your hallway. And a used clock would look just as good. That's right! They carry both new and antique clocks and who would know the difference? (Unless of course, the antique clock is running a few hours behind the times.) Repairs are available and take about two weeks which is pretty standard since most clock stores we shopped consistently averaged about two weeks for repairs. (Or they're all using the same repair service?) And if your watch needs aid, other than financial, they can repair them, too. All clocks are mechanical or battery — don't expect an electric clock here. Closed on Sundays and Mondays, because everybody needs some time off.

★★★★★★ Wigand's Gifts & More   214/222-8525

890 N. Mill Street   Mon-Sat 9-6 Sun 12-5
Lewisville, TX 75057

 When you're at your Wig's end, here's where to put you over the top. Ever wonder where all the merchandise comes from that you see en route in all those gift and truck stops along the way? Even if you're not a big fan of knick-knacks, admit it, at times that wooden Indian or that collectible beanie-type baby is just perfect to wrap up and take on the road. This Lewisville wholesaler has opened his doors to the public and both Dean Jr. and Dean Senior welcome you with open arms. Closer to Christmas, they pull out all the stops and stay open 7 days a week. But for regular hours, expect them to be open Monday-Saturday from 10-6. Their A to Z inventory is at best described as a little of this and a little of that. From ceramic birds to birdhouses, knives to reading glasses, vases and urns to wall hangings and wind chimes ....

stacked floor to ceiling. Store them in your gift closet and you'll always be prepared for a great little something for most any occasion. From executive desk accessories for that man who has everything to life-size carved wooden-like Indians, what more can you want (except to find out if they take reservations???) Even if you don't appreciate my humor, you will appreciate the prices here because everything's half price. I promise — you won't be able to stop with just one!

★★★ World Market (Cost Plus)   972/509-1843

1201 N. Central Expressway   Mon-Sat 9-9; Sun 10-7
Plano, TX 75075
www.costplusworldmarket.com

All the world's a stage, and that means, shoppers, you should act the part. Enter World Market (formerly Cost Plus), when fun and functional furnishings fit the bill. Over 220 stores in 27 states, their almost national presence creates a worldly environment from which to unearth the deals. The buyers for the World Market travel the globe uncovering the treasures from remote and centuries'-old villages and foreign bazaars. Based in California, they now bring forth their delicacies like baskets from Bali, chocolates from Belgium, pottery from Portugal, other gourmet foodstuff and wine. Do they have the wine! Over 450 varieties, all at inexpensive prices. Not described normally as a discounter, they would best be described as a value merchant where products are affordable. From soup to nuts, Chardonnay to Cabernet, Merlot to Zinfandel, the pickings are vast and veritable. Merchandise arrives daily. They even produce their own coffees and biscotti and bring it out to settle comfortably between floor lamps, sleeper sofas, rugs, chairs, pottery, housewares, home accents, even blinds. One of the most notable blinds were the cinnamon bamboo varieties, the matchstick versions, rice paper and paper accordion ... not your usual or customary garden varieties and I've only seen them at World Market. Check directory for one of the seven or is it eight Metro locations, as well as locations throughout the USA. New just as we went to press, two new stores just threw open their doors: Flower Mound at Long Prairie and 407 West in the Highlands, 972/539-3355; and in Denton at 1400 Loop 288, 940/381-9014. *Call toll-free: 800/COST-PLU*

Jewelry

★★★★ **All that Glitters**   972/355-5910

Grapevine Mills Mall #507   Mon-Sat 10-9; Sun 11-7
Grapevine, TX 76051

Fashion accessories and jewelry sparkles at All that Glitters at Grapevine Mills. Enter the theatre side of the mall and you'll be right on target to hit the bullseye for rings, necklaces, designer-style purses, bracelets, watches, scarves all priced WHOLESALE to the public. Saving the tourist a trip to Sam Moon's, this store provides an extensive selection at low, low prices so why not give it a whirl, girl. Don't expect investment grade diamonds, but they look good enough to pass the mustard. But of course, not Sam Moon, but a lookalike and growing. Too bad there's not a gem of a website. In fact, if you type in www.allthatglitters.com, you'll get a search engine for jewelry but not for a store of the same name.

◆◆◆◆ **Artful Bead, The**   817/294-2903

Wedgwood Village   Mon-Sat 10-6
5304 Trail Lake Drive. Fort Worth, TX 76133
www.artfulbead.com

It's so easy to get to, you're practically there once you take Loop 820 South from Fort Worth to the Old Grandbury Rd. exit. Turn south on Grandbury Rd. The store is located in the Wedgwood Village. From Dallas, take I-30 or I-20 West to Loop 820 South. Then take the Old Grandbury Rd. South on Grandbury to the Wedgwood Shopping Center. If you want to learn the art of beading, here's the place that will teach you the ropes. A $15 deposit is required which will be credited toward your class fee. You'll receive a materials list and a coupon good for 15 percent off the materials that you purchase in your class. This store has the largest selection of beads and jewelry making supplies in Fort Worth. See what you can create with a little help from The Artful Bead. Go online to learn about their up and coming schedule of classes including a brief course description. They also have a map to guide you there.

★★★★ **Bermuda Gold Custom Jewelers**   817/481-5115

404 S. Main St.   Mon-Fri 10-6; Sat 10-3
Grapevine, TX 76051

They are smack dab in the middle of the downtown Grapevine historic district. Go figure! What is still terrific about this store, especially if you'd like to strike it rich with gold, is it's location — inside an old bank. Where else can you strike it rich anyway? In the jewelry business since 1984, the building's claim to fame was that it was once held up by Bonnie and Clyde. You'll find jewelry utilizing 14-Karat and 18-Karat gold and platinum. If you want a more contemporary look, don't overlook their large selection of colored stones. Strike it rich or strike it for less in diamonds (round, emerald-cut, pear-cut, princess-cut, a solitaire, whatever's your pleasure), available in small sizes or large enough for you to impress the neighborhood. Gary Meek is not meek about being bold about gold. His prices, selection and service are right on the money.

★ Bova Diamonds   214/744-7668

2050 Stemmons, Suite 7729   By Appt. Only
Dallas, TX 75207
www.bovadiamonds.com

This upstairs jeweler offers shoppers an ideal cut. Consider this, for starters: an 1.8 K pendant that retails for $10,000, their price $5,900. Similarly discounted rings, bracelets and an extensive selection of certified loose diamonds are also part of their repertoire. Although prices may appear exceptional, shoppers do not live (or buy) by price alone, they will grill you like the FBI when you call. They were emphatic to know who you are and why you're calling so be prepared for the third degree. Either you want to sell to the public or you don't — I hate it when it's both ways." Just looking" is an unacceptable response when they ask you what you're interested in purchasing. Perhaps on a particular item, though, if you have the cash on hand, they might be receptive and present a new attitude. I found it a turnoff. All of their our mountings are carved with 14K or 18K gold and use the best quality diamonds with Color D-F and Clarity VVS-VS1/2. One ring 4.11 carat diamond ring, custom made, was a deal for $20,000 (H SI2) but it was either my mortgage for the year or a ring. Which do you think won?

★★★★★   Bracelets, Etc   972/353-8177

1565 W. Main Street, Suite 220   Mon-Fri 10-5; Sat 10-6; Sun 12-5
Lewisville, TX 75067

This neighborhood haunt has one thing going for it that Sam Moon doesn't — a parking place. Pull up and get a front-row space and leave the armor at home. You won't need it as there was plenty of elbow room to work your way through the bracelets, earrings, teen jewelry, toe rings and anklets, sterling silver, watches, purses, candles, crosses, children's jewelry and more. Wholesale prices is closer to home at the Garden Park Shopping Center whether you're looking for scrunchies or interchangeable watches, Italian charms ($4.99-$5.99), coral, turquoise and onyx necklaces or inexpensive handbags that you see up and down Harry Hines. This experience is darn like taking baby steps rather than leaping over tall buildings and armed guards. You might want to circle your wrists for $15.99, for example, which were the same prices seen on HH. Save gas and shop in Lewisville. Smaller, yes, but less frenetic and certainly very family-friendly. Deck out, too, in Frisco at 2728 Preston Rd., in the Toys R Us Shopping Center, 972/334-9277, 7 days a week at least through the holidays.

★★★★★   Castle Gap   214/361-1677

8300 Preston Rd., Suite 500   Mon-Sat 10-6
Dallas, TX 75225
www.castlegap.com

Head to their stores or check out their website and see what Charlotte Bennett has brought back from the reservations. Castle Gap closes the gap on paying exorbitant prices for Indian jewelry. For more than a quarter of a century, Charlotte and her family have collected North American sterling silver, handcrafted wares from Indian reservations. In fact, she has served on many prestigious Indian craft jewelry organizations such as American Indian Arts Council and as a judge for the North American Indian Art for the AIAC in Dallas. From the ordinary to the extraordinary, Castle Gap is your conduit to Indian jewelry, and, now, they've expanded to showcase silver jewelry worldwide via their website. Hop into their Plano location at the northeast corner of Preston and Park, next to Boston Market and in Fort Worth, 6224 Camp Bowie Blvd., 817/989-1677. And if it's beads you're after, bead it to one of their locations. Choose from over 400 sterling charms alone! Inventory includes bracelets, necklaces, rings, earrings, pendants, pins, as well as buckles, bolos and belts — with bragging rights to their "reasonable prices." An 18-inch turquoise and apple coral necklace was corralled for a measly $35, but most items escalated from there. At least you don't have to make a "reservation" to shop their finds. But now that I've found Nadine's at Vikon Village in Garland, I've moved Nadine's to the 100 BEST as I liked her jewelry prices better. But it was a close call. *Call toll-free: 800/880-7407*

★★★★   Charles Cohen Manufacturing Jewelers   817/292-4367

4747 S. Hulen St., Suite 107   Tues-Sat 10-6
Fort Worth, TX 76132

With a name like Cohen, of course, they know how to sell it to you wholesale. Since 1947, Charles Cohen Jewelers has provided a personal touch to generations of shoppers. This family-owned jewelry store offers jewelry repair to appraisals, and custom design help in picking out the perfect stone or setting. It's like having a gemstone in the family tree. Value pricing on diamonds, colored gemstones and gold jewelry are how they've managed to stay around for more than 50 years. Want to trade up to a larger diamond? Fine, that's their secret trade-in policy: if you buy the diamond from them, you'll receive the full current price back. Bigger is better, you know that. In addition to their raw gemstones (inlaid malachite, lapis, precious opals, black onyx and more), they have a staff of graduate gemologists (GIA) ready and able to help you with their two-year, no-interest layaway plan. They sell gold wholesale by weight. Specials are active throughout the year on gold and diamonds. Set your dial to a discounted ROLEX or the newest addition, the ROVEN DINO watch with a five-year warranty (comparable to TAG HEUER) and still their favorite watch. Located between Pearle Vision and Bank of America across from Hulen Mall in a small office complex at the back. It's worth the treasure hunt.

★★★★★★   Choice (Jewelry & Accessories)   972/818-3133

17194 Preston Road, Suite 120   Mon-Fri 10-7; Sat 10-6; Sun 12-4
Dallas, TX 75248

Located at the northeast corner of Preston and Campbell (in the Kroger Shopping Center), it's your choice but given your choice, would you opt for the real designer purse or the "knock-off?" Let's call them like we see them. Some of these purses look so real, you'd think they were. But when you see the prices, you'll know they're not. Is it real or is it Memorex? Only your hairdresser should tell you. Right? What is, is what is. You pay for what you get and these look-alikes do look the part. If you never want to leave home without your COACH, DOONEY & BOURKE, FENDI, KATE SPADE, LOUIS VUITTON, PRADA — and many more, here's where to bag a bargain. They even have some of the real McCoys at fabulous prices as well. But what makes them stand apart from the crowded jewelry and handbag category is their one-of-a-kind creations, their boutique atmosphere and the service of the owners. Faux-give me. I can't resist sharing this north Dallas's best-kept secret. This is the only discount boutique of it's kind where you'll see knock-out handbags and jewelry with a top-notch hair dresser (Jose Eber's former partner) in the back doing hair cuts and color. What a combination. I live and I love making Choices!

★★★   Claire's Boutique   972/524-6442

I-20, Exit 501   Mon-Sat 10-9; Sun 11-6
Terrell, TX 75100
www.claires.com

Dare your little girl not to drag you to Claire's! Catering to the young and restless, regardless of her age, Claire's wants her! Play dress up at this Tanger Factory Outlet location in everything from rhinestone earrings to tiaras, friendship bracelets to fuzzy-top pencils; it's glow and go for all the girls. You go, girl. To the prom! They've got you covered from glitter glow to sparkles for your hair. Perfect little purses to handle only those little things, or back packs to carry your change of clothes and makeup must-haves. Add in your key chains, cartoon character diaries and their "buy one, get another for FREE" whatevers, this is a must stop on the 99¢ trail. Or buy a certain dollar amount and get something else for 99 cents. Prices ranged from cheap on jewelry to I-can-get-that-cheaper-somewhere-else, especially on accessories and other little goodies. But if you watch the shoppers in action, you'll notice how they grab and go, regardless of their allowance. Fun, fun and more fun, but watch those mini-mavens lest they go crazy with their babysitting money. Piercing of ears is free — which is why they can claim over 50 million ears pierced! If you buy their starter kit that includes studs and antiseptic ($16-$40), you must show proof of age as you have to be over 18 to get stabbed. With thousands and another thousand of locations in malls everywhere, surely there's one near you.

★★★★   D-Wholesale Exchange   972/386-9088

5000 Belt Line, #250
Dallas, TX 75254

Buying or selling, the Axels don't have an axe to grind. The only thing they do grind, however, is diamonds, as they are experienced diamond cutters and jewelry manufacturers selling loose diamonds, mounted jewelry, estate jewelry and pre-owned **PATEK** or **ROLEX** watches at a price that is hard to resist. Check them out if you want a relative in the business to get it for you wholesale. Well, if not related, let's just say you're friends.

★★★★★★   Dallas Gold & Silver Exchange   972/484-3662

2817 Forest Lane   Mon-Fri 10-6; Sat 10-4
Dallas, TX 75234
www.dgse.com

 Crack open this oyster and you'll find more than a grain of sand inside. Billy Oyster's the pearl in charge at DGSE and when Mother Nature wants to transform something from the earth into a gem, they know where to recommend you buy the completed reincarnation. From a lump of coal into a diamond, or lava into tanzanite, well, just step back and watch how nature works it magic with gemstones here. Dallas Gold & Silver Exchange is one of the few public jewelry companies in the Metroplex with a single location that has its own stock exchange symbol (DGSE). Find the best prices on pre-owned **ROLEX** watches that come with a two-year warranty and a price tag that's substantially less than new. Considered a category killer without a million-dollar ad campaign, they're one of the power players who can deliver great prices on diamonds, estate jewelry, watches, pearls, gold jewelry, and one of the largest selections of wedding bands in the city. They also buy your old rings and things. When it came time to impress my son's Russian father-in-law for his 50th birthday, this Rolex/Mercedes-only man would of course only wear a Rolex. Josh bought him one for $2,000 with the black face and diamonds. Can you believe it? Did he love it? Does he now think my son's the best? Thanks to Dallas Gold & Silver Exchange. Go online to their different jewelry shopping sites such as www.FirstJewelryExchange.com, www.USBullionExchange.com, www.SilvermanLiquidations.com and others. Their other location's in Charleston hence the name Charleston Gold & Silver Exchange, 900 Pine Hollow Rd. in Mt. Pleasant, SC. Online, when I last checked the webcam showing their Dallas store, I saw that there was NO jewelry and NO people inside. Then I realized the date — July 5 and it was a holiday. That's why 'cause the store's filled to the brim with jewelry and they are usually packed — any day of the week. They do have to be open, though. Shopping online or via their auctions is fun and lucrative. From **ANNE KLEIN** watches brand new for $15 up to....well, hundreds of thousands. From estate jewelry, coins, bullion, it's one of the premier and trusted jewelry companies in the country, in Dallas and online. And now that DGSE bought Silverman's jewelry consulting company, they'll continue to help the thousands of retailers throughout the U.S., Canada and the Caribbean Islands by conducting professionally run retirement, liquidation and promotional sales. *Call toll-free: 800/527-5307*

★★★★   Dallas Watch & Jewelry Co.   972/484-6700

12801 Midway Rd., Suite 505   Mon-Fri 10-6; Sat 10-3
Dallas, TX 75244
www.dallaswatch.com

One of the largest retailers of reconditioned **ROLEX** watches, it should come as no surprise that they've been around for 30 years, from the days of my first book in 1972. Twenty years later, they merged with Promenade Gold and Silver, and now they're even a member of NAWCC. (Aren't you impressed, whatever that stands for?) Watch out, they carry **BREITLING**, **OMEGA** and **ROLEX** to name-drop a few star-watchers, but these are nothing without the addition of a custom-diamond-emerald bezel around that dial. Custom bezels add a very special touch with oyster- or emerald-colored faces. Shop online for it for $1,095, instead of $1,800. They will install any new bezel that you buy, at no additional charge. A bezel is that gold and jeweled ring-around-the-watch face. And watch out, you will! A diamond and sapphire bezel that retailed for $2,650 was $1,100. They specialize in reconditioned Swiss watches, so any kind should do. If your taste turns to tennis and you want to ace a large tennis bracelet, then wrap up a dozy; a 10.42 kt diamond tennis bracelet that retailed for $8,995 was $7,800. Yes, it's more than a tennis membership to Brookhaven Country Club, but, then again, you can't wear a country club! And if you want to assert your manhood and shower her with a trillion engagement ring, this rock was a whopping 3.25 carats for only $3,500. Now she, too, can own a piece of the rock. *Call toll-free: 800/345-0428*

★★★★★   Designs by Flora   214/747-3510

2050 N. Stemmons Freeway, Suite #7519   By Appt. Only
Dallas, TX 75207
www.designsbyflora.com

For more than three decades, Flora has been designing and creating fine jewelry in platinum, 14K, 18K, yellow and white gold. It's in her blood. It's in her genes. She can get it for you wholesale. Now in it's second generation, her professional staff (her sons Michael and Greg now own the business) are well versed in the subjects of gemology, appraisals and custom designs. Offering G.I.A. and E.G.L certified loose diamonds (the best way to buy diamonds is out of the setting where flaws can easily be hidden) and colored gemstones from around the world. (My personal favorites, love those colors!) When it comes to buying that engagement ring, wedding band sets, anniversary bands, anything that relates to that special day when love is all around, Designs by Flora should be there for any special occasion. They carry fine gold designer jewelry as well as sterling silver and the combination of both. Besides, they even can help you obtain personal jewelry insurance to protect your treasures. Customers are offered annual appraisal updates, inspection and cleaning at no additional charge. How's that for a gem-uine service. And if you want your item shipped, they ship UPS insured with signature required as well as Registered Mail. All of their work is guaranteed for quality and workmanship. Now you can say you've got a friend in the business. Meet Flora and the boys...., you're new best friend but you MUST have an appointment or you can't get in. *Call toll-free: 800/553-9357*

★★★★   Diamond Cutters   972/386-9088

14811 Inwood Rd.   Mon-Fri 9-6; Sat 9-4; Sun By Appt.
Addison, TX 75001

The name is so long, it ran off the line but Diamond Cutters Jewelry Mfg. Wholesale Exchange is its complete and official title in its entirety. The Father of the business was celebrating his 82nd birthday when we stopped by so it doesn't look like he's showing any signs of retiring. We talked to the son who is willing to work seven days a week to fill in the gaps when Dad is wanting to take a day off. Diamond Cutters have been around a long time. As a matter of fact, since 1921 they have been laying out the velvet carpet showing you loose diamonds, mounted jewelry with diamonds, watches with diamonds and estate jewelry with diamonds. If diamonds are not your best friend, you might shop elsewhere. If you prefer a pre-owned **ROLEX**, a work of art, an elaborate silver tea service, they take in those for cash and resell them for cash. Located between Spring Valley and Belt Line on Inwood. Like a high-class pawn shop (very high) and a wholesaler-to-the-public, a most intriguing source for all things bright and beautiful.

★★★★★★   Diamontrigue   972/934-1530

5100 Belt Line Rd. #808   Mon-Sat 10-5:30
Village on the Parkway Dallas, TX 75254

 Located at the Village on the Parkway, behind Bed, Bath & Beyond, look for the first fountain, park your car in between the Rolls and the Mercedes, and you have arrived. Since they grow their own stones in a lab, these man-made diamonds look every bit like the real thing. Though they are fake, experienced jewelers have trouble detecting them from the real. The rocks are cut and set in 14kt, 18kt or white gold, as well as platinum. If you keep your mouth shut, nobody can tell the difference. Just get used to brushing your diamonds daily with a toothbrush and jewelry cleaner. All stones come with a lifetime guarantee that they will not turn cloudy. Since Bob bought my engagement ring at Diamontrigue, I can tell you first hand that I wear it on the fourth finger of my left hand and everybody gawks! Since 1978, Judy Mason and her band of merry mavericks treat you with kid gloves. The showroom is elegant, the service sublime. With over 500 rings in stock, as well as accompanying bracelets, earrings, anklets, pendants, neck pieces and other gems of any color, they only *look* expensive. Then celebrate with a FREE Happy Hour buffet across the way at Blue Mesa. Now you can really impress your wife or girlfriend. Ask her to marry you with a Diamontique ring at the bottom of a frozen Margarita. Well, then again, it may be better served where the chances of her drinking it isn't possible.

★★★★★   Dixie's Fashion Accessories Outlet   817/649-1112

2500 E. Randol Mill Rd., #113   Mon-Fri 9-6; Sat 10-5
Arlington, TX 76011
www.dixiesoutlet.com

You'll whistle Dixie when you cross over to this side of the Mason-Dixie line. It seems like only yesterday when we uncovered this little gem, but it was really nine years ago that we discovered this Dixie was a real Pixie. Dixie will make you feel like one of the family. And so does her entire family and crew. It's such a happy place to buy jewelry, handbags, gift items, candy, soaps, bath products, candles, garden decor accessories, totes, well you never know what lies in-store. From her wholesale business that originally kept her and her husband Roy on the road, she decided to open a little retail shop in order to stay closer to home to sell her fashion jewelry lines at wholesale prices. And now, look at her now. She's even got an online store that you can order from without looking for a parking place. *Call toll-free: 800/535-6825*

★★★★ Euless Gold & Silver   817/540-5242

1201 W. Airport Frwy., Suite 305   Mon-Sat 9:30-5:30
Euless, TX 76040

Here's another Gold & Silver, but no relation to Dallas's premier Gold & Silver. Nevertheless, you can save here and that's what turns us on our heels. Oh, how we danced on the night we were wed. Remember that song? Doesn't matter, as long as you remember your anniversary! Turn around and head to Euless, for those little nothings that cost less in Euless. Or, maybe buy an anniversary band that has been worn before to celebrate your own wedding, one that didn't last throughout the night. Who cares? If it's beautiful and you like it, that's all that counts. Look for ARTCARVED wedding and anniversary rings that are brand new at substantial discounts, too. Diamonds are sold at 20 percent over cost, giving both the buyer and the seller a fair and square deal. They are here to serve you at the intersection of Airport Freeway and F.M. 157 (near BURLINGTON COAT FACTORY).

★★★★★ Fossil Company Store   254/582-7785

104 NE I-35, Exit 368   Mon-Sat 10-8; Sun 11-6
Prime Outlets of Hillsboro Hillsboro, TX 76645
www.fossil.com

Dig up a good deal at the only Fossil Outlet around. This hometown favorite with customers and Wall Street has their only company store in Hillsboro, so if you want it, you'll hit the road, Jack. To be cool, you've got to buy the HARRY POTTER limited-edition watch starting at $90. All FOSSIL collectible watches come with special packaging. Fossil started in 1984 with just watches, but has now expanded to over 300 different styles. Plan to save 30 to 40 percent. Fossil also licenses other items such as purses, leather belts and wallets for men and women, jewelry and more. They have online shopping for everything except listing their other outlet locations. For that, go to www.outletbound.com. Receive second-day air shipping free.

◆◆◆◆◆◆ Friendze   817/514-7700

654 Grapevine Hwy.   Mon-Sat 10-6
Hurst, TX 76054
www.friendze.com

Located in the Mayfair Shopping Center, two doors down from Tom Thumb, their motto is pure and simple: "LOOK like a million without spending a fortune!" This place is for the bead junkie but withdrawal pain is not covered in their prescription for doing it your way. There are a few pre-made pieces, but this is mostly a create-your-own jewelry store with all the supplies you'll need to start and finish. Beads, crystals, trinkets, you name it, they've got it. They give you a supply list for a specific readymade jewelry project or you can design you own. Check online for workshops and discussion groups, if you want an entire wardrobe of jewelry for yourself and your home. *Call toll-free: 888/591-4394*

★★★★★   **Grissom's Fine Jewelry**   **817/244-9754**

9524 Spur 580   Tues-Fri 10:30-5:30; Sat.10:30-5
Fort Worth, TX 76116

Tarrant County's golden goose is Grissom's Fine Jewelry. If only you can find them. Just half a mile off Loop 820, you'd think it would be a cinch as they've been in the same location for 35 years. Try them on yourself. You know the old saying, "If the shoe fits," well, same goes with the ring. The traditions that have been handed down to the next generation of family jewelers make them proud to be the manufacturer of much of their wares. Now twice the size from their humble beginning, once you've entered through their custom doors, you will take a seat and be waited on hand to neck. Their inventory runs the full spectrum from loose diamonds to custom designs. In fact, Grissom's certifies more diamonds than any single outlet operation in Tarrant County. All diamonds are independently graded (certified) which helps when comparative pricing. Choose custom designs in platinum, gold and silver. These are the good guys with jewelry and watch repair on-site. *Call toll-free: 800/362-6645*

★★★   **International Gems**   **214/521-1555**

3811 Turtle Creek   Mon-Fri 8-6 (Closed for lunch)
Dallas, TX 75219

Well, Henry Kostman is on the move again. Now under a different name (A Fine Jewelry Salon was the old name), he is still considered one of Dallas' premier "private" jewelers. I just wish he wouldn't stay so private. One can get lost while he's protecting his privacy, so how can you shop when you can't find him? Anyway, he does have some beautiful bijoux (that's jewelry, 22 kt hand-crafted, freeform designs) as well as platinum accents in many designs. Too, he's a provider of world-renowned fine watches and exquisite diamonds, gemstones and pearls. Bring in your design or bring in a picture of your "gotta have," and they will make it from scratch. Just don't expect to save a bundle of scratch. Ah, what price jewelry? *Call toll-free: 800/380-0522*

★★★★★★   **J's World Trading, Inc.**   **972/243-4707**

11422 Harry Hines, #106-#107   Mon-Sat 9-6:30
Dallas, TX 75229
www.jsworldtrading.com

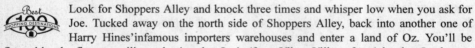

Look for Shoppers Alley and knock three times and whisper low when you ask for Joe. Tucked away on the north side of Shoppers Alley, back into another one of Harry Hines' infamous importers warehouses and enter a land of Oz. You'll be floored by the floor to ceiling selection that Jay's (from Vikon Village fame) brother Joe has on display. Pick a packet or two just waiting to adorn those fingers, necks, ears, wrists, toes, ankles and hair. June will take you by the hand and point you in the right direction as you could get lost in costume jewelry overload. It is a condition that many women suffer from. Its remedy is to buy a few pairs of earrings, for example, and drop them in one of those carrying baskets. Up one aisle and down another, it's wall to wall stuff to buy, from jewelry sets to jeweled boxes, rings to things, scarves to sundries, it's a general store with something for everyone. Looking to bring something home from Texas? Then the rhinestone Dallas pins are a must. Too, the DIVA pins were hard to resist and the initial key rings were snapped up for under $5 — so that should give everybody something of their own that personalized. J's has you covered in both fine jewelry and fashion jewelry. Either way, put on the Ritz with lots of glitz. From 10K, 14K, diamonds to costume jewelry, handbags, sterling silver, earrings, necklaces, rings and things, since 1988, this place has created its own legend in its own time across from the old Sam Moon on Harry Hines. Probably running a close second to Sam Moon, there's certainly enough inventory to keep you shopping for hours. And being in second place always makes you work harder. Why not jump in with both feet without getting soaked? At the intersection of Harry Hines and **ROYAL** lane, look for the sign that says "Shoppers Alley," across the street from the old Sam Moon's.

★★★★ Jewelry By Floyd   214/821-9155
3300 Swiss Circle   Mon-Sat 9:30-5:30
Dallas, TX 75204

Meet Floyd Bickel by heading toward Baylor Hospital, on the corner of Hall and Swiss Circle, and near Floyd Street. Look for the white building with black trim and tell him the Diva sent you. He's a one-man show and it's now showtime. Floyd is like Lloyd's of London in one respect. He insures that he sells the best for less. He has new jewelry but in today's economic climate, there's a lot of buying and selling of estate jewelry going on. Pre-owned jewelry can be liquidated and converted to cash, fast. And Floyd is a buyer. Estate jewelry, closeouts and pre-owned watches fly in and out of his store, so check often. He does his own casting and does beautiful work. An old-fashioned artisan with old-fashioned values make a perfect match.

★★★★★ Jewelry Connection   972/247-1477
11427 Harry Hines Blvd.   Mon-Sat 9:30-6
Dallas, TX 75229
www.jewelryconnectioninc.com

Though strictly wholesale to retail stores, they still welcome you through the door, but please be discreet while you're there. There are retailers shopping and they don't like to offend their bread and butter traffic. So while you're inside, keep your mouth shut! Did you hear me? Zip it up! Say nothing. Get whatever you want at true wholesale prices and go home (laughing all the way to the bank.) At the Jewelry Connection, you'll connect to fashionable costume jewelry, great-looking handbags, totes, clutches, rings and things. One of the absolute best selection of scrunchy bracelets and matching jewelry sets in the Metroplex and at the best prices in town. And now, online, if you're a store or have a tax ID#, you can shop from home. *Call toll-free: 800/878-1493*

★★★★★ Jewelry Exchange, The   972/404-9400
15721 Coit Rd., #100   Mon-Sat 10-6; Thurs 10-8
Dallas, TX 75248
www.jewelryexchange.com

Though they've moved off Central Expressway to Coit Road, they're still technically (I think) in Richardson though their address is Dallas. You've never heard of them? Do you watch television? These guys flood the airwaves with millions of dollars of TV advertising. With so much jewelry at such good prices, who'd want to make an exchange? They brag about cutting out the middleman, and they do. They manufacture, design, market and staff-develop everything in-house. About 90 percent of their inventory is manufactured at their state-of-the-art factory. And the reason they can keep prices lower is because they import diamonds by the cartons, the cheapest and most direct way of acquiring diamonds. They have loose stones, semi-mounts, earrings, pendants, gemstones, pearls, men's jewelry and custom designs. Other jewelers claim their diamonds are not the very best grade but do you really care or know the difference? Online, I saw everything from a $35 pair of gold earrings to a $26,000 diamond necklace. Of course it was 15 carats but no grading was revealed so it's difficult to compare to another's diamond price. They import much of their diamonds directly from Israel and India and they range dramatically from a one-carat pair of stud earrings for $399 to a one-carat diamond solitaire stone from as low as $599 but usually much higher. *Call toll-free: 800/441-0715*

★★★★   Jewelry Factory, The   817/633-3333

2800 Forestwood Drive, Suite 114   Mon-Fri 10-6; Sat 10-5
Arlington, TX 76006

If your watch has lost its band width or your dial has died, you might rush your instrument to The Jewelry Factory for an emergency fix. Watches that are in need of repair can be made whole in no time. But The Jewelry Factory does more than watch repair; they are also home to custom-made jewelry and fine stainless steel watches at 25 percent off. Try on a CITIZEN watch or one that is called a BELAIRE that they consider one of the finest. BELAIRE watches, they claim, are the best timepiece for the money. Made in America for more than 50 years, all with Swiss movements (the same as found in OMEGA, TAG HAUER, GUCCI), they start at $50, but for around $200 (rather than $2,000), you can have yourself an exceptional timepiece. They stay on their toes by shopping the competition and pride themselves on keeping abreast of the latest jewelry trends. But their strength still lies in repairs. This husband-and-wife team can save you up to 66 percent on repairs. Located one block west of 360 off NE Green Oaks Boulevard in northeast Arlington, take a peek at them in action. Manufacturing, importing, wholesaling and designing in 10-, 14-, 18- and 24-carat gold. They could be your link you your unchained melody: chains, earrings, pendants, bracelets, rings, watches, silver and platinum jewelry. Pay the same price for quality stones that retail stores do and laugh all the way home. All services are performed on site — in most cases, while you wait! Layaway, available, for those who have to wait.

★★★★   Jewelry Gallery, The   214/369-5361

5924 Royal Lane, Suite 170   Mon-Fri 10-5
Dallas, TX 75230

Did your dearly departed mother leave you her cache of crown jewels? Want to turn them into cash? Then, consigning her jewelry here makes perfectly good sense. Tucked away in an office building that is kind of tricky to find, consignment jewelry is priced at half of retail. Letting the folks at The Jewelry Gallery sell it entitles them to receive a 17 percent commission (2 percent goes for insurance). You'll be dazzled with estate rings, necklaces, earrings and bracelets, but don't expect to get away cheap. A pair of dangling tanzanite and diamond earrings was $2,895, and an accompanying floral ring of tanzanite and diamonds in 14 kt was $1,600. Wait for sales when prices are reduced even more. Margaret Gronberg, ISA, GG owner and certified jewelry appraiser gathers her lode through estate sales, bank-ordered liquidations and closeouts from other retail stores and they're priced at least half off or more. At the southwest corner of Preston Royal, this is quite the jewel. Too bad they don't have a website in this day and age. It should would entice shoppers to come in to buy.

★★★★★★   King Arthur Clock and Jewelry   972/423-2205

1201 N. Central Expwy., #3   Mon.-Wed & Fri 10-6; Thurs 10-7; Sat 10-5
Plano, TX 75075
www.kingarthurclock.com

King Arthur Clock and Jewelry has been holding court for more than 18 years. As one of the premier retailers of grandfather clocks, cuckoo clocks, curio cabinets, mantle clocks, wall clocks on one side, and the other side is jewelry, this combination of odd bedfellows works to save you time and money. Their incredible selection and low prices have held firm in spite of the rise and fall in the economy. Grandfather clocks started at $999 and up. HOWARD MILLER and SLIGH are two popular manufacturers who meet King Arthur's qualifications, and they rest easy next to all sorts of clocks including wall, table and novelty models, tick tock. Shopping online makes it easier than ever. Visit the shop located behind the

Fina station at the southwest corner between Office Max and Einstein Bros. Bagels. Then check into their certified watch makers (horologist) and gemologists who also design jewelry right there on their laptops. From jewelry appraisals, jewelry repair and restoration, custom jewelry, there isn't much that they don't do in the way of jewelry. Just to have four gemologists on their staff is worthy of note. *Call toll-free: 877/883-8300*

Luanna's   972/218-9114

137 Historic Town Square   Tues-Sat 10:30-5:30
Lancaster, TX 75146

 Don't expect Luanna to answer, or even an answering machine, on Sunday or Monday. They are not available to speak, period. But when Tuesday morning rolls around, the place is hoppin'. Luanna's carries mostly ladies'clothing from size 2 to 22, but also fashion accessories like belts and purses. But women do not live in clothes alone. What about candles, bath products, floral arrangements and jewelry. Okay, so a sucker is born every day. I am a sucker for custom jewelry which is designed and made by a stay-at-home Mom from Coppell utilizing natural stones, crystals, mother of pearl and other of nature's offerings. The line includes earrings, bracelets and necklaces and is priced from $48-$95. If shopping makes you hungry, enjoy a relaxing respite next door at the Tea Room. A pot of tea and now you can sip and shop.

★★★★★★ Manufacturer's Expo   469/429-6000

Ave. K & Spring Creek   Mon-Fri 10-9; Sat 10-6; Sun 11-6
Plano, TX
www.manufacturersexpo.com

 It's all about you and they call it ME — Manufacturer's Expo. You start at this 15,000 square foot emporium where this importer has brought together fine jewelry, designer watches, leather apparel for the entire family, handbags, bed and bath domestics, giftware and put it all together under one big discount emporium. They even offer the services of three gemologists so if you want a piece appraised, bring it on in. One of their proudest moments is when they discovered that by heating the diamond with radiation, they could create a teal-colored diamond. Talk about something that they can brag about. It's something to write home about. Flash for less cash is the Diva's mantra, you know. What doesn't sell at these low prices are further reduced and shipped to their outlet store called Extempo at 2200 Vantage St., 214/267-1318, open Wed-Sat 10-6 and Sun 12-5. With the three big categories, you should be able to dress you or your home for less. And for jewelry, they are a cut above! They call it "the Jewelry, Leather & Gift Superstore" and it's a start. You have to experience the store to know you're in good company. Website is simply informational — one page and a map to get you there. *Call toll-free: 877/8-LEATHE*

★★★★★★ Manufacturer's Expo   469/429-6000

Ave. K & Spring Creek   Mon-Fri 10-9; Sat 10-6; Sun 11-6
Plano, TX
www.manufacturersexpo.com

 It's all about you and they call it ME — Manufacturer's Expo. You start at this 15,000 square foot emporium where this importer has brought together fine jewelry, designer watches, leather apparel for the entire family, handbags, bed and bath domestics, giftware and put it all together under one big discount emporium. They even offer the services of three gemologists so if you want a piece appraised, bring it on in. What doesn't sell at these low prices are further reduced and shipped to their outlet store called Extempo at 2200 Vantage St., 214/267-1318, open Wed-Sat 10-6 and Sun 12-5. *Call toll-free: 877/8-LEATHE*

★★★   Nature's Gallery   972/446-1994

1106 South Elm St.   Tues-Sat 10-5:30
Carrollton, TX 75006

You can't fool Mother Nature or anybody else that is made and nurtured from the stones, minerals and gems molded here. West of the gazebo in old town Carrollton, Nature's Gallery is where Donald molds nature's wonders into art. See them glisten and glimmer as they are transformed into beautiful jewelry that bedecks the finest necks in town. Add a few ear pieces and encircle a matching bracelet, and, hands down, you've got a down-to-earth work of art. Quality, price and the variety of minerals, gems, custom lapidary items, gifts and carvings are unearthed by this guy who doesn't mind getting down and dirty. He happens to be a geologist and chemist turned artisan who was forced into an early retirement from the oil industry and has parlayed his passion for minerals and stones into a business. We dig this classic entrepreneur who's worth applauding.

★★★   Oscar Utay Jewelry   214/363-6591

8300 Douglas Ave., Suite 725   Mon-Fri 9-4:30; Sat. By Appt. Only
Dallas, TX 75225
www.utay.com

Like father, like son. In the '30s, Oscar Utay began as a watchmaker in downtown Dallas. He moved to the Preston Center location in 1981 and continued to work every day until his death at the age of 85. Dedication was his middle name. Like the song in *Fiddler on the Roof*, "Tradition!" brought his son Eddie Utay into the business when his father passed away. He continues as his father before him with a jewelry business off the beaten path selling quality jewelry below retail prices. In fact, he works with each customer personally, with more than half of his sales being custom-made. Diamonds are hand-picked per design, as are other gemstones, to ensure the best quality and pricing. He's so sure of his pricing that if you show him a comparable deal that he can't beat, he'll tell you to buy it even if it's elsewhere. He'll gladly bring out all the jewelry left in the vault that his father hoarded from the early '30s and '40s and let you see what real "estate jewelry" is all about. (No, not real estate!) Talk about a pack rat. A two-tone 14 kt **ROLEX** that retailed back then for $5,300, Eddie sold for $1,600. What a steal! But it wasn't to me, so that's no deal.

★★★★   Palazzo Diamond Importer   972/239-3131

4532 Belt Line Rd.   Mon-Sat 10-6; Thurs 10-8
Addison, TX 75244

A short throw from the Tollway, shoppers at either end can exit for custom designs and imported diamonds at prices in cruise control. In Dallas for almost 20 years, they provide an on-site resident **GIA** gemologist, custom jewelry designs and watch repairs on the premises, and certified loose diamonds every day except Sundays. Specializing in large diamonds, maybe Mark Cuban bought his bride a really big basketball size one here! Find something special for the special lady you're courting. You don't want to appear cheap or a skinflint, do you? Prices from $2,820 to $37,000 were advertised specials, including the three-carat marquise that my fingers'beckoned, "Here ye, Here ye!" All hands on deck. A big ring happens to be one of those coveted items necessary to wear when you walk down the Promenade Deck on the cruise we're taking to Costa Rica. For a mere $20,000, wouldn't it be grand if my wallet were as big as my wants? They also carry the **SWISS ARMY** knives, **BERTOLUCCI** watches, a favorite of Josh's, and another that started with an E — made by **MOVADO**. Well, that could mean the Eliro, Elliptica, Esperanza or Estimo —

and now I don't remember which one he was referring to. But I do remember not to type in www.palazzo.com by mistake as it will take you to a marketing company by the same name. No website. Boo Hoo! That's not keeping up with the times.

★★★ Parkhill's   817/921-4891

2751 Park Hill Drive   Mon-Sat 10-5
Fort Worth, TX 76109
www.barse.com

It may not be Park Avenue, but Parkhill's has all the rudiments of success. Just like the high-priced boutiques in New York City, but without the high price tags, look for this little white house near TCU without all the presidential trappings. The building alone is worth a trip. Lower prices on silver jewelry because they are the manufacturers. They own a factory in Bangkok, and, although, you may not be as familiar with their line called **BARSE**, it is very similar to **BRIGHTON**, **MARY LOUISE**, **MEDALIAS** (see write-up under Jewelry) and **ROBERT CHIARELL**, which they also sell. **BARSE** specializes in sterling silver jewelry combined with semi-precious stones and it's styles are trendy but quality at very moderate prices. Expect at least 30 percent off their own line. Silver chains, bracelets, rings, toe rings, anklets, earrings, keychains — if it dangles in silver, no doubt they've got it! Where else can you expect to buy a money clip? Not every store has them in their inventory but at **PARKHILL**, just park your car — not high on a hill — and shop for everyone on your gift list. Don't overlook the very popular crystal jewelry that is in such demand today, as well as some fab night lights, candle sticks, and other giftie-type items should you need an occasion to buy. Then, call it a wrap and away it goes. Lots of inspirational items with delicate crosses embedded with turquoise and other precious stones. BARSE & COMPANY is down the street from Er'go Candles at 7800 John Carpenter Freeway, Dallas, TX 75247, 214/631 0925; FAX 214/631-1001. But so far, I haven't heard if they have an outlet there. If they don't, they should.

★★★★★★ Sam Moon Trading   972/484-3083

11826 Harry Hines Blvd.   Mon-Sat 9-6:30
Dallas, TX 75234
www.sammoon.com

 Uncle Sam wants you! Enlist his help if you want the premier source for gifts, handbags, luggage and jewelry on the street of dreams, Harry Hines. In fact, when he opened his grand slam new centers (at the intersection of 635 and Harry Hines and in **FRISCO**, at Hwy. 121 and Preston Road), he will be justifiably one of the major independent retailers in this city that can move mountains as well as locations. This 125,000 square feet shopping center across the 635 freeway from his old Harry Hines location on the south side of Harry Hines was the second move in less than a year, or so it seems. He moved to bigger digs down the street first and then outgrew that location in months; so he had to move again. And this time, he even has room to house a third Sam Moon store, this time centered around Home Decor. His new Frisco store at Highway 121 and Preston Road is also up and flourishing. Is there no stopping this bull-dozer of bargains? And to set the record straight, Sam Moon is very much alive and well, nor was he a party to the counterfeit bust that was done a while back on Harry Hines. He is the grand-daddy and a legend in his own time. His sons Sam and Daniel are carrying on the tradition and expanding now to epic proportions. The only thing Sam Moon doesn't import is Moon drops, but watch for those soon. Everything else is fair game. The lines are formidable, the traffic logjam something you don't see often in this city, but ask any woman where she heads to buy her jewelry, handbags, scarves, luggage, small leather accessories, hair accessories, totes, small electronics and gift items, and if she is a "wholesale"-type of gal, she'll say Sam Moon. Sam Moon's. Sam Moon Center....or some variation of the above. Oh, did I forget to mention it's THE source for brief cases and attachÈs, picture frames, toys, backpacks, hair pieces and perfume and now lamps, mirrors, furniture and home dec items. Just one small step for womankind! After all, this is **TEXAS** and Sam Moon has landed! In Frisco, at 121 and Preston Rd, 2449 Preston Rd., 214/297-4200. Always shop the original — imitators are flattering, but never the same as the real thing.

★★★★ Sentimental Jewelry 972/271-3420

2918 S. Jupiter, Suite D
Garland, TX 75041

Tues-Sun 10-7

Wanna take a "Sentimental Journey?" That's easy. Just head to this jewelry store that has been in the same place for decades. The second generation of family is now residing alongside the founding mother of invention, Dorothy Norris and believe it or not, she's a horologist, something she's proud to boast. Who would have thunk that outside the perimeters of Vikon Village, this fine jewelry store would reside but indeed, there it is with both sterling, fashion and fine jewelry in 10Kt, 14Kt gold plus diamonds, watches, what you see is almost what you get (though special orders are not out of the question.) From time pieces to custom work, a deal's a deal when it comes to creating something that in time would have sentimental value. Here is a good place to start with prices reflective of the good ole days and service equally nostalgic.

★★★ Silver Vault 214/357-7115

5655 W. Lovers Lane
Dallas, TX 75209

Mon-Sat 10-5:30

Taking a flying leap over to this vault and see silver, "Hi, Low Silver." Expect savings of 25 to 50 percent, yet they deny being a discounter. I guess they feel it would look bad to acknowledge that even Highland Parkers appreciate a good deal. Merchandise changes routinely, but not the categories. Expect to find the largest selection of unique silver gifts, collectibles, silver jewelry, silver photo frames, baby gifts, cigar smoker accessories, barware, decanters and other wine items, as well as antique and estate silver at this shop just west of the Tollway. Custom engraving services and gift-wrapping are also available. They'd get a higher rating is they'd acknowledge that they are proud of their discount prices.

★★★★★★ Solitaires 469/241-0590

7140 Bishop Rd.
Plano, TX 75023

Mon-Fri 10:45-5:30; Sat 10:45-4

 At last, bigger is now better. Making his moves in the Metroplex, Winston Davis moved out of his yucky Plano location to uptown, upscale Legacy. He still sells good like a 5-star (now 6) jeweler should. One visit to his shop will confirm his lone star proof. He's a long-time winner in our book, and the jeweler who took an onyx and pearl Buddha pin that was a treasure my mom brought back to me from Hong Kong, but transformed it into a ring. Yes, THAT ring — the one that wherever I am, in the elevator, the ladies'restroom, at a restaurant, in the courthouse, someone asks, "Where did you get that ring?" It's THAT ring that has made Winston Davis a star in my jewelry box. After 30 years in the business, he does have a few connections to get it for your wholesale. That means, up to 50 percent off at his jewelry salon, across from the Angelica Theatre. After 30 years, he is your solitary connection to getting it wholesale in the northern corridor of Plano/Frisco. He has a full-time watch and jewelry repair artisan on staff alongside his designers, including himself and a gal who has been by his side for years, starting as a former customer and now, his front showroom aide de campe.

★★★★ Travel Jewelry   214/369-4722

6123 Berkshire Lane   Mon-Sat 10-5
Dallas, TX 75230
www.traveljewelry.com

Don't travel with an armload of jewels that would give anybody a reason to stop and shop (without your permission, that is.) Simulate those diamonds and other precious stones with a Cubic Zirconia and leave the real jewels at home in the safe. Wouldn't you rather be safe than sorry? Don't travel and tempt the crooks. From costume and CZs, to custom and estate jewelry, this place is a virtual trip in itself. Wander through cases of 14kt, 18kt and platinum — all glimmering like the sun setting on a beach horizon. Ask for Larry Albeita and he will create anything your imagination can conjure. Into charm bracelets? (Which by the way is all the rage.) Then you must shop here for a vast selection to charm you. Their selection of diamond loops is always expanding. You can select from a rainbow of diamond, pearl and semi-precious stone dangles in various shapes and colors. Have jewelry you wish to sell? Consign it here and let them do all the work! Ever think of name bracelets for your wedding party as a gift? Choose from a large selection of 18kt and stainless letters, hearts and other symbols. Travel Jewelry will help customize a bracelet just for that special occasion. You may even like one for yourself. And if you prefer to deck out from home, an online special of diamond-like bracelets for $19.99 was irrestible. With every online purchase, you'll get a free jewelry pouch. Now how's that for bagging a bargain!

★★★★★ Two Divas   214/696-6719

4412 Lovers Lane   Mon-Sat 10-5:30
Dallas, TX 75225

If you think one Diva is all you can handle, think again. Double the fun is twice as nice. And azurite is the simulated gem that they prefer to Sharon the stone. It is not a CZ because, it will never cloud like a CZ. Too, take a look at their other simulated colored stones as well. They will take your breath away. All stones are set in white, yellow gold or platinum. Now we're talking the height of arrogance with a twist of savvy. A simulated diamond set in platinum, that's a good one. Don't leave home with the real McCoys. Travel with the faux, and go with the flow. Nobody can tell the difference. Some bridal couples have even resorted to choosing the simulated stones in the better setting to save enough money to put a down payment on a house. Now that's a smart duo. Of course, the savings are huge compared to the real things. I would describe their designs as fashion jewelry for the jet set and surely something that is just what the doctor would prescribe. The Azurite collections will knock your socks off. And if they ever decide to create a line of toe rings, then they really will knock your socks off — literally. Until then, think lots of flash for a lot less cash. Strictly for the discriminating hoi-polloi. Don't look for any websites, yet. When you type in two divas into a search engine, my name comes up first. See, I told you there's confusion on there as to how many stores I have, how many columns I write, well, you get the message. They would be in the 100 BEST if they had a website. Maybe next year.

★★   Ultra   **972/724-1966**

3000 Grapevine Mills Pkwy.   Mon-Sat 10-9:30; Sun 11-8:30
Grapevine, TX 76051
www.ultrastores.com

Can you imagine? Fixing what's broken right before your eyes? Well, it's true (but broken hearts do not count!) It's just one of the extras that this value-jewelry retailer, who was named among the top 10 national jewelry chains by *National Jeweler Magazine* as one of the largest and fastest growing in the country, provides to area shoppers. Locations besides Grapevine Mills (above) include Allen Premium Outlets and Prime Oulets at San Marcos. As an example, an 18 kt gold (nice weight) claddah charm with an emerald heart (not lab created) was regularly priced at $125, but I walked out with it around my neck for $38. You'd better like what you buy, because there are no returns — just exchanges within 10 days. But with savings of 20 to 75 percent everyday, jewelry is just dessert — enjoy it if you can afford it. Rings, bracelets, diamonds and gemstones, watches with names like AUCUTRON, BULOVA, LUCIEN PICCARD and MOVADO come to mind. A sleek gold men's MOVADO with a black leather band and gold face would retail $295 elsewhere, but here you'd pay $221 — a 25 percent savings. Okay, I didn't say it was dialing for substantial dollars off, did I? Jewelry repairs done on site while you watch (but no watch repairs).

★★   Zalde's Trading Company   **817/488-2287**

120 N. Main St.   Mon-Sat 10-6
Grapevine, TX 75051

No, this isn't someone's grandpa, as I first suspected. (At first glance, I though their name was Zadie and in Yiddish that means Grandpa.) But even on a Friday afternoon, they didn't answer their phones — twice. Suppose they were so busy with customers, they couldn't? Well, rumors of another Sam Moon wannabe were heard and so off we went a-shopping. No way, Jose. But nice try. This small store on the north side of Main Street between Rothchild's Home Decor and British Emporium, across from Elliott's Hardware, is a nice neighborly draw for a last-minute accessory that is typical of Sam's, but without the impact of selection or prices. Nice try, though, with packaged jewelry, BRIGHTON-like sunglasses, purses with sequins, MARILYN MONROE silkscreen prints, some rhinestone tiaras and jewelry sets, but it's no Sam Moon's. And prices of $36 don't make our purse strings sing!

Zales (The Diamond Store) Outlet   **214/689-0492**

8701 John W. Carpenter Frwy., Suite 200   Mon-Sat 10-6
Dallas, TX 75247
www.zalesoutlet.com

  Zales did not get to be the largest jewelry retailer by sitting around on the sidelines. No, sir. They know their business. And their business is diamonds. Zales has multiple outlet locations including the newest one they acquired from one of their own, the Barry Zale's location in Preston Center (214/363-0066), as well as Grapevine Mills (972/874-7403) and the Allen Premium Outlets (972/678-2090). Shopping at the outlets means you're shopping with prices of 20 to 70 percent off traditional retail. Win the war on high prices, from diamond solitaire earrings to a pair of gold hoops that could run circles around the competition. Most jewelry is, if you didn't realize, especially purchased for their outlet division. And my diamond pave wedding band cost $99 and Bob's with channel-set diamonds was $199. Not bad for a couple who started off their second-time around on the right foot with rings on their left hands.

Legal & Financial

◆◆◆◆◆ **AA USA Insurance Agency**   **972/644-7010**

9319 LBJ Fwy., Suite 214   Mon-Fri 8-6; Sat 9-4
Dallas, TX 75243

Start out revving their motors for your car insurance. You'll be tickled pink if they save you some green, then you can pursue their other insurance offerings. If you're longing for a company that represents more than 30 different companies and seeks out the best price and value for your money, you might find this agency a refreshing change of pace. Family-owned and operated, each member participates in the company's goings-on. No customer is denied coverage, regardless of past driving records. Seniors, young drivers under 25, first-time drivers, ticketed drivers, drivers with accidents, drivers with no prior insurance — no problem! So be it. Coverage is available for all 50 states and Canada. They even offer short-term policies (like one or two months), but they are no Rodney D. Young. If you prefer, they'll even split your down payment. Now, where else have you ever heard of such generosity?

◆◆◆◆◆ **Abe Factor**   **817/222-3333**

6301 Airport Freeway, Suite 160   By Appt. Only
Fort Worth, TX 76117

"Whatever happened to the guys who appeared in that best-selling *Greatest Little Bachelor Book in Texas* that you wrote way back when?," they ask. Well, some are in jail, some were murdered, some have died, and some have married and then died. But the dark-haired hunk on page 130 moved from Corpus Christi, where he was the assistant county attorney, to being one of the most experienced DWI lawyers in the Metroplex. "I'll drink to that!" Well, on second thought, perhaps I better not, but if YOU do, here's the attorney to call if you run afoul of the law. Counselor Factor is one factor in your defense. He's board-certified in Criminal Law and has defended over 2,000 DWI-DUI cases. He's also a member of the National College of DWI Defense, which I guess is like having a black belt as a DWI Defender. Check him out and see if his status has gone from NBM (Never Been Married) to no longer eligible! Disregard the office setting. The Massage School has taken over all but the Mr. Factor's office. If you need a criminal attorney, though, consider him the Fear Factor.

◆◆◆◆◆◆ American Reliance Mortgage   972/724-1515

2717 Cross Timbers Rd., Suite #400   Mon-Fri 8:30-7; Sat 10-3
Flower Mound, TX 75028
www.americanreliance.com

 Here's where we separate the wheat from the chaff, the men from the boys, the mortgage companies from the mortgage companies. Tom Cooper's a former radio show
mortgage hour host and does he know his stuff. His office, his work ethic, his family
life, his community life, his social life — all based on Christian principles. His wife, Kristen, has a
title company with similar philosophies. It's very convenient to have both of these services all
under one roof led by such ardent professionals. Together they are credited with being one of the
area's most respected and admired businesses. Tom and Kristen both have offices full of experts
for one-stop shopping. With lower interest rates, you might even want to convert your 30-year
mortgage into a 15-year version and save yourself thousands of dollars of interest, plus have your
house paid off much earlier. Tom will throw in a free $500 home warranty along with your mort-
gage if you tell him the Diva sent you. Talk about savings! Check out their second office in Grapevine if that is more convenient at 611 S. Main St., Suite 400, 817/410-4727; 817/410-4728 FAX.
See their Grapevine offices is you want to see Christian Painters workmanship.

◆◆◆◆◆ Better Business Bureau   214/220-2000

1600 Pacific Ave., Suite 2800   24/7
Dallas, TX 75201
www.dallas.bbb.org

Let me introduce you to the other BBB, the Better Business Bureau. While we used to call our
book, Bigger Better Bargains, we have always abbreviated our name to BBB but gave credit to
those that came before us. Now that we're back to being The Underground Shopper, it's easy to
refer you to the original BBB, the one and only. Since they have a fabulous website, you can
access tons of information without having to ask me for it. For example, if you are looking for
roofers, first check out if there are any roofers listed as unacceptable on the BBB's website.
Another valuable service is their project estimates. You can also check on a business or file a complaint — and the phone line is open round the clock. We'll intervene, too, with complaints, but not
'round the clock. We haven't had to very often, but when we call, we usually get immediate results
I'm happy to say. Discount merchants by and large are honorable or we wouldn't refer them in our
book. Ever now and again, we get a rummy. This year is was TD Landscape. But had we really
dug deeper into the guy's MO, we would have learned he has done these disappearing acts before.
So, when spending a lot of upfront monies, do your homework (or at least be a member of the
Home Improvement Coordinators — listed in Home Improvement chapter) and see to it that they
have checked the company out first, if you haven't.

◆◆◆◆◆ Bloom Legal Search   972/385-6455

14001 N. Dallas Parkway, Suite 725   24/7
Dallas, TX 75240
www.bloomlegalsearch.com/rank.html

If you're a law firm looking for a lawyer, this is the site for you. Howard Bloom has been a legal
matchmaker for more than 20 years and has a few things to say to consumers looking for a lawyer.
An educated consumer is a better legal consumer. There are several sites that consumers should
know about — and check up behind the scenes about a prospective lawyer they're thinking of hiring; or who to call to see what school their lawyer went to, what were their rankings in their graduating class, etc. Just like you'd want to know if you've got a doctor operating on you who was

ranked at the bottom of his class, you don't want a lawyer drawing up a contract that's still illiterate in English, can't add or subtract (you'd think many lawyers suffered from this lack when you get their bills), or they are been disciplined by the Bar Association for co-mingly client funds with their own personal checkbook. Well, this is where Howard Bloom recommends you look: Martindale-Hubbell Law Directory and the Texas Bar are two great websites that will dispense lots of good information. Howard Bloom's business has collected information from law firms based on the law schools attended by each lawyer in every firm or office having 25 or more attorneys. That's important if you only want to seek the counsel of an attorney who went to Harvard, for example. Or if you want someone who is also an Aggie because "they understand about certain things," this source knows who they are. Other factors that were considered in this rank and file includes the names of attorneys with advanced legal degrees, honors they received while in law school (such as Order of the Coif, etc.), and their level of participation and accomplishment in activities such as Law Review and Moot Court. Read how they determined the rankings and what other rankers such as the and the Gorman Ranking of Law Schools also think. Only firms that score 4.0 or above are included in the ranking.

◆◆◆◆◆◆   Bud Hibbs, Credit Counseling   817/589-4284

PO Box 16513   By Appt. Only
Fort Worth, TX 76162
www.budhibbs.com

 This Bud's for you! But instead of just specializing in Credit Counseling, Bud has expanded into Financial Counseling as well. Once he becomes your om-Buds-man, move over, credit bureaus. Bud Hibbs will tell you all the alternatives to filing for bankruptcy or resigning yourself to the so-called nonprofit credit-counseling agencies. His book *Guilty! Until Proven Innocent* is FREE — you can't beat that! Get it all on his website: learn what to do if you're drowning in debt, get a FREE "cease and desist" letter, know what you need to know before dealing with debt collectors and collection agencies and even learn who are America's WORST collection agencies. If you should need the assistance of a consumer attorney regarding illegal collection efforts, credit bureau misreportation or other consumer abuses and don't know where to look, just send Bud an email outlining your problem and where you live and he'll give you the advice you need, even if you have to resort to an attorney. He's smart. Cuts to the quick. And has done his homework. Meet him online and introduce yourself. He's the best friend a consumer can have. With almost 20 years in the business, he can guide you along the Bankruptcy Alterative Plan to get you back on your feet while keeping you on your toes, too!

◆◆◆◆◆   Complaint Department

Arlington, TX 76012   24/7
If you're not a happy camper, hire the Complaint Department for a letter writing campaign that usually gets results. Forget taking legal action if you're dissatisfied or feel you haven't been treated fairly. Sometimes the Diva can intervene but sometimes not. Instead, invest a $100 into the hands of this bulldog complainer and she can turn that lemon into lemonade. I've watched her first hand and trust me, you'll appreciate her tenacity when she sics her tentacles into getting restitution from a merchant, even if it is an isolated case. After several tries, if you're still not happy, let her have at it. This is a service that is only available via email initially. Then, if the Complaint Department sees that they can help you, a check for $100 will be issued — with no guarantees that it will work. However, she really does go to bat on behalf of disgruntled shoppers. If you don't have email access, call our offices for the Complaint Department's phone number directly. We just don't want the whole world to be calling — after all, this is just her part-time contribution to "get-

ting your money's worth!" This is what she'll need in order to help you: 1. Send your name, address, telephone number, details of the complaint and how to contact the company. In addition written permission/request must be given for the Complaint

◆◆◆◆ Consolidated Funding   972/644-4663

2301 Travis   By Appt. Only
Plano, TX 75093

Well, lo and behold. Getting advice from this slugger, who's on your side, is a breath of fresh air. Want to know how to do your own mortgage and save a few hundred, maybe a few thousand on that mortgage loan? Well, Larry Dugger has a better idea. His one-page loan application is simple. You can't go wrong if you follow his instructions. Whether you're purchasing or refinancing, it pays to save with advice from this expert. At the time of our research, we could get a 7 percent interest rate on a 30-year mortgage and a 6.5 percent rate on 15 years with no points. See for yourself and save the old-fashioned way.

◆◆◆ Consumer Credit Counseling (CCCS)   214/638-2227

8737 King George Drive, Suite 200   Mon-Fri 8:30-2:50
Dallas, TX 75235
www.cccs.net

Since 1973, this Dallas-based credit counseling service (CCCS) has helped the full spectrum of maxxed-out consumers. From financial counseling to debt management, their funding comes from contributions made by creditors and is usually given as a percentage of your payment to that company. You can even get advice online. However, credit counseling is noted on your credit report, and, from what I hear, most creditors see it similar to bankruptcy; so don't think you're off the hook. And for sure, erasing your debts by filing bankruptcy is not at all like wiping the slate clean. Getting a handle on your finances is one of CCCS's best contributions to your out-of-control indebtedness. There are at least a dozen offices throughout the Metroplex, with some having ATMs to take your payments. To get to their main location, take I-35 to Regal Row, then east to King George and turn right. They're on the second floor of the second building on the right. Betty Banks is their consumer spokesperson and has been a friend to the beleaguered credit-card maxxed out shopper for years. *Call toll-free: 800/783-5018*

◆◆◆◆◆◆ Doc Gallagher/The Gallagher Group   817/992-8294

1845 Precinct Line, Suite 215   By Reservation/Appt.
Hurst, TX 76054

 Retire safe, early and happy is Doc's mantra and indeed, he delivers. His financial services company has a team of investment counselors that take your money seriously. As independent brokers, they are dedicated to doing what's "Best" for you rather than which product they represent. They can represent the universe of products and have a wealth of expertise on retirement options for you. From long-term care protection to income investments, estate planning that will allow you legally to avoid paying estate taxes, turning old life insurance policies into long-term care policies, roll over IRAs, well the list is endless and the recommendations with your best interest is always foremost in Doc's mind. Tune in to KAAM where Doc is the resident financial advisor daily and on Saturdays where you'll often hear the Doc and Diva Show. And, too, join Doc and his experts somewhere in and around the Metroplex where he gives popular sell-out seminars during the lunch or dinner hour at popular restaurants around town. (Surely it's not the free lunches or dinners that attract the crowds.) Call for information especially if you want to learn "The 15 Tragic Mistakes Retirees and Pre-Retirees Make that Turn

Peace of Mind into Panic." You don't want to wind up a "bag lady," do you? (Even if it's a Louis Vuitton bag!) *Call toll-free: 800/434-4362*

◆◆◆◆◆ Great American Realty   972/965-8100

Richardson, TX 75080   By Appt. Only
www.realtor.com/ntrelis/barbarasommers

Barbara Sommers had a better idea, and rather than sitting still and keeping her mouth shut, she has become a leading authority on saving consumers some money when it comes to real estate. In fact, her theory about the importance of who manages the sale of your home, rather than who actually brings you the buyer, may be the ultimate truth. She has designed a program that offers a negotiable brokerage fee. In today's market, if you want to save money on real estate transactions, you either have to sell it yourself, without a real estate professional, or pray. Barbara Sommers has provided a package that allows you to cancel the listing agreement if it isn't working. She'll also offer you the opportunity to exclude those who have already shown your home, prior to the listing agreement. And that's some of her money-saving programs she brings to the table. If you need to do battle with the tax-assessor's office for your property taxes, she can help you out in that department, too. All you have to do is ask.

PS Hayman & Company   214/953-1900

Dallas, TX   Call for Reservation

Here's a new twist on an old subject — bankruptcy. This licensed attorney offers a $99 package seminar on avoiding judgments. Hey, I know a few folks who could or should be first in line! If you want to learn how the law permits you to restructure your assets and protect your income, you might want to find out when the next seminar is. Such hot topics as learning which assets a creditor can't touch, how to protect your spouse's assets, how to settle your judgments cheaply (hey, I didn't think a lawyer even knew that word?), how to set up checking accounts your creditors can't find and garnish, how to hide your money in untraceable credit and debit cards, even what to do when the constable knocks on your door — I'm not suggesting you sit in the front row, but you never know when this information could come in handy.

◆◆◆◆◆◆ Healthy America Agency   469/293-7467

                                                          By Appt. Only

Lewisville, TX 75067
www.undergroundshopper.com

 We've made contact with the best broker in the business — and gave him the challenge of getting Underground Shoppers the best health insurance options available. And so he did. Plus anybody in the state of Texas is safe with this agent, who won't let you go broke (even though he's a broker!) He will look after you like one of the family. From the best individual and group insurance rates with only A-rated companies and above to discount medical cards called Healthy America. Just click on our website and head to the button that says Insurance for dental, medical, prescriptions and such. Special Diva rates to all who sign up for information or call our number above. One call will get you connected to the broker who in turn will analyze your situation and come back to you with the best plan for mice and men. Get the most bang for your buck before you duck out permanently. There are two discount medical card programs from as low as $30 and up and they can't be beat. It's a card for the entire family and especially meaniful for those who lack insurance altogether. The only drawback (for non-Underground Shoppers) is that there's a $70 enrollment fee. For readers of the Underground Shoppers, that fee is waived. See it pays to save with the Underground Shopper. But you must identify yourself in order for you to reap that savings. Feel secure in the knowledge that the companies represented in every referral are solid as a rock. But our expert broker says the newest insurance route to consider these days is an HSA account (Health Savings Account) which was approved into law with the new Medicare legislation, signed December, 2003. It's treated in the tax code as a medical IRA with basically the same tax benefits. According to our top notch insurance agent, he said, "The HSA 1-deductable plan for Major Medical is the best bet for insurance for your money." He further exclaimed, "It the best deal that has come down in insurance in 25 years." For more information, give us a call and become an educated insurance consumer.

◆◆◆◆◆   **Home Warranty of America**   **888/HWA-RELY**
PO Box 850   24/7
Lincolnshire, IL 60069-0850
www.HWAHomeWarranty.com   ☟ *Top Online Store!*

If you want to protect your most valuable asset (your home), you'll want to always have a home warranty plan. But they are expensive. One way to save is to get your home mortgage or refinancing program through American Reliance Mortgage — Tom Cooper throws it in with a mortgage or a re-fi. Another way is to buy it online at Home Warranty of America. This one is one of the premier providers of home warranty coverage. Enjoy the security of knowing that when problems in your home occur, you're covered for major kitchen appliances, electrical systems, heating, air conditioning or plumbing for starters. Pick and choose which covered items you want. Expect a lower price for a fairly comprehensive warranty. It's worth it! Don't you remember moving in that dream house that you were going to remodel one day and the next, the motor to the A/C unit goes out? *Call toll-free: 800/236-4215*

◆◆◆◆◆   **Jack Duffy, Jr.**   **817/332-2022**
101 Summit Ave.   By Appt. Only
Fort Worth, TX 76102

Okay, so he's not certified by the Texas Board of Legal Specialization; most lawyers are not. But he is located at the Mallick Towers in Fort Worth and if it's one thing I know, if a lawyer is good at his craft, it doesn't matter if they're certified or not. Duffy is good. Real good according to one speedy Gonzales who has gotten several speeding tickets while driving a little faster than the posted speed limit while coming from his house to work. After a few tickets, he put this attorney on speed-dial. For $20, I hear he can keep you out of hot water. Although that's not all he does in his law practice, it might be a good introduction. Mr. Duffy also handles DWI, divorce, personal injury, auto accidents, slip and falls, medical malpractice, nursing home neglect — a lot of these are on a contingency basis, so you know he's got to be good. If he wins for you, he collects; if he loses, he doesn't. Frankly, I think that's how all lawyers should charge and it would immediately cut at least most lawsuits in half. If a lawyer doesn't think you have a good case, maybe he shouldn't have taken that big fat retainer and laugh all the way to the bank. Imagine how the court's docket would shrink; there are way too many frivolous lawsuits already. But that's another story. If you have a Tarrant County traffic ticket that needs defending, here's who to call.

◆◆◆◆◆   **Jeffrey H. Rasansky, P.C.**   **214/747-HELP (4357)**
Dallas, TX   Calls answered 24/7; By Appt. Only
www.texasinjuryattorney.com

And here you thought you were going to school to learn the 3 R's: Reading, 'Riting and 'Rithmatic? Eh? Instead, this lawyer will teach you a thing or two about the law — especially if it has to do with medical malpractice, nursing home abuse or accidents at the work place. Jeffrey Rasansky's law firm has another idea for the 3 R's: Reputation, Resources, Results! Who better for a plaintiff's lawyer than one who practices what he preaches. His staff of legal and medical professionals goes right to the heart of the matter. With the potential cap on malpractice suits, they have to fight doubly hard to get what their mistakes have cost you. Jeffrey Rasansky is not only considered one of the best lawyers under 40, but one of the best lawyers, period. He is the attorney who goes to bat for you, and he's usually on a contingency fee. That means, if he wins, you win. *Call toll-free: 800/704-3578*

◆◆◆◆◆ JK Harris & Company   800/435-4459

4514 Cole Ave., Suite 618   By Appt. Only
Dallas, TX 75207
www.jkharris.com

With almost 500 offices nationwide, this company says, "Go Away IRS!" Veteran ex-IRS agents and tax professionals will intervene on behalf of anyone being pursued by the IRS, so you don't have to face them yourself head-on. Ah-h-h, how do you spell RELIEF? Toll-free 24-hour voice message on "How to End IRS Problems Forever!" For your Free copy, just ask and ye shall receive. All on the up and up, they will legally help reduce the monies owed to the IRS. What H & R Block did to the tax preparation business, he's done with the IRS. To schedule an appointment, call 800/925-9609. Since 1997, over 100,000 troubled tax-payers have been helped by this company which The Wall Street Journal touts as the nation's most successful tax resolution company. *Call toll-free: 877/451-9111*

◆◆◆ Law Offices of Michelle L. Smith   214/521-4605

4111 N. Central , #102   By Appt. Only
Dallas, TX 75204

Here's a gal who gets it done with no frills, no fancy overhead, no bells and whistles. Why pay for more when all you want is a simple will, child support, someone to handle a DWI or another kind of traffic ticket (most cases $55), or a divorce that's not complicated or anticipated as a court battle. Fees start at $95, plus no court costs if in Dallas county and there are no child custody or property issues involved. Contested divorces can get costly as well as ugly. So try to have all the i's dotted and the issues settled before seeing any attorney. That's good advice for anyone, but especially for those who don't have the luxury of lots of money to blow on attorneys. She accepts Visa or Mastercard and se habla Espanol. And, as always, she is not certified by the Texas Board of Legal Specialization, if that is an important criteria you hold dear before hiring an attorney. Ever wonder why attorneys don't have hours that coincide with your days off? Well, this attorney has office hours on Saturday from 9-12. Now, that's convenient. Several Hispanic fans appreciate that she speaks their language. Si!

◆◆◆◆◆ McPherson and Associates   972/381-9800

17400 Dallas Parkway, Suite 112   By Appt. Only
Plano, TX 75287
www.mctexlaw.com

If you are a business owner and need representation consider Mark McPherson, a lawyer who's up to speed in business and consumer law. Subscribe to his free newsletter where he rights the wrongs of the legal world. If you are interested in commercial real estate, for example, and want to make money with it as a developer, landlord, or tenant, don't make a move without letting him draw up the necessary paperwork that will protect you down the road. Go to one of McPherson's informative websites and find information that will cut to the quick: articles on recent cases and other topics of interest to owners of Texas businesses, downloadable booklets on business law, choice of business entities and asset protection. And all of the information is updated monthly.

 Nick Mayrath, CPA   **972/661-9055**

13612 Midway, Suite 603   Mon-Fri 9-5 By Appt. Only
Dallas, TX 75244

 Here's the scenario: My former CPA did my tax return and said I owed
$600; Nick Mayrath did the same return, and said I was entitled to a
$6,000 refund. Now, which CPA do you think I trust? You'd be wise to
seek his expertise and counsel. He won't steer you wrong. He is one of the most efficient CPA's in town, not only with his information and accounting expertise but he makes time for all of his clients. In fact, he treats you like one of the family. You always feel special. He looks after your books and tax consequences and never misses a beat. And of course, you'll always want somebody looking out over your business so that there's no "hanky-panky" going on with your books. He can spot a rat with a paper trail a mile long. This guy's the best. His references is as long as the aforementioned above-mentioned paper trail.

 Pre-Paid Legal   **469/644-7551**

PO Box 1188   By Appt. Only
Dallas, TX 75244
www.prepaidlegal.com/info/denicegames

 You've heard of a gag order, well in this day and age, that's what happens when you visit with an attorney — you gag over their high prices, upfront retainers before they even do one thing on your behalf. And don't you just love those hourly charges that are assessed minute by minute. And then, how about those **XEROX** charges? $3 for every single sheet they copy? Well, is there a way around it? The only way I know around the system (besides never getting involved with the system to begin with) is to join the group. The more the merrier and the bigger the clout when it comes time to sing, "Here comes the judge!" Join for as little as $17 a month to ensure you will get quality legal counsel — you're as close as a phone call away. If you've got teenage drivers (or you're one of those who's midlife crisis has just kicked in with a Corvette), you are ripe for a speeding ticket, trust me. These legal eagles soar with information on getting you out of a jam, whether it's personal or business. You never want to jump into most relationships these days without legal counsel. From pre-nupts to leases, starting a business to someone slipping and falling inside your house, be prepared. (That's not only the Boy Scout mating call.) Having a lawyer on your side is the best advice a Mother can give you. Otherwise, you'll wind up in a sticky situation and that jam may linger and escalate into a major hornet's nest. Get help with legal issues from personal to business, they handle both. The IRS is bragging that they're going to audit more persons this year than ever before. Are you going to be one of them? Don't leave yourself open to potential disaster without somebody on your side! Have their audit legal department ready to back you. From updating your will to evicting a roommate, securing a piece of real estate to adopting a baby, one call will put your mind at ease. Whether it's part of the package and it comes with the program at no additional charge, or it's something that you need that will require a 25 percent discount off their usual and customary rates. Either way, did I say how much money you'll save? I know a great little boutique you can celebrate with the savings, unless of course you like paying your lawyers big bucks! And listen to this: All members who sign up for the business legal plan get an autographed football from Fran Tarkington. At least when that subpoena arrives, you can tell the process server to....take a "hike!" *Call toll-free: 866/708-4891*

◆◆◆　Property Tax Protest

Dallas, TX   By Appt. Only

www.propertytaxprotest.com　🖱 *Top Online Store!*

Did you know that for $300 a property tax consultant will represent you at the County Appraisal Review Board. What does that mean? Well, first they will file your protest, conduct a personalized search for relevant comparable sales, and ultimately represent you before the Appraisal Review Board. They even offer a limited conditional money-back guarantee which may reduce your out-of-pocket risk. If your property has been appraised higher than you think it should be, you may want to consider this. (However, check out the write-up earlier in this chapter for Barbara Sommers, at Great American Realty, who seemingly does a similar service of preparing comps in your area and doesn't charge for it.) Lastly, visit Dallas-based www.PropertyTaxProtest.com to learn more so if savings can be realized, you can pocket the difference for years.

◆◆◆◆◆　Simple Law   817/838-6263

2816 Denton Highway   By Appt. Only
Fort Worth, TX 76117

www.simplelaw.com　🖱 *Top Online Store!*

Ver-r-r-r-y interesting. Save money by preparing your own legal documents. That's right, with a little help from your friends at Simple Law. SimpleLaw Central Building even has their own building by the same name. Choose forms that will help you do some of the following: name change, wills and trusts, divorce and general documents which includes affidavits, assumption deeds, land contracts, organ donation, power of attorney and more. All four come in a CD, downloadable version as well as in book form. Also, online updates available for Free. Founded in 1996 by Attorney L. Keith Martison, a licensed and practicing Texas attorney, they do not give legal advice with these products, but they do provide accurate forms for you to do it legally for a whole lot less. And most importantly, these forms are applicable in Texas as opposed to other forms that you can buy at an office supply store based on another state's laws or on a national basis. Too, the lawyer who developed all of the forms is available by email (and phone by appt. only) should you need further help along the way. Don't you just love it. KISS high prices good buy and Keep It Simple Stupid (KISS!) *Call toll-free: 800/585-8481*

Texas Tenant Organization   512/477-8910

508 Powell Street   24/7
Austin, TX 78703-5122

www.TexasTenant.org　🖱 *Top Online Store!*

To access the Texas Tenant Organization, call, write, or email your concerns to the: Texas Housing Income Information Service and you'll be in good hands. If you are renting a property, know your rights. To learn all about them, turn to this website for answers. Even before you call an attorney, the Texas Tenant Advisor via this website is intended to provide general information regarding TEXAS residential tenancies only. If you have a problem in Georgia, you can whistle Dixie. There's no help for you here. Understand your rights within certain given situations. There may be one just like the one you are experiencing and by reading about others'problems, you will glean information that may be helpful for your situation. At least be armed with factual ammunition to fight back. Get the facts and then, if necessary, call an attorney if the suggestions do not result in satisfaction with your landlord. Here are some of the issues under discussion: Your application deposit, breaking a lease, discrimination, eviction, house rules if your Landlord seizes your property, all about late fees, what if you get locked out? Issues with mobile homes, privacy, rent repairs, retaliation, roommates, security deposits, smoke detectors, subleasing, termination, utilities, who owns the property and more can be answered via this organization. How to fight back, sue your landlord, contact government and the media, form a tenant organization, and things like "Don't sign anything" before seeking counsel. Don't look back and say, "If only." Read your rights. An educated tenant is a smart tenant.

◆◆   Universal Passports and Visas   214/739-3400

7515 Greenville Ave., Suite 910   Mon-Fri 8-5
Dallas, TX 75238
www.upandv.com

Procrastinators by nature will love the services available at Universal Passport and Visas. Even if your trip is sudden and unexpected, you can't get around the issue of needing a passport to enter certain foreign countries. But if you dragged your heels for months, and are planning on traveling to Rome tomorrow, don't do as the Romans do and wait to-ga without a passport. If you need a last-minute passport (or to renew your existing expired one), these two veterans of the visa wars can help expedite matters. Cathleen Stroud has more than 20 years of experience getting folks across the border(s) in record-breaking time. To expedite a new passport in one week, expect to pay an additional $60 plus whatever the government charges for passports these days; if you need it in three days, plan on an additional $80 charge; and to get it in TWO days, add $110. This year, the cost was $145 for a new passport or $115 for a renewal. Visa prices depend on the country you are going to, how soon you are leaving and other particulars. Passports, however, can be expedited through the post office as well. There are a few branches that take same or next day appointments or walk-ins. The fee for an expedited passport is just $25 but if you don't have the time or patience to tolerate the long lines, just call Universal instead. *Call toll-free: 800/831-2098*

Lighting & Lamps

G&S Sales

★★★ A to T
720 Valley Ridge Circle
Lewisville, TX 75057

972/219-9660
Mon-Fri 7-6:30; Sat 8-3

Or is it A & P? A to Z? Or A to T? Couldn't quite get a handle on their name, but I guess it takes a while for the lights to go on here. First, how did they get their name? A stands for arbitrary (basic light bulbs) and the T stands for tubular lights. Go figure. Now in their new Lewisville location, consider them experts when it comes to bulbs or ballasts. So, it's not lamps but rather lights that they sell. That's all you need to know to make the switch. They carry fluorescents, floods, ballasts and specialty light bulbs including the full spectrum and daylight fluorescents. Call for a lightening quick quote on any of your lighting needs and get out of the dark ages. They used to be called A to T Lamps, but somewhere in the process of moving, they've lost the Lamps.

★★★★ ARC Fan & Lighting
120 W. Bedford-Euless Rd.
Hurst, TX 76053-4098

817/268-2218
Mon-Fri 9-6; Sat 10-2

No need for a curve ball, ARC Fan & Lighting is on the straight and narrow when it comes to good deals. Cool your heels with ceiling fans from CASABLANCA, CRAFTMADE, ELLINGTON, HUNTER and more. Let them show you the light with over 50 different manufacturers of home lighting including landscape, decorative, or utilitarian lighting. Still can't see your way clear? Then why not put on your reading glasses and flip through pages of catalogs 'til you find just "watt" you're looking for; but since most fixtures are on display, deciding between CALCO, CLASSIC, DOLAN, KICHLER, MINKA and WILSHIRE may still be the hardest part. Ordering is easy and prices are still competitive and, in some cases, they make a clean sweep of the competition. Life's all aglow with heavenly fixtures and fans from ARC.

★★★★★★ Barrow Electrical & Lighting
2820 E. Belknap Street
Fort Worth, TX 76111

817/834-2177
Mon-Sat 7-5:30

Play it again, Sam (our wonderful guide to the showroom this year). Open to both the public and to the trade industry at factory-direct prices, Sam's the woman who will make it happen, whether you're in the market for one piece or a houseful. Expect a showroom full of ceiling fans, sconces, chandeliers, ceiling lights, well, it's a lighting store, dim-watt! After 32 years in the business, you can expect them to at least shed some light on the subject. Items chosen that are in stock are ready to hang once you get them home. They don't do installation, but they can refer you to the business down the street (BCS) that can fix you up. If you're building a new home or are having some problems with your old electrical hook-ups, you'll want to at least give this narrow Barrow an opportunity to shine. They do repair and rebuild fixtures as well as selling new. They also provide electrical supplies and lighting for the great outdoors. Landscape lighting can really put your azaleas on the map. Choose from an abundance of brands priced at wholesale or factory-direct prices. Brands included **GENERAL ELECTRIC** breakers, **PHILLIPS** light bulbs and **THOMAS LIGHTING** at contractor prices. *Call toll-free: 800/255-2177*

★★★★★   Benson Lighting   817/590-2266

2325 E. North Loop 820   Mon-Fri 8-5; Sat 9-1
Fort Worth, TX 76118
www.bensonlighting.com

Looking to shed some light on the subject of high-end lighting at lower prices? Then let this Benson bend your ear with their selection. If you're still living in the Dark Ages or under a rock, this family-owned mother-and-son business has been lighting the homes of Tarrant County for years. New this year is the addition of hardware including knobs, drawer pulls, bathroom hardware and, best of all, you're welcome to shop their lighting showroom even if you're not a card-carrying resident of Tarrant County. Their only request? You remain orderly and not grab the sconces from the walls, see if the crystal chandeliers "ping," or play with the dimmers on all the light switches. You see, they expect a more sophisticated audience and prefer that when you see the prices and the selection of old world, Mediterranean and rustic styles that have joined the others on display, you will remain calm and collected. From contemporary to traditional, eclectic to elegant, economical to extravagant, it's all under one roof here. Expect to brighten more than just your space by adding some dramatic finishing touches such as mirrors, paintings and furniture.

★★★★★★   Classic Galleries   214/630-4074

7101 Carpenter Frwy.   Tues-Fri 10-5; Sat. 10-4
Dallas, TX 75247

 Classic Clearance Center (CCC) is to lamps and shades what the BBB is to bargains (bigger, better ones, that is.) Over 10,000 square feet, to be exact, at their Dallas location (exit Mockingbird off the Carpenter Freeway, and enter what appears to be a run-down brick warehouse). Once inside, you'll throw abandon to the wind and buy, buy, buy. More than 5,000 lamp shades and more than 500 lamps in stock. Hundreds of lighting possibilities with lampshades starting at $5. Top it off with any one of their choice finials, hang out around the framed pictures, decorative accessories and pillows, and appreciate that life is good. At least 50 to 90 percent off those that have seen better days - market samples, items that have been discontinued, or things that are slightly shopworn but still worth every penny. The Fort Worth store is over 5,000 square feet and carries more than 2,000 lamp shades and 200 in lamps. (2435 S. University Drive, Fort Worth, TX 76109-1145, phone 817/207-8180.) So—between the two stores, there is no doubt they carry the largest selection in the Metroplex. As for finials, well I stopped counting after I hit 1,000. And if you still need encouragement, what about all the framed art from their wholesale division with new market samples arriving monthly—selling of course at wholesale prices. Too, look to Classic Galleries for lamp repair. Nobody does it better. Better price. Better turnaround time. Better workmanship.

★★★   Elect-A-Van/dba EVS Supply   972/231-5351

1350 E. Arapaho, Suite 126   Mon-Fri 8:30-5; Sat 10-3
Richardson, TX 75081
www.evssupply.com

If it's portable and you need it to run, go to EVS supply. Battery packs are the specialty of the
house—for laptops, camcorders and cellular phones, but remember, they haven't gotten so big that
they've forgotten the little guys. They still sell watch batteries even if the big boys call on them for
large-scale, down-well drilling operations. Get powered up with batteries from DURACELL,
ENERGIZER, HAWKER, LENMAR, PANASONIC, POWER-SONIC, RENATA, SAFT, SANYO,
TADIRON, VARTA and others. You now can take care of all your battery and light bulb needs
online, as you may find their physical location a little tricky to find. (In the same "L" shaped building as National Tire and Battery.) *Call toll-free: 800/776-5267*

★★★   Fan and Lighting Gallery   817/244-5888

7948 Hwy. 80 West   Mon-Sat 9-6
Fort Worth, TX 76116
www.fansales.com

Formerly the Fan Factory Outlet, you can still get a good deal here—it's a breeze. Getting their
website up and running is, however, not so easy. Somewhere in between, this 10-year-old-plus
business has put up with a lot. A lot of fans, that is. From inexpensive to 52 inch HUNTER Original fans for $245, you will become a fan of the Walter's family and forever keep your cool. There
are fans everywhere hanging out with others of the same ilk: AIRWIND, HUNTER, LIGHTO-
LIER, ROYAL PACIFIC and others. Whether you're blowing hot or cold, you can choose from
lots of inexpensive fans priced lower than those at home centers, and in a variety of styles and a
multitude of colors for under $39.95. Just don't expect them to last a lifetime or to be as effective
as others with sturdier motors and higher price tags. Mostly made in Taiwan or by low-end USA
manufacturers, some were even as low as $25, but they do the trick. Again, for a small utility room
or a bathroom, it should do a good job. Special orders are welcome.

★★★★   Ft. Worth Lighting   817/568-9127

2746 S.E. Loop 820   Mon-Fri 8:30-5:30; Sat 10-3
Fort Worth, TX 76140-1021

Formerly Lee's Ceiling Fan & Lighting, isn't it time you took a break from the stale and ordinary?
Turn into the 820 Business Park between Campus & Wichita and get ready to make the switch.
Turn on and fix up those dark places in your life with lights. Close-outs, red tags, overstocks and
one-of a kind finds in bathroom fixtures, chandeliers, sconces, ceiling fans, outdoor lighting, etc.,
is what Fort Worth Lighting has in store. Lee has merged his front showroom, where he had fixtures to be ordered, with his backroom bargains so now it's practically a free-for-all. Now is the
time to head out to SW Loop 820 near the Everman Exit. It's not the easiest place to find, but once
you do, you'll not be in the dark any longer.

★★★★★★ Innova Lighting   972/353-4550

701 S. Stemmons, #140 @ Fox Exit   Mon-Fri 9-5; Sat 10-4
Lewisville, TX 75067-3536
www.innovalighting.com

 Looking for your "Lights in shining armor?" Exit Fox Ave. off 35E into Lewisville and go left over the freeway, behind Black Eye Pea Restaurant. You never know when your lights will go out on Broadway but when and if they do, don't worry, get happy. Innova Lighting has the best selection at the lowest prices around. An occasional blowout sale slashes these low prices even lower to reflect a 90 percent savings. Get to Innova any time because there's always something spectacularly priced (besides their everyday low, low prices.) Seeing is believing. Keep current via my radio show or the website so I can alert you to electrifying price cuts. There's 100 years of combined experience on the floor according to owner Ray Harper, an experienced lighting man himself.

★★★★ Lakewood Lighting   214/826-5980

341 Hillside Village   Mon-Fri 9:30-5; Sat 10-4
Dallas, TX 75214

For almost a quarter of a century, Lakewood Lighting has been illuminating the area—but forget the lake, there isn't one in sight. However, expect to see a sea of values floating around this store in the Lakewood area. As this shop caters to those in the neighborhood, expect them to be both shopper-friendly and personable. Light up the night with some of their custom transformations. Yes, although they carry traditional lighting fare (lamps, fixtures, ceiling fans, chandeliers), their forte is topping them off with a shade (as low as $10), or taking your favorite or unusual container and transforming it into a one-of-a-kind lamp. They are an authorized **STIFFEL** repair service center and turnaround time for the average fix-er-upper is about four to six weeks.

★★★★ Lamp House   214/946-2372

923 Wynnewood Village   Mon-Sat 10-5:30
Dallas, TX 75224

Try leaving the porch light on, just in case you've gone shopping. After 30-plus years, these folks don't flicker; they don't speak English very well, but they do offer some pretty fluent deals on lamps. The flame burns brightly in the same location with the same hours and the same mission—not to leave a light unturned. No need to leave the home fires burning; the Lamp House will light the way with all kinds of lamps in every shape, size and intent. From decorative table lamps to floor lamps to sit behind a couch, a grand **SCHONBEK** chandelier for the dining room table or a smaller version for the entry way. Tiffany-styles mean a stained-glass look and wall sconces mean you can throw some light off the wall. The market samples were not a filament of our imagination, either. They were half price and a Lamp House fixture. Excellent prices throughout and this standard of excellence hasn't dimmed over the years. No ceiling fans and only a few fancy bathroom fixtures, but lots of chandeliers, lamps and shades make this an Oak Cliff fixture to try.

★★★ Lamps Plus   214/520-2995

3319 Knox Street   Mon-Fri 10-9; Sat 10-6; Sun 11-6
Dallas, TX 75205
www.lampsplus.com

Lamps Plus, since 1974, has been the largest specialty lighting company in the U.S. Their brightly lit, state-of-the-art showrooms carry a huge selection of functional and decorative lighting, with a complement of furniture and accessories. Save 10 to 50 percent on hundreds of items, and a smaller selection online. Expect prices to be lower than those at the typical lighting or department store with online coupons and offers of FREE bulbs as additional incentives. A TIFFANY mission-style torchiere that retailed for $249.99 was $199.95 (a $50 savings). Stick lamps, in several different finishes, were $14.95 and could accommodate those little lamp shades with the beads that are the hit this season. Nothing out of the ordinary, but a shining example of a full-service discounter of traditional lighting, chandeliers, indoor and outdoor lighting, torchieres and more. The selection is gigantic with over 660 chandeliers to choose from alone, making it a difficult task to remain in the dark for too long. Second location in Plano at 1705 Preston Rd., corner of Park and Preston, 972/447-0019. Lights out! (Don't forget to check out those seven-year bulbs—imagine, not changing bulbs for years?) *Call toll-free: 800/782-1967*

★★★ Lighting Connection, Inc.   972/964-1946

2001 Coit Rd., #164   Mon-Fri 9-6; Sat 9-4
Plano, TX 75075
www.lightingconnection.com

In 1989, Lighting Connection, Inc. came upon the midnight clear and showed us another way to buy lighting fixtures in the Dallas/Fort Worth area. Since their inception, they've opened two other showrooms, in Irving and Austin/San Antonio. Each location displays an A-to-Z inventory of possible lighting options. From chandeliers to ceiling fans, outdoor and landscape lighting, hall and bath lights, and table and floor lamps. With more than 2,000 fixtures in stock, and savings of at least 20 percent, let them be your Lighting Connection. Online, there's a small closeout section and an online catalog with a few pictures (no shopping online yet). Hang around with brands like ART, FORECAST, GEORGIAN, MAXIM, THOMAS, SAVANT and WILSHIRE—both classic and contemporary—at prices several watts below retail. Connect to some of the best, but not at the very least. Turn on to their Irving store at 3301 Royalty Row. If it's good enough for David Weekly homes, it's good enough for me.

★★ Nathan Frankel Electric   817/336-5656

1109 Lamar   Mon-Fri 8-5; Sat 8-Noon
Fort Worth, TX 76102

Let's be frank, Nate, I don't like to pay retail. That's why I like Nathan Frankel Electric because they fit the bill for service and low prices. Ceiling fans started at $50 but before you buy, they make sure you're getting what you need. What's the room size where the fan is going to hang? What's the primary reason for the fan—to cool, circulate warm air, or just for looks? What is the motif of the room? Is it already wired? Who would think there are so many questions that needed answers? But when you finally select a fan, you'll be sure it'll get the job done. Then, don't forget the light for the fan, too. This small mom-and-pop neighborhood shop keeps the overhead low, hence lower prices. There's plenty of name brands to choose from with quality and familiarity, and although some brands were unfamiliar, they appeared to be a good value.

Pettigrew Associates, Inc.   214/745-1351

1715 Market Center Blvd.   Mon-Fri 9-5; Sat. By Appt. Only
Dallas, TX 75207

Do they or don't they? The Design District used to be a stickler for selling exclusively to the trade, but, since business is sluggish everywhere, they've been inviting the public in and selling their lighting wares to you and me, babe! Although they have dealt exclusively with designers and retailers, they haven't turned us away....yet. Pettigrew Associates, Inc.

has offered professional chandelier installation, cleaning and restoration for years, and, no doubt, is in it for the long haul. Greg Clayton has 18 years of experience installing and restoring chandeliers, so he's one of the few specialists in an arena of generalists. If you are looking for a spectacular lighting fixture, sconces to chandeliers, Pettigrew won't just grow on you, they'll root you right out of your back pocket. Watch out! It'll cost you—but then again, it's to die for and if you're going go out, it might as well be with the lights on!

★★★★   Texas Lamp Manufacturers   972/564-5267

505 E. Hwy. 80   Mon-Sat 8:30-5
Forney, TX 75126

This is no blarney. Forney is where lamps are made for Texas homes. If you live in Texas and you haven't shopped here, you might as well move back to Detroit. Y'all visit them one time and you might be hooked. Several shoppers this year complained about the rise in prices. Custom lamps take two to four weeks' turn-around time to make—not bad! And new this year is a large selection of furniture. Exit Talty Road and enjoy one of the largest lamp manufacturing showrooms in the Southwest. If you can't find a lamp here, they'll custom make one. The savings are 30 to 50 percent off! So even if the prices have skyrocketed, you're still saving up to 50 percent and that's still pretty electrifying in my book. *Call toll-free: 800/537-2675*

G&S Sales
See writeup on page 379

Linens & Bath

★★★★★ **Back Alley @ Peacock Alley**   **214/520-6736**

4311 Oak Lawn, Suite 150 @ Hershel   Mon-Sat 10-6
Dallas, TX 75219
www.peacockalley.com

Okay, so they've moved south. Sometimes good things come to an end and they have to make their move to accommodate bigger and better plans. In this case, as of mid-April of 2003, this outlet location has joined forces with their retail store in Oak Lawn, carving out a 2,000-square-foot area so you won't be left high and dry. You can still count the Pope, Oprah Winfrey and Bruce Willis as fans of Peacock Alley's linen products. For the finest in luxurious bed and bath linens, here's where to start for the highest in thread counts. Wrap up in sumptuous bath towels, bed linens, comforters and bathrobes. See samples, discontinues or slightly flawed in the outlet department or flawless in their retail showcase. Save a dramatic 50 to 60 percent less on the Egyptian cotton towels and sheets. They've launched an entire baby's bed collection. In Fort Worth, sleep chic at 4601 West Freeway, 817/731-3443. Tune in to our website or the radio show to be alerted to their next blow-out warehouse sale or call 214/689-3755. Watch for a spring clean-out-the-warehouse sale and when it's on, look for the last door and enter the "no-spin" zone at 2050 Postal Way in Dallas, 75212. *Call toll-free: 800/652-3818*

★★★★ **Bed Bath & Beyond**   **972/991-8674**

5100 Belt Line Rd., #1000   Mon-Sat 9 AM- 9:30 PM; Sun 10-7
Dallas, TX 75240
www.bedbathandbeyond.com

This New Jersey-based chain of bigger, better bed and bath items was founded in 1971 and today is one of the dominant forces for better quality domestics and home furnishings in the world. With more than 300 stores (11 in the Metroplex), ranging in size from 30,000 to 80,000 square feet, they leave no room for you to shop elsewhere. Offering a huge selection at what they call everyday low prices, they provide everything you could ever need or want when it comes time to living the good life....for less. The B B & B inventory list exhausts even the doyenne of domestics: air purifiers, blenders, coffeemakers, cookware, cutlery, dinnerware, down comforters, duvets, espresso machines, flatware, food processors, irons, pillows, scales, sheets, stand mixers, tablecloths, toasters, toothbrushes, towels—did I miss anything? A national computerized bridal and gift registry makes it easy to buy the perfect gift. More than 70,000 items are within their confines with customer service a priority. Some of the brands highlighted included ALL-CLAD, CALPHALON, FARBERWARE, LE CREUSET, JOYCE CHEN and T-FAL cookware to dinnerware by DANSK, MIKASA, PFALTZGRAFF to linens by BAY LINENS, CROSHILL and WAMSUTTA.

Watch newspapers for frequent 20 percent off coupons. A great place for college students to load up for the dorm and for brides to register. It's a one-stop shop. Check directory for location nearest you. *Call toll-free: 800/GO-BEYON*

★★★★★★ **Bedroom Solutions**   **214/905-9121**

1326 Inwood Rd.   Tues-Sat 10-6
Dallas, TX 75247

 Want to sleep cheap and chic? Cover up on luxury bedding at these prices (50-75 percent off retail) at Bedding Solutions, your solution to your bedroom blahs. Comforters, duvets, bedspreads, drapes, trims and more from one of the Southwest's most prestigious bedding manufacturers. Check out the sensational pillows, shams, bed skirts, high-end thread count sheets all displayed in eye-catching vignettes. This manufacturer for major department, specialty stores and catalogs has opened a little outlet refuge from high prices at the Inwood Outlet Center. It's literally floor to ceiling here so don't miss looking up and looking down so you don't miss a thing. Comforters, duvet covers, bedspreads, pillows, shams, bed skirts, fabric, trim, beads, frou-frou lamps, long-lasting candles, draperies, even high-end thread count sheets were displayed in tempting arm's reach—enough to transport you to the specialty boutique shops on an Amtrak ticket. Lots of accompanying feathered and beaded boudoir lamps, to set alongside your night tables, will finish off the look to designer perfection. Located on the south side of the Inwood Outlet Center, next door to the Calendar Bakery. Sandi and Brandi are your conduits to design perfection.

★★★★★ **C & E Custom Bedspreads**   **817/485-4422**

4209 Clay Ave.   Mon-Fri 8-5
Haltom City, TX 76117

Get the look you've been looking for in your bedroom. C & E will custom-craft your bedding ensembles—but bring your own fabric. Then it's up to the wizards at C & E to zip (or sew) your bedding into shape. The prices quoted are all-inclusive of labor and batting. Strike up a good deal with their nimble fingers to make you a match. It's a sham if you don't! From twin to king size, they can cover you from head to toe for less dough. Listen to these prices for labor only: $174 (twin), $180 (full) and $215 (king), dust ruffles from $51-$73 and pillow shams ($31-$39.50). Trust me, it doesn't get much better than this. Cording, ruffles and extra stuff costs more, but that's standard operating procedure. Prices vary depending on whether you get a comforter, bedspread, duvet cover, and whether it is reversible or not. For pricing examples, let's say it takes seven yards of fabric for a queen size comforter (plus seven yards for the backing). The cost for medium batting and assembly on that would be $236. The cost for a full size with the same specs, $210. Naturally, a twin would be less than the full—and a king size more than the queen. Tailored corners, box pleats and addition of trims are just some of the extra add-ons that would be tacked on to the ultimate final price. Allow three to four weeks for turnaround time, but isn't it time you went undercover?

★★ **Charles Curtain Co.**   **214/630-7967**

1352 Crampton   Mon-Fri 8-3:30; Sat 9:30-Noon
Dallas, TX 75207

It's curtains for this Charles—but not in the cardinal sense. After all, he's been selling his curtains out of his factory for years. A lot of water has passed under the bridges of the Trinity River at this 1,000-square-foot outpost. It's small enough to house plenty of overstocks and samples of his manufactured draperies and bedspreads at 50 percent off and more. Remnants of fabric are also available for your creative splurges at $2 to $10/yard. Complete a bedroom ensemble with pinch-pleated drapes, scarf valances, pole top drapes, tailored panels, blouson valances, jabot and filler valances. Dress up your bed with matching spreads, shams and dust ruffles. What a shame, you're saving so much money. Take Stemmons to Irving Boulevard; Crampton is between Wycliff and Motor Streets. Their target customer? A JC Penney shopper. But do get there early as they still hold dear to their timetable. A queen-size bedspread would cost you from $45 to $100, or up to $200 to order one, so it's not dirt cheap. What's a windfall? They also have matching ready-to-hang draperies. Expect fabric to run between $5 to $10/yard, still a bargain in anyone's book.

★★★★   Linens 'n Things   214/265-8651

10720 Preston Rd., Suite 108   Mon-Sat 9-9; Sun 10-7
Dallas, TX 75230
www.linensnthings.com

Since 1975, Linens 'n Things has been just that, Linens 'n Things—a leading home textiles, housewares and home accessories superstore coast-to-coast. With names that have made America famous: ALL-CLAD, BRAUN, CALPHALON, CUISINART, HENCKELS, KRUPS, LAURA ASHLEY, WAMSUTTA and WAVERLY to name drop a few. Say beddy-good-buys to their increasing presence of private labels which supplement their brand name products, yet give shoppers more bang for their buck. Of course, "we won't be undersold," is their everyday low pricing strategy with about 40 percent of their sales coming from "things" such as frames, area rugs, candles and small electronics. Get a LNT Natural Down standard pillow for $19.99, a CUISINART CHEF CLASSIC seven-piece cookware set for only $99.99, a set of three EMESS Bronze room lamps for $59.99, or a ROOMBA iRobot Automatic Vacuum for $199.99. Check directory for other area locations—11 in the Metroplex alone and 350 nationwide. Watch for $5 off coupons in the newspaper circulars.

★★★★   Luxury Linens @ Burlington Coat Factory   972/613-1333

2021 Town East Blvd.   Mon-Fri 10-9; Sat 11-9; Sun 10-6
Mesquite, TX 75150
www.bcfdirect.com

How do I love thee? Let me count the ways. Burlington Coat sells more than just coats. They sell ladies, men's, children's apparel and shoes, plus fragrances, baby items, home decor, luggage, and at this particular store, linens. Some brand names you've come to love over the years and their newest exclusive offering by CHRISTOPHER LOWELL of HGTV fame. With his designer eye, he coordinates the entire bedding ensemble for you. With almost 300 stores nationwide, it all began back in 1924 when Abe Milstein launched a successful wholesale outerwear business. Then, when Monroe Milstein joined his father in the '50s, they began selling retail. When I caught up with him in my first book in 1972, they had just acquired a coat factory and outlet store in Burlington, New Jersey—hence the name Burlington Coat Factory. Save up to 60 percent off department and specialty store prices on more than one thousand designer and name-brand fashions for the entire family. Check directory for multiple area locations or log on to their website and shop online at www.bcfdirect.com.

★★★★★★   **Quilt Factory Outlet**   **972/206-7800**

2969 Red Hawk Drive   Mon-Fri 8:30-5; Sat 10-4
Grand Prairie, TX 75052
www.americanhometex.com

 Once you've found the intersection of Mayfield and Hwy. 360, you're almost ready to hunker down for the night. Say nighty, night night to some of the best prices on quilt coverlets in town. Well, how can it get any better than wholesale prices or less? This wholesaler of quilts leaves nothing to the imagination. Look for the last building on the block, and begin your search for the all-American cover up. (Only these are mostly made in China). Prices are ridiculously cheap. From Christmas throws (50 x 60) for $5.99 to a quilted king-size model called "Harmonious Mist" for $69. Now shop the glass-enclosed front to their 20,000 square foot warehouse and load up for gifts, going-away-to-college, bridal showers, Christmas, Mother's Day, there's a million occasions that call for something up close and personal. And if you can take the chill off, all the better. Don't forget, there's a FREE pillow sham with every purchase as their Diva Dollar deal. It keeps getting better and better. At least, it will keep you from "hocking" the family jewels just to keep the old fires burning. Look for their front door sign which says "American Hometex, Inc." *Call toll-free: 877/373-1638*

★★★★★   **Quiltcraft Outlet Store/Bed Dressing 214/376-1841**

1230 E. Ledbetter Drive   Second Saturdays 8-2 (main outlet)
Dallas, TX 75216
www.quiltcraft.com

If you are looking for a class act, consider one of our own. Based in Oak Cliff, where a lot of the manufacturing action takes place, expect this output to be outstanding as a bedding manufacturer. With only the latest decorator trend designs, their outlet carries the overruns, discontinues, samples and returns from some of America's biggest department stores. Then, lay thee down to rest in a matching bedspread, comforters, duvet covers, pillow shams, bed skirts, accent pillows and down pillows. Always save 50 to 90 percent! They're the ones who bought the former **VINEYARD** manufacturer (that I used to rave about) who made all the bathroom coordinating ensembles. Oh dear, I forgot about the 310 thread count sheet sets: queen size, $39.99 and king size, $49.99. Turn over, Martha. These 100 percent cotton sateen high-thread count sheet sets are the lowest priced in the Metroplex, maybe even in the country. But you're best to shop their other outlet stores called Bed Dressing at the Tanger Factory Outlet in Terrell and in Hillsboro at the Prime Outlets where they are open seven days a week. Look for a yellow brick building and follow the road to luxury for less during the Second Saturdays when they're open at their main plant. Call before you go to verify their inconsistent hours at their Ledbetter location. *Call toll-free: 800/462-2805*

★★★★★★   **Quilted Star, Inc.**   **972/530-4663**

301 E. Buckingham, Suite 1   Mon-Fri 9-4
Garland, TX 75040
www.quiltedstar.com

 We hate to make you feel quilty, but these quilts are not your typical poly-filled, machine-made and limited in detail. This company offers one of the largest selection of colors and designs in quilts at the wholesale level for you to resell; or you can buy them for yourself. The quilts are lovingly and painstakingly quilted entirely by hand with extensive and detailed quilting patterns and made from 100 percent cotton fabrics especially chosen to uphold and complement traditional quilt designs. Most quilts these days are mass-produced using poly/cotton blend fabrics and light polyester filling; however, a star was born the old-fashioned way at the Quilted Star—utilizing 100% cotton batting. Cotton is all natural, it is warm and comfortable, and gives their quilts the star quality that consumers demand these days. An incredible website to order from listing each quilt pattern for easy decision making—from patriotic stars to broken stars. These are all high-quality, handmade primitive looking quilts like Grandma use to make. *Call toll-free: 800/390-4278*

Right At Home   817/641-8060

3101-B North Main   Call for Hours
Cleburne, TX 76033

You'll feel Right At Home with this fabulously funky, fine bedding source that rounds out the reason to drive to Cleburne to shop Furniture By Design, Old West Stitches and Right At Home. And you will feel right at home! When Mommy had Annie, she decided not to run herself ragged driving all over the Metroplex to serve her design clients. Instead, she only has to drive to her shop so Annie can help her sell her stuff. (Even at three years old, she can be a formidable saleswoman!) But believe me, the stuff here needs no selling. From custom bedding that will knock your socks off (who sleeps with their socks on anyway?) to custom pillows made from old VICTOR COSTA dresses—(Remember him? The BILL BLASS knock-off king?) Well, had I had more couches and beds that required more pillows, I would have bought every one of them. In fuchsia taffeta with a black satin rose in the center, you won't be able to stop with just one. The pillow collections are eye-stopping. For a low of around $10 to $49, these pillows will bring Metroplex and Metropolitan shoppers to their knees. Trust me. And don't forget to look at Annie's collection of custom bed frames. Be glad that her Mommy has turned her sights to innovative beds and bedding. Now which store is looking to launch their own signature line? If they were smart, they should call Right At Home.

Rose Tree Linen Outlet   214/520-6400

3201 Knox St. @ Cole   Mon-Fri 8-3:30
Dallas, TX 75205
www.rose-tree.com

Since Rose Tree opened their luxury linen emporium in the Knox/Henderson corridor, we wonder where the outlet went? At last try, no one was answering their phones at 7900 AMbassador Row, 214/637-0011. You may have better luck getting someone to answer Mon-Fri 8-3:30. So instead, this year, we decided to throw abandon to the wind and rave about their full Uptown retail store. This manufacturer of custom, traditional bedding and other soft goods for the home has now opened its first retail store and we wonder what happened to their shar-pei dog. Did he or she go to the dogs and join them at the retail store or is he/she back at the warehouse? This store is a welcomed relief to a shopper with little imagination. In fact, one visit and you'll exclaim, "I want it all!" Founded by mother Lydia Rose in 1979, she started first as a manufacturer of tailored place mats with a former background in women's fashion. ROSE TREEÍS line of luxury bedding is but an extension of her flair for design as she envelops her unique concepts into everything else to coordinate with the luxury linens. The store is a series of vignettes that incorporates entire bedroom packages. So rather than build their bedroom piece by piece from a variety of stores, it's Rooms-to-Go for the high-end shopper. They offer all the bedroom accessories, nightstand, lamps, even a coordinating vase and everything's exquisite. They pride themselves on quality workmanship, custom products at affordable prices. But let's not kid ourselves, this isn't the outlet. Their linens are sold at 19 fine department stores plus their own company store on Knox Street. But where or where has the outlet gone? Remember, what doesn't sell at the retail store may wind its way to their outlet. Ooh wee! Bark if you see their Shar-pei (you might want to invite him to our **BOTOX®** clinics since we use one as our cover girl!)

textileshop.com   877/TexShop (839-7467)

55 Edward Hart Drive
Jersey City, NJ 07303

www.textileshop.com   🖰 *Top Online Store!*

Mon-Fri 9-5:30 (EST)

If you're fed up with wading through the sheets to find the ones that match up, or the king bottom that inadvertently got paired with the twin pillowcases, then let me introduce you to www.textile-shop.com. It's no wonder it has been given the star rating by Yahoo! The BBB (U.S.) concurs along with the security factor of shopping at a safe and secure site. FREE shipping on all orders of $100 and more (and that's not hard to do), you can be assured that they DO NOT sell, rent, or trade your personal information to any third party. Okay, now that you're armed with all the security factors, it's time to shop for sheet sets starting at $14.99; duvet sets at 63 percent off, same with 100 percent cotton, waffle-weave throws for only $9.99, half off blankets starting at $14.99, 75 percent off **LOONEY TUNES** beach towels (isn't that just ducky), bed pillows as low as $4.99, half price window coverings, 58 percent off cotton tote bags, 77 percent off rayon chenille 50 x 60 throws, 70 percent off wine bags (great to bring with a bottle of wine to a family gathering) and more. Bed and bath never was so inviting. Without being soaked, you can stay dry with all your bed and bath items that make for a domestic goddess lifestyle for a whole lot less. Why not live like a Diva—and shop like the Diva. Up to 75 percent off on rugs, throws, table linens, bed and bath products, hip, hip, hurray! Textileshop.com is a venture of a large industrial group that has manufactured home textiles since 1968 and has been shipping to stores in Europe and Japan. Now, they have brought their expertise and product mix to the USA and are based in New Jersey. Lucky for you, you can shop from home and avoid the crowds (or show a passport).

★★★★   Westpoint Stevens Factory Outlet   940/565-5040

5800 North I-35, Suite 508
Denton, TX 76201
www.westpointstevens.com

Mon-Sat 10-8; Sun 11-6

Even if you haven't an appointment to WestPoint, you can graduate to this outlet for savings on items for your kitchen and bath. Forget department stores and paying full price; head to the Denton Factory Stores where there are some of the best brands in the business: **GRAND PATRICIAN**, **LADY PEPPERELL**, **MARTEX**, **RALPH LAUREN**, **STEVENS** and **VELLUX**. They also maintain quite a line-up of licensed brands such as **DESIGNERS GUILD**, **DISNEY HOME COLLECTION**, **DR. SCHOLL'S**, **GLYNDA TURLEY**, **JOE BOXER** and **SERTA PERFECT SLEEPER**, and they are the manufacturer for the **MARTHA STEWART** bed and bath line. Discounts can soar to 70 percent on everyday popular brands in this 10,000-square-foot emporium. The inventory's extensive: towels, bath sheets, duvet covers, comforters, pillows and pillow shams, blankets, throws, pot holders and table tops; you can buy the works without getting short-sheeted. Directions: I-35 North to exit 470 or I-35 South to exit 471. For more than 187 years, Westpoint Stevens has been a giant in the textile industry. They are the nation's largest producer of bed and bath fashions. Sleep tight at their second outlet at the Allen Premiun Outlets (972/678-2420) in Allen. ***Call toll-free: 800/533-8229***

Lingerie

Big Girls' Bras, etc.   877/475-8110
3905 Melcer Dr., Suite 502   24/7
Rowlett, TX 75088

www.biggerbras.com   🖱 *Top Online Store!*

It's always great to see something big bust out of Big D. This online lingerie shop has you covered in every kind of bra from push-up to minimizers, soft-cup to underwires, from a training size to a maxi-size, this site has it all under wraps. Brands are traditional to exotic, ones you'd see everyone; ones you'll see only here. Buy three-in-stock bras and they'll throw in another FREE; buy six in-stock panties or thongs and they'll throw in another three FREE. And that's just the start of this lingerie site that showcases bras, lingerie, stockings, accessories, camisoles, tops and jeans, swimwear, sleepwear, pantyhose, shoes and slippers and men's unmentionables. Organized by budget (under $26; middle of the road, $25 - $45; or luxury, over $45), bras that are new for the month, bras that are the most popular, by size, by color, by design or shop by manufacturer. Then, there are pages and pages of sale merchandise which is where the buys are. This site is a treasure, not only because it fills a niche for larger-size lingerie for the big and beautiful, but becasue of its mammoth selection, ease of shopping and being a local online merchant success story. Just listen to some of the manufacturers represented: AVIANA, BALI, BARELY THERE, BIOFORM, CHANTELLE, EVA NIXI, EXQUISITE FORM, FANCEE FREE, FANTASIE OF ENGLAND, FELINA, FLEXEES, FREYA, GLAMORISE, GODDESS, GOSSARD, GRENIER, JUST MY SIZE, LADY MARLENE, LEADING LADY, LEONISA, LILY OF FRANCE, LILYETTE, LUNAIRE, MAIDENFORM, NATURANA, PADDED ATTRACTION, PLAYTEX, QT, SCHIESSER, SNOB, VABIEN, VANITY FAIR and WONDERBRA. Yes, there are other manufacturers out there and some you'll recognize because of their outlet stores, but none can compare to having them all in one place. Plus, if you're looking for seamless or seamed stockings, fishnets, ones that shimmer, ones that are thigh high, ones that go over the knee with a bow, well they've got 'em. Also, where else can you find a collection of opera-length gloves? Try them, you'll like them. *Call toll-free: 877/475-8110*

★★ Frederick's Of Hollywood   972/231-6576
501 S. Plano Rd., Suite 611   Mon-Sat 9-9; Sun 10-6
Richardson, TX 75081
www.fredericks.com

Well, I can dream, can't I? Play dress-up in the fanciest of lingerie from Frederick's of Hollywood at this Richardson Square outpost. Ooh, la-la, what an uplifting experience. Why not become a jungle kitty with a sexy outfit from here? Laced corsets to other unmentionables from $50 and up. And just because you're a BBB (big, blonde and beautiful) doesn't mean you can't get something sexy in your size. Full-figured females can get their fill to thrill. Choose appliquÈd gowns to pleated lace baby dolls, bustiers to thongs, indulge in something from Frederick's of Hollywood, you devil, you. You can also find lace bodice gowns and peignoirs, teddies, fantasy wear, chemises, body stockings and pantyhose, it's your call. Check directory for locations.

★★★★★★   L'eggs Hanes Bali Playtex Outlet   972/881-1006

1717 E. Spring Creek Pkwy.   Mon-Sat 9-9; Sun Noon-6
Plano, TX 75074
www.myfavoriteoutlet.com

 Let comfort be your guide and savings (20 to 50 percent off) be your reward. Find **BALI, BARELY THERE, BEYOND BARE, L'EGGS, LOVEABLE, PLAYTEX** and **WONDERBRA** in everything you need underneath it all. Whether it's bras, panties, intimates, socks, hosiery, legwear, sleepwear, slippers or apparel, you'll weather the storm of high prices here. From first-quality **HANES HER WAY** panties that were $1 less than Wal-Mart, to getting the scoop, the whole scoop online for everything else that's going on in the outlets. Find the closest one to you, order their catalogs, or shop online and forever have it your way. Four metro outlet mall locations.

★★★★★   Maidenform Outlet   972/355-4056

3000 Grapevine Mills Mall   Mon-Sat 10-9; Sun 11-8
Grapevine, TX 76051
www.maidenform.com

From fair maidens to old hags, **MAIDENFORM** will shape, hold, firm and tuck you back into place. Save as much as 50 percent off department store prices. From full figures to petites and all sizes in between, save big on crop tops, minimizers, push-ups, soft cups, strapless, underwires and water bras. Panties were as low as 99 cents a pair and shapewear was priced well under $20. There's underwires, push ups, strapless, bikinis, boy shorts, high cuts, low rises, g-strings and ouch....thongs. Expect savings to be around 40 percent off. Shopping at this outlet is hardly a bust! It's a boom.

★★★★★★   VF Factory Outlet   903/874-1503

316 Factory Outlet Drive   Mon-Sat 9-7 Sun 10-6
Corsicana, TX 75110-9045
www.VFFO.com

 Vanity Fair is far from being fair. As a matter of fact, it's way above average. It's the cleanest concept for an outlet operation in the country. Take one of the most powerful names in manufacturing and put in an outlet way out in the boonies at the Factory Stores of America and they will come. Shop here and you will save! That's right....half off the lowest ticketed price. That's how it was during one of their blowout sales. Otherwise, it's just 50 percent off, everyday. Their brand names are never-ending. The line-up is mind-boggling: **BRITANNIA, HEALTH-TEX, JANSPORT, JANTZEN, LEE, RED KAP, RIDERS, VANITY FAIR, VASSARETTE** and **WRANGLER**. Closest to the Metroplex, you can shop in Corsicana by taking I-45 S to Exit 229 to Highway 287 S.; or 4500 Highway 180 East in Mineral Wells, TX 76067-8385, 940/325-3318; from either Fort Worth or Dallas, take I-20/Highway 180 to Mineral Wells;

Wichita Falls: Highway 281 S to Highway 180 E. Visit online to find the VF Factory Outlet nearest you. Drive a little but save a lot!

★★   Victoria's Secret   214/987-9034

1030 Northpark Center   Mon-Sat 10-9; Sun Noon-6
Dallas, TX 75225
www.victoriassecrets.com

Do you know Victoria's signature? Well, it's probably "Pretty in Pink" since it's their signature color and name of one of their fragrances. Do you know Victoria's Secret? Well, I don't think it's much of a secret any more. They've been front and center for years. If you're a hip, fashion-forward gal who's anxious to stay abreast of the latest in lingerie (bras, panties, sleepwear, robes, hosiery, slippers, swimwear, clothing, cosmetic cases and more), this is the place to land. They now they even provide some support for the plus size figure; but, it's not as affordable as it is sexy. Online or via their toll free number, ordering can be done 24/7. Slip into any one of their 11 area locations but don't expect to find a deal. VS panties were five/$19.50, shapewear panties three/$29.50 but FREE shipping online for purchases over $100. *Call toll-free: 800/888-8200*

Medical & Dental

John A. Standefer, Jr., M.D.
Bob Blair's Before and After Photos

★★★★★ **1stDiscountRX.com**

2201 Midway Road, Suite 112   Mon-Fri 9-5 (CST online)
Carrollton, TX 75006

www.1stDiscountRX.com   🖰 *Top Online Store!*

It shouldn't come as any new news that Canadian Pharmacies can save you 40-60 percent off of the price you are currently paying for your prescription, generic, and OTC (over-the-counter) drugs. And this Canadian pharmacy is no exception. You must, though, have a recent script from your doctor which is faxed or mailed to 1stDiscountRX.com in Canada before it can be dispensed. However, this company makes it a cinch if you are a resident of the Metroplex to get help in ordering as they have an office in Carrollton to help you with the paperwork or if you prefer not to order over the internet. You'll fill out the forms and start using their service in just a few short steps. For those who love to shop online, their website is easy and well-organized. Navigate to wellness with a few clicks of the mouse. Hey, even pet prescriptions can be ordered at a substantial discount. With headquarters in Calgary, all prescriptions for 1st Discount RX are dispensed by Extended Care Pharmacy, License #1636, licensed by the Alberta College of Pharmacists, Licensee: Diaa Arsany, 109-2915 21st St. N.E., Calgary, AB, Canada T2E 7T1. It will cure your budget with what ails you. *Call toll-free: 866/901-DRUG*

◆◆◆◆◆ **A & T Moore Health Care Corporation   817/277-8606**

PO Box 121202   By Appt. Only
Arlington, TX 76012

When the going gets tough, the tough take care of it. This company is the one to call when you're dealing with a loved one who requires special in-home care. From sitter services to personal care, custodial to respite, even medical staffing, this company is licensed by the Texas Department of Human Services as a home health agency that provides that welcomed personal assistance. Up to 24-hour care is provided whether in local nursing homes or assisted living facilities, in your own home or the patient's home. For personal care, what exactly do they do? Well, just about everything from providing companionship to bathing and dressing, assisting with ambulation to meal preparation or assistance with meals, light house-keeping, laundry and more. They ensure your loved one is well cared for. Call for your private consultation and customized package as each patient is different.

★★★★   Accurate Medical Supplies   817/870-1240

550 Hemphill St.   Mon-Fri 8:30-5
Fort Worth, TX 76104

Durable medical supplies is this Accurate's claim to fame. What are durable medical supplies, you ask? Well, let me list the ways: wheelchairs, walkers, nebulizers and such for assisting those in need of moving about and in some cases, living a better life. Maybe a gel mask, for about $8- $10, would suit you to a T (rather than the old wives tale about tea bags). It may even be the perfect remedy for a certain employee's migraine headaches. (I won't mention any names, but she answers your calls at the office.) It never hurts to ask—how do you spell relief? For those who have price-checked other medical supplies in the area, these folks came out ahead of the competition in the price department. And that's relief right there. Now, doesn't that feel better?

◆◆◆◆   American Dental Care, Inc.   800/452-4468

11111 Katy Freeway   Membership Program
Houston, TX 77079
www.americandentalcareinc.com

Looking for a way to keep your mouth in good working order? Then consider this plan as an option for paying 30 to 80 percent less for dental services. There are two plans available: the first is for dental and optical care. For a family of up to six members, the yearly fee (which includes a five percent discount and the one-time $25 registration fee) amounted to $321.40; semi-annual fee was $181 for the first half (it includes registration fee) and $156 for the second half. For monthly payments by credit card, the fee was $26/mo plus the $25 registration fee. The second plan is for dental, optical and prescription discounts. Fees for yearly enrollment were $412.60; semi-annually, $229 and $204 or monthly payments by credit card would be $34 plus the one-time $25 enrollment fee. For dental, most of your basic services, for example, (cleaning, x-rays etc.) would be discounted as much as 80 percent with other services like fillings, crowns, etc., they were discounted about 30 percent. You have a choice of providers. Smile if all you want for Christmas is your two front teeth. Now, here's the way to save the day. (Check out our Insurance Button on our website for other options, though, before you join here. We offer a much more comprehensive plan for less money and no enrollment fees .... yes, I got a better rate and the enrollment fees waived for readers.) Go to www.undergroundshopper.com and click on the Insurance Button. Again, it pays to save with the Diva.

◆◆◆   Auditory Hearing Services   972/296-1600

210 S. Main Street, Suite 5   By Appt. Only
Duncanville, TX 75116-4763

When they announce their FREE audiometric testing, take advantage of their generosity and find out, once and for all, whether you're experiencing hearing loss, or if it's just a build-up of ear wax. Having a thorough examination is step one. Finding the right hearing aid is step two. And when they're running a sale is when you step up to step three. A CLASS A ITE custom-fitted full shell was reduced by 51 percent, from $800 to $389 during their blow-out sale and that is when you jump and when you can hear the resounding floor when you land! A PHONAK AERO CIC 100 percent digital signal processor "DSP" was reduced 40 percent off MSRP (manufacturer's suggested retail price); same with the PHONAK CLARA model, the only hearing aid to win the "Good Housekeeping Seal of Approval." These two are the nearly invisible, completely digital models that adjust to your environment, reduce wind noise, are cell phone-compatible. It's like having "three hearing aids in one." Forty percent off is probably music to your ears. For a custom canal Class A ITC, during the sale, the price was reduced by 50 percent, from $1,400 to $695. But remember, if you snooze you lose. Pay attention to their sales that occur periodically. Also available at their Sulphur Springs location at 1217 S. Broadway, 903/885-8357. Did you hear me?

◆◆◆◆◆◆ Barix Centers 972/429-8150; 972/429-8000

801 South Highway 78, Suite 300
Wylie, TX 75098
www.barixclinics.com

By Appt. Only

 It is now 2004, almost 2005—many years under the bridge (or is it over the bridge?) For me, it 2001 that was my pivotal year for my personal journey that took me to weight-loss surgery. It changed my life (and saved it at the same time.) See the "Before and After" pictures on my website, www.undergroundshopper.com to see what I looked like with an additional 140 pounds. I won't bore you with the gory details. You saw it up close and personal with Deborah Ferguson and me (unconscious) on Channel 5 when she chronicled my story in a three-part series of how I went from "morbid obesity" to svelte. Well, losing a 140 wasn't chopped liver. (Come to think of it, maybe it was the chopped liver!) Today, I am movin'and groovin'! I am out of the wheelchair, no longer suffering from congestive heart failure and sleep apnea or the agony of DE-FEET! Gastric Bypass Surgery was my path of least resistance. The operation called a Roux-en-Y worked and I am forever grateful. Now, it's your turn. Turn to the Barix Centers (formerly the Bariatric Treatment Center in Wylie (For other locations, log on to www.barixclinics.com.) If you are morbidly obese, a BMI index of 40 and 100 pounds or more overweight, then call for your consultation now. If you're a physician, you can make a referral to 888/797-8400; and if you're a potential patient in need of a consultation, call 800/282-006. These doctors have performed over 22,000 bariatric surgeries so consider this group one of the most experienced in the country. They understand the total care that you need—before, during and after your surgery and have built a clinic to meet all of those needs. *Call toll-free: 800/363-4303*

NR Boston Medical Group 469/374-0439

6380 LBJ, Suite 288
Dallas, TX 75240
www.bostonmedicalgroup.com

Mon-Fri 8-8; Sat-Sun 9-5

Anyone who advertises, "Sex for Life—the future of mankind rest assured," gets my attention. Of course, when you go to their website, you'll see a shirtless man and woman smiling....under the sheets. This international medical group has locations around the world claiming a 95 percent success rate over **VIAGRA**. This is a particularly sensitive issue and they take a medical approach in helping couples who are struggling with sexual issues complicated by diabetes, high blood pressure, heart conditions and stress. Not having tried it, I can't tell you if it works or not, but you're welcome to email me in confidence. Use an alias, if desired. *Call toll-free: 800/337-7555*

★★★★★★ BuySmart Medical Supply 214/358-0007

10031 Monroe, Suite 200
Dallas, TX 75229
www.buysmartmedical.com

 It doesn't take a genius to figure out what's been missing in the Metroplex. That's right, a store that sells pre-owned medical equipment. How many requests have I gotten for a deal on a scooter or a wheel chair? Well, I've run out of fingers counting. Hundreds, if not thousands. Thank goodness for BuySmart, the latest addition to our CMO (Community Medical Outreach) providers. I knew it was inevitable. Who better than Joe Williams to bring to the marketplace a better and smarter way to shop for Medical Supplies? Afterall, he has been selling brand name medical equipment for years; now, he's got a resale version where you can sell what you don't need or can't use anymore, and buy what you do need at a substantial savings. Every piece of equipment is sanitized so don't worry about the bed bugs biting! Here's where you can find the largest selection of pre-owned and refurbished medical equipment that has been inspected, sanitized and sold with a warranty. Since August 2003, BuySmart Medical Supply is the first company of its kind in the Dallas - Fort Worth and none too soon. Find Mobility Scooters, Seat lift Chairs, Wheelchairs, Walkers, Crutches, Hospital Beds, Safety Equipment—get the picture? Of course, there's more in store, but the idea is for you to visit just west of Stemmons and Walnut Hill. Turn left on Monroe and look for 10031. You won't be sorry and if you can't get to them, they'll come to you. They, of course, deliver, set-up and service the equipment after the sale. Get a preview of what's available on their easy to navigate website and order their FREE BuySmart Medical Supply Catalog to have "buy" your side for your next order. They also sell medical supplies and equipment from all the leading manufacturers. Financing available. If no one answers their phone, that means they are busy with a customer or out on an appointment. Leave your name and number and someone will get back to you shortly. If not, hit them over the head with your reburbished cane!

★★★★★★ Citi Uniforms   214/630-4000

1348 Inwood Rd.   Mon-Fri 10-6; Sat 10-5
Dallas, TX 75247
www.citiuniforms.com

 Just opening in the nick of time, this could be the best remedy for the high cost of health care yet—a place for doctors and nurses to get their uniforms, factory direct. Located at the Inwood Outlet Center. In fact, there's another uniform outlet in the same center so you'll have two options to choose from; the other outlet is Judy's Scrubs, also an excellent relief to the pain of full-price scrubs. Of course, it does nothing for you unless you are in a profession that requires the wearing of a uniform. But this outlet doesn't stop at just medical uniforms, they also provide discount medical accessories and supplies, too. That means the kind of shoes that someone who stands on their feet all day can get some relief in and a stethoscope to take a quick blood pressure. Mix in all the accessories that the medical profession calls upon in a pinch, and then add restaurant uniforms to the roster and make everyone who needs a uniform happy. It could outfit a lot of people in this town for less. And that is good. Very, very good. Remember, there are many professions that require a uniform and not just in the health care arena.

◆◆◆ Comfort Keepers   972/503-2222

2201 N. Central Expressway, Suite 175   By Appt. Only
Richardson, TX 75080
www.comfortkeepers.com

Let's face it. We may need some in-home assistance as we age. Perhaps one day we start to lose some of our mobility. What to do? What if it's your parents you're worried about and the trip across town, or across the country on a daily basis, is just out of the question? Here's that middle-of-the-road, affordable alternative. Comfort Keepers can tend to minor services like housekeeping, fixing a snack, running an error, helping with beauty treatments, taking clients for a manicure or a haircut or most any other non-medical acts of kindness. Currently, there are five Comfort Keepers (a franchised chain) in the Metro area (Plano, Bedford, Fort Worth and two in Dallas). Each office is individually owned and operated so rates vary. A daily phone check-in costs as little as $20/week and that alone could bring upon some comfort. A physical check-in costs $40 hour/with a two-hour minimum. That's for starters. *Call toll-free: 800/387-2415*

◆◆◆◆ **Cosmetic Solutions**   **214/526-LOBE (5623)**

12221 Merrit Drive   Mon-Fri 8-5 By Appt. Only
Dallas, TX 75251

Even if you merit a raise, you might not get one at this time and place. But if you have a raised mole, cyst, keloid or other kind of raised blemish or skin eruption that may even be a tumor, have off with it! And here is the place that cuts to the quick. Board-certified surgeons who specialize in the above procedures particularly skin abnormalities is their raison d'Ître. (I think that means reason for being in French, but I'm not sure—just move right along.) Preceding your appointment, you can fax a copy of your insurance card along with your name, address, phone number and social security number, along with what you need done and they can get it all approved prior to your arrival. And if it's a torn earlobe, they will perform a FREE ear piercing with its repair. Those repairs, however, are only done on Tuesdays from 2 PM-early evenings.

◆◆◆◆◆◆ **David Provost, M.D.**   **214/648-3069**

5323 Harry Hines Blvd   By Appt. Only
Dallas, TX 75390-7216

 If I hadn't had a Gastric Bypass myself, I'd hardly be qualified to recommend this doctor. But I did have the surgery and I whole-heartedly recommend Dr. David Provost of the Southwestern Medical Center. All I can say is, he sure made me a loser and I am the one who came out weigh ahead. I will be celebrating my third year anniversary soon and the loss of 140 pounds. Read more of my saga on my website but suffice to say, Dr. David Provost is the doctor who saved my life and added at least a few more decades of shopping onto my lifespan. Go to our Insurance Button on our website if you need help finding insurance that will cover this surgery. For a reference website about obesity and thousands of "before and after" life stories, go to www.obesityhelp.com. Be prepared for a wait for a consultation—a long wait.

◆◆◆◆◆ **Dental Depot, The**   **972/488-2123**

3326 Forest Lane   Mon-Thurs 7:30-5:30; Fri-Sat 8-2:30
Dallas, TX 75234-7712

Charles Nunnally, D.D.S is the dentist who drives the train at the Dental Depot. They also speak Spanish. (Se habla Español?) Well, they not only speak the language, they train all their patients (both grown-up and kids) to sit back and relax while the dentist is in the conductor's seat. There's something special about a dental office that is built with a train depot theme, complete with railroad crossings and other accoutrements of an actual train station depot. What happens when you pull into their parking lot? You smile. And that's the same philosophy that the dental office wants to convey to all their patients. To improve your smile through regular dental care. Here's an office that actually takes "walk-ins" and handles emergencies the same day without you having to beg and plead. All of the standard procedures are handled—from cleanings to wisdom teeth extractions. And Nitrous Oxide is provided if you request it. Crowns, bridges, cosmetic procedures and bleaching, root canals, full and partial dentures, whatever is necessary, hop aboard the dental train and let's not say, "A Choo-choo" until you've completed your appointment.

★★★★★   **DentalDepot.com**   **978/681-1170**
35 Woodberry Lane   24/7
North Andover, MA 01845
www.dentaldepot.com   ⌁ *Top Online Store!*

No, I don't expect you to travel to Massachusetts to make an appointment with this dentist, Dr. John A. Schrader, DMD, a practicing general dentist. What he has done that I approve of is having a shopping component with all the dental products that they recommend that you can't find except for a few products at your local dentist. Then, on top of the extensive selection for products for Dry Mouth, Halitosis, Headaches (TMD, TMJ), Athletic Mouthguards, Electric & Non-Electric Toothbrushes, Irrigators and **WATERPIKS**, Dental Floss and Floss Aids, Dental Tapes, Interdental Brushes, **OXYFRESH** (Hey, that's what I use), Stimulators, Lip & Tongue Care, Denture Supplies, Specialty Toothpastes, Braces, Bleaching & Bite Guard Supplies, Sugar-Free Candies and Gums, Natural Products, Medications (no pain medication, sorry about that) Pet Oral Care, even Goat's Milk Products. But the best part, they sell it at the lowest wholesale prices. Now, you can really smile.

◆◆◆◆◆◆   **Diva Discount Health and Insurance Programs**

469/293-SHOP (7467)
1079 W. Round Grove road, PMB 428, Suite 300   By Membership Only
Lewisville, TX 75067
www.undergroundshopper.com

 Log on to our website and click on the button that refers you to money-saving health plans, from discount medical cards to Health Savings Accounts. When you buy the big book this year, you'll save thousands of dollars with Diva Dollars (those are the checks that you present to area merchants for additional discounts), but new this year is our negotiated group rate for a discount medical card. Instead of having to pay an enrollment fee of $70 to Healthy America, they have waived the fee for Diva Readers. It's not insurance but rather a discount card. Read more about it on our website under the Health/Medical/Dental Insurance button. We also have access to fabulous A rated and higher rated companies at competitive rates (rates are all regulated by the state so they're basically the same). However, the secret is to have an expert independent broker who cares to give you the very best for your money—even if he doesn't make a dime. Fill out a quick questionnaire and click the mouse to be taken immediately to the broker's office and insurance is on its way. Enrollment fees for the discount card ($70) is automatically waived if you tell them the Diva sent you. This program will literally save hundreds, if not thousands of dollars on health care services.

★★★★★   **DoctorSolve.com**   **604/597-5952**
#200-2055 152nd St.   Mon-Fri 9-5 (PST)
Surrey, BC V4A 4N7, BC
www.doctorsolve.com   ⌁ *Top Online Store!*

If KIRO in Seattle ranked this Canadian Pharmacy #1 for prices, it was certainly worthy of my consider. Lo and behold—they're right. And not only were they the lowest, most of the other Canadian pharmacies didn't carry one of the drugs that I was checking on for a radio show caller. For example, even with her insurance co-pay of $25, the same drug **MAXZIDE** was available for a three-month (90 day) supply for $42.34. That's the price she almost pays for one month's supply.

Go figure! Within two business days after receiving your prescription order, a nurse will call to review your health profile. What great TLC. Save up to an additional $60 or more if you refer customers to them of $15 off your next prescription drug order when you give a Referral Card to a friend. There's no limit to their generosity. Furthermore, receive a complimentary pill box with your first order. I'm liking this company better with every word I write. A member in good standing of CIPA, the organization that monitors Canadian pharmacies for safe and reputable dispensing of medications, this company is a one-stop shop for ordering not only your prescription drugs, but generics, OTC (over-the-counter medications) and even for your pet. And by the way, Canadian drug standards are among the most stringent in the world. So, be assured you are getting all first-rate drugs at cut-rate prices without sacrificing quality or service. Trust me. The DoctorSolve Health Care Clinic is a 1,100 square foot office in Surrey's Windsor Square, a typical suburban strip center where clinic doctors are available for service to those Washingtonians who come over to BC for their doctor visits and prescriptions. What's a person to do if they can't afford their medications? Buy them in Canada, that's one way to save the day. Shopping for your prescriptions via email is even cheaper than buying them in person. So if you're uninsured, disabled, on a fixed income, or just plain can't afford to lay out often a thousand dollars or more a month just to stay alive, think DoctorSolve.com to the rescue—a real RX to savings. CIPA RX is the organization that sets the standards of safe, reputable Canadian Pharmacies. Always make sure the pharmacy requires a valid prescription from your doctor—as does DoctorSolve.com. This is a sure-fire way to determine if a website is legit. Doctorsolve is run out of a clinic and pharmacy in White Rock, British Columbia. Dr. Paul Zickler owns Doctorsolve, where you are charged $39 every time you order for a doctor to review your case. Like all online Canadian pharmacies, you have to fax or send your U.S. doctor's prescriptions, fill out a medical questionnaire and sign a consent form. Business from the states is booming. Is it any wonder? *Call toll-free: 866/732-0305*

◆◆◆◆ Dr. Bush Zhang   972/279-4888

10851 Ferguson   By Appt. Only
Dallas, TX 75228

If you are open to alternative medical treatments, consider this Korean doctor of acupuncture somebody to needle. Let's get to the point: If you're in pain and nothing else has worked, what do you have to lose (except the pain)? Be on pins and needles as a therapeutic procedure and see if there's any relief. But pain is not the only reason to seek out an alternative route to improved well-being. Several friends of mine swear this doctor has relieved them of everything from constipation to acute pain, back aches to weight loss. Try it. English barely spoken but understandable.

★★★★★   Flower Mound Pharmacy   972/355-4614

1001 Cross Timbers, Suite 1050 (Main Street)   Mon-Thurs 8:30-6:30; Fri 9-6; Sat 8:30-12:30
Flower Mound, TX 75028
www.fmherbalrx.net

If you're allergic to the outer casings of a prescription drug or your child can't swallow a pill without gagging, what to do is simple—call a compounding registered pharmacist. They provide custom made prescriptions (so the medicine will go down and not come up!) Not every pharmacist wants to or is trained to perform this customized service. That's where Dennis Song and three registered pharmacists come in, three certified pharmacy technicians and a manager to keep everything running smoothly in this 2,000 square foot oasis that has set themselves apart from the Walgreens and Eckerds on every street corner. Located on the west side of the Atrium Mall facing Braum's on Main Street in Lewisville, picture the famous Norman Rockwall painting of a pharmacist, and you'll get the picture. This one-stop neighborhood pharmacy offers the same or lower prices than Sam's. They charge you the cost of the drug plus $10 for his profit on each and every prescription. How about that? So for all of the mom and pop pharmacies out there complaining that Wal-Mart is making it impossible to compete, here's one that not only competes pricewise, but does it better. This full-service pharmacy offers everything you'd expect and more including aromatherapy products, pet products, bath products, books, BURT'S BEES, diabetic supplies, hair and skin products, herbal remedies, natural medicines, durable medical equipment and an extensive website for information and product ordering online. Next door is FM Specialty Foods store for all the rest.

◆◆◆◆◆   **Genesis Wellness**   **940/497-8500**
4851 I-35   By Appt. Only
Corinth, TX 76210-2348
www.hyperbaricwellness.com

Want to improve you health? How about your life? Are you fed up with being sick? Tired? Are you looking for that miracle cure for the aches and pains of rheumatoid arthritis, Fibromyalgia, chronic fatigue syndrome? A ha, now I have your attention! Then, look to Genesis Wellness for FREE tests and turn the tide towards something new, different, state-of-the-art and revolutionary. Stop running all over town looking just to treat symptoms. Instead, let me introduce Dr. Les Schachar, a medical doctor with years of experience and world-wide acclaim who is devoted to several major treatment modalities that are both non-evasive and cost-effective. For one, the Hyperbaric Oxygen Therapy (HBOT), a painless procedure in which the patient breathes 100 percent oxygen in a chamber. That's it. It's like going to a tanning salon, it's that simple with powerful results. Over and over again, studies have shown that a variety of medical conditions will benefit with an increase in oxygen (it enhances the body's ability to kill germs and to increase healing.) Take a deep breath and say H2 Oh-h-h! *Call toll-free: 877/367-4268*

◆◆◆◆   **Grace Medical Association**   **972/420-6777**
560 W.Main, Ste. 205   Mon-Tues & Fri 8-5; Wed 8-1; Fri 9-6
Lewisville, TX 75057
www.gracemedical.ehcmd.com

Looking for an alterative medical treatment, such as chelation therapy, but would rather not travel outside the traditional medical milleau? Well, look no further than Lewisville and save more than just grace. This medical group consists of Internal Medicine Specialists as well as Primary Care Physicians who provide excellent medical care, from the routine to the most complex medical problems of adolescents and adults. They treat all the usual cases of hypertension, heart diseases, cholesterol problems, arthritis, diabetes and its complications, kidney problems, respiratory diseases and more. In other words, they do it all. But they also offer other procedures that many family practioners do not, such as laser therapy for varicose and spider veins, permanent hair removal, skin toning with some of the most advanced and effective FDA-approved techniques such as Nd-YAG laser device "LYRA-XP" by LASERSCOPE and more. In fact, their website recommends you take the time to learn more about these latest techniques and become an informed shopper before you make your appointment. Another bit of good advice for saving Grace.

◆◆◆◆◆◆ Healthquest Chiropractic/Wellness Ctr.   972/724-7247

2221 Cross Timbers Rd., # 137   Mon-Fri 7 AM-7 PM By Appt. Only
Flower Mound, TX 75028
www.chiropractic-doctors.us/Healthquest_Chiropractic__24721-chiropractor.html

How do you spell relief? Well, it just might be—if you check into the Healthquest Chiropractic & Wellness Center. Nothing mysterious about seeing a chiropractor and at HealthQuest, there are three of them. Twelve hour days Mon-Fri to heal your mind, body and spirit, really; from top to bottom with some of the most incredible diagnostic devices I have ever seen demonstrated. Ask about Dr. Mary Jo Ellig's testing equipment. One visit and you will be flabbergasted. That's all I'm going to say. Though she is a board-certified chiropractor (DC, DACBN, CCN) as are all of the other doctors, she is not interested in impressing anyone with all of her credentials. In fact, she prefers you call her Mary Jo. (She also is a certified nutritionist and knows lots about how your diet affects every aspect of your life.) Then meet Dr. Mike Cox, he's a chiropractor, too, but his specialty is acupuncture. Wow! Let him needle you to your heart's content. Pain, pain go away and that's easy, according to Dr. Mike. Weight loss and smoking cessation are tougher to affect a change but he says he's up to the challenge. There is also a RMT (registered massage therapist) on staff, Livia Prue's her name. Expect lots of information alongside adjustments and natural homeopathy remedies. They also work closely with Dennis Song, one of the few compounding pharmacists in the city at the Flower Mound Pharmacy down the street (which is, by the way, the talk of the town with people who like to heal the natural way.) While other medical treatments may fail, sometimes correcting the cause of the physical problem rather than just treating the symptom is the cure to what ails you. At least that's the path taken by the chiropractors at Healthquest. With a normal functioning spine and healthy nervous system, your body can heal itself. Makes sense, doesn't it? If there is something interfering with the spine's normal functioning, then the goal is to get rid of it through specific chiropractic adjustments. By George, I think they've got it! Again, ask Mary Jo about her diagnostic tools. Going through it will make you a believer. Don't ask me how or why it works—it just does. Even babies can benefit from a chiropractor's advice and adjustments. Why be plagued with problems your entire life when there is help right around the table? Meet me there if your back is giving you a pain in the neck. Many insurance carriers now underwrite a chiropractic visit, so check into it. Then call me in the morning. This is your home for health, homeopathy, nutrition, acupuncture, chiropractic treatment and the latest in computer technology. How to you spell relief? H.E.A.L.T.H.Q.U.E.S.T.

★★★★★★ Hearing Aid Express   972/241-4620

11888 Marsh Lane, Suite 111   Mon-Fri 9-5
Dallas, TX 75229-2660
www.hearingaidexpress.com

Now hear this. Hearing Aid Express has four locations: Congratulations! If you have trouble hearing the fine print, you need Hearing Aid Express. At last, someone is meeting the needs of the aging population by providing discounts on private label hearing aids (HAE brand). Both in the ear (custom, $495 and canal, $595) styles can get you hearing right off the bat. Save $400 off a pair of SONIC INNOVATIONS 2SE Digital Hearing Aids. With all the new and improved technology for the hard-of-hearing, nobody has an excuse these days to be reading lips. Hearing Aid Express has been in the Metroplex for over 10 years. They offer a 30-day trial period, so what do you have to lose? Expect a one-year warranty, full FDA compliance, qualified repairs ($89-$119 any brand), batteries (50 cents) and fast service. Look what you get for FREE: hearing exam, office visits, programming, supply of batteries, cleaning any time, consultations. After that the batteries cost 50-cents (Wal-

Mart charges $1.00) Locations in Dallas, Houston, San Antonio and Austin. Remember, if you buy a hearing aid through the mail, who are you going to take it to if something goes wrong? You can't get an adjustment at a post office box. Visit the Marsh Lane location (in the Tom Thumb S/C across from Hancock Fabrics) and see the lab where your hearing aids are made. HAE is the only factory-outlet of hearing aids in the state that I know of so it's the only real hearing aid resource that can save you money. Did you hear me loud and clear? Save money! Save the embarrassment of having to ask folks to continually repeat themselves. Enjoy the theatre whereby you can hear the jokes and laugh at the right times. Other locations at 3330 North Galloway, Suite #322, Mesquite, Texas 75150, 972/270-4441; Plano at 926 East 15th Street, Suite # 102, 972/881-4327. There's always a special going on such as $100 off linear / $200 off each **SONIC INNOVATIONS II** or **III** purchase of any hearing aid. Aids start as low as $495 and go up to $2,800. Hearing Exams are FREE and take about an hour. Appointments recommended, but walk ins welcome. They can pre-arrange Saturday appointments in advance. Bring in a copy of our FREE monthly magazine and receive $400 off a pair of digital **SONIC INNOVATIONS NATURA 3** or take advantage of Hearing Aid Express's Diva Dollars. *Call toll-free: 800/628-8250*

◆◆◆◆◆◆ J. Glenn Smith, D.C.   214/956-0999

2608 Inwood Rd., Suite 150   By Appt. Only
Dallas, TX 75235-7433
www.coldlaser.com

Dr. Glenn Smith made my pain go away in my legs. No ifs, ands or butts! Actually, the pain in my buttocks, attributed to a sciatic nerve problem, is better, too, not gone but after one visit, what do you expect? OK, so what did he do that years of orthopedic visits didn't or couldn't? Well, he used the cold laser on me and I am here to tell you, it worked. One treatment and the pain behind my calves that I have suffered with for years did not hurt today. One treatment. Am I a believer? You bet. In fact, Dr. Smith, in my opinion, is a wunkerkind with more than 10 years of experience using the cold laser. It's a medical device that is credited with almost miracle-like results in many areas of medicine and dentistry. Forget scalpels. Lower costs. Reduced risks. And yes, maybe better and faster results. For sure, faster healing. Hey, I'm for that! Using a cold laser beam that pierces the skin and stimulates the white blood cells to come to the inflamed area to reduce pain and swelling—well, who can argue with that? Success is just a laser beam away. Approved for the treatment of carpal tunnel syndrome by the FDA as well, Dr. Smith has been a proponent of the cold laser for years. This non-burning therapy is used to treat soft tissue injuries which means it may be useful in the treatment of sprains, Tendonitis, disc injuries, arthritis, wounds, shingles, mouth injuries (like TMJ syndrome) and sciatica. Workers Comp and Insurance pays for laser treatment, so what are you waiting for? Even without insurance, the treatments are very affordable. Oh, I almost forget to mention that it also helps with edema (swelling) and acute conditions like sports' injuries and has even been successful for sufferers of rheumatoid arthritis. Is this too good to be true? Not in my case; hence, I want to shout from the highest stair case—I can climb to the highest mountain with no shooting pains in the back of my legs. Try it, you'll like it. And if it works for you, too, thank Dr. Smith. Three minutes from Love Field on the south side of the airport, is it any wonder folks fly in for treatments? In fact, one patient drives from Chicago, no kidding. Treatment times vary. Though several are recommended, a day or so apart, if you are traveling a long distance, Dr. Smith may perform them twice a day for a week to accelerate the healing process.

◆◆◆◆◆◆ **John A. Standefer, Jr., M.D.**   **972/296-1587**

1014 E. Wheatland Rd.   By Appt. Only
Duncanville, TX 75116
www.facedoctor.com

 Ageless Beauty Cosmetic Surgery is how Dr. Standefer separates himself from other cosmetic surgeons in the Metroplex. Operating, so to
speak, in the Duncanville area for the past 20 years, he wants YOU! In
fact, he recently ran a Makeover Special whereby he and other physicians and local shops donated
their services to make YOU over. Watch our website for another Extreme Makeover. Send him a
recent photo and a paragraph as to why you want or need an Extreme Makeover and you never
know—one may be in the cards just around the corner. Starting at the top and working his way
down: eyelid surgery, forehead and eyebrow lifts, neck liposuction, Otoplasty, cheek implants and
of course, the facelift itself. Then, his aestheticians step in and the fun begins: Laser Hair
Removal, Microdermabrasion, **OBAGI** Skincare Products, **JANE IREDALE** makeup (mineral
based and fabulous) and much more. The fact that he did a complete face lift on you-know-whose
husband is reason enough to recommend him above all others. Check out Bob's button on our
website, www.undergroundshopper.com and see what you think of his "Before and After" pictures. Graduating from the University of Texas Health Science Center in 1978, he completed his
internship and residency at the Bexar County Hospital specializing in Otorhinolargygology (big
word for head and neck surgery) and then going back for a second specialty in Facial Plastic and
Reconstructive Surgery. He is board-certified in both. Is it any wonder they call him the Face Doctor? He is active in all of the medical societies and has written and presented numerous papers on
head and neck surgery as well as facial cosmetic surgery. He is also compassionate and giving of
his incredible skills to people in need. There's one little boy out there who now has perfect ears
thanks to the generosity of Dr. Standefer and his able medical staff. They were featured on Channel 11 News locally and nationally on Inside Edition with Deborah Norville. Too, he's our doctor
of choice for our 4th Saturday monthly **BOTOX®** Clinics. I'm the first in line every three months
for BOTOX and when it comes time to have another **RESTYLANE®** injection (the newest col-
lagen filler), I will be again right up there. Having both is possible because Dr. Standefer's prices
are so much more reasonable for the Botox® and Restylane® that I can afford it. What a difference an injection makes. So, if you look like a Shar-pei, go to our Shar-pei button on our website
and see where we'll be next.

◆◆◆◆◆◆ **John Launius, M.D.**   **972/315-8588**

713 Hebron Parkway, Suite 220   Mon-Fri 9-5:30; Sat 10-3:30
Lewisville, TX 75057
www.affordablehealthlewisville.com

 By George, I think he's got it! This is one MD who you'll never want to write a Dear
John letter to. Instead, you will want to write a thank you note, because he is a Dear!
When was the last time you didn't have to beg a doctor to see you on a Wednesday,
much less a Saturday? Here's just point #1 that makes this doctor stand apart from the crowd, a
one-of-a-kind jewel in the arsenal of medical practitioners who actually thinks of their patients
first. Second point, there are no appointments necessary. Okay, so you sign in and wait a bit but
nowhere near the wait when you have an appointment at a designated time and have to wait two
hours. Point #3. Here is where we separate the weak from the cheap. He's affordable. Yes, can you
believe I am using that word in the same breath as when I say Doctor? Dr. John specializes in folks
who have no insurance; or whose deductibles are so high they will probably never meet them in a
year. And lastly, Dr. Launius wants to cater to those of us who are self-employed and do not have
the benefit of gigantic group health insurance. (Do any of these apply to you? Do you resemble

this remark?) Parents, do you need a school exam for your kiddo who wants to play sports? How does $10 sound? Or what about a standard exam for $49 or a complete physical for $99 which includes an EKG, Cholesterol, diabetes and kidney screens, PSA (Prostate exam for men), Thyroid Panel (women), Urinalysis and lastly, a physical exam. Yes, there's a full lab and X-Ray department also within his offices making it a one-stop shop. But mostly, we applaud this doctor because it's obvious he cares. This Emergency Medicine specialist is one medicine man who has found a better way and if there were Nobel Prizes for noble deeds, he would be first on my list. And if my recommendation isn't enough, on one website, he was voted one of the top ten best thyroid doctors in Texas and another patient said, "He treats symptoms, not just numbers. He really listens to what you have to say." All of this and affordable, too?

★★★★ Judy's Scrubs & More 214/634-3734

1342 Inwood Rd.
Dallas, TX 75247

Mon-Sat 10-6

Two blocks west of Stemmons on Inwood Rd. at the Inwood Outlet Center, say hello to Judy's Scrubs & More. Across from the Crate and Barrel Outlet, you can straddle both sides of the street to shop for the sunny side up. Brand new to the family of merchants who have congregated within this in-town outlet complex called the Inwood Outlet Center, whether you shop the north or south sides of the street, the message is clear: savings are in store everywhere. But at Judy's, here's a place that provides an equal opportunity to save money on just about everything in the store; more specifically scrubs at Judy's. Whether you're a fan of CHEROKEE, DISNEY, LANDOW or the PEACHES brand, you can wrap up a scrub and look the part of the professional. From the medical profession to the hospitality industry, the tops and bottoms here are made for comfort, durability, flexibility. After all, you don't sit still for very long in your job, do you? Find unisex drawstring bottoms and those oh those comfy tops in solids and prints starting as low as $9.99. Whether you're working, lounging or wanting to dress up for Halloween, expect them to be marked with a price that's right. And during sale times, they discount over and above their everyday discounts.

◆◆◆◆◆ Lynn K. Glover, M.A., Speech Pathologist 972/407-6050

16990 Dallas Parkway, Suite 255
Dallas, TX 75248

By Appt. Only

Lynn Glover is a certified speech and language specialist holding all the appropriate licenses to hang out a shingle and call herself a Speech Pathologist. If there's an area of speech that is suffering, she is the professional to consult. From those who suffer from a speech impediment to victims of a stroke who are looking to regain their speech, here is a caring and dedicated professional who will offer special Diva rates for groups, in-home, in-office, in-school or in-hospital visits. From work at early childhood centers to private speech-language clinics, Lynn has worked for many non-profit organizations and societies before entering private practice. She provides evaluation and treatment for language disorders, auditory processing, articulation disorders, fluency, voice treatment for Parkinson's and stroke patients, as well as the ability to work closely with families to facilitate carry-over into the home. You couldn't get a more genuine care-giver or a more competent consultant when speech is problematic.

★★★★★★   **Medical Arts Pharmacy**   **817/645-6619**

604 N. Nolan River Rd.   Mon-Fri 9-6
Cleburne, TX 76033-7008

 Medical Arts is a masterpiece of value and quality wear for men and women in the medical profession. But no website unfortunately. So it's up to you to show up in person for scrubs to medical duds, all offered at discount prices. Since staying on your feet all day can be taxing, CALZUROS shoes are just the right remedy. The fact that they will match competitor's prices and sever another 10 percent off the price can be almost therapeutic. Get an extra jolt by bringing in the whole gang. They'll give an extra 2 percent off the purchase price. But, with all that, we still haven't gotten to their best feature. Discount prosthetics for women with mastectomies. Who would have thought swimwear, bras and lingerie for women with special needs would ever be discounted? Well, they are, with the same low price guarantee. Rest assured Medical Arts DME is just what the doctor ordered.

◆◆◆◆◆◆   **Natan Yaker, M.D.**   **972/985-7474**

4100 W. 15th Street, Suite 106   By Appt. Only
Plano, TX 75093
www.dryaker.com

 Dr. Natan Yaker, MD is the Medical Director of Cosmetic Surgery Associates of Texas in Plano and has been in practice in the Dallas/Plano area since 1978. Having done his internship and residency programs in Miami, Florida and New York in Plastic and Reconstructive Surgery, he ultimately moved to Dallas to begin his practice. Board-certified since 1979 by the American Board of Plastic Surgery, he has held many administrative positions in the Dallas Society of Plastic and Reconstructive Surgeons and is imminently qualified to perform all types of cosmetic (both plastic and reconstructive) surgery. He is a member of the American Medical Association, American Society of Plastic and Reconstructive Surgeons,

◆◆◆◆◆◆   **New You Weight Management Center**

3820 W. Northwest Hwy.   By Appt. Only
Dallas, TX 75220-5160
www.newyouwmc.com

 Less invasive than a Gastric Bypass (like I had), the Lap-Band is often the procedure of choice for many morbidly-obese patients (those with generally over 100 pounds to lose.) Here's where it's one-stop lap banding with a team of three surgeons, two of whom do the lap band and the third, Dr. David Leland who sculpts the body with his plastic surgical skills for breast lifts, tummy tucks, liposuction—ah, return to the days when everything didn't point south. Joining Dr. Leland, Drs. Nirmal Jayaseelan and Dr. Thomas Diaz are part of the New You team where "losing is everything." Be a loser. Attend one of their FREE monthly information seminars which are held monthly at the Park Cities Hilton Hotel, 5934 Luther Lane in Dallas, two blocks south of Northwest Hwy. and east of the Tollway. If you're ruluctant to try gastric bypass, this is a less risky "WEIGH TO GO!" *Call toll-free: 800/383-0605*

★★★★★★   **PASS (Prescription Assistance Specialized Services)**
8344 E. RL Thornton Freeway, Suite 100   **214/367-8200**
Dallas, TX 75228   Mon-Fri 8-5
www.pass4rx.com

                Kerry Price and Kellye Staub are the driving forces behind the Prescrip-
                     tion Assistance Specialized Services. Do PASS go because this is your
                     get-out-of-debt relief if you're struggling to pay for prescription drugs.
Their service is so easy and affordable, it's hard to resist. Did you know that pharmaceutical companies will provide FREE prescription medicines to those who qualify? The only problem is,
"Who are they? Who to call? What does your doctor have to do to get those prescriptions for you
and why isn't he doing it?" Well, first off, doctors are so busy that filling out forms is the last thing
they have time to do. But if they did, perhaps you could be saving hundreds even thousands of dollars a month on your much needed (live or die) prescriptions. To read if you qualify, log on to their
website and stop worrying. To meet in person, they are inside the Guaranty Bank Building on the
first floor in very attractive offices at the intersection of Jim Miller and I-30. There's a $25 Enroll-
ment Fee, $30 Medication Application Fee which covers the application and the first three months
of each prescription; then there's a $15 Monthly Service Fee per prescription. If you are needing to
take what they call Complex Medications, (Medications that are oncology/virology (HIV)/narcot-
ics-controlled substances/or any medication which requires monthly participation between the
physician, PASS and the PAP,) there's a small surcharge but nothing compared to the retail cost of
these drugs. Most patients taking three or four drugs per month will literally save hundreds a
month and hence thousands in the year. A small price to pay to LIVE—the good life at all even at
half the price! *Call toll-free: 800/727-7479*

◆◆◆◆◆◆   **Patients Comprehensive Cancer Center 972/395-1010**
4352 N. Josey Lane   By Appt. Only
Carrollton, TX 75010
www.pccctx.com

                Watch for a 20 percent discount and then a 50 percent discount off the second scan
                     when the first one is purchased at Patients Comprehensive Cancer Center
                     (pccctx.com). Their website is extensive for inquiring minds, detailing their philoso-
phy, staff and procedures. There's no doubt in my mind that when the dreaded word of "cancer" is
uttered, most folks are more than just disheartened. But at this Cancer Center, you can take heart.
It is fast becoming a clinical setting where there is hope, where every doctor's specialty is oncology. Find medical oncology, infusion therapy (that's chemotherapy), diagnostic radiology and
radiation therapy services all under one center. So for preventative treatment before you're diag-
nosed and then when the treatment begins (and after, too), this is a one-stop shop to have all of the
cancer disciplines involved in your treatment plan to be right there under one roof. They have all
the newest CT scanners whereby early detection through the full body scan, the Heart, the Lung, a
virtual scan of the Colon (you mean I could have avoided TWO general anesthetics just to have
the exam done on me this year?) Where was this center when I needed them most? Do you think
you're young and therefore out of cancer's path of destruction? Wrong. Isn't it a shame that this
wasn't around during the time when Gilda Radner could have taken advantage of them and continued making us laugh. As she so often lamented, "It's always something!" Here is the perfect
opportunity for you to take a proactive role in your healing. Even if your Mother told you you better shop around, you don't have to here. Early detection is the key to survival and I vote for the
pccctx.com website if you want to read more about achieving that all important "peace of mind."
Call for your appointment. There are four facilities (all listed on their web site in Plano, Grand
Prairie and Farmers Branch). The one above is located northeast of Hebron Parkway and Josey

Lane (at Josey and Cheyenne on the North), directly east of Trinity Medical Center. ***Call toll-free: 866/4PCCCTX***

◆◆◆◆◆ **ProSource Medcost Containment**   **214/222-2400**

359 Lake Park Road, Suite 128   Mon-Fri 10-5
Lewisville, TX 75057-2326

If you know someone who needs to get around so they can shop around, here is one source to contain costs. Most items are at little or no cost to you via Medicare and secondary insurance. For example, Medicare will cover one pair of diabetic shoes and three pairs of inserts per year. So here's one step for man or woman kind that I applaud. As a matter of fact, this company will even come to your home or office for a FREE Medicare pre-qualification consultation. Call to see if they are still willing to accommodate you even if you don't have a coupon. Here's what they routinely provide towards your medical needs: power chairs, scooters, lift chairs, walkers, manual wheelchairs, lifts and ramps. Don't let your disability limit your mobility. There is help out there and all it takes is a phone call. Do it or lose it as we say.

◆◆◆◆◆ **Radiant Research**   **214/265-1624**

7515 Greenville, Suite 801   Call For Appt. Mon-Fri
Dallas, TX 75231
www.radiantresearch.com

Chances are, whatever ails you will eventually end up on a list of investigative pharmaceutical medicines. If you want to be on the cutting edge of medical research, then volunteer yourself and your ailments to Radiant Research. Programs change frequently, but to find out the latest trials, log on to their website and read on. One week's problems included athlete's feet, contraceptives, gastrointestinal ulcers, hot flashes, obesity, osteoporosis and overactive bladder. Well, seven ailments, and I suffer from 6 of them. Where do I sign up? The list doesn't stop with just those seven sent. There were 10 other medical conditions also being researched. This may be an alternative to high-cost doctor's office visits and prescriptions. Each study has certain requirements such as age, gender, etc., but most conditions offer FREE study-related medications and examinations, as well as travel compensation. When was the last time you got a check from YOUR doctor? ***Call toll-free: 888/220-7715***

◆◆◆◆◆ **Renaissance Laser Centers**   **214/361-9226**

11661 Preston Road, Suite 128   Mon & Wed 9-6; Tues & Thurs 9-8; Fri 9-5; Sat 9-3
Dallas, TX 75230
www.renaissancelaser.com

Looking for state-of-the-art hair removal and other high-tech skin care treatments? You don't have to be a Renaissance woman to enjoy the services exclusively. Men are welcome, too! Utilizing the **LUMENIS LIGHTSHEER** Diode laser, this system offers breakthrough features and distinctive advantages. It was the first system to provide permanent hair reduction using state-of-the-art, high-power diode technology. It's fast and offers non-invasive treatment that is nearly pain-free, and you can get up and go with virtually no downtime. All kinds of skin types can get the benefits, even if you're tanned and lovely. The system has endured long-term clinical trials and has shown to permanently reduce hair growth and treat the entire range of skin colors and hair types. Hundreds of thousands of patients have become hair-free as a result of this treatment. But if you think there is life beyond hair, then consider some of the other high-tech skin care procedures such as FotoFacials, Microdermabrasions, **BOTOX®** injections and **ENDERMOLOGIE** for the removal of cellulite. Cellulite? Who's got cellulite? Check directory for other locations.

◆◆◆◆◆◆ Richard J. Martin, DDS   972/434-0050

591 W. Main St.   By Appt. Only
Lewisville, TX 75057-3628

Here I thought implants were those things that women sought to increase their busts. Well, that was before I met Dr. Richard Martin, Oral and Facial Surgery of North Texas, PC. After my consult with Dr. Martin, everything became right with the world. He is a specialist in the field of Oral and Maxillofacial Surgery and has every credential within his field with years and years of specialized training including all of the years necessary beyond dental school. He is up on all the current techniques to ensure each patient receives the highest quality of care with the most compassion rare to see demonstrated by a medical person in this day and age of "pack 'em in and get 'em out." When you see the results of his work, you can understand that he can literally transform a person's life. As for me, personally, all I can say is that he is the finest oral surgeon I have ever gone to. My beautiful three bottom implants are in my mouth as if they were there from the very beginning. Not only is Dr. Martin a technical perfectionist but you won't meet a more caring dental office ensemble of nurses and assistants. They treat you like one of their family even when I got a little scared on the day of my surgery, they put me at ease and before I knew it, I was walking out with nary a regret. Call for a FREE consultation for any special dental concerns you've been putting off for years. If you're a candidate for dentures, talk to Dr. Martin about transplants. If you're fearful, he'll allay your fears. And whatever he performs, it will be painless. Remember, Dr. Martin trained many years after dental school to performed intricate and complicated dental and facial restorations that literally change peoples lives. From jaws that are out of line to clef palates, wisdom teeth extractions to dental implants, he's a skilled surgeon dedicated to the cutting edge (pardon the expression) on new techniques and procedures. You might even smile on your way out the door. I did.

◆◆◆◆◆ Senior Friends   972/420-1000

500 W. Main St. (Lewisville HCA Hosp.)   Membership Club
Lewisville, TX 75057-3629

Are you a senior? Do you love a bargain? Is your name Goldstein or Blair? Well, CODE GREEN, CODE GREEN, all bargain hunters report to the hospital with their *Senior Friends* membership card and upgrade to first class. For $15 a year or $25 for couples, enjoy the benefits only this club can grant. Oh, mighty one. Want a private room for the price of a double? Want your spouse (or other family member) to enjoy a meal on the house while they're visiting you? These and other benefits await you just by knowing who to call. Her name's Mary Sue and she's the coordinator of this program that grants you these wonderful upgrades. And you don't even have to be a frequent crier to be granted these special awards. You just have to join the club. Then, on your next visit to the Lewisville Hospital, you pay for a semi-private room but get placed in a private room at no additional charges. Now, that's a deal even in these difficult times.

◆◆◆◆◆◆ Solace Counseling   214/522-4640

2519 Oak Lawn Ave., Suite 100   By Appt. Only
Dallas, TX 75219
www.solacecounseling.com

Unlike any other counseling center in town, Solace Counseling presents itself as "a New Direction in Intensive Therapy." Sounds sobering and perhaps ominous; instead, it's the opposite. It's enlightening and hopeful. This caring team of professionals have dedicated themselves to a creative program of day treatment for addictive behavior— alcohol, drugs, prescription RX, food, sex, anything that would be considered as out-of-control compulsive behavior. From crisis stabilization to intensive treatment, long-term support and after-care, they are the licensed specialty center for detox, addictions, psychiatric care, borderline personality disorders, suboxone/subutex treatment for opiate dependency (like anyone addicted to a pain medicine like Oxicodone who needs to withdraw but is afraid of the withdrawal complications.) The latest research, the latest medications, the latest techniques for treatment that can often be described as miraculous. Individual and group therapy available to teach you coping skills so as to live your life to its maximum. Don't expect a bunch of stuffed shirts, suits and ties. It's a casual, warm and inviting environment with a full-time physician and RN on staff. It's also cost-effective, compassionate and caring. Wouldn't it be wonderful to learn how to manage life's everyday activities without a dependence on anything that could be damaging? It's the only center for day treatment for addictive patients who do not want to enter an overnight facility like Betty Ford. And as it's name implies, it's comforting. Creative solutions to life's everyday problems that can be managed almost overnight with the newest medicines combined with counseling. Call for an appointment today; they might just be the solace needed to turn your world around to a new, healthier you.

Southwest Medical   800/236-4215

Mon-Fri 8-5; Sat 9-1

513 W. Thomas Road
Phoenix, AZ 85013
www.southwestmedical.com   🖱 *Top Online Store!*

Southwestmedical.com is an online discount medical supply company that has a huge selection at deeply wounded prices. Owned and operated by industry professionals, they have more than 20 years of direct selling experience in providing customers with all types of home medical equipment and supplies. Why pay retail while trying to maintain a healthy outlook on life? From strictly rehabilitation equipment for the new user to a full line of products ranging from ultra-light wheelchairs and ambulatory aids to urology supplies and wound care, there really isn't much they don't attend to (with the exception of "scar therapy" which is what I was particularly interested in). The menu of supplies and equipment is extensive with discounts equally as substantive: bathroom aids, daily living aids, diabetic care, diagnostic products, personal protection, respiratory and accessories—and the ability to search by category, by product, or by brand.

◆◆◆   Southwest Patient Care Solutions   972/867-4613

Mon-Fri 9-6:30; Sat 10-2

3221 Independence Pkwy.
Plano, TX 75075

Just call and ask about a product, any product and you'll get more information than you bargained for. But then, an armed consumer always wins out in the end. Fortified with an arsenal of medical supplies including GUARDIAN SUNRISE, INVACARE and LUMEX—even custom-built supplies, such as wheelchair baskets, can be procured. Actually, just go ahead and get the wheelchair here, too, while you're at it. They're prepared for any medical problem with wound care and diabetic supplies being a specialty. Catalog orders, from infant pediatric supplies to rehabilitation needs, are at your fingertips. Get the answer to all your problems by receiving a discount for payments in full at time of purchase or let their insurance center take care of the details. And just in case you're confined to quarters, delivery is also available.

◆◆◆◆ Southwestern Medical Center   214/648-3111

5323 Harry Hines Boulevard   By Appt. Only
Dallas, TX 75390
www.utsouthwestern.edu

The University of Texas at Dallas has a superb medical complex that has probably every kind of medical specialty under one roof—more than you have to choose from than your corner meet market. Take a number and hope it's the right one. My only beef here has to do with the numbers, too. Where's the phone numbers? It's almost impossible to know which number to call if there was such a thing as a general switchboard to the entire complex? Or is there a number for each and every doctor? If so, how do you connect to a main number to ask for a recommendation for the myriad of doctor specialties. To reach many of their clinical trials, and even their staff doctors, it's sometimes an impossible maze to direct your finger to the right dial. And to make it even more problematic, each clinical trial is offered by a different doctor. For example, if you're depressed (and who isn't these days), the National Institute of Mental Health was running a cognitive therapy treatment program for FREE if you qualified. Are your depressed or sad? Have you lost interest in activities? Have difficulty sleeping or sleeping too much? Are you feeling tired? Do you feel guilty or worthless? If you feel this way ALL the time, then you may be a candidate for their FREE treatment. Call 214/648-5351 which is their Depression Clinic. And I'm just depressed over all of this confusion. Make it simple, please. Such a great medical center, such a great medical maze.

◆◆◆◆◆◆ Steven W. Titensor, DDS   972/355-9545

1901 Long Prairie Road, Suite 320   By Appt. Only
Flower Mound, TX 75022
www.smilesbysteve.com

 Peering out of a strip shopping center (look for Chili's) at the intersection of 2499 and 3040 (Round Grove and Long Prairie Roads), enter
this totally blissful worldly state-of-the-art 21st century dental oasis. If
nothing else, you've got to see their new Tuscany-inspired offices complete with an indoor fountain to recognize how far dental environments have come. You WILL open your mouth but instead of saying, "Ow!", you'll say, "Wow!" Make it beautiful. Make it painless. And the people will come. Then put Dr. Steven Titensor at the helm and you'll be in good hands. You are greeted with the plushest ambience in town, maybe even the country. There is nothing that can compare. When I say state-of-the-art, I'm not just talking dental technology. This office is a work of art from pillars to posts, columns to hardwood floors, stone facades to intricate moldings, just take a seat and you'll see. Add in the massage padded chairs and head phones that access over 50 different kinds of music, and you'll think you're at a spa. View your favorite news or TV show with their new "eye trak glasses: or use the chair-side monitors. Call for your appointment now! And ZOOM® those stained teeth into a new and improved whitened smile. If you're are really discolored, ask for the super strength technique. From sedation therapy (no pain, I promise) to digital X-Rays, caps and crowns, veneers and problematic bites, TMJ and implants, Dr. Titensor is up on it all. And don't forget to check into our website, www.undergroundshopper.com for the announcement on our Extreme Makeover. Dreams really do come true.

◆◆◆◆◆ Texas Lap Band   972/842-THIN (8446)

610 N. Coit Rd, Suite 2120   By Appt. Only
Richardson, TX 75080-5457
www.Texaslapband.com

Nothing personal, mind you, but so many of my readers and listeners swear by the lap-band procedure for weight loss that who can argue with success? Though I am a 140 lb. loser with the Roux-
en-Y gastric bypass surgery, I can't attest to what a lap band is all about; but I've been to enough
support groups, visited with hundreds of those who have had it done, I am confident that this
FDA-approved procedure is a weigh-to-go. If you are "morbidly obese" (having at least 100
pounds or more to lose or in the case of the Lap-Band 75 pounds or more to lose), shedding those
excess pounds is now within the realm of possibilities. The **LAP-BAND®** is FDA approved, is
performed laparoscopically on an outpatient basis and is fully reversible. Most patients can even
return to work within a week. These doctors at The Surgery Center of Richardson encourage you
to visit their website for FREE seminars and more information. This is a fairly non-invasive and
safe surgical procedure that has been a boon to those who have failed at every other kind of
weight-loss program. So, what do you have to lose?

◆◆◆◆ Texas Spine Medical Centers   972/289-1200

400 W. Kearney, Suite A   Mon-Fri 7:20 AM-5 PM (First Treatment Begins at 7:20)
Mesquite, TX 75149
www.vaxdtexas.com

Don't step on that crack 'cause it'll break your Mother's back—remember those warnings? But
your Mom may not have told you about the latest in back treatments, if yours is killing you. With
four Metro locations—Mesquite, Grand Prairie at Hwy 360, Plano at I-75 and Arlington at 360
and Pioneer Parkway, the Texas Spine Medical Centers use a non-invasive treatment called Vax-D
for the treatment of painful, herniated, degenerative and bulging discs. They have treated over
2,000 patients using this method with a 70 percent success rate. There is no hospitalization. No
surgery. So what is it? **VAX-D** is a patented, FDA method for back treatment that has been
approved since 1996. It's a decompression system which over the course of 20 to 30 treatments
uses a vacuum system to draw the disc back into place. Most insurance plans are accepted. The
consultation is FREE, just bring your medical records, CAT scans, x-rays or MRIs to determine if
you are ripe for the procedure. ***Call toll-free: 888/543-7747***

◆◆◆◆◆ Vital Imaging   972/378-6858

3304 Communications Parkway, Suite 201   Mon-Fri 8-5 (By Appt. Only)
Plano, TX 75093
www.vitalimaging.com

What price do you put on your health? Why would I include an expensive x-ray procedure in a
bargain shopping book? Simple. I have a touch of claustrophobia and refuse to go for an MRI for
fear of being enclosed. And, too, my husband is a "smoker." I love him but let's face it, it's a death
sentence and a sure-fire ticket to developing lung cancer. I worry about him all the time. He thinks
he's immortal. But with the cutting edge technology of the EBT, early detection could provide him
with the gift of life. Vital Imaging is a safe and accurate procedure that captures a crystal clear 3-D
image of your heart, lungs and abdominal organs. It only takes 10 minutes. It's a cinch. The full
body scan, including the virtual colonoscopy, is $1,395; without the virtual colonoscopy, it is
$845. That's a bargain right there because with a colonoscopy you have to drink an awful tasting
liquid the night before to clean you out, go into the hospital, and then be put under a general anes-
thesia to even have the procedure done in the first place. All in all, it costs a lot more. A heart and

lung scan was $645; a heart scan was $445; a virtual colonoscopy, $950 and a cholesterol test, $50. Many PPOs cover some of these procedures, but HMOs do not. Therefore, full payment is due at the time of the service. Again, finding and treating heart disease early, for example, can usually prevent sudden heart attacks, bypass surgery or angioplasty. So, what price are you willing to pay to live the good life? *Call toll-free: 866/VITAL-1-1*

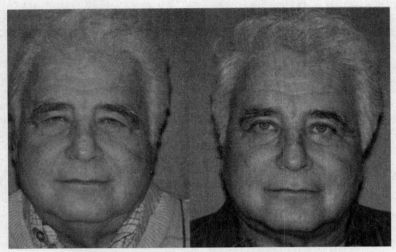

John A. Standefer, Jr., M.D.

Bob Blair's Before and After Photos

See writeup on page 475

Music & Books

★★★★★   75% Off Books   972/239-5545

4545 LBJ Freeway
Farmers Branch, TX 75244
www.75offbooks.com

Nothing suits me better than curling up in a comfortable chair, cross-legged, with a good book, sipping on a tall glass of iced tea with a hint of mint. Now where to buy the book? That's easy. Thou headest to the bestest bookstore, and this is it! No leaf left unturned. Consider reading this small chain of bookstores from cover to cover. With nine locations in Texas Bookmark savings of 75 to 95 percent off—as that is a constant. Books retailing for $15, $25, $50, $100 (and sometimes more), for under $5? Truer words were never written. It doesn't get better than this. Every category of reading matter covered including novelty books, gifty-type books, children's books that could be construed as a toy, as well as art books, cookbooks, computer books, health and fitness books, maps, fiction, but what can't be beat are those gorgeous coffee table editions that impress the neighbors as well as make perfect gifts for folks who have everything. Keep on the edge of your seat with a nail-biting mystery or a well-crafted piece of fiction, learn about your roots with a Texas gardening book or dream of far away places with a book about, what else, traveling. If it's in print, expect it to be sandwiched between my lunch hour and my late night reading. I can't get enough. And at these prices, load up—these are all a cheap read. Check directory for other locations in Plano, Mesquite, Austin, Gainesville, Greenville, Tyler and two in Houston.

★★★★   Below Wholesale Magazines   800/800-0062

1909 Prosperity Street
Reno, NV 89502

Read on, this gets good. Real short, sweet, and to the point. Want your favorite magazines at below wholesale prices? Not just below cover prices but below wholesale prices. Did you hear that? Eyes, don't fail me now! Love the gossip from Hollywood, sports updates each season, latest fashion trends, cutting edge technology, great recipes, interesting advice or just want the news? With over 733 subscriptions to choose from, this might just be a gift worth giving. No need to read between the lines, the name says it all with Below Wholesale Magazines. Call toll-free and get your FREE subscription catalog. ***Call toll-free: 800/800-0062***

★★★★   **Bill's Records**   **972/234-1496**

8136 Spring Valley   Mon-Thurs 10:30 AM-10 PM; Fri-Sat 10:30 AM-Midnight; Sun 12 -10 PM
Dallas, TX 75240
www.billsrecords.com

Hear it. See it. Buy it at Bill's. There's no other record store like it in the Metroplex. Is it a hang-out? Yep! Is it a worldly source for rock 'n'roll history? Yep! Is it the place to strike gold, plati-num or any other record that has made it to the top? Yep! Will you feel old if you shop here? You might, but that's life. If you want the current rage on the Top 10 Billboard Chart or you want one that was a hit way back when, Bill's Records has it. Their fully operational website is www.billsrecords.com. FYI—you can go to the store every Friday from noon to 1:30 PM for a lunch break with FREE food offerings and country music. Have you ever seen such a glutton for punishment for store hours? This is survival of the fittest while the power chains have reeled havoc with small, independent stores like Bill's, he has managed to remain right up there with grit and determination—and doing it just a little bit better.

Book Liquidator   **214/724-5456**

124 Daugherty Street, #1   Mon-Sat 10-5 (CST)
Denton, TX 76205-7111

www.bookliquidator.com   🖰 *Top Online Store!*

How does saving 75 percent off brand new books sound without even getting out of your PJ's? Brand new books at below wholesale prices at this book liquidator's website is almost too good to be true. For example, The Complete Book of Vitamins and Minerals selling for $9.98 was a pit-tance at $2.49; you save: $7.49 (that's 75 percent off). Do this all in the comfort of your own home, where you can shop online for books, books and more books.

PS   Book Market   **972/459-4286**

2416 S. Stemmons Freeway   Mon-Sun 10-9
Lewisville, TX 75067
www.book-market.com

The Book Market is the limited traveling sale to the Book Warehouse where you can save up to 80 percent off the publisher's original price. Over 100,000 grand new books that transverse the com-pendium of titles: fiction, kids'books, computer, travel, cookbooks, religious and all at rock bot-tom remainder prices. All the major publishers are represented but once they're gone, they're gone and relocated elsewhere to be dispersed to their other permanent stores around the Metroplex. Be sure to call ahead before you head out—this kind of holiday warehouse sale does not always appear in the same spot next year. This year, they opened their stores in the previous location at the intersection of Stemmons and Hwy. 3040 (Lakepointe Crossing) but closed the minute the Christmas shopping season was over. When that occurs, try their full-time stores called the Book Warehouse at the Allen Premium Outlets, the Prime Outlets at Hillsboro and the Tanger Factory Outlet. And if you're a teacher, don't forget to ask about their "teacher appreciation program." Yes, they offer special prices to teachers. I wonder if ex-teachers count?

★★★   **Book Rack**   **214/221-0064**

10233 E. Northwest Hwy., Suite 432   Mon-Sat 11-7
Dallas, TX 75238

Here's the epitome of "Trading Places." Even Eddie Murphy would find the Book Rack a laughing matter (if he were looking for funny books). Their trading policy, though, is somewhat not so humorous. They only take back their books (previously sold) or new releases. No other trade-ins are allowed at this time—that tells me their shelves are overflowing. Thumb through thousands of paperback books that have been read before, ending up at their final resting place. Take half off the cover price or trade two-for-one, it's all the same to them. They also take magazines for in-store credit, but comic books? Forget it! Leave the funny stuff to Eddie Murphy. Well-organized, alphabetically by author and category, so if you're looking for the "Life of Reilly," you'll find it under biographies, or if Danielle Steele's your must-read, find her under romance. But if you're looking for love, you're looking in all the wrong place. Try www.matchmaker.com instead.

★★   Book Swap   817/284-2513

6618 Grapevine Hwy.   Mon-Fri 10-6; Sat 9-5
Richland Hills, TX 76180

As youngins', a good trade was a jump rope for hopscotch chalk (and you couldn't have one without the other.) Now that we're older, it's time to be sensible. Trade in those already read books that have been sitting on the shelf collecting dust and "swap 'til you drop" at this shop. If you bring in Children's, Harlequin Romance novels, Westerns or Sci-Fi, you have to swap for books in the same genre. Those move out "lickity split." Credit given is basically 20 percent off the publisher's price and if they purchase the books outright, discounts are about 40 to 50 percent off the cover price. If your interest is as long as Longfellows and you're looking for a Wordsworth of savings, you've landed face-up at the right shop.

Booked Up   940/574-2511

216 S. Center St.   Mon-Sat 10-5
Archer City, TX 76351

 If you're looking for some *Terms of Endearment*, this is the place that is all booked up. Larry McMurtry, author of *Terms of Endearment*, *Lonesome Dove* and *The Last Picture Show* has carved out his place both on the page and in the bookstore. History is in the making. Small towns and bookstores that are unique, different and a place where people meet is what McMurtry had in mind when he opened Booked Up a decade or so ago. Still, four stores are scattered throughout the square, each with their own unique categories. Go to the main store (referred to as Store No. 1) and get the lay of the land of their other bookstores, each organized by categories. Since none of their inventory is computerized, you'll only get a list of books by authors. Well, this is one chain store that does not want to be linked to the 21st century. I guess visiting where Cybil Shepherd slept is as close to contemporary as you're going to get. Often you'll run into Larry hauling off books or see other famous folks thumbing through signed first editions or rare books. You never know who you're going to bump heads with, but do not expect to find any new books. This bookstore is in a class by itself, a rare find indeed.

★★★★★★   Budget CDs & Records   972/278-4333

2918 S. Jupiter, Suite C   Tues-Fri 11-7; Sat-Sun 10-7
Vikon Village Garland, TX 75041
www.budgetcd.com

 Owner Don Baker spent 33 years in the music business and wanted to do something else. So, what did he do? Opened Budget CDs & Records. Then in 1999, another milestone occurred and Budget CD went online. Talk about hearing the sites and sounds of music—now you'll never run out of options. Their extensive inventory contains thousands and thousands of new and used CDs, LPs, vinyls and cassettes. You'll also find hard-to-find and favorite posters, concert T-shirts, photos....I mean, it's music-buyology 101. Pony-tailed owner who still works extra jobs to make a living during the week and operate Budget CD as well, certainly spins a tune to a different color but is one cool dude in the music biz.

★★★★★   CD Source   214/890-7614

5500 Greenville Ave.   Mon-Thurs 10-10; Fri-Sat 10-10:30; Sun Noon -10
Dallas, TX 75206

This Old Town source is for new town, uptown, downtown and all-around town CD music lovers. Celebrating their 10th anniversary, CD Source is the place to add to your "Chopin Liszt," just don't expect Chopin to be high on the list of frequent buys here. Stop doodling around and turn up the volume at the intersection of Greenville and Lovers Lane. The Rap Trap is just part of the scene here. Find old and new music on old and new CDs. In fact, they have more than 70,000 in stock at some of the best prices in this town. And what's nice is that they are co-mingled, quite harmoniously, with new and old, imports and rare products sharing space rather than isolated in a world of their own. Expect thousands of new titles at $7.99 or less. Can't beat it (even if your name's Michael Jackson!) A 30-day guarantee assures your complete satisfaction; returns are accepted only with receipt. CD Sources pays more for your old CDs ($4.50 and up) than the competition.

★★★★   CD Warehouse   817/469-1048

1114 N. Collins St.   Mon-Sat 10-10; Sun Noon-8
Arlington, TX 76011
www.cdwarehouse.com

Another success story out of D/FW. Can you "Handel" it? Okay, let's get down to business. CD Warehouse was started in a flea market in 1992 by Mark Kane, an attorney, who obviously didn't want to practice law. He sold the concept in 1997 and an IPO was instituted, giving the investment group who bought it plenty of cash. Today, there are almost 400 franchises, not only in the U.S. but Canada, England, France, South and Central America. Talk about running with a good idea! Another of the companies they acquired under the CD Warehouse banner was the Disc Go Round stores. In 1998, they really expanded their reach when their website went live. Inventory, including rare, difficult and hard to find titles, from all the company stores was up-loaded onto the website and today, they're probably the largest supplier of pre-owned CDs on the Internet with over 1,000,000 items. I can't even fathom 1,000,000 anything, let alone CDs. But wait—where are these one million CDs? Anybody who can find them on their website, please let me know. No doubt, pre-owned CDs are the way to go as far as prices are considered. All of these still have plenty of listening hours yet to go. No vinyl, period. And everybody comes out a winner, whether you're buying, selling or trading. As I say, when you build a better mousetrap, flaunt it. There are over 20 CD Warehouses in the Metroplex where you can expect savings of 30 to 50 percent off used and discounts on brand name titles, too.

★★★★★★   CD World   214/826-1885

5706 E. Mockingbird, Suite 170   Mon-Sat 10-10; Sun Noon-8
Dallas, TX 75206

The world may take 24 hours to navigate, but it'll only take you two to four minutes to find what you need and be on your way here. Why so short? Well, it's so well-organized and well-stocked without the long lines, you can get in and out in minutes. You'll even stay grounded as the inventory won't make your head spin, like some superstores. Being overwhelmed is not necessarily a good thing especially if you're a serious shopper. Furthermore, if there are lines forming at the checkout counter, it will sometimes tempt you to turn around and leave. Though smaller than the superstores, their prices were as good, if not occasionally better. And, too, you can listen to anything before you buy it. Over 300 DVD's per store that are always priced to sell is one way to hear the world. Yes, they buy, sell and trade and were voted as the best new/used CD Store by the Dallas Observer. Hey, don't we count, too? But it's the used CD selection that could really spin you out of control. Also visit at the Dallas North Tollway at Belt Line in Addison, across from Hooters, 972/386-6565.

Earful of Books   972/239-4028

11810 Preston Rd.   Mon-Fri 8 AM-9 PM; Sat 9-9; Sun 11-6
Dallas, TX 75230
www.earful.com

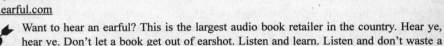
Want to hear an earful? This is the largest audio book retailer in the country. Hear ye, hear ye. Don't let a book get out of earshot. Listen and learn. Listen and don't waste a minute waiting for the bumper-to-bumper traffic to get your dander up. Fill up your down time with a good book. Since the average commute is approximately 25 minutes each way, surely you can find some time to hear a few chapters in route. (Of course, on Saturdays from 11-1 on KAAM 770 AM, I hope you're listening to the Diva and let me tell you where to shop right from the pages of The Underground Shopper.) If you have an opinion about a certain book, hop online to the audio book cafe for chats with authors or book discussion groups. Get to "hear" all the writing genres including biographies, classics, health, fiction, children, history, poetry, mystery, education, foreign, inspirations, business books and more. Pick up your audio books in Dallas, Arlington and Plano. This is where to go for selection not for savings as you'll usually pay a premium for the words to be heard. *Call toll-free: 800/532-7385*

★★★   EB Games   972/874-1619

3000 Grapevine Mills Parkway   Mon-Sat 10-9:30; Sun 11-8
Grapevine, TX 76051
www.ebgames.com

Once you shop any one of their multiple Metroplex outposts or hop aboard online, you're sure to understand this company's gameplan. It's games. And they "take games seriously!" During a special, they might offer a "buy two preowned games and get one free," or buy any two platinum hits, the greatest hits, or **PLAYER'S CHOICE** game (when each usually costs $19.99 each) for $25. (That's for two, remember.) Or get a **GAMEBOY** Advance SP system for only $59.99 when you trade in your working **GAMEBOY ADVANCE SYSTEM**. They sell preowned **PLAYSTATION 2**'s or **XBOX** systems for $129.99 if you're lucky enough to have a coupon from one of their many direct mailers. There's always something special going on for any game you want to play (hop scotch and kissing games are not on the menu), so why not play it for less? Lots of buying and trading going on at their stores in Arlington, Burleson, The Colony, Dallas, Flower Mound, Fort Worth, Frisco, Garland, Irving, Mansfield, Mesquite, North Richland Hills, Plano, Richardson, Rockwall so check directory for the closest location and let the games begin! Take your game playing to the next level and get in on the action. Enjoy new releases without paying new release prices. *Call toll-free: 877/432-9675*

Film Caddy   877/622-2220

PO Box 10048   9-5 PST
Mesa, AZ 85216-0048

www.filmcaddy.com   🖱 *Top Online Store!*

If you want an easy way to rent your favorite DVDs, you can sign up for this service right now for
FREE. How long they will keep it this way is anybody's guess. But here's the deal: You can rent
unlimited DVDs, every month, with up to four titles checked out at any given time. Delivery and
return of your DVDs is handled entirely through the mail and they pay the postage. There are no
additional fees, other than your monthly membership, which means you can keep your movies as
long as it takes you to watch them during your membership term. If you like what you see and hear
for one month free, you can continue for a fee of $19.95 a month plus applicable taxes. Want to
"Lose a Guy in 10 Days" or see the "Gangs of New York?" Well, here's a way to start the popcorn. You can sign up online to register for the FREE trial, but be sure you read all the fine print.
An interesting, though lazy man's way to eliminate running to Blockbuster's and having to cram
four movies down your throat over the weekend. You can at least enjoy them at your leisure.
Movie's on! *Call toll-free: 877/622-2220*

★★   Half Price Book Barn   817/335-3902

1001 Hemphill   Mon & Thurs-Fri 10:30-5:30
Fort Worth, TX 76104

Beside difficult hours, they make it difficult to trade. First, they only accept paperback novels (and
ONLY novels, no children's books, short stories, instructional books, how-to books, cookbooks,
period). Now here come the REALLY confusing instructions. However many books you bring in,
you get half as many FREE and you have to buy three. Sound confusing? You bet. For example, if
you bring in 10 books, you get five FREE, but you still have to buy three. Oh me, oh my. When
you've got 100,000 books in stock, I guess you can call the shots. Plus, look at the hours. Who in
the world prefers to shop during those three days? Isn't anybody out there working? Who's got so
much time on their hands? Retirees, seniors, well, that's at least two target audiences. Read on. So
be it.

★★★★★   Half Price Books   214-360-0833

5803 Northwest Hwy East   Mon-Sun 9:30 AM-11 PM
Dallas, TX 75231
www.halfpricebooks.com

Got writer's block? Go to any location of Half Price Books, there's inspiration a block-long—and
all at half price. See the millions of words that have been created in thousands and thousands of
books from writers who have probably had, at sometime in their career, a few writers'moments!
At their flagship store, thumb through 53,000 square feet of books; surely you will find something
to spark your interest. And think of the passion that was the foundation of this now 60-store chain,
when they first started. Today, there's a "Half Pint Books" children's area, a community room for
events, a coffee shop/bistro and, even, a post office substation. Due to these amenities and their
fabulous shop-online website, Half Price Books continues to be one of the leaders of the previ-
ously-read pack. They are also a vast reservoir for half price software, videos, LPs, cassettes, CDs
and, even, reading glasses. Whether it's new or used, they've probably got it. Look for 22 stores in
the Metroplex.

★★★★★ **Movie Trading Co., The**   **214/361-8287**

6109 Greenville Ave. @ Caruth Haven   Sun-Thurs 10 -11; Fri-Sat 11 AM-Midnight
Dallas, TX 75206

I knew Mark Kane was up to something after he sold his fast-growing empire of CD Warehouse to start another chain, hence The Movie Trading Co. He shifted gears to concentrate on the next major trade in, trade out, trade up concept. Or at least for a while. It wasn't long before he was up and running with this concept and nine Movie Trading Company stores. Then, it was sold to Blockbusters. They are the best and most extensive movie/video/DVD store in town. The more than 20,000 copies of over 15,000 titles should keep you entertained for a lifetime. Whether it's "Sesame Street," "Barney," or "Die Hard," check 'em out. Look for stores on Oak Lawn, Belt Line, Central Expressway in Plano, Arlington and Irving. Another Mark of authority!

★★★ **Paperback Trader**   **972/219-8400**

1112 W. Main   Mon-Wed, Fri 10-6; Thu 10-8; Sat 10-5; Sun Noon-4
Lewisville, TX 75067

What a novel idea! After all, who reads a book more than once? Unless it's the Bible or a dictionary, perhaps. The only thing good about having all those books around is to fill your library's shelves. Maybe a few you've read twice, but the others are either decorative objects or space-wasters! Who cares if the book's been read or the pages are dog-eared? It only makes the book easier to digest, and easier to open. You know, it's the groove and if you want to know how Stella got her groove back, there are thousands of options here. After eight years in the same place, turn to this neighborhood shop where used paperback, hardbacks and audiotapes are available for at least half off the cover price (and even cheaper for most hardbacks). For bigger, better savings, bring in books to trade. For each traded-in title, you'll receive a credit of 25 percent of the publisher's price. Use that credit to buy another title and you'll end up saving at least 75 percent off the cover price. Isn't love lovelier the second time around? Well, so are books.

★★★★★★ **Recycled Books, Records & CDs**   **940/566-5688**

200 N. Locust   Mon-Sun 9-9
Denton, TX 76201
www.recycledbooks.com

 Since 1983, this Denton tower of babble has been the source of reading material for miles around. I really didn't want to "Title Tattle", but it's one of the best in the county. From required reading and esoteric titles to books for under the hammock or around the fireplace, there are over 200,000 of them, 7,000 records and 16,000 CDs. A lifetime of collecting, and a lifetime of pages to turn before you sleep. If you're on your way to court, you can't miss it. Just look for the color purple (that's their building color) and then go inside and see how many books these days have the word "purple" in their title. Three floors of books, records, CDs and more for 50 percent off and less. No sales. No fooling. No overpriced anything.

★★★ **Top Ten Records**   **214/942-7595**

338 W. Jefferson   Mon-Sat 10-6; Sun 1-5
Dallas, TX 75208

Top 10 anything always gets my attention and this is no exception. No matter the state of the economy, the competition around them, the thrill of it all, this record store probably has surpassed all local records. They keep going and going. And yet, you'll find that this "oldies but goodies" store will always come up swingin'. If you're in the mood for love, you'll probably have to dance bi-lingually. Spice up your life with a little salsa and merange! If they don't have it on the shelves, they can order it for you through their huge yellow reference book. If you place your order before Tuesday afternoon, chances are, it'll be turning up on your turntable the same week. No deposit required to place an order, so why not hip-hop over and see what Ricky Martin's up to these days. Take the 12th Street exit off 35.

Musical Instruments

★★★★★★ **Brook Mays Warehouse**   **214/631-0921**

8605 Carpenter Freeway   Sat 10-7
Irving, TX 75247
www.brookmays.com

Though no relation to babbling brooks, this Brook runs deep....but they now have opened a warehouse store and clearance center (above.) Expect to see them playing a different tune here. Throughout their retail chain, however, they do offer a low price guarantee which means if you find it cheaper within 30 days, they'll refund the difference. In business over 100 years, they opened in 1891 and are still playing music, music, music. Everything you need for guitars, amplifiers, the orchestra or band, keyboards, drums, recording, lighting, DJ equipment and musical education. There's a Mail Order Department for educators, even a Pro Shop at the above location, but note, the warehouse is only open to the public on Saturdays, while their retail stores are open traditional hours Monday through Saturday. Check the website for specifics. *Call toll-free: 800/637-8966*

◆◆◆◆◆◆ **Carroll's Piano Service**   **817/431-8501**

Keller, TX 76248   By Appt. Only

Want to make your piano sing? Call and get Miked (not milked!) For $70 plus tax, Mike will bring his ear and all that goes with it to tune your piano. Though based in Keller, he has no problem being a travelin'man. Mike Carroll is a Maestro when it comes to tuning, repairing, rebuilding and refinishing pianos. You won't go wrong calling upon his services, as he is a masterful craftsman and has the calling to keep pianos he works on in tiptop shape.

◆◆◆◆ **Cousins Piano Moving**   **972/926-1920**

1801 Stratford   By Appt. Only
Garland, TX 75041

Don't expect to move the ivories cheap. But if you're needing to move a piano, I only remember the best (like an elephant, "Tusk, Tusk!") This family-owned business are the folks to entrust your 88s to. Most movers, if you haven't already discovered, hate to touch a baby grand, especially if it's going to the Van Cliburn competition. For local service, expect to be charged a flat fee. A 15-mile trek from Grapevine to northeast Fort Worth, for example, would cost about $205 for a console or spinet. Expect a grand to be grander. For long-distance moving, though, they contract with a nationwide carrier that picks up weekly and gets it to your final destination without a hitch. The fees are calculated by miles. (Note: All My Sons Moving has a specialist piano moving team on staff. See write-up elsewhere in this chapter.) *Call toll-free: 800/878-8795*

★★★★   Dallas Piano Warehouse & Showroom 972/231-4607

9292 LBJ Frwy.   Mon-Thurs 9-8; Fri-Sat 9-6; Sun 1-6
Dallas, TX 75243

Billy Joel may have been the piano man, but it's Walt Birchfield, owner of Dallas Piano Warehouse & Showroom, who's stealing the show these days. Stop at his showroom on LBJ (exit Abrams Road) and look inside. Even if you're driving by, you're sure to remember the red (or whatever color) piano is being showcased in the window! Tickle the ivories of **BOSENDORFER, KAWAI, ROLAND, SCHIMMEL, STEINWAY, TECHNICS, YOUNG CHANG** and more in pianos and keyboards. In fact, they are said to be the largest Young Chang dealer in the country. But what if you wanted to "Play It Again, Sam?" Used pianos started at $1,495 (and there were at least 20 to choose from.) The most expensive piano we saw was $2,200, on the floor, which is not a bad price, if you're just a budding Beethoven. But it was the player pianos that really caught our ears. What fun! Lay-away is available for up to six months with 25 percent down, 90-days financing is the same as cash, or 10 percent simple interest for three years and 11.5 percent for five years. A "sound" investment for the burgeoning Bach or an enterprising Elton. A clean **BALDWIN** console in cherry wood was $1,685 and included delivery, tuning and warranty. Now, they're playing our song!

◆◆◆◆   Dallas School of Music, The   972/380-8050

2650 Midway Rd., Suite 204   Mon-Thurs 10-9; Sat 9-4
Carrollton, TX 75006
www.dsminfo.com

You've heard of "Tickle me, Elmo," haven't you? Well, what instrument tickles you most? If it's the piano, you're really sharp because this school can teach you the difference between sharps and flats, rests and clefs. In fact, they can teach you how to play almost any instrument. Lessons are available at their location or via the Internet at www.MusickEd.com. Piano lessons via the web? They also offer vocal education: soprano, alto, tenor, bass and speech therapy, plus all the instrumental instruction you need to join the orchestra or band. For the summer, there are camps for infants at $55 for one week, Monday through Thursday with mom and baby, and a three-hour ensemble camp through the ninth grade at $155 for one week, Monday through Thursday.

◆◆◆   Glen's Piano Service   972/768-0531

6900 Preston Rd., #2611   By Appt. Only
Plano, TX 75024

Sorry, Charlie, if you're looking for a tuna, Glen is not the guy to call. But if you're looking for a tuner, he's the one. Pianos are his specialty and if your piano hasn't been given a tune-up in a year, expect a charge of $85, plus tax. But if you have really neglected your piano, and it's been years since it's been tuned, expect him to tighten those strings and things for $145 to $165, depending on how flat it is. No charge for on-site visits. Expect Glen to spend about two hours for the tune-up (unless of course you'd rather bring it in on a gurney!!) Oh yes, be sure to ask him if he spells his name with one N (Glen) or two N's (Glenn)?

★★★★   **Guitar Center**   **972/960-0011**

14080 Dallas Pkwy.   Mon-Fri 10-9; Sat 10-7; Sun Noon-6
Farmers Branch, TX 75240
www.guitarcenter.com

The story began the night the Beatles appeared on "The Ed Sullivan Show" in 1964, although the actual business began in 1959. On that night, rock 'n'roll was introduced via this English singing group, and the electric guitar made its TV debut. Now, you can cut a rug at Guitar Center's four area locations, but they are hardly the same as they were when they were first getting into the groove. Today, Guitar Center has evolved into a multi-faceted music store where musicians connect both locally and nationwide. It's also the country's largest retailer of musical instruments at the guaranteed lowest price. Every music specialty is represented—keyboards, MIDI peripherals, music software, pro audio recording equipment, dance music gear, drums, accessories, and, even vintage instruments can be found. Ask a pro where to go and generally it's the above (who is above all others!)

★★★★★★   **Jack Whitby Piano**   **214/381-9571**

8326 Scyene Rd.   Mon-Thurs 10:30-7; Fri-Sat 10:30-5; Sun By Appt.
Dallas, TX 75227
www.jackwhitbypiano.com

 The piano scene starts and ends on Scyene, however you pronounce it. This three-generational scion of the piano business has the corner on pianos, late model used pianos in pristine condition. Like new inside and out, can you imagine having one of those beauties wrapped up with a great big yellow ribbon at the holidays. Texas pianists like it big and Jack Whitby can supply them in a grand way. Since the early '70s, they have maintained an inventory of over 30 pre-owned grand and upright KAWAI and YAMAHA pianos. They also have BALDWIN, MASON & HAMLIN, PEARL RIVER, SAMICK and STEINWAY. They provide all the pianos at Master's Touch studio in Grapevine and Chuck even does all of the tuning. Piano tuning costs $75. Now, even that's a harmonious ticket to sounding A-OK. Don't expect a showroom befitting a Carnegie Hall performance. They save on overhead to pass the savings on to the pianos.

◆◆◆◆◆   **Karl's Piano Tuning**   **214/381-7390**

Dallas, TX   By Appt. Only

If your C is flat but your F is sharp? It's time to call in the tune-up medic. Karl maintains his home business by coming to your home for your piano's checkup. Don't wait until it's an emergency when Van Cliburn's coming to dinner and you've got to tune up! No, if you think dogs have great ears, you should see Karl in action. He can hear a flat a mile away. He'll come to the rescue with his perfect pitch and tuning fork anywhere in the Metroplex. Expect to pay a minimum of $75 for a house call. Make an appointment a few days ahead, but sometimes, he will make a special appearance for a calamity. Don't let your diminuendos sound like crescendos or have your pedal hit the metal. He can work magic but not miracles; in those cases, you may need to call an organ transplant surgeon.

★★★★★★ Lone Star Percussion   214/340-0835

10611 Control Place Drive   Mon-Fri 9:30-5:30
Dallas, TX 75238
www.lonestarpercussion.com

 This is where a star can be born, if drums are the search object. In fact, consider this a drummer's paradise for marching or concert bands, rock or reggae aspirants. There are over 6,000 items in stock and the leader of the band is none other than the famed Bobby Roundtree. Drums, snares, quads, cymbals, mallets, drum heads, sticks, well, if you're a drummer, here is where it's at! In business for 24 years with a new online shopping site that includes an awesome clearance section, you may go wild before your time. A pair of ZILDJIAN drumsticks were $4.98 (list $10.40), and VIC FIRTH drumsticks, reguarly $12, were $6.15. Drumset cymbals retailed at $320, but sold here for $159.95. Marching cymbals, usually priced at $690, banged all the way home for $250. But it was the PEARL snare drums, originally $825, that pounded the pavement at $375 and really made us sound like we were destined for big time. If you can't beat 'em, try shopping at Lone Star Percussion instead; that way, you won't miss a beat! Skin up to 40 percent off across the board and have a bang up day!

★★★★★ Piano Outlet   972/490-5397

14235 Inwood   Thurs-Sat 10-6
Dallas, TX 75244

Bob continues to play his song, only now he's calling it the Piano Outlet rather than the Clearance Keyboard Outlet. Grand opening specials of half price pianos were just the beginning to the musical madness. BALDWIN, KAWAI, NORDISKA, PETROF, WEINBACH, YAMAHA and others were touted as being all half price—all refurbished to a fine and upright condition. No trade-ins, but credit cards and financing acceptable during their abbreviated three-day work week. They much prefer serious buyers who don't hem and haw about their intentions. No digital or electric keyboards, folks. A $30,000 beauty could be had for $9,999 and a $3,000 was out the door to somebody's house for $799. Payments are often made directly to the bank because they are bank repossesions. Now that has a nice sound to it.

◆◆◆◆◆◆ Piano Restoration by Bill Powell   972/285-9755

1320 Hwy. 80 E.   Mon-Sat 8-6
Mesquite, TX 75149

Nothing quite compares to a piano that has been restored by Bill Powell. That's where my BALDWIN went for it's complete make-over. Make an appointment for an estimate. But be prepared to wait a few days, maybe a week for his appraisal as he's very busy. The $50 consulting fee will be taken off the final bill, if you have him perform the necessary plastic and/or internal surgery. He can transform that pale and pathetic 88-keyed instrument to one in mint condition, both inside and out! But really, it's the innards that make him a Master of Pianontology, a new and neglected discipline soon to be added to Southwestern Medical School's roster. An old, neglected BALDWIN that I rescued in an estate sale for $2,000 was restored completely inside and out, included a new keyboard, sounding board and other intricate workings. When it was returned two months later, for approximately $5,500, it brought tears to my eyes. That investment brought an appraised value of over $15,000 and I'd say well worth the money spent. Dr. Powell, as he should be addressed, is the Miracle Man who has worked magic on many other pianos, grand or otherwise, in the Metroplex. Even dealers use him and then charge you twice the price. Shop direct and save. Sounds good to me, eh?

★★ Rhythm Band, The

817/335-2561

1212 E. Lancaster
Fort Worth, TX 76101-0126
www.rhythmband.com

Mon-Fri 8-5

Even if you don't practice the rhythm method, you'll want your kids to march to the tune of a different drummer. Whether to create their own jam session or strut their stuff around the block, you'll want to buy them the tools to make it happen. After more than 40 years of beating around the bush, here is the place to find tom-toms for $9.95, xylopipes for $8.95 or marching drums for $11.95. How many other places in town offer such a school-size selection? If you love the no-frills approach to warehouse shopping, you'll love The Rhythm Band, a Fort Worth landmark with their hand-painted mural on the front of their building. Shop by mail or online, either way you'll save about 15 percent. September is when the new catalogs come out and you can receive yours, FREE of charge, in about three days. *Call toll-free: 800/424-4724*

★★★★★★ Richard's Band Instrument & Repair 972/446-4081

1311-B E. Belt Line Rd.
Carrollton, TX 75006

Tues-Sat 10-6

Richard's Band Instrument Repair is a great place to strike up the band, if your children are looking to blow their own horn. But before you shell out a lot of cash for some brass, think again. Remember, they frequently change their minds, so before making the financial commitment to join the band with a brand-new $800 trumpet, check out Richard's stock. Save on those expensive instruments and buy them pre-blown. Just swing by, if indeed, your brass is sounding crass and you're ready to donate it to the dump. Richard's the original Music Man but he's more than just a Johnny One-note. This band teacher (he's taught all instruments except the guitar and drums) repairs, refinishes, restores, replaces, rejuvenates old brass to like new condition. He himself is a sax virtuoso and is available to play at parties. All instruments sold are guaranteed to be back to making sweet music in no time at all.

★★★★ Speir Music/Roomscapes

972/272-1700

510 S. Garland Rd.
Garland, TX 75040
www.speirmusic.net

Mon-Fri 10-8; Sat 10-7; Sun 1-6

Music started blaring out of Speir's Music Store in 1962 and has been resounding loud and clear ever since. Cutting to the heart of the music industry, they offer band instruments, guitars, keyboards, percussions and amplifiers at very competitive prices. You have probably heard them around the world with amplifiers by AMPEG, BUDDA, CARR, CRATE, DR. Z, GIBSON, GOLDTONE, SWR and TOP HAT. Then be sure to record every note with components by AKG, ALESIS, AUDIO TECHNICA, CAD, EV, ROLAND, SENNHEISER, SHURE and others. All under one roof, you'll find all the instruments, repairs and a policy of 90 days same as cash. Now, where else can you find more than 1,000 guitars with this helpful financing incentive? All sales personnel are specially trained by the factory. Take note. The four S's make them a logical choice to escape to: service, sales, selection and Speir's. Oh, by the way, the TOCA conga drums for $299.95 came with a FREE stand, so we couldn't resist. On the other hand, we just ogled the $5,000 top-of-the-line MARTIN. Beat the bands in any battle at Speir's, an old-time favorite places long before places like Mars came into the picture. Now, look where Mars is? (Out of business, that's where.) They could easily outfit a pro with a 1965 reissue of a FENDER STRATO-

CASTER for $3,200, though they didn't have an original 1973 FENDER that would have cost me about half of that. *Call toll-free: 800/497-1703*

★★★★★   **Sword's Music Co.**   **817/536-8742**

4300 E. Lancaster Ave.   Mon-Sat 10:30-7
Fort Worth, TX 76103

Let's cut to the quick. First, ask for Anthony or Dave (they're always there) and let them lead the way. Since 1969, Sword's has been helping slash high prices on all band and orchestra instruments to beat the band. If your child is in the band, have all of their instruments serviced and overhauled here—especially if they are marching in the Macy Thanksgiving Day Parade! Start out with FENDER, GIBSON, IBANEZ or MARTIN guitars; add in CRATE, FENDER, MARSHALL or ROLAND amps; strum on a CB-700, LUDWIG, PEARL, or TAMA drum; tickle on a KORG or ROLAND keyboard. Jump on the bandwagon and show them a price that was advertised elsewhere, and they'll match it. Plain and simple. *Call toll-free: 800/522-3028*

Office

★★★★ A-Box Connection 214/357-2088

2671 Manana
Dallas, TX 75220

Mon-Fri 8:30-5; Sat 9-1

Help yourself, folks, when you're ready to pack it all in. This small store is housed in their offices, but it's set up to accommodate you whenever you're ready to move. Buy new and recycled boxes when packing time draws near. A perfect stop to shop before you call in the movers. Get packed and keep organized. You'll be so much happier when you finally reach your destination. Mark your boxes - Living Room. Bedroom. Kitchen etc, then when you get there, the movers can deliver it to the right room. Save time and money, and buy your boxes here. Overruns and misprints in boxes, just like in other merchandise categories, will save you a bundle. From small recycled packing boxes to the heavy-duty varieties that can handle the big stuff, to the delicate stuff such as glasses and dishware. From a low of 50 cents for a 16 by 12 box to one that can house your entire closet for $8, complete with metal bar rack so you can keep it all on hangers, you can be sure that your wardrobe can go from house to house with nary a wrinkle. Plus, after you've unpacked, you'll have an extra closet for the garage. Buy all the packing materials to ensure a perfect move, like bubble wrap, markers, foam and sealing tape. It's your connection to boxes. So let's get moving!

★★★★ Aaron Rents/BackRoom 972/385-9472

14105 Inwood
Dallas, TX 75243
www.aaronrentsfurniture.com

Mon-Fri 9-6; Sat 9-5

If you haven't seen panel dividers for $19, folding tables for $19, computer desks for $39, desks for $99 or file cabinets for $39, you haven't been to Aaron's Back Room. Remember, these are the guys who rent furniture for both home and office, and these are their rental returns. So what? Unless you believe that what goes around, comes around, you can make your business a success, regardless if your supplies came from a dot.com business who didn't. Your bottom line will know the difference. Office suites, desks, files and other storage units, seating, tables, panel systems, business equipment and more, at a great savings. Aaron Rents is one of America's leading names in furniture rental, sales and leasing, so give them an "A" for their leadership and another "A" for effort. Aaron Rents and you can be the benefactor by going to the back—the Back Room.

★★★   Acquisition Specialists Inc. (ASI)   972/888-1500

15160 Marsh Lane   Mon-Fri 8-5
Dallas, TX 75001

Acquisition and mergers. Acquisition and office equipment. Of course, now I get it! Housed in
CompUSA's old location and next to Fuller's Jewelers, this jewel may be the pearl in the oyster of
office equipment. Got an old copier that doesn't work like it should? Well trade it in, trade it up, or
go for the gold and get one that works from scratch. They sell refurbished copiers with three-year
warranties on models and five-year warranties on new. Now you can start making copies by the
copier. They carry other new and used electronic office equipment beside copiers. After all, man
does not live by copiers alone. They also carry printers and fax machines and sometimes very specific machinery, such as a plotting machine or industry-specific equipment. Just don't ask me to
explain. Get one of their sales reps to lead you by the hand. They're the specialists, remember?

◆◆◆◆◆◆   Action Trophies & Awards   972/245-0105

1701 S. I-35E   Mon-Fri 8:30-6; Sat 9-2
Carrollton, TX 75006
www.atawards.com

Well, they sure win the award for stability. This family-owned business should have
been nominated in many categories, but it would be self-serving, as they're the ones
making the awards in the first place. After 15 years, they have settled into their new
5,000-square-foot facility housing their office, showroom, engraving, assembly and warehouse.
They are one of the largest trophy dealers in the Metroplex, with one of the largest inventories in-
stock, they needed to spread their wings. And now they're soaring. Today, they can ensure prompt
service, quality custom products and competitive prices on such items as plaques, trophies, name
badges, acrylic and glass awards, as well as promotional products, signs and banners. Samples of
their gift line include jewelry boxes, a wooden golf ball box for storage and display at $78 and a
red marble business card holder for $32.30. They have clocks (all types) in wood, acrylic, glass
and metal. They do incredible etchings, yet we don't expect you to use the line, "Come on up and
see my etchings sometime!" If you're a business who's bottom line is out-of-control, take Action.
Reward your employees with recognition, even if you can't give them a raise. Appreciation is
almost the next best thing! *Call toll-free: 877/805-8501*

◆◆◆   Administrative Purchasing, Inc.   972/620-1500

2755 Valley View Lane, Suite 101   Mon-Fri 8:30-5:30
Dallas, TX 75235

Mr. Kelly Antwine has all the answers when it comes to solving your office needs. He's in the
know about all the latest and greatest in the office machinery industry, and passes that information
on to small businesses. In other words, he's taking care of business. Acting as a liaison between
vendors and suppliers and the ultimate office end-user, his company negotiates contracts, based on
the size of your company and your needs, with equipment dealers, furniture manufacturers, computer factories and more. How does it help you? Well, you have your own purchasing agent without having to hire one in-house. What a great idea! Get in on the action, without having to invest in
an entire purchasing department. With negotiated deals, you should get better prices. Let me know
how your bottom line has been affected, won't you? *Call toll-free: 888/505-9337*

★★ American Discount Office Furniture   817/640-0179

2251-A E. Division   Mon-Fri 8:30-5:30
Arlington, TX 76011
www.beiexpress.com

Well, when you compare office offerings to office offerings, American doesn't come out on top. They have a website, but it's missing about 400 additional lines that they carry. What you can carry (out), though, are items that have been discounted in their back room. There's no financing, delivery is available for an extra charge, and savings of about 20 percent doesn't sound like they're keeping up with business. Though they like to call themselves a "business interiors company," you don't need a course in Shopping 101 to calculate the overall feeling that it is not way up there on our priority list. If you need office furniture, like executive chairs, computer tables, or printer stands, whether you prefer to buy or lease, be sure to consider all the variations when making your office expenditure decisions. The inventory, too, is limited. You can, however, expand your official boundaries, the all-American way, by shopping via their *Quikship Catalog*. There you'll see all of the popular office lines from **DMI**, **HON**, **LA-Z-BOY**, **NATIONAL**, **PAOLI**, **RIVERSIDE** and **STEELCASE**, for starters. Then add in your style preference, from contemporary Scandinavian to traditional classic, choose computer furniture to bookcases, lateral files to stackable chairs, is there anything else you need? Is this your final answer? ***Call toll-free: 800/727-2484***

★★★★ Bob Carney Office Furniture   214/827-2537

3901 Main   Mon-Fri 1-4; Sat 8:30-4:30
Dallas, TX 75226

This Carney isn't as funny, but when he's open for business, he means business, with furniture spilling out the front door. At the corner of Main and Washington (he recommends parking on Washington and coming in through the middle entrance,) the furniture is parked out front, too. I suspect he's hanging on for something to do in his free-time, post-retirement, but it's not over 'til it's over. The discounts are what makes most shoppers flock to on the more than 350 items in stock. You can buy good-quality used office furniture cheap, whether it's a dented or scratched reject or a manufacturer's return, it's your bottom line that takes precedence. We carted off a four-drawer legal file for $75 and a teacher's desk, for old-time's sake that brought back nightmares from my former teaching days, for $100. Of course, I should have thought twice and considered the one for $45 and then refinished it myself. Just look for the two-story, red brick building and follow the stone walkway to the side door. Truly a remarkable shopping experience where office furniture, traditional and contemporary, sells to savvy purchasing agents, like you and me. If no one answers the phone, it only means they're out delivering. Call ahead. And if you develop labor pains while you're waiting, Baylor Hospital is five blocks away. Delivery is available there; just don't expect Bob to deliver, he doesn't. He will recommend some area movers for you to hire.

◆◆◆ Business Environments   214/637-6336

8900 Chancellor Row   Mon-Fri 8-5; After-hours By Appt. Only
Dallas, TX 75247

If you are buying furniture (and, hopefully, from Express Furniture, their sister store), you're going to need someone to install it. Who to call for this labor-intensive task? Here is where the answer lies, the operational team that will deliver and install it all: Uncrate it, level the glides, make sure everything's in tip-top shape, even hang the **PENDAFLEX** file bars and then haul away the empty boxes. Somebody's gotta do it. (You could break a fingernail and then what?) Express Office Furniture, their sister store, is located at 909 N. Industrial Blvd, near the corner of Industrial and Continental. Gee, that address sounds familiar. Phone 214/-416-0013. Selling both new and used office furniture (see write-up elsewhere in this chapter.) *Call toll-free: 888/637-6337*

★★★★★★   **Copy-Write Business Center**   **972/874-8744**
Flower Mound, TX 75028   Mon-Fri 8-6:30; Sat 9-3

Want the best printer in town? Want the best price? Want to publish a book "on demand," which means you don't have to order 50,000 to get a book published? What about a complete letterhead package with business cards, stationary and envelopes, etc? Want to know what we know about doing the right thing? Then pay attention. When doing the "write" thing means giving your printing needs to the "right" printer, Copy-Write should be at the top of your list. Both full-service and self-serve copying can be accomplished in a jiffy. So, enjoy making copies by the copier, or give it to the pros to copy it right. Color copies, over-sized prints, posters and banners, laminating and binding, faxing and scanning, internet access, projector rentals and more, this is the stomping ground for many area business-types who like to chew the fat and get their printing done, all in one run. Just knock three times, ask for Joe and whisper low. He picks up and delivers. Just give him a call.

★★★★★   **Corporate Interiors Group**   **214/622-5950**
Dallas, TX   By Appt. Only
www.cig-texas.com

This former Executive Privilege honcho has evolved into a newly morphed, bigger and better resource for office design and furnishings. Doug Lack (the "handsome one") and Lynda Barnett have formed a new company that continues to represent all of the better manufacturers in the office arena: CREATIVE WOOD, EUROTECH SEATING, FLORENSE, HICKORY LEATHER and LA CASSE as well as showcasing some of the best pre-owned office furnishings in the Metroplex. Expect only high-end and specialty-store designer looks. They provide interior design and space planning at no charge while you furnish or refurbish your offices. Plus new to their resource list, they will provide new, pre-owned and refurbished business phone systems and voice and data cabling. Now we're talking entering the 21st century. Then if you run into a computer problem, staffing problem, need a mover or an expert in networking, they have a team of experts ready and able to jump into action. All you have to do is say, "How high!"

★★★★★   **Dallas Desk**   **972/788-1802**
15207 Midway Rd.   Mon-Fri 8:30-5:30; Sat 10-5
Addison, TX 75001
www.dallasdesk.com

If you are looking for an impressive front, then Dallas Desk is where you should shop for your office ensembles. This is a one-stop extravaganza, all at discounted prices. Desks, workstations, tables, leather and executive seating, ergonomic seating, all purpose seating, industrial seating, guest and reception furniture, lateral and vertical files, filing accessories and storage, then relax in their custom finishes and fabrics room....it's all under one roof. It's either too hot or too cold to shop from store to store. It's nice you can get it all together in one place. They also offer modular as well as systems furniture, plus filing cabinets, bookcases, art and accents. For a tour de force, ask for designer Victor Lefeve or for sales, Gary Powers. ABCO, ARTISTICA, BEST CHAIRS, BRADINGTON-YOUNG, BUTLER, HERMAN MILLER, HOOKER, LA CASSE, LA-Z-BOY, PAOLI, STANLEY, STEELCASE—get the picture? And pictures, too alongside a stellar selection of desks and hutches, computer cabinets, conference tables, decorative tables, executive seating, sofa and lounge chairs. I even saw an executive washboard unit for a bathroom with a drop in sink for under $800. They offer modular as well as systems furniture, even some antique-looking armoires and desk units that are as beautiful as they are functional. A beautifully ornate curved leg, three-drawer table desk by HOOKER was $699.99; these are particularly appealing for the home office that doesn't want to look like office furniture. That is what sets Dallas Desk apart from the crowded office front. They look like a home furnishings design center, everything's discount and everything you can imagine for office—regardless of where it's housed.

★★★★★   Dallas Midwest   972/866-0101

4100 Alpha Rd., Suite 111   Mon-Fri 7:30-7; Sat 9-1
Dallas, TX 75244
www.dallasmidwest.com

Any company that is in business over a half a century must be one step from heaven. And that's exactly the chosen ministry at this industry treasure. Specialists in institutional furniture for schools, churches, day-care centers and libraries, you can finally get a new pew, a mobile desktop lectern ($79), a coat and hat rack ($59), a park bench, a picnic table, a bike rack, storage unit, bulletin or magnetic boards with markers or magnets, indoor and outdoor signage, and you still save 30 to 60 percent off list. Order online or via their catalog, which now has more than 120 pages of pews for churches, pulpits, choir risers, office furniture and more. They provide FREE color samples on some items and some come with a 50-year guarantee (instead of the usual 15-year). Some assembly required but, usually, only the basic tools are needed. Prices are quoted with and without customer assembly. Additional savings are available for volume purchases over $1,000. If you'd prefer utilizing your own fabric for chairs, for example, they are likely to oblige. If you're a church, school or government agency, sometimes, there's special credit extended. You can even lease furniture, if your order exceeds $2,000. Holy rollers! *Call toll-free: 800/933-2731*

★★★★★   Express Furniture   214/637-1600

909 N. Industrial Blvd.   Mon-Fri 9-6
Dallas, TX 75247

If you're buying office furniture, you will find that deep in the heart of the industrial district, your wholesale connection to the actual furniture awaits. Save at the corner of Industrial and Continental, with more office furniture down the street. New office furniture at wholesale prices, showroom samples, and used furniture for even additional savings is the ticket here. PAOLI is one of the big names in the business that will transform your business into a first-class act. Others are likely to do the same: COUNCIL CRAFTSMAN, EFI and others, again at 50 percent off. Express does offer financing, but you have to visit the store for more information. It's plenty confusing. The same operator answers for several different companies but they're all related. So whether you're looking for Express Furniture above or Business Environments elsewhere, the same receptionist will connect you. Go figure.

★★★★★★   Front Desk Office Furniture Outlet   214/904-9045

10401 Harry Hines Blvd.   Mon-Fri 8:30-4:30; some Sat 9-1
Dallas, TX 75220
www.frontdeskdallas.com

With more than 1,000 chairs in stock, take advantage of others' misfortunes and grab a leather side model for $99 or a high-back leather chair for as low as $119. Jay and John Crisford take front and center at their showroom's warehouse door and lead you through the vignettes of new and used furniture.

Whether yours is in the front or not is immaterial, as long as the price is right. Clean up your act and get ready for the laundry list of options: new and used office furniture, including executive chairs, reclining chairs, retro-looking chairs in a variety of cool colors; ergonomic computer task chairs, storage units great for the garage, credenzas, bookcases, vertical and lateral file cabinets, metal desks and accessories. The brands have all passed an official inspection: **HERMAN MILLER, KNOLL, LA-Z-BOY, STEELCASE, THOMASVILLE** and more. They can no longer say that they are proud to be rated 5 stars by The Underground Shopper. This year we've raised it another star and the best merchants have now been issued 6 stars along with their 100 BEST designation. ***Call toll-free: 800/299-8095***

◆◆◆◆◆◆ Lone Star Overnight

Dallas, TX   By phone or Online ordering
www.lso.com

 Log on to their website to see the closest drop off location to your zipcode; or call for pickup as this is a boon to your office's bottom line, over and out! If you're got a CFO who squeaks or a boss who's cheap, you will look like a hero by suggesting this overnight delivery service. To expedite an overnight delivery in Texas (and now Oklahoma, too), cut your costs in half and five percent by using this service rather than the national carriers. How's that, you cheapskate, you. Utilizing both air and ground transportation, within and between Texas and Oklahoma, LSO's price structure allows for up to a 55 percent savings over the national carriers just based on lower operating costs within a regional service area. You know the routine. Lower overhead, pass the savings on to the consumer. I urge you to compare the rates of FedEx and UPS that you thought you couldn't live with, and change your thinking by calling on this Lone Star. As they say, fill a niche and the customers will come. If you're looking for reliable "next day" shipping options, this is it. Talk about service with a smile at half the price, well, it doesn't get better than this. LSO's basic services include next day delivery by 8:30 AM, 10:30 AM, 3:00 PM, End Of Next Business Day and Saturday Delivery. All deliveries are guaranteed to be on time or you get your money back plus they have hundreds of convenient drop-off boxes throughout the Metroplex, an additional declared value option, toll-free customer service, on-line shipping, FREE shipping supplies, up to a 150 pounds capability per Priority Package and up to 70 lbs. for Ground shipments. Visit their website and see for yourself. It sounds like Fed Ex, it offers superb service like Fed Ex, it has supplies like Fed Ex—the only difference....the price! Oh, I didn't even tell you they have a 99 percent on-time delivery record. I'm telling you, they're the greatest. ***Call toll-free: 800/800-8984***

★★★★★★ Metroplex Enterprises   817/284-9336

7324 Baker Blvd.   Tues-Fri 9-6; Sat 10-3
Richland Hills, TX 76118

 If saving up to 80 percent on a weird combination of used store fixtures and new and refurbished computers is what makes your world go around, then establish a relationship at this store—one block from where the old Sam's Club was in Richland Hills. See everything under one roof that you could conceivably utilize in outfitting an office on a tight budget. Turn on to the light fixtures, shelving, store displays and counters waiting for display merchandise. Metroplex Enterprises is a 30,000 square foot combination resource for saving a ton of money from store displays to computers (new and used) so that you can take care of business in setting up a store or keeping a store running. Industrial shelving, slat walls, peg hooks and display cases will keep you organized and posting notices for all your employees to see. Fireproof safes will keep your corporate papers, your will, deed of trust, stocks and bonds, real estate contracts, insurance papers and such. Check them out if you want to net a sizeable savings the salvage your cash flow.

★★★★★★ **OFCO Office Furniture** 817/429-3553

200 W. Rosedale
Fort Worth, TX 76104

Mon-Fri 8:30-5:30

That's it. Shop at the W. Rosedale location only. This year, they lost their leases at their other locations, so they are concentrating on the hospital district in Fort Worth. Get covered from the top drawer to the waste basket and everything in between. OFCO is all about selling new, used, even scratch-and-dent office furniture at low, low prices. Delivery is available with set up and installation a sure thing. OFCO stands for Office Company and if it's your company's office furniture you're needing to buy, why not buy it as direct as it gets. Everywhere you look, you'll see that price tags are prominently displayed with the retail price and the OFCO price. If the executive chair you're looking at is used, depending on condition, it will be marked 60 to 90 percent off; or, if new, prices are marked 40 to 60 percent off. Now, ask for that raise! (Or at best, a corner office with a view.)

★★ **Office in My Home** 214/348-4741

10101 Royal Lane
Garland, TX 75238

Mon-Sat 8:30-5:30; Sun 9-5

If you're one of the millions who have started a business from home, or are sent home to do your business, hello. Go east on LBJ, exit Royal and Miller Road, watch for the big sign facing LBJ; or if you're going west on LBJ, exit Plano. Either way, you wind up in an industrial area where making a home office is all under one roof. They offer the A to Z variety, new, reconditioned and refurbished office furniture, but many items need to be ordered, with some select brands taking as long as six weeks to arrive. Joan was our official greeter and gave us the lowdown. **RIVERSIDE** will take about six weeks, **ASPEN**, four, and **THOMASVILLE**, three. You can expect a discount on some, but not always. So it's up to you to discern. Your best bet is the refurbished items. Lots of custom opportunities such as computer armoires, color-matching to existing furniture and a complete reupholstering department. Ah, home, suite office, home.

★★★★ **Office Liquidation Center** 972/438-4499

3215 E. Carpenter Frwy.
Irving, TX 75062
www.officeliquidationcenter.com

Mon-Fri 8:30-5

This 35,000-square-foot showroom was bland next to the colorful Lone Star Boot building, but that company doesn't exist anymore, so today, they'll have to stand on their own merit. These folks liquidate office furniture fast, and have finally gotten their website up and running. Whether only new will do (closeouts), or used where price is the major consideration, here resides the best of both worlds. Expect to save as much as 60 percent from this 15-year veteran of the official war against high prices. Look behind closed doors for the hundreds of desks, credenzas, conference tables, bookcases, filing cabinets, artwork, partitions, cubicles and more. Put more than your mind at ease with lots of chairs, including side chairs, task chairs, executive chairs, manager's chairs, secretary's chairs, guest chairs, conference chairs, banquet chairs, and at last, you can even table the issue. They also offer minor refinishing services in case there's a nick or a scratch. Delivery is $40 (if it will fit in a van) or $75 (if a truck is needed.) Same day delivery is available, if it's do or die!

★★   Paper Plus   214/748-7587
2025 Irving Blvd.   Mon-Fri 7:30-5:30
Dallas, TX 75207

The paper trail ends here at this division of Monarch Paper, though they did hold steady with prices on copy paper with the same price this year as last. ($22/case.) Spread your wings and fly-in to buy paper in bulk. Ad agencies and printers have known about them for years, but you may not. They do not sell cheapo paper, so consider them for special events only. When it comes to ordering invitations or announcements, be it weddings, births, anniversaries, holidays, whatever the occasion, they stock every catalog in the world, alongside a substantial stock of paper goods. Pick up your paper, graphic and office supplies all in one place, that's a plus, and visit their other location at 2101 Midway Rd. in North Dallas, 972/490-8809. Forget their website. It's out and about. That's no plus in my way of thinking. Ordering paper on line should be a cinch and much more convenient that schlepping down to Irving Blvd. It's way too close to KAAM studios and I'll think I'm going to work.

★★★★★★   Plano Office Supply   972/424-8561
705 Avenue K @ Plano Parkway   Mon-Fri 8-5; Sat 8-12
Plano, TX 75074
www.planoofficesupply.com

Fifty years and life is just beginning for the family who founded Plano Office Supply. Buying direct from over 100 factories makes for not only a terrific selection of binders, calendars, planners, files, furniture (even the ergonomic kind!), paper, pens, computer and office equipment, presentation and meeting supplies, but they also offer imprinting services. All items in their catalog, though, are not necessarily in the store, but, quick as a bunny, they can be ordered with next-day delivery. Multiply the savings and the convenience and it all adds up to decreasing your initial outlay. Try 'em, you'll like 'em, especially if you want to do business with a home-town favorite son. Like being the #2 "buy" in town, they can provide the additional personal touches that the giants, too busy doing business around the world, are unable to provide for the local yokels.

★★★★★★   PS Business Interiors   214/688-1925
3131 Commonwealth   Mon-Fri 8:30-5
Dallas, TX 75247
www.psbusinessinteriors.com

PS: Don't forget to save some money when shopping for your favorite office furniture and modular workstations. With offices in Florida, Pennsylvania and Texas, you can expect the best money can buy, wherever you shop. For the fastest and bestest prices, pre-owned is what's recommended for the common cause. Since 1984, Dallas-based Robert Paul (the P) and Jack Shure (the S) collaborated and developed the concept of buying and selling office furniture that was three to seven years old and in acceptable, if not superb, condition. Some of the brands to note include: GLOBAL, HAWORTH, HERMAN MILLER, NATIONAL, PAOLI and STEELCASE. Expect to save between 70 and 80 percent off retail on desks, secretarial chairs, lateral and vertical filing cabinets, conference tables, storage cabinets—whatever it takes to run your office. In other words, spend about 27 cents on the dollar compared to new. A gorgeous traditional cherry wood conference table AND the 4 chairs, you will spend only $1200.

★★ S.P.E.C. Fax Plus 972/484-5522

12801 Midway Rd., #111
Dallas, TX 75244

Mon-Fri 10-5; Sat 10-1

Got the specs? Need a fax? Put these two together and it spells Fax Plus with new fax machines being their specialty. A few refurbished ones, okay, I liked the prices on these better! But this year, they've added new copiers and printers, too. Saw a particularly appealing **OKIDATA** fax that you can hook up to your computer and use it as a laser printer as well for $299. Just the fax, ma'am. Less expensive models were $249, but in the long run, could be more expensive to operate. Most faxes, though, started out in the $599 price range, a bit steep for the in-house office set-up. If you're looking for price, you better shop around (just like Mother told you!)

★★★★★★ Sav-on Office Supplies 817/926-7071

2508 W. Berry St.
Fort Worth, TX 76109
www.sav-onofficesupplies.com

Mon-Fri 8-7; Sat 10-5

First there was Snap-on, now it's Sav-on and specifically, Sav-On Office Supplies. Save on a little or save on a lot from this Fort Worth favorite son. With their full complement of name brand office, computer and school supplies from 20 to 70 percent off, you can get off to the right start with the right stuff. They have everything you may need to pass the grade in school and in business, from paper clips to copy paper, furniture to fax machines, computer printers to cartridges. Then, pay attention to the other services, such as making those rubber stamps, printing business cards, faxing, special orders and the area designated, "Copies and More," a full copy center located in each of their stores. With locations currently in 10 states, you can hone in on two new locations: In Dallas at the northeast corner of Mockingbird and Abrams (214/887-1245) and in Bedford at 1524-B Airport Freeway (817/571-0866). Don't overlook their complete online catalog, convenient to shop from home, or your home office. They are the largest independent office supply discounter in Texas with enormous buying power. Since they buy in bulk quantities, direct from manufacturers, they can pass the savings on to those in need. I guess that's why they've called themselves "Sav-on." And we say, "Right-on!" Here's one up for the small business owner—one up for the Gipper!

★★★★★★ Signs Manufacturing Corp. 214/339-2227

4550 Mint Way
Dallas, TX 75236
www.signsmanufacturing.com

Mon-Fri 8-5

What sign are you? If you don't know, you might want to give this sign company a call. After all, their signs have been seen in national magazines, as well as newspapers, movies and commercials. So, why not let them do yours, too? If you want to compete with the big boys, get your name out there. Choose channel letters, neon, illuminated or non-illuminated sign cabinets, pole signs, plastic lettering, trim-cap lettering, monuments, pylon signs and more! Their philosophy is, "If a sign is costing you money, it's not doing its job." In fact, on the contrary. They use only the highest quality technology available while presenting a competitive bottom line. FREE estimates are available.

★★★★   Staples   972/353-3877
997 Valley Ridge Blvd.   Mon-Fri 7 AM-9 PM; Sat 9-9; Sun 11-6
Lewisville, TX 75067
www.staples.com

This $9 billion Massachusetts-based retailer of office supplies, furniture and technology to con-
sumers and businesses is a top dog in the office supplies industry. From home-based businesses to
Fortune 500 companies, Staples is credited with inventing the office superstore concept, and today
is the world's largest operator of office superstores. With more than 46,000 employees at more
than 1,100 locations plus business via their mail order catalog, e-commerce and contract business,
expect if it has anything to do with cut-and-paste, you can find it here, for less. Similar to Office
Max and Office Depot, this completes the triangle of superstores where you can literally run
around in circles. In my humble opinion, I preferred the good old days of small, neighborhood
office supply stores, except for the power buys the big boys seem to finagle. And online, there are
easier websites to navigate and better prices elsewhere. There, I said it! Check directory for location nearest you. *Call toll-free: 800/STAPLES(*

★★★★★★   TCS Corporate Services   972/238-9123
1212 Presidental Dr.   Mon-Fri 7 AM-6 PM
Richardson, TX 75081
www.tcstoner.com

In business since 1986, TCS is headquartered in Dallas with locations throughout the
state though this is their ONLY location in the Metroplex. No one comes close to
them when it comes to volume sales. They are the largest direct-seller of remanufactured toner cartridges in the country, and if you don't get to this one, you've got to be toner-deaf!
Save up to 40 percent and keep that printer going and going and going. Stop paying full price for
new cartridges and consider this your money-saving option. I finally met my Prints Charming—at
least when it comes to replacing my cartridges. TCS is authorized to sell and service all major
brands of printers, too. Again, another office nightmare solved. Who do you call when your printer
crashes? But with this service, you've got to put the cart ahead of the horse and bring it in to be
fixed. (Rescue-Tech is who will come to you and fix it!) Let them help you uncover cost savings
on your printing needs without sacrificing quality. Start with laser printers, faxes, scanners, remanufactured toner cartridges, inkjet supplies, printer accessories and more. Stock your office with
envelopes, markers, labels, shelves, pens, hole punchers, clips, cords, binders, even coffee supplies. Brands include: AVERY, BUSH, CANNON, GENICOM, HEWLETT-PACKARD, TEX-
MARK, PITNEY BOWES, TEKTRONIX and XEROX for starters. Additionally, TCS-direct, a
division of TCS Corporate Services, provides specialty advertising and promotional products,
products just for business-to-business use, products for the non-profit, educational and government organizations....just about everyone. Pay 50 percent less than new on remanufactured toner
cartridges and 40 percent less on your printing costs. *Call toll-free: 800/633-4935*

★★★★★★   Tiger Paw of Dallas, Inc.   214/358-2332
2636 Walnut Hill, Suite 309   By Appt. Only
Dallas, TX 75229
www.TigerPawLaser.com

Between the FREE delivery and preventive maintenance, put a tiger in your tank at
the office and save yourself some gas. (Fuel, that is.) Since 1989, they have been in
the remanufactured office supply business—all for less, of course. Expect full service for laser printers, fax machines and copiers with a 100 percent guarantee. They sell and ser-

vice remanufactured toner cartridges for laser printers, printers, copiers and faxes. They specialize in **CANON, HP** and **LEXMARK** and have many other brands, as well. You can save up to 50 percent on your purchase AND take another 10 percent off if you are a new customer. You will also receive another 5 percent off if you purchase six or more cartridges at a time.

★★★ **Trophy Arts**   **817/336-4532**

519 Pennsylvania   Mon-Fri 9-5:30
Fort Worth, TX 76104

Shelve the idea of going anywhere else when you need to bestow an award of excellence. Trophy Arts, near the hospital district of Fort Worth, is the place to get custom trophies and engravings along with plaques, medals and awards of achievement when the deed warrants it. Give those employees a pat on the back once in a while for a job well done. It doesn't hurt to acknowledge and motivate for a continued performance. If men can have trophy wives, why can't employees have something to show for their hard-earned efforts, too? From sports to academic excellence, be proud and show off for a change! Turn around time is generally only three to five days for just about any order. Employers may want to reward sales efforts, for example, if a certain goal is achieved with something that serves a double purpose such as a trophy clock or plaque that doubles as a penholder. Whether it's carved in wood, engraved on a trophy or medal, printed on a ribbon, everybody wants recognition. Even if they spell your name wrong, it's still appreciated. If they don't carry what you want in stock, you can catalog shop for the likes of acrylics, award clocks, and pricier specialty awards with delivery in about three weeks. Quantity discounts can be had, BUT they have to be the same item with the same imprinting—like merchants who are voted into the 100 BEST. Watch for those honors, coming soon to a merchant nearest you.

Outlet Centers/Old Towns

★★★★★★ **Allen Premium Outlets** 972/678-7000
820 W. Stacy Rd. Mon-Sat 10-9; Sun 11-6
Allen, TX 75013
www.premiumoutlets.com

Fifty-plus outlet stores are up and ready for inspection just by heading north on US 75 N (Central Expressway) and exiting Stacy Rd. (Exit 37). This far northern outpost is Chelsea Property Group's latest addition to the north Texas bargain shopping scene. If discount designer clothing, shoes, handbags, luggage, housewares, home furnishings, gifts, books, music, vitamins, jewelry and accessories get your attention, I won't even mention food. The lineup here includes: ADIDAS, BANANA REPUBLIC FACTORY STORE, BARNEYS/NEW YORK, BIG DOG, BROOKS BROTHERS FACTORY STORE, CASUAL CORNER, COLE HAAN, DKNY, DRESS BARN, EDDIE BAUER, ESCADA, FUBU, GEOFFREY BEENE, GREG NORMAN, GUESS?, IZOD, JONES NEW YORK, KENNETH COLE, L'EGGS/HANES/BALI/PLAYTEX, LIZ CLAIBORNE, MAIDENFORM, NAUTICA, PERRY ELLIS, POLO RALPH LAUREN, PUMA, REEBOK, SAMSONITE, TIMBERLAND, TOMMY HILFIGER, VAN HEUSEN, WESTPOINT STEVENS, WILSON LEATHER OUTLET, ZALES OUTLET....got room for more? Well, go see it all for yourself! It's the chi-chi outlet mall but doesn't hold a candle—yet, to Woodbury Commons, Central Valley, NY, the largest outlet center in the world. But it's close. Hope aboard online for a 20 percent discount coupons before you head out the door.

★★★★★ **Bishop Arts District**
Bishop Street Varies with Merchants
Dallas, TX 75208-4657

It's so haute, it's hot. Shop the Bishop Arts District in Oak Cliff because it's a throwback to the days when people felt a sense of neighborhood and everyday was a holiday. Even with the closing of Mistletoe Boot, I still find it nostalgic to shop in Oak Cliff. My monthly treks to Dallas Food Depot for my gourmet garnishes for half price are legendary! But it's the vintage spin on retailing that is drawing crowds to the Bishop Arts District in record numbers. More and more folks with flair are looking for zoot suits and something out of the ordinary. Between Hate's Restaurant and Bishop Arts Floral is Zola's (a vintage resale shop) who has appetizing merchandise for both men and women. And prices, well, definitely a throw-back to the good old days. Though the two cousin owners named their store after their grandmother (Zola), inspiration for its flavor and force is written in every nook and cranny. They both work in full-time jobs elsewhere, but they ooze with spirit and determination. Where can you dress up in an evening dress for $50 or throw on a silk blouse for $15? Scarves from the 80s are making a comeback today (just look at the PUCCI's and GUCCI's running rampant in chi-chi boutiques around town.) Mix in both old and new and somehow the total package turns out funky and blue. The Bishop Arts District is surrounded by many notable alternatives to the same ole, same ole retailers. Don't miss making these a must-see when you're out and about in the District. Patina Bleu for antiques, the Oak Cliff Mercantile Building for architectural salvage, Dave's for new **FIESTA** dinnerware and antiques, and you've got to see the Book Doctor in action as she binds old books into like-new condition; too, she also designs custom covers for books in various states of disrepair. Imagine your family's bible that has come unglued that you treasure more than anything else in the world. She can restore it to pristine condition. Talk about a miracle! She can meticulously restore it, one page at a time. Then, don't miss Fet for the fusion of Oriental art objects, candles, custom-made accessories....there's no end to the imagination that oozes from this District. It's our SOHO....so say HELLO. There's always something going on to whet your appetite. You see, whatever Zola wants, Zola gets!

★★ Denton Factory Stores   940/565-5040
5800 N. I-35, Exit 470   Mon-Sat 10-8; Sun 11-6
Denton, TX 76207
www.dentonfactorystores.com

You don't have to drive a million miles for one of those sought-after styles, because, now, just north of the Dallas county line, there's a line-up of outlets under the umbrella of Denton Factory Stores. No doubt, Denton residents know a good thing when they see it. You can, too, just by heading north on I-35 past the Denton exits to Exit 470. What they lack in quantity, they make up in quality. One reason to cross the county line, when the season beckons, is the Bridal Company Outlet (See Bridal Chapter). Bridal gowns for as low as $99 which is a good bet in anybody's book. Just ask my niece, who bought her gown there. Dress Barn and Dress Barn Woman's are also good companion pieces for the trousseau—but nothing you can't live without. Need comfortable shoes? Try Famous Footwear which has locations everywhere. Need a wedding gift? You'll love the Lenox Factory Outlet, Suite 501, 940/891-6011. And lastly Antiqueland is trying to save them from fading into the sunset. So far, I doubt it it's helping. Even their website was inoperative each time I tried. They need help and I bet I could. But they probably will never call. I wonder if the Hunts still own the property?

★★★ Factory Stores of America   903/439-0118
I-30, Exit 124   Mon-Sat 9-7; Sun Noon-6
Sulphur Springs, TX 75482

Just one new addition since last year and that's the World Beauty and Gifts outlet. And that could be a beaut! However, this alone would not make you do a Wheelie and head to Sulphur Springs. If you want to salute the savings in total, you will find it patriotic to enlist the help of a few friends and make the drive if only for the Vanity Fair outlet. (They are 6-stars—see Lingerie Chapter) It is definitely worth the drive; I support them wholeheartedly. But the rest of the offerings leave me wanting to stay closer to home. A smattering of other bargain stops could give an additional incentive to make the trip but most of these outlets can be found closer to home: **BASS SHOES, BONWORTH, DRESS BARN, EASY SPIRIT, FIELDCREST/CANNON, FACTORY BRAND SHOES, FACTORY CONNECTION, KITCHEN COLLECTION, L'EGGS/HANES/BALI, MORGAN ASHLEY, PAPER FACTORY, RUE 21, VAN HEUSEN** and **VANITY FAIR**. Whether it's a comfortable pair of shoes that you buy after a few hours of walking, or a dress shirt for dad, your kid's birthday party invitations, a queen-size sheet set, believe me, you'll have enough choices to come home bearing gifts. A real deal, I almost forgot, can be had at Kitchen Collection. Then again, you can shop there online and save on the wear and tear on your car and your feet. Again, the reason to shop here is Vanity Fair. And that's the way it goes.

★   Festival Marketplace   817/213-1000
2900 E. Pioneer Pkwy.   Wed-Sat 10-8; Sun Noon-6
Arlington, TX 76010

You can't get a straight answer even if you wanted one here. Questions about anything and every-thing can only be answered by fax. So, what's the deal? If you're looking for a place to bring your family visiting from Ohio, if they won't talk to us, imagine how they'll ignore you? Of course, they have also been the object of law enforcement in the past, so it's best you probably avoid them all together, except for the Dillard's Clearance Outlet which is open Mon-Sat 10-7 and Sun 12-6. Their direct number is 817/649-0782. But rumor has it that its presence may be short-lived, which leads me to believe there's trouble in River City. There's a lot of space vacant, although they claim there are 100 vendors representing mostly ethnic goods, Mexican curios, imports, costume jew-elry, flowers, baskets and a food court. There wasn't. Whoopee-Do! But Whoopee didn't. We left empty handed and headed to Dillard's. *Call toll-free: 877/877-3378*

★★★★★   Grapevine Mills Mall   972/724-4900
3000 Grapevine Mills Pkwy.   Mon-Sat 10-9:30; Sun 11-8
Grapevine, TX 76051
www.grapevinemills.com

If you've heard it through the Grapevine, it's probably true. Exit Bass Pro Drive off Highway 121, this mega-marvel at the cornerstone of D/FW means over 1.5 million square feet of pure shopping pleasure. Not all stores, though, offer the biggest discounts, or even the littlest discount, but it's still a place to spend the day and, no doubt, you'll bag a few good items, or grab a bite to eat and enjoy a movie. From the big attractions like the AMC 30-screen theater to Bass Pro Shops Out-door World, Bed Bath & Beyond, Books-A-Million, Burlington Coat Factory, GameWorks, Group USA, JC Penney Outlet, Last Call from Neiman Marcus, Marshalls, Off 5th, Off Rodeo Dr, Old Navy, Polar Ice, The Sports Authority, Virgin Megastore and Western Warehouse, it's all here and more. Ann Taylor Loft, Carter's For Kids, Donna Karen, GAP Outlet, Guess? Outlet are sure bets. But Off Rodeo Drive is not Pricey, pricey. Then again, you can make it with a few cheeses from The Mozzarella Factory in a kiosk. It's a home run. Score cheeses without having to drive down-town to their factory. Lastly, stop by their Information booth and pick up a Discover Card coupon book that allows for bigger savings when shopping with your discover card. And always check which outlet has discounts just for stopping buy. Check with the Mall's Management. A great place to connect for a regular heart-healthy regime. Their partner is Baylor Hospital Systems so you can bet they can get you up and running.

★★★★★★   Inwood Outlet Center   214/521-4777
1311 Inwood Rd.   Hours Vary with Merchants
Dallas, TX 75247

For an in-town shopping experience that's an outlet shopper's easy in-and-out dream, here's where it's happening. Regardless of which side of the street you shop, the bargains are equally divided. The line-up delivers an equal-opportunity for you to save the big bucks, from evening glitz to bedtime Puttin'on the Ritz. Starting on the south side of the street, some favorites include the Special Occasion Dresses Outlet Store, where they've con-solidated what hasn't sold at their discount chain around the Metroplex. Next door, you can bed down on the most glamorous bedding ensembles made expressly for specialty stores and catalogs at Bedroom Solutions. This is THE place to sleep tight and outfit your bedroom like the rich and famous. The only difference is, here you can afford it. Check directory for location. Other favorites include 7th Ave Plus Sizes, Suzanne's, Crate and Barrel Outlet Store, the Interior Alternative (Waverly/Schumaker Outlet) and Circa Interior Designs. Medical and profession personal need scrubs and medical supplies, so there's Judi's Scrubs and Citi-Uniforms. Discount Dresses for After 5 dresses, the Simmons mattress outlet called World of Sleep for sleeping in after a night on the town, did I forget anybody? Let me know if I did. Sorry about that! Oops, I almost forgot, Closeout Corner is around the corner and where the decorators are shopping now for all of their accents. See write-up in Furniture Chapter. Owned and managed by Vantage Management.

★★★★★   Old Downtown Historic Carrollton

I-35 and Belt Line   Varies with Merchants
Carrollton, TX 75006
www.oldcarrollton.com

In spite of tight parking, shopping in Old Downtown Historic Carrollton is a real treat—it's so neat with even some super-duper places to eat. Of course, having the Gazebo for a backdrop to send a photo to friends and family back east doesn't hurt, either. Pick up a brochure of all of the shops and have yourself a field day by taking a field trip to each and every one. Pierson's Fine Quilts is a friend to all of us at KAAM, Stained Glass Overlay has their own write-up and has so for many years, the Herb Market for freshly grown herbs and candle making glasses and the Old Craft Store which combines an old-fashioned U.S. Post Office which is housed in one of Carrollton's original bank buildings from the 1930's with quilts and other antique country store gotta have's. Too, there's the Carrollton Skin Care Spa, Mary Lou's (see write-up under Apparel) and Antiques and More (see write-up under Antiques). A thrift store, a massage depot, a coffee house, the Prairie House Barbecue favorite hang-out and so much more. Walk the walk, talk the talk, and enjoy shopping in the slow lane.

★★★   Old Town/Historic Garland

Garland, TX   Varies with Merchant

Need another reason to shop in Garland besides my all-time favorites of the Cabbage Patch and Vikon Village? Then, consider the downtown Garland historic hideaways that have been tucked into mini niches up and down Main Street, State Street and North 6th and 7th. You won't believe how this little town percolates with small town deals and big time conversation. Getting to know each merchant has been the job of the town's crier and her charitable resale shop "I'll Never Tell." Christina Nappi is the pied piper of old-town Garland . Around the corner, enjoy an hour or two at Maude & Murel's, a leisurely lunchtime repast at Patricia's Coffee and Tea Diner on State Street because they're right next door to each other. (See individual write-ups under antiques or food). Then on Main Street, you'll need to make an appointment to see the steals at Rena Taylor's Estate Gallery (1235 Main Street, 972/494-0295, by appt. only) specializing in antiques and estate sales. Then if you've got room, you can enjoy lunch at Tea Time Treasures, 700 Main Street, 972/205-9995, Mon-Sat 11-5 where private tea parties, bridal and baby showers, and dress-up birthday parties are the focal point.) So when you're not dining, think tea parties or private parties and let them bring out the good china. (I'll drink to that!) Now you're off to Alston's Old Home Place at 212 N. 7th Street, Thurs-Sat 10-6, 972/272-3970. You don't want to miss the place if you love to scrounge for architectural antiques, furniture and collectibles. Think Canton, only front-in parking and better prices and you've got a glimpse into Garland's resurrection of their Old Town. And that's for starters. There's more. Walk the walk and talk the talk here, too.

★★★★ Old Town/Lewisville

Main and Mill Streets   Varies with Merchants
Lewisville, TX 75057

At last, my hometown is going uptown with major renovations and an attempt to embrace the return to the good ol'days. Shopping in the older section in Lewisville has always had its good points, but mostly it was just the "other side of Stemmons." Except for the hospital, I rarely graced that side of the street unless it was via ambulance. Today, however, the street is abuzz with renovation and excitement. Things are on the move, you can tell. And there are some pretty good reasons to shop on the other side of town. Antiques Etc. Mall, Bargain Depot, Home Sewn Solutions, Wigand's and Bridal Boutique were some of the better reasons and it's still glowin'and growin'! After-Glow Antiques and Refinishing (417 E. Church, 972/221-6907) is a glowing resource for touch-ups and major restorations of your favorite sideboard; CCA (Christian Community Action) has moved to bigger digs on Highway 121 and 3040, and Bridal Boutique, 119 W. Main St. even has its own website., www.bridalboutiquelewisville.com. More than likely, you've never heard of Wigand's, north of Main on Mill Street, but if you want wholesale prices on knick-knacks that look a whole lot more expensive than head to Wigand's, you'll flip. You'll find Old Town Lewisville an up-and-coming bargain shopping district. So, keep your fingers on the pulse of this small town that is finally growing up. Watch this space for improvements. And check for individual merchant write-ups throughout the book in their appropriate chapters.

★★★★ Plano Market Square   972/578-1591

1717 E. Spring Creek Pkwy.   Mon-Fri 10-9; Sat 10-10; Sun 10-6
Plano, TX 75074

With 22 merchants under one roof and the "potential" of a website, things are not staying the same in and around downtown Plano. Still, should they ever put monogrammed towels in the public restrooms, they would say "PMS" (Plano Market Square!) I think this is initially a wonderful spin-off to proclaim a monthly sales event, don't you agree?) Conveniently located in the 'burbs, shop Garden Ridge (open 9-9), TJ Maxx, The Dollar Store, Dress Barn, L'eggs/Hanes and more. Don't expect a lengthy run-down of all of the merchants as even the telephone operator was out of breath after the first few stores. Located on Spring Creek Parkway, just east of Central Expressway, it's a good place to run down your weekly shopping menu list of "Things to Buy!" Some merchants better than others but overall, a reason to stop by often if you're in the neighborhood.

★★★★★ Prime Outlets at Hillsboro   254/582-9205

I-35 South, Exit 368A   Mon-Sat 10-8; Sun 11-6
Hillsboro, TX 76240
www.primeoutlets.com

Eighty-five stores and holding at their Prime, these outlets are worth the one-hour drive south from Dallas/Fort Worth. Sign up online and get email notifications of special sales and events or if not online, call their toll-free number. Some of the big names are represented: Big Dog, Black & Decker, The Bombay Company Outlet, Bugle Boy, Carter's, Casual Corner, Corning Revere, Dress Barn, Duck Head, Eddie Bauer, Elizabeth, Farberware, Florsheim, Fossil, G & A Furniture, Gap, Guess?, Haggar, J. CREW, Jones New York, Kasper, L'eggs/HanesS/Bali/Playtex, Liz Claiborne, Maidenform, Mikasa, Motherhood, Nike, Oshkosh B'Gosh, Polo by Ralph Lauren, Reebok, Rue 21, S & K Menswear, Samsonite, Sunglass Outlet, Ultra, Vitamin World, Zales, The Diamond Store Outlet and more. If your tummy starts a grumblin', then get your motor rumblin'over to the food court for everything from Subway Sandwiches, Pepperidge Farm, Rocky Mountain Chocolate Factory and well, give me strength to carry on! Groups of 10 or more get special coupons for additional savings. One of the three Prime Outlet developments within the North Texas marketplace.

★★★★★   **Prime Outlets of Gainesville**   **940/668-1888**

I-35, Exit 501   Mon-Sat 10-8; Sun 11-6
Gainesville, TX 76240
www.primeoutlets.com

Another Prime example of what you can deliver when you put 80 or so name-brand outlets and specialty stores under one roof. Just three miles south of the Red River en route to Oklahoma, stop—in the name of the love of bargains. More than 80 stores line up to tempt each and every dollar out of your wallet into their coffers. From A to Z, they've got it all! Start out at Big Dog's and work your way to the infamous jewelry store, Zales not to mention everything in between.

★★★★★★   **Sam Moon Center**   **972/484-3084**

11826 Harry Hines   Mon-Sat 9-6:30 (Dallas); Mon-Thurs 10-7; Fri-Sat 10-8 (Frisco)
Dallas, TX 75234
www.sammoon.com

 Now that Sam's the man in the shopping center business, is it any won- der he's considered THE legend of Harry Hines? When he made his first move to bigger quarters on Harry Hines and LBJ on the south side of the freeway, this center was a roaring success but NO PARKING. People were parking on Harry Hines and having to literally walk miles to get into the stores. So Sam Moon went across the street on the other side of LBJ. We did a live radio remote to celebrate the grand opening on Valentine's Day and there was a winter avalanche of three inches of snow. So much for a "snowy" opening. Even God got into the act. Now, the lot continues to fill to the brim, but not the breaking point. There's enough parking and every good reason to shop at Sam Moon Center (but Sam Moon is still the biggest draw.) The Haggar Outlet is more than likely the other. This 125,000 square feet of bargain shopping U-shaped center tries all to live up to the legend of Sam Moon, but it's a tall order to fill. Another 400,000 square feet of bargain-shopping is happening with a second Sam Moon Center in Frisco at Hwy. 121 and Preston Rd. Many shoppers are in search of a good bargain, especially in light of today's economy, and those in the know have long frequented Sam Moon Trading for the best deals. Now those in the northern suburbs of the Metroplex can enjoy the same bargains that Sam Moon Center brought forth to the Harry Hines strip. Sam Moon himself has three stores in his center. One's for jewelry and purses (which first made him famous.) Next is one for luggage and gifts, which now is making him king of luggage and small electronics with the addition this year of perfume and cologne for men and women; and most recently, his Home Store for frames, lights, lampshades, mirrors and furniture. When will it ever end? We hope never! A miscellaneous grouping of other stores for apparel, bedding, beauty supplies, candles and more. This is America and Sam is the perfect role model that with hard work you can make it big!

★★★★★   **Tanger Factory Outlet Center**   **972/524-6034**

301 Tanger Drive   Mon-Sat 9-9; Sun 11-6
Terrell, TX 75160
www.tangeroutlet.com

Being one of the pioneers in the outlet center business, Tanger can be proud of its contribution to helping bargain shoppers save money everywhere. Open since 1981, Tanger is no Sanger-Harris, but if you're a department store devotÈe, make a detour down I-20 (Exit 501) in Terrell. After all, you're going to be making at least a dozen trips to G & S Sales in Terrell for all your home improvement supplies at half the price anyway, you might as well veer off the highway and see what's cookin'at Tanger. With over 35 stores including Bass, Bible Factory Outlet, Big Dog, Bon Worth, Book Warehouse, Casual Corner, Claire's, Corning Revere, Welcome Home, Dress Barn, Factory Brand Shoes, Factory Shoe Warehouse, Full Size Fashions, Gap Outlet, Jockey, K-B Toy Outlet, Kitchen Collection, Koret, L'eggs/Hanes/Bali/ Playtex, Levis, Liz Claiborne, Mikasa, Old Navy Outlet, Oshkosh B'Gosh, Paper Factory, Perfumania, Rocky Mountain Fudge Factory, Reebok, Rockport, Rue 21, Samsonite, Seiko The Company Store, Totes/Sunglass World, Tupperware, Van Heusen, Vitamin World and Wilson's Leather Outlet, what do you have to lose? Well, unless you're talking about the money you're not having to shell out? It's a fair trade-off, don't you agree? Show your AAA card at the mall office and get a coupon book. One per day per AAA member. One of their highlights are their special events'days like their 4th of July and Labor Day sidewalk sales, even extra sales on Tax Free shopping days. "It's always something," as Gilda Radner used to say. ***Call toll-free: 800/4TANGER;***

Party & Paper

★★★   Alert Signs and Banners   972/416-3639

3208 E. Belt Line, Suite 240   Mon-Fri 9-5
Farmers Branch, TX 75234

Only sign language spoken here and full service every step of the way. Magnetic, vinyl, aluminum, coroblast (whatever's your pleasure), they do it all and....all in house. That means, your sign never leaves their sight and from start to finish, expect about a three-day turn around. A 2'X 5'vinyl banner (for a trade show, for example) would run about $60—add $25 onto that if you need to add your logo. Aluminum signs 18'X 24" would run about $29 (and $18 for the frame), but you can get a 20 percent discount for buying in quantity, for the sign only. Stay Alert and follow the signs.

★★★★★★   All for Less   972/509-5368; 469/569-2893

Windy Meadow Drive   24/7 online; By Appt. In-House (Mon-Fri 10-7:30); Sat 11-2
Plano, TX 75023-5004
www.allforlessweddings.com

 If I have but one party left to plan, let me call Sharon Nichols at All for Less to help me make it through the night. Her attention to detail since 1994, the savings of 20 to 40 percent off every kind of invitation and all the extras that she makes available in person or online turns you into a fool if you fool with it yourself. Leave your name and she'll return your call. Grooms are not neglected as they rent tuxedos, too. Just bring in your correct measurements (and don't lie); then they do the rest (except for pick up and return of the tuxedo.) Expect only the finest invitations and accessories at THE BEST discounts in town. They also do Floral/Gown Preservation (at less than retail) with connections to other services a bride may be looking to purchase. Take a walk down her aisle of wedding products: invitations, accessories, veils, engagement announcements, bridal shower invitations, rehearsal dinners, plus the full spectrum of greeting cards including anniversary, birthday (for kids and grown-ups), calendars, congratulations, a new line of COURAGE CARDS, get well, sympathy, thank-you cards and more. Then, for personal or business use, what about letterhead, business cards, envelopes, mailing envelopes, customized stamps, advertising labels, POST-IT NOTES, shipping labels, personalized labels, memo pads; well, make a note to call Sharon ASAP! And if you are looking for specialty and premium items, don't forget to peek at her selection: address books and planners, pens, T-shirts, mugs and cups. If you want to promote your business, here's the place to place your bets. Remember, they do MUCH more than invitations! Member of Association Of Bridal Consultants and the Association of Wedding Professionals International.

★★★★★★   Card & Party Factory   817/274-8044

2215 S. Cooper @ Arkansas Lane   Mon-Sat 9-8 Sun 12-6
Arlington, TX 76013

If you're like me and are burning the candles at both ends, you might as well save money in the process. Here's where to turn to huff and puff those candles right out without creating a five-alarm fire. Party, party, burning bright, head to Card & Party Factory for a hula good time night. Say hello to **AMERICAN GREETINGS** and the like in the card department. The store in Arlington (above) took over a former Kroger location with 20,000 square feet. Having a luau? Bring on the grass skirts and pineapple honeycombs. For any holiday, wait until after the date, and then stock up for even greater savings. Whether you are planning a wedding, graduation, baby shower, over-the-hill, kids'party, retirement, going away, bachelor, whatever, here's where to start the ball rolling. Three Fort Worth locations—on Western Center Blvd., 817/232-7866, 5240 S. Hulen St. at Hulen Fashion Center, 817/423-1026 and 6226 McCart Ave., 817/294-1566; in Desoto at 360 E. Belt Line, 972/223-3123 and others throughout the state (Cleburne, Corsicana, Sherman, Waco, Amarillo, San Angelo, Baytown, Brownwood, Temple, college Stations—well I'm exhausted already. Check out their newest Dallas superstore opened as we went to press. Call 214/824-6223 for directions. Looks like the Irwin's, based in Ennis are making their moves as party stores are moving in and out of business, these guys are steady plodders who are probably having the time of their lives (surely not partying day and night, I hope.) Go to the towns where the big boys are not and clean up. Be the biggest fish in a small pond and rise to the top. The Wal-Mart philosophy of specialty party stores if I've ever heard, and what a swell party it is. With the amount of inventory they carry, including Christmas trees when the season dictates, I don't understand why I can't get a website up. I've been looking for it since 1999. Do you suppose it's still under construction? Or what? Please let me know when you find it.

★★★★★   Constructive Playthings   972/418-1860

1927 E. Belt Line   Mon-Fri 9-7; Sat 9-5; Sun 12-5
Carrollton, TX 75006
www.ustoyco.com

Party, party, let's have a party, smarty. And if you're one of us, you already know where to get your party decorations. When you enter their store, in person, via their catalogue or online, you know there is no one better when it comes to educational toys, party novelties and in general inexpensive doodads for school, play or party. Most things are priced so low, they cost more to mail than to buy. Browse through three different divisions until you find the perfect....whatever. There's an immense selection and a full line of challenging stage magic supplies, tricks, videos and magic books, too. In fact, in Kansas City, they have the largest magic store in the world. Choose from a clowning section with videos, costumes, professional make-up and more. Constructive Playthings is made up of the School Division and the Parent/Family Division, award-winning suppliers of the finest early childhood educational toys, equipment, books, records, tapes, videos, art supplies and teaching aids. They search the world and pick only those products that promote, enhance and enrich the growth of children. The catalog is FREE for the asking. Imagine, every festive occasion can be celebrated with something from here at up to 70 percent off. Lucky for us, we can spin the wheel and land in Carrollton to shop their store as well. *Call toll-free: 800/841-6478*

◆◆◆◆◆ **Entertainment Alliance**   **972/495-3768**

2001 Lancecrest Drive   Mon-Fri 9-6 (Office Hours)
Garland, TX 75044
hometown.aol.com/mwmagic/page/index.htm

You can't help but smile when you place a call to Entertainment Alliance. They're the folks to call to arrange the perfect party, all the way down to the entertainment. So, start the ball rolling. With 25 years of experience, Marty the Magician (a.k.a. Marty Westerman) has more than magic up his sleeve. They also are "cape-able" of providing the catering, arranging for the decorations and supplying other entertainers like sketch artists, musicians and others. Why worry about who's going to tend to all those details? It's hats off to this group of dedicated master planners! *Call toll-free: 800/395-3768*

★★★★★ **Invitation Company**   **972/233-3344**

                                                               By Appt. Only
Dallas, TX 75248

Cindy Spechler has invitations for every occasion and, always, at discounted prices. Operating her home-based business in the far north Dallas corridor, remember, an invitation is a guest's first impression of things to come. Nobody sends brown paper bags anymore. So, if it's a plain vanilla invitation, you can expect a plain vanilla occasion. Add some oomph to your invite, and watch what happens! All the latest offerings from the New York paper shows are available for your discriminating selection. Enjoy invitations and party accessories by such notables as ARLENE SEGAL DESIGNS, ARTSCROLL, CARLSON CRAFT, C'EST PAPIER, CHASE, ENCORE, JANSSON, MAZEL TOV, NU-ART, ROYAL IMPRINTS and others. Browse through the books and books of options with plenty of options for personalization. Expect a two-three week turnaround and a slice of 30 percent off the retail price. All you have to do now is RSVP!

★★★★★★ **Nowlin Trading Company**   **214/366-3206**

2666 Brenner   Thurs-Sat 10-5
Dallas, TX 75220

He's back. Now you can shop Ronnie Nowlin's infamous warehouse sale on a 3-day week regular basis. Now the doors to his warehouse are opened Thurs-Sat from 10-5 1/2 block west of Harry Hines, five blocks north of Northwest Hwy, four blocks south of Walnut Hill—well, close to all of the other activity in the Harry Hines shopping Mecca that is slowly becoming internationally known as the "strip." Oops, didn't mean to get so graphic. X marks the space where the deals are three days a weeks. Get all of your gift wrapping accoutrements all under one roof, for starters. Ronnie Nowlin is back without any hiccups in his store hours. Finally, he's having a regular gig in a 4,000 square foot warehouse location that will be open each and every week until further notice. Load up one or two shopping carts with everything you've ever wanted to "call it a wrap." He's back and for those of you who remember him, he was the CBI Warehouse guy when the outlet was on Luna Rd. in Carrollton. (They're back, too. Check out their write-up under Beauty.) Think of it as your last stop to get what you need to wrap that gift, but make it the first stop when it comes time to buying what you need. Great prices on everything. Speaking of prices, expect wholesale throughout, from 50-75 percent off. For example, at a certain wholesaler in town, wire ribbon was selling at a WHOLESALE price of $20—Nowlin sells it for $10. Or fabulous floral arrangements are always 50 percent off (and some 50 percent off wholesale!) Sort of like fleurs-de-less. He welcomes shoppers with open arms and treats them like royalty. See tons of wrapping paper, package trim, bags, tissue, ribbons, tags, boxes, candles, home accessories, note cards, floral arrangements, decorative accents and tons of little gifty items that could be classified as "odds and ends." Remember the good old days of the Susan Crane ware-house sale? Well, this is it....reincarnate. And don't overlook the separate Christmas department of over 1,000 square feet devoted just to this holiday. See what's in store and be prepared to load up the carts but be sure to tell him the Diva sent you!

★★★★ Palmer Sales   972/288-1026

3510 E. Hwy. 80   Mon-Fri 9-6; Sat 10-4
Mesquite, TX 75149

Saving one-third on all your party favors, fund-raising and carnival supplies is how they've staked their claim at Palmer Sales. Since 1948, they have been selling balloons, toys, holiday and other religious items through their "wholesale" catalog. Have a ball. Celebrate your next happy occasion with thousands of little doodads that every teacher or parent would love. Items like plush animals, holiday decorations, confetti, party supplies, trinkets and charms, paperware, party favors, piÒa-tas, all the accoutrements of a fun time in the old town tonight. You're nuts if you pay full price when you can save on all the LOONEY TUNES plush animals. One thing you won't find is popu-larly-themed children's party decorations. But if you want to be a POWDER PUFF GIRL, you better go POKEMON someplace else. On all returns (30-day return policy), there is a 10 percent restocking charge, so be sure it's what you want. Most orders are shipped the same day they are received. Order in their FREE catalog and see what kind of party's just around the corner. No web-site? Boo hoo!

★★★★ Party City   972/509-2200

3308 N. Central Expressway, Suite A   Mon-Fri 9:30-9; Sat 8:30-9; Sun 10:30-6
Plano, TX 75093
www.partycity.com

Eight is a charm for Party City, the number of PC locations in the Metroplex, and each with over 30,000 items. Open seven days and six nights, I can't think of an occasion when you can't throw a party and provide the necessary accoutrements. It's always somethin'....from half price periodic deals to regular everyday savings of at least 20 percent, you might as well enjoy your party from every value vantage point. Everything is discounted from the MSRP (manufacturer's suggested retail price.) In fact, if you can find the same merchandise advertised for a lower price, they will refund you 15 percent. From catering trays to plastic tumblers, plastic table covers to luncheon napkins, go ahead, "Make My Day." Whether it's a birthday or a Halloween party, wig out. Bal-loon bouquets to Easter baskets, you'll be stuffed at the end of the day (or night). With over 450 stores across this great expanse, you might as well let them entertain you. Don't forgot there's 50 percent off gift wrap, 50 percent off tableware patterns, 30 percent off wedding invitations, what more do you want?

Trax City USA   972/252-7827

3909 W. Airport Frwy.   Mon-Fri 10-7; Sat 10-6
Irving, TX 75062
www.traxcityusa.com

Just west of the Irving Mall, this 20-year veteran of the party biz is looking to crank up the volume at your next karaoke clambake. From jive to hip hop, rap to mambo, cha-cha to the Lindy, golden oldies to country-western, big band to the blues, rent a karaoke machine, roll up the carpet and start filling up your dance card. Pick your sounds from over 80,000 sound tracks and if you really want them to trax down something out-of-the-ordinary, they're up for the challenge. For the past two decades, they have been whoopin'it up for churches, schools, auditoriums, clubs; your next big party can next be the talk of the neighborhood! Whether you want to have something recorded, gather hours of musical pleasure for the karaoke machine, make a cassette or CD of your favorite tunes, these are the recording pros. Whether it's a personal or a professional event, any aspiring "American Idol" can use their studio for $49.95/hour which includes editing and mixing by a recording engineer with over 30 years'experience. They can also connect you to an agent to get bookings, help with promotions and set up your own website.

★★★★★   Under Wraps   972/724-4900

3000 Grapevine Mills Pkwy.   Mon-Sat 10-9:30; Sun 11-8
Grapevine, TX 76051
www.millscorp.com/grapevine

Like the **ENERGIZER** Bunny, these brothers are still going strong but it looks like, at last, they have landed at a permanent location at Grapevine Mills. Let me see, how long has it been that I been writing about them? 20-25 years? Gee, they must be as old as I am—and still haven't called it a wrap! Sure enough, they learned early to roll with the punches. And it's their rolls that have fed the Metroplex with savings of 50 percent off and more. Get real! Twenty-five running feet of nice gift wrap for $3.65—doesn't get much cheaper than that! Always half off retail, up to 80 percent, means gift givers never let their gifts leave home without them. Designer gift-wrap, tie-ons, ribbons and bows, including several bins of 99-cent rolls on clearance, are the tip of the paper chase. Accent all of your packages with punch. And finally, being in a mall, they have to stay open through the lunch and dinner hours. (I remember the days when they closed for lunch!) Now, they have to sell right through it. Let's just hope they aren't dining on wraps, though. Their corporate offices are still on Floyd Circle in Dallas, but I'm glad to see they are still in various states of unwrap.

Pets & Vets

◆◆◆◆◆◆ **Abbey's Pet and Housesitting**   **817/735-1486**

Fort Worth, TX   By Reservation Only

Kelly and Mary Claire Sullivan are a most happy couple who share their love of pets with the business of pets and house-sitting. After all, if yours is like Miss Cleo (who would not tolerate sleeping on a concrete floor or a stiff, cold cot), before you leave home, give this service a call. Are your pets spoiled prima donnas used to down comforters and food served fresh daily in a crystal bowl? If so, you wouldn't want to inflict a cold and isolated crate to your best friend, would you? Abbey's is one of the oldest professional pet and house sitting services in the Fort Worth/Tarrant County, and the Sullivan's are not only blessed with their own two-legged children, but consider all of their four-legged friends to be part of their extended family. Instead of taking them screaming to the kennel, keep them at home while you get a much-needed rest away from the barks and purrs. They are members of the PSI (Pet Sitters International), offer a pre-meeting before you leave, are bonded, insured with references a mile long. Besides, after pricing their competitors, Abbey's came in as a bargain without taking a bite into our vacation budget. Just ask the over 250 satisfied pet owners who never leave home without calling Abbey's first.

◆◆◆◆ **Aussie Pet Mobile**   **817/318-7387**

Arlington, TX 76010   By Appt. Only
www.aussiepetmobile.com

All the way from down under, this Australian import is better than carrying your pooch (or it is pouch?) to the groomers. A lot better. In fact, there's nothing better I'd rather do then get my brood's hair-does at home without keeping them locked in isolation with all the other barking bow-wows at a groomer's kennel. Plus, Miss Cleo goes absolutely bonkers if she even hears us getting her traveling **SHERPA** out of the garage to pack 'er up. This mobile grooming company attaches a trailer to their cars; only need water and electricity when they arrive (making it a tough haul if they're coming to a high rise.) One of the fastest growing industries, what parents won't spend on themselves, they'll spend on their four-legged children, whiskers, tail and all. All products are environmentally-friendly, and the groomers take pride in their innovative trailer design, heated hydrobath and 15-step grooming maintenance process. Created in 1996 in Sydney, Australia, others were itching to hop on the gravy train (so to speak). So they began franchising throughout Australia and now in this country. They are headquartered in the U.S. in Dana Point, California. Stacey Magee, co-owner is based in Arlington, TX 76010, but have pet, will travel anywhere in the Metroplex. Leave your name and number on their answering machine and they'll get back to you. *Call toll-free: 888/677-PETS*

★★★★★   **Backtalk Bird Center**   **972/960-BIRD**

14560 Midway   Mon-Tues, Sat 10-6; Wed-Fri 10-7; Sun Noon-6
Dallas, TX 75244

If Polly takes flight, take her in for a wing clip and nail trim, only $10. Birds need their regular salon appointments, too, even if they continue to give you back talk. These sassy little critters can also be boarded when you go out of town. Bird sitting now joins the ranks of other pet-sitting services around town. Bird-watching costs begin at $5 a day, but you must bring your own cage. Leave any special meds, vitamins, instructions and if Polly likes her special crackers, bring them, too. Now onto the other birds. Many were below dealer's cost and that means, "cheep, cheep!" Cockatoos to Cockatiels, Macaws to Amazon parrots, this is aviary heaven here on earth. Bring these flying friends home and get acquainted. The more exotic, the more expensive.

★★★   **Boutique Pet Shop & Aquarium**   **214/321-1219**

9035 Garland Rd.   Mon-Fri 8-7; Sat 8:30-6; Sun Noon-5
Dallas, TX 75218

We fell for this store hook, line and sinker, until we had to give them a call. Though they've been a favorite since 1968, it's hard to believe this is a combination grooming salon and fish store. Yes, they're a popular hang-out, but surely there's not a line-up of fishes waiting to fin-agle a salon appointment. They sell aquariums and all the accoutrements: plants plus tropical and marine fish on one hand; and dog supplies for your dogs and grooming for same with charges from $30-$50, depending on size and condition of your dog on the other. Yes, same-day grooming is possible unless Max has to be de-toxed and de-tangled. This full-service pet store and grooming salon includes pet food and toys as well. Thank goodness, they're not grooming fins or fish.

★★★★★   **Canine Commissary**   **214/324-3900**

11504 Garland Rd.   Mon-Wed, Fri 9-7:30; Thurs 9-9; Sat 9-6; Sun Noon-6
Garland, TX 75218
www.caninecommissary.com

This is the ultimate in fancy feasts for your four-legged friends. Gourmet treats, peanut butter pops, biscuits and bones are just the beginning to whet their growing appetites. Bring Fido along when you shop and let him beg for his supper. Give him something exotic to nosh on only if you didn't have to call for the pooper-scooper afterwards. (When are they going to learn to clean up after themselves?) Both cats and dogs are treated as equal opportunity pets with discounts across the kennels, dogs runs, show supplies, grooming supplies, doggie fashions, car seats and carriers, bowls, bones, toys, "how-to" manuals and books, even cards that are dog-eared. Arf. Arf. Don't be catty and take the bite out of barking up the wrong tree. Spread the good word. Premium to economy-brand food, yummy in their tummies. But if you're one of the new breed of pet owner, you might serve it on "bone" china. To satisfy all of your animal instincts, the pet patrol is also maintained at 3614 Greenville Ave., Dallas, 214/821-7700 and 1301 Custer Rd., Plano, 972/985-3900. Watch for their website, which is still under construction one year later.

★★★★★★   **Diamond Pet Center**   **972/442-7500**

1275 E. FM 544   Mon-Fri 10-7; Sat 8-6; Sun 1-5
Wylie, TX 75098

 When a bird flies the coop, all hell breaks loose in this store. Imagine our chagrin when this exotic birdhouse had such a "beakout." Close the escape hatch! All hands on deck! You can imagine the chaos that ensued when all we wanted was to bring

Tweetie in for clip job. Anyway, all's well that ends well, especially since he got his nails done FREE with a wing clip. Parrots, Cockatoos, Cockatiels and several varieties of Macaws, including Green Wings, Harlequins and Camelots were swinging from their perches when we flew in. They have one of the most extensive and best-priced lines of bird products and accessories in the Metroplex. Now nested in their new Wylie location, you should know that they breed their own birds. Their stock varies from Parakeets to Macaws, Cockatoos to Amazons. They have all the accessories you'll need to keep your bird in an environment to which they soon grow accustomed.

◆◆◆◆ Find-A-Pet   214/827-4357

6301 Gaston Ave., Suite 600   Mon-Fri 8:30-5:30
Dallas, TX 75244
www.petdata.com

When Fifi or Fufu lose their way, where to go for help? Try this FREE Find-A-Pet service, but only if your pet has been registered. Registration costs $7 for spayed or neutered pets and $20 for those that aren't. Senior citizens have up to three FREE registrations, as do the pets that assist the disabled. Statistics show that you are 90 percent more likely to find your lost pet if they are registered with the city. Currently, there are nine cities using this service. All information is shared via an automated phone line. Register every year and when the tag expires, it will be the same expiration date as the expiration of your animal's rabies'shots. Help solve animal control problems and the heartache that goes with losing your best four-legged friend. *Call toll-free: 888/738.3463*

★★★★★★ Flower Mound Animal Adoption Center 972/874-6390

3950 Justin Rd.   Mon-Fri 9-5; Sat 10-3
Flower Mound, TX
www.flower-mound.com

 How can I not fall in love with every last Tom, Dick and Harriet. You can't help it. Flower Mound Animal Adoption Center provides shelter for as many as 50 dogs and 50 cats now that their new $2.8 million center capacity has expanded to accommodate more stray animals than their previous digs. You might say their new facility is going to the dogs, so to speak. See what I mean by logging on to their website—and clicking on the top right hand corner: "Adopt a Pet Today!" There is currently no charge to adopt a dog or cat; however, the state and town ordinances require that the adopter get the animal's rabies vaccinations and have the animal spayed or neutered within 15 days from adoption. This is mandatory and must be complied with. All animals have a safe haven in cages behind glass so it's not nearly as noisy as other shelters and children can look without fear of being snapped at. The animals have a play area, sick dogs and cats are isolated from the rest and there is a treatment room for the veterinarians. Any docs looking to help? Like in all shelters, shop here before looking to buy from a breeder because these dogs and cats need you or else—well, let's not think of that. They usually are terrific pets with temperaments that are not as temperamental as those with a pedigree. Just love 'em and they melt in your laps.

PS Flower Mound Humane Society   888/738-7864

1601 Arrowhead Drive   Hours Vary
Flower Mound, TX 75028
www.fmhs.org

Every second and fourth Saturday, you can see the Flower Mound Humane Society's populace waiting to leave the pound. From 10-4, you can ogle the poodles and others who will love you forever, regardless of your attitude. Even if they're having a bad hair day, they never turn their backs on you once they know where their bread is buttered. This all-volunteer, non-profit organization keeps unwanted, neglected and abused animals from being euthanized. Come on, have a heart! It's the only way to access a love in your life that is truly unconditional (and often save yourself the cost of their pedigree). Now, if you want them to participate in Westminster, that's another story. You'll need to be a millionaire for that. Check other humane societies to adopt your next best friend. On various Saturdays, you can see the Lewisville Humane Society at PetsMart where adoptive dogs and cats, puppies and kitties are panting with baited breath. Expect to pay about $125 for dogs and $85 for cats with all current shots, spayed and neutered. As we speak, there was a darling little poodle mix by the name of "Diva!" Was destiny speaking to me....again? *Call toll-free: 888/ 738-7864*

Four Paw Bakery   972/219-8991

PO Box 294677
Lewisville, TX 75029
www.fourpawbakery.com

Even Fido has to watch his or her weight....especially if he's undergone stomach stapling. You know how those who've had the gastric bypass surgery can't eat sugar anymore. So, if your dog has to give up sugar, they might as well get a treat that still is sweet. These custom treats for canines contain no sugar OR salt. (Just in case they're suffering from high-blood pressure, too!) Plus, if you're like my Sherman, forget the preservatives. He can tell and will turn up his nose. This company has a booth in the Nostalgic Craft Mall at Hwy. 121 and 35 in Lewisville, but their specialty is offering gift baskets, Frisbee gift packs, doggie birthday cakes, holiday treats and a bone-of-the-month club. Arf-Arf!

Funky Fido and Company   256/734-2660

204 1st St., NW   24/7
Cullman, AL 35055

www.funkyfidoandcompany.com   🖰 *Top Online Store!*

If you want to drop up to $2,500 for a custom dog bed, here's where to do it—with panache. I'm talking about the most gorgeous yet expensive beds that any dog would love to curl up into—extravagance fit for a King—a Cavalier King Charles Spaniel, that is. Solid wood Bunkie Beds or wrought iron beds are hand-crafted for a dog who has everything and a master who wants to give him more. It's one thing to build a dog house in the backyard that would serve the purpose of providing shelter for your animals during inclement weather or the heat of the Texas sun, it's another thing just for the privilege of sleeping in their own bed (and that's not just the floor or in YOUR bed.) Each bed comes complete with mattress, pillows, quilt and dust ruffle in a variety of fabrics and covers. You've never seen thrones like these before. The wood Bunkies are hand-crafted in solid wood featuring a pull-out drawer/trundle, plush mattress and decorative pillows. They come in three sizes and a variety of unique styles and colors. Of course, you can have one custom made to match your own furniture. But living the life of Riley in bed doesn't come cheap! (even for Riley.) The price of each bed includes one mattress. A small bed measuring 29" long, 28" high, 20" deep and 12" high in a decorative design sells for $1,499.00 + $50.00 shipping; in a solid color, it's $1,200.00 + $50.00 shipping. Custom Beds are priced upon request. Please allow six to eight weeks for delivery. The full site for unique, unusual pet products for dogs and cats, can be accessed at the full website, www.prestigiouspets.com. Same phone number as above, same email, too. From rhinestone DIVA collars ($7.99 plus $2.99 per slide initial) to **MICHAEL SIMON** Raincoats, this world is no doubt going to the dogs.

Future Pets (formerly Pet Expo)   888/738-3976

11600 Manchaca Rd., Suite 101,   24/7
Austin, TX 78748

www.FuturePets.com   🖱 *Top Online Store!*

 The future of pet supplies is online here at up to 50 percent off. Meet Future Pets, formerly Pet Expo, the site for your future savings on pet supplies. Everything is discounted. Yippee! Not only name brands but some unusual and unique items as well. Where else can you find clothes for the big and tall Alpha dog? The problems you see in the real shopping world is similarly problematic in the canine world. But here, the selection is stupendous. So much to choose, so little time. Can you fathom 8,000 products all under one roof for almost any kind of pet that lives under your roof? Buy online via a secure shopping cart with ease and speed. Shop for dogs, cats, fish, ferrets, ponds, small pets, birds, reptiles, horses, bugs, butterflies and collectibles. Great prices. Great selection. The future of pet shopping lives on. *Call toll-free: 888/738-3976*

◆◆◆   Golden Retrieval   972/691-3979

PO Box 271391   By Reservation Only
Flower Mound, TX 75027
www.goldenretrieval-texas.com

If you're looking for someone who does your dirty work, this couple is right on target. Pooper-Scoopers may not be on the top of your honey-do list, but if it is and your honey won't, call on these residential pet waste removal retrievers. Somebody's got to do it and it might as well NOT you. Rhonda and David Polvado are the picker uppers with their own specialized poop scoops. I wonder how they handle double dips? Let not ask and let them go about their business in silence.

◆◆◆◆◆   Kittico Cat Rescue   214/826-6903

PO Box 600447   Call for hours
Dallas, TX 75360
www.kittico.org

Funded entirely by donations, this kitty-cat rescue group provides veterinary care, food and shelter for unwanted, abandoned and feral cats and kittens in Dallas and surrounding areas. They also offer an adoption/placement service for homeless adoptable felines and do their part to educate the public on the prevention of cruelty to animals, pet abandonment and responsible pet ownership. A worthy cause run by people who really care! They often appear in feline force at Pet Supplies Plus in Plano, Custer and Parker which rumor has it that this is one terrific pet store. Let me know but please don't be catty. If you don't have something nice to say about them, save it. If you love it, post it. Either way, tell us what you think on our website.

★★★★★   Martin Spay/Neuter Clinic   214/651-9611

362 S. Industrial Blvd.   Sun-Fri 8-4; Sat-Sun 9-3
Dallas, TX 75207-4405
www.spca.org

Bark when you see the nine area Dallas and Collin County locations of these clinics (an offshoot of the SPCA—Society for the Protection of Cruelty to Animals). Specializing in the issues surrounding the surrender or admitting of abandoned, adoption, rescue of, cruelty towards animals as well as low-cost vet services. To low-income residents who qualify, they provide spay and neutering services which are FREE, whoopee! There's no excuse not to get them in by 9 and off by 4 (or whenever they close!) For those on a limited budget, regular rates are low cost and as follows: Felines, $40 for spay, $35 for neuter. For canines, costs are determined by weight and range from $45 (up to 24 pounds) to $95 (for a dog 100 pounds or over.) In addition to spay and neutering, the clinic also provides after-surgery care, vaccinations, first aid and preventative medications (heartworm, flea and tick, for example). Vaccinations, rabies shots and discounted pet supplies are just the beginning in building a sound and stable foundation for your dog or cat and should not be overlooked, especially now that you know there's a low-cost alternative.

Moodys Feed   325/388-6217 (Days)

4623 Hwy. 1431   24/7
Kingsland, TX 78639

www.moodysfeed-texas.com   🖰 *Top Online Store!*

Though the Moody's sell and trade horses and mules, ponies, offer stud services, tack and links to other animal sites, they are well known, as well, for their custom dog and cat houses. Featured in *Texas Monthly*, they were showcasing an incredible multi-level barn complete with stalls, barn doors, balconies and such which any cat would love to claw their way to the top. Only problem, it's $400. But you, too, can keep your money in Texas and find fun for your feline or canine habitat with a sketch or a picture idea and never leave the comfort of your own. One click and the building will begin. OK, so put me and Tammy Faye to shame. I dare you!

Nixon's Top Dog Bakery & Boutique   972/668-3125

2601 Preston Rd. Frisco, TX 75034   Mon-Sat 10-9; Sun 12-6
www.jazzersnap.com

You may not have another Nixon to kick around any more, but lets not bite the hand that feeds us. Three area locations of this Nixon rates a top dog status: Besides the one at the Stone Briar Center above, there are bakeries at Willow Bend 469/366-0104, and North Park Center 214/378-6739. Though not a bargain by a longshot, their fresh-baked treats, breed collectibles, beds, dishes, toys, collars and more, really jazzed my dog Jazz. The North Park and Willow Bend locations have a "Yappy Hour" every Thursday from 5 to 7—doggies invited (but not in the Mall) and during those times, there are specials throughout the store. Yap! Yap! This store's a hoot for haute dogs.

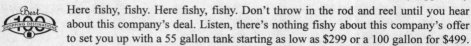

★★★★★★   North Texas Aquarium Maintenance   214/755-9286

Grand Prairie, TX 75051   By Appt. Only

Here fishy, fishy. Here fishy, fishy. Don't throw in the rod and reel until you hear about this company's deal. Listen, there's nothing fishy about this company's offer to set you up with a 55 gallon tank starting as low as $299 or a 100 gallon for $499. Whether you are looking for a fresh or salt water aquarium, they not only offer the set-up for your home or office but provide the monthly or bi-monthly maintenance. It's like having an au pair for your Tetras. Once the fishies get use to their regular fish-sitters, it's important to keep the introductions to new sitters to a minimum. You know how fishes hate meeting new fish faces? Plus, they get use to a sitter's feeding techniques and they hate changes in their routine. So keep them in the swim of things and in good spirits. Keep them well-fed and clean and you'll not have any mean or famished Piranhas lurking behind any coral colonies. It wouldn't speak well of your parenting skills.

◆◆◆   North Texas Emergency Pet Clinic   972/323-1310

1712 W. Frankford   Mon-Thurs 6 PM-8 AM; Fri-Sun 24 Hours
Carrollton, TX 75007
www.ntepc.com

Bark if you have an emergency, for $75 if before 11 PM and $100 if it's after. Bring in medical records, if possible, and then we're in business. This almost-new medical facility caters primarily to dogs and cats, but they also have been known to take care of an occasional ferret or rabbit. Birds and exotic animal owners should call, in advance, to see if there's a specialist on duty; otherwise, they will recommend you to another clinic. As always, bring your dog on a leash and your cat in a carrier or box. Otherwise, they will provide one so as to not add insult to injury. Though expensive, what's a mother to do when they get sick or hurt in the middle of the night? You're at their mercy so get use to the extravagance. It's a matter of life and death so you pay whatever. If you have pet insurance, it may come in handy if it's a serious accident and requiring expensive X-Rays, surgeries, transfusions—well, it'll add up. Then instead of them barking, you'll be barfing! *Call toll-free: 800/362-8600*

◆◆◆◆◆◆   Operation Kindness   972/418-7297

3201 Earhart Drive   Mon-Wed, Fri-Sat 11-4:30; Thurs 11-8; Sun 12-4:30
Carrollton, TX 75006
www.operationkindness.org

I double dog dare you to find a better place for finding a new home for your dog or cat, whether you're giving or getting. Their new and improved expanded facility is one mile north of Belt Line and one street south of Keller Springs, west of Midway in Carrollton. Adoption rates have increased this year to $115 for dogs and $100 for cats. If you're ever hungry, stop in at CiCi's Pizza on Trinity Mills in Carrollton (second Thursday of each month) and then bring in your receipt and drop it in the box at Operation Kindness. CiCi's will donate 10 percent of all receipts collected to this no-kill animal shelter that finds love and gives love for the rest of your life. If you're ever looking for a perfect pet present, what about a state-of-the-art litter box or crate, umbrellas, jewelry, photo frames, whatever's got a pet connection can be found in the gift shop. Johnnie England is its Mother Hen guiding her brood to Herculean heights. She is one reason Operation Kindness is such a success and why many of us leave endowments in our wills to Operation Kindness for all the years of love one of the dogs or cats from OK have given to their adoptive parents.

◆◆◆◆◆◆   Paul's Pet Food   214/222-PETS (7387)

1491 N. Kealy, # 42   By Reservation Only
Lewisville, TX 75057
www.paulspetfood.com

If your dog is a galloping gourmet and used to premium dog food, you can stop running to the vet's when the pickin's are slim. Instead, have Paul deliver. Yes, FREE home delivery of super premium pet food in a stay-fresh storage bin. They guarantee your dog will love it. If not, return the unused portion for a complete refund. Interested in a FREE sample? Just tell them the Diva sent you. Your dog deserves the best and my dogs and cats went ga-ga over it. Their flavors include Chicken, Lamb and Rice, specifically formulated to fulfill all of your pet's nutritional needs, using only the finest ingredients - no fillers, animal by-products or chemical preservatives. No artificial colors or flavors, either. In fact, they eat it up! Expect delivery on Tuesday if you live in Tarrant County, Wednesday for Dallas County, Thursday for Collin County and Friday for Denton County. Head online to their website to compare the other premium brands in relation to ingredients, service and price. You'll be impressed. A 50-pound bag delivered was about $41. *Call toll-free: 888/814-PETS*

Pet Food Direct   215/699-4535

203 Progress Drive   24/7
Montgomeryville, PA 18936
www.petfooddirect.com   *Top Online Store!*

 Pet food is one big category of your household budget, right? How to cut the cost without denying your animals the name brand foods they are use to? Go online. This company offers 11,000 pet products without leaving home. Products for dogs, puppies, cats, kittens, birds, small animals and fish, all delivered to your door. Besides food, there's FREE shipping and an automatic five percent savings coupon waiting for you to download. But on the day we went online to shop, 20 percent was going to be deducted at checkout time on everything we were ordering. Don't miss their clearance corner outlet where there were over 1,000 products up to 70 percent off. Then, too, there's the toy section, the jewelry and accessories button, the animal wellness center, even a specialty boutique. There is so much to their website, it's almost overwhelming. Maybe I, too, need **9 LIVES**? It's hard to know where to stop before we are satiated with pet products for years at a time. Any of these brands are on your shopping list? **9 LIVES, ANNAMAET CAT FOOD, ARTEMIS, AVODERM, BREEDER'S CHOICE, AZMIRA PET FOODS, BIL-JAC, CHEF'S BLEND, CHICKEN SOUP, COUNTRY VALUE, DIAMOND, EAGLE, EUKANUBA, EVOLVE, EXCEL FOR CATS, FELIDAE, FRISKIES, HILLS'S SCIENCE DIET, HOLISTIC BLEND, IAMS, KASCO, LICK YOUR CHOPS, MEOW MIX, NATURAL BALANCE, NUTRO, PINNACLE-BREEDER'S CHOICE, PRECISE, PREMIUM EDGE, PRISM, PRO PAC, PRO PLAN CAT FOOD, PURINA, PURINA ONE, SENSIBLE CHOICE, TENDER VITTLES, WHISKAS**—see, whether it's a premium blend or an everyday brand, they can have it their way....direct.

◆◆◆◆◆◆ Pet Love   972/243-8331

10909 Indian Trail, Suite 101   Mon-Sat By Appt. Only
Dallas, TX 75229
www.petlove.com

 And they call it, Puppy Love. Or at least they used to - now they call it Pet Love to better reflect that they groom both dogs and cats. Jazz and Sherman and Miss Cleo (our Himalayan cat) would not leave the house—but they will jump into the purple pet salon with Lidabel as their stylist of choice. She is incredible. Doesn't even believe in restraining Miss Cleo to groom her, claws and all. She just has her way with words. Book your appointments about two weeks in advance for Saturdays and one week for weekdays for this mobile groomer. (Hey, when you're haute, you're hot!) Grooming rates vary by breed, but $3 is the only additional charge for the convenience of pulling up in your driveway. You won't get away cheap but, then again, having a Bichon means detailed and meticulous grooming. Now, a Shepherd mix doesn't require the same deft hands. Anyway, we can't sing their praises loud enough. The convenience alone is worth the price of admission. Before Pet Love, I did truck them to get their nails done with moans and groans; today, they have a monthly standing (or sitting or lying down) appointment. And believe it or not, there are days when they actually jump with glee, rather than flee, when they know Pet Love's pulling up in the drive-way. Their service extends to the Mid-Cities, Arlington and all of Dallas, and their multiple purple-pleasing vans are manned by professional groomers who know all the cuts, from French Poodles to Yorkies, Malteses to Akitas. And yes, certain groomers also do "lion cuts" on our Himalayan cat. (If I'm lion I'm dyin'!) Color them beautiful as their vans whiz in (but dye jobs are not part of their salon service.) Still, color them P for Perfect.

★★★★★   Pet Pantry, The   972/899-2262

126 Natches Trace
Coppell, TX 75019
www.thepetpantry.com

Rated FIVE paws, how can you go wrong? Generic prescriptions save you money, right? Well, what about a private labeled dog food product that is like or better than the brand names. Woof! Woof! Meow! Meow! This national franchise has a local distributor who'll deliver quality pet food for your dog and cat right to your front door, and delivery is FREE. Nothing beats a fancy feast better than home delivery, don't you agree? No more late night runs to the store when you're out of food. When they're hungry, there's no living with them. It's like they've not eaten in weeks, the way they carry on. Forget lifting those 50-pound bags of food. And prices, well, they are delicious, too. I got a FREE sample and Jazz and Sherman gobbled it up; Miss Cleo and Little Bit, well, we did have to serve it on a **WATERFORD** dish, but so what? They deliver the food via a bin system which makes the reordering process a snap. Doug Lovelace is the Pet Pantry's person in charge. There's a link to Pet Insurance on their site as well as links to each of the major brand of dog or cat food that they are likening themselves to. Guaranteed freshness because their dry foods are produced, shipped and received by the local Pet Pantry within one to two weeks which means that they can get it to you in record beating time. The big pet superstores can hold a handle, nor can most dot. coms, or so they say. So if quality control, no fillers, freshness, price and convenience are top priorities for your pet ad you, pick the Pet Pantry for your next meal. Unless it's their last, and then I'd take them to Del Frisco Steak House.

★★★★★   Petco   972/221-8816
Mon-Sat 9-9; Sun 9-7

201 N. Summit Drive
Lewisville, TX 75067
www.petco.com

Go, pet, go. This pet company means business, and if you don't know it, you haven't been to one of their stores where pets sometimes out-number humans. Petopia.com is now part of Petco, so shopping online makes even more sense. In fact, their website is dog-gone great! If you want to adopt a pet, check with your nearest Petco location for times and dates for humane society adoption events. Grooming facilities are open seven days a week, dog-training classes are offered in-store and even veterinary services are available (though the location above is one of the few that doesn't offer grooming). Veterinarians are mobile and have varying schedules; call in advance for times and dates. If you use their vet, expect to take advantage of their low-cost vaccinations, feline fecal exams, deworming and all of the other routine services that a stationary clinic would provide. *Call toll-free: 877/738-6742*

★★   Petland   972/874-0770
Mon-Sat 10-9; Sun 11-6

420 E. FM 3040, Suite 680
Lewisville, TX 75067
www.petland.com

How much is that doggie in the window? The one with the waggity tail. But it's not just how much, it's also which one's right. Are you the perfect master to a Miniature Schnauzer or are you an Alpha-kind of guy? If so, you'll find the Akita to be your soul mate. From Beagles to Terriers,

Bassets to Bloodhounds, Boxers to Black Labs, even a few mixed breeds thrown in for humility, now you can buy your pet from the largest Petland in the country. This franchise is owned and operated locally, but it also provides other pets for our land aplenty: Kittens, tropical and marine fish, reptiles, birds plus all the accoutrements to keep your pet alive and well and living in the laps of luxury. American Kennel Club registerable puppies and Cat Fancier Association kittens are available, too. They closed their Coit Rd. location, but tails are still wagging in Southlake at Southlake Marketplace, 2125 W. Southlake Blvd., Suite 345, 817/488-2488, in Arlington, 642 Lincoln Square Shopping Center, 817/861-0131 and in Tyler at The French Quarter, 4512 S. Broadway #A1, 903/561-3143 besides Lewisville. But pets are pricey. A Yorkie was priced in the four digits. Yikes! And weighed less than two or three pounds if my memory serves me correct.

★★★★★ Petmed Express, Inc.   800/738-6337

1441 SW 29th Ave.   24/7
Pompano Beach, FL 33069
www.petmeds.com

Order **HEARTGARD, ADVANTAGE, FRONTLINE**, or other pet medications from the largest pet prescription service in the country and have it delivered right to your front door - for less! All major brands and prescriptions are in stock at the largest pet pharmacy, online or off. Forget disguising the trip to the vet since Jazz always knows when we're going for a check-up. Forget waiting it out in the waiting room with a few dozen other dogs who are not as well behaved or well-coifed as Miss Precious. Stay home and let them deliver prescription and non-prescription pet medications along with health and nutritional supplements at substantial savings. More than 100,000 items and over 6,000 pet medications per day are shipped nationwide from their pharmacy to your front door. Whew! Be sure you've got plenty of cheese and hot dogs around; if they're like my "mules," they will refuse their pills unless they're wrapped inside a treat. Pet Meds is fast changing the way America buys their pets'medications—now by phone, fax, mail or online. And why not? What, you like to pay more, wait in line at PetsMart or drive to the vets? This way it's so easy, convenient and economical. (So says Dr. Marc Puleo, president of PetMed Express.) Check with www.drsolve.com as well in Canada because the pet prescriptions may cost even less., Just do your homework so you can squeeze every dollar savings possible. *Call toll-free: 800/ 738-6337*

◆◆◆◆◆◆ Petmobile Hospital & Mobile Clinics   972/423-7387

608 West I-30, Suite 411   Mon, Wed, Fri 9-6; Tues 11-8; Thurs 11-6; Sat (ER Only) 2-5
Garland, TX 75043
www.petmobile.com

For full service, make an appointment at their Petmobile Hospital ($45 per appointment); for spays and neuters, you must make an appointment and your pet must have all of its current vaccinations, (heartworm tests are mandatory for dogs.) If your pet is over five years of age, bloodwork is offered for $40-$60, and if they are an aggressive breed, there is an additional charge (husbands don't count!) To spay or neuter a cat, it costs $25 for males and $45 for female felines; for canines, cost is by weight—similar to Southwest Airline's policies! Then, check their website for their mobile clinics at various locations around town: Balch Springs, East Dallas, East Plano, Garland, Irving, Oak Cliff, Richardson and West Plano.

★★★★   PetsMart   **972/407-0101**

6204 W. Park Blvd.   Mon-Sat 9-9; Sun 9-7
Plano, TX 75093
www.petsmart.com

If you're sMart, you'll shop PetsMart. If you're not, you'll pay retail. That's just how the raw hide goes. Similar websites makes fairly equal competitors, but PetsMart comes out ahead in the pricing department. Pennies from heaven are shaved from their site compared to Petco's, though I found Petco's site easier to navigate. With dogs, cats, birds, hamsters, fish, reptiles and wild animal supplies, you can literally shop from A to Z. They also have a VetsMart inside with it's own separate phone line (972/250-6428—no clinic hours, yet.) The VetsMart in East Plano, though, has clinic hours already, (which most locations do) so call 972/423-6032 and they can get vaccinations for just the cost of the shots. The office visit is FREE but it's only during special clinic hours, which vary by location. Get smart, shop PetsMart—or PetSmart, however you slice it. Do your part for the hundreds of thousands of dogs and cats in Texas that wind up in area animal shelters. All it takes is one dog or cat to bring love into your life while you save a life in the process. During special promotions called Luv-A-Pet, this discount superstore allows humane societies to adopt their animals. This warehouse superstore distinguishes itself from the competition with a line of gourmet goodies from Three Dog Bakery. Also look for a chuck wagon full of rawhide treats, beef ears, pig ears, tail chips and ham bones. Shop for everything that will keep your new pet set for life—dog houses, leashes, food, toys—all at discounted prices. Then again, what price can you put on love? Check directory for location nearest you.

◆◆   Plano Pet   **972/423-1610**

1120 E. Parker, Suite 112   Mon-Sat 8-9; Sun Noon-6
Plano, TX 75094

From premium foods to made-in-Texas varieties, it's food for thought for all your pets, including ferrets and birds, grooming supplies and more. The lineup is all over the map from ALL GLASS, HIKARI, KENT, KT, LM PRODUCTS, OSI, PRETTY BIRD and WARDLEY with the main pest control line being PHOENIX. Doing-it-yourself can be a blessing or a pain in the patootie. Call back in a few months when their website should be up and purring for online ordering. Red Rover, Red Rover, get Rover combed all over with fine-tooth combs, slicker brushes, nail clippers and more. Then, when all is said and the do is done, add the final spritz of cologne and dog-gone-it, let's be on our way. Oh, don't forget the breath spray so the liver and bacon treats'odor will be-gone. At least at Plano Pet, they maintain their sense of humor while Jazz went wee-wee all the way home - but she was "smelling like a rose!"

◆◆◆◆◆   Riding Unlimited   **940/479-2016**

9168 T. N. Skiles Rd.   Tues-Sat: Call for times
Ponder, TX 76259
www.ridingunlimited.org

Three cheers for their sponsors: Lone Star Park, Texas Instruments and Wal-Mart. These folks provide horseback riding as therapy for both children and grown-ups. Ride 'em cowboy. Saddle up for their 10-week sessions in the spring and fall and a six-week session in the summer. Want to help, but they can't squeeze a penny out of a turnip? Then listen up: Albertson's, Kroger and Tom Thumb donate a percentage of your purchases to Riding Unlimited. To acquire an Albertson's Community Partners Card or Kroger Cares Card, simply call the Ranch above or the next time you are at Tom Thumb, ask the cashier to program your Reward Card with Riding Unlimited's number (4842). How's that for a galloping gourmet? They are always looking for volunteers, so if you're a horse person who loves people, too, this program needs you. Now, that makes horse sense, neigh? Another similar program, also in Ponder, is called Reata Rehabilitation, and they treat physically- and mentally-challenged children using horseback riding as therapy. They are open Mondays, Tuesdays and Thursdays. Contact 940/479-2612 for volunteer information. Both are always look- ing for volunteers.

★★★★   Southland Farm Store   214/350-7881

5855 Maple Ave.   Mon-Fri 8-6; Sat 8-5
Dallas, TX 75235

Who would have thought that an out-of-the-way feed store would be the primo pet place for sav- ing money? Make this a ritual as you make your monthly rite of passage for pet food. After all, these guys are the distributors of premium pet food, so why not shop where the retailers shop and be guaranteed a lower price? Shop and compare and you'll see why man's best friend laps it up here. Visit this 5,000 square foot, air-conditioned warehouse/showroom. Finish the rest of your shopping in the remaining 30,000 square feet of warehouse (un-airconditioned), then pull your car or truck up to the loading dock and pile it in. Retailers, who are buying wholesale, need to shop at their new warehouse in Irving (400 Cascade Drive), while the rest of us pet parents fill up our canine pantry at the Maple Ave. location, now, with more elbow room. All of the popular and vet- recommended brands are available: **IAMS, KAL-KAN, KEN-L-RATION, NUTRO, PRO PLAN, SCIENCE DIET, SENSIBLE CHOICE, WAYNE** and more. Check out the prices online at the var- ious online webstores first before you plunk down your hard-earned cash here for the same prod- ucts. Plus online, will be delivered to your front door. *Call toll-free: Metro 972/44*

◆◆◆◆◆◆   Spay-Neuter Assistance Program   214/372-9999

4830 Village Fair Drive   Wed-Sat 7:30-6 (Appt. for surgeries)
Dallas, TX 75224
www.snaptx.org

 In by 7:30, off by 6! For less than it costs to tune-up your car, you "auto" fix your dog or cat. The Humane Society of the United States operates the Spay-Neuter Clinic as well as the Animal Wellness Center (Open Wed, Fri & Sat from 10-6, with walk-ins welcome). Though the prices are reduced, the state-of-the-art equipment and veterinar- ian's services are not. Top notch all the way, from spaying and neutering to rabies'shots (required by Texas law), nail trims, physicals, heartworm testing, flea and tick control and prevention, the works—for less. Located six miles south of downtown Dallas near I-35E and Ledbetter Drive (Loop 12), please help control the animal population. Do your part so there's no unwanted strays without a loving home. For cats, the set price is $30 for spaying and $20 for neutering. Dog prices are by the weight of the dog; a female Yorkie would run $35 and a male miniature Schnauzer would run $30. See, even the little boys get a break big time!

State Line Tack   800/228-9208

PO Box 935   24/7
Brockport, NY 14420

www.statelinetack.com   🖱 *Top Online Store!*

How tacky of me to look for a discount on tack! But it's time to stop horsing around and get down to brass tacks. Whether you order via their slick 236-page catalog or shop online, you can find dis- counts from 15 to 50 percent. Mount and then count the savings on breeches, chaps, jodhpurs, tights, jackets and coats, shirts and boots for the entire family (men, women and children). If you're part of the jet set and ride the fox hunt, you'll find both formal and less formal footwear, outdoor gear, helmets and such. But now that we've dismounted, let's look to outfitting the horse next. Equipment and supplies for horses are available, including saddles, bridles, horse-related jewelry, trailer equipment, blankets, medical aids. Then be sure to check out the selection of "how-to" books. Both English and Western are covered. The catalog provides the more extensive selection of products and horsy-themed items, like mugs, watches, t-shirts, knives, place mats—all with an equine in mind. For anything to do with riding the range, State Line Tack is definitely the "Whoa" to go! With over 100 physical stores around the country, locate your nearest at their website above. ***Call toll-free: 800/228-9208***

Plants & Gardens

★★★★★★ **Advantage Services Landscaping**   **469/855-7286**

Flower Mound, TX   By Appt. Only

This Andy's quite a dandy—a lion when it comes to saving you green. Andy Smith helps you keep up with the Jones's. Take it or leaf it. The Advantage is now in your court. If you want to net success, then this company is the ace up your sleeve. Let's root for their business plan because it'll help save you money on landscaping. If you are building a new house and your builder has given you a "landscape" allowance, call this company and at least get the most bang for your buck. Since they can save you 30-50 percent on trees and shrubs, you might be able to get twice the shrubs for the money if you left it up to the builder to buy and install. Handpick your own trees and shrubs at one of the largest selection of nursery stock in North Texas. Be your own dirt diva (and leave the Doctoring to Howard Garrett.) Get more for your money. More of a selection. Better quality. Higher value all rolled into one nursery. For example, a 2.5' Live Oak elsewhere was $595 but here you'd pay $275; 3' Grand Magnolia was $580 elsewhere but here you'd pay $317; a 2' Bald Cypress was $199 elsewhere but here was $117 and a 4-6' Mexican Fan Palm was $125, seen elsewhere for $199. Saving on Azaleas ran from about $8 on the three-gallon varieties to almost $20 on the 7-gallon. When you buy a dozen or more, it all adds up. So let the blooms begin. Call, email or fax for more information. You won't be sorry.

Blooming Colors Nursery   **817/416-6669**

221 Ira E. Woods (Hwy. 26)   Mon-Sat 9-6; Sun 12-5
Grapevine, TX 76051
www.bloomingcolorsnursery.com

Whether you're in Grapevine or Coppell, you can be rooted in luxury at an affordable price at this family-owned and operated nursery and landscaping service. To really save, shop for items on sale. On the day of our last visit, trees in stock were on sale for 30 percent off. Is it any wonder we were inspired to surround ourselves with towering leaves? We couldn't resist the Oaks, Elms, Maples, Pistachios, natives, Hollies, Conifers, Cypress, fruit, Red Buds, Dogwoods and more. And that was just what we could see through the forest. Their website is a blooming bastion of color and my, oh my, how their garden has grown. Now with two locations, (Coppell location, 1701 E. Belt Line, Phone 972/393-8660; coppell@bloomingcolorsnursery.com), there isn't much they don't do when it comes time to add color to your yard. For professional input, there's a landscape designer on site and if you let them plant the trees, they will guarantee them for a year; if you do it yourself, the guarantee's reduced to three months. But if you want to plant yourself in their Bloomin Coffee Cafe for a leisurely breakfast or lunch, I guarantee you won't leave hungry or empty-handed. Shop their antique-filled dining area for some housewarming gifts and house plants, pick up a special brew and stroll through the wooded garden path. The Cafe is as good as it gets. Home-cooking by owner Barry Johnson's mother, Sally "Mimi" Johnson is open Mon-Fri 6:30-2; Sat 7:30-2, 817/416-6669 and you don't want to miss it. If you have room, Mimi's "Good Stuff" desserts are legendary. Her ice box coconut cream pie, ice box lemon pie and the Baptist Peach Pie was my mother-in-law's (a former Baptist preacher's wife) her all-time favorite. My husband's favorite, "Sally's I'm Not An Angel Cake." Go figure. And by the way, ladies, the Cafe would be a great backdrop for an evening garden club meeting. But back to the basics. The 12,000 square foot greenhouse allows them to grow the highest quality plants so as to supply their two retail locations and their landscaping division. One of their specialties is roses and in addition to the **TEXAS EARTHKIND** roses, they feature one of the largest collections of the **GRIFFITH BUCK ROSES** in the Metroplex. A rose by any other name wouldn't smell so sweet. Enjoy! Take time to smell the roses and the coffee. Both are intoxicating.

◆◆◆◆◆◆ Blooming Creations   972/236-2337

Carrollton, TX   By Appt. Only
www.bclandscape.com

With four crews digging up the dirt in and around the Metroplex, you can expect a Blooming Creation to ultimately emerge in all it's glory splendor. It takes a women to build a garden. And Kerrie Smith is that woman. She has created many splendors in the grass and all the coordinating fleurs to accompany that landscape. She's also a native of Dallas so she has been getting her hands dirty since she was knee high to a grasshopper and knows which plants, which grass, which trees are rooted in prosperity in the Metroplex. Expect her to be a hybrid between Howard Garrett and Neil Sperry in her philosophy of gardening as she prefers to go with the flow. She is your one-stop shop for towers of flowers, from specialty landscaping to water features, arbors, gazebos, hot tubs, patios, awnings, trees and scrubs, outdoor lighting, decks, scored concrete, wood planked decks, greenhouses—well, just about anything as long as it goes in the front or back yard. That is, except a sunroom. She leaves that to others. But this landscape architect is an imaginative go-getter who makes things come alive with attention to detail and a green thumb to make your neighbors green with envy. Go online to her wholesale-plus nursery where you can pick the plants, scrubs and trees just with a click of the mouse and watch it then magically appear on your doorstep, ready for planting. All plants and trees that they plant are guaranteed for one year. Special is as special does. Expect the unique and they'll deliver the extraordinary. Whether you want a design to do-it-yourself, or you want the VIP (Very Important Planting) treatment, this is the company to root for! One visit to the website, and you will be drooling through the Daisies and savoring the Safflowers, Snapdragons, Spider Mums, Sweetpeas, Sweetheart Roses, Sweet Williams, Sunflowers and Stephanotis. Ah, the sweet smell of excess. At these prices, who's counting?

★★★★★ Bright Flowers   972/247-8818

11363 Denton Drive, #104   Mon-Sat 9:30-5:30
Dallas, TX 75229

Flowers, flowers burning bright, want to bring a little sunshine into your life? Even if you can not speak the proprietor's first language, the language of flowers is, first and foremost, universal. Instead, carry on a conversation with the plants and flowers as they will last forever or until the last dust mite eats them first. These flowers never die - though they may just fade away. Save 50 to 80 percent on thousands of flowers and greenery that can be bought individually or in an arrangement. Large centerpieces and bridal bouquets are another specialty of the house. Located in the International Plaza complex (at Royal Lane) with lots of other imported worldly finds, shop year 'round or during the holidays for Christmas trees and it's guaranteed that you won't be cut out of the loop. Shoppers Alley is next door dripping with purses and dress shops. If you concentrate, their flowers, green plants and arrangements could be the bright spot in your day.

★★★★★★ Bruce Miller Nursery   972/238-0204

1000 E. Belt Line Rd.   Mon-Fri 8-5:30; Sat 8-5:30; Sun 10-5
Richardson, TX 75081
www.brucemillernursery.com

If all your plants go from green to brown, then take a look around here. If you need help, gardening expert Rick Rayburn is available Tuesday, Wednesday and Saturday. Go ahead, pick his brain. Bruce Miller's the place for anyone looking for high-quality trees, shrubs, flowers, fertilizer, seeds, bulbs, soil, pots, tools and more—especially if you're beyond the nursery stage. Now that organic is becoming the "in" thing, you can expect plenty of the pure stuff here as well. Since they're located in a former Dairy Queen, what did you expect, a blizzard? Yuletide brings a mad rush for Christmas trees, and Bruce Miller is right up there front and center. Save some green from their seedlings that are all grown up and ready to be carted off. Looking for a great gift? What about a potted Rosemary plant shaped like Christmas tree, or a Christmas cactus, an ivy candelabra, wind chimes or the all-time favorite, Poinsettias? See, you don't have to just bed down with the plants out front. There's plenty of the green stuff inside, too. Their website is ground-breaking as a handy-dandy resource for knee-deep gardening information. Isn't that right, Widetrack? Or is it Sidetrack? Second location now in Prosper, Country Road 4, 972/346-2760. One of the longest landscape resources in The Underground Shopper. What is it now 25? 30 years, Bruce Miller?

★★ Calloway's Nursery   817/861-1195

900 Lincoln Square   Mon-Sun 9-6
Arlington, TX 76001
www.calloways.com

There's no beating around the bush. I shop at Calloway's, too, in a pinch. Their ads are just one reason that I succumb. Another reason, they have locations everywhere and one's near my house. (They've got two of them in Arlington alone!) They've got a commendable selection and lastly, there's always a sale on, which is when I buy that occasional plant, bush, fertilizer bag or two. Overall, this is where to amass nursery items for the masses. Not always the fullest, not always the most knowledgeable sales personnel, not always the best selection in a particular species, and not always the best price....but convenience counts for something. So stick that in your wheelbarrow and plant it! Check directory for the location nearest you.

★★ Countrybrook Florist   972/245-5606

2150 N. Josey Lane, #210 @ Keller Springs   Mon-Fri 8:30-6; Sat 8:30-3
Carrollton, TX 75006
www.countrybrookflorist.com

When it comes to a neighborhood florist with a worldly sense of design, consider hiring the Bakers—who'll handle the candlesticks along with every other accouterment that would go into a floral arrangement. Located in the Albertson's Shopping Center, if you want to pay your condolences or send your congratulations, make it the best. The Bakers have owned and operated this store for eight years (it's been in business for 18) and they've learned how to arrange the petals to the medals and earned many honors by doing it the right way. Why send flowers only to discover they come "droopingly" on the vine? Here they use only the freshest flowers in unique baskets and vases with delivery anywhere in the Metroplex. Consider them for big events or small, baby's birthdays to bar mitzvahs, with weddings being high on their list of priorities. If you don't believe me, go to their website and see their creativity in action. ***Call toll-free: 800/453-4492***

★★★★★★   **Cristina's Garden Center**   **972/599-2033**

6250 Mapleshade Lane   Mon-Sun 8 AM-7 PM
Plano, TX 75252
www.cristinasgarden.com

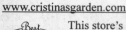

This store's got flower power as well as buying power. With 18-count flats at $10.80 each, they were the lowest-priced nursery in town. That's elementary, my dear. Figure it out. That's 60 cents each, folks. On the border of Plano at 190 and Preston (across from Lowe's), can you believe they outsell them petal by petal, flat by flat? Bedding plants were all over the place, side by side with shrubs and hanging baskets. They've got it all, from Alyssum, Begonias, Celosia, Shade Coleus, Dianthus, Dusty Miller, Impatiens, Marigolds, Moss Rose, Petunias, Snap Dragons, well, the list is exhaustive enough to tire even Tiny Tim as he tip-toed through the tulips. They could have the best prices in town, with plants on sale all year long. When we visited, all shrubs and shade trees were 50 percent off and the selection of hanging baskets and perennials was breath-taking. They grow all of the 3,000 plants they sell and sell all of the plants that they grow! One of the few independent growers in town with one other location at 4617 Lovers Lane (214/357-5626) just west of Inwood in Highland Park. Even plants covet that zip code where there's already plenty of green. I wait to see their website grow and flourish as well.

★★★★★   **Decorators Warehouse**   **972/985-1078**

2819 West 15th   Mon-Sat 10-6
Plano, TX 75075

Having the decorator's touch is like the Midas Touch at this Decorators Warehouse. Kin to founder Dave Hanson, this 15,000-square-foot warehouse is overflowing with fabulous foliage for less. The forest is flourishing with some of the lushest artificial trees, floor plants, silk flower arrangements and table toppers in the Southwest. But it's their custom-made trees, as tall as 12 feet, that brings us to our knees. Want a Ficus? No fuss. No muss. How about a Palm? No problem. The six-footer was tall, dark and handsome. Select your tree branch and go from there. Save 40 to 60 percent off retail on florals, plants, trees, framed art, mirrors and occasional tables, too. Shop where the decorators shop and grace your high ceiling ballrooms or atrium, if need be. Choose your tree type and watch them grow. (No watering required.) With several floral designers on staff, expect DW to offer creative solutions to boring blooms. Their original location that launched The Underground Shopper magazine back about ten years ago is located at 1535 S Bowen Rd., Pantego, Phone: 817/460-4488. But calling them umpteen times with no return calls gave us reason to feel slighted. So when Dave calls me back, I'll be happy again in the old town tonight. Scott Lincoln, his brother-in-law doesn't return calls either. So you, too, will probably need to leave a voice mail and then see if he'll return your call. No website. Another thorn in their side.

★★★   **Diana's Silk Plantation**   **817/788-0222**

9155 Grapevine Hwy   Mon-Sat 10-6; Sun1-5
North Richland Hills, TX 76180

Carry me back to ol' Virginia where plantations reigned supreme and Diana's showcased silk flowers are so real she could fool Mother Nature. Most flowers are so botanically-correct that they even collect dew drops on their petals. If they don't have what you're looking for, they'll order it for you. Regardless of the project, they'll bring in the supplies, vases, whatever you need, even if they don't do the arrangement. Diana's flowers are eternally available and only need a few nips and tucks when they start to sag. While fluffing up the flowers, you won't be able to ignore the stacks of decorative accessories, knick-knacks and table accents such as candlesticks, picture frames and other collectibles....you can never have too much or too many. Designers on the spot are available for in-home or office design consultation. Their showroom is a 4,000-square-foot arbor blooming with color. Spring flowers and other seasonal entries bring about a 25 percent discount. Now that's a nice touch.

★★★★   Doan's Nursery   972/790-3500

622 S. Belt Line Rd.   Mon-Fri 8-5; Sat-Sun 9-4
Irving, TX 75060
www.doansnursery.com

Since 1991, they've been boasting the "lowest prices in town," so if you're suffering any pain over the high prices of plants and shrubs, go back to nursery school and start over from here. Over 50,000 square feet to aid and abet the greening of America: shrubs, annuals, perennials, fertilizer, bird feeders, pots, statues, the works. Sure gets my attention. Add these to your studies: Butterfly Vines, Mandavilla, Purple Passion, Angel Wings, Blue Daze, Boston Ferns, Fuchsia, Geraniums, Ivy And New Wonder hanging around or in pots watching over the flats of Dianthus, Dusty Miller, Marigold, Moss Rose, Purslane, Salvia And Zinnias. Color, color everywhere but not a square inch left to plant. What a dilemma! Well, what about starting over? Okay, that sounds like a good idea. This time, should I choose Asian Jasmine or English Ivy? I declare. Is it any wonder my neighbors are green with envy? So what did they do to compete? Headed to Doan's and loaded up with Azaleas, Boxwoods, Dwarf Buford, Red Tip Photinia and Waxleaf Ligustrum. Why don't they just leaf me alone, already? However, we generally lose something in the translation here as it's very difficult to communicate with them. That gives us the biggest pain and we wind up going home empty handed and taking two **TYLENOLS**. Maybe we should call them in the morning?

★★★   Fannin Tree Farm   972/747-9233

Hwy. 121 @ Custer Rd.   Mon-Sat 8-5; Sun 1-5
Plano, TX 75024

Down by the old mill stream is where Fannin Tree Farm now resides. At the northwest corner of Highway 121 and Custer, the forest now has some breathing room. There's nothing more idyllic than sitting under the shade of that ol'apple tree, and then being able to buy it. Of course, the staple crops here are the Red Oaks, Live Oaks, Cedar Elms and Chinese Pistachios. Hundreds and hundreds of them are waiting to be uprooted and reestablished at your home and garden. This farm is a legacy in its own time. Expect prices, depending on the season, to be about $100 per caliper inch. A three-inch tree (round), for example, would cost around $330 delivered, planted and guaranteed, while a four-inch beauty could be yours for around $490. Delivery charges assessed the further away the tree goes from Plano. Trees are not available for you to pickup since Fannin delivers them all. All trees are guaranteed for one year with the option of purchasing another year guarantee for 10 percent of the price of the tree. Located 1.5 miles north of Legacy, this grower and tree contractor is waiting for you not to bark up the wrong tree.

★   Flower Market   214/521-8886

5315 N. Central Expwy.   Mon-Fri 9-6; Sat 9-5
Dallas, TX 75205

Looks like this flower has wilted some more this year. Whatever happened to one of my favorites? Just the basics, ma'am. Just the basics. Claiming good prices for a dozen long-stemmed roses,

$37.50, I'd say they are sleeping under a rock—that price is a thorn in the side of savings. No big deal. Delivery of different color roses in a vase and delivered to a small area (within Highland Park, where they need the savings the least,) left us wonderful just how service oriented they were. (They were hardly willing to go the mile—that is, if you lived in Colleyville where we were calling.) Then, if you wanted balloons, you had to give plenty of advanced notice. (What, is there really a shortage of balloons in the Metroplex?) Tulips, though, were only available in springtime, they said. Well, wouldn't you think April was springtime? Sure enough. They were out. But in fact, they were kind enough to refer us to another florist for tulips and if truth be known, he said, tulips were just too costly for us to order this year. Honesty, is indeed, their best policy. Give them credit where credit is due. Find them on the southbound service road of Central Expressway, south of Mockingbird near McCommas. Whatever happened to Bud? This Bud used to be for me! *Call toll-free: 800/659-5249*

★★★ Flower Ranch   817/431-3830

901 Pearson Lane   Mon-Fri 8-5; Sat 8-2 (open longer hours during high season)
Keller, TX 76248

The hours may fluctuate in the high-demand seasons, but for right now, you can expect to be singing, "Don't Fence Me In" with flowers bought at this Flower Ranch. Giddy-up and get going. If you're looking for a flat of anything, ask before you pack up the kids and pack up the car. When you round the bend, there's usually upwards of 20,000 flats waiting to be lassoed. Expect most flats to cost $13.75 and up; compared to Cristina's at $10.80, you may want to bar this ranch this year. This commercial grower has been open to the public for the past few years and should be able to sell at dirt-cheap prices. Even though the economy is "flat," everyone in the Metroplex still wants to stay in the pink with Alyssum, Begonias, Bougainvillea, Celosia, Coleus, Ferns, Hibiscus, Impatiens, Joseph's Coat, Marigolds, Moss Rose, Petunias, Salvia, what did you expect? A colorless canvas of nudes? High season includes April, May, Oct and Nov where the hours are Monday-Friday 8-7; Saturday 8-6; Sunday 8-5; in June, they are open weekdays until 5 and Sundays until 2. In July and August, they close at 4 on weekdays and are closed on Sunday. Got it? Just keeping track of their hours is work enough for most city slickers.

★★★★★★ Hartwell's Landscaping Nursery   972/436-3612

1570 N. Stemmons Frwy.   Mon-Fri 8:30-5:30; Sat 8:30-5; Sun 10-5
Lewisville, TX 75067

 What's a tree growing in Lewisville? I thought it was supposed to grow in Brooklyn? Even though she didn't have a New York accent, we understood Tammy very well. She's the decorator to consult for your garden. For $250, she'll completely map out a recommended and functional design, but if you then proceed with buying the plants, shrubs, trees, ground cover, it comes off the final bill. In other words, there's FREE design service with purchase; or bring in your own plans, designs and ideas, and let them bid on it, for no charge. Nevertheless, just take a look at the Crepe Myrtles—one-gallon pots for $1.89 or five gallon (five-six feet tall) for $9.95. Lots of trees line the freeway of opportunities: Bradford Pear, Chinese Pistachio, Fruit, Pecan—have them planted by their crew or plant them yourself and have a backache on Monday. Prices were also slashed on one-gallon shrubs and Hibiscus, two-gallon Wax Myrtles, Cedar Elms, Silver Maples, Live Oaks, Loblolly Pines, Globes and Weeping Willows, with a one-year guarantee. Wholesale's in their name, being in the 100 BEST is their claim to fame. Respected by home owners, builders and even their competitors as allowing you to strike paydirt when shopping here. They are one of the best in the business. Ask for Scott and tell him the Diva planted one on Hartwell's.

★   Herb Market   972/446-9503

1002 4th St.   Tues-Sat 10:30-5:30
Carrollton, TX 75006

Just over the railroad tracks, this former train depot is now a caboose for herbs. Owner Lana Jones, cook and gardener, grew her own until her private garden was so big that she had to open a store. Now, she sells her overruns in this little choo-choo. Buy bulk herbs and enjoy the roots of her labor. They're fresher and cheaper than the typical grocery store. For example, garlic was around $3 at Tom Thumb and $1.25 for about one ounce of organic garlic here. Lana mixes and matches between dry and fresh herbs depending on the season but....you "or-eg-a-no!" Be sure to inquire if they're still offering their candle and soap-making classes. Though they may keep you burning the candle at both ends, you'll still come out squeaky clean! After leaving several messages, we gave up calling back or maybe they were just off the track.

★★   Joy Silk Flower Outlet   972/241-1466

11252 Harry Hines Blvd., #201   Mon-Sat 9:30-6.30
Dallas, TX 75229

How many shops in the Harry Hines area can turn around a custom arrangement in two days and occasionally speak English? Not too many, that's for sure, but here's one that will bring some joy into the equation. Bring in your own container or find one here, it's your choice. Lots of silk arrangements ready for planting with nary a green thumb required; individual stems are alone and available, just waiting to be picked up. (After all, they are located on Harry Hines, aren't they?) You needn't read *The Joy Luck Club* to get inspired. Inspiration will come from the fabulous silk flowers, custom-made arrangements or the possibility of making-your-own which will help turn over a new leaf in your life. Stems started at $1 and are perfect for any occasion. Do buy them, 'cause they never die or require much attention. The more exotic the stem, the more expensive, but the time comes when you just have to spring for it. Occasionally, that's a thorn in my side, but it only hurts for a little while. For sprucing up those you wish to plant as a centerpiece on your dining room table, nightstand, bathroom counter or elsewhere, here is where to buy all of the silk flower cleaning supplies you might need—even if not all at dirt cheap prices. It's still a way to clean up your existing arrangements without having to spring for a complete major overhaul.

★★★   Lake June Garden Center   214/391-4005

8634 Lake June Rd.   Mon-Sat 9-6; Sun 10-3
Dallas, TX 75217

Don't get hosed by paying through the nose. Instead, plant your garden from the terra firma here. Knowledgeable staff make your gardens grow. In fact, one staff member has been there for over 16 years, so he's rooted in lots of information about Texas soils and plants. Robert does the landscaping design but by appointment only. Expect him to be booked a week to 10 days in advance. Though there's a charge of $25 for his computer generated design, it is deducted from the cost of the plants and services should you choose to implement the design with their products. Plants, plants and more plants can be found at Lake June, minus the lake and during more months than just June. They've even busted out with a sister store called Pickerings, 8950 Kingsley Rd., in Dallas, 214/349-1077. Expect discounts to be at least 20 percent off competing nurseries and more during special sales. Well, it's better than nothing. And you're not suppose to look a green horse (or is it gift horse?) in the mouth (or is it your eye?) I am definitely confused.

★★★★★   **Little House on Pearl, The**   **214/748-1443**

514 S. Pearl   Wed-Sun 9-5
Dallas, TX 76201

What a gem! This pearl is a girl's best friend when it comes time to add some greenery to the mountainless scenery of north Texas. In the heart of Farmer's Market, here's another house of repute, but hardly ill. Millions of shoppers descend on downtown Dallas to shop Farmers Market and the Little House on Pearl is no exception. Mix and match, pick and play with a bunch of dried flowers, the more the merrier, all at a fraction of the cost if purchased pre-arranged. Gather ye rose buds while thee may. Add a touch of sunshine with sunflowers, throw in some pepper or tallow berries, poke around the artichokes and, for spice, add some cinnamon sticks. For local color, assemble a gaggle of okra pods and a cayenne of chili peppers, gaze upon some pine or star cones, rough up some raffia, and tuck in the birch twigs—what a great little housewarming for a new-comer moving to Big D. Nobody west of the Mississippi can rival the selection at this Little House on Pearl. Curl your fingers around a bevy of dried flowers and plants that sit gingerly alongside candles and other tabletop accessories and enjoy your trip that will wax nostalgic. My only beef? Dragging the garden statuaries to my car when it was time to pack up and head home. Remember, I also had to stop at Ruibal's and The Mozzarella Factory!

★★★   **Mary's Flowers**   **972/243-4333**

Farmers Branch Shopping Center   Mon-Fri 9-5; Sat 10-2
12895 Josey Lane Farmers Branch, TX 75234

Mary had a little flower shop and decided to sell her cut flowers at cut prices. Whatever the occa-sion, she tries to accommodate both the traditional requests she gets from customers as well as the unusual. She specializes in utilizing a plethora of pots, containers, unusual baskets, urns, tea pots, whatever she can find to display the flowers that's not the usual and customary and still save you 25 to 30 percent. April showers bring more than May flowers. Mary sells a dozen roses at $54.99, which includes the vase, greenery and baby's breath, that is a tad too high when you can get a dozen of gorgeous roses from proflowers.com for $29.95 plus a few bucks for delivery. Anyway, at least she didn't quibble about delivery. It was a given—at that price. Also, she carries a large selection of Mylar and Latex balloons for all occasions (I guess she hasn't heard that there's a bal-loon shortage in town, just ask Flower Mart) and in-stock, pre-made arrangements beginning around $19.99 and going up to $40, on average. A springtime bouquet could be had for around $39.99. Delivery was available with a minimum purchase of $25 ($5-$8 delivery charge added to the cost.) Exotic arrangements with such unusual varieties as Birds Of Paradise, Spider Mums, Halliconia, Pineapple Plants, Honeycombs, Baby Orchids on the one side, well, you get the pic-ture. Add ribbons and stuffed animals, maybe a green plant on a pedestal, and there you have it. One call, that's all it takes to have a blooming bouquet—delivered. Flower arrangements that are imaginative, economical and fun all rolled into one continues to make this Mary not contrary. *Call toll-free: 800/222-6507*

◆◆◆◆   **Metro Irrigation**   **817/877-5052**

1622 Rogers Rd.   Mon-Fri 8-5; Sun 8-Noon
Fort Worth, TX 76107

If your lawn's begging for a drink and the occasional downpour in the hot Texas sun doesn't quite quench its thirst, consider calling Metro Irrigation. But don't expect Metro Irrigation to do repairs. In fact, they are so expert at the system itself, they can pretty much talk you through any repair job for FREE. Family-owned and operated, their other location is at 8020 North Richland Hills, 817/ 485-8638 where they can also keep you in the green so that your garden will grow into maturity.

They continue to specialize in installing custom irrigation systems, from one-inch heads. If you want smaller ones, they recommend you go elsewhere. Again, I repeat: Do not call them for repairs. Choose from stationary, pop-ups and gear-driven heads for just the right combination of coverage. Off I-30, exit University and go south toward the Fort Worth Zoo. Of course, chances are, you won't need to go to them—as they come to you.

◆◆◆ North Dallas Garden Design   214/914-5865

PO Box 111667   Call anytime
Carrollton, TX 75011-1667

How's this for down-home friendliness? Call anytime for complete design, consultation and instal-lation if it's a garden you wish to create. Competitive bids for services include installation of land-scapes and hardscapes such as walkways, stonework, ponds and maintenance. What they DON'T do? Fences, folks. They will even given you a break on plant prices, if you have them do the plant-ing. Sow? What are you waiting for? Complete landscape greenprints (or blue if you prefer) are $400. Then, you're on your own. They are complete and not cheap but they are firmly planted on a quality performance.

★★★★★★ North Star Florist   972/276-6956

301 N. Garland Ave.   Mon-Fri 8-5:30; Sat 8-4
Garland, TX 75040
www.northstarflorist.com

Who'd ever thunk that when I was in a funk, a bouquet of flowers would pick me up? Well, North Star became my shining star when we were in a pinch for a corsage for our Makeover Prom Winner. She was all "Pretty in Pink" but was carrying a white chiffon pearlized wrap over her pink two-piece gown. We wanted a pearlized white chiffon wrist corsage and North Star delivered. A matching boutonniÉre for the male escort and the couple went merrily on their way. (Their coach, though, was a shocking yellow Corvette, rather than a submarine!) In business for more than 27 years, they have grown to two sizeable but personable floral emporiums with buckets of fresh flowers overflowing at their doorsteps. Whether you need to wire flowers to someone cross country or deliver a local arrangement for any occasion, expect them to be Johnny on the Spot. Always with a smile, they exude small town friendliness with each and every custom floral arrangement. From ordinary to extraordinary, they will get extra creative if the occasion calls for it or the customer asks for it. They have sample custom arrangements already made up on the floor for you to choose from, or bring in a picture and they will show you their stuff. If you want a balloon bouquet, no problem, they're not blow-hearts! (And they've not heard of the balloon shortage sweeping Highland Park.) Blooming and colorful as well as verdant green plants, they've got the right stuff with their green thumb. Plus you'll save some green in the process. Plant an order at their Centerville location, too: 130 East Centerville Rd., 972-271-9545 (Mon-Fri 8-5:30; Sat 8-3.) *Call toll-free: 800/441-0743*

★★★★★ P & E Plants   214/741-9209

1204 S. Central   Mon-Sun 6 AM-6 PM
Dallas, TX 75201

If you love flowers, you'll want to buy them out at P & E, lock, stock and barrel. I hate to accuse them of being bloomin'idiots, but a three-gallon Azalea pot that last year was $15 was priced $8 this year. How's that for cutting prices to the bare roots? The price of flats was $12 (same as last year and the year before.) Though Pansies were out-of-season at the time, we were particularly pleased with the Periwinkles. Is it any wonder that millions of shoppers make the trek to Farmer's

Market just to get into the thick-of-et? P & E Plants and Mr. Eddie Comer are a big draw to plant yourself downtown and add color to them thar front and backyards. If your landscape is challenged, bring a truck or your trunk will runneth over. Three-gallon shrubs were gathered up as thee may: Azaleas, Boxwoods, Buford Holly, Red Tip Photinia And Yaupon Holly were all at jolly-good prices, $5.50. With over 20,000 scrubs to choose and over 10,000 hanging baskets, is there any other reason why folks from miles around come to cozy up to the greenery? Don't expect a lot of personal service. They are so busy, they can hardly come up for air.

★★★★   Plant Market, The   972/239-0049
7989 Belt Line Rd. @ Coit   Mon-Sun 9-5:30
Dallas, TX 75254-8129

To market, to market, have yourself a field day. Just how green is your valley anyway? If it's not, The Plant Market is the place to sow. At the intersection of Belt Line and Coit, it's all a matter of how your garden grows. From custom landscaping to flower beds, this company has it all. Planted on solid ground, turn your barren back yard into a blooming arena. From Alyssum to Passion Vines, don't overlook the myriad of possibilities of planting it all. And for eager beavers, there's nothing better than your own vegetable or herb garden. Adding wonderful color, aromatic aromas, and pretty accents for cooking, the time is ripe to consider all the growing options. All plants are grown in their own greenhouses in McKinney, hence "Direct from Grower." Expect prices to reflect this. Have it all, from landscaping plants, seasonal flowers, some trees, Christmas trees, clay pots and other seasonal items to a complete line of organic products for the yard including Howard Garretts', in case he has you under his thumb. Spring and summer, expect hours to extend to accommodate the rush for Begonias and the petulance for Petunias. Their Plano location near Thunderbird Skating Rink has melted. But their Belt Line location is on terra firm ground. Spring into action. Please don't fall!

◆◆   Plant People Landscaping, The   817/237-4439
3017 Caddo Trail   Mon-Fri 8-4:30
Fort Worth, TX 76135
www.theplantpeopletx.com

This isn't some "Little Shop of Horrors." Au contraire! These Plant People will make your home the showplace you always knew it could be. Win that "Yard of the Month" award and be proud of your accomplishments (even if you had a little help from your friends!) First impressions are lasting. Let these people lay it on thick, with green shrubs, colorful flowers and easy-to-maintain perennials along the walkways, but keep in mind that they prefer to concentrate their efforts in west Fort Worth. They have ventured out on occasion to the Mid-Cities, but you'll have to make it worth their while or they'll be reluctant to show up. Talk about limiting your curb appeal! Nevertheless, if you are geographically desirable, they could turn your pool into a tropical paradise and then you can enjoy a vacation every time you take a swim. Look out weeds! They're masters at keeping them at bay, mixing and switching plants as the season dictates, and following through on a weekly, monthly or yearly basis for maintenance. Though limited in their geographic area, there was no boundary in their imagination.

★★★★★★ **Plants and Planters**   **972/699-1281**

1050 N. Greenville Ave.   Mon-Sat 9-6; Sun 10-6
Richardson, TX 75248

Just north of Arapaho, plant this twosome on your "To Shop" list and get thee to their greenery. Herbs for $1.19, Geraniums for $4.95, Fruit Trees for $19.95, Azaleas from $4.95-$12.95, well, what you get here is basically twice as many plants for the money. From organics to perennials, vegetables to pots, get that landscape and flower bed in tip-top shape with the custom green thumbs here. Whether it's landscaping or your own weekend project, these folks can keep you bedded down for life. From ground cover to houseplants, floor-size Tropicals to baby versions for $1.25, life is good. Life is green. Life is saving you money. Now, how much green was your valley? Second location at Northwest Highway and Plano Rd., 214/340-1020. For houseplants, these folks can't be beat! Make this Bud's for you.

Pro Flowers   **888/373-7437(FRESHEST)**

5005 Wateridge Vista Drive, Ste. 200   24/7
San Diego, CA 92121
www.proflowers.com    *Top Online Store!*

He loves me, he loves me not. If that is where the state of your flower-power is, then it's time to put the petal to the medal—this online source is where to buy your flowers and in my book, they win hands down. Since 1998, with Bill Strauss at the helm, they are not only the freshest and bestest for flowers, but the lowest prices, too. The ease of ordering at Pro Flowers and its flawless delivery makes for a satisfied customer with each and every bouquet. How do they do it? First, their flowers are individually selected and picked by the best growers in the country and then shipped directly to you or whoever you're wanting the flowers to go to, usually within 24 hours of being cut. Because their flowers never wait around in a warehouse, truck, or retail florist's cooler, you're getting the absolutely freshest flowers available. Many times, the flowers arrive with their buds closed so they can begin opening on arrival and hence last well over a week or two. You are notified when your flowers are picked up and delivered. It's simply the best. Don't even think 1-800 flowers or flowers.com. They don't hold a candle to the quality of these flowers. Furthermore, they've expanded their offerings to now include gourmet desserts, baskets, teddy bears and more. You won't wilt under the pressure. One call does it all.

★★★★★★ **Redenta's**   **817/488-3525**

6230 Colleyville Blvd.   Mon-Sat 9-6; Sun 10-5
Colleyville, TX 76034
www.redentas.com

With locations in Dallas (2001 Skillman, 214/823-9421) and Arlington (5111 W. Arkansas Lane, 817/451-2149) as well as Colleyville, they have the ground covered in the Metroplex with their annual and perennial quality plants, herbs, old garden roses, Texas native shrubs and trees for grandeur and grace. You might have expected as much since this is part of the family's blooms at Kings Creek Gardens, a retail nursery in Cedar Hill (813 Straus Rd.) If you've not seen this once rural setting of bluebonnets and rolling hills, you may not know Redenta's heritage. Founder Rosa Finsley, a landscape architect in her own right, has seeded the nursery to the Kindler family of Arlington who already operate the Redenta's Garden organic nurseries. Add to the mix, garden accents in every shape and function (from fountains, statues and glazed pots to gift items.) When you think you've hit rock-bottom, dig a little further and you'll discover a wealth of organic gardening supplies, landscape design services and the building of secret gardens. Redenta's offers a plethora of opportunities to rewrite "The Greening of America." Evironmentally-sensitive, all plants are organically grown and every item sold is earth-friendly. If you're after herbs, they have enough to shower any garden with their herb appeal.

★★★★★ Ruibal's Plants of Texas   214/744-3434

601 S. Pearl Expwy.   Mon-Sun 8-6
Dallas, TX 75201
www.ruibals.com

Now we're talking a blanket of carpet bushes, climbing roses, rose bushes and more than what meets the eye of any Ivy Leaguer at Ruibal's Plants at the Farmers Market downtown. The Ruibal boys are at it seven days a week, knee-deep with bedding plants, Tropicals, landscaping, topiaries and making deliveries to area offices and household gardens. Pat those Petunias and Sweet Peas for $12 a flat. Lilies, well, they're the hottest flowers growing. Create stunning vertical color online, too, with their topiary basket system. A 12-inch basket that fits a 14 to 16-inch pot was only $24.99. Their world-famous topiaries bring folks from around the world to check them out. Going online, though, brought a skeletal template of what their website will look like when it gets filled in. Trust me, you'll wind up a basket case after you've taken a look at the over 5,000 baskets hanging overhead. Keeping their own overhead low is one of the reasons they can sell their plants-to-go so low. And growing about 80 percent of their own bedding plants, annuals and perennials and some of their herbs is another. From their shed to your yard, patio, pool, front or back yard, ground cover, bedding plants, perennials, Tropicals, herbs, what is it that you want? Two sheds full of all the garden varieties from simple to elaborate, dainty to dramatic, if it's green, has flowers, can grow, Ruibal's is the place to stake out.

★★★★★★ Season Flower International   972/488-3073

11398 Harry Hines Blvd., Suite 101   Mon-Sat 9:30-6
Dallas, TX 75229

 You can't smell the roses, but what the heck, spray them with air freshener or cologne instead. There's nothing seasonal about the flowers here. In fact, they cover all the seasons, never die, and live on in infamy. From silk to latex blooms, these folks are blooming with them all. From delicate roses to magnificent magnolias, you can join the Bush administration and blow your tax rebate all in one place. Prices start as low as 50 cents for a single stem to $7 for potted bushes. Flowers and fruits are their specialty, all arranged for easy picking. Have yourself a field day with the artificial fruit - from apples to grapes, bring on the reds and the purples and set them in bowls, on tables, in vases, in stands throughout your house. No watering required. An occasional dusting should do the trick. One of the treasured plums for artificial florals on Harry Hines can be found at Season Flower International.

★★★ Sunshine Miniature Trees   214/691-0127

7118 Greenville   Mon-Sun 9-6
Dallas, TX 75231
www.sunshinebonsai.com

Add a little sunshine to your life and you'll be better off in every direction. It's true, Sunshine Miniature Trees has the largest bonsai nursery in North Texas and has been refining their delicate art for the past 35 years. The Sunshine's have been serving the needs of the discriminating plant enthusiast for years based on the proposition that "Excellence at the most reasonable price" makes for good bed-fellows. Expect to save 20 to 40 percent. Though they do import some of their plants from Asia, most are started from seed, tissue cultures and cuttings and grown right in the heart of

Texas. Looking for a good deal? Then ask about their monthly specials like a Bonsai Juniper. This hearty two-year-old plant comes completely landscaped with moss and rocks and planted in a brown plastic bonsai pot. If you are not happy with your purchase, you may return it with a receipt within 10 working days for a full refund. For orders outside the area, there's FREE UPS shipping available. Sunshine on my shoulder makes me happy (but I have no luck with bonsai's, I'm sorry to say.) *Call toll-free: 800/520-2401*

Twigs

740 N. Walnut Creek Drive
Mansfield, TX 76063
www.twigs-floral.com

 If you want a bunch of flowers, shop elsewhere. If you want a floral inspiration that speaks to owner Darr Fuller's imagination and creative spirit, then turn to Twigs for your custom arrangement with a European flair. Designs are contemporary and unique so expect the unexpected. Using only the freshest and highest quality blooms, you can expect whatever leaves their store is going to bring a "Wow" to a recipients'lips. Incorporate home accents into the arrangements or buy them just for room decor, there's candles and crosses and framed art and more. Choose from a veritable variety of urns rather than just a plain glass vase and make a statement with every bouquet. For parties and weddings, Twigs can deliver from stem to stern. Make it memorable. Make it magnificent. Make it colorful. And don't let the Mansfield address deter you. They deliver to Arlington, Fort Worth, Dallas as well as in their own backyard. Located right off Highway 287 in Mansfield, you will be smelling the sweet scent of success. This shop is a baby's breath of fresh air and guaranteed to be the highest quality with imagination thrown in for good measure. When I spoke to a ladies'club group in Mansfield, I couldn't help but notice the table centerpieces. Log on to their website and you'll see why I'm so impressed. Expect the unusual, the beautiful and exotic in both flowers and color with florals shipped from growers around the world. And don't overlook quality dried florals. Bring in your containers and they'll design an arrangement to your specifications.

Weston Gardens in Bloom   817/572-0549 (Metro)

8101 Anglin Drive   Mon-Sat 9-6; Sun Noon-5
Kennedale, TX 76060
www.westongardens.com

 Although technically in the Fort Worth area, you might describe it more aptly as heaven on earth. It's one reason we had to create a "to die for" category. Think outside the box—actually outside terra cotta four-inch pots. Even outside, the green vinyl or plastic holders are tacky and that's one thing you will never say about Weston Gardens in Bloom. Never. Take a leisurely walk through the many acres of pristine gardens across the street from the nursery and drool. They describe themselves as a "real nursery and garden center for those who love plants and gardens." They are not the kind of bait and switch retailer who sells an occasional plant under the guise of really wanting to sell you a lawnmower. Instead, these are serious gardeners with a passion for plants. Everything's labeled from whence they came and whether they are good for butterflies or hummingbirds. There's so much to see, so much to take in, so much to buy. The garden originated in the early '30s with an English garden and lily pond. Today, there's an incredible demonstration garden and even a gift shop. Featured in many of the shelter magazines and TV news shows, everything your heart desires can be unearthed here, from water plants to koi. And if you want fish that specifically eat pests, they'll direct you to the mosquito fish; or if you want fish that won't eat the plants, they'll reel in a Shubunkin. (That's a new one, eh?) If you're not inspired after a visit here, you probably have gone to the wrong address. They have combined science, art and nature's inspiration in developing this magnificent tribute to all things of Mother Earth. They make a point of planting native plants that will acclimate to our Texas climate rather than force-fitting plants that don't belong. They design gardens that uses water responsibly by including the latest in Xeriscape methods. They use less toxic and more natural, organic products than in days gone by, and in general, keep up with the latest planting techniques. If you're desirous of a specialty garden (butterfly, hummingbird, bird-attractor, wildscape, cutting garden, antique rose garden, water garden, herb or rock garden), you've landed at the right spot. If you're "anglin" for the best, this is simply the one "to die for!" During select holidays like Easter and Mother's Day, take your family in walk the walk at Weston Gardens in Bloom. It's a day that you can commune with nature and see God's artistry at work.

Willhite Seed   817/599-8656

PO Box 23   Mon-Fri 8-Noon; 1-5 (Closed for Lunch)
Poolville, TX 76487
www.willhiteseed.com   🖱 *Top Online Store!*

Call for their FREE catalog and soon you'll be able to suc-seed from the union. Shop online or from their catalog pages and see what a 75-year-old source for top-quality seeds is all about. Though they started out with watermelon, today's a whole other ballgame. From peanuts to beans, peas, tomatoes, onions, spinach, potatoes—well, there's corn, cucumbers, squash and peppers, too. Plant your garden in July and come fall, you'll be wallowing in the fruits of your labor. Willhite Seed is one of the largest mail-order seed companies in the country. Texas-born and bred, Willhite's actually located between Weatherford and Bridgeport; so if you're in the area, why not "see'd it" for yourself? Family-owned and operated, dig around and see what materializes. Sow what? Whether you plant the seed directly into the ground or seed ahead for planting after the last frost, you will be able to turn your garden into a lean, green, eating machine. It's fun. It's cheap. And it's so satisfying to watch your garden grow. *Call toll-free: 800/828-1840*

★★★★★★   Wisteria at Home   800/767-5490 (Customer Service)

151 Regal Row, Suite 205   Thurs-Fri 10-5 (Only)
Dallas, TX 75247-5609
www.wisteria.com

Here's a last minute beauty that we couldn't resist planting onto your Bargain Homes and Garden scene. Take two talented shoppers and put them out there in the worldwide arena and let them find neat little items to bring back and sell through their beautiful catalog. Andrew and Shannon Newsom are the ones behind this two day a week outlet for their mail order closeouts. Their catalog is the repository from their around-the-world travels where they pick up wonderful accents for the home and garden. Antiques (mostly imported from China or India, though not exclusively), garden and patio conversation pieces, kitchen, bedroom and bath decorative items, vases and planters, furniture, tableware, linens, toys for kids and pets....whatever they find that would add to splendor in the grass is disposed of weekly at their warehouse. Cast iron urns to zinc flower containers all make dramatic centerpieces to your dining room or outdoor entertainment areas. Online, you'll love all the "purple tag sale" items, where you'll save 30-50 percent. Remember, when you're old, you can shop the purple tags. Not much in the way of a selection online, but their warehouse is always brimming with a bounty of bargains. *Call toll-free: 800/320-9757*

★★   Your Florist   214/361-7707

3213 Knox Street   Mon-Fri 8 AM- 9 PM; Sat 8-8; Sun 10 AM-5
Dallas, TX 75205

Ah, a name from the past. It's been years, maybe even decades since I've done a write-up on Your Florist. But recently, I ran into a special that was almost reminiscent of the good ole days. How does two dozen roses for $20 sound? Too good to be true? No, this is the deal. But don't expect equally drop-dead (but alive and in color) similar prices on anything else. That's the come-on. Somebody has to pay for their Highland Park, Knox-Henderson location where finding a parking place is like finding that the Highland Park Cafeteria has returned. It won't happen. Still, you can dream the impossible dream. But at this florist shop, you won't just be dreaming. You will see lots of different floral varieties in cut stems, plants, Euro-Gardens, other party bouquets and flowers for most any occasion, from weddings to funerals (unless they're one in the same.) Also, expect Your Florist to provide other cut flowers like Gerber Daisies, Tulips, Tropicals, Carnations, Lilies, all kinds really. Premade arrangements in containers started at $25. Potted plants—large and suitable for a gift or door prize—started at $25. Gift baskets started at $50, plus fruit baskets, gourmet food baskets, balloons and other floral and gift goodies—but not at cut rate prices. If you type in www.yourflorist.com, it won't pull up this florist but somebody else's florist. How's that for some undercover underground information.

Pools & Yards

★★★★★★   **A 1 Grass Sand & Stone**   **972/780-7283**

1501 N. Highway 67   Mon-Fri 7:30-5; Sat. 7:30-3
Cedar Hill, TX 75104
www.a1grass.com

 With four area locations, how can you not rock around the clock? Cedar Hill (above), Plano (972/242-4023, Mon-Fri 8-5; Sat 8-12), Rockwall (972/771-3997, Mon-Sat 8-5; Sun 10-5) and Prosper (972/346-2274, Mon-Fri 7:30-5; Sat. 7:30-3), this family-owned dynasty has been moving mountains since 1969. Whether it's retail or whole-sale, they can usually get you covered and delivered to your designated bald spot (no matter how big.) If you need topsoil, masonry sand, play and yard sand, loam sand or hardwood or pine bark mulch, they can help with the cover-up. Nothing clandestine, mind you. Just grass, and not THAT kind either. Whatever type of grass you're needing, for your home, sports'field, even a golf course is available with one call. How does Bermuda, St. Augustine, or Zoyzia and the seasonal Fescue sound? Right up your alley? They also have Oklahoma and Arkansas Flagstone, if you even knew there was a difference, moss boulders, quarried stone and Colorado river rock. What if you wanted different-sized crushed rock, pea gravel or washed concrete for your flower beds or water features? Here is your rock of Gibraltar. And now you, too can implement all of those garden ponds and water garden features in your own back yard.

★★★   **AAA Nursery Sand & Stone Inc**   **214/342-1794**

10550 Miller Rd.   Mon-Fri 7-4:45; Sat 7-2; Sun 9-2
Dallas, TX 75238-1212

Unfortunately, going to this nursery won't propel you to the head of the class but you won't flunk the course, either. Start at the corner of Miller and Plano Roads for your landscaping materials (not sod) like sand for play or patio areas and stone for patios, walkways and gardens. Start here for building your own little walkway or seating area. Consider the favorite Arkansas Flagstone ($225 a ton for pickup, or delivered with a two-ton minimum for around $65-$85.) Now, start your weekend project and don't look back. (That mound behind you can sure look like a mountain, though!) Get the lemonade, tea or beer handy and don't forget to wear sunscreen. The 214 area code number above is the number they've used for 20 years in their previous location on Jupiter Rd. However, it does go directly to their new location, and we've listed it above as a courtesy to their long-time customers. They do get an A in service; are you going to get an A in implementation?

◆   **Adams Landscaping**   **214/349-9006**

By Appt. Only

Dallas, TX 75218

If your sprinkler system's gone kaput, here's the guy to call. He charges $18.50 an hour (parts extra). Have you compared prices for sprinkler head replacements lately? He's got all the necessary know-how and is a licensed irrigator #3449, so if your pop-ups have gone down-under, give Adams a call. But don't ask a lot of questions. He yelled at us!!

◆◆◆◆◆◆   **All Things Great and Small**   **972/965-2569**

Dallas, TX   By Appt. Only

www.allthingsgreatandsmall.com

 Interior or Exterior, things great or small, this company does it all. Call them for a **FREE** consultation for your decorating or landscaping needs—or both. Carry your inside out or outside in and make it all one grand design experience. Whether you're a do-it-yourself buff and need a little help or you want it off your hands into the hands of a pro, this is another way they can go. They do space planning, rearranging, color schemes, fabrics, furniture, flooring/carpet, art objects, hardware fixtures and plants, bedding and window treatments, faux painting and more. Too, they'll work within your budget. They then take digital photos to analyze and evaluate your needs to create a computerized plan on how they're going to do it on a budget. Then they make it happen. And that is strictly for the indoors. Wait 'til you see what can be sculptured for the yards. Click through their landscape photo gallery, their landscape design and installation jobs to see work previously executed: trees, flower beds, shrub planting, seasonal planting, lawns and groundcovers, landscape lighting, sunrooms, outdoor living rooms, patios, decks, arbors, walkways, concrete staining, retaining walls, fence installation and repair, water features like ponds and fountains, sprinkler systems....well, one call and you're practically home free. Well, not exactly ....though the experience will be flawless as well as priceless if not free.

◆◆◆◆   **Alpha Pool Services**   **972/345-2170**

Dallas, TX   By Appt. Only

Call on this Alpha dog for doing your pool service, repair and/or renovation. He'll take the bite out of paying full price since the more you take advantage of their discount pricing to upgrade and safeguard your pool, the more you'll save. Here's a menu of their services: replaster, tile work, coping, decks, leaks and the replacement of equipment. Too, if you need some plumbing work done in conjunction with the pool service, they can help in that department, too. Weekly pool service and chemicals at some of the best rates in town. They don't do Fort Worth, Arlington or the Mid Cities but I-30 North (Garland, Mesquite, Richardson, Plano, Valley Ranch, Irving, Highland Park.) Call them for specific assignments before they rule you out as a geographic pariah. Expect at least 25 percent off their low prices on labor.

★★★★   **American Stone Inc**   **817/589-0051**

6500 Airport Fwy.   Mon-Fri 8-5; Sat 9-2

Fort Worth, TX 76117

You don't have to get stoned to appreciate owning a piece of the rock. There are over 20 different types of stones to use inside or out here that should keep you high and dry. Go to Hwy.121 and Minnis and check out their yard full of choices. Take 121 South to 183 where it curves around near 820 in North Richland Hills; then go back on 121 south about 1 1/2 miles near the Minnis Exit. If you need help, which we did, twice, give them a call. Prices ranged from 7 cents a pound or $140/

ton to 32 cents a pound or $4,520/ton. It all depends on the rock you're selecting and how hard it is to get out of the mountain. Don't expect to shop at an inside showroom because, after all, their stone is water resistant and can only be displayed outside! Delivery charges apply depending on where in the Metroplex you live, how much you order and whether you want your stone forklifted off the truck or just dumped. A load of flagstone to Colleyville, forklifted off, would run an additional $7 for delivery. Consider that a good price for the Mother Lode.

Aqua Pool Warehouse   316/267-2014
Wichita, KS   24/7

www.aqua-pool-warehouse.com   *Top Online Store!*

Don't want to drown in the high cost of maintaining your swimming pool? Then do as other smart pool owners do and dive in to the Underground. These folks have been delivering the savings on swimming pool supplies, equipment, heaters, automatic pool cleaners, diving boards, water slides, pool paint and deck coverings, pool filters, pool filter cartridges, spas, fiber optical pool and spa lighting, water chemicals, floats, above ground pools and pool covers since 1996. They also have fountains, lawn and garden products and barbecue supplies through their sister sites. Tired of being bitten by the bugs? What about a **COLEMAN** Mosquito Deleto that retails for $199.99 but here for $175? I know, that's only a $24.99 savings but we're talking not paying retail, folks. Every little bit helps. Want to build your own little water oasis? Then consider the one that provides a tumbling stream, a bubbling fountain and a cascading waterfall, if you want to engage your senses and enhance your outdoor landscape. Do-it-yourself and it can be yours for less than you think with **LITTLE GIANT**, the leader in water gardening products and design. Make sure you insert the hypens in their online address. And be sure to check out all of their sibling sites. *Call toll-free: 877/891-7665*

◆◆◆◆◆◆ Aquatic Landscapes   214/327-POND(7663)
9132 Sweetwater Drive   By Appt. Only
Dallas, TX 75228
www.aquaticlandscapes.com

 Oh, how I wish I could go with the flow. Though no Henry David Thoreau, there's nothing quite as inviting as dreaming by a golden pond created by these specialists. Over a decade strong, they maintain their own 7-acre garden design center for you to get ideas, create a wish list, or take their products for a test drive. See beautiful gardens, patios, retaining walls and other custom features that only germinate into more ideas. Their philosophy is simple—build it right the first time and make it low maintenance. Believe it or not, almost 70 percent of their business is fixing or rebuilding others'designs that are less than 24 months old because they are too complicated for the average consumer to maintain. Their staff continues to create award-winning, user-friendly water gardens and koi ponds, as well as movie and television set designs and exquisite low light designs, just to name a few. Also, they create living eco-systems that not only increase the value of your home, but help to rejuvenate the soul. Creative touches such as low-voltage lighting, cedar arbors and hardscape construction, as well as ecologically safe organic planting methods, set them apart from the crowd. Visit their model home near White Rock Lake where they've converted a plain 3-bedroom home into their offices and model showplace where you enter the garden through the mine shaft just past the working waterwheel. See Koi dancing in the stream. See an outdoor boulder fireplace and seating area underneath a cedar shade gazebo. If you're thinking of a themed garden, your imagination will be titillated into 5th gear here.

★★★★   **Aries Spa Manufacturer**   **972/771-6286**

4176 I-30   Mon-Fri 8-5; Sat 9-3; Sun 10-4
Rockwall, TX 75087
www.ariesspas.com

So, what is your sign? If you're an Aries, you might have found a place to cool off. Since they're
the manufacturer, customization for your spa is no problem. Start by simply choosing your color
and finish. Then go a little deeper, under water that is, and feel the placement of each jet as it personally is retrofitted to suit your needs, aches and pains. Every spa is available as a portable
model, a spa shell with or without plumbing or a deck model. A few noticeable differences
between Aries and other spas include the extra depth, a user-friendly top-loading filtration system
and topside controls, an extra-heavy shell and easy-care finish. Over 15 years in business should
tell you something. Here, at least, you can try to keep your head above water. They also sell all the
hot tub and spa supplies. Located on the eastern edge of Rockwall near I-30 and FM 549 (Exit 70),
they are some of the best-priced spas in town. Why spend a fortune? You'll end up all wet anyway! They service all the spas they sell. (If it's not an Aries Spa, though, forget it!) And if you'd
rather do it yourself, they carry a complete line of parts and components. Watch for an online store
coming soon, where you can view and purchase all your spa chemicals, supplies, accessories and
parts.

★★★★★★   **Artforms Fountain Outlet**   **972/494-6787**

3826 Cavalier Drive   Mon-Fri 8-3:30
Garland, TX 75042

Best Shopping Destinations   Well, how art thou form? If you want your fountain to appear as a work of art, try
shopping in Garland, of all places, as opposed to Venice or Paris. What's there?
Copper fountains, whimsical garden sculptures, garden and gift accessories, all
priced at wholesale or close. Don't let your cup runneth over - try a fountain instead. If not, you
may have to have your head examined. They don't always answer their phones, but assuming
they're still creating forms that follow function, you'll score at this garden bonanza.

★★★★   **AWS Advanced Wall Systems**   **817/540-1313**

903 Cresthaven Drive   Mon-Fri 8-5
Euless, TX 76040-6901
www.advancedwallsystems.com

Sticks and stones may break your budget, but never at AWS (Advanced Wall Systems). Here they
offer stone and brick walls with monolithic concrete construction and steel reinforcement, while
giving your project the warmth of natural stone - all at competitive prices. So, Humpty-Dumpty
may have fallen off the wall, but not from one from here. AWS offers a natural choice for a retaining wall, replacing failed railroad ties, brick and stone fences and decorative landscaping. Want to
find out more? Give them a call for a FREE estimate and see what a difference a stone or brick
wall can make. Ah, I wonder if Scotland Yard knows about them?

◆◆◆◆◆   **Backyard Environments**   **972/242-9902**

1740 South I-35, Suite 140   By Appt. Only
Carrollton, TX 75006
www.backyardenvironments.com

Backyard environments has moved to Stemmons and now concentrates on this single full-service -
your backyard. Here's what they can do for it: design and construct a custom pool (Eden Pools),

spa and landscape to fit both your yard and your budget. The finished product is as individualized as your thumb print, even if you have a green one. From palm trees to waterfalls, rock sculptures to grottos, here's a waterfront specialist that can do it all. How about a gazebo or an outdoor kitchen? Let them grill you with their artistry. They can also build an outdoor fireplace or firepit should the occasion call for a functional open hearth. An arbor with trailing roses, a cabana for changing clothes, a flagstone patio, an irrigation system, yard and decorative lighting, retaining walls, custom rock work - they're as solid as their work.

★★★★ Barbeques Galore   817/468-3939

4605 S. Cooper St.   Mon-Fri 10-7; Sat-Sun 10-6
Arlington, TX 76017
www.bbqgalore.com

Ah, the smells of summer. Did you get a whiff of that? If you're ready for a grilling, shop at America's largest chain of barbecue stores (multiple locations throughout the Metroplex.) Have a hot time in the old town tonight. Invite a few friends, get the fire started or turn on the gas, and fire away. Remember, where's there's smoke, there's usually some guy wearing an apron and holding a spatula in his hand. Smokers and grills are the specialty here. Go online and print out BBQ Bucks that you can use toward an in-store purchase. Brands included **BROILMATE**, **CAJUN COOKIN'**, **CAPT'N COOK**, **FIESTA**, **GREEN DIAMONDS**, **NEW BRAUNFELS** and more - all competitively priced. **FARBERWARE** was also decidedly discounted 20 percent to make serving your final fare all the more appetizing. Check directory for locations. They are firing up all over the Metroplex! ***Call toll-free: 800/752-3085***

★★★★★★ Binford Supply Co.   972/286-2881

2915 Hickory Tree Rd.   Mon-Fri 8-5; Sat 8-Noon
Mesquite, TX 75180

Not exactly "Tool Time" with Tim Allen, but Binford Supply will put you on the right path to savings. Actually, they'll keep you fenced in so you can't get lost. This company is like a lumber yard for fences—wood and chain link only. Since they mostly sell to fence companies, they don't provide much in the way of service, but you can buy at the same prices as the contractors buy and get it wholesale. Although no installation is available, they will gladly recommend installers. Because this is all they sell, the grade of the chain link is higher than at your home improvement centers. (Theirs is heavier and the diamond size grid is smaller.) Cedar and spruce are all #1 grade and all 1'X 4's are true to size and not an inch smaller or larger either way. Truth in advertising, how refreshing! They are also selling pickets and posts now, so you can do it all. Take the do-it-yourself challenge and maybe next year, you'll have your own reality series. Serving the Metroplex since 1950, Rick Istre has been the fence guru for contractors and for those who would like to build their own fortress with a fence surround. Just watch those fingers.

★★★★★ Brandon Industries   972/542-3000

1601 Wilmeth Rd.   Mon-Fri 8:30-5
McKinney, TX 75069
www.brandonindustries.com

Since 1983, Brandon Industries has been leading the way out of the Dark Ages. As a manufacturer of aluminum outdoor lighting, signage and mailboxes, they have made antique reproduction lamp posts, period street lights, deck lights, wall sconces, stop signs, cast aluminum mailboxes and mailbox posts for both commercial and residential use. Look to them for many charming styles and sizes that are made to complement any landscape or architecture. Expect only quality exterior fixtures in their FREE catalog or shop online. Everything they craft is similar to the originals after which they were modeled. Combining turn-of-the century casting methods with today's technology, Brandon Industries offers the best of both worlds. Orders delivered to your home or office via UPS usually arrive in about two weeks. They only use name brand UL-approved parts from **ADVANCE TRANSFORMER, GENERAL ELECTRIC** and **LEVITON** to electrify the way. Whether you're a builder, a developer, or a property owner (of your own home or office), you might consider adding something more attractive to light the way. All prices are wholesale or below. Find them one exit north of U.S. Hwy. 380 on U.S. Hwy 75.

★   Breez-Lite Awning Co.   214/321-2626

8940 Garland Rd.
Dallas, TX 75223

Mon-Fri 9-4; Sat 9-1

About 30 percent less than the competition, this company's a breeze to consider for the long hot Texas summers. One way to reduce your electric bills is to shade your windows or cover your patio with an awning. Canvas awnings may need to be replaced, but the baked-enamel aluminum models don't. They come in a myriad of colors and include a lifetime FREE of maintenance. That means they don't have to be replaced. Stay warmer in the winter and cooler in the summer. Your initial investment may be higher than you'd like (about $1,000 or more), but remember, you're never going to replace it. Breeze-Lite also builds patio covers and carports. If you like that look, you'll like their price. They will gladly come out, but make sure the estimate will be FREE. It's a "maybe" or "sometimes" proposition. And that's too "iffy" for me.

◆◆◆   Chair Care   214/638-6416

8804 Sovereign Row
Dallas, TX 75247
www.chaircarepatio.com

Mon-Fri 8-4; Sat 9-12 (during the season)

Why buy a whole new chair when repair will do? The remedy is Chair Care, where there are two businesses rolled into one. Chair Care and Custom Powder Coating operate out of their Sovereign Row location while reigning supreme in the category of restrapping or restoring your better brands of patio furniture. Here, every strap is replaced and, if need be, your frames are restored to like-new condition. Brands such as **BROWN JORDAN, TROPITONE** and **WOODARD** meet the criteria for cost-saving repairs. If, for example, you had a Brown Jordan set that you wanted re-strapped and repainted, the arm chairs would cost you $130 per chair. Restrapping four chairs, for example, will take approximately two weeks. (Well, unfortunately, there were several late arrivals this year) though this strapping family-owned business has been around since 1988. Hours vary depending on the season. March through July, they are open every second and third Saturday.

★★★   Chesshir Stone & Rock Supply   214/350-6781

2841 Lombardy Lane
Dallas, TX 75220-2638

Mon-Fri 7-5; Sat. 7-2

If you are looking for a local source for water gardens, take a splash of color here. Start with a copy of the 2003 "Tour of Ponds" guidebook and "Resources for the Modern Water Gardener" for ideas. Then rock and roll out to the garden. Sample rock prices (without delivery): Arizona River Rock, $120/ton; Colorado Flagstone, $239/ton. Mexican Beach Pebbles, 39-cents/pound. There are no designers on staff—so let your imagination be your guide. Walk gently and carry a strong back through the two large stone yards. Use stone in a myriad of home projects, from walkways, patios, fireplaces, fire pits, water gardens, weight training—whatever lifts your spirits. Delivery available in the Metro area.

★★★★★★ Classic Stone   817/222-9735

5703 Airport Freeway (Hwy. 121)   Mon-Sat 9-6; Sun 1-5
Haltom City, TX 76117

Plant these fine statues in your back yard and attract more than just birds. Just like the gardens of the rich and famous, this manufacturer can provide some of the most beautiful planters, table sets, statues, benches, fountains, animals and more. Ah, such elegance and affordability in the same breath. A three-tiered fountain with pump was only $395 and looked like it would fit comfortably at the Gardens at Versailles. This manufacturer of classic stone statuary is not to be confused with the Classic Stone (the other Classic in Gainesville.) These are the ones in Haltom City that make classic custom statuary for the home and garden. They may even consider renaming their outlet "Better Homes and Bargains" as one could certainly write a book about the possibilities that lie in wake for the garden here. It's classic! They can even mix up a special marble dust into their statuary molds that make them look exactly like marble. Pay attention to our website and radio show because we shall be letting you in on the below-wholesale sales. Delivery available. Owners Mike and Mary James are a classic couple themselves.

★★★★★★ Comfort Cushion   214/748-2242

1717 Levee St.   Mon-Fri 7-3; Sat 8-1 (summer only)
Dallas, TX 75207

This manufacturer and wholesaler is a cut above the others, especially if you want to cushion the blow of paying retail. Whether you want new ones, replacements, or repairs on your old, make sure you know your sizes, since all cushions are not created equal. Both ready-mades and custom cushions are available. Standard sizes can be anywhere from 18 x 18 inches up to 23 x 72 inches. From PVC furniture slings to umbrellas, you can pick from hundreds of fabric swatches and coordinate your entire patio ensemble with matching fabric. Open on Saturdays during the summer months only.

★★★★★ Contractors Stone & Landscape   972/516-1468

6620 Ave K   Mon-Fri 7-5; Sat 7-3
Plano, TX 75074-2511

You don't have to be a contractor to shop here, despite the name. But you still can take advantage of contractor prices. The stoneyard is where you'll be shopping, so walk through with sturdy shoes (ballet slippers are hardly appropriate.) Choose your stone: flagstone, slabs, pavestones, pea gravel, river rock, crushed rock—whatever. In fact, there were boulders that would even function beautifully as benches. Don't be rigid. Create something wild and/or imaginative. Don't come traipsing through looking for flowers or landscaping services, although many landscapers know this place like the back of their hand. Delivery available throughout the Metroplex.

◆◆◆◆◆◆◆ Crack Doctor, Inc., The   972/420-6442

1702 S. Hwy. 121, Suite 401   Mon-Fri 8-5 (By Appt. Only)
Lewisville, TX 75067
www.thecrackdoctor.com

Here is the scoop. If you've got a crack in your pool, don't crack up. You're a fool to think you have to replace the entire pool. For $150, they'll come out and do a structural damage analysis, then it's $4 a foot for crack repair. Other cracks around skimmers, drains, pumps, etc. are priced $75/an hour and are billed at actual time. The Crack Doctors are underwater repair specialists who can repair any crack in your pool regardless of its origin. Cracks, grout, tile, mastic repair, stain removal and leak detection are just part of their everyday repair duties. They perform underwater inspections, acid washes, and year-round underwater service. But NO more FREE estimates. Only a warranty comes FREE with every repair job. Don't ignore it. Your water bills will soar and ultimately, you'll have serious pool damage that may be irreparable. Expect a three-week wait for an appointment. Founded in 1990, Rick Garrett started this business as a way to enjoy his hobby of scuba diving. Now, look at him! Services provided throughout the Metroplex and now Austin. Though they specialize in underwater repair, they also do underground plumbing leak detection and repair, repair or replacement of equipment, tile, coping, mastic, as well as full restoration and renovation of pools. So, if you've got a problem, take two deep breaths and call this doctor in the morning. ***Call toll-free: 800/404-8234***

◆◆◆◆◆◆ Creative Water Gardens   972/271-1411

2125 W. Kingsley   Tues-Sat 10-6; Sun 12-4 (Mar-Oct); Tues-Sat 10-5 (Nov-Feb)
Garland, TX 75041
www.creative-watergardens.com

 Note expanded hours during the warmer months when creating creative exteriors is foremost in shopper's minds. But every day is a creative one at this aquatic garden. There's not an aquatic plant since 1988 that hasn't grown from one of their water gardens yet. Located northeast of Dallas, north of 635 on Garland Road, this garden invites you to take a stroll amongst the fountains and ponds surrounded by native trees, wildflowers and birds while enjoying the fruits of another's labor. Vivid waterlilies and gliding fish are schooled in these proper environments. Think "On Golden Pond" (a 10,000 gallon one for starters) and marvel at the giant water lilies and robust koi. More than 300 varieties are raised on site including both the rare and the usual, plus new varieties that are under experimentation. Then, tiptoe through the lotus - graze through the oxygenating grasses—take a whiff of the hardy and tropical waterlilies and then on to the pond fish. Okay, so I'm a sucker for koi, both domestic and imported and I love to look a goldfish in the mouth! For do-it-yourselfers, there are tons of pond products, from waterfall pumps to floating alligators, granite fountains to unique bronze statuary. Also, shop online. Wave good-bye to boring landscapes. It's a humdinger!

★★★★ Custom Stone Supply   972/335-4122

9207 FM 2934   Mon-Fri 7-5; Sat 7-3
Frisco, TX 75034-3224
www.customstone.com

This Collin-county custom stonery is just one of three (others in Dallas, 972/243-1144 and in Tarrant County in Keller, 817/337-4408), so the tri-county area is etched in stone, so to speak. Here is a source for natural stone for fireplaces, countertops, backsplashes, floors, shower and tub walls and that's just for indoor use. Think out of the box to the outside, too, and you'll see the stones that can be used in waterfalls, pools, retaining walls and home exteriors. Over 3,000 square feet of displays showcasing native Texas stone, Calico Limestone, Pennsylvania Bluestone, Tennessee Crab Orchard and Arizona Flagstone. Did you even know there was such a variety—let alone such funny-sounding names? Tennessee Crab Orchard, that's a real cracker-upper. Garden stones, patio stones and random rectangulars are waiting patiently for you to walk all over them. What's holding you back? Your back? They offer delivery, just ask.

★★★ Dallas Custom Swings   214/341-3727

11660 Plano Rd.   Mon-Fri 9-5; Sat 10-5
Dallas, TX 75243
www.customswingsoftexas.com

Since its founding in 1984, Deborah Muse has been musing over Custom Swings. Their northeast Dallas factory and showroom has been the building block to backyard fun for kids (of all ages). If she's any relation to the founder of Muse Air, she's a high flying entrepreneur in her own right. Her "Explorer Series" is, as are most, kits and a real challenge to assemble, but surely you have a honey-that-can-do it for you. If not, they have trained installers who do it—for a price. Equipment can be installed and then sealed as well. Regardless of age, you can be a swinger in no time. For other backyard swing-ding -a-lings, don't forget all of the other accessories that Dallas Custom Swings is famous for: swing hangers, tent tops, porch swings, picnic tables, swing frames and slides. Have a field day on the "Amazing Imagination Machine Play Systems," their large systems designed to spark a child's imagination and improve playtime on the equipment. Their Preston Road location in Dallas has swung shut; note the difference in name at their website.

◆◆◆ Decks Appeal   972/964-8821

3131 Custer Rd., #250   Mon-Sat 10-5
Plano, TX 75075-4426
www.decksappeal.com

If your decks appeal has gone south and you want to find it, restore it, rekindle it, replace it, or start from ground zero, you might want to start at this 2,600 square foot showroom in Plano at the southwest corner of Custer and Parker. Since 1988, they've combined a quality design staff and master craftsmen to custom craft redwood decks, arbors, overhead structures, gazebos, benches, planters, railings and necessary lighting, for all of the above. Looking to get some luster back in your faded redwood deck that has otherwise lost its decks appeal? Here's the place for color restoration and/or repair. Whether you imagine yourself in an elaborate pavilion or just sitting lazily under an awning, an archway or a patio cover, it doesn't take a brain surgeon, but it does take a company like Decks Appeal. Although we were interested in a gazebo initially, we were told that it may not be the best way to go. An eight-foot eight-sided gazebo started at $4,790; whereas, a pavilion would be less pricey, with far less waste and much easier to construct. You can dream inside their showroom gazebo for a trial run—and then decide which way to go. But you'll pay for it. Nobody said Decks Appeal would come cheap!

◆◆◆◆◆◆ Diamond Pool Services   972/353-2449

Dallas, TX   By Appt. Only
www.diamondpoolservices.com

 If diamonds are a girl's best friend, then here's her choice for pool services as well. Weekly pool service is a drag so if you'd rather not do-it-yourself, here are the guys that make it their business, their family business. John Rhodes and Company provide weekly pool service but it doesn't stop with just the dirty work. They also build custom pools and spas. Starting as low as $27.50 a week including chemicals, you can have your pool in tiptop shape instead of scum and glum. They empty all the skimmer baskets, brush pool tile, steps, seats, benches, sides and slides. They remove all floating debris (dead bodies excluded), vacuum pool, if needed, test pool water and maintain the appropriate chemicals. They also backwash every four to six weeks as needed and will inspect and maintain all of your pool equipment so that there are no surprises just when you least expected them. At the end, you've got a pool that glistens and is in tip-top shape; they leave with a smile and a door tag that tells you they've been there and done it!

Repairs are an option for a service call plus parts. If you sign up for weekly service, they were offering a filter cleaning special for $62.50, a **POLARIS** Tune-up for $120/retail $145 and if only wanted chemicals, they are up to delivering them for $65 per month. Now, it's okay for you to dive in with both feet.

◆◆◆   Dickson Brothers   972/288-7537

204 N. Galloway Ave.   Mon-Fri 8-5:30; Sat 8-5
Mesquite, TX 75149

The Wright Brothers knew about blue sky and what makes planes fly and the Dickson Brothers know the ropes about blue waters and the pumps that make them flow. Bring in broken parts from your spa, pool or pump and someone in their service department will point you in the right direction. Better yet, have them service the part or system on location. (It's a bit much to haul in a pool, don't you agree?) They are the fixer-uppers to do the job. Though they used to build water gardens and ponds, today they just sell the equipment and hook you up with those that do. Broken pool filters, no-bubble **JACUZZI'S**, clogged-up pipes on your pond, that's what they're all about. They also sell water gardens, pool supplies and service water wells as well. Well....what are you waiting for? Pond scum?

◆◆   Elliott's Spas, Pools & Service   972/562-7902

1505-B W. University Drive   Mon-Fri 10-7
McKinney, TX 75070

Call before you dive, as the Elliott's may be out on a call for a spa that's got a leak or a pool with a problem. After more than 15 years in the business, Sunbelt Spa Manufacturing Company has designated them as the authorized dealer for Sunbelt's 15 models and five jet system spas. You can choose from 14 different colors in gemstone, marble and granite and each comes with a three-year warranty and lifetime structural warranty. They know their stuff and if you want a value-priced spa, these are about 20 percent less that California Pools or Morgan Spas. Besides selling them, they can service them. If there's something that goes on the blink, give them a call though each time we called, their answering machine picked up the call. See if you get a live operator and tell Malcolm and Marianne Elliott we called.

★★★★★★   Executive Jungle   817/488-9608

567-B Commerce St.   Mon-Fri 9-4; Sat 9-Noon
Southlake, TX 76092

In business almost 20 years, when it comes to interior or exterior landscaping, this is the place to make those executive decisions. Afterall, it's a jungle out there and you don't want to be swinging from one vine to the next. These folks are rock solid. They offer landscape maintenance services and design services, par excellence. If you want to transform your home into a showplace, in and out, consider the options here - everything is priced at wholesale prices. See iron tables, accessories and pottery with some of the same items that have decorated restaurants such as El Chico and others. Since 1979, they've been one of the best-kept secrets. (Well, so much for hidden treasures.) When you think pottery, chimeras, talavera, sconces, iron, gazing balls, baskets and more, turn to the one and only, Executive Jungle. You don't need to be a CEO to figure how this company will help you climb the corporate grapevine.

★★★★ Fiber Fence   817/379-4411

715 Katy Rd.   By Reservation Only
Keller, TX 76248
www.fiberfence.com

Makes sense, doesn't it? Buy direct and save up to 30 percent on your next fence be it commercial or residential. Nationally-franchised, this trademarked fiberglass fencing system offers a lifetime warranty and since it doesn't rot, never splinters, and is completely weatherproofed. That means, you'll never need to replace it. Yea!! Molded-in colors means never having to paint. Too, the choice of styles and colors is up to you: privacy, stockade, picket, shadow box, ornamental, ranch or board on board are your fence style choices. In essence, any fence that is built with wood, plastic or metal can be made with the **FIBERFENCE**™ components. Too, you can buy the components and install them yourself to save even more. Doors and gates are built on the same principles with the same hardware that is used for wood fences. Heights vary and determined by local ordinances from 3-foot fences up to 8-foot. And if your vigorous lawn mower whacks at weeds growing next to the fence, don't worry, it won't even damage your Fiberfence. My favorite is the black wrought iron look since everyone thinks it's the real thing and greatly enhances the value of your property. Smart, isn't it?

★★ Flags USA   817/589-2525

3404 East Loop 820 South   Mon-Fri 8-5; Sat. 9-1
Fort Worth, TX 76119

Around June 14th, Flag Day, the calls start coming. Where do I buy a flag? Well, here's a place to buy 'em, all of them except those that we are fighting with. (Pakistan and Iraq) are two countries that are the endangered list. Just the good ole USA flags and Texas flags are their specialty. A few other state flags are waving (but why?) alongside a few college flags such as UT (my husband claims there isn't any other, although he's an A & M grad!) Wave your allegiances loud and clear. If you're proud to be an American, salute the flag. Wave the flag. Sing around the flag and let Bruce Springston know that you are glad to have been "Born in the USA."

★★★★★ Future Fence & Deck   972/298-6659

639 E. Hwy.67   Mon-Fri 8-5
Duncanville, TX 75137
www.futurefence.com

At least, Future Shock will not be in store for you with this company. But it may be the last fence you will ever need. Ah, isn't that special! No more staining and painting, and staining and painting, again. No more rotting slats and broken down boards. You can see their products at their showroom in Duncanville, if you need convincing. These guys are licensed wholesalers, distributors and fabricators of **KROY** vinyl out of York, Nebraska. They build decks, arbors, gazebos, trellis, patio covers and more, in your basic white. For additional colors, tan or gray, add another 15 percent more. Then, for khaki, it's an additional 20 percent more. All colors come in a textured wood grain and cost an additional 22 percent. All products come with a lifetime warranties, making it virtually maintenance free, and the warranty can be transferred to future owners.

★★★★★★   **Hartwell's Landscaping Nursery   972/436-3612**
1570 N. Stemmons Frwy.   Mon-Fri 8:30-5:30; Sat 8:30-5; Sun 10-5
Lewisville, TX 75067

 What's a tree doing growing in Lewisville? I thought it was supposed to grow in Brooklyn! Even though she didn't have a New York accent, we understood Tammy very well. She's the decorator for your garden. For $250, she'll completely map out a recommended and functional design, but if you proceed with buying the plants, shrubs, trees, ground cover, it comes off the final bill. Or bring in your own plans, designs and ideas and let them bid on it, no charge. Imagine this great oasis of greenery sitting between all the boat dealerships, barbecue joints, funeral homes and RV outlets on Stemmons. Whether it's for a complete landscape overhaul, or a corner niche, these warriors can help you beat the high cost of a backyard transformation. Go with the pro's; it will pay off in satisfied dividends in the end. All's well that shops at Hartwell's.

◆◆◆◆◆   **Hobert Pools**   **972/690-8118**
300 S. Central Expwy.   Mon-Fri 8-5; Sat 8-4; Sun 1-5
Richardson, TX 75080
www.hobertpools.com

Ho-Ho-Hobert. This business started in 1975 when Central Expressway was just two lanes, and today there are five locations throughout the Metroplex and Central is still as slow as it was when it was just two lanes. With 100 percent financing (with approved credit), you, too, can jump in over your head with manageable payments. A FREE consultation is available to have someone give your yard a once-over. They will build a pool within a 70-mile radius of Dallas and they take pride in building one pool at a time and building it to last. Along the way, they try to save you time and money. A timely completion date, quality construction and a competitive price sums it all up at Hobert Pools. If you want to take a peek, they have pools on display at select locations. Check directory for the location nearest you. Other locations in Flower Mound, Corinth/Lewisville, Allen and Rockwall. Come on in—the water's fine.

★★★★★   **Hot Spring Portable Spas**   **972/633-1085**
1725 N. Central Expwy.   Mon-Sat 10-6; Sun 1-5
Plano, TX 75075-6910
www.hotspring.com

If you want a hot time in the hot tub tonight, then consider this award-winning spa manufacturer, Hot Spring Spas. It's considered the world's number one selling brand and has been the market leader since 1977. HOT SPRING is a recognized name throughout the country, Canada, and over 50 countries. So, no matter where you live, there's somebody already soaking in one. These manufacturers are the only three-time recipients of the spa industry's prestigious "John Holcomb Silver Award for Technological Innovation." Expect state-of-the-art technology and specially-trained delivery and installation technicians. Also, visit in Fort Worth at 4820 SE Loop 820 (I-20 at Anglin Drive), 817/572-0004, and 1419 Hwy 114 W at William D. Tate in Grapevine, 817/481-4288. Enjoy! It's a wonderful way to end your end after a day at the office.

◆◆◆◆◆   Into the Wind   817/267-2069

1610 W. Euless Blvd.
Euless, TX 76040
www.inthewindflags.com

Mon-Fri 9-6

We're not just blowin'smoke, we are telling you once and for all, where to buy a flag. If I have been asked once, I've been asked a million times. Whether it's at the appropriate holiday time or for folks who are just plain proud to proclaim their pride at being an American, this is the place to contact. Whether it's wall-mounted flagpoles, nautical flagpoles, steel flagpoles to 150-feet, counterbalanced tilting flagpoles or flagpole parts and accessories, these are the folks who will help you fly the high and the mighty. They sell them. They repair them. They custom make them with your logo or whatever. They install them. They also make pennants and banners. What do you want to put up to the test? For team or corporate support, what's better than holding up a banner or flag with your name on it? Nobody knows the business of flags better than here. Looking for the Mexican flag? Canadian? Whatever country you wish to honor, shimmy up the flagpoles here and pick your flag. Listen to this banner special: 3'x 10'banner, $95. Get on the bandwagon and start waving your name out there at the soccer game. *Call toll-free: 800/725-FLAG*

★★★★   Jackson's Pottery   214/350-9200

6950 Lemmon Ave @ University
Dallas, TX 75209

Mon-Sat 9-6; Sun 12-5

If the subject turns to calling the kettle black, chances are they're talking about something from Jackson's Pottery. But don't limit your thinking just to black outdoor urns and pots. This is a garden seeding for a gallery of ideas. Lawn sculptures and statuaries, fountains and water gardens, gas lights, other outdoor lighting fixtures and lamps and all the expertise that goes along with setting up in the great outdoors is under the tutelage of Jackson's Pottery. Then if it's pottery, concrete, marble or terra cotta bird baths or fountains, they've got your yard covered. Then, when it comes time to turn up the heat, expect Jackson's to be your grill headquarters, from the smallest to the grandest gas grills with all the bells and whistles. No patio furniture to date but they will custom order cushions. Bedding plants to fill out your need for green. And if you covet a **HASTY-BAKE** charcoal oven, they smoke out the competition. Selection and quality warrants a look see but sales net the "gratest" savings to buy. But if bugs are bugging you, don't miss their magic mosquito be-gone. They have a product that folks are raving about. I haven't tried it yet so they're still biting me; but it gives me a good reason to shop them before the time when I want to sit out on my patio. I'll let you know if I'm itchin'next year. But "Boo-Hoo," why no website?

◆◆◆◆◆   Jay Ling Landscaping Specialties   214/850-1621

4911 Smith Road
Plano, TX 75094

By Appt. Only

If you want to transform your landscape into a work of art, you call on an artist with plenty of years of experience. Jay Ling's no newcomer to the yards of the Metroplex. Many corporate accounts are showplaces because of his contributions to outdoor walkways, waterfalls, ponds and sculpture. And, too, many homeowners are benefactors of his wondrous landscape, waterscape and color laden additions to their yards and gardens. When a well-known watch-maker titan wanted a bridge to connect over his babbling brook to the barbecue pit without wading through the river, Jay built "The Bridge Over the Water Why" or was it Kwai? Jay Ling is who folks in the know call because he can get the job done better and with less extraneous costs. He gives you a lot of bang for your buck and will never load you down with things that you don't need just to make the project more expensive. He's an honest man with integrity. Doesn't mean he's cheap. But compare him to the big nurseries in town (Lambert's, North Haven, etc.) and you can readily get the picture his prices are a fraction of the cost without sacrificing the quality of his workmanship. From pools to fences, even 100-year-old trees are entrusted to his care to be moved. Each job is unique. Each job is considered his number one priority. That is just one reason his repeat business is his mainstay and he receives a myriad of accolades for his artistry. Don't forget to ask about his small ponds to give you a taste of why everybody's clamoring for the ones with those overturned pots with water spewing forth. Look for teak furniture, he is also a distributor. Yes, he can do it all so you'll never have to go elsewhere to complete the deck, the patio, the new stamped concrete sun deck. He's a one-stop shop in a truck. He supervises all of his crews so you're never left holding the bag of mulch. He delivers what he says and will no doubt give you a reason to enter your yard this year into the "Yard of the Year." Betcha win!

◆◆◆◆◆◆   Joy Pools   972/539-SWIM (7946)

506 S. Stemmons   By Appt. Only
Lewisville, TX 75067
www.truejoypools.com

There's nothing better than a personal recommendation. I'll swim to that! I have a Joy Pool that is simply a joy to behold. Five years later, it's still purring like a kitten, looks like a million bucks (lagoon-shaped and all) and if you happen to have a pool in the Lewisville/Flower Mound area, you'll jump for Joy at the chance to utilize their expert services all year round. From pool maintenance to remodeling, here's one happy camper. Swimming has been my choice of exercise since my gastric bypass and though I still have to drag out the water wings, it has certainly helped in the toning department. Like a duck takes to water, the Diva dives in to her Joy Pool and is grateful for every lap I take. Joy Pools has offered remodeling services as well as new construction for over twenty years and builds all the latest kinds you ogle over on Home and Garden TV. They also offer custom outdoor kitchens and grills. FREE quotes and first-class service tags along with their first-class building. Founder Mike Truesdell established Joy Pools in 1981 and the company has grown from 10 installations per year to over 160 per year - always a good sign. You don't want to have somebody use your backyard as a test site, dig a hole and disappear. Joy Pools is known for their quality and timely installations and that is why I have no hesitation to recommend them.

★★★★★   Kids Playthings   972/416-7748

2717 E. Belt Line Rd., #105   Mon-Sat 10-5; Sun 1-5
Carrollton, TX 75006
www.kids-playthings.com

One block west of Marsh, there's always something to kid about when it comes time to send them out to play. "Get out of the kitchen and go play" was my mom's favorite phrase when we got too noisy. If you suffer from the same disturbances, send your kids to play with ready-to-assemble playthings at 30 percent off; and 40 percent off everything else. You just missed the 50 percent off on all special pine and NATURALINE® swing sets. Swing sets started around $699. This division of the formidable Creative Playthings down the street on Belt Line has been designed with children's play in mind. The showroom sports wallpaper with a rainforest jungle theme along with ample room around the playsets for play. All sets carry comprehensive warranties, so they're likely to outlive your back yard. Their Frisco location is located 1 1/2 blocks N of Hwy 121 at The Center at Preston Ridge (NW Corner of Preston and Gaylord) or call 214/618-1910.

★★★★★★ **Kiva Pottery**   **214/821-1700**

1916 N. Haskell Ave.   Tues-Sat 10-6
Dallas, TX 75204

Viva la company! Long live Kiva, a popular name in the world of Southwestern, primitive and Santa Fe pottery. If you've ever lived in Arizona, New Mexico or Southern California, trust me, Kiva is like a middle name to designer products. Now shop like you mean it—especially when I tell you the prices are wholesale. Located between City Place and Ross Avenue, there are yards and yards of decorative planters (usable inside or out) for you to choose. The shapes, sizes and styles are plentiful including the popular chimineas. For indoor accoutrements, the pottery, the rustic wrought iron and patio furniture and accessories make for warm and inviting conversation pieces, containers for plants, or just laid down on their sides as a decorative accent (in truth to cover a stain in your carpet or that blank space in your floor plan.) For example, a decorative urn, sold elsewhere for $155, was unearthed here for only $50. Their selection includes 150 lines of clay pottery with an old-world Greek style. Pottery is a wonderful decorative accessory in any home, indoors or out.

★★★★★ **Leslie's Swimming Pool Supply**   **972/231-3793**

1260 W. Spring Valley Rd.   Mon-Sat 10-6; Sun Noon-5
Richardson, TX 75080
www.lesliespoolsupplies.com

They're everywhere, they're everywhere, which tells you there's a pool practically within walking distance from a Leslie's neighborhood locations. With more than 38 years in the business, they are the largest and most well-know swimming pool supplier who'll keep you in the swim of things. With over 430 retail stores, in 36 states across America, plus the availability of mail order (800/537-5437) and Internet shopping, Leslie's offers every customer the ultimate shopping experience. Dependable and well-priced, Leslie's is an AQUA QUEEN, ARNELSON, KREEPY KRAULY and POLARIS pool-sweep dealer, but they also carry solar covers, pumps, heaters, motors and lights. They offer repair service and leak detection, so you won't have to float a note to keep from drowning in debt. Look to Leslie's private-labeled goods for their best buys, as well as specials. For example, with any inflatable purchase over $49.99, you would get a FREE electric pump. You don't have to be a blow-heart to appreciate the wind-power that you will conserve. One of my favorite features is their FREE water tests. That's just one of the in-store perks. They offer FREE labor on in-store repairs, FREE seminars, an X-press parts program, a 100 percent satisfaction guarantee which is right up there with their 120 percent best price guarantee. Float to the center of the pool with a fort and slide; or hydra-lounge around complete with water guns for a real duel, $49.99. Check directory for the location nearest you. FREE catalog upon request. *Call toll-free: 800/537-5437*

◆◆◆ **Marjorie's Lawn & Garden/ Fence Repair** **214/350-4238**

3044 Webb Chapel Extension   Mon-Sat 8-5; or By Appt.
Dallas, TX 75220

It may take a village to—well, it may take a woman to deliver good, old-fashioned service at affordable prices. Marjorie's is a one-stop landscape service business. If it has something to do with your yard, she's the one to call. Overcoming poverty by working is her motto, and she offers ten-year guarantees on new fences and five-year guarantees on fence repairs. For your yard, she does weekly maintenance, one-time yard sprucing up, sprinkler systems and tree trimming. Don't be a prune, your trees need attention, too. They're not the cheapest, but they're one of the most reliable. They actually show up, do the job and leaf without leafing a mess. And in a pinch, they offer plumbing, aid-conditioning and handyman services, too. What don't they do? Well, we haven't found them willing to cater my Thanksgiving dinner.

◆◆◆◆ **Mobile Mini**   **214/333-2222**

3550 Duncanville Rd.   Mon-Fri 8-5; Sat 8-Noon
Dallas, TX 75236
www.mobilemini.com

This is so cool—containers delivered to your home or office to act as mini-storage units. Low-cost, ground-level and portable, they pick up and deliver these mini-storage vaults and you're practically home free. They are custom-built from five to 40 square feet and delivered to your site direct from the manufacturer. Hate keeping those lawn mowers or pool equipment strewn about the lawn? Are your golf clubs, tennis rackets, racing bike and mini-gym units cluttering your garage? Then, pack it up and store it if you're not using it. Same with all your Christmas paraphernalia. Pack up the tree, trimmings, ornaments and such in a storage unit such as a Mobile Mini until next year. With one call, they'll be returned coming down the chimney. (Okay, so it's really the driveway.) Moving boxes and supplies also available. Click online for special coupons like a $50 off rental. Have a business? Become a Preferred Customer. It's FREE and you'll get reduced rates, rebates, FREE clean up on returns, priority pick up and delivery and your satisfaction guaranteed or your next local delivery is FREE. *Call toll-free: 800/950-6464*

◆ **Mower Medic**   **972/466-9093**

2540 Dickerson Pkwy.   Mon-Fri 8:30-5; Sat 8:30-2
Carrollton, TX 75006

Got a sickly mower on your hands? Take it to the Mower Medic for a tune-up and expect to pay at least $79.95 for labor plus parts. For example, the parts for a tune-up on a BRIGGS & STRATTON motor were estimated around $40. However, unless you've got an expensive mower, you're almost better off buying a new one. They are paramedics for almost any brand: Briggs & Stratton, HONDA, HUSQVARNA, MONTGOMERY WARD, MTD, MURRAY, SEARS and TECUMSEH, for starters. Expect a two to three day turnaround time for the average; for example, fixing the gas line to a RYOBI trimmer. Bring your mower to their parking lot. They're not welcome inside their store. Forget their website, it's no longer running, but don't forget what I said about their gruff greeting. They still sound like they could care less if you or your mower's ailing. You can see their sign from I-35 E. and Trinity Mills.

★★ **Mower World**   **972/298-7554**

435 E. Danieldale Rd.   Mon-Fri 8-6; Sat 8-5
Duncanville, TX 75137

Mow'er down and keep that lawn cut to the quick with a new HONDA, LAWN BOY or TORO lawn mower, trimmer or blower. If it was meant to do hard labor on your lawn or garden, this place presents a football field worth of options. From a Lawn Boy single-speed, self-propelled mower for a low of $324 to a MASSEY FERGUSON tractor for several thousand, cut to the quick at the largest lawn, garden and outdoor equipment store in town. Orbit around and while you're at it, save some green. If it's mowers you want, they have every brand, every size, and every price range. Bet you didn't know there are special lawn mowers just for women? (I can just see me now. Full makeup. Darling sling mules and a mower! Wow!) The same holds true for garden and lawn tools. Sales are where you'll get the best price, though, as much as 60 percent off. Forget the Christmas store; it has closed permanently. And their gardening store has diminished drastically.

The emphasis here is mower sales, parts and service. Repairs available but only during the busy season (spring and summer). Expect about a two-week wait, unless it's minor and then it'll take only a few days. During slow times, though, repairs take only a week or less. ***Call toll-free: 888/ 80-MOWER***

◆◆◆◆◆◆ Mustang Contracting 214/369-3353; 972/488-9889

Dallas, TX   By Appt. Only
www.mustangcontracting.com

If you want to know a pro in the sprinkler and irrigation service business, let me introduce you to owner/general manager Shafford McKinney. Since 1990, this locally-owned contractor has been soaking it in to area lawns without having you drowning in debt. Schedule an appointment online or give them a call, they actually answer their phones without having you talk to a robot or going into a voice mail maze of extensions. How drippingly refreshing. These guys know how to get you a "-head" of the competition and believe me, they take the business of installation and irrigation systems seriously. Furthermore, since I first discovered their sprinkler services, they have expanded into residential and commercial remodeling (for office finish outs), driveways, patios and retaining walls. Hey, that reminds me. I sure could use a new retaining wall for my front yard walkway. Right now, I'm experiencing a serious mudslide.

Outdoor Decor   205/345-1103

4446 Hendricks Ave., #399   24/7
Jacksonville, FL 32207

www.outdoordecor.com   ⌁ ***Top Online Store!***

The product list is exhaustive enough to tire out even my inexhaustible dog Jazz. From address markets, arbors, birdbaths, bird feeders, bird houses, bridges, clocks, cupolas, decorative signs, doorbells, door mats, door knockers, downspouts, faucets, flags, fountains, furniture, garden bells, garden sheds, garden stakes, gazebos, gazing globes, hammocks, herb markers, hose guides, house numbers, lanterns and torches, lighting, mailboxes, patio heaters, patriotic markers, pedestals, pest control, pet items, planters, and, of course, dog and cat beds, even houses and memorials for your dog or cat. Oh, did I tell you I also fell in love with their shades, statuary, thermometers, wall art, weathervanes and wind chimes, too? ***Call toll-free: 800/ 422-1525***

★★★★★★ Patio One/Fullrich Industries   972/633-5522

1401 Summit Ave., Ste 3   Mon-Fri 9-5; Sat 10-6; Sun 1-6
Plano, TX 75074
www.fullrich.net

New location, whoopee-do. Didn't find the first one too easy to get to, so imagine how happy I was to learn that they had moved. That's until I found out it was from 1501 Summit to 1401. So, it's still hard to find, though it's closer than their headquarters in Jakarta, Indonesia. Now open on Sundays, amen, Brother. Don't expect to get away cheap all the time, though prices are what drives most people to buy. For example, a teak four-foot swing that retailed for $200 was $99.99. Director's chairs were priced at $75 retail (a bit too high for my bottom....line) but were priced during a special sale at $25 for two. Now, that's more like it. Patio One is no second best. In fact, they're probably the only designer teak garden furniture manufacturer's outlet in the Metroplex and they're at your service. They've been manufacturing patio furniture for over a decade with sales to companies like Alsto's Mail Order Catalog, Crate and Barrel and Pier One, to name drop a few. Outfit your outdoor environment with direct savings on imported teak and **NYATOH** furniture displayed in their 3,000 square feet warehouse/showroom. Shower your outdoor environment in tables, chairs, benches, sun umbrellas, lounges and more.

Pool Merchants   **888/430-4NET**

PO Box 3266   24/7
New York City, NY 10163

www.poolmerchants.com   🖰 *Top Online Store!*

 I told you, if I can't refer you to someone in the Metroplex who can get it for you wholesale, I will refer you elsewhere. And other than Leslie's, there's really no deep blue discounters of pool supplies and equipment in the Metro area, I'm sorry to say. Enter these Pool Merchants who since 1997 have been selling everything you've ever wanted or needed for your pool or spa at the guaranteed BEST PRICES. Pool merchants is the lowest prices on swimming pool, spa and automatic pool cleaners, equipment and supplies period. Not only do they guarantee the best prices but shipping is FREE to the continental USA. So, unless you're living in Hawaii or Alaska, you can't get these products anywhere for less. They still have the lowest prices day in and day out, plus their sales on top of that and links to manufacturers for additional money-saving coupons and rebates. Put it all together and it spells savings, savings and sometimes even more. The lineup of categories includes everything but the inground pool. Expect to find aboveground pools, alarms, alternative sanitizers, automatic pool cleaners, chemicals, chlorinators, chlorine generators, covers, electronic controls, filter cartridge replacements, filters, floats/lounges, fountains, heat siphon heat pumps, heaters, ladders, lighting, liners, maintenance equipment, motors, ozonators, pool and deck paint, pumps, sealants and epoxies, solar covers and reels, solar heating, test strips, toys and games and **SWIM WAYS RECREATIONAL PRODUCTS**. *Call toll-free: 888/430-4NET*

NV Price Lawn   **817/296-4428**

2015 Springcrest   By Appt. Only
Arlington, TX 76010

Now here's a novel idea. Name your own price for your lawn care needs. Obviously, if it's ridiculous, they won't consider; but if it's reasonable, they will, and you'll feel like you're in the driver's seat. Start saving. Get a group of your neighbors together and agree on a fair price, but lower than what you're paying now, and make them an offer. You'll never know what some guy would find acceptable. If they're young enough and hungry enough, you may have a deal of a lifetime. If this is just a clever marketing ploy, well, if they're not as good as what you've got going now, don't switch. But if they're good and will do it for less, perhaps they'll cut it low enough for you to seal the deal. We've not met them so we can't vouch for them; but you'll have to admit, it's very interesting!

★★★★ REC Warehouse   **972/509-9707**

700 Alma Rd., Suite 116   Mon-Fri 10-8; Sat 10-6; Sun Noon-5
Plano, TX 75075
www.recwarehouse.com

Head north to Plano for a plain ole source for recreational products like tanning beds, spas and above-ground pools. At the northeast corner of Plano Parkway and Alma, you can fill up your after-hours with recreational activities that are sure to relax, refresh or reduce the stress of everyday living. They guarantee the lowest prices on all LEISURE BAY products. No big deal since they are the only source for them and we couldn't compare the prices if we wanted to. But you have to give them credit where credit is due. They are one of the largest factory-direct retailers of above-ground pools, portable spas, billiard tables, tanning beds, gas grills and patio furniture in the U.S. so you can get some pretty decent deals. What they don't manufacture, they have made to their specifications. What started out in 1974 out of Buffalo, New York, two brothers (Don and Gary Doebler) founded RFW and have only looked forward since. For $99, you can just add water to an above ground, family-size SEA RAY pool. But, read the fine print. That is for installation only! The cheapest way to take a dip is around $699 up to $999. Swing to their other locations and see what you think: 6801 NE Loop in 820 North Richland Hills (817/498-4811) and at their newest store in Arlington, 4634 S. Cooper, 817/557-2011 with hours Mon-Sat 10-9, Sun 12-6. Looks like their Garland location on Belt Line bit the dust.

★★★★★★   Rustic Wall Tile & Stone   972/436-6194

Mon-Fri 8-5; Sat 8-4

511 Simmons Road
Lewisville, TX 75077-8238

 If you are looking to create a rustic look in your backyard, look no further than this open-to-the-public stone yard. No showroom, just the stones, ma'am, just stones (although your kidneys are not involved). If you want to decorate a kidney-shaped pool, that is a different story. Get to the bottom and dig your way to the top with stones and tile that would be of use in interior and exterior surfaces. Interior uses would be flooring, counters and backsplashes, fireplaces etc.; exterior uses would include landscaping, retaining walls, patios, walkways and outside fire pits. Oh, did I forget about utilizing the stones for building an outside fireplace, too? They can do it all, from helping you pick the right stones to making it happen, all at a very reasonable price. Get those spits ready to roast those marshmallows over an open firepit in your backyard. Every girl and boy scout troop should put in their reservations. Soon your backyard could be winning badges.

★★★★★★   Sid Parker Stone Co/Taylor Grass   817/281-9111

Mon-Fri 7:30-5:30; Sat 8-5

8225 Grapevine Hwy
North Richland Hills, TX 76182
www.sidparkerstone.com

 You can see the stone yard from Grapevine Highway (Hwy 26) in NRH. You've probably passed it a million times, but, then, you didn't have a need to shop for rocks. Now that you've figured on a million different projects that could use some, this is the place to get them. Call the above SOS (save on stones) if you need to build something that's rock solid. Flagstone, Colorado River Rock, ($126/ton), come and see the variety to be used for patios, walkways and steps, waterfalls, decorative boulders, edging and retaining walls. Don't worry about how much you need to do the job. They'll help you figure just how much you will need. No grass or nursery items here, but if you want delivery, tack on another $50. They also own Taylor Grass and Stone in Lewisville at 1120 Texas St., Old Town Lewisville, in Lewisville, TX 75057-4833, phone 972/436-7973. (See write up under Taylor Grass & Stone.) The website will really impress you if you didn't know there was a million variations on the theme of flagstone, ledgestone, building stones, boulders, cobblestones and gravel. Isn't it time to rock and roll out a weekend project and save money in the process? Playing the tune from "Rocky" will give you additional inspiration.

Spas Unlimited   972/317-3700

2999 N. Stemmons Frwy.   Tues-Sat 10-6; Sun Noon-4
Lewisville, TX 75067
www.spas-unlimited.com

 One spa-stop, that's all it takes to find an unlimited selection of everything you've ever
wanted but didn't know who to call if the subject is a pool or spa. Bingo! You've hit the
jackpot. They carry the AQUA SWIM spa - the one that you can do laps in within a 14-
foot, 19-foot or 21-foot configuration at about $1,000 per square foot. Just north of Garden Ridge
Road on Stemmons, they also carry **AQUA**, **COLEMAN SPAS**, **CATALINA SPAS**, **SPLASH**
SUPERPOOLS, that's if you want all the popular brand names. Get an ozonator to clear up your
spa and reduce your need for chemicals by 90 percent. Now, that's a savings in the long run, plus
it's better for your health and the environment, too. This decade-old veteran is a Texas-based contractor so he knows his stuff. Surround yourself with a solid mahogany deck, for the final finishing
touches. No accent is left unturned. The internet site, www.spas-unlimited, is an internet shopping
site for many spa retailers.

★★★   Splash Pools & Spas   817/590-0333

827 Airport Frwy.   Mon-Fri 10-6; Sat 9:30-5:30; Sun 1-5
Hurst, TX 76053

Splash round in one of their pools or spas, but expect cash to reign supreme here. The lowest-
priced model started at $4,000 and did a double gainer up to $9,000. Though financing is available, it's no cheap proposition. If you still want to bring the water to your backyard, take a splash
here. But what may be a better idea is to dry off in any of the more than 500 patio sets in stock.
What a selection: wrought iron, aluminum, resin—pick your pleasure. They promise a low price
guarantee, but not the lowest. Nevertheless, you certainly can count on them to deliver on their
promise. In business since 1951, they carry only top-of-the-line products, like **HOMECREST**,
RANDAL and **WINSTON**. Because they deal directly with the manufacturer, they can cut you
some slack—especially during clearance sales.

◆◆◆◆◆◆   Sundek Products/All Texas Decks   817/265-2406

805 Avenue H, Suite 509   By Appt. Only
Arlington, TX 76011
www.sundek.com

 Don't plunk down your hard earned money for just another boring driveway. If
you've want drive-up or drive-on appeal, why does it have to be bland? Instead, consider laying down a Sundek Product and you've got an improvement worth talking
about. In fact, Charlie Plunk and Steve Thomas want to help walk you through the transformation.
Transform your outdoor environment of gray concrete to a resurfaced walkway of beauty. Whether
it's for your pool deck or driveway, porch or patio, save the expense of tearing out the old concrete
and starting from scratch. Instead, all you need to do is Sundek it. It's cooler than regular concrete
and resistant to fading and staining, slipping and falling, even freezing and thawing. The product is
much more porous; hence, it can ultimately be impervious to nature's wrath. Just like a cracked
tub which can be resurfaced instead of replaced, your outside surfaces can be resurfaced, as well.
It not only adds an improved look but it also increases the overall value of your home. It's a concrete coating process that offers a vast array of colors, patterns and textures so the designer in you
can really have a heyday. They've been in business for 30 years and will stand behind their product and labor. The versatility is astounding, from classic Texas looks to a masonry effect, a weath-

ered surface to a sunburst, aggregate to scored concrete, it's all in the making. Go online and check out their photo gallery, if you need more convincing. The special effects are spectacular.

★★★★★   Superior Forest Products   972/539-6948

1000 Spinks Drive
Flower Mound, TX 75028

Mon-Fri 8-5

Formerly Decksource, this is now a subsidiary of Superior Forest Products providing homeowners with an opportunity to deck out their backyards at the price of what the contractors pay. If you want to build your own deck, they will help you design it and install it at their store or over the phone, and sell you all the ingredients at 10 percent less than the competition. Woodn't that be loverly? And why not? What you get delivered to your back yard is pressure-treated cedar, CHOICE DEK, pine, redwood or TREX, at no charge for delivery (unless you are building a lanai in Costa Rica.) If you'd rather just save on the materials and have someone else build it for you, they have several reliable deck hands they will recommend. Remember, you're just ordering the supplies here. These guys are not one to lend a helping hand.

★★★★★★   Taylor Grass & Decorative Stone   972/436-7973

1120 Texas St , Suite A
Lewisville, TX 75057
www.taylorgrassandstone.com

Mon-Sat 9-6

 If I've heard it once, I've heard it a million times. Where can I get landscape stones and rocks? Well, rock on over to Taylor's and get stoned. It'll cost you, though, a $50 delivery fee plus your materials, but at least you're not the one driving! In fact, it's quite simple. Measure out what it is that you'd like to lay down: flagstone, building stone, decorative gravel, boulders, sandstone, limestone, lava rock or ledge stones and they'll tell you how much you'll need to get the job done. And if you're looking for grass (the legal kind, silly), the popular ones are described in detail, so you know what you're getting and what to expect, once it arrives. Choose Bermuda, 419 Tifway, St. Augustine, Buffalo, Fescue and Zoysia. And, too, they're open to special orders. Their website walks you through the sod installation, if you choose to do-it-yourself. Sod is sold by the square yard. Measure your lawn area (length x width = square foot, divide by nine = square yards) to determine the amount of sod you will need. (Example: 12'x 24'= 288 feet (288 divided by 9 = 32 square yards of sod needed.) But, if you're a clod, you might want to reconsider calling in the landscaping troops. Remember, this is also a sibling to Sid Parker Stone, so you'll have your choice of either or. (See write-up elsewhere in this Chapter.)

★★★★   Texas Greenhouse Co.   817/335-5447

812 E. Northside Drive
Fort Worth, TX 76102
www.texasgreenhouse.com

Mon-Fri 8-5; Sat 10-2

Growing since 1948, you can stay in the pink with the greenhouses here. Manufacturing their own greenhouses and accessories, expect prices to be factory-direct. Don't be a hot-head, either. If you really want to build your own and save a lot of green, go with a Texas Greenhouse kit, plain and simple. Let your plants get steamed, not you. Carrying a full line of accessories including heating, cooling, ventilation, misting and watering systems, shaders, timers, controls, benches, shelves and hundreds of other items to enable your green thumb to not turn black and blue, choose your style and you're on your way. Styles include free-standing, lean-to, bay window and outdoor fog systems. They'll even help novices find the right style to suit their space and needs. But don't expect them to make house calls. They also carry other brands beside their own including MODINE heaters and **CHAMPION** coolers. Prices are extremely competitive and most orders are delivered in six to eight weeks with a one-year guarantee. Also, take note: If you return it because of indecision on your part, you'll be paying a 15 percent restocking charge. A 50 percent deposit is required upon ordering and balance is due upon delivery. Call, write or order online for their catalog. *Call toll-free: 800/227-5447*

◆◆◆◆◆◆ Texas Lawn & Landscape   866/818-3459
Dallas, TX   By Appt. Only

When you're mow-tivated to have your lawns mowed, edged, weeded and maintained on a regular basis, here's one company that is rooted throughout the Metroplex. That means their trucks can service your yard regardless of your metro location. When I tell you the price quote we got, $26 for mowing, edging and clean-up on front and back yards, you will wonder how fast you can sign them up. This complete landscape, design and installation company is a one-stop shop. Most lawns cost $20-$35 (includes mowing, edging and blowing). Not bad, for a cut and curl. They can do it all including full-service maintenance anywhere in the Metro area including tree service, weed and insect control, fertilization, sprinkler systems, drainage, sodding (see Taylor Grass's write-up for sod), outdoor lighting, fence installation and repair. This is the company to call for either residential or commercial assignments. And around holiday time, don't hesitate to call upon them for your Christmas lights. (My yard is limited to a few lights for the Chanukah bush so they wouldn't have to do much for me.)

★★★ Texas Patios   817/831-2266
5742 Airport Frwy.   Mon-Fri 9-7; Sat 9-5;30; Sun Noon-5
Haltom City, TX 76117
www.texaspatios.com

Between Haltom Road and Carson on Highway 121, guess what I found? That's right. A perfectly pleasing patio set on my way to City Mattress. Exit Haltom Road and circle back on the service road, and low and behold, this two-story behemoth sits overlooking the Fort Worth skyline. I hate to name-drop but with all of the star-studded sets to extol, here goes: **DAYVA, HATTERAS HAMMOCKS, HOMECREST, KETTLE, LANE VENTURE, TELESCOPE CASUAL, TROPITONE** and **WOODSTOCK CHIMES** while winding through the myriad of patio sets and patio accessories on display. We sought out the water fountains, waterfalls, even the black fiberglass lines to add to a kidney-shaped fish or lily pond, but it took us forever to decide—koi or joy? We finally went with koi. Frankly, this 30,000-square-foot showplace is a landmark for many Tarrant County old-timers. If you care enough to sit on the very best, you might as well buy it here, for less. Exclusive lines such as **BROWN JORDAN, TROPITONE** and others made us ready for some R & R. But instead, we started digging our koi pond. You, too, can reel in similar opportunities at their second location, 6080 S. Hulen St. in Fort Worth, one mile south of Hulen Mall, 817/292-7599.

★★★★★ Texas Stone & Tile Inc.   214/358-4698
2683 Lombardy Lane   By Appt. Only
Dallas, TX 75354-0755
www.texasstone.com

You know most manufacturers, distributors, wholesalers and such are straddling the fence between their traditional customer base and YOU. But slowly and surely, YOU are becoming more and more popular as the way to survive in tight economic times. That is why so many formerly, "only open to the trade," builders, contractors, designers and manufacturers have been closed to the general public; that is, until now. This company provides top-quality natural stone, cast stone, brick, ceramic, quarry and paver tiles that make for exquisite flooring materials for us Material Girls. The structure of the company is multi-faceted but runs the gamut from small to large, commercial to residential, decorators to individual home owners. Expect marble, granite, limestone and other natural stone products to be the material of choice and their installers know which works best and where it should go based on the material used, structural concerns, attachment methods, etc. These are all important considerations. That's why you need to shop with the pros!

★★★★★ Vita Spa Factory Outlet   817/226-7727

2542-C E. Abram St.   Mon-Sat 10-6; Sun 1-5
Arlington, TX 76011
www.vitaspa.com

We softened our appraisal of them being a smacked mackerel last year to one of being more like a catfish this year. A few whiskers still tickled our thoughts of their hard-sales approach but, some-how, this 27-year old company greeted us this year with greater warmth and no sales pressure. Hurray! They must have read their write-up in last year's book and taken a few notes. So, let's move on to bigger and better reports. All of their spas come with a 25-year warranty and a lifetime structural warranty. We saw well over 100 to choose from in a price range from as low as $1,000-$6,000. All spas were user-friendly with top-loading filters and since they use silver and zinc, there's no need for chlorine. Then to make you even more relaxed, they offered aromatherapy scents to add a lot more punch to your spa experience. To make you jump in with both feet, though, let's talk price. Yes, their pricing can't be beat and it includes the spa, delivery, cover, chemicals and redwood steps. Now get this: They also include beverage holders, Euro-tech han-dles and a filter cover that converts to an ice bucket. Spas started at just over $1,000 but can esca-late to as much as $6,000—which are at the lower end of the spectrum of spas in general.

★★★★ Wooden Swing Co./Children's Furniture 972/386-6280

13617 Inwood Rd.   Mon, Tues, Wed, Fri 9-5; Thurs 9-7; Sat 10-6
Dallas, TX 75244
www.woodenswing.com

For the active tykes, get a tree house in the August moon. Imagine keeping them up a tree, without costing a fortune. Just think what a pool costs? Sleep-a-way camp? A trip to Grandma's? For a fraction of the price, build them a vacation retreat in the backyard and keep them looking up. Or keep them occupied indoors with lots of space-saving bedroom suites such as modular bedrooms that grow with them through their teen years and beyond. What kid wouldn't have dreams of sug-arplums when sleeping in a bunk bed, complete with a slide or canopy, trundle beds, captains beds, or in an imaginative hand-cut twin bed? Then, add in all the matching furniture and accessories to complete their sweet dreams. Lots of styles, from big to bigger, to keep them out of your hair and having fun in the sun. **BRIO** toy railroads are always 10 percent off suggested retail. Since 1978, this company has been building their business while building their market share selling market samples of children's furniture, taking over about half the store. Children's furniture was definitely a void in the marketplace and, often, at the lowest prices in town. Novelty beds will bring a smile, from racecars to bunk beds. And of course, outdoors, they can be swingers in wooden swing sets, or on the lookout inside the fort. Imagination and safety's always tantamount in their strategy.

◆◆◆◆◆◆ Wylie Plastering, Inc.   972/442-0017

110 Regency Drive   By Appt. Only
Wylie, TX 75098
www.wylieplastering.com

Looking to renovate your pool? Then call on the experts who have been getting plastered since 1978. They are specialists in complete pool renovations, not just minor repairs. Being the largest DFW contractor of pools, you are getting the power behind the experience. Family-owned and operated, if you need replastering, retiling or recoping, these are the guys to call. You'll save money because you are eliminating the middleman and going direct to the subcontractor that the designers would call upon to do the job in the first place. They are board members of the National Plasterer Council and offer a separate office for Tarrant County called Flower Mound Plastering. Either area, you'll have your pool fixed without a hitch—in other words, covered by the best for less. *Call toll-free: 800/677-7228*

★★★★★★ Yard Art Patio & Fireplace   817/421-2414

6407 Colleyville Blvd. (Hwy 26)   Mon-Sat 10-6; Sun 12-5
Colleyville, TX 76034-6279
www.myyardart.com

I think that I shall never see a yard as lovely as a one from thee. Yard Art Patio & Fireplace has it all made in the shade. If you're seeking chic furniture for the patio, the gazebo, the outdoor bar but don't know where to shop, here's a place to start and finish in the same stop. Combining comfort, durability as well as good looks makes for a winning combination. Their solid wood furniture utilizes only Number 1 Grade or better Southern Yellow Pine that is CCA pressure-treated. After that treatment, the wood is thoroughly dried, surfaces are planed to a super smooth finish and edges are rounded for safety. Since 1994, this spacious showroom has been overflowing with patio furniture with as many as 15 different manufacturers represented at any one time. KINGSLEY-BATE, LANE VENTURE, OUTDOOR LIFESTYLES, TROPITONE and WINSTON are just some of their star performers. They are so confident you'll love their furniture, they back it by what they call their exclusive "Platinum Promise." Too, they guarantee the lowest prices. Their second location is at 3500 Preston at Parker, Plano, 972/769-0093. Make their Yard Art Patio & Fireplace, your Yard Art Patio & Fireplace.

★★★★★ Yard Ideas   817/379-5644

136 N. Main St.   Mon-Sat 10:30-5:30
Keller, TX 76248

This husband-and-wife team had a better idea. In fact, they had plenty of ideas, so they decided to make their own yard art and go from there. Located on the Main Street drag in Keller (the old Hwy. U. S. 377), you'll find a home for small statues starting at around $25 all the way to giant garden varieties for $225. Yard Ideas offer mostly rounded models; very few square ones will fit nicely into backyard corners. You can lust after their massive yard display as you drive down Main Street and marvel at their ingenuity. Prices are so low, a shopper said even when she was in the nursery business herself, she couldn't find wholesale containers or fountains priced as low as these. Furnish your entire back yard with concrete bird baths, benches, tables, decorative animals, bird-houses, children's tables and both white and terra-cotta pottery. Save at least 20 to 40 percent on statuary, fountains and concrete patio sets and you will never have to tiptoe through the garden again. Most everything is displayed outside, so what you see is what you can buy.

Shoes

★★★★★ **DSW (Designer Shoe Warehouse)** **972/233-9931**

13548 Preston Rd. Mon-Sat 10-9; Sun Noon-6
Dallas, TX 75240
www.dswshoe.com

Joining the movement north, DSW (Discount Shoe Warehouse) has entered the fray in Frisco and now boasts two stores on Preston Road, the newest being the one at 3333 Preston Rd., north of Stonebriar Centre at Hwy. 121 and Preston, 972/668-4510, Mon-Sat 10-9; Sun 11-7. Ladies and gents can slip into either one of their other Metroplex locations and be shod to the nines (though their sizes go from 5 to 12 for women and 7 to 15 in men's). If you're "shoesy," then only the best will do. Guys line up in **BALLY, FLORSHEIM, NUNN BUSH** and **STANLEY BLACKER** for starters and gals slip out in **AIGNER, AMERICAN EAGLE, ANNE KLEIN, BASS, COLE HAAN, DEXTER, ENZO, EVAN PICONE, HUSH PUPPIES, LIZ CLAIBORNE, NINE WEST, SELBY, VIA SPIGA, ZODIAC** and more including the coveted **DOC MARTENS** for both men or women. Over 36,000 pairs to choose from in 900 different styles. Their "Reward Your Style" frequent shoppers' program gives you $25 off for every $250 spent and that's another good reason to shop. This division of billion-dollar off-price Value City Department store (headquartered in Columbus, OH), has lots of stores nationwide; and multiple stores to try on in the Metroplex where everything's 20 to 50 percent off department store prices. Also, you can bag discounts on handbags, totes and hosiery. It looks like their lower price/clearance location called Crown Shoe Warehouse has been de-feeted and closed its doors. *Call toll-free: 800/477-8595*

★★★ **Famous Footwear** **817/732-8491**

Overton Park Shopping Center Mon-Sat 10-9; Sun Noon-6
4656 SW Loop 820. Hulen Fort Worth, TX 76109
www.famousfootwear.com

Want to be one of the "shoe-sen" few who have met their sole mate? Then slip into a Famous Footwear and see if you're a match. This power chain (with over 900 locations nationwide) is famous for brand name shoes for the entire family. Save 20 to 40 percent across the platform, be it athletic, dress, casual, boots or slippers. From hiking to slippers, sandals to accessories, name your favorite: **ADIDAS, ASICS, AVIA, BASS, BUSTER BROWN, CARLOS FALCHI, CATERPILLAR, CLARKS, CONNIES, CONVERSE, DEXTER, DOCKERS, DUCKHEAD, EASY SPIRIT, ESPRIT, ETONIC, FILA, KEDS, FLORSHEIM, FOOTJOY, FREEMAN, GOOD TWO SHOES, HUSH PUPPIES,** KEDS, **LIFESTRIDE, MAINE, NATURALIZER, NEW BALANCE, NIKE, NUNN BUSH, PUMA, REEBOK, ROCKPORT, SAUCONY, SEBAGO, SKECHERS, SPERRY,**

STACY ADAMS, TIMBERLAND, VANELI, WEEBOK, WESTIES, WOLVERINE and more. Full size ranges in both mediums, wides and narrows, well, pretty slim in narrows, sorry to report. Watch newspapers for additional savings when coupons appear. Online shopping's a breeze, even if it's just for a new pair of slippers. Check directory for location nearest you. Their outlet store is still located in the Fort Worth Outlet Mall downtown, but since there are only four stores left in the mall at the time of our research, their future is uncertain. *Call toll-free: 800/40FAMOUS*

★★★★ Fossee's   214/368-1534

600 Preston Forest Shopping Center   Mon-Sat 10-6; Sun 1-5
Dallas, TX 75230
www.fossees.com

Fossee's has gone to not just kicking up their heels with shoes but also with novelty bags such as the MAY FRANCIS collection which is darling, all embellished to the hilt. They alone give reason to acknowledging that you're a bag lady! They are now carrying lots of fashion jewelry such as turquoise necklaces, earrings and custom bracelets for every occasion. Here is where to buy designer shoes and unique accessories for any star-studded opening. Home to sizes 4 through 12 with a particular bent in the long and narrow department. Shoes are discounted here, especially dramatic during sales! Generally, across the arch, savings averaged 20 to 60 percent during sales. Unfortunately, accessories were paired at close to retail. Nonetheless, it's hard to "stop" with just one, especially when you see so many of the high-end designer brands beckoning. Here are some of the stars that take a bow: AEROSOLES, AMALFI, ANDRE ASSESS, ANNE KLEIN, BANDOLINO, CALVIN KLEIN, CHARLES JOURDAN, COLE HAAN, DONALD PLINER, EVAN PICONE, FERRAGAMO, I. MILLER, J. RENEE, LIZ CLAIBORNE, MR. SEYMOUR, PREVATA, SESTO MEUCCI, RANGONI, STUART WEITZMAN, UNISA, VANELI, VIA SPIGA and YSL. Slip into their second location closer to Plano at 19009 Preston Rd., (972/380-0992).

◆◆◆◆◆ Mehl's Shoeland   817/924-9681

2900 S. Hulen St.   Mon-Sat 10-5:30
Fort Worth, TX 76109

Call before you go because they had a terrible fire just as we went to press. Hope everything is fine. Myer Mehl opened this Shoeland in 1950 and from day one, solved many a foot problem. In his particular land of plenty, you'll find names like CLARKS, EASTLAND, HUSH PUPPIES, KEDS, MUNRO, NATURALIZER, NEW BALANCE, REIKER, SPERRY, STRIDE RITE and TROTTERS. Well, that's just the start of it. Women can finally find a full size range, from Cinderella's size 4s to big and tall size 12s. At last, gals with a lot of leg room don't have to get blisters squeezing into too-tight shoes. Widths are offered in S, N, M, W and WW. And, too, footwear here can accommodate inserts and orthotics (the prosthetic for your feet.) Mehl's offers a FREE shoe clinic with a certified orthotist on the last Monday of each month. Rest assured, even kids can be sized up. Website went by way of the button down shoes.

★★★ Off Price Shoes   214/327-1150

410 Big Town Mall   Mon-Sat 10-7:15; Sun Noon-5:15
Mesquite, TX 75149

With new hours and a new location for their Dallas store, expect everything to be the same ole, same ole. Conversation here is still a hit and a miss - mostly a miss. Nary a word was spoken, but we were able to manage a few sporadic bursts such as—"Yea!" Still, you can be off (price) and running in women's shoes for $9.99. Occasionally, they were even lower....like $6.99. Men, too, have plenty to choose in sizes 6 1/2 to size 13 (and a few 14's) with prices tagged $14.99. Now, how can you lose, unless you snooze? Choose sandals, canvas slip-ons, boots, dressy and casual, lace-ups, tasteful, professional and perfect for that lost sole you've been searching for. Locations include Wynnewood Village Shopping Center in Dallas, Montfort at Preston in Dallas and Six Flags Mall on East Division Street in Arlington.

★★ Payless ShoeSource   817/460-4714

1071 N. Collins St.   Mon-Fri 10-9; Sat 9-9; Sun 11-6
Arlington, TX 76011-6133
www.payless.com

You may not consider Payless Shoes as some little secret that you haven't heard about before, but maybe their baby program is one that will catch you by surprise. It's the baby's first shoes pay-ola. Bring in your little one when you think it's time to move their feet from under their jammies to their first pair of shoes, fill out a registration card and choose from a little pair of white, pink or blue canvas sneakers for FREE. Okay, so they don't stay on, but they're so cute. This nice gesture surely will endear you to Payless, where you do pay less for lots of shoes for the entire family. Being the biggest and offering some of the best values for your money means you can slip into a pair and not have to take out a second mortgage. A Star is born? (Do you believe Star Jones really shops at Payless?) Check out their website and read about FREE shipping and handling for online purchases when picked up at any of their stores nationwide. Payless ShoeSource is your source for inexpensive shoes that are indeed fashionable. I would consider Payless to be like knockoffs. Find a style that's in-style and copy it for less. That's how you can Pay Less. Check directory for the location nearest you.

★★★★ Rack Room Shoes   214/327-3663

Casa Linda Plaza, Suite 294   Mon-Sat 10-9; Sun Noon-6
Dallas, TX 75218
www.rackroomshoes.com

Rack up the savings at this power player. Get a toe-up with this ten-store shoe store chain—your link to a store that had its start in 1920 with 12 stores. In 1984, they were acquired by a European family and now can boast 330 stores and are now the largest privately-owned shoe retailer in the world. So, what are you waiting for? This powerhouse is walking all over the competitors with number of stores and certainly establishing their footprint onto the Metroplex pavement. So why not rack up savings every step of the way? Choose from more than 17,000 pairs in each store's inventory at discounts from 15 to 50 percent in brands such as ADIDAS, AIRWALK, BONGO, CANDIES, CAPEZIO, CHILIS, DEXTER, EASTLAND, ESPRIT, FLORSHEIM, GAROLINA, IMP, MIA, MOOTSIES TOOTSIES, MUSHROOMS, NEW BALANCE, NICOLE, 9 & CO., OSHKOSH B'GOSH, ROCKPORT, SKECHERS, TIMBERLAND, WEEBOK, WHITE MOUN-TAIN and more. Rack after rack, don't get your back up against the wall, even if you're a redneck Mother. They sell shoes for men, women and children with their slogan being, "The Big Brands! The Big Savings!" Online, download coupons (though at our last visit, there were none being offered) and see what specials are in-store. Check site for the location nearest you: Grapevine Mills, Cedar Hill, Irving, North East Mall, Southlake, McKinney, Rockwall, Dallas and Arlington.

★★   SAS Factory Shoe Store   972/296-6185

3643 W. Camp Wisdom Rd.   Mon-Sat 10-6
Dallas, TX 75237

Some women swear by these shoes. Some women just swear AT these shoes. Did you know that
SAS stands for San Antonio Shoes and these are their direct-to-retail stores? If you are interested
in comfort, these shoes were made for standing, walking, strolling down the River Walk or wandering through the new American Airlines Center. Most professionals who are on their feet all
day—beauticians, medical personnel, retailers, warehouse workers, young mothers—as long as
you're not wanting to be considered a fashion plate because in reality, you're a work horse, these
shoes are for you. Ugly, but comfortable. The only place you're able to get a deal on them, though,
is in San Antonio, at their outlet. Otherwise, you'll have to hold your breath for their sales. Don't
expect to order online, either; that service has been discontinued. Sizes 4 to 12 in women's sizes,
in the $40 to $50 range and men's sizes 6 to 15. Check directory for other retail locations including
one in Fort Worth where walking with ease is their claim to fame.

★★★   Shoe Cents   972/668-4350

3333 Preston Road, #401   Mon-Sat 10-9; Sun Noon-6
Frisco, TX 75034
www.shoecents.com

One store left....but all's right at their Preston Road location that sells both men's and women's
shoes. (More stores in Houston.) If you're Cents-bile about your shoes, take the walk test and step
into a pair from here. At the northeast corner of Preston and Park (next to Ulta), load up on lipsticks and loafers, you never have enough, right? Department store brands at discounted prices
include: AIGNER, BASS, CALICO, CLARKS, ESPRIT, HUSH PUPPIES, IMPO, KEDS,
LIFESTRIDE, MUSHROOMS, NATURALIZERS, NICOLE, NINE WEST, RED CROSS, REE-
BOKS, SAM & LIBBY, SRO, WESTIES and more—your basic standard fare, but solidly built to
last. Pick your pair—from dressy to casual, career to play—if it's shoes, they've got you covered
from 20 to 40 percent off. Go online for the latest sales such as select women's athletic shoes for
$10 and thousands of spring styles that were out the door for $19.99, if you ever took time to count
how many's in store, you might hit as many as 14,000 pairs on any one given day, in any one location, priced under $25. They even have extra small and extra large sizes (to size 11 in pumps, loaf-
ers and casual leather shoes.) Is it any wonder why I recommended you hook up with Closets by
Design to build an extra shoe rack to accommodate all of your shoe purchases?

★★★   Shoe Fair   214/631-7463

1320 Inwood   Mon-Sat 10-5:30; Thurs 10-6:30
Inwood Outlet Center
Dallas, TX 75247

If the shoe fits, you'll find these to be priced at more than fair prices. Savings on men's and
women's shoes soar to 60 percent off, but generally 20 percent will be represented everyday.
Career, casual and special occasion footwear for both men and women are their stock and sock(s).
Names to celebrate include AMALFI, BANDOLINO, CALICO, ENZO, DEXTER, EVAN-
PICONE, G. BRUTIN, J. RENEE, MARGARET JERROLD, MR. SEYMOUR, PROXY, STACY
ADAMS and more. And one of their best features, ladies, is they go to size 12W. Find them tucked
into the corner next to Bedroom Solutions. What a great duo. All you have to do is kick them off
and fall into bed after a night out on the town. (Find a strapless gown for $19.99 at 7th Ave. across

the street.) Kick up your dancing shoes with plenty of glitz to take you to the Ritz. You'll still have money left over to tip the limo driver and call it a night!

★★★★★★   **Vantage Shoe Warehouse**   **214/678-9967**
2222 Vantage St.   Mon-Sat 10-8; Sun Noon-6
Dallas, TX 75207
www.handmadeinitaly.com

  This is it! Each Vantage Shoe Warehouse has different hours but the same best-shoes-for-the-lowest price day in and day out, hand's down. Good to the last buck. How they do it is anybody's guess, but they will go down in history as writing the saga on CHEAP FEET. Women (and men, too) within a 500 mile radius surely have slipped into a pair or two from here over the years. My shoe wardrobe numbers in the hundreds, maybe thousands since the early 1970s when I bought my first pair of STUART WEITZMAN shoes for a song (and then I went dancing!) Vantage is THE best place to shop for the best shoes at THE best prices. Period. They win hands down and feet first. Brand names include: ANNE KLEIN, ENRO, ENZO, DONALD PLINER, FERRAGAMO, J. RENEE, MARGARET JERROLD, NATURALIZER, STUART WEITZMAN, VANELI, ZALO—for starters? Then, make sure your man can keep up appearances, too. Men can shop for BASS, BOSTONIAN, FLORSHEIM, ROCKPORT, SEBAGO, ROCKPORT and more. But the selection is miniscule compared to the women's. At the Preston store, there's a smattering of women's fashions, handbags, jewelry, too. Their promotional offerings are legendary. Leave it to the Glickman's to institute a 2 for 1 sale; a 3 for 1 sale; everything's $19.99 in the store; everything's $6.99 on a select half of the store. You never know what they're going to do but Liz Taylor, I know, is a big fan of Vantage Shoes. We even wear the same size, six. Fancy that! (So does Tammy Faye, another fan.)

Sporting Goods

★★★★ **Academy Sports & Outdoors**   817/346-6622

6101 W. I-20   Mon-Sat 9-9; Sun 10-7
Fort Worth, TX 76109
www.academy.com

This super-duper sports chain offers an academic lesson in saving money. Since 1938, when Max Gochman opened the first Academy Tire Shop in San Antonio, he began selling military surplus and called the business Academy Super Surplus. He expanded to four stores in Austin. In 1973, his son Arthur began opening similar stores in Houston and the rest is history. Now selling sporting goods and outdoor items, Academy is one of the biggest sporting goods discounters in the Southwest and exploding on to the Southeast scene with over 50 stores in seven states. The selection is broad enough to satiate most sports'enthusiasts with equipment, apparel and footwear at everyday low prices. Combining low prices with a large selection, Academy Sports & Outdoors has the highest sales per store and highest sales per square foot of any sporting goods retailer in the country with a consistent 25 percent sales growth for the past ten years. Whether it's golfing, fishing, skiing, or hiking, why not get in gear for less? *Call toll-free: 877/999-9856*

★★ **Alpine Range Supply Co.**   817/572-1242

5482 Shelby Rd.   Mon-Sun 8-6
Fort Worth, TX 76140

Shoot 'em up and get to the point. This is where they shoot straight from the hip to save you a few shell-kels. From $4-$13, you can get on the shooting range, but to hit the short range, it'll cost you $7.50 per person. Go skeet shooting with 25 shots for $4 and table pillars are $13 for 135 birds. Watch for the new and improved archery range. Don't know how much it'll be yet (it was $7.50 per person before), but they have upgraded and added a lot more stuff, so you'll have to see it before you hit the bullseye. Alpine Range Supply is a full-range gun store with a gunsmith on the premises and mounting on the spot. Even clothing and over 20 gun safes are in stock. Talk about a full-service operation. Shoot 'em, then stuff 'em with their in-house taxidermist. For hunters alone, buy all the reloading equipment you will ever need including primers, casings, presses for pistols, and the "how-to" books to ensure you're doing it right. Save about 10 percent and more during sales on all the better brands in rifles and pistols: **BROWNING**, **COLT**, **MAGNUM**, **REMINGTON** and **WINCHESTER** are all aimed to please. If they don't have it, they'll get it, assuming it's legal. Practice with what you buy on any of their four pistol ranges, a rifle range, three skeet fields, a trap field, five-stand sporting clays as well as an archery range. Ready? Aim? But don't fire 'til you see the whites of their eyes, or their hankerchiefs, whichever comes first.

◆◆◆◆ Aquatic Academy at Cooper Fitness Center 214/692-8888

12100 Preston Rd.
Dallas, TX 75230-2222

Hours vary after Memorial Day

Let them jump in with both feet and learn how to get into the swim of things. Reduce your anxiety over having your kids around water. Teaching them to swim gives them confidence, too. It doesn't have to be sink or swim for your little fishies. The earlier they learn, the better for their safety and your peace of mind. The Cooper Clinic offers swimming instruction for children of all ages and at all different levels—up to competitive events often taught by Olympic Gold Medallists such as Jerry Heidenreich. Jump into the pool at The Aerobics Center (Preston Road just north of Forest) and learn to avoid swimming with the sharks. Classes start after Memorial Day. Call and leave your name and address, information will be mailed out to you. Prices were $135 for a two-week course and $35 for a half hour for private lessons when last we checked, but don't hold us to it. They could have gone up on their prices or....taken a nose dive!

★★ Army Store, The 817/531-1641

2466 E. Lancaster Ave.
Fort Worth, TX 76013

Mon-Sat 9-6

You're in the Army now—but not for real. Camouflage your latest trek into the woods with all the appropriate gear. Lots of camo apparel including pants, short- and long-sleeve shirts, thermals, coats, field jackets, hats and more. Even boots and cold weather gear like heat packs should keep those tootsies warm and toasty. So, if you'd like to replicate the fashions of F-Troop, hit the bunkers with bargain apparel. But beware, you'll not be armed to engage in much more than looking the part. Though there was some camping equipment, like backpacks, duffel bags and a few hammocks, the savings are hardly enough to stay out in the woods for longer than a day or so. With their lack of cooking utensils and camping gear, you're likely to starve to death, too. Though you may not get armed for survival here, chances are, you won't be naked!

★★★★★ Athletic Warehouse 972/219-0073

1780 N. Stemmons Frwy. East
Lewisville, TX 75067
www.athleticwarehouse.com

Mon-Fri 10-7; Sat 9-6

The Athletic Warehouse finally has hit a home run. Shop in person from their catalog, or now online. You can strike while the game's still hot: Bats, balls and gloves by ATEC, DIAMOND, EASTON, LOUISVILLE SLUGGER, MARKWORT, MIZUNO, RAWLINGS, SSK, WILSON. Actually, you can shop here for shoes and accessories for any major sporting event. Be a baseball fashion plate and a slide into home base with T-shirts. Or don any of the related baseball fashion jackets and jerseys by all of the place plus NIKE. Whether it's padding, bats, balls or any of the other accoutrements to play the game, you can find children's and youth sizes all at one playing field. Older kids and their dads are not in their game plan, though. Ordering from their outlet store online is a new feature. (Even if you type in their new website URL, www.athleticware-house.com), you will get to their old URL, www.baseballwarehouse.com) so you don't have to learn much to get to the bottom of it all. www.athleticwarehouse.com. Weekly specials and all their new products are showcased on their website alongside all of the favorite standbys. *Call toll-free: 800/435-6485*

Ball Billiards Ltd.   **972/424-4533**

1305 Summit Ave, Suite 10   Mon-Fri 7-4:30; Sat 9-3:30
Plano, TX 75074

 You might as well rise to the summit and get out from behind the eight-ball. Arthur
Ball is the owner of this custom-billiards business. In business for eight years, looks
like eight is his lucky number. Don't expect him to ever pressure you into buying a
table; he probably won't even ask you to buy one. Simply stop by, he'll give you a tour and
explain how all his custom tables are made, and then tell you to have a nice day. But if you're in
the market for a billiard table, you probably will place your order here if you want to cue up with a
custom pool table starting at $2,395. Now we're talking custom-made, complete with delivery and
set-up. Take your pick of felt and pocket colors as well as four cue sticks and cue rack, a slate top,
oak or mahogany wood, **BELGIUM ARIMUS** balls and chalk, too. No assembly-line here; each
table is hand-made and carefully crafted. Even an exotic African mahogany table with six legs is
within the realm of possibility. Have you priced ready-mades lately? This is their *only* business
and unless your name's Minnesota Fats, there's none better in the Metroplex. Exit Plano Parkway
off Central, go east to Avenue K, turn left and take the first right, which is Summit. They shoot
straight but don't expect a big sign on their door, as they like to keep a low profile. Except during
Christmas, they can produce a custom table in about two weeks. Order before Thanksgiving to be
guaranteed delivery in time for the holidays. All tables come with a lifetime guarantee and are
totally handmade. Do you think their name had anything to do with their ultimate life's work?

Bass Pro Shops/Outdoor World   **972/724-2018**

Grapevine Mills   Mon-Sat 9-10; Sun 10-7
2501 Bass Pro Drive Grapevine, TX 76051
www.outdoorworld.com

 Without a doubt, the design, style and ambience of Outdoor World will make a visit
here worthwhile, even if all you want to do is walk through. Stop complaining that Dallas has nothing to show off when visitors come and want to see something besides the
Kennedy Museum. The Bass Pro Shop is a world all its own. The store includes areas for boats
and boating/watersport accessories, camping, hiking, fishing, hunting, bowhunting, golf, footwear,
general outdoor clothing, specialty clothing and more. Located in the center of the Dallas/Fort
Worth Metroplex, Bass Pro Shop Outdoor World is convenient to get to and is surrounded by
other great attractions, dining and lodging. *Call toll-free: 800/BASS-PRO*

★ Bicycle Exchange   **972/270-9269**

3330 Galloway, Suite 170   Mon-Fri 9-7; Sat 9-5
Mesquite, TX 75228
www.bicycleexchangedallas.com

Now under new ownership, you can wheel and deal but prices in this store are pretty much retail in
my book. If, however, you say "you saw them on their website above," you can expect a five percent discount. If you'd like to skateboard, you can now shop here for all of your wheelies but
expect only an exclusive line of them. Mostly new bikes (with an occasional used one) available
here but if you're looking for expertise, they boast over 60 years of combined experience. If
you're looking for great prices, turn left at the door. They carry these bike lines: **DIAMOND
BACK, FREE AGENT, HARO, KHS, MASSI, MONGOSS PRO, REDLINE, SCHWINN, TREK**
and others. Sorry, Charlie, we only tout the best. *Call toll-free: 800/583-7269*

★★★★★★ Billiards & Barstools   817/355-1355

1803 W. Airport Frwy.   Mon-Fri 10-7; Sat 10-5; Sun 12-5
Euless, TX 76040
www.babstools.com

This power player has cued up and placed five locations in the Metroplex for your gaming pleasure (and most recently added dinettes to the metro mix!) Pool tables, for sure, started at $1,395 and included delivery and set up. Choose from over 31 cloth covers and not pay extra for the option of choice, doesn't that rope you in? Financing with approved credit is a plus, since this hobby doesn't come cheap. The selection here is probably the best around with at least 50 pool tables and over 200 bar stools in stock. Too, they offer an in-home service for anyone wanting decorating advice for accessories. Check directory assistance for other locations in Richardson, Lewisville, Frisco and Arlington. And on occasion, watch for their outlet center's warehouse weekend sales where you'll save an additional 30-70 percent off of their pool tables, accessories, custom bars that have not met the mark, game tables, foosball, hockey, assorted cinema chairs, electronic games and closeout dinette sets. First come, first served. That warehouse location is 1702 Vantage Drive in Carrollton, 972/418-8921. At least at this B & B, you won't be caught behind the 8 ball!

Brass Register, The   972/231-1386

Richardson, TX 75080   Mon-Sat 9-5:30
www.brassregister.com   🖰 *Top Online Store!*

Hop online to see a few of the highlights of the store, but don't expect to shop on their website, yet. Well it looks like you missed it. Now you'll only want to make a pit stop because they are no longer doing anything like they did. No more mini-diner counters or jukeboxes. Forget turning back the clocks to rock around The Brass Register. When you click on their website, you'll see that all that has gone and what they started as a side-line business has grown into a full-time gig. That's right. For a fun ride, they are now in the Extreme Scooter business online. Call or shop online, either way, if you have an need for speed (or is it greed?), you can shop her for extreme toys like the GO-QUAD or a VIZA land machine. Go-Carts start at $670 and we're not talking a drop in the bucket. Of course, these could be a handy-dandy transport for getting around the back roads or the shopping center parking lots. And since this is their only business now, this is where to go-go. Shipping approximately $30 within the continental U.S. Read all about it online.

★★★★★ BSN Sports

PO Box 7726   Mon-Fri 7:30-6
Dallas, TX 75209
www.bsnsports.com;

After a quarter of a century, BSN Sports is still going strong. If you want a place to soccer-to-me, call for your FREE BSN Sports catalog or shop online. This is your one-stop sports headquarters for any sport available at the high school or college level. Shop where the coaches and athletic directors shop. Brands include ATEC, BULLDOG, EASTON, GAMECRAFT, HUFFY, IGLOO, MITRE, MIZUNO, PORT-A-PIT, PRO DOWN, REEBOK, ROL DRI, SPALDING, VOIT, WILSON and WORTH. There's always a deal, a great deal. *Call toll-free: 800/292-7772*

★★★★★ **Buddy's Sporting Goods Athletics**   **214/941-5506**

123 W. Jefferson Blvd.   Mon-Fri 9:30-6; Sat 9-5
Dallas, TX 75208
www.buddyssportinggoods.com

Look great, no matter your passion. Is it football, basketball, baseball, soccer, track, boxing, volleyball, hockey—even the best-looking officials around can make the call in these uniforms. This is the customized place for team uniforms and equipment with your name emblazoned via screen-printing or embroidery. We found some blow-out prices on gear like chest protectors for only $5, socks for $3 and helmets as low as $10. How low can they go? Well, if limbo was a sport, they'd be on the floor! Sales mean taking an extra 20 percent off their already discounted-priced gloves and finding baseballs, softballs and 12-inch softy balls starting at just $1.99. Name brands include ADIDAS, CONVERSE, HIGH FIVE, NIKE, RAWLINGS, REEBOK, WILSON and others. This sporting goods resource is an institution in Oak Cliff. Teams have been courting them for years. See what's online and get in the mood with the *Rocky* theme song. You'll be ready to climb the stairs of the Philadelphia library when you're finished outfitting the kids and the refs. Play ball at their second store in Duncanville at 749 W. Wheatland Rd. (972/780-8177) and then call it a day.

★★ **Busybody Home Fitness**   **972/960-7573**

5403 Arapaho Rd., Suite 103   Mon-Fri 10-8; Sat 10-6; Sun Noon-5
Dallas, TX 75248
www.bikesandfitness.com

Though their national headquarters are in Carrollton, you won't be shopping there but rather at one of their many stores in the Metroplex. With many tries at their website, we left empty-handed. But if you want to get fit and get with the program, surely, you can find a storefront somewhere in the Metroplex. One of the early providers who have been a driving force in the field of fitness, you can expect to see a large selection of treadmills, elliptical cross-trainers, home gyms, exercise bikes, fitness accessories, supplements, free-weights and more. You don't even have to be a busy body to get your body busy! Getting bored with the same old routine? Retail and commercial accounts and equipment for in-home and in the gym are available as your chain link to fitness. At the store level, there are on-site service teams as well as warranty protection plans to ensure your complete satisfaction. Brands include: ALLIANCE, BFL, CONCEPT, CYBEX, HORIZON FITNESS, KEYS, NORTHERN LIGHTS, PACEMASTER, PRECOR, SCHWINN—recognize a few of these? If not, get acquainted at any of the multiple Metroplex locations. *Call toll-free: 800/ 466-3348*

★★★★★★ **Camping World**   **940/898-8906**

5209 I-35 North   Mon-Sat 8 AM-7 PM; Sun 10-5
Denton, TX 76207
www.campingworld.com

 With locations in Mission and New Braunfels, Texas, their first Metroplex store has just opened in Denton. Watch for more as they are already have done in Arizona, California, Colorado, Florida, Illinois, Kentucky, Michigan, Minnesota, New Jersey, New York, Ohio, Utah, Virginia and Washington. Don't expect them to congregate in major markets, just on the outskirts, where the overhead's less and they can offer their members the lowest prices possible. Within their 31 locations, you can expect their reputation as the best and biggest supplier of RV and camping accessories to be the talk of the town. View their magazine filled with detailed information on new products, technical tips and much more. Plus get this: FREE RV accessories are given to members at random to test and to keep before they are approved for mass introduction into their stores. Of course, your complete satisfaction is guaranteed. Order or call toll free for your RV accessories catalog. Products include outdoor bikes and racks, tables and chairs, tents and camping gear, steps and mats; then for upkeep and storage for camping and your RV, you'll see covers and much more. No camping must-have is left *Call toll-free: 866/784-3399*

★★★★★★　Cheaper Than Dirt　　　　817/625-7171

Mon-Fri 9-8; Sat 9-6

2522 NE Loop 820
Fort Worth, TX 76105
www.cheaperthandirt.com

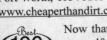

Now that the millennium scare is over, enter the War on Iraq. Looking to protect yourself at "Cheaper than Dirt" prices, try this 4,500 square foot resource of possibilities. Don't expect the website and store to carry the same merchandise; however, the store can order anything you find on their website. Come and admire their trophy room with game animal mounts and full-body mounted Black Bear, African Lion, Jaguar, Trophy Deer, Elk, Cape Buffalo, Alligators and dozens more to sneak up upon. For hunters, shooters, law enforcement and collectors who intend to be armed with the best, here are some of the top brands: BERETTA, COLT, DAKOTA RIFLE, GLOCK, H & K, KELTEC, KIMBER, MARLIN, REMINGTON, RUGER, SAVAGE, SIG, S & W, TAURUS, WINCHESTER and more. Check FREE catalog for more products that keep you alive and well. *Call toll-free: 800/421-8047*

★★★★★★　Cycle Spectrum　　　　972/480-9588

Mon-Fri 10-7; Sat 10-6; Sun Noon-5

1360 W. Campbell Rd., #101
Richardson, TX 75080
www.cyclespectrum.com

Take advantage of their FREE Service For Life policy on all bikes sold. That's right—this solid performer has been riding the high road since 1970 and they have all 35 of their shops nationwide humming. The spectrum of cycles here is monumental. From road bikes to mountain bikes, from a cruiser to a BMX; even kiddy bikes complete with training wheels for that very first ride will start your relationship with this bike shop early. For the serious biker, we eyed the MOTOBECANE LE CHAMPION bike that retails for $1,600 but was here for $1,095. Expect other top dogs to complete their discounting cycle with brands from BELL to VISTALITE, and everything in between—at some of the best prices in town. Check directory for one of their eight locations.

★★★　Dallas Golf　　　　972/270-0989

Mon-Fri 9-7; Sat 9-6; Sun Noon-5

2118 Eastgate Drive
Garland, TX 75043
www.dallasgolf.com

Dallas may be known to have the quickest draw in the Southwest, but Dallas Golf has the quickest repair service. And believe me, that should count for something when these 18 holes are beckoning. After seventeen years in the business, they know a panic attack when they see one. Since they specialize in custom-fitting clubs, it doesn't matter if you're a Sunday golfer or tournament pro, they treat you the same. Four locations and swinging, you can also see them in action at 3963 Belt Line Road, Addison, 972/866-0007; 429 N. Central Expressway, Richardson, 972/231-9399 and in Irving at 2326 W. Airport Freeway, 972/255-3639. Want to demo the equipment on your home course? No problem. Have at it! Their knowledgeable staff shouldn't tee you off with any of the popular brand names on the floor: MCHENRY METALS, PING, PRO-LINE, TITLEIST, WIL-

SON and others. Just don't expect sizeable slices in the prices. Look online for the best deals on auctioned and used equipment. Now we're getting closer to that hole-in-one. Congratulations to Dallas Golf for achieving the Titanium Power Seller Rating, eBay's highest seller status. Now you can shop online since their new PayPal-enabled shopping cart makes it easy to add to your eBay order or shop any of their deals. They take trade-ins on both new and used clubs. Bring or send in your clubs and turn them into cash! *Call toll-free: 800/955-9550*

◆◆◆◆◆ Dive West   214/750-6900

5500 Greenville Ave., Suite 910   Mon-Fri 10 to 6; Thurs 10-8; Sat 10-5; Sun 12-5
Dallas, TX 75206
www.dive-west.com

If you want to join a school of fish, here is the place to learn. This company is a full-service scuba-diving and aquatic center serving the entire Metroplex with a complete training program. Certifi-cations are offered at all levels up to and including being a scuba instructor. They have an indoor heated pool for your diving pleasure. Expect to see one of the most comprehensive selections of the latest dive equipment. Dive West carries all the best brands such as **BODY GLOVE**, **OCE-ANIC**, **SCUBAPRO**, **SEAQUEST**, **SPEEDO** and **U.S. DIVERS** in both new and used varieties. They also offer a full repair or upgrade on any manufacturer's equipment. Even by mail, you can send them your equipment for service. They offer the full service "Enriched Air Nitrox" diving services with certified gas blenders on staff as well as Enriched Air Nitrox certified instruction. No, you're not going to the dentist. This is no laughing matter. If you want to join a group of divers, Dive West is famous for their Dive Vacation Trips—if you want to sink to the lowest com-mon denominator—like Belize. Have kids 8 to 12 join in the fun with the Scuba Rangers, a way cool scuba club for youngsters. Pay attention to their occasional rummage sales when prices really take a nosedive—up to 85 percent off.

Diver's Direct (formerly Performance Diver)   800/727-2433

PO Box 2741   24/7
Chapel Hill, NC 27514

www.diversdirect.com    *Top Online Store!*

 Hold your nose and take the plunge. I couldn't resist giving you this online and cata-log site for America's largest and most experienced diver (or is it div-a) retailer. Founded in 1984 in Key Largo, Florida, they acquired Performance Diver and now converted all of their scuba sites to one name—Divers Direct. Many divers have shopped their original super store in Key Largo at Mile Marker 106. Since then, they've opened five additional stores in Florida, a catalog and internet division which is where you come in. Shop with them for everything you'd every need or want if you're a diver. If you happen to be going to the Keys, their stores are Divers Direct Outlets. Call for their FREE catalog or shop online from the Metroplex for over 25,000 products known to scuba divers and snorkelers at any level.

★★★★ Edwin Watts Golf Outlet   817/861-6677

901 W. Lamar   Mon-Fri 9:30-7; Sat 9:30-6; Sun 12-5
Arlington, TX 76012
www.edwinwattsgolf.com

If you're looking for a "Swinging Summer," (that fabulous movie starring my husband opposite Racquel Welch), best you should shop here. The movie is available online (or send $10 and I'll be happy to make you a copy.) If given his druthers, he'd rather be playing golf these days. If that is your pleasure, too, you'll find it here—from balls, bags, belts and books to clubs, cleats and carts. Look good in men's and ladies'apparel, gloves, hats, sunglasses and even magnetic bracelets. Be prepared with large umbrellas, training aids, software and travel covers. Even gifts for the real golf enthusiast like "Golf Monopoly" for $30 and "Golf Scrabble" for $20. What a great gift for the golfer who has everything. From one small pro shop in Fort Walton Beach to almost 50 super-stores today, Edwin Watts and his brother Ronnie are still going strong. Swing to their other Dallas locations at 2320 Stemmons Trail in Dallas, 214/352-9431 and 5955 Alpha Road, 972/404-4424. Each year since 1986, Golf World Business Magazine recognizes the ì100 Best Golf Shops in Americaî and Edwin Watts is consistency listed in the top 100. *Call toll-free: 800/874-0146*

★★★★   FitCo Fitness Center Outifitters   972/503-6060

2101 Midway Rd., # 240   Mon-Sat 10-6
Carrollton, TX 75006
www.fitcofitness.com

Save $300 to $700 on the world's No. 1 Health Club EFX Elliptical Crosstrainer—if you are so inclined! Also, save on PRECOR treadmills and more plus six months with no payments, no inter-est with approved credit. Not too shabby. Located off Belt Line just south of Keller Springs, this 5,000-square-foot expanded showroom also includes NAUTILUS equipment. FitCo will outfit your home or business, school, university, apartment complex or hotel with exercise equipment by CYBEX, LIFE FITNESS, NAUTILUS, PRECOR, STAIRMASTER and VECRA (some of the best in the business), and once you get with the program, you will, rest assured, live a long and healthy life....for less. Locally, they have taken care of the TCU Student Recreation Center and the Coppell Aquatic & Recreation Center. I'd say those are pretty good references. They offer sales, Auto Cad design, delivery, installation and service for your equipment. Stay focused on their clearance area for new, overstocked and discontinued equipment, with great buys on used, trade-ins and demos—some at or below cost. Don't worry about any of the equipment, as it all comes with complete war-ranties; used, however, comes "as is." If it breaks, lotsa luck!

★★★★★★   Fitness HQ   972/980-7788

11930 Preston Rd., Suite 140   Mon-Thurs 10-8; Fri-Sat 10-7; Sun Noon-5
Dallas, TX 75230
www.fitnessheadquarters.com

 Both commercial and residential equipment at "competitive prices"— what price are you willing to pay for your good health? Ask me about my recumbent bike. It's the best investment I've ever made 'cause it's a bike I can actually ride, read, write and listen to CNN all at the same time. Expect superb advice from pros on only top brand name equipment at very competitive pricing. All sales includes a FREE in-home training session (but they don't stay around to see to it that you do your exercises daily!) They even offer owner transferable extended warranties valid throughout the U.S. on all equipment. So, even if you sell it, the warranty goes with it. Another Preston Rd. location in Plano as well as locations in Southlake and Fort Worth. Check directory for the one nearest you. Exercise your options with treadmills, rowers and cycles like ELLIPTICALS, LIFE FITNESS, SPORTS ART, SCHWINN, TUNTUNI and other sought-after makers. Then, what about home gyms, free weights? Everything when the subject of fitness comes up—everything that is except motivation. *Call toll-free: 877/479-4444*

★★   Foot Locker Outlet   817/451-4602

5116 E. Lancaster Ave.   Mon-Sat 10-8; Sun Noon-5
Fort Worth, TX 76112
www.footlocker.com

Isn't it amazing? The Foot Locker Outlet in Fort Worth has the same lousy attitude as the one we
visited in Orlando. Looks like the apple doesn't fall far from the tree. They must have had the
same corporate trainer. If you're looking for brands, they've got you covered from toe to toe.
ADAM BUCKS, ADIDAS, AIRWALK, AVIA, BIRKENSTOCK, BULOVA, CANDIES, CHAM-
PION, CONVERSE, DKNY, EASTON, HARLEY DAVIDSON, HUSH PUPPIES, JANSPORT,
KEDS, MIZUNO, NAUTICA, NIKE, OAKLEY, PONY, RAWLINGS, REEBOK, ROCKPORT,
SALOMON, SKECHERS, TIMBERLAND, UMBRO and VANS to name those that stand out.
They also carry regular Foot Locker merchandise at retail prices. The other outlet is at Grapevine
Mills but as you can see, I have already put my foot in my mouth with this write-up.

★★★★   For Divers Only   972/317-2822

1015 N. I-35 E. #324   By Appt. Only
Carrollton, TX 75006

Not only can Barbara cook, she can deliver the deals on dives and equipment. Her motto is
"Everything's always on sale" and she means it. There's an on-site heated pool for diving lessons
and they sponsor some of the best dive trips in town. No, the dives are really out-of-town, to places
that are south towards the ocean blue. You learn "how-to" in Dallas first and then dive in elsewhere. Call in the evenings or call the cell phone at 469/867-DIVE (not DIVA!) I don't promise
deep dives but she promises deep savings. Hold you nose if you're not in to machinery. And enjoy
the dive! *Call toll-free: CALL 31-SCUB*

★★★★★★   Galyan's   817/987-4800

3891 S. Cooper St.   Mon-Thurs 10-9; Fri-Sat 10-9:30
Arlington, TX 76015
www.galyans.com

Joining their Plano store at Stonebriar, add The Parks in Arlington to make two
Galyan's locations in the Metroplex. Guess who is the healthy benefactor? With
over 90,000 of the best products to get you into shape at the guaranteed best prices,
whether you're into mountain biking, racing or just riding around the neighborhood, you can ride
in and out of Galyan's for the best bike at the best price. Choose from an awesome selection for
adults and kids. No matter what day it is, your bike will be a deal including a full year of FREE
adjustments. Galyan's is your one-stop source for all the right gear, clothing, shoes and advice for
a great time in the great outdoors. From a good old COLEMAN lantern to some of the most
sophisticated camping gear in the industry, from strollers to trawlers, climb every mountain and
ensure a peak performance. Be a sport: Fish, swim, walk, play golf, any team sport, the world of
adventure is just around the corner. Galyan's Trading Company is a most unique, active lifestyle
retailer and welcome to the Metroplex from Plainfield, Indiana. (They were destined to be in the
sports business, look where they're from?) *Call toll-free: 888/GALYANS*

★★★★★   **Golfsmith Pro Shop**   **972/991-9255**
4141 LBJ Frwy.   Mon-Sat 10-8; Sun Noon-6
Dallas, TX 75052
www.golfsmith.com

I remember them well. Ah, Carl and Frank Paul, brothers from Plainfield, NJ, who started out in one little basement location and moved to Austin in 1969. Today, they're one of the big boys in the industry who have struck it rich, first selling their own line of golf equipment via mail order, then to their bricks and mortar stores and now their online supercenter. Inside their stores, you'll find Golf Simulators (featuring virtual golf), SWINGTEK swing analyzers, expansive putting greens, and large screen TV(s) showcasing the current tournament or latest in golf and sports programming. Shop the major manufacturers including: ADAMS, ALIEN SPORT, ASHWORTH, BEN HOGAN, TOP FLITE, CALLAWAY, CLEVELAND, COBRA, DATREK, ETONIC, FOOTJOY, FORESTERS, GOLFSMITH, IZZO KILLER BEE, LA JOLLA, LYNX, MAXFLI, MIZUNO, NIKE, ORLIMAR, PING, PRECEPT, REEBOK, SNAKE EYES, STX, SUN MOUNTAIN SPORTS, TAYLOR MADE, TITLEIST, WILSON—there's enough to link you up to every golf course in the country. Check other locations in Plano, Arlington and their newest store in Frisco. Their outlet store is online only. But that's par for the course. Remember, too, if you find it for less "Before or After" the sale, up to 30 days, they will not only match the price, they'll give you an extra 15 percent of the difference. Unused merchandise may be exchanged or returned within 30 days. Used merchandise, special orders, custom clubs and personalized items may not, however. *Call toll-free: 800/815-3873*

★★★★★★   **Home Fitness**   **972/488-3222**
3340 Garden Brook   Mon-Fri 10-7; Sat 10-6; Sun Noon-5
Farmers Branch, TX 75231

 Formerly Consignment Sports & Fitness, they have now consolidated into their former warehouse location, closing their Coit Road store and now you can swing over to their 95,000 square foot super duper new and used fitness location. (What a difference a location makes—from 2,000 square feet to 95,000 square feet. From small to gigantic.) Smart move. Whether you're consigning or buying, they are a solid source to reduce the fat. The choice of sports equipment is as varied as the myriad of sporting activities and it's forever changing with the times. One customer, though, called about manual treadmills and their answer was, "We just threw out four of them in the dumpster." He was supposed to look for them as she waited on the phone but gave up after 15 minutes. I guess the trash man had already come and gone. Too bad, customer service is also part of the sales equation. And one wrong move and you've lost a customer for life. But you will see all kinds of fitness gear, from STAIRMASTERS to PRECOR, weight benches to circuit weight training apparatus, hockey skates to in-line skates, racquetball and tennis rackets, golf clubs to an occasional recumbent bike or WEE JOGGER, you just have to be a sport and shop a lot. Equipment comes and goes just like the craze.

★★   **Innovation Skate Shop**   **817/417-5283**
1201 W. Arbrook Blvd., Suite 101   Mon-Fri 1-7; Sat 11-6; Sun 1:30-5
Arlington, TX 76015

If you're still into skateboards and in-line skating, you'll want to es-skate from the general sporting goods store and skate to a specialist. This is it. Complete boards start at $69.99 and that's not a cheap sandwich from the sandwich board. Sandwiched in between your school work and your after-school job, see if you can slip into a pair of shorts from COUNTER CULTURE, HURLEY and **REBUILD**. For a complete wardrobe, they carry both youth and adult sizes including lots of T-shirts and shoes, plus posters for your bedroom. Located near the Parks Mall, just a few doors down from Starbucks, round the corner, just get in-line for their in-line menu of options.

★★★★★★ Larry Black Sporting Goods Outlet 972/484-2527

13880 Stemmons Frwy   Tues-Fri 11-7; Sat 9-6; Sun 12-5
Farmers Branch, TX 75234

Keep your budget in the black (or is it the red?), I never could remember which color is the good one. Generally, I like a combination. It's better than black and blue, which is often the result of your game plan. Shirts, shorts, shoes, cleats, balls (for most sports), warm-up suits in name brands like **ADIDAS** and **NIKE** can be bought up at a steal, without stealing any bases. Overstocks, closeouts and clearance items are fit to be tried. Let's play ball! Looks like the owner of Fitness Headquarters is also behind the ball here. So, it looks like this store comes with a great genetic link.

★★★★ North Texas Golf World   817/457-9345

1100 E. I-820 S.   Mon-Fri 8-5; Sat 9-2
Fort Worth, TX 76112

Golfers, take a back seat and relax. Here's your source for new and used golf clubs and carts. I bet if you could have but one piece of equipment, you would die for a cart before a **BIG BERTHA**. Eh? Golf carts with names like **BOMBARDIER**, **E-Z-GO** and **YAMAHA** at prices from $750 for a fabulous three-wheeler to more expensive models three to five years old. Like-new, rebuilt carts range from $2,850 to $3,400, but new ones can set you back $4,000 or more. The store in Granbury is no longer, but you can still fly like an eagle and take a swing at their new and used club selection in Fort Worth with names like **CALLAWAY**, **COBRA**, **PING**, **TAYLOR MADE**, **TITLEIST** and more. There's always something new (well, new to you even if it's used) coming and going. Word of finding a Tiger in the Woods was a hoax!

★★★ Oshman's SuperSports USA   817/467-0090

4620 Cooper & I-20   Mon-Fri 10-9; Sat 9-9; Sun 11-6
Arlington, TX 76017
www.oshmans.com

When you're big, there's nowhere to go but up. And that's what Oshman's has done. They have experienced monumental store growth since Jake Oshman first opened Oshman's Dry Goods in Richmond, Texas, in 1919. After moving to Houston and opening another store by buying up bankrupt stock of another dry goods store while liquidating the inventory of his store in Richmond, he was on to something. In 1990, the Oshman's SuperSports USA megastore concept began to take shape in 80,000-square-foot monster stores with so much going for them, you'd get dizzy walking the perimeters. There are product demo areas where you can try out the equipment. They sell equipment and accessories for those into "xtreme" sports including **CWB SLAYER WAKEBOARDS** and **FILA FF 70** In-Line Skates for women. They also sell **HOT WHEELS** Folding Kick Scooter With Front Suspension for $79 (retail $109). Ride out on a mountain bike with names like **HUFFY**, **JEEP**, **MONGOOSE** or **ROYCE UNION**. And you still haven't experienced half of the savings or selection from this power player. Check directory for location nearest you.
Call toll-free: 800/PLAY-OSH

★★★★★   **Play It Again Sports**   **214/821-7737**

6465 East Mockingbird, Suite 366   Tues-Wed-Thurs 10-7; Mon-Sat 10-6; Sun 1-5
Dallas, TX 75214
www.playitagainsports.com

With seven area locations, how can you not get with the program? Though this is not a Humphrey Bogart-licensed store, this Sam plays sports and doesn't pay attention to Lauren Bacall. Play It Again Sports is in the game of selling sports equipment, as long as it's been played before. This franchised nationwide network of sporting goods stores sell it again and again. They also service what they sell and with so many opportunities to consign and buy fitness equipment, you can exercise your options and get physically as well as fiscally fit. Bedford, Carrolton, Flower Mound, Fort Worth, Mesquite and Plano are their home bases, so you've got no excuses not to hop aboard. Whether it's a skateboard or a exercise bike, you'll surely get your heart rate into its target zone. Trade in or trade up to something more advanced or retreat back to something more elementary, my dear. Exercise the myriad of options by checking the directory for the one nearest you. As Seen in Bottom Line Magazine, I sent them a copy of the article I wrote and still waiting to see if they've read it. *Call toll-free: 800/645-7299*

★★★★   **Ray's Sporting Goods**   **214/747-7916**

730 Singleton Blvd.   Tues-Sat 9-6
Dallas, TX 75212
www.rayssportinggoods.com

Since 1949, Ray's has aimed to please. With their killer instincts, is it any wonder that big game hunters and other gun enthusiasts consider Ray's a sanctuary from high prices? Called "the firearms specialist," Ray's has been the target of pot shots with my puns for years, but if you're a serious shooter, when it comes to custom rifles, shotguns and pistols, there is none better in the Metroplex. Their arsenal of weapons are not the only items for sale in their game plan. Dress the part in camouflage clothing, sign up for a deal on their frequent hunting trips, and buy all of your supplies, optical equipment and accessories to hit the mark, too. Major brands to brandish include BENELLI, BERETTA, BIANCHI, BLASER, BROWNING, COLT, DESERT EAGLE, GLOCK, GRIZZLY, HAHR, H&K, KRIEGHOFF, MOSSBERG, REMINGTON, SKB, SMITH & WESSON, UBERTI, WALTER, WEATHERBY, WINCHESTER and more. Whether it's a pistol, a rifle, a shotgun, ammo, knives, even targets, you can be sure the conversation turns to ease, reliability and price. Remember, though, safety comes first. *Call toll-free: 800/440-3323*

★★★   **REI Recreational Equipment**   **972/490-5989**

4515 LBJ Frwy.   Mon-Fri 10-9; Sat 11-7; Sun 11-6
Farmers Branch, TX 75244
www.rei.com

One block west of the Galleria and actually within the boundaries of Farmers Branch, you only have to have a zest for the great outdoors to escape city life and head for the hills. Maintaining one of the finest catalogs for the well-endowed sporting class, if you'd like to climb to greater heights, REI is the place to camp. They offer the most extensive clothing and equipment inventory for the serious mountaineer in the world. And if anything breaks, be it a zipper on a jacket, pair of pants, sleeping bag, or you need to patch a parka, tent or backpack, they will fix you up. If you are a member, prices on zipper pulls is $8 while non-members pay $10. Are you looking to explore a new sport? Then take advantage of their rental gear program and try before you buy. If it's Adventure Travel, get your discounts here. Sign up for your own REI Bankcard with cash back and other benefits alongside their $15 yearly REI membership, where you get cash back at the end of the year on your total purchases. Online, load up on gear too!

★★★★★ Richardson Bike Mart   972/231-3993
1451 W. Campbell Rd.   Mon-Fri 10-8; Sat 9-6: Sun Noon-5
Richardson, TX 75080
www.bikemart.com

Stop spinning your wheels riding the wave of new retailers who take you out for a spin and then, drop you like a hot potato. No, ma'am, this is a long-time name in the area, and even though their name implies only a Richardson location, they're also at 9040 Garland Rd., near White Rock Lake, 214/321-0705, Mon-Fri 10-7; Sat 9-6; Sun 12-5. There you'll see plenty of riders getting in gear for a ride around the lake. If you, too, want a leisurely bike ride, get in shape for a triathlon, or are a first-timer rider, here's where to go. Expect to see brands like **BIANCHI**, **CALFEE**, **CERVELO**, **CIOCC**, **COLNAGO**, **COPI**, **DE BERNSRDI**, **GRIFFEN**, **IBIS**, **INDEPENDENT FABS**, **KLEIN**, **LEMOND**, **MERLIN**, **QUINTANA ROO**, **SCHWINN**, **SEROTTA**, **SEVEN**, **SPECIALIZED**, Trek—well, all I was looking for was a **SCHWINN** since that was a name I remembered from my childhood. Visit their website too! That's all, spokes!

★★ Sports Authority, The   972/874-0500
3000 Grapevine Mills Parkway   Mon-Sat 10-9:30; Sun 11-8
Grapevine, TX 76051
www.thesportsauthority.com

This Grapevine Mills location is often the leader of the pack when it comes time to clean up at their end-of-the-season merchandise sales. That's when your heart rate gets up to your target heart rate, after you're ranted and panted around this great expanse of savings. Run, don't walk, to their tent sales where you can save up to 90 percent. Paintball merchandise, you could have taken another 20 percent off the lowest ticketed price. Downhill skis and snowboards were slashed to as low as 90 percent off. There isn't a sport left unrecognized. Volleyball, badminton, beach and lawn games, dart boards, darts and accessories from **ACCUDART**, **HALEX**, **SPORTCRAFT** and **WINMAU**, golf balls, tennis balls, coolers, fishing reels (rods and lures, too), tackle, firearms, hockey game tables, handheld electronic games, golf bags, shoes and accessories, boxing equipment and much more. Visit also the Plano Sports Authority at 6500 Preston Meadow Drive, Plano, TX 75024-5259, 972/208-5437 or shop online. At the outlet online, you can save 20-50 percent. But pay heed to the fine print which says, "retail price does not mean that anything sold at that price, but rather it's just a reference point." That means, someone arbitarily suggested you sell something for $200 at the MSRP (Manufacturers Suggested Retail Price) and if you want to claim it, even though nobody ever bought it at that price, you can use it for comparison purposes. In other words, the MSRP of this book is $99.99, but for you, it's only $14.99. I thought that was illegal? Oh well, selection does count for something. ***Call toll-free: 888/LOOK-4TS***

★★★★★★ Sportsman's Warehouse   214/488-2700
723 Hebron Parkway   Mon-Thurs 10-8; Fri 10-9; Sat 9:30-7; Sun 10-6
Lewisville, TX 75057
www.sportsmanswarehouse.com

 Be a sport and consider this warehouse if you want a surefire hit on hunting, fishing, camping, reloading, outerwear and footwear gear. This company hits the mark with a bullseye—they are right on target. Born in 1986 in Midvale, Utah, Stu Utgaard and his family purchased a 26,000 square foot initial retail store. Soon, they began to make their move and expanded their initial store plus open another 35,000 square foot store in Provo, Utah. It didn't take long to hit the road on a pretty impressive expansion plan. They were on a roll adding Riverdale, Utah; Meridian and Idaho Falls, Idaho; Loveland, Colorado; Spokane, Washington; Grand Junction, Colorado; Salem, Oregon; Kennewick, Washington; St. Cloud, Minnesota; Aurora, Colorado; Coon Rapids, Minnesota; Missoula, Montana; Portland, Oregon; Phoenix, Arizona; Twin Falls, Idaho; Thornton, Colorado; and Ankeny, Iowa—all of which are big hunting and fishing headquarters. They employed 65 people six years ago. Today, there are more than 1,400. Recently, they've opened their first location in the Metroplex at the Lake Pointe Center in Lewisville. With a $10 coupon, I was lured into the store. All of the products are shipped in from a 1,000,000 square foot distribution hub. Six more stores on the horizon this year including one in Anchorage, Alaska. Watch out bears! The Sportsman's Warehouse offers a unique yet extensive mix of merchandise serving these industries: hunting, fishing, camping, optics, clothing and footwear merchandise, including more than 1,000 firearms, 80,000 flies for fishing, over 100 models each of tents, sleeping bags and back packs, and over 150 different types of binoculars and spotting scopes. With the most knowledgeable personnel, they can offer superb customer service on the highest quality merchandise. There is no other store like it offering so much at such low prices. Endless rows of merchandise make the shopping experience a bang-up event. They never fish for compliments, but this is the store to shop if you're a hunter or a fisherman because you can reel in a whopper each and every time. Log on to their website for their Waterfowl Weekend Dates, goose contests sanctioned by Avery International. Prizes for the duck events are all delineated online. Prize money runs from a low $100 to a high of $10,000 which isn't goose liver! These events are always well attended with guest seminars so make your reservation early when it comes to your town. Lewisville opened June 5 just east of I-35. Give 'em a real Big D welcome.

★★★★★★   St. Bernard Sports Outlet   214/352-1200

3120 Commonwealth Drive   Mon-Fri 10-7; Sat 10-6; Sun 12-5 (Winter Hours)
Dallas, TX 75247
www.stbernardsports.com

 Bark when you see this St. Bernard coming to the rescue. Great prices (Arf! Arf!) like a pair of **SALOMON X-SCREAM** skis for $550 (MSRP: $675) or a pair of the new 2002 **VOLANT** Gravity Chubbs for $300. Some hard-to-find brands that you might find only in the more exclusive ski boutiques like **BURMA & BIBAS**, **CHACO**, **DIESEL**, **FRESH PRODUCE**, **HELEN KAMINSKI**, **LUCKY**, **MAUI JIM**, **OAKLEY**, **PAUL FRANK**, **QUICKSILVER**, **REEF**, **SOLITUDE** and **TOMMY BAHAMA** plus all the popular brands you'd expect in the typical ski shops like **BURTON**, **K2**, **NORDICA**, **SALOMON**, **TYROLIA**, **VOLANT** and others. From bindings, boots, poles to skis, snowboards and accessories, you'll find it all under one roof. Head to their warehouse where savings descend to 50 percent off. Start at the top of their 3,500-square foot warehouse store complete with carpeting and so well-organized, you'll wonder where the jammed-crammed to the gills look went. Savings soar to up to 75 percent. But the real beauty of the Goyers, Ann and Wes's baby is how to get them lined up when the snow starts to melt. Well, all you have to do to experience what they've done is to shop during the spring and summer and see for yourself. I came away with tons of unbelievable deals on ladies'sportswear and accessories. I couldn't believe my eyes. Why didn't they start this sooner. I would have been shopping sooner. But now, I'm giving you a heads'up. Now you can shop year 'round and have an up-to-the-minute chic wardrobe for a fraction of retail. Exit Commonwealth off Stemmons to the west. And it's immediately on your left in the old Bierner & Son's Hat Building. If you want to avoid the crowds totally, you can always shop online. ***Call toll-free: 800/444-6937***

★★★★★★   **Supreme Golf Warehouse Outlet Hub   817/332-5318**

203 S. Calhoun St.   Mon-Sat 9-6
Fort Worth, TX 76104
www.supremegolf.com

Here's a swinger who has been around since 1973. Expect all their locations to offer discounts, but the Fort Worth store is the warehouse outlet. Have you ever considered a Professional Club Fitting? It's a process that matches your swing characteristics and setup to a specific club shape and shaft style. Online, you can really get teed off. Everything that's in the stores is just a click away. Supreme Golf always tries to be the best price on name brand golf clubs, balls, bags, shoes, apparel and accessories, with more than a quarter of a century of experience getting you on the green. Names like ADAMS, CALLAWAY, CLEVELAND, ETONIC, FOOT JOY, KINGSTON CLASSIC, MACGREGOR, MIZUNO, NIKE, PING, TAYLOR MADE, TITLEIST and others are in the forefront. Other stores in Hurst, 817/590-2582; Irving, 972/869-1035; Southlake, 817/251-0808 and their supreme-O Outlet above.

★★★   **Texas Army Navy Store**   **972/235-9781**

111 N. Central Expressway (exit Belt Line)   Mon-Sun 9-7
Dallas, TX 75080
www.afmo.com

Gear Up is the slogan used by the Army Navy stores but you don't need to sign up to enjoy the gear. Expect to see both Army/Navy gear, but there's more. Online, it's a worldwide selection beyond the wild blue yonder. Salute the savings online with Army/Navy surplus, from camo clothing to survival gear. Military-quality footlockers are perfect to send kids off to school or to camp and what campus BMOT would not like to tote an **ATB** Gear Bag on Wheels around campus constructed from 1200 denier cordura with PVC waterproof backing? Camping gear, law enforcement equipment, eyewear for rugged individualists, first aid, foot and headwear for the great outdoors, insignias, knives, manuals, novelties, optics and lights to guide you, and all important survival needs can be secured all with one mission. Gear up at their second location on Hwy 121 at Harwood in Bedford at 817/335-0481. *Call toll-free: 800/282-3327*

★★★★★★   **Tour Line Golf**   **817/560-4700**

7616 Camp Bowie West (Spur 580)   Mon-Fri 10-6; Sat 9-5
Fort Worth, TX 76116
www.tourlinegolf.com

The game doesn't get better than this. Play with the pros—their equipment that is. The pro shops from country clubs nationwide send their clearance items and used clubs that they take in trade to these two shops in Dallas and Fort Worth. They are, in fact, the largest clearinghouse in America for such pro lines. In turn, they sell the clubs at a fraction of the cost of new. Major players include CALLAWAY, CLEVELAND, HOGAN, KING COBRA, PING, TAYLOR MADE, TITLEIST, TOP FLITE are typically on hand, but they do keep their "eagle" eye out for others like: DEXTER, DUNLOP, FOOTJOY, LIQUID METAL, MAXFLI, MIZUNO, ODYSSEY, PRECEPT, PROLINE, US KIDS, WILSON, YAMAHA, ZEVO and others and grab them when they can so as to make an occasional appearance. You can return your buys within 48 hours (even if you used the equipment) for a full refund. After that you have 30 days, but there will be a 20 percent restocking fee. Also, swing into their Old Town location in Dallas at 5500 Greenville, Suite 502 at Lovers Lane (NE corner), 214/692-9411. *Call toll-free: 800/530-5767*

★★★★   **Wally's Discount Golf Shop**   **817/261-9301**

900 E. Copeland Rd.   Mon-Fri 9:30-6:30; Sat 9-6
Arlington, TX 76011
www.wallysdiscountgolf.com

Make a detour on your way home when the traffic is backed up bumper to bumper on Stemmons. Start your golf game at their outlet location, inside their discount store at 9090 N. Stemmons Freeway in Dallas, 214/637-2944, before you lay down the green. What a sport! Wally's will help you keep your score as low as it goes. He wonders why you haven't taken up his favorite game yet, after all these years? Since 1970, he's been taking off Sundays, so only expect to shop and save Mon-Sat. Whether you're looking for one club or a set, stay focused on Wally's because with his multiple stores, he has what you're looking for. In fact, he can get most anything within two days since he stocks the most popular sizes and brands in his Garland warehouse. Otherwise, the wait may be up to two weeks. All the top names from ADIDAS, BEN HOGAN, CALLAWAY, MIZUNO, NIKE GOLF, PING, STRATA, TAYLORMADE, TOP FLIGHT, TITLEIST, WILSON, well, he carries them all. Shop online or via the phones toll-free Mon-Fri only. *Call toll-free: 800/249-2559*

Surplus, Pawn & Thrift

★★★★ **American Pawn Superstore** 972/203-2020

484 W. I-30
Garland, TX 75043-4456
Mon-Sun 9-9

An all-American activity that has been ignored in good times comes back into favor when times go south. What is it? The lowly pawn shop—sometimes the only place that provides much-needed cash in bad times. (Try taking your computer or your **ROLEX** watch to the bank. Other than admiring it, they won't give you squat.) When shopping here, though, try to avoid Frank. He's so fast-talking, you may pawn the clothes on your back without wanting to do so. But the good news is that almost anything that can be bought, sold or loaned-on is somewhere on their shelves. With 32,000 square feet, it's probably the largest pawn shop in the Metroplex. Pawn shops, in general, are great places to learn to shop with the sharks because you won't be over your head in debt shopping for sporting goods, electronics, musical instruments, electronics, luggage, lawn mowers, vacuum cleaners, TVs and stereos, more TVs and stereos, VCRs, clocks, guns, jet skis, bikes, power tools, clocks, lamps, jewelry (costume and fine), diamonds, watches and more. Or if you're drowning in debt, this is a good place to relieve some of the pressure by pawning things for ready cash. Either way, it's the American way. Visit their smaller satellite locations at LBJ and Midway and another in Arlington.

★★★★ **Cash America Pawn** 214/948-1522

626 W. Jefferson Blvd.
Dallas, TX 75208-4724
Mon-Fri 9-7; Sat 9-5; Sun 11-4

Remember not so long ago when pawn shops were scattered all over the country and the industry was but fragmented mom-and-pop concerns with no universal voice? Well, welcome to the world of high finance and smart marketing. Headquartered in Fort Worth with other companies under their corporate umbrella (they also own Mr. Payroll and Rent-A-Tire), Cash America Pawn not only has the largest number of pawn shop locations in the United States, but is the most recognizable name in the pawn shop industry. Just for your edification, pawn loans were around as far back as 3,000 years ago, so the concept is nothing new. When Cash America Pawn was born in 1984, the image changed dramatically. Now it's known as the "non-bank" with over 470 locations in 18 states. It's where people go to get cash as well as a great place to buy something at a great price. In fact, CAP is a little shopping Mecca of previously-owned stuff, like TVs and VCRs, guns, cameras, sporting goods, guitars, bicycles, drums, saxophones, treadmills and some household items like blenders, microwaves and silver. Conceivably, it's a gold mine. And if you want jewelry, you can buy jewelry. Lots of it. Examine all merchandise before making that final decision. Get cash quick; loan documents take minutes to print and then you're outta there. Visit the 42 other Metroplex locations and tip your CAP when you leave with a bargain under your hat.

★★★   City Store   214/670-5729
1201 Turtle Creek Blvd.   Wed-Fri 9-4
Dallas, TX 75207-6613

What a steal! Yes, even the City has gotten in on the act and not soon enough, I might add. Since it was nearly impossible to find out when and where police auctions were taking place, for example, there may not have been a need for a permanent sale site. But now that there is, you and I can be cell mates. It's a perfect relationship. At the corner of Turtle Creek and Irving Boulevard, you will find a warehouse site loaded with ammunition for the robber barons—those who would rather steal from the robbers and profit from their cache. Though limited in hours and selection, the city's retail store disposes of what police have seized from crime scenes and what city offices no longer use. Office equipment to knock-off handbags, you never know what lies behind closed doors. Cars and other big ticket-items are still sold via the auction. It's always a good source for automotive parts, kids'toys, holsters, beauty supplies, Bibles, air-conditioning units and small appliances. What a marriage between steals and deals!

★★   Disabled American Veterans   972/790-2185
2310 Rock Island   Mon-Sat 9-5:30
Irving, TX 75061

If you are between a rock and a hard place, this may be the place to gather up your closet has-beens, your attic's dust-gatherers, or your kitchen cabinet overflow and bring it to the Rock Island Line. For economic reasons, they can no longer pick up your donations, but they will certainly be helpful when you're unloading. Be sure to get your tax receipt as your generosity does have its blessings. They're located near the corner of Story and Rock Island in Irving; regardless of the items, from furniture to fabric, toys to tools, clothing to car parts, everything that you don't want could be number one on someone else's wish list. Generosity begins at home. And 'tis better to give than receive or vice versa in this case.

★★★★   Discount Outlet, The   903/583-7792
Hwy. 56 (117 Sam Rayburn Drive)   Mon-Sat 9-5
Bonham, TX 75418

It's described as a "hole in the wall", but nevertheless, it does have plenty of devotees. They buy pallets of stuff from what doesn't sell through at Target, so you can often find a deal or two that would warrant a bullseye. But beware: some things are incomplete, some chipped, others, well, you wouldn't want them at any price. Still, it's always half of what you'd pay at Target. We did find a bookshelf for $45, regularly $89, with nary a nick in sight. A set of CALPHALON cookware was $60 for the complete set, though a ding was noted in one of the lids. You'll find dishes, toys, electronics, clocks, linens, candles, lamps, frames, and a few clothes. I know it's a drive but you can save a bundle, remember?

★★★★   Freight Outlet, The   972/240-6678
6545 Duck Creek Drive   Mon-Sat 9-7; Sun 1-5
Garland, TX 75043

New address and phone number do not a difference make. But they have made a move in the right direction by getting closer to the greater good. (Garland is closer than Balch Springs.) That means, the freight stops here, where "it's been shipped by truck." They famous motto is, "We have it, had it, or will have it." And everything's on the up-and-up, and all killer-priced. New merchandise is sold on an old premise: buy it right, sell it low and the customers will come. The adventure of it all is one big surprise. You never know what lies ahead in the search. Standard surplus items included food items (canned and boxed), sundries, beauty supplies and your typical grocery and drug store items. Occasionally, they offered some perishables, too, like corny dogs and bacon. But man does not live by the fat of the land only. Save lots by buying lots. Load up and make every dollar count. Personnel are helpful and typical of small-town America. They're located near the corner of Duck Creek and Broadway, across the street from Bartain Town (formerly a K-Mart.) Trek over to their second location, called Freight Outlet Plus, in St. Joseph, Texas. If you need directions, call 940/995-2776.

★ GSA Personal Sales Office 817/978-2352

Fort Worth, TX   Mon-Fri 7:45-4:15 (Periodic Sales)

Expect the typical government run-around. The GSA has auctions, but to get clearance you probably need a code name and a magic wand. Still, an occasional windfall occurs and you actually talk to a person who knows when the next sale is. That, however, takes an act of God and an amendment to the Will of Rights. But when you get the bill, if you do attend one of their auctions, you can pay only with a cashier's check, money order or personal check with a bank guarantee. It's so complicated, I give up. But what do fans get by being persistent, dedicated and loyal beyond a Boy Scout merit badge? When they're selling real estate that for some reason was confiscated, the number to call is 817/978-4275. For personal property sales, call 817/978-2352 and punch in "1" when cued by the recorded message. What they're selling is surplus inventory that has been seized by the government (except from the Post Office and the Department of Defense) and can often include vehicles, office furniture, computers, office equipment and just about anything that can be sold at an auction. Everything's sold "as is" so you take your chances. When you land, there's no telling what will turn up or how it will turn out. It's all in the cards. Business hours are Mon-Fri 7:45 AM to 4:15 PM (to avoid all that traffic!) But it's anybody's guess as to when, where and how you get to a sale on time. Nobody is anxious to talk to you. *Call toll-free: 888/878-3256*

★★★★ Goodwill Industries 214/638-2800

2800 N. Hampton Rd.   Mon-Sat 9:30-6; Sun Noon-6
Dallas, TX 75212
www.goodwilldallas.org

How about Goodwill hunting? Well, you won't have to look very far. Goodwill Industries means not only are you buying right, you could be giving for all the right reasons. Benefit this worthy cause and strike a deal in any of the area Goodwill stores around town. Besides knick-knacks and odds and ends, you'll see small appliances, dishware, glassware, family clothing and toys. We crowed loud and clear when we discovered a MURANO glass rooster for $14.99. Drop-off locations throughout the Metroplex are open seven days a week. Just about anything can be found but it's definitely a hit and miss affair. They always have, though, clothing, household items, electronics, small sporting equipment, small accent pieces of furniture, small office equipment and small appliances. Don't expect large furniture or appliances; Goodwill does not accept them.

★★★★★★ Habitat for Humanity Outlet Stores 972/303-0203

Mon-Sat 8 AM- 7 PM

451 W. I-30
Garland, TX 75043
www.dallas-habitat.org

Ready to sweat the good stuff? Then ReStore is the place for in-store savings on all your home improvement projects plus you'll be benefitting the magnificent charity "Habitat for Humanity." Their newest resale ReStore is quite the place to be seen....buying. You will find new and used appliances, doors, windows, tile, tubs, sinks, plumbing supplies, flooring, hardware, fixtures, wiring and more for any home improvement project. Illuminate the possibilities with 50 percent off wholesale prices on premium manufacturers'lighting. Visit, too, to double your pleasure, their location at 3420 S. Grove St, Fort Worth, TX 76110-4307, or call 817/926-3585 and in Dallas at 3020 Bryan, 214/827-9083. And head online to www.habitat.org for printing out additional coupon savings. ReStore your faith in humanity and support the cause as you put savings back into your pocket and add your contribution to mankind.

★★★★★ Hope Chest   214/520-1087 (Hope Chest)

Mon-Fri 10-5;Thurs 10-7; Fri 10-5; Sat 12-5

4209 McKinney
Dallas, TX 75204
www.hopecottage.org

If there's hope, there's charity if you make this thrift store your guiding light. New and gently used resale with all of the proceeds benefiting Hope Cottage, (where parents are made through adoption). Expect to see lots of babies', children's and maternity wear, as you should, since their audience is expectant parents and their offspring. Donations are welcome. Now, their parking lot sits on the property of my old office building on Fitzhugh, so you can see, "How the World Turns." And as an adoptive mother myself, I feel even closer than most to this charitable cause. Besides, where else would I suggest you fill up a hope chest than with the finds from here? It's worth a lifetime of happiness to other prospective parents everywhere—with a little help from our community. Expect to be treated royally like I was when I bought all of the novelty sculptures that were $25 for $5/each, brand new, in their box. Wow, did I score a shopping coup or not? *Call toll-free: 800/944-4460*

★★★★★ Nuevo Sol (Hotel Liquidators)   972/780-7600

Mon-Sat 9-5

3650 Marvin D. Love Freeway (67)
Duncanville, TX 75224
www.hotelfurniture.us

When you have thousands and thousands of square feet of selling space and want to attract thousands and thousands of bargain shoppers, let me introduce you to Nuevo Sol Partners, Inc. Hotel Liquidators. From budget to opulent, when a hotel is ready to refurbish their rooms, they delegate all of the room's furnishings to a few select liquidators, one being this one in Duncanville. A cherry armoire that retailed when new for $5,000 was marked down to a pitiful $150. Almost flawless, including the space to fit a large-screen TV and a mini-refrigerator. In their new location on Hwy. 67, nothing much has changed. This is the place for the $5 lamps, the $295 complete bedroom suites, the $25 sofas, the $75 entertainment centers, the $100 industrial stoves, well, seeing is believing. Choose mirrors, chandeliers, industrial kitchen equipment and thousands of accents that will boggle your ever-loving bargain-shopping mind. From downtown Dallas, follow 35 South to the 67 (Marvin D. Love) split. Take 67 to the Polk Street exit and U-turn back onto the northbound service road, one half block on the right. Owner Bob Lloyd and his right hand helper

Jeff are there to see to it that there's an abundance of surplus. Go online to see what you will see and then find someone with a truck and go, man, go!

★★★   Pennies From Heaven   214/821-9192

4301 Bryant Street   Tues-Sat 10-5
Dallas, TX 75204
www.reconciliationoutreach.org

Penny pinchers might just find that their prayers have been answered at Pennies from Heaven. When you're feeling under the weather and want to bring a little sunshine back into your life, donate what you're not using to this charitable cause. Whether it's an item of value or your valuable time, you will be giving to Pennies From Heaven without experiencing a thunder shower. Discounts on thrift goods such as clothing, dishes, small housewares, books, belts, shoes, furniture, bric-a-brac, books, lamps and whatnots arrive Tuesdays through Saturdays, via the gracious generosity of others, and recycled back to those in search of a good deal. Every little bit helps. They accept many of their volunteer helpers from those who are serving out their community service sentence but so what? They take the help where they can get it.

★★★★   Prime Time Treasures   214/369-7446

9845 Central Expressway @Walnut Hill   Tues-Sat 10:30-4:30
Dallas, TX 75231

At the northwest corner of Walnut Hill, the senior artisans at Prime Time Treasures will tickle your fancy, without being so. If it's something for gift-giving, consider this a one-stop shopping experience from experienced hands. This project of the Assistance League of Dallas offers something for everyone, besides being a source of pride for folks in their prime. Lots of holiday decorations and home-made crafts made by senior artisans are donated and sold to benefit the Assistance League of Dallas. A source of pride for not ready for prime-time players. See what a difference it makes to all who are involved in this worthy cause.

★★★★   Resale by CCA /CCA   972/315-6544

2202 Business Hwy. 121 @ Corporate   Mon-Fri 10-8; Sat 10-6 (donation area closes at 5)
Lewisville, TX 75057

Formerly Bargain Depot, this Christian Community Action charity is one of the most successful Lewisville as ever seen. Somewhere, every day, you'll see their trucks tooling up and down the streets loading up from one home to the next cast-offs that eventually are put out to pasture at their big, spacious resale shop called ReSale. Isn't that an imaginative name? Do your duty and contribute your hand-me-downs, hand-me-offs and hand-me-aways, too, to this community action program who is now settled into their new digs in the Albertson Shopping Center. Fill up a shopping cart and when it overflows, it's time to check out. Then, when the cash register totals $50, you'll be shocked that they've tallied five shirts, three pairs of men's pants, four pairs of shoes, two hats, a sports jacket, a baseball cap, a baseball jacket and let me see, what else? That's because most things are $1 or $2. If you want to donate some items, give them a call and they'll set up a pick-up time.

★★★   Salvation Army   214/353-2731

6500 Harry Hines   Mon-Sat 10-6
Dallas, TX 75235
www.salvationarmy.org

We want you! To be a price-conscious shopper, that is! Even if it means stopping by the local Salvation Army to rummage around the boxes, shelves, racks and displays, it's highly recommended
as an aerobic activity. You burn off at least 100 calories just running around looking for things in
their main resale shop on Harry Hines. You'll never know what you'll find. The hunt is on for per-
fectly-priced clothing for men, women and children who are big, small, short or tall. Fall in love
with the housewares, baskets, lamps, toys, bikes, furniture, small office equipment, yard tools and
appliances and come out a winner. Win the war on high prices. One man's trash is another man's
treasure, so just about anything goes here. And don't forget to give your unused items along with
your spare change to the ringing bells during the holiday season. All those pennies you save at the
store can be turned around and put to good use. Spare a dime? How about a hundred? A thousand?
These days, anything goes. The Salvation Army is now accepting boats, cars, motorcycles and
trailer donations. Don't forget—it all goes to a worthy cause and every penny is tax deductible.
This generosity could be your salvation come tax time. Watch for their online store soon and if
interested, you can donate online. Their website is internationally full of feature material and
information on their charitable activities. Rummaging is the key, digging down deep is your salvation, both when your shopping and when you're donating.

★   T-Mart Bazaar   817/534-7709

3137 E. Seminary   Mon-Thurs 10-8:30; Fri-Sat 9:30-9
Fort Worth, TX 76119

This bazaar might look at you as a little bizarre if you ask too many questions but. But if you just
dig around, there are deals to be found....just don't bother asking a lot of questions. It's like pulling
teeth—your own! We didn't find anything to really rave about in furniture. The price on dinettes
was small but so were the dinettes. You can buy an inexpensive dinette table and four chairs with
a glass top for $119 that should hold up long enough to scarf down a pizza or a box of Kentucky
Fried wings. Children's headboards were priced low ($29) but didn't seem like they'd hold up to
much horseplay. In fact, none of the furniture, quite frankly, looked like heirloom quality (useable
after a year or more.) Choose the typical metal versions that you see all over town in a variety of
colors for the same price. About the only thing that really rang our chimes were pagers for $15.99.
That price included the pager, the activation fee and the first month. After that, the monthly fee
was just $9.73 and there was no need to pay for a full year in advance to get that rate. It's up to you
to find them, shop them, rate them and buy what you find in worthwhile condition. Mostly, it's
stuff that doesn't quite meet the grade (unless it is low-grade).

★★★★★   Thrift Town   817/625-2864

2444 Jacksboro Hwy.   Mon-Fri 9-8; Sat 10-7
Fort Worth, TX 76114
www.thrifttown.com

A thrift store that gives tours? Now, how about that? It's like going behind the scenes to see how
the other half lives, if truth be known. Being thrifty is thrifty spent. Prudent shoppers all unite at
one of the four Metroplex Thrift Town locations. With plenty of room in which to roam, their
well-lit and organized showrooms gladly accept tax-deductible donations. All proceeds benefit
ARC, the Association for Retarded Citizens. We liked the fact that the dressing rooms were not
only available but clean, too. Find clothing (including some vintage), furniture, housewares, shoes,

toys, bedding, jewelry, belts, purses, books and more, all at reasonable prices. Saturdays are busy, so try stopping in on a weekday when shopping is less chaotic. The good stuff goes quickly, so early birds gather the best deals. If you have something that you would like to donate, even serviceable items, call for pick up at 817/624-7001. Enjoy their corporate website and consider them a First Class Second-Hand store. The beauty of their efforts is that they really help the mentally challenged, plus provide top-quality pre-owned merchandise for fiscally-challenged customers. For the past 30 years, you, too, can join the group of most happy fellas. If you want to clean up what the other guys left behind, enjoy the mystery of the hunt separating the cheap from the chic on top of the heap. Visit their other locations on Westmoreland in Dallas, North Richland Hills and Arlington.

★★★   Thrift Village   972/278-1026

1829 S. Garland Ave.   Mon-Sat 9-8; Sun 11-6
Garland, TX 75042

If you're in the neighborhood, stop by Thrift Village and make this your lucky day. Then again, maybe not—this Village is a hit or miss on good deals. Hillary, you may be wrong as to what it takes to make a Village. Some items were right on the money while others resembled the Village People's rejected wardrobe. A township of clothing for men, women, children and infants were the bulk of the inventory with a few scattered outsiders hanging on. Stragglers included some housewares, furniture and sporting goods that were hanging on by a thread. If you're looking to frame something, consider buying the used frames here. For $5 a framed picture, it won't matter if you don't like the picture. Surely, within this garage sale/thrift store, you can find something of value. But if you donate, you'll have the double pleasure of providing something of value to someone in need and buying something of value that brings you pleasure as well. That's an entirely different story. Proceeds benefit the Cancer Federation, so be sure to give Janet a call if you need large items picked up. Located in the Garland Shopping Center. They do have solicitors that call to let you know when there's a truck in your area for donations but they also encourage you to call and verify the name of the solicitor with their store since so many fraudulent companies are out there posing as non-profit organizations. An educated consumer is ....

★★★★★★   Top Line Warehouse Store   972/262-5326

433 E. Church St.   Mon-Sat 9:30-6
Grand Prairie, TX 75050

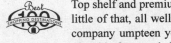

Top shelf and premium brands line the aisles of this warehouse. A little of this and a little of that, all well-organized and priced low. That's how Bud Bobbitt started his company umpteen years ago and it's how he continues to maintain the Top Lines today. No membership fees needed to get the deals just as we reeled the steals on pet food and supplies like **NATURE'S RECIPE** five-pound bag for $1.99 and a 40-pound bag for $12.95. **WALTHAM** eight-pound bags were $8 and **IAMS** canned food was a mere 89 cents. Other brands included **ALPO, CYCLE** and **PEDIGREE**, but brands come and go around here. From pet supplies to paper goods, groceries, office supplies and more, it's all here at big savings. There's even a pharmacy in the front of the store. But don't forget to look across the street to their other store, Top Line Select, which specializes in clothing, fabrics, toys and books. This location is at 208 N.E. 5th St. and is open Tues-Sat 10-5.

★★★★★   **Trading Post**   **972/263-7117**

818 W. Main St.   Mon-Sat 9:30-6; Sun 9:30-5
Grand Prairie, TX 75050

Mosey on over and stake your claim at this station of value. Hear thee, pardner, the Trading Post exchanges quality merchandise for cash or trade. From TVs to VCRs, appliances, furniture, tools, whatever, it's all fair game. Dust if off, polish it up and bring it on in. New and used as long as it hasn't been abused. Merchandise changes frequently. Last month, washers and dryers tumbled in and cleared out. This month it was refrigerators and stoves that changed the temperature in these here parts. Next month, it might be a stampede of CD players. (Now that would be music to my ears.) Ride 'em off into the sunset but before howling at the moon, be sure to pull on those heart-strings. Dress the part and round up your posse. Head out to the Trading Post where they'll wheel and deal their way into your heart, too. Don't dress in your finery; they might think you don't want to save money. From appliances to tools, electronics to housewares, **BEANIE BABIES** to animal bean bags, you'll roar with the best of them—both new and used. What fun, even if you're not Emily Post. Shop if for no other reason than to see a dying breed of bargain haunts. From **AVON** to **TUPPERWARE, GE** to **KENMORE**, there's always more right around the corner. Hey, get a load of those tools and that TV set? My, my, my dear, what low prices you have!

Telephones

10-10 Phone Rates

603/484-1273

PMB #119, 1125-B Arnold Drive

24/7

Martinez, CA 94553-4104

www.10-10PhoneRates.com 🖱 *Top Online Store!*

You need a Phd. to discern the various phone rates just to have a fair chance at determining who to call, what to buy, who's got the best rates. You give up in desperation. Not any more! Save time and money with rate comparisons of more than a dozen 10-10 and 10-x dial around phone plans. Avoid bad deals like 10-10-220 and compare cheap long distance services like **EVERDIAL** or 10-15-335. In fact, making calls with most 10-10 services does not require signing up or switching your regular long distance service. Dial the plan's seven-digit code (such as 101-6868 or 10-15-335, for example), then the phone number you are calling. Another way you can save money. Believe it or not, some dial around plans keep billing current customers old rates. When new, lower rates are offered to attract new customers, existing users still continue to pay the higher rates! That's a no-no! By checking 10-10PhoneRates.com you will know to call your current telephone company and ask them to switch your phone to lower rates. Consumer Alerts! There are often tons of mistakes, surcharges to mobile phones, increases in reconnect fees, over billing, and you can't find out who to talk to complain yet there's no one to talk to to correct the problems. At this site, when, for example, when a plan doubles their connection fee, often times you will be automatically assessed the higher rates because you would have missed the deadline—conveniently. Refer back to the website since the changes can make your crazy. At least this web site can clear away some of the confusion and gobbly-gook. Hear ye, Hear ye. Read the Consumer Alerts where all those secret changes are posted. You can be connected to comparing phone rates in all 50 states and over 200 countries. You can also click on Dial-1 plans and other types of long distance fees. Compare state rates and link to other interesting and/or related sites such as to find out an area code, to U.S. phone books, how to contact a telephone company and their phone numbers and more. Want to connect to 4.9 cents a minute for state-to-state rates with no monthly fee. The ultimate goal of this site is, of course, to save consumers money. Make educated choices instead of stumbling in the dark. They do not want to sell any long distance plans or work for the phone company. They will alert you "before" the fact to any rate increases. How to get adjustments from your phone company? Well, a prayer wouldn't hurt; but too, listen to the expert, Rick Sayer of Martinez, California who's behind the scene at this website. He'll reveal company tricks shoppers need to know to protect themselves from unscrupulous telephone companies. For questions about specific 10-10 plans, this website will direct you to their toll-free customer service numbers for individual phone companies. Same with the "dial 1" plans and other types of plans. Remind them you read about it on the 10-10 Phone Rates site. Avoiding dial-around run around is the key. Matching the service with the type of phone call you wish to make is pretty time consuming but it's almost the only way to save any money. As always, read the fine print. A price quote on a phone plan doesn't always include everything—one shopper chose a plan for $49.99 a month. She signed up but instead of the bill she expected, she got billed in June and July for $74 per month. So, it pays to pay attention and it pays to shop around. This site will help you do so. Another website by this consumer advocate is www.phone-bill-alert.com. Get involved by helping alert other consumers by watching your phone bill and reporting rate or fee increases to www.Bill-Alert.com.

101 Phones

63 W. 38th Street, Suite 806   24/7
New York, NY 10018

www.101phones.com   🖰 *Top Online Store!*

This specialty store features products by such well known telephone operators as **AT&T**, **NORTEL**, **PANASONIC**, **PLANTRONICS**, **SIEMENS**, **UNIDEN**, **VTECH** and others. After five years refining their online site, they've got their act down pat and are really connected now. One ringy-dingy, and you, too, can order single-line or multi-line portable and desktop lines and more with a top rating by Bizrate naming them to be in the top 1 percent of all consumer electronics sites on the internet (even out-performing big name competitors such as Officemax, Radioshack, Compusa, Buy.com, Officedepot and others.) Hello competitors. Are you listening? Great customer support makes for flawless transactions that are often overlooked in corporate America. Their phone support staff use all of the phones themselves and can therefore recommend one with some degree of familiarity to meet your needs. Their website makes it a snap to shop for phones with your first course in telephone shopping 101. Fast and FREE SHIPPING plus the benefit of getting many name brand phones and different systems at a discount. (Now we're talkin'!) If anything comes defective, or if you're not satisfied, don't worry. Each purchase comes with a 30-day satisfaction guarantee on brand new items only. On factory-refurbished items, they are guaranteed to work upon delivery; if not, you've got 30-days to exchange it for the exact same one that does. Factory Serviced Phones come with a 30-day, 90-day, or one-year warranty depending on the model of the phone. They do assess a 10 percent restocking fee if you return or cancel a product plus shipping costs. (But that's pretty standard in the business.) Leave it to the Cohen's to come up with a better plan; there's a phone just waiting for you, priced for less on their site. Shop for cordless and corded phones, multi-line phones, the new 5-86GHz phones, conference phones, beamer video phones, fax machines, special need phones, novelty phones, designer phones, headsets, batteries, accessories, answering machines, booster antennas, caller ID, two-way radios, music on hold in both new and refurbished phones with closeouts sprinkled through the site. *Call toll-free: 877/374-6635*

ABTolls

Dallas, TX   24/7

www.ABTolls.com   🖰 *Top Online Store!*

In concert with www.tollchaser.com, this company has a handle on helping you figure out the cheapest long-distance phone plans. It's a FREE website for all of us to share their findings and post them on this site. The founders estimate that they have about 10,000 researchers out there who donate their time and experience to ensure that the site's data is up to date. They have all kinds of interesting comparative tools to rate your current service, including comparing international rates, should you be so lucky as to live in Afghanistan, Albania, Algeria, Antarctica....well you get the picture, all the way to Yugoslavia, Zaire, Zimbabwe. They've got a good consumer corner to answer your questions, giving help when needed in reading your phone bill, a complaint resolution arena, how to stop telemarketers, where to get Free Directory Assistance and more. At the time we checked, they were working on the same comparative services for cellular phone plans as well. This is not part of some giant telecommunications provider's website. The reason they don't have a phone number is because this site is managed by three guys with full-time jobs elsewhere who try to run this cool website. It's a start to getting down to the nitty-gritty so you can determine for yourselves whether you're getting a good deal or not. Good luck.

★★★★   Cellular Warehouse   Hot Line 972/467-009

701 S. Stemmons Frwy.   Mon-Fri 9-6:30; Sat 9-6
Lewisville, TX 75067

With five locations in the Metroplex, turn to this juggernaut when you're ready to join the cellular revolution. Supposedly, it's cheaper by the dozen, the length of time this company's been wiring us up, and, now, you can hook up to the Dish Network through them with no equipment to buy. Get a grip on your monthly cable costs for $40.99 and a $49.99 activation fee. What you get is FREE installation, two receivers, 100 digital channels, 100 digital CD music channels and an in-house service policy. Pretty good deal. Check first for even better deals as they seem to get better all the time. And yes, they also "cell" all the other keeping-in-touch gadgets that we've grown accustomed to, like cell phones and pagers. Too, window tinting is still part of their repertoire. Call their Hotline for the location nearest you.

Digital Cellutions

Dallas, TX   24/7

www.digitalcellutions.com   ⌐ *Top Online Store!*

There are many cites on line to easily compare and purchase popular cell phones and plans specific to the Dallas/Fort Worth area. Tons of FREE phone offers, many with FREE accessories. Regardless of your needs, they can get you connected; there are even sites that included cash back. With FREE long distance and no roaming fees on many of the rate plans, don't just shop for a cell phone by listening to the commercials. Let the computer do your comparative shopping for you. For one, www.digitalcellutions.com is a good place to start. Other online comparison sites include: www.point.com and www.letstalk.com. As they say, don't shop for cell phone plans without them.

DO NOT CALL LIST   888/382-1222

Dallas, TX   24/7

www.ftc.gov/donotcall   ⌐ *Top Online Store!*

For the DO NOT CALL FTC's list to keep telemarketers from tying up your phone lines, cut 'em off at the quick. Registration is FREE online or through a toll-free number above. For details, see www.ftc.gov/donotcall.com. The ban takes place within three months after you register and you remain on the list for five years or until your phone number changes. The registry should eliminate most unsolicited calls, except for those from charities, political fundraisers and firms with which you do business. Phone calls made directly to consumers by banks and insurance companies are already regulated by the Federal Communications Commission rather than the FTC, but they are likely to be covered by the list as well. This list goes into effect in July, 2003.

◆◆◆   **Nextel Wireless**   **972/241-8400**

2905 Forest Lane   Mon-Fri 9-7; Sat 10-6
Dallas, TX 75229
www.nextel.com

Hang up on Telephone Warehouse—they are now kaput with a new telephone company in their place. Called Nextel Wireless, they operate at the same location with the same phone number, and these guys give direct connect a whole other meaning. They've got cell phones that work like walkie talkies with those on your network: business network, family network or association network of colleagues. Wireless web services are also available. Whatever web you want to weave, get 400 minutes with all incoming calls FREE, all direct connects are FREE and long distance is FREE for only $69.99 a month. (Or at least that was one modis operating plan when we checked.) Log on to their website to view current talky walkies. Considering what you might be paying for long distance, cell phones often put a real boost to your savings. Or if you'd prefer a plan with FREE nights and weekends, then how does 300 minutes and 100 direct connect minutes for $39.99 sound? Lots of plans and so many choices. This is probably one of the better plans for business communication between employees, if your company's more than a party of two. Find a cell phone on sale for as little as $49.99 and you may even be ready for the wireless web! Are you?

Reverse Phone Directory

Dallas, TX   24/7

www.reversephonedirectory.com   🖱 *Top Online Store!*

Every once in a while, www.switchboard.com or www.411.com doesn't come through with a listing. And, here I sit, wanting to know where someone is but all I've got is their address. No problem. You should be able to secure who lives there by going to www.reverseaddress.com or, if you're looking for a phone number or all you have is the phone number and you want to know who lives there, check out www.reversephonedirectory.com. So there. Go play private detective.

Uniden   **800/297-1023**

4700 Amon Carter Blvd.   Mon-Fri 7-7 (CST); Weekends & Holidays 9-5 (CST)
Fort Worth, TX 76155

www.uniden.com   🖱 *Top Online Store!*

Calling all UNIDEN fans? Say hello to their online store where there's a variety of "like-new" Uniden products. No one will know the difference and the price savings on their refurbs is substantial. But there have been times when the products ordered just looked good....but weren't! Be sure to pay attention to the condition of the item before ordering. The condition is listed so you're the first to know. And although their intentions you can rely on, sometimes their products aren't as reliable. (Personal experience taught us a lesson.) Choose from a variety of product categories including cordless phones (2.4 Ghz Digital, 900 Mhz Digital, 900 Mhz Analog), FRS radios, radar detectors, scanners, marine radios, CB radios and Roger and out! Available at their website are manuals, a variety of rebates and coupons, how-to register your products, repairs and a bevy of other helpful hints. They also offer accessories for all Uniden products and various other accessories such as cellular batteries, scanner headphones and universal remotes. One noteworthy item that piqued our interest included the TRU248, 2.4 Ghz Digital Spread Spectrum Cordless with Call Waiting/Caller ID and Digital Answering System for $100. That is a Wow kind of product worth considering.

Toys

Collectible Trains and Toys
214/373-9469

10051 Whitehurst Drive, Suite 200
Dallas, TX 75243
www.trainsandtoys.com;

Mon-Fri 10-6; Sat 10-5

 Since 1981, they have been on the right track for saving on collectible trains and toys. Choo-choo boogie and see what this depot is all about. Keeping it all in the family, they have weathered a tough year and come up with some interesting ways to save the day—and it's called "pre-sale." Their expansion to 12,000 square feet in the Skillman Crossing Center at Skillman and LBJ, just a few minutes north of their original site, is evidence they are doing something right. Check out their library of over 1,000 book titles, if you're a hobbyist on the track for a good read. Lone Star Toys shares this newly-reconstructed building with Collectible Trains & Toys along with "The Lone Star Backshop," a warehouse-type area where collections are sorted and stacked. The Backshop is open to the public for browsing and buying. Their Toys of Yester-year can be viewed on their lonestartoys.com site. *Call toll-free: 800/462-4902*

★★★★★ Constructive Playthings
972/418-1860

1927 E. Belt Line
Carrollton, TX 75006
www.ustoyco.com

Mon-Fri 9-7; Sat 9-5; Sun 12-5

Party, party, let's have a party, smarty. And if you're one of us, you already know where to get your party decorations. When you enter their store, in person, via their catalogue or online, you know there is no one better when it comes to educational toys, party novelties and in general inexpensive doodads for school, play or party. Most things are priced so low, they cost more to mail than to buy. Browse through three different divisions until you find the perfect....whatever. There's an immense selection and a full line of challenging stage magic supplies, tricks, videos and magic books, too. In fact, in Kansas City, they have the largest magic store in the world. Choose from a clowning section with videos, costumes, professional make-up and more. Constructive Playthings is made up of the School Division and the Parent/Family Division, award-winning suppliers of the finest early childhood educational toys, equipment, books, records, tapes, videos, art supplies and teaching aids. They search the world and pick only those products that promote, enhance and enrich the growth of children. The catalog is FREE for the asking. Imagine, every festive occasion can be celebrated with something from here at up to 70 percent off. Lucky for us, we can spin the wheel and land in Carrollton to shop their store as well. *Call toll-free: 800/841-6478*

★★★★★   **Discount Model Trains**   **972/931-8135**
4641 Ratliff Lane   Mon-Sat 10-6
Addison, TX 75248
www.trains.com

I think I can, I think I can—well here, you definitely can!!! For an extensive website about toy trains, read all about it at www.trains.com. Then shop at this brick-and-mortar store in Addison and get on the right track. Discount Model Trains, since 1989, has provided in-stock trains to the tune of over 60,000 G to Z scale, with most products discounted 20 percent off manufacturers'suggested retail price. Every little bit helps with this hobby that can get quite expensive. Only a small sampling of their inventory is on their website, but most things in the current Walther's Catalog, plus hard-to-find and unique items, are either in-stock or readily available from here. Model trains in sizes HO (the most popular size requested), N and G are available, too! They have the largest selection of anybody in town, that we know of, anyway. You might want to check out Mike's Hobby Shop on Stemmons in Carrollton (1740 S Interstate 35E; Phone: 972/242-4930).

★★★★★   **Dolls of Yesterday & Today**   **972/242-8281**
1014 S. Broadway, # 108   Wed-Sat 10:30-4:30
Carrollton, TX 75006
www.dollsoldandnew.com

Hello, Dolly! Say hello to hundreds of current and discontinued MADAME ALEXANDERS in stock. Great prices on clearance BARBIES, GENES and TONNERS, too. (They are so expert in the doll business, they can even provide an ALEXANDERS appraisal in case you need it for insurance.) Looking for dolls, well, how can you keep them in boxes forever? Put them in an upright position on a doll stand and show them off! They have a large library of collectors'books and catalogs available for sale. All of the books are in new condition. You'll find ALEXANDER BABIES, ANN & ANDY, RAGGEDY ANN & ANDY and other vintage dolls that only get better with age. Yeah! Want a play doll or a bear to hug? They've got them, too. Did you miss the Jackie White House fashions'exhibit? No problem, as you can still buy fabulous JACKIE dolls online and at their overstock clearance price. Wow! Since 1981, Marilyn and A. Scott Dundon have made shopping for dolls state-of-the-heart. Shopping online is a cinch. FREE shipping on U.S. orders of $100 or more. Layaway available. What a doll! *Call toll-free: 1/800-327-DO*

★★   **Hammett's Learning World**   **972/270-3155**
63 Driftwood Village   Mon-Fri 9-8; Sat 9-6; Sun Noon-5
Mesquite, TX 75150
www.hammett.com

If it's in their catalog, it's online, too. From office and art materials, teaching resources to furniture, plus audio and visual tools and aids, if you think there's an end to learning, you haven't met Hammett. This educational resource was formerly called The Teacher's Store, but, now, more than just teachers are interested in teaching their children out-of-school, in-school skills. Delivering school tools at educated prices, it won't bring a raise but it might make the load lighter. Ideas can start to flow for children in grades K-6. After that, encouragement is probably the best teacher. Pick the possibilities from an A-to-Z selection of paints, crayons, scissors, stickers, pens, pencils, flash cards, letters, poster board and classroom "stuff" that students want so they keep up to "snuff." If it's not in the store, you can order through their catalog which costs $5. The catalogue is sold at all their locations except the Mesquite store; in Carrollton at Frankford and Josey; Arlington in the Lincoln Square Shopping Center; and Plano at Independence Parkway. Everything offered in their catalog is available online as well. From office and art materials, teaching resources to furniture, audio-visual tools to learning aids, you can only make an "A" by shopping here. ***Call toll-free: 800/955-2200***

Hobby-Warehouse   859/986-0020

128 Mt.Vernon Rd.   24/7
Berea, Ky 40403

www.hobby-warehouse.com   🛒 ***Top Online Store!***

Easy in and easy out for all hobby lovers. One click and you're at one of the best discounters online. For N Scale Train sets, regular price on the **BACHMANN** Highballer Union Pacific E-Z Set N Scale was $79.99; their price $46.99; and the Yuletide Special Set was $89 for $69.99. So, see, you don't have to come up on the caboose side if you know where to shop. Also, great prices on batteries for everything, though not as dramatic a savings since some of the prices are low to begin with. For example, the 3V Lithum Battery is regularly $7.99 and their price is $4.99. Look for all kinds of things on their website: Accessories, airplanes, apparel, arts & crafts, bumps and flying saucers, boats and submarines, cars and trucks, diecast models, engines and motors, games and collectable, helicopters, kites, nitro fuel, paintball, radios chargers, science and learning projects, software and videos, tanks and military vehicles and of course trains and racetracks. Spend almost as many hours browsing online as you'll spend on the activities. But it's all in the name of fun. These call carry manufacturers warranty and are all new (not refurbished or used.)

★★ Iron Horse Hobbies   972/317-7062

1400 Moccasin Trail, #5   Tues-Fri 11-6; Sat 10-5
Lewisville, TX 75067
www.ironhorsehobbies.com

Get on track to collecting trains, a hobby that will carry you through to the end of the line. One of the area's few full-service train shops, here is where you can start a relationship with trains—but only if you intend to be a collector (and not a conductor!) The discount is only 10 percent, but the conversation and wealth of information is priceless. To get that discount, ask to join their "gold card" program. Each purchase gets a hole punched on the card; after 10 purchases, you get a $25 in-store credit toward your next purchase. All popular scales and gauges for model rail equipment are available, while others can be special ordered. Rack up the tracks! They carry N, HO, O, G and S as well as a nice selection of "how-to" books and magazines. Expect their stock to increase dramatically around October in anticipation of the holiday rush.

★★★★★ Just Jump'n   972/485-5006

2021 Copper Street   By Reservation Only
Garland, TX 75040
www.justjumpn.com

Do you think this belongs in the back yard chapter? Entertainment? Probably yes, on both counts; but if you think Kids—Toys—Fun, all go together, then you're in the right chapter, the Toy Chapter. A full day's rental for these inflatable bounceable house rentals, slippy slides, circus clowns, Jurassic Parks or Princess Palaces is worth the joy it brings to girls and boys. At Hannah's 4th birthday party, about a dozen kids were occupied for several hours inside these bounceable, whatever you want to call them—houses of fun that keep them out of the sun. And when all things are said and done, you can't beat it—as low as $49. FREE Delivery! FREE Setup! Lowest Prices! See the number above to call and have a ball. Many different styles to choose from and same day service. Don't overlook the weekday specials, especially during the summer when any day will do for a birthday bash. *Call toll-free: 877/771-5867*

★★★★★   K-B Toys Outlet Store   254/582-1052

Prime Outlet Center at Hillsboro   Mon-Sat 10-8; Sun 11-6
104 I-35 NE Hillsboro, TX 76645
www.kbtoys.com

It's A-OK at K-B Toys if you're looking for the ABCs of gift-giving. Thousands of toys, collectible toys, video games and software titles at great prices. You'll have no problem finding what you want. Browse the main departments: Toys, Software, Video Games, Collectibles or just land at the Outlet. Or if you prefer, simply shop by age, price or brand. It's so simple, even a child could do it! If you're looking for a birthday or holiday gift, visit the Gift Center. Find expert gift advice and specially-created Gift Guides. Can't resist a bargain? Check out the Surprise of the Day—and don't miss their "Great Values." Thousands of items in every brand: BARBIE, CRAYOLA, FISHER-PRICE, LITTLE TIKES, POKEMON, RADIO FLYER, STAR WARS, trading cards and more. It's like being in a candy store without the calories. If you need to return or exchange a product, you can take it to one of the 1,300 K-B Toys stores nationwide. Also,since they recently purchased the eToys name, features and merchandise, there is nary a toy that can't be found online. Watch for new features like "Wish List" and "Gift Wrap" coming soon. Overall, this is the best toy store if you dismiss Toys R Us as a competitor. *Call toll-free: 877/522-8697*

★★★★★★   Mattel Toy Club, The   817/302-3360

501 Meacham Blvd.   Mon-Sat 10-5
Fort Worth, TX 76106-1969
www.mattel.com

This club has written "The Toy Story," both chapter and verse for years. If it's toys you're wanting, the MATTEL/FISHER PRICE clearance center is the place to win, place and show. Well-versed in the toys that your children love to play with, day in and day out, The Toy Club is the source for undivided attention. Buy it all at wholesale prices; then pick up an additional 10 percent off discount card (it's FREE) in the store and you'll be saving even more. Names like BARBIE, FISHER PRICE, HOT WHEELS, MATCHBOX, SESAME STREET PRESCHOOL, TYCO and more. Could life get any better? This warehouse is brimming with the biggies. Some damaged, unclaimed, overstocked, or undersold—who cares?! What a lifesaver at birthday party time. Load up when the price is right. Have you noticed how educational most toys are these days? (They teach us how little we can get for our money!) Not here. There were lots of BARBIES (even collector Barbies—even Barbie Bazaar magazines) and other hotties that were discounted as much as 70 percent. Weekly specials result in an ever-changing inventory, so call before you shop. Note their new address near the Meacham Airport. This is your last chance to beat the other parents and grandparents who line up. Be sure to check prices carefully as some may be closer to retail than I'd like to report. Strike only when the deals are hot! Mail order available.

★★★★ Merrill Discount Trampolines   972/424-2285

1909 Hillcrest   Mon-Sat 9-5
Plano, TX 75074
www.discounttrampolines.com

Jump around, turn around and do a pirouette. Jump on the only discount trampoline source in town, be it round or rectangle. Since they represent a company who manufactures them locally, you'll be a jumping bean in no time. Both new and used models available, from $300 to $500. They're the only dealer in the U.S.A. to carry the **JUMP KING** European Model, a rectangular 9 x 15-foot model with heavy-duty pads, brand new, for $550. Check the website for pictures of models which can be ordered and available almost immediately. Though inventory was low, stock is always a phone call away. *Call toll-free: 800/449-3598*

Not Just Dolls   972/412-2525

2801 Lawing Lane, Suite B   Thurs-Sat 10-5
Rowlett, TX 75088

www.notjustdollsdallas.com   🖰 *Top Online Store!*

Oh, you beautiful doll, you great big beautiful doll. But if you think there's just dolls, think again. Since 1988, Suzanne has been one of our doll-babies of choice with one of the largest selections in Texas. Not only on line, but in their new, limited-hours location in Rowlett. Consider any of these dolls part of your new family and add generations to your collection. From **ANNETTE HIMSTEDTS** to **DADD'S LONG LEGS**, **MADAME ALEXANDER** to **MARIE OSMOND**, take your pick. Line up the beauties. **BARBIES** are waiting to be picked up while **ANNETTE FUNICELLO BEARS** and **BEANIE BABIES** were waiting to be hugged. They now have a local online store. They are always adding inventory, so stop by often.

Squadron Mail Order   972/242-8663

Carrollton, TX 75011   Mail Order Catalog Sales Only

www.squadron.com   🖰 *Top Online Store!*

After more than 30 years, Squadron Mail Order is the oldest and considered the most reliable mail order firm in the United States specializing in military models, books and modeling supplies. They scour the world to find just the best modeling supplies, maintaining an inventory of over $2 million within their 50,000-square-foot warehouse in Carrollton. Say "Tanks" for the memories. This defender of discounts on model airplanes, motorcycles, bombers, battleships, tanks and other military items can win the war on boredom single-handedly. Saving 30 to70 percent is one easy way to call a truce. Then order from their catalog, the latest one we have is 104 pages with 32 pages in color. Then, expect 12 monthly updates to keep you up-to-date on new products as well as additional bargains. Orders are shipped within 24 hours, really. While they cannot accommodate shoppers in person, you can order from their catalog or by phone or fax. Squadron is known throughout the world for publishing a catalog that is also considered a reference guide. With over 10,000 modeling items, and a subscription of $5 per year (that includes the 12-monthly newsletters that contain some 3,000 listings), you'll be accessing both new and sale items including what they call their Super Sale items. Make your day, but you better be a "model" customer!

★★★★★ **Ace Cruises Inc.**   **903/887-6339**

1360 V.Z.C.R 2719
Mabank, TX 75147
www.acecruises.com

By Reservation Only

Hook your wagon to the stars and dream; but call Ace Cruises to set your sails. Whether you want to hop aboard a cruise for a few days out of Galveston for practically pennies on the hour or look for an around-the-world, get-away-from-it-all long, long time trip, these cruise specialists can book it and save you money. They're the one....no I mean, two cruise aficionados, Donnie and Sharon Finley. Some sample trips included a five- day cruise from Galveston, $409.15 for an inside cabin and $459.15 for an outside cabin. Remember, that also included all of your meals....and there are lots of all-you-can eat 'til you split a gut gluttony on board. Try a Mexican cruise for $364.15 inside cabin and $414.15 for an outside cabin for seven days. What about an Alaskan cruise on board the "Mercury" for $775 for an inside cabin or $975 for an outside cabin. And that's just the tip of the iceberg. Go online and see where else they'll lead you. Ship Ahoy, mates! *Call toll-free: 888/295-9266*

★★ **Air King Travel & Tours, Inc.**   **972/931-8991**

17440 Dallas Parkway , Suite 262
Dallas, TX 75247

Mon-Fri 9:30-5:30; Sat 9-1

Occasionally, it's nice to be treated like royalty. Fly to the moon if that is on your vacation itinerary. Buckle up and hop aboard Air King's wholesale travel network. If ever there's a family emergency, don't panic—they specialize in both domestic and international fares on average about $398 for same day travel. Cross over the moat for that personal touch. No automation here; each person is like a special delivery. Ride the waves in Hawaii, Monday to Monday, for $598; or maybe you'd like to walk the Commons in Boston—a real bargain for $198. Don't leave your heart in San Francisco even though the fare was a heart-felt $150. While Miami simmers at $180, you can take a bite out of the Big Apple (New York) for only $185. Rates change every Monday, Wednesday and Friday so when you know where and when you want to go, get your boarding pass and be gone. Then, if you want to escape from the mundane, they also specialize in exotica—tours that include everything from safaris to white-water rafting, adventure tours for cross-country skiers to mountaineering for that record-setting climb. Expect to wait five to seven minutes to speak to a travel consultant. It's maddening waiting on the phone.

★★★★★   **Anglin Rose Bed & Breakfast, The**   **817/641-7433**

808 S. Anglin

By Reservation Only

Cleburne, TX 76031

Cleburne is bursting with bed and breakfasts and this one is a real beaut! Without sticking you with the thorn of extravagant prices, The Anglin Rose is a charming Victorian home that has been faithfully restored to its original 1892 elegance and authenticity, but with prices in line with the turn of the century. Don't miss the two "theme rooms," Grandma's Room and Uncle Sam's. Even if Uncle Sam doesn't want you, you can still appreciate rates of $90 during the week. Check in at two and out at noon, with a seven-day cancellation policy. Enjoy a full breakfast, snacks, beverages and complimentary basket upon departure. You won't even have to give up your cable TV and you'll have access to a small kitchen area and a balcony view of the majestic oak tree. Tie a yellow ribbon on your finger so you won't forget this travel stop. *Call toll-free: 800/899-4538*

★★★★   **Buffalo Girls Hotel**   **903/567-7829**

Hwy 64 East

Reservation Only

Canton, TX 75103

www.buffalogirlshotel.com

When you're ready to commit to a weekend of serious shopping at First Monday in Canton, why not make it a weekend for serious relaxation, too? Why drive back and forth to Dallas or Fort Worth? You know good and well you can't see it all in a day and do justice to the Mountain, the Old Mill Marketplace, the Trade Days market and its six pavilions. A sleepover with the girls at The Buffalo Girls is some kind of fun. With their nine different period-decorated rooms all with TVs, VCRs and private baths, expect to shell out $95-$250. A continental breakfast is thrown in and your children and pets are welcome. No smoking inside the rooms. All the rooms are authentically decorated overlooking the Mountain where you can shop 'til you drop in old time 1800's pioneer shops, eat and ride the shuttle to the original First Monday Trade Grounds; or, sip cappuccino on your balcony and watch the real western shootouts.

★★★★★   **Carson House & Grille**   **903/856-2468**

302 Mount Pleasant St.

Mon-Fri (Lunch); Mon-Sat (Dinner)

Pittsburg, TX 75686

www.carsonhouse.com

What do you get when you have two Dallas-based gourmet cooks who want to raise their children in a small town in East Texas? You get the Carson House & Grille. Clark and Eileen Jesmore and family gave birth to the Carson House, the oldest occupied house in Pittsburg, Texas (home to Bo Pilgrim). Since 1991, the Carson House has been a bed and breakfast with beautifully appointed guest rooms for overnight accommodations, each with their own bath. Pick out a video to pop into the Vcr, curl up with a diet Coke and enjoy a relaxing respite. In the morning, you'll awaken to the aroma of freshly-baked muffins and a full-course homemade breakfast. Visit their website for room views and menu; enjoy the amenities of nearby lakes for fishing and water sports and don't overlook the antique shops around the bend. *Call toll-free: 888/302-1878*

★★★★ Cruise Masters   972/458-1000

13101 Preston Rd., Suite 300   Mon-Fri 10-6; Sat 11-3; Sun Noon-5
Dallas, TX 75240
www.bestcruisevalues.com

If you'd like to be in the Captain's chair, then board the bargain boat when they're traveling in December from Galveston to Cozumel. Set sail on a Mexican three-day cruise for a low of $290 per person plus tax. Now, that's a deal. No doubt, you'll eat enough food to justify the price. (And that doesn't even account for the fuel the boat eats up!) Or kick back for seven days on the Royal Caribbean. A seven-day Mexican cruise for four people would cost $335 per person. But if you think bunking for two is a bit crowded, imagine cramming four people, all with luggage, into one stateroom and one loo. Moo-ve over, baby. They represent all the major lines: CARNIVAL, CELEBRITY, COSTA CRUISES, HOLLAND AMERICA, NORWEGIAN, PRINCESS, RADISSON SEVEN SEAS, RENAISSANCE, ROYAL CARIBBEAN, ROYAL OLYMPIC and more. Cruise almost anywhere from Africa to Alaska, Antarctica to Australia, the Bahamas to Bermuda, Costa Rica to the Caribbean, Hawaii to the Holyland, the Mediterranean to....well, the world's your oyster. Most of their cruise specialists are CLIA accredited or are master-cruise counselors, so they know their stuff. There's also land vacations and accommodation specials on their website which is always loaded with values up the kazoo. Weather and passport links make vacation travel a breeze.

◆◆◆◆◆ Cruise Report   817/446-8962

Arlington, TX 76017   24/7
www.cruisereport.com   🖰 *Top Online Store!*

If you're a travel agency, you must subscribe to this unbiased cruise ship report. But if you're a cruise shopper, it's the most valuable resource you can log in to BEFORE taking the plunge. You don't want to jump in and be over your head in a cruise that won't suit your expectations, lifestyle, or dreams. With over 100 different ships, this company will help determine the right ship for you and chronicle the worse. See which four cruise lines are listed as the only 6-Star Awards of Excellence worthy of your consideration. Find out all of the extras you'll enjoy by hopping aboard a 6-Star cruise line: gratuities are included, for example, soft drinks and water are complimentary, wine with dinner, complimentary, and open bar is complimentary throughout the ship, complimentary champagne and caviar, in-room bar set ups, impeccable service, all the little extras and much more!

★★★★★ D-FW Tours   972/980-4540

7616 LBJ Frwy., Suite 524   24 Hours
Dallas, TX 75241
www.dfwtours.com

Established in 1978 as a wholesale tour operator, they are one of the largest volume airline consolidators. Don't be fooled by the localized name. These guys can fly you anywhere except the moon. Having contracts with over 35 major air carriers, D-FW Tours offers the almighty discounted consolidator fares. Anywhere you want to go, except the moon for the time being, there's a flight for it. Destinations are worldwide from more than 200 U.S. departure cities. Online, you'll find a scheduled airline service at wholesale rates. Most international fares are sold as air only, and usually don't require an advance purchase. D-FW Tours also offers senior, student, military, missionary and child fare discounts. Internationally-published sale fare-matching is permitted for select carriers and destinations. Visit them online to request a fare quote, to book a reservation and for information on domestic tours and reservation policies. *Call toll-free: 800/527-2589*

★★★★ Discount Travel 817/261-6114
Mon-Fri 9-6

5024 Trail Lake Drive
Fort Worth, TX 76133
www.bestfares.com

Imagine our surprise to find this travel agency is now part of the Best Fares network. Nevertheless, it always pays to check them out since they eke every last discount out of airfares. With every travel site wooing you, you might as well know the ropes. A round trip to New York city was $196.20 plus tax and Miami was $218 plus tax. From D/FW, that's a great price for a quick get-away. But remember Tom's warning, "You snooze, you lose!"

◆◆◆◆◆◆ Eagle Travel 972/387-9252
Mon-Fri 9-6

5301 Spring Valley Rd., #100
Dallas, TX 75254
www.EagleTravelInc.com

If you listen to the Diva, you know I'm no schmo. I like to save dough, but not if it means traveling cargo class. I'm there for the rest and relaxation, the fun, the pampering, breezes, music, dancing and food. Ah the food, glorious, food! So, how do I travel luxuriously for less? I put my travelin'cruise plans in the hands of owner of Eagle Travel, Marge Finstead and her right hand gal Mary Jean Thompson, two expert travelers who make my vacations once-in-a-lifetime experiences. I've been on three-day and seven-day cruises to the Caribbean and decided I've been there and done that. Where to go that I haven't been before? And do I want to forgo the a hip-hop cruises for the luxury of a six-star ship? Well, what do you think? We even raised our 100 BEST merchants to a 6-star status in honor of a six-star cruise that we are taking to Costa Rica. Eleven glorious days leaving from Fort Lauderdale and hitting Barbados, St. Barts, Martinique, the Panama Canal and then Cost Rica, baby. Eagle Travel is my agency of record. From Lori who has booked many weddings in Mexico and the Caribbean for Underground Shoppers to Elana, who's Russian and handles all of Josh's trips to his wife's native land. Plane—and simple. You don't want to leave home without them. Some agencies rock; this agency soars. They're the pro's in the know. In business since 1983, Eagle Travel has made its mark by providing bend-over-backwards service to their customers and to listeners of KAAM and the Diva. In fact, they are designated in the industry as a Virtuoso Agency, which reflects their top-notch status amongst other travel agencies. Since my father was a travel agent for 40 years, I know why folks use a travel agent and Eagle Travel is who is the agency of record for Underground Shoppers. Luxury for less. We're older now and expect the best—but of course, we want a deal! You might be able to navigate the internet for a variety of money-saving fares but then again, for a vacation, a trip-of-a lifetime, service from folks who have shopped from one port to the another (visit Eagle's offices and you'll see Marge's artifacts bought on the cheap from around the world,) an experienced agent can make the difference between just a trip and an experience. Owner Marge Finstead is a woman who stands head and shoulders above the crew—if shopping is what you want to do. Mary Jean is a dynamo who's always on the go and will take you along with her enthusiasm. Their new offices set the stage as a backdrop to their many years of travel experience. Every nook and cranny has a memento brought back from one trip or another. Get the picture? There are artifacts and handicrafts from around the world, each with a price tag of a few dollars or more. It's like a travelogue museum, elegant and entertaining. Every trip had memories and every trip had a story wrapped around the item on display. For example, Marge's shoe collection is worth the price of admission. Always tune in to the Underground Shopper's call-in show and check out the Travel

Button on www.undergroundshopper.com web site for Diva Specials with Eagle Travel. Getaway with the Diva and Marge and let's shop. From Martha's Vineyard to the flea markets of Buenos Aires, there's not a port that will remain un-shopped or untapped. If you're thinking about sailing with the Diva (and her awarding-winning golfer face-lifted husband), call Eagle Travel. We'll be taking detours when we land to shop, ladies (and gents are welcome too) and guys can play golf with Bob (ladies can, too.) Both reflect what we do best and we'd love to take you along, "if you lova us!" *Call toll-free: 800/326-7172*

Fantasy Suites   940/387-0591

820 South I-35 East   By Reservation Only
Denton, TX 76205
www.dentonramada.com/FantasySuites.htm

 If there is one destination that I plan to book a reservation at this year besides the new Gaylord complex, it's the Fantasy Suites in Denton. Yes, you heard me. In Denton, Texas? What a shocker to find a plain ole Ramada Inn transformed into one of the most "fantabulous" nights on a moonbeam. Book a room Sunday through Thursday and expect rates for these incredible rooms to be $149; Friday and Saturday, $199 and special occasions $249 but boy, what will be a night to remember. Expect to give a 72-hour cancellation notice. Certificates are available for a sensational surprise gift. Reservations are made only with a valid credit card. Now that you have all the poop, here's the scoop. Fantasy Suites are indeed just that. Great themed rooms that will drop your drawers as well as your jaws. Listen to the room's decor with pictures available for viewing online: Arabian Nights, Caesar's Court, Geisha Gardens and Pink Cadillac. Somebody really did it all up with creativity and fun. Though not part of the Ramada Inn corporate hierarchy, reservations for the Suites are made directly with their front desk. You can even make a reservation online. See ya there! What a trip!

◆◆◆◆◆◆   Hall Motor Home Rental   469/721-5047

6615 East I-30   Mon-Fri 9-5; Sat (By Appt. Only)
Royce City, TX 75189

 What a wonderful way to see the USA. Dinah Shore, move over in your Chevrolet. Here's a better way to go. At Hall Motorhome Rental, you'll be hooked up with just the right vehicle to see the sights up close and personal. This family-owned and operated business is about 20 minutes east of I-635 and I-30 in Royse City, in the Rockwall area with easy access from I-30. Matthew and April Hall want to put you in the driver's seat. They even want you to practice on the country roads before you hit the big city in one of their monstrous RVs. Renting one of their new vehicles or one with low mileage ensures that you will be dependably-backed by excellent customer service. They represent only the most reputable manufacturers like **MONACO; HOLIDAY RAMBLER'S** the Vacationer and Atlantis; **DAMON CORPORATION'S** Ultrasport and Challenger and more popular luxury land-cruisers.

★★★   Hoopes House Bed and Breakfast

417 N. Broadway   By Appt. Only
Rockport, TX 78382
www.hoopeshouse.com

Here we go Hoope-Dee-Do. Here we go Hoope-Dee-Da. And this time it's to Rockport, Texas to the Hoopes House. Built in the late 19th century by a local banker and land developer, it has been transformed into a B 'n'B for the past 100 years for guests, offering the private luxuries of a larger hotel. A swimming pool, hot tub, gazebo and beautiful gardens are just a few of the comforts that keep the surroundings intimate in this eight-room capacity hotel. The location keeps you within walking distance of downtown Rockport, where you'll find shops, galleries and museums for those inclined toward natural pursuits. Rockport, in case you didn't know, is a birder's paradise. There are several nearby parks to choose from for hiking, bird-watching and fishing in and around Goose Island State Park and the Rockport Beach Park. The rooms are lavish and elegant and run about $120 per night for either a single or double occupancy. Wood-burning fireplaces and a book parlor are just some of the amenities in the common living rooms. Say hello to your hosts, Mike and Paula Sargent, but you won't have to salute! *Call toll-free: 800/924-1008*

★★★★★★ Hotel Reservations Network   214/361-7311

8140 Walnut Hill Lane, Suite 203   24/7
Dallas, TX 75231
www.hotels.com

 After they were acquired by a big online travel site and went public on NASDAQ, Hotel Reservations Network instantly became the internet's primary source for discount accommodations worldwide, with savings up to 70 percent off regular hotel rates in some of the world's most popular and expensive cities. Of course, that makes talking to Bob Diener, one of the founders, beyond possible. No doubt he's curled up with a good book on his yacht in the Gulf of Mexico. Some of the best rooms, for a moderate rate, can be booked quickly and efficiently. Compare price, quality, location, amenities and availability of hotel rooms, then make your reservations which is confirmed in just seconds. They can even get you a room in a city where rooms are sold out. They have discount accommodations in more than 7,000 premiere properties in over 300 major destinations. To contact Customer Care, log on 24/7; to speak to a Customer Care Agent, call 800/219-4606 between 7 AM-8 PM CST, Mon-Fri. For hotel reservations, book online or call 800/2HOTELS. *Call toll-free: 800/964-6835*

Miss Molly's   817/626-1522

109½ W. Exchange   By Reservation Only
Fort Worth, TX 76106
www.missmollys.com

 Take a room at Miss Molly's and enter into the history of the Fort Worth Stockyards. Miss Molly's is a historic hotel furnished in turn-of-the-century unique Texas style. Only in Texas, though, could you pull this off. Housed in a building built in 1910, Miss Molly's is located on the second floor above what is now the Star Cafe, one of the Stockyard's oldest and best restaurants. Shutters, lace curtains, iron beds, antique quilts and oak furniture are found in every room. Breakfast is served in the parlor beneath the stained-glass skylight where guests can enjoy coffee, tea and juice, with fresh fruit and a basket full of specialty breads. Yumm-m! You can smell the yeast rising while you are reading the paper or visiting with other guests from around the world. Seven of their eight rooms are basically the way the hotel was when it was new, only updated for all the right reasons. The bathrooms, for example, have iron tubs, pull-chain toilets and pedestal sinks and are just down the hall, (they provide robes for use during your stay and when taking that walk in the middle of the night!) Rooms range from the Oilman and Gunslinger to Cowboy's and Miss Amelia's and rates range from $125 to $200, depending on the room. Once a proper boarding house, later a bordello (When else have you slept in either?), it's now a slice of Fort Worth history. *Call toll-free: 800/99-MOLLY*

Off Peak Traveler

37 E. 28th St. @ Park Ave. S., Ste. 608,   By Reservation Only Online
New York, NY 10016

www.OffPeakTraveler.com   🖱 *Top Online Store!*

Talk about a vacation Nirvana. Travel during the non-peak season and get twice the bang for your buck. Enjoy a rendezvous in Rio de Janeiro, stay at the hub of Copacabana, but book the deal before December 23rd, for example, and a deal awaits. (Or it did.) Yes, you'll need a visa to leave the country and re-enter the country. They also recommend using a visa service. If you'd rather take a stroll along Michigan Ave., get tickets to see an "Oprah" taping and spend two nights in a first class hotel, how does $256, including airfare, sound? Or want to travel like a Queen on a serf's paycheck? How does seeing Big Ben at the bargain price of $389 from New York sound? And yes, that includes air. Based in New York, this power bargain house offers spectacular deals for air and hotel packages allowing everyone to partake in wonderful travel options.

Priceline

Norwalk, CT   24/7

www.priceline.com   🖱 *Top Online Store!*

William Shatner jumped aboard this Starship and made a fortune in stock options. What a smart captain he was, indeed. But you've got to give Priceline the credit for being also at the right place at the right time. Raise your hand if you invested in this start-up that took-off and now has expanded into other categories to save consumers a ton of money? Though it came upon the internet scene with a bang, its impact was immediate when the subject of travel was raised. It could, would, should save consumers money. And it did! Name-your-own-price is now the business model for gasoline, groceries and, of course, airline tickets, hotel rooms and rental cars. It also has a much smaller niche for cruises, new and used cars, mortgages and telephone services. *Call toll-free: 800/PRICE LI*

◆◆◆◆   Shallow Creek RV Park   903/984-5335

568 East Wilkins Road
Gladewater, TX 75647
www.shallowcreek.com

Nothing shallow about this country club. But if you sink a hole-in-one, I guess you will think you've hit pay dirt at this shallow little hole. Otherwise, this is quite a complex showering you with some interesting and plush amenities for both RVs, golfers, shoppers and families. Shallow Creek Country Club is actually a semi-private golf club, open to the public with memberships available, that is located not too far from the Louisiana border where gambling is but an hour's drive away. Speaking of drives, what about the course itself? Located just 1.7 miles north of Interstate 20 on Hwy 135, this beautiful course is nestled in the Piney Woods of East Texas. For a low monthly fee, you can store your personal cart in their cart barn. With senior memberships starting at a low, low $60 per month, it is easy to see why people say, "They only look expensive." Those fees are irresistible. Make your reservation online or through their phone numbers above. *Call toll-free: 877/742-5569*

★★★★★   **Snowballers Tours**   **817/335-SNOW**

714 Shady Creek   By Reservation Only
Kennedale, TX 76060

I don't have a snowball's chance in you-know-where to ever make it beyond the Bunny Slope. But whatever your skill, there's only one way to go....up. And there's only one way to get there and that's down. Unless you've got a friend who pilots a helicopter, this is an inexpensive way to go. Snowballers Tour is a Metroplex tradition that makes the downhill slope less slippery. All you have to do is join the club. They make ski trips affordable by providing group rates without hefty membership fees. Just put down a deposit when you sign up for one of the multiple trips this group arranges each year. Ski outings and other options are available, too, with prices usually under $400, and many in the $250-$300 range per person. Getting there is half the fun. Travel varies from sleeper bus to a 727 charter jet. Destinations include Crested Butte, Squaw Valley, Mount Rose and Taos. Since 1972, this club has been satisfying many skiers regardless of proficiency. Even if you're a master of hot toddies, you're welcome to participate. Since trips sell out even before the season gets under way, get on the list so you can make that downhill journey for less and won't get left behind the 8-ball while you powder your nose. Pay attention. The T-Bar's calling you. *Call toll-free: 800/SNO-SKII*

◆◆◆◆◆   **St. Botolph Inn Bed & Breakfast**   **817/594-1455**

808 S. Lamar St.   By Reservation Only
Weatherford, TX 76086
www.stbotolphinn.com

On the days you don't feel like much of a saint, book a reservation here to get your groove back. St. Botolph Inn Bed & Breakfast, the home of Dan & Shay Botolph, is a large, beautifully-restored Queen Anne style mansion built in 1897 by William E. Tate, a local mercantile dealer. With over 5,500 square feet, the opulent splendor includes fifteen rooms, repainted as a "Victorian Painted Lady" in twelve historic colors. The home is furnished throughout with antiques from Europe, Asia and America and sits on five pastoral acres of terraced hillside, complete with swimming pool and the original windmill well-house. If you think I am envious, you're right. Can you picture the Diva on the front lawn enjoying a game of croquet or bocce ball while Bob is pitching horseshoes across the way? When he tires of the game, we can engage in a quick game of volleyball or badminton. Yeah, right! Well, then again, maybe we'd be better off relaxing in one of the bedrooms all with private baths, some with Jacuzzis. Not only are children welcome but you'll find they have their own playground. Prices range from $80 to $165 and are worth every penny. Don't stray too far. They serve a four o'clock tea with lots of food. Cheerio. Weatherford is the birthplace of Mary Martin and the setting for Larry McMurtry's novel, *Lonesome Dove*. *Call toll-free: 800/868-6520*

◆◆◆◆◆   **Thee Hubbell House**   **903/342-5629**

307 West Elm   By Reservation Only
Winnsboro, TX 75494
www.bluebonnet.net/hubhouse

The history of this Bed & Breakfast is part of the wonderment of staying at Thee Hubbell House. Built in 1888 by Winnsboro merchant J.M Lankford, for his personal residence, it was purchased by Col. J.A. Stinson in 1906 and reconstructed into its present Colonial style. Today, you can play the part of a Southern gentleman, or if you want to get a group together, Thee Hubbell House can accommodate bus tours, corporate retreats, church retreats, family reunions, full wedding services and romantic candlelight dinners. If you need some relaxation, spend some quiet time in the Hot

Tub House, a private and secluded outbuilding on the estate which has its own central heat/air, piped music, refreshment bar, light dimmers, and a double-occupancy shower and bath. Pick your room from the five main bedrooms (priced from $90 to $175 per night) or choose a room in the Cottage or Carriage House from $75 to $85 per night. If you want a candlelit dinner, it's dinner for two, but BYOB as you're dining in a "dry" area. There is so much to rave about, take a sneak peek online and it won't take long to say, "When can we go?" *Call toll-free: 800/227-0639*

◆◆◆◆◆◆ Victorian House (The Angel House) 817/599-9600

PO Box 1571, 1105 Palo Pinto St.   By Reservation Only
Weatherford, TX 76086
www.texasguides.com/angelsnest.html

Be an angel and make a reservation at the Angel House, would you, please? Weatherford is a dream destination for bed and breakfasts and this 1896 restored three-story, 10,000-square-foot Victorian mansion is no exception. You might even think you've died and gone to heaven. Whether you call it The Victorian House or The Angel House, they're interchangeable and come complete with 10 huge bedrooms, (we're talking 18 x 22 feet big), with private baths, custom bedspreads and draperies, cable TV, armoires and museum-quality antiques. This is not what you'd call "roughin'" it! Hardly. One bed alone cost $25,000. Take in the 3½ acres of landscape green, savor a three-course breakfast and return to the days of yesteryear. If you're looking for a perfect wedding site, just descending the spiral staircase is enough to generate an avalanche of tears. They can accommodate 300 guests for outside weddings or 100 guests inside. Caterers in the area are recommended, or you can hire your own. Consider this location for any special occasion, a private dinner party, a bridal shower; it's more than just a weekend getaway. Rooms range from $99-$199. Ogle online or call their toll-free number for information and a brochure. They are very gracious and Weatherford or not you've ever met an Angel, it won't be for lack of trying. *Call toll-free: 800/687-1660*

◆◆◆◆◆ Woldert-Spence Manor   903/533-9057

611 W. Woldert St.   By Reservation Only
Tyler, TX 75702
www.tyler.net/woldert_spence

Be sure to make your reservations early. This peaceful and historic 1859 B 'n 'B sells out quickly, and you'll be disappointed otherwise. It's the closest of its kind to downtown Tyler and a great respite from a weekend at Canton's First Monday Trade Days, the weekend before the first Monday of every month. Pick your pleasure from their six rooms featuring 12 foot ceilings, some with tiled fireplaces, private baths for every bedroom (some even feature an antique claw-foot tub or a glassed-in tiled shower). The rates, which range from $80 to $110 per night, are a small price to pay for a comforting retreat after a day of serious bargain shopping. For complete privacy, consider the 1920s carriage house in the rear of the main house. It's a private 660-square-foot private garage apartment on the second floor and includes a gas log fireplace, a small balcony (I can just see my husband wooing me with "Rapunzel, Rapunzel, let down your hair!") and dining room. The dining room continues into a fully-equipped kitchen with its original cabinets. The full bathroom even has the original corner sink and tiled floor, all for $125 with a two-night minimum. So, book it before you go out of style. *Call toll-free: 800/WOLDERT*

◆◆◆◆◆   **Woodbine Cottage Bed & Breakfast   817/706-4936**

6020 Walnut Creek Drive
Grandbury, TX 76049
www.woodbinecottageretreat.com

By Reservation Only

This 1900 prairie-style farmhouse is not your typical bed and breakfast retreat. Designed for a group of women who want to get away and work on a craft, from scrapbooks to making jewelry, the cottage comes equipped to accommodate a twin bed in one of three rooms with private bath and dressing area. Every guest is provided a large work table and comfortable chair as well as their own trash bag and drink holder. Everything you'll need to be creative and productive. Watch for weekend retreats for pottery or bag making, interior decorating on a budget, faux painting and more. Just getting to the country with a bunch of my friends seems like a great idea. Breakfast is served both Sat and Sun on a large farmstyle table; a light lunch and dinner is also included just 40 minutes southwest of Fort Worth and ten minutes from Granbury. What a creative getaway from the hassles of every day life. How about meeting at the Hobby Lobby. See ya!

Windows & Walls

★★ 3 Day Blinds

951 W. I-20, Ste. 107
Arlington, TX 76015
www.3day.com

817/784-9200
Mon-Fri 10-6; Sat 10-5

Ask for Paul Stevens if you want the "blind" of your life. Why go to Six Flags in Arlington when this guy goes like a roller-coaster when it comes to window treatments? If your windows are in need of some energy, pop into this Arlington location and see what materializes. If you're lucky enough to live in California, where 3 Day Blinds are made, your windows will be dressed in 3 Days. Otherwise, expect to wait 10 days or more to get your windows dressed. Vinyl shutters will cost you $35 per square foot, which means a 32 x 72-inch window can be shuttered for....you figure it out. Not a deal, sorry to say. (No bargain in my book.) Their Shop-at-Home Service's (800/590-SHOP) scheduling department is open for business seven days a week. Their own brand of blinds and **ATLA, COMFORT TEX, PRESTIGE** (bamboo-type), and **HUNTER-DOUGLAS** plus a smattering of **KIRSCH** and **WAVERLY** thrown in for good measure you'll see at their showroom. Expect an in-home measurement fee of $35 to be assessed up to 50 windows. Visit other locations throughout the Metroplex including Arlington, Denton, Fort Worth, Irving, Mesquite and Plano. While the savings (from 10 to 50 percent) aren't nearly what you'd expect, it's still better than retail! Besides, they represent the **CHRISTOPHER LOWELL COLLECTION** of custom window coverings exclusively. Now when they come to represent the **DIVA** line, we've got something to talk about. *Call toll-free: 800/800-3DAY*

◆◆◆◆◆ Barbara Kirk

Lewisville, TX

972/436-0484
By Appt. Only

When it comes to hanging out with the best of them, Barbara Kirk rolls out the red carpet, but she does it with wallpaper. And to keep you on the edge of your seat, she hangs borders on the edge, too, but with a woman's touch. Bringing 25 years of experience to the table, she provides FREE estimates and quality workmanship (or is it womanship?)

★★★★ Blind Connection, The

Dallas, TX

214/731-1599
By Appt. Only

Susan is waiting with baited bargain breath, ready to remedy all those interior aches and panes! While you won't find anything in stock, you can custom order blinds and shades from **ROYAL, KIRSCH, SKANDIA, TIMBERLAND BLINDS** and others. A standard wood 32 x 72-inch blind in white wood will cost $99, or slightly more if you prefer a little color. No curtains or draperies can be found hanging around, but if you are in need of window hardware, there's hardly a better place to make a connection. With discounts ranging up to 75 percent off, color your budget happy. *Call toll-free: 877/708-3361*

★★★★★★ Budget Decorators, The   469/293-SHOP (7467)
Lewisville, TX 75067   By Appt. Only
www.thebudgetdecorators.com

 There's nothing like it so far in the Metroplex, but if you like Design On A Dime, you'll love the Budget Decorators™. It takes one to know one. Since I'm great at launching new businesses, let me introduce you to my latest—and maybe my greatest. Called The Budget Decorators™, it's my answer to being glued to Home And Garden Television. I love to play decorator. I know who some of the good ones who charge $200 an hour; and I know some of the good ones who charge $65 an hour. Who would you prefer? Ok, so now we're on the same wave length. If you are interior design challenged, you will love the Budget Decorators. We even intend to sponsor a total room Extreme Makeover later on in the year. Designers, afterall, have been sneaking around the "underground" for years and yet charge clients ten times what they find because nobody would believe how cheap it was. In fact, that's who we're marketing to. We'll pass the savings on when we find it on the cheap. Window treatments, upholstery, working with fabrics are are specialty, but we do it all. Meet The Budget Decorators (and the Lone Arranger) at our BD headquarters or at your home or office. An appointment is still necessary. Call the number above and we'll get you connected. Our Budget Decorators come with plenty of experience and charge half the usual and customary designer rates. Then, once you've laid out your plan of action, they shop at "underground" approved resources. Wholesale or less, staying within your budget, I guarantee it. We shop at only the best who charge you the least—and then pass on their low prices to you. The look may be one of opulence; the price tag will be more pauper-like. From chandeliers for $95 to floral arrangements right out of the lobbies of the Mansion Hotel for under $200, painting inside and out, faux painting to murals, to complete kitchen or bath remodels that will save you thousands, you'll can count (the savings) on us. We'll share our secrets, teach you a few design tricks, and hope you'll recommend us to your neighbors in the process. Nobody can beat our prices. The Budget Decorators™ are on our website. You're but one click away for your design makeovers. From commercial lobbies for businesses, corporate offices, waiting rooms for doctors, lawyers or any professional who wants to make an impression for less; but mostly for home owners in need of a face lift, a room rearrange, a total house makeover, a room addition, or a new home from scratch. Here we come, ready or not. We've combined the talents of several designers who have the eye for color, scale, fabrics, room arrangements, how-to-mix and match and the Lone Arranger who will come out and just re-arrange with what you have already have to create a whole different look. Reality does have to come into play, however. They can't redo an entire room complete with 10 pieces of furniture, art work, accessories, florals, new carpet, wallpaper, faux painting, window treatments, an Oriental rug for under $1,000. We can do some of it, but let's get real! Expect to pay a small (considering the competition) hourly wage and then, let's go shopping!

★★★ Charles Curtain Co.   214/630-7967
1352 Crampton   Mon-Fri 8-3:30; Sat 9:30-Noon
Dallas, TX 75207

It's curtains for this Charles—but not in the cardinal sense. After all, he's been selling his curtains out of his factory for years. A lot of water has passed under the bridges of the Trinity River at this 1,000-square-foot outpost. (Or is it outhouse?) Off Irving Blvd. between Wycliff and Motor Street, it's small enough to house plenty of overstocks and samples of his manufactured draperies and bedspreads at 50 percent off and more. Remnants of fabric are also available for your creative splurges at $2-$10/yard. Complete a bedroom ensemble with pinch-pleated drapes, scarf valances, pole-top drapes, tailored panels, blouson valances, jabot and filler valances and dress up your bed with matching spreads, shams and dust ruffles. What a shame—you're saving so much money! Besides, he's practically a dinosaur in the business seeing as they're not many bedspread and ready-made drapery workrooms left in the business to even recommend. Take Stemmons to Irving Boulevard; Crampton is between Wycliff and Motor Streets. One of their biggest customers is JC Penney and you know how particular they are in quality control.

★★★★★★ Christy's Resale Draperies　　　　972/403-1543

1300 Custer @ 15th　　　　　Mon-Wed 10-6; Thurs-Sat 10-8; Sun 11-6　Mall Hours
Plano, TX 75075

 Christy's is located inside Antiqueland at 15th and Custer in Plano and has been expanding like mad to showcase a growing inventory. If you think you've heard it all, you haven't. Christy's is in a class all by itself, filling a huge, gaping void in the marketplace. She does this by combining window treatments and accompanying bedding that are both resale and brand new. One-of-a-kind treatments from beautiful homes in the Dallas area can be found here. From their homes to yours, Christy's may be just the thing to provide the cure-all for all of your window "panes!" Ah such luxurious names: can you believe you will see hanging around such stars as **BRUNSCHWIG & FILS**, **KRAVET** and **SCALMANDRE**. If you are wanting to sell your drapery or window treatments, please call ahead and schedule an appointment; otherwise, if you're a shopper, you're welcome seven days a week for your convenience. Christy's has expanded with a large selection of new custom items. There are loads of ready to hang silks and other fine fabric panels in lengths up to 120". These can also be accented with a beautiful collection of new ready to hang valances, table rounds, table runners and bedding sets in the latest fabrics and colors. Christy provides the "Custom Look" and quality without the decorator pricing. Now get this: you can take any item out on a 24-hour approval. See what it will look like in your home BEFORE you commit. Once you've decided they are for you, write a pre-nuptial agreement to love and honor it all the days of your life. What a great service. How many other home furnishings stores encourage you to try before you buy? Love it and keep it. Love it but no thank you, the color is all wrong. Christy has the finishing touches to an extreme makeover for your home. Just hang around with her and you'll that see if you like "The Curtain Exchange" (and who doesn't), you can have that look without the pricey price tag.

★★ Cornelius Draperies　　　　　　　　　817/731-8469

3520 W. Vickery　　　　　　　　　　　　　　　　　　　　　　Mon-Fri 10-5
Fort Worth, TX 76107

At the intersection of Vickery and Montgomery, we asked a clerk about the price of a particular blind. When the question was broached, the clerk stood there dumbfounded. In fact, she mumbled, "Mum's the word!" She wasn't particularly forthcoming except to say, "The boss would know." Well, it's not easy shopping when and if only the boss can talk....prices. So we decided to pass the buck and leave it up to you. Without prices, however, we couldn't tell you if they were selling at a good price or not. We could understand her dilemma if we were asking about custom draperies, but standard window sizes, in our opinion, should roll off the tongue with ease. If they don't know the prices, how can you discern the bargains? All she was able to tell us was to expect to pay half down when we placed an order with the balance due upon delivery. The good part? How does FREE in-home estimates sound? Installation charges are extra, depending on the difficulty of the project. Bring in a picture and they can usually duplicate the look. Most brands of fabric and hardware are available. It's your call. From **KIRSCH** to **LEVOLOR**, **WAVERLY** to **WESTLAKE**, it's all in Cornelius's hands. For their lips to our checkbook, see if they know a little more when you shop their shore.

★★★★★★   Curtain Exchange, The   214/350-3045

5470 West Lovers Lane
Dallas, TX 75209
www.thecurtainexchange.com

 It's curtains on custom draperies here. A concept whose time has come, this new money-saver lets you hang it up with gorgeous ready-mades for less money. Think of it like a boutique for your windows instead of for clothes. Located in the heart of Highland Park, at the Inwood Village Shopping Center, they have been seen in *Southern Accents* and *Metropolitan Home* so consider yourself to be in good company. The Curtain Exchange is expanding across America with franchisees offering shoppers a cost-effective, high-quality and immediate solution to their window covering needs. All have been custom-made and rather than taking a small fabric swatch home to see if the color works, they invite you to take the entire drapery panel home to see if it fits and if you like it. Now, that's a switch (or is it a swatch?) They also sell ready-made draperies in fabulous silky and sensuous colors: toffee, mocha, cinnamon, merlot and plum to match your color scheme. The first franchise opened in Baton Rouge, Louisiana in August,1998 and the rest is history. Their second location is in Plano at Lakeside Market, 5813 Preston Road, 972/243-2300. Though not particularly cheap, the value is in the ease and speed with which you can get those windows covered in elegance economically. And one visit to their online gallery and you'll be wanting to hang up on them immediately.

★★★★★   Custom Shutters   903/488-3224

Como, TX 75431   By Appt. Only
www.customshutters.com

If you are you looking for love in all the wrong places, stop in the name of love at Custom Shutters. That is, if you want to love your new custom Plantation Shutters. Monumental savings direct from the manufacturer is what you'll get just by knowing who to call. One toll-free call, that's all, and ask for Sara. You don't even have to travel to East Texas to pay homage to their artistry. Instead, they come to you. Shutters are installed with custom finishes, moldings, whatever it takes to fit each window to a T. Shutters are made with solid hardwood, with your choice of finish and installed to your complete satisfaction. With more than 22 years of experience, expect them to know a thing or two about what it takes to make a perfect plantation shutter. FREE estimates and installation. Quality from this East Texas family-owned company and great prices makes for a slam-shut case for shopping with them. *Call toll-free: 800/323-8458*

★★   Designer Draperies, Floors & Furniture   817/451-6890

5715 E. Rosedale, Suite E-1   Mon-Fri 9-5:30; Sat By Appt. Only
Fort Worth, TX 76112

Max and Beverly are reigning supreme as the "designing duo" of Fort Worth. Their motto, "You want it, we have it!" That means you can find quality furniture with names like ESTATE HOUSE and FLEXSTEEL. You can see what's here ahead of time if you simply check the possibilities at www.flexsteel.com. But for windows, amaze your eyeballs with window hardware from GRABER, HUNTER-DOUGLAS and KIRSCH with the added touch and whisper of luxurious fabrics from ROBERT ALLEN, WESTGATE and WAVERLY - all favorites of designing women. Lengthy in-home estimates do require a minimum of a $50 charge which is waived upon purchase, while installation fees depend on the individual products and services chosen. You will find that everyday prices are lower than "below MSRP" promised elsewhere but not by much! With up to six months same as cash and all major credit cards accepted, what are you waiting for? So if your eyes are sore, soothe them with fresh designs, bright colors and a fresh new landscape - indoors, of course!

★★★   Draperies by Linda   214/371-6463

Dallas, TX   By Appt. Only

Stop hanging around with just anybody; be selective and go custom! Whatever your windows are lacking, let Linda have a look. Go window shopping through the magazines, show her a picture and Voila! - it will materialize before your eyes. Whether you're looking for a residential make-over or a commercial project, Linda can coordinate it all. From drapes to shutters, wood blinds to all the matching coordinates for your bed and bath, this is one-stop shopping for your window treatments. Then, if you want a chair upholstered, a chaise recovered or a bench or a stool to pull up to your makeup table, she offers custom upholstery to provide the perfect complement to your home's decor.

★★★★★   Dungan's Floors/Blinds & More   972/562-9444

2306 Virginia Parkway   Tues-Fri 8:30-5:30; Sat 10-4
McKinney, TX 75070
www.dungansfloors.com

How can you explain the phenomenon of this husband and wife's longevity—both personally and professionally? Meet the happy couple who have stayed happily married for more than 20 years, raised a family and cornered the McKinney market on window and floor coverings before the boom hit that corridor. What is their secret? Just ask Lennie and Lou Jenkins. They're one of the originators of custom tile on both floors and counter-tops, laying imaginative patterns you'd see only in million-dollar mansions. Let them install **ARMSTRONG**, **BRUCE**, **MANNINGTON**, **PHILADELPHIA** and **SALEM** carpet and hardwoods. Choose adobe, brick, ceramic tile, hard-woods or laminates. It's a never-ending quest to overwhelm customers with options; there's the newest stain-resistant fibers, custom ceramic tiles to match your wallcoverings, to match your back splash, to match your—whatever. They're noted for being a one-stop three S shop: Style, Selection and Service = savings.

★★★★★   Elegant Shutters Plus   972/437-9081

13566 Floyd Circle, Suite G   By Appt. Only
Dallas, TX 75243
www.elegantshuttersplus.com

Why not enjoy a room with a view with Elegant Shutters? Keep the riff-raff out. Open sesame and let the sun shine in; or close out the world and cocoon, the choice is yours with custom shutters from this company. Plantation shutters, one of the most sought-after window treatments, as well as wood blinds and mini-blinds cover a multitude of options for your window panes. The double-pleated cellular shades not only filter light and soften the glare but also provide additional insula-tion for any room in your house. Don't shutter. These folks have been shuttering the world for the past 25 years. In-home consultations, professional installation, FREE estimates and lower over-head equals lower prices, plain and simple (or plain and elegant, depending on your outlook.) Eliminating the middleman, and displaying your craftsmanship is all you need to call it a day. Check out their special of eight windows or more at $19 a square foot, including rectangular shutters, trim, paint finish and installation. For special windows such as doors or arches, call for pricing and expect a trip charge for traveling outside of the Metroplex.

★★★   Elite Blinds   972/418-1380

2145 N. Josey @ Keller Springs   Mon-Fri 10-4:30; Sat 10-5
Carrollton, TX 75006

Elite only considers the hard window treatments, so please don't call them for draperies. They're tired of answering for the umpteenth time, No, NO, a thousand times NO! But if you want the elite treatment at 70 to 75 percent off, consider honeycomb shades and two-inch PVC wood look-alike blinds. They're in because they're so sensible and easy to maintain. Or maybe you'd like an entire orchestra of **HUNTER-DOUGLAS** treatments. Just have your measurements ready, and you can start ordering now. Pick out the best from **KIRSCH**, **GRABER** and **TIMBERLAND BLIND** and you can ensure your privacy at a discounted price.

★★★★★   Fancy Windows   972/690-8666

940 E. Belt Line, Suite 160
Richardson, TX 75081
www.fancywindow.com

Fancy this: This family-owned business is a true-blue window treatment source to reckon with. Their guaranteed-in-writing best prices on the same window products is sure to be a hit with bargain shoppers. Though there's nothing clandestine about their cover ups, you can expect to save on name-brand blinds, shutters, shades and custom draperies. Over 10,000 customers in the Dallas area have engaged their services and with over a decade of experience, they must be doing something right. Now, with business booming, their son, the engineer, has joined the business and invites customers in for a spot of Persian tea—and a deal on window treatments. Lifetime limited warranties and superb installation (FREE on five windows or more) makes for an additional incentive worth noting. Online, check out the sizes and prices, then call for a FREE estimate. They will beat all written estimates on the same products and offer interest-FREE financing. You can't beat that!

◆◆◆◆◆   Fine Art Finishes   817/426-5252

1470 Wilshire Blvd.   By Appt. Only
Burleson, TX 76028
www.fauxtalk.com

Fee, Fie, Faux, Fun. That's what you'll see by enrolling in the classes at this finishing school. If you're looking for that Trompe Card, this is where they teach you how the palette meets the painter. You'll learn a myriad of painting techniques for your walls and ceilings; one which is particularly mesmerizing is multi-color glazing over hand-troweled plaster. You'll probably pick the textured and realistic faux brick placed throughout a room. Faux concrete walls can be antiqued to resemble those of ancient Italy which have begun to crumble and are discoloring with age. Head online to learn more about where and when their faux painting courses will be underway. They are the talk of the decorative painting message boards. They will introduce you to imported materials and layering techniques and explain why certain materials are used the way they are. All aspects of this business, including installs, pricing and design, are included in your coursework. Too, they have plenty of accomplished faux painters to recommend if all you want is to have somebody else do the dirty work. ***Call toll-free: 888/508-FAUX***

◆◆◆◆   Grace's Draperies   972/304-6868

150 S. Denton Tap Road, #111   Mon-Fri 10-5; Sat 10-3, or later By Appt. Only
Coppell, TX 75019

It used to be that the Moon wasn't over Miami but rather Coppell. Now, they are called Grace's Draperies (formerly Moon's Draperies). They are sticklers for detail and are specialists in custom-made window treatments from top to bottom including swags, cornice boards, balloon shades, the whole kitsch and kaboodle. When you want coordinating bedroom ensembles (spreads, duvets, coverlets, throws) added to the shams, the pillows, accent trims, tassels, tiebacks are in a lush lineup of fabrics with matching upholstery. Give us your tired, your worn. Just like the Statue of Liberty, liberate yourself from the tyranny of boring window treatments. Replace them, dress them up, do something but doing nothing will not a transformation make. You'll be saving, Grace, by calling Grace's. Amen.

◆◆◆◆◆   Home Sewn Solutions   972/436-9083

125 N. Mill St.   Mon-Fri 10-5; Eve & Sat By Appt. Only
Lewisville, TX 75057
www.homesewnsolutions.com

This home-grown workroom has been custom sewing draperies, bedding, pillows and other fabric creations since 1994. Their design showroom showcases their creativity but they can create an idea from scratch or you can bring them a picture and have them just re-create it. Other window treatments include brands such as **HUNTER-DOUGLAS** and **KASHMIR** fabrics. Home Sewn Solutions has everything for your home to make a personalized and dramatic statement: custom window treatments, bedding, pillows, toppers, table skirts, accessories and more made right there in their workroom. When shopping their showroom, you will see how easy it is to pick your next design project. They pride themselves on differentiating between merely being a seamstress and a fabricator. Just having the ability to sew does not ensure the best draperies. Fabricators are the highest skilled in one particular area of sewing and have additional training in creating custom treatments with professional tools and equipment. They draw, lay out, prepare and create a custom project with specialized sewing techniques. In-home measurements and design service are also available with itemized quotes listing everything from lining to labor.

L. J. Anthony   214/340-0359

10420 Markison Rd.   By Appt. Only
Dallas, TX 75238
www.jlanthony.com

Ready to take a leap from the ordinary? Then look to order handsomely crafted hardware for your windows from L. J. Anthony, a division of Lancaster & Associates, Inc. with craftmanship unparalled by any competitor. They produce to your exacting specifications, a furniture-quality work of art to position your custom draperies so as to stand apart from the crowd. Using only fine hardwoods and the best architectural quality hardware, J.L. Anthony produces an unbelieveable product. Finishes are nothing but the best, similar to what you see on higher-priced furniture in an array of colors, textures and classic designs. Choose your size, style, and ultimate finish and what you wind up with is a one-of-a-kind dramatic accompaniment to your windows. All poles are available in your choice of 2¼ or 3 inch diameters, and fluted and smooth style rods may be obtained in lengths up to 16 feet in one piece. If you think you might need a built-in traversing system, they can do that, too. All their products are available unfinished, if you choose to do it yourself. You can ask for their FREE brochure or order online.

★★★★★★   **Leland Interiors**   **817/226-7890 (Metro)**

2021 S. Copper, Suite A   Mon-Fri 9-6: Sat 10-5; Sun Noon-5
Arlington, TX 76010
www.lelandswallpaper.com

 Celebrating their 21st year anniversary, Leland Interiors offers everything from antique reproductions, window coverings and blinds and draperies to stencils, murals, wallpaper and more! Forget their humble beginnings. These folks have grown to gigantic proportions with their online presence. Get a look—and pick a pattern. Find manufacturers like **ASHFORD HOUSE**, **GRAMERCY**, **PARKVIEW DESIGNS**, **SCHUMACHER/ WAVERLY** and **YORK**. They offer a discount book list of wallpapers for online customers only, as well as FREE shipping on orders over $100. Their online border catalog is unbelievable, including a closeout section. As part of their line-up, expect 45 percent off in-store wallpapers and all special-order books, and cut 30 percent and more off the MSRP. Say hello to Gary Leland and congratulate him on coming a long way, baby. Another must-shop store on Cooper Street. (Remember to grab a donut at Krispy Kreme down the street or going the other way, a patty melt at Buck n' Loons.) *Call toll-free: 800/560-9725*

★★★★   **Lone Star Blinds**   **214/766-0330**

Dallas, TX   By Appt. Only

This is strictly a shop-at-home business that can provide a remedy for any window treatment. Ram will knock on your door armed with samples and ready-to-please pricing. Low overhead equals lower costs to you, and forget the time-consuming effort it takes to get in your car, find a parking place, sweating all the way and then having to stand on your feet while looking at all the window options possible. Shop for hours in the comfort of your home environment. Hassle-free, relaxing and effortless, that's what shopping at Lone Star Blinds is all about. Take your time and take care of all your window needs from blinds to solar screens without leaving home. The discounts vary between manufacturers and installation difficulty. All the national brands like **GRABER**, **HUNTER-DOUGLAS**, **LEVOLOR** and **KIRSCH** are represented and more.

★★★★★★   **Louver Shop, The**   **972/355-0853**

Dallas, TX   By Appt. Only
www.louvershop.com;

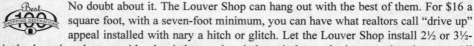 No doubt about it. The Louver Shop can hang out with the best of them. For $16 a square foot, with a seven-foot minimum, you can have what realtors call "drive up" appeal installed with nary a hitch or glitch. Let the Louver Shop install 2½ or 3½-inch plantation shutters with what is known in window circles as the lowest prices in town. All hardwood construction with the frame included was purchased by several customers in one neighborhood....en masse. The only limitation was at this price, frost white was the only color to choose, so shoppers can't be choosy. But if you want 'em, you buy 'em like they have 'em. Another promotion that was ongoing until the end of the year one year was the same $16 a square foot pricing for hardwood construction and standard paint finishes rather than just the one white one including installation. Catch them while the iron is hot (or haute) and don't get blind-sided by others who advertise the lowest prices. This shop usually is. For ordering online, go to www.louvershop.com or www.louvershipblinds.com. How's that for comfort shopping? Their main office is outside Atlanta, with local-area representatives in both Dallas and Fort Worth, Houston and San Antonio. They make FREE in-house appointments, with no obligation to buy. (The price is right, so why would you not?) At that time, they'll show off their product samples, take your window measure-

ments and you'll be covered in no time. They also sell **HUNTER-DOUGLAS** blinds and shades if that piques your interest. ***Call toll-free: 800/528-7866***

Magnolia Plantation Shutters

972/668-2600

8600 Preston Road, Suite 106
Dallas, TX 75225-3111
www.magnoliashutters.com

Mon-Fri 10-6; Sat 9:30-5:30

The 1992 winner of the American Window Covering Manufacturers Association Award for Best New Technical Innovation, Magnolia's technical design and advanced manu-facturing methods have brought about the first custom shutter with new innovations in over a century. At Magnolia, their goal has been the pursuit of excellence. And this year, they moved out of their Irving Boulevard warehouse and now have an upscale showroom at the inter-section of Hwy. 121 and Preston (where you can see Sam Moon as well.) Having sold and installed shutters made by other companies for over twenty years, they recognized problem areas encountered by their customers. They addressed the challenges by manufacturing their own shut-ters. Magnolia Plantation Shutters makes custom shutters, provides FREE in-home estimates, FREE installation and FREE measuring. They feature no divider rails and no visible operating bar. Every shutter is flush-mounted, which may be a must-have consideration if you're a perfectionist. All their shutters have been constructed with the finest details, mortising, louvers, magnets and tight tolerances, so there's no flapping in the wind. You also can pick custom colors and stains and the size of your slats: 2½-inch, 3½-inch and 4½-inch. What's not to love about them? ***Call toll-free: 800/395-7948***

★★★★★★ Metropolitan Window Covering

817/222-1070

5206 Airport Freeway
Fort Worth, TX 76117
www.mwcblinds.com

By Appt. Only

Consider the importance of keeping your privacy. You don't want the whole neigh-borhood to really know what goes on behind closed doors, now do you? Then con-sider protecting your comings and goings and cover up. Here's a company that feels window covers are as important as your home furnishings, an integral part to your decorating scheme. Just make an appointment with an in-home representative and together pick what best suits your needs. Their motto is our motto: "Why pay retail?" With over 25 years in the business, they offer professional installation, FREE in-home discount packages, evening and weekend appointments and FREE estimates. For a cosmopolitan approach to window coverings, Metropoli-tan's extensive website showcases many of the window covering options is open to the sophisti-cated shopper. Their shutters are a premium quality product manufactured in Fort Worth and offered in a variety of styles and colors. ***Call toll-free: 888/273-6692***

★★★★ Mini Blind Warehouse

817/277-1014

2707 S. Cooper, #105
Arlington, TX 76015

Mon 10-5; Tues-Sat 10-6

Forget name brands here. Mini Blind Warehouse manufactures their own and after 15 years of doing so, you can expect quality at a price that can't be beat. In business for 15 years, they shop their competitors to ensure quality, which to them is the most important ingredient in duplicating the other, well-known brands. Everything from blinds to shades are custom-made to size except shutters. A standard 32 x 72-inch two-inch wood blind will cost $119. They will gladly come out to measure or if you already know what you need, then just call for an estimate. Mini's are back in style but not at maxi prices so here's where you should start.

★★★★★   Shutter Factory, The   972/881-7511

601 J Place, Suite 700
Plano, TX 75074-1310
www.theshutterfactory.com

Hate living with plastic? Then don't buy it! Get custom wood shutters with wider panels, custom paint and stains direct from the factory. Did you know you can add the cost of shutters to your home mortgage? That way, you can cover all the windows with elegance and curb appeal and not feel the pinch up front. You can contact your builder or designer or shop direct at the factory. Either way, you can save the day. This family-owned business can help you see the way and close the slats to paying retail! *Call toll-free: 800/424-7497*

★★★★★★   Shutter Masters, Inc.   972/423-0210

5401 E. 14th St.   Mon-Sat 8-4:30 (Out to Lunch 12-1)
Plano, TX 75074
www.shuttercraftmfg.com

Shuttermasters, Inc. is located in Plano, Texas, but the driving force behind it is the Morrows from Smart Looks in Richardson. Serving the Metroplex since 1974, they were the original manufacturers of exterior shutters, so it was a natural eventuality for them to branch out (pardon the pun) to interior shutters as well. So, there you have it. Custom shutters in every shape and style at factory-direct prices—and that's the truth. They *are* the factory. They are already well-known for quality window treatments generally, and now with their custom shutters as well, they represent the full spectrum of options. Choose from custom wood shutters, wood blinds, poly shutters, faux blinds and much more. Whether you're wanting to sell them as a retailer or you want to buy them wholesale and you're the public, here's the real McCoy. See their artistry in work on their website and achieve a phone or online quote without even leaving home. Haven't you mastered the "Art of the Deal" by now? Then don't even think about paying more! And visit their site to view a sample of the superior products they offer. *Call toll-free: 800/ 400-8632*

★★★★★★   Smart Looks Window & Wall Decor 972/699-1151

101 S. Greenville Ave.   Mon-Fri 9-5; Sat 9:30-5
Richardson, TX 75080
www.smartlooksdecor.com/

Forget running around all over town to coordinate your entire house, or even just a room, if that's your plan. Instead, be smart. Shop smart. Smart shoppers are the "norm" here at this old-time favorite. In 1972, both The Underground Shopper and ERS Exterior Shutters were born. ERS was their name before they changed it to Smart Looks. (They manufactured exterior rolling shutters—hence ERS.) What was once a shop for exterior shutters has now evolved into a worldly wall and window emporium featuring the best for less. More than 30 individual vignettes showcase ideas for you to embrace. In-stock wallpaper, plus hundreds of books to browse through, will keep your nose buried in the books for hours. Norm and Lucy Morrow have been in the business, at the same corner location, for more than 20 years. Without compromising service one iota, they continued expansion beyond the usual custom blinds, verticals, Plantation shutters, exterior shutters, balloon shades, pleated shades, Silhouettes, rolling shutters, woven woods and, of course, custom draperies. Want them motorized, so you don't have to get up to close the drapes? No problem. Want matching bedspreads, pillows, boudoir chair, bench, ottomans? No problem. See why they've been your best friend in this business for years saving you 30 to 75 percent on the finest fabrics by **FABRICUT**, **KASMIR** and more. And expect the lowest prices on **SHUTTERCRAFT SHUTTERS** because they are the factory. Always FREE estimates and all prices include installation. From commercial to residential, bay-bow or arched, they've got you covered.

★★★★★★ Stained Glass Overlay 972/570-4685

6311 N. O'Connor Blvd.
Irving, TX 75039
www.dallasdesignerglass.com

Not a stain on their fine reputation, shop at this national window transformation company via their local representatives, Karen Rae or Margo Rudder. Designer Glass is by Stained Glass Overlay, Inc, an Orange, CA national company (www.sgo-Inc.com or toll-free 800/944-4746). What you get is a custom stained-glass look for windows and bath shower doors that generates nothing but rave reviews. I even have a desk sign made in stained-glass that has dignified my desk for the past six or seven years that simply states "The Diva." Stained Glass Overlay does a lot to add custom accents anywhere in your home, from front-door sidelights, skylights, ceiling light panels, shower and tub enclosures, light boxes, mirrors, sliding glass doors, over-the-tub windows, cabinet and furniture doors, table tops, room dividers, windows, well....anywhere. And no need to worry. All workmanship comes with a 10 year-limited warranty and a lifetime of pleasure. Prices are cheaper than if you had a custom stain-glass artist come in to custom-craft one, but their designs will certainly enhance the value of your home's selling price. Seeing something made from Designer Glass will usually make a believer out of you. To visit in Carrollton, head to 1014 S. Broadway, #102, 972/245-5454 and speak with Margo Rudder. You won't crack up either place but you will get a work of art to call your own. The shower doors alone will make you a believer.

★★★★ Sunburst Shutters 214/343-2601

10990 Petal St., Suite 100 Mon-Fri 8:30-5
Dallas, TX 75239
www.sunburst-shutters.com

With a burst of energy and a Sunburst Shutter, life on the fast slat is good. Keeping the rays at bay, Sunburst Shutters has been crafting wood shutters for almost 25 years. They offer a unique louver tension system, premium finish and one of the highest structural integrity. In fact, their reputation has followed them all along the way. Being "The Best Built Shutter in America" does have its burdens; however, it takes a real commitment to continue on in the path that has been carved out from preceding products. But don't expect them to rush the process. Turnaround time is between five and seven weeks. **POLYWOOD SHUTTERS** are made of an engineered wood substitute that won't chip, crack, warp or split. They are moisture- and fire-resistant and impervious to termites. Made of natural gas with 50 percent more insulation than traditional wood shutters, in-home measurements are taken to ensure the perfect fit. Pay $22.50/square foot which includes tax and installation. Located just off 635 and Jupiter, they are easy to find and easy to fall in love with!

★★★★★   **Texas Galleries**   **972/396-1001**

206 N. Greenville, Suite 300   Mon-Fri 10-6; Sat 10-4
Allen, TX 75002
www.texasgalleries.com

If you want to spend a lifetime browsing through wallpaper books, start now and don't miss a lick. This online superstore is literally a one-stop shop. Wallpaper brands are staggering with prices slashed to 80 percent. Over 1,000 books from all the national suppliers will be at your beck and call—the only difference is the price. Not bad, not bad at all. Then, to complete the picture, try their personalized service for custom window treatments in wood and PVC blinds, Plantation shutters and draperies. There's a limited lifetime warranty on window coverings but expect to pay a $50 charge for an in-home estimate (about one and one-half hours' worth), but it is credited back to your total purchase price. Visit a wallpaper retailer in the area, pick your wall covering, manufacturer's name and number, then record that information on their online form for a price quote. Manufacturers include all the popular ones: BAYSIDE, BEACON HOUSE, BEACON STUDIO, BIRGE, EISENHART, FOREMOST, HORIZON, IMPERIAL, MAXWELL, PATTON, PELICAN, REGALIA, SCHUMACHER, SEABROOK, SHELBOURNE, SUNWALL, SUNWORTHY, TALMADGE, WALL TRENDS, WESTCHESTER, YORK and others. See how much they'll save you in the long run. Voila! You're in the money. *Call toll-free: 877/347-1001*

★★★   **Twin Designs**   **972/712-TWIN (8946)**

7151 Preston Rd., #101A   By Appt. Only
Frisco, TX 75034
www.twin-designs.com

Double your pleasure, double the fun, by shopping at Twin Designs, some of the best under the sun. From window treatments, bedding, fine art and furniture to lamps and shades, even awnings, this place will definitely have you seeing double! Creativity is the operative word of the day, every day with these twins. For some of the best-looking shutters, shop here. Specially hand-crafted by a retired cabinet maker, these shutters are exclusive to Twin Designs! Find names like R & M, WESTCO, WESTGATE and other major brands in fabric. Pay a $45 fee for an in-house consultation and installation cost varies with products. Buy $500 or more, and the fee is FREE. All manufacturer's pricing is competitive and affordable. With combined experience spanning 25 years in the business, this twosome, Trudie and Julie, can take you from start to finish with any decorating assignment. Mention you saw them on their web page, and they'll provide a 20 percent discount off a fabric purchase, but you better live in the following areas as they limit their services to: Dallas, Highland Park, North Dallas, Richardson, Plano, Frisco, Prosper, Celina, Carrollton, Lewisville, The Colony, Mckinney, North Garland. Though Flower Mound wasn't listed, they would make an exception. Check out your area before you make the drive to Frisco to see if they can get you covered. Beautiful work with your budget in mind, but price is not the only consideration in their mission statement.

★★★★★★★   **V2K Window Fashions**   **972/355-5556**

1301 Justin Road, Suite 209   By Appt.
Lewisville, TX 75077
www.v2kDFW.com

    Here's the newest way to buy draperies and other window treatments to come down the pike. And they are at the Peak of perfection. Where else can you buy custom window treatments at a discount, not leave home, have them measure right then and there while they are at your home or office, and then show you on their laptop, what you window treatment will look like in a matter of minutes. No, I'm not pulling the curtains in front of your eyes. This is a new kind of underground shopper. Talk about it being so easy, so convenient, so much fun. Shutter at the thought of paying retail but first, you have to do some due diligence. You've got to shop Home Depot and Lowe's and get a price as your benchmark so that you know how much you'll be saving. Then buy what you need from V2K, ok? Wishful thinking? A pipedream? Or are you listening and reading every word? Sure enough, this brand new franchise hit town with all the bells and whistles of the most sophisticated business opportunity for a home business I've ever seen. Literally shop for hundreds of fabrics in your own home or office for custom draperies. Pick your fabric and see it displayed on the screen in a matter of minutes. They come to you complete with laptop, measuring tools for your windows and walls, records them in their computer and then WOW! They hit the button with your new window treatment. It's totally awesome. Same thing goes with other hard treatments as shutters, blinds, hardware in all the popular names from **ROBERT ALLEN** fabric to **GRABER** and **HUNTER-DOUGLAS** blinds. Nothing is left to this imaginative but this is high-tech shopping at its best. With the savings alone, you can buy it all: custom bedding, fabric walls, pillows, swags, cascades, cornices and valances, shades, outside awnings and yes, even upholstery—you might as well not hide but rather get a peek inside the world of window shopping in the 21st century. By appointment, what do you have to lose? Check out their website, read about their business opportunities, and then kick yourself for not thinking of this first. They make shopping for custom draperies and other window treatments an absolute dream come true. Six months no down payment, no interest and six months to pay for custom draperies and plantation shutters. It doesn't get better than V2K. (Oh, I take that back. Did you see their Diva Dollar offer?) ***Call toll-free: 866/305-5556***

★★★★★★ **Wallpaper Source & More**   **214/987-2369**

612 Preston Forest Shopping Center   Mon-Thurs 10-6; Fri-Sat 10-5
Dallas, TX 75230
www.wallpapersource.com

Paper! Paper! Read all about it. Business must be booming since their expansion. Wallcoverings, of course, are their specialty with only name brands you've come to know and covet. Wade through the over 1,200 in-stock patterns and over 1,500 special order books that are the mainstay of their repertoire. Their wall and window covering options are extensive alongside all the coordinates and accessories such as rugs, art, custom draperies, bedding and floral arrangements. Conveniently located at the intersection of Preston and Forest (SE corner), they've been a popular shopping choice when it comes to wallcoverings at a savings of 30 to 75 percent off. Laura and her staff of angels provide everything you need to shop for window and wall treatment with that all important personalize service and decorating know-how that you just can't get online. Furthermore, they have taken on the design challenge of the Budget Decorators. Now you'll have a place to land, a place to meet, a place where all the fabrics and books are right there for your shopping pleasure—and of course, then they'll take you "underground shopping for the rest." That means, all of the outlets, the secret remodelers and landscapers we have under our wing, this is Design on a Dime in real time. Don't you just love it? I do, or I wouldn't have let them take it over and run with it. I'm too busy telling everybody about it, but it's the next best thing I've done since the birth of The Underground Shopper. So, when you need a bed and a new mattress and the bedding and the faux walls and the drapery treatments and the accents, they know who are the best and who are the best priced. ***Call toll-free: 800/987-2369***

★★★   Wallpaper Unique Home Accents   972/219-9985

1288 W. Main, Suite 109   Mon-Sat 10-6
Lewisville, TX 75067

If accessorizing your home for less sounds appealing, then consider the expanding inventory at Wallpaper Unique Home Accents (formerly Wallpaper for Less). This neighborhood wallpapering hole serves up savings on your liquid assets. Unique home accents now permeate the rolling inventory including plate racks, plates, lamps, framed prints, crosses, candles, plant stands and more. Custom bar stools, mantel pieces and wall shelves complete the picture. Want to paint over old wallpaper? No problem. They carry the product, "Readywall", which does the trick. No paint, though, but enough paste and buckets to wallpaper the town from the ground floor up. Then, if you remember what you came in for, don't forget they do have wallpaper and fabric, for less.

★★★★   Wallpapers Galore for Less   972/381-7664

17194 Preston Rd.   Mon-Fri 10-6; Sat 10-5
Dallas, TX 75230

With over 300 wallpaper patterns in stock, Wallpapers Galore for Less will keep you glued to your money! But that's not all. You'll also find window treatments, blinds, shades, wood shutters, fabric and more, all rolled into one neighborhood outpost. They don't do FREE estimates or installation but will recommend those that do at a charge. You'll find discounts off MSRP (Manufacturer's Suggested Retail Price) ranging from 30 to 80 percent. While they carry most name brands, you won't find any HUNTER-DOUGLAS products here. Don't know why, but who cares? With so many wallpaper books to wade through, who has time to look behind company policies. Some of the brands of wallpaper included: ANTONIA VELLA, GRAMERCY, LAURA ASHLEY, KATZENBACH & WARREN, MOTIF, RALPH LAUREN, RONALD REDDING, SEABROOK, STERLING PRINTS, VILLAGE, WAVERLY, WESTMONT and YORK. And that's just a few to impress you. Though wallcoverings are their forte, they also showcase KASMIR, LADY ANNE and NORBAL fabrics and custom blinds at similar discounts. Remember, windows to your soul start with the appropriate window treatments; otherwise, they'll catch you, butt naked!

★   Wallpapers To Go   817/485-6094

5152 Rufe Snow Drive, #332
North Richland Hills, TX 76180
www.wallpaperstogo.com

Down to one lone star location, Wallpapers To Go has weathered the storm and has survived the fallout of the economic times. Now, they are selling HUNTER-DOUGLAS mini-blinds, pleated shades, verticals, honeycomb shades for 65 percent off and that's not too shabby. Shady, maybe. Over 1,000 books to look through with a five to seven day turnaround time, all with 33 percent off or $9.99 per single roll (regularly from $12.99-$18.99). For their designer collection, they only discount 10 percent. Do you see why they have not grown to epic proportions? With some of the online sites selling hundreds of thousands of different patterns over the net at up to 75-80 percent off, they can't compete. They try, though, as they are a nationwide chain offering over 850 of the world's best borders and wallpaper - though they don't stop with wallcoverings. They have now extended their reach to framed art, coordinating fabrics and home accessories. Go online to visualize the transformation that's possible with the additions. Learn how to measure for those hard window coverings like blinds and shades. But don't expect to order anything on their website, as it's strictly for learning the basic A-B-Cs.

★★★   Window Fashion Center   817/261-5009

2901 West Pioneer Pkwy.   Mon-Tues 8-5 Wed-Fri 8-6; Sat 10-3
Arlington, TX 76013

You don't have to be a pioneer to celebrate your independence from high prices. This high-fashion window store exudes all of your window needs right down to the bedding and upholstery, so that everything can mix and match. Nary a whim is left unattended. Want some good-looking furniture that you can sit on as well as count on? Consider names such as **BASSETT**, **BECKMAN**, **HOOKER** and more. But it doesn't stop there. Add up the discounts of up to 75 percent off name brand blinds such as **HUNTER-DOUGLAS** and 30 percent off wallpaper on any name in the book. While an in-home estimate for windows is FREE, expect to incur a $75 retainer for interior design work which is then deducted from your total bill. Debbie does decorating! Seek them out and ye shall prosper. Custom draperies, shutters, upholstery, mini-blinds, verticals, pleated shades, wood blinds, area rugs, carpet, plus the bedding ensembles and window treatments are just the beginning to a *House Beautiful*.

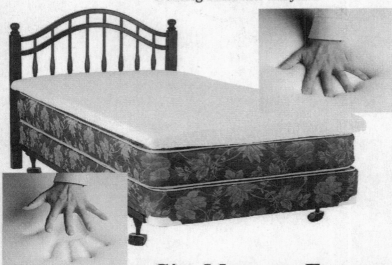

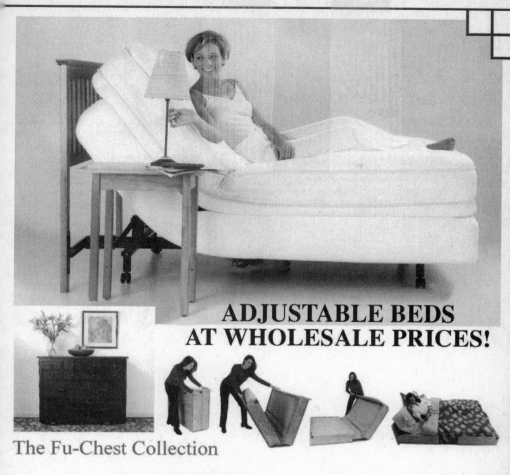

ADJUSTABLE BEDS AT WHOLESALE PRICES!

The Fu-Chest Collection

Futon Sofa Sleepers

100's of Styles & Fabrics To Choose From

See City Mattress Factory write-up on page 119.

Diva Dollars

On the following pages you will find over $7,000 worth of savings from merchants in this book. Clip the Diva Dollars and take them with you wherever you go.

the Underground
• Shopper

1079 W. Round Grove Road
PMB 428, Suite 300
Lewisville, TX 75067
469/293-SHOP

VALUE: D$ Up to **40** per $100 (see other side)

ISSUED TO:

2004/2005 Edition
Underground Shopper
Shopping Guide Purchaser

REDEEMABLE AT:

7th Avenue Plus Size Outlet
1331 Inwood Road
Dallas, TX 75247

214/638-9033

---

the Underground
• Shopper

1079 W. Round Grove Road
PMB 428, Suite 300
Lewisville, TX 75067
469/293-SHOP

DIVA DOLLARS

VALUE: D$ **10** off per $100 purchased

ISSUED TO:

2004/2005 Edition
Underground Shopper
Shopping Guide Purchaser

REDEEMABLE AT:

At Your Service Flooring
4400 Airport Freeway
Fort Worth, TX 76117

817/831-3113

---

the Underground
• Shopper

1079 W. Round Grove Road
PMB 428, Suite 300
Lewisville, TX 75067
469/293-SHOP

DIVA DOLLARS

VALUE: D$ **15** off per $100 purchased
(see other side)

ISSUED TO:

2004/2005 Edition
Underground Shopper
Shopping Guide Purchaser

REDEEMABLE AT:

BOCA Leather Gallery
4051 LBJ, #140
Dallas, TX 75244

972/620-1011

---

the Underground
• Shopper

1079 W. Round Grove Road
PMB 428, Suite 300
Lewisville, TX 75067
469/293-SHOP

DIVA DOLLARS

VALUE: D$ **50** off consultation fee

ISSUED TO:

2004/2005 Edition
Underground Shopper
Shopping Guide Purchaser

REDEEMABLE AT:

Bud Hibbs, Credit Counseling
PO Box 16513
Fort Worth, TX 76162

817/589-4284

DIVA DOLLARS

$40 off per $100 purchased in beaded/embellished suits.
$30 off per $100 purchased in career suits.
$20 off on hats $50 and over.
$10 off any dress (*regularly priced items only*).

the Underground Shopper ◇ 469/293-7467 ◇ 1-866/273-SHOP

DIVA DOLLARS

$10 off per $100 purchased.

the Underground Shopper ◇ 469/293-7467 ◇ 1-866/273-SHOP

DIVA DOLLARS

$15 off per $100 purchased, based on the lowest sale price or other advertised price.

the Underground Shopper ◇ 469/293-7467 ◇ 1-866/273-SHOP

DIVA DOLLARS

$50 off on consultation fee.

the Underground Shopper ◇ 469/293-7467 ◇ 1-866/273-SHOP

the Underground
• Shopper

DIVA DOLLARS

1079 W. Round Grove Road
PMB 428, Suite 300
Lewisville, TX 75067
469/293-SHOP

VALUE: D$ **75** off any permanent cosmetic treatment

ISSUED TO:

2004/2005 Edition
Underground Shopper
Shopping Guide Purchaser

REDEEMABLE AT:

Vicki's Making Faces
Arlington, TX
By appointment only

817/692-6639

NO CASH VALUE - NOT REDEEMABLE FOR CASH

---

the Underground
• Shopper

DIVA DOLLARS

1079 W. Round Grove Road
PMB 428, Suite 300
Lewisville, TX 75067
469/293-SHOP

VALUE: D$ **50** Off on a move *(call for details)*

ISSUED TO:

2004/2005 Edition
Underground Shopper
Shopping Guide Purchaser

REDEEMABLE AT:

All My Sons Moving & Storage
9761 Clifford, #150
Dallas, TX 75220

214/219-8900

NO CASH VALUE - NOT REDEEMABLE FOR CASH

---

the Underground
• Shopper

DIVA DOLLARS

1079 W. Round Grove Road
PMB 428, Suite 300
Lewisville, TX 75067
469/293-SHOP

VALUE: D$ **10** off per $100 purchased

ISSUED TO:

2004/2005 Edition
Underground Shopper
Shopping Guide Purchaser

REDEEMABLE AT:

Changing Places
101 S. Coit Road, #82
Richardson, TX 75080

214/570-0077

NO CASH VALUE - NOT REDEEMABLE FOR CASH

---

the Underground
• Shopper

DIVA DOLLARS

1079 W. Round Grove Road
PMB 428, Suite 300
Lewisville, TX 75067
469/293-SHOP

VALUE: D$ **10** off per $100 purchased

ISSUED TO:

2004/2005 Edition
Underground Shopper
Shopping Guide Purchaser

REDEEMABLE AT:

Christy's Resale Draperies
1300 Custer @ 15th
Plano, TX 75075

972/403-1543

NO CASH VALUE - NOT REDEEMABLE FOR CASH

DIVA DOLLARS

CONDITIONS

$75 towards any permanent cosmetic procedure.

the Underground Shopper ◇ 469/293-7467 ◇ 1-866/273-SHOP

DIVA DOLLARS

CONDITIONS

$50 off on the price of a move - call for details.

the Underground Shopper ◇ 469/293-7467 ◇ 1-866/273-SHOP

DIVA DOLLARS

CONDITIONS

$10 off per $100 purchased.

the Underground Shopper ◇ 469/293-7467 ◇ 1-866/273-SHOP

DIVA DOLLARS

CONDITIONS

$10 off per $100 purchased.

the Underground Shopper ◇ 469/293-7467 ◇ 1-866/273-SHOP

the Underground • Shopper

1079 W. Round Grove Road
PMB 428, Suite 300
Lewisville, TX 75067
469/293-SHOP

DIVA DOLLARS

Expires January 1, 2006

VALUE: 10% off specific item - see back

ISSUED TO:

2004/2005 Edition
Underground Shopper
Shopping Guide Purchaser

REDEEMABLE AT:

Bedroom Solutions
1326 Inwood Rd.
Dallas, TX 75247

214/905-9121

NO CASH VALUE - NOT REDEEMABLE FOR CASH

---

the Underground • Shopper

1079 W. Round Grove Road
PMB 428, Suite 300
Lewisville, TX 75067
469/293-SHOP

DIVA DOLLARS

Expires January 1, 2006

VALUE: D$ 10 off per $100 purchased

ISSUED TO:

2004/2005 Edition
Underground Shopper
Shopping Guide Purchaser

REDEEMABLE AT:

City Mattress Factory Outlet
900 S. Haltom Road
Haltom City, TX 76117

817/834-1648, or 800/834-2473 toll-free

NO CASH VALUE - NOT REDEEMABLE FOR CASH

---

the Underground • Shopper

1079 W. Round Grove Road
PMB 428, Suite 300
Lewisville, TX 75067
469/293-SHOP

DIVA DOLLARS

Expires January 1, 2006

VALUE: D$ 100 off order of $1,000 or more
(see back)

ISSUED TO:

2004/2005 Edition
Underground Shopper
Shopping Guide Purchaser

REDEEMABLE AT:

Closets by Design
4301-A Lindbergh Dr.
Addison, TX 75001

972/361-0010, 817-416-9250
or 800/BY DESIGN toll-free

NO CASH VALUE - NOT REDEEMABLE FOR CASH

---

the Underground • Shopper

1079 W. Round Grove Road
PMB 428, Suite 300
Lewisville, TX 75067
469/293-SHOP

DIVA DOLLARS

Expires January 1, 2006

VALUE: D$ 70 enrollment fee waived

ISSUED TO:

2004/2005 Edition
Underground Shopper
Shopping Guide Purchaser

REDEEMABLE AT:

Healthy America Agency
Lewisville, Texas
By appointment only

469/293-7467

NO CASH VALUE - NOT REDEEMABLE FOR CASH

DIVA DOLLARS

10% off purchase of any Classic Creations bedding.

DIVA DOLLARS

$10 off per $100 purchased.

DIVA DOLLARS

$100 off any order of $1,000 or more. FREE installation with any complete unit order of $500 or more.

DIVA DOLLARS

$70 enrollment fee for discount medical card waived.

the Underground
• Shopper

1079 W. Round Grove Road
PMB 428, Suite 300
Lewisville, TX 75067
469/293-SHOP

DIVA DOLLARS

*Expires
January 1, 2006*

VALUE: D$ **10** off per $100 purchased

ISSUED TO:

2004/2005 Edition
Underground Shopper
Shopping Guide Purchaser

REDEEMABLE AT:

Cutting Corners
13720 Midway Road, Suite 200
Farmers Branch, TX 75244

972/233-1741

NO CASH VALUE - NOT REDEEMABLE FOR CASH

---

the Underground
• Shopper

1079 W. Round Grove Road
PMB 428, Suite 300
Lewisville, TX 75067
469/293-SHOP

DIVA DOLLARS

*Expires
January 1, 2006*

VALUE: D$ **10** off purchase - see other side

ISSUED TO:

2004/2005 Edition
Underground Shopper
Shopping Guide Purchaser

REDEEMABLE AT:

Bruno di Nola Classic Cheesecake
3613 Gaitland Circle
Flower Mound, TX 75022
By appointment only
972/539-3429

NO CASH VALUE - NOT REDEEMABLE FOR CASH

---

the Underground
• Shopper

1079 W. Round Grove Road
PMB 428, Suite 300
Lewisville, TX 75067
469/293-SHOP

DIVA DOLLARS

*Expires
January 1, 2006*

VALUE: D$ **10** off per $100 purchased *(see back)*

ISSUED TO:

2004/2005 Edition
Underground Shopper
Shopping Guide Purchaser

REDEEMABLE AT:

Dallas Gold & Silver Exchange
2817 Forest Lane
Dallas, TX 75234

972/484-3662 or 800/527-5307 toll-free

NO CASH VALUE - NOT REDEEMABLE FOR CASH

---

the Underground
• Shopper

1079 W. Round Grove Road
PMB 428, Suite 300
Lewisville, TX 75067
469/293-SHOP

DIVA DOLLARS

*Expires
January 1, 2006*

VALUE: **15%** 15% off any purchase

ISSUED TO:

2004/2005 Edition
Underground Shopper
Shopping Guide Purchaser

REDEEMABLE AT:

BuySmart Medical Supply
10031 Monroe, Suite 200
Dallas, TX 75229

214/358-0007

NO CASH VALUE - NOT REDEEMABLE FOR CASH

DIVA DOLLARS

CONDITIONS

$10 off per $100 purchased.

the Underground Shopper ◇ 469/293-7467 ◇ 1-866/273-SHOP

DIVA DOLLARS

CONDITIONS

$10 off the purchase of any order of $40 or more.
Call number on other side to order and arrange for delivery.

the Underground Shopper ◇ 469/293-7467 ◇ 1-866/273-SHOP

DIVA DOLLARS

CONDITIONS

$10 off per $100 of jewelry purchased ONLY, no more than $100 reduction for total sale.

the Underground Shopper ◇ 469/293-7467 ◇ 1-866/273-SHOP

DIVA DOLLARS

CONDITIONS

15% off any purchase

the Underground Shopper ◇ 469/293-7467 ◇ 1-866/273-SHOP

the Underground
• Shopper

1079 W. Round Grove Road
PMB 428, Suite 300
Lewisville, TX 75067
469/293-SHOP

VALUE: *See back for details*

ISSUED TO:

2004/2005 Edition
Underground Shopper
Shopping Guide Purchaser

REDEEMABLE AT:

Cantoni Outlet
4245 Simonton (off Midway)
Farmers Branch, TX 75244

972/720-0052

---

the Underground
• Shopper

1079 W. Round Grove Road
PMB 428, Suite 300
Lewisville, TX 75067
469/293-SHOP

DIVA DOLLARS

VALUE: **FREE CANDLE** with purchase of $20 or more

ISSUED TO:

2004/2005 Edition
Underground Shopper
Shopping Guide Purchaser

REDEEMABLE AT:

Er'go Candle Outlet Store
9200 W. Carpenter Freeway @ Regal Row
Dallas, TX 75247

214/905-9050

---

the Underground
• Shopper

1079 W. Round Grove Road
PMB 428, Suite 300
Lewisville, TX 75067
469/293-SHOP

DIVA DOLLARS

VALUE: D$50 off $500 or more purchase

ISSUED TO:

2004/2005 Edition
Underground Shopper
Shopping Guide Purchaser

REDEEMABLE AT:

Ethan Allen Outlet Store
633 Northeast Loop 820
Hurst, TX 76053

817/595-0490 or 888/EAHELP1 toll-free

---

the Underground
• Shopper

1079 W. Round Grove Road
PMB 428, Suite 300
Lewisville, TX 75067
469/293-SHOP

DIVA DOLLARS

VALUE: D$50 off $150 or more purchase

ISSUED TO:

2004/2005 Edition
Underground Shopper
Shopping Guide Purchaser

REDEEMABLE AT:

EyeLane
2288 Valley View Mall
Dallas, TX 75240

972/233-4113

DIVA DOLLARS

Your choice of either 10% off any one item *or* free delivery on any order of $1,000 or more.
Only one offer per coupon. Cannot be combined with any other offer.
Valid only at the Cantoni Outlet.

the Underground Shopper ◇ 469/293-7467 ◇ 1-866/273-SHOP

DIVA DOLLARS

Free candle with purchase of $20 ore more.

the Underground Shopper ◇ 469/293-7467 ◇ 1-866/273-SHOP

DIVA DOLLARS

$50 off purchase of $500 or more.

the Underground Shopper ◇ 469/293-7467 ◇ 1-866/273-SHOP

DIVA DOLLARS

$50 off purchase of $150 or more.

the Underground Shopper ◇ 469/293-7467 ◇ 1-866/273-SHOP

the **Underground**
● **Shopper**

1079 W. Round Grove Road
PMB 428, Suite 300
Lewisville, TX 75067
469/293-SHOP

DIVA DOLLARS

VALUE: D$ **50-200** off *(see back)*

ISSUED TO:

**2004/2005 Edition
Underground Shopper
Shopping Guide Purchaser**

REDEEMABLE AT:

Fitness HQ
11930 Preston Road, Suite 140
Dallas, TX 75230

972/980-7788 or 877/479-4444 toll-free

---

 the **Underground**
● **Shopper**

1079 W. Round Grove Road
PMB 428, Suite 300
Lewisville, TX 75067
469/293-SHOP

DIVA DOLLARS

VALUE: D$ **20** off any framing job

ISSUED TO:

**2004/2005 Edition
Underground Shopper
Shopping Guide Purchaser**

REDEEMABLE AT:

Framing Warehouse & ArtHouse Gallery
2760 E. Trinity Mills, Suite 126
Carrollton, TX 75006

972/416-3626

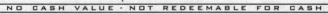

---

the **Underground**
● **Shopper**

1079 W. Round Grove Road
PMB 428, Suite 300
Lewisville, TX 75067
469/293-SHOP

DIVA DOLLARS

VALUE: D$ **25** leather chair purchase *(see back)*

ISSUED TO:

**2004/2005 Edition
Underground Shopper
Shopping Guide Purchaser**

REDEEMABLE AT:

Front Desk Office Furniture Outlet
10401 Harry Hines Blvd.
Dallas, TX 75220

214/904-9045 or 800/299-8095 toll-free

---

 the **Underground**
● **Shopper**

1079 W. Round Grove Road
PMB 428, Suite 300
Lewisville, TX 75067
469/293-SHOP

DIVA DOLLARS

VALUE: D$ **50** off $250 or more purchase

ISSUED TO:

**2004/2005 Edition
Underground Shopper
Shopping Guide Purchaser**

REDEEMABLE AT:

G & S Sales
4304 Highway 80 W.
Terrell, TX 75160

1/972-563-3201, 1/972-563-7821 or
800/926-9534 toll-free

DIVA DOLLARS

DIVA DOLLARS

DIVA DOLLARS

DIVA DOLLARS

DIVA DOLLARS

CONDITIONS

$3 off on entrees and specialty items from the menu.

the Underground Shopper ◇ 469/293-7467 ◇ 1-866/273-SHOP

DIVA DOLLARS

CONDITIONS

A FREE home warranty with the purchase of a full-service marketing plan.

the Underground Shopper ◇ 469/293-7467 ◇ 1-866/273-SHOP

DIVA DOLLARS

CONDITIONS

$5 off purchase of $50 or more.
$10 off purchase of $100 or more.

the Underground Shopper ◇ 469/293-7467 ◇ 1-866/273-SHOP

DIVA DOLLARS

CONDITIONS

$10 off per $100 purchased on plants and trees only.

the Underground Shopper ◇ 469/293-7467 ◇ 1-866/273-SHOP

DIVA DOLLARS

DIVA DOLLARS

DIVA DOLLARS

DIVA DOLLARS

the Underground • Shopper

1079 W. Round Grove Road
PMB 428, Suite 300
Lewisville, TX 75067
469/293-SHOP

DIVA DOLLARS

VALUE: D$ **75** off any laser service

ISSUED TO:

**2004/2005 Edition
Underground Shopper
Shopping Guide Purchaser**

REDEEMABLE AT:

Light Touch Laser
6351 Oakmont Blvd.
Fort Worth, TX 76132

817/361-8838

---

the Underground • Shopper

1079 W. Round Grove Road
PMB 428, Suite 300
Lewisville, TX 75067
469/293-SHOP

DIVA DOLLARS

VALUE: D$ **10**

ISSUED TO:

**2004/2005 Edition
Underground Shopper
Shopping Guide Purchaser**

REDEEMABLE AT:

Linda's Penta Water By The Case
Home Delivery Only
By Appointment Only

214/337-0107

---

the Underground • Shopper

1079 W. Round Grove Road
PMB 428, Suite 300
Lewisville, TX 75067
469/293-SHOP

DIVA DOLLARS

VALUE: **10¢** off per foot on any wood purchased

ISSUED TO:

**2004/2005 Edition
Underground Shopper
Shopping Guide Purchaser**

REDEEMABLE AT:

Lumber Liquidators
1620 N. I-35
Carrollton, TX 75006

972/323-5077 or 877-Mill-Direct toll-free

---

the Underground • Shopper

1079 W. Round Grove Road
PMB 428, Suite 300
Lewisville, TX 75067
469/293-SHOP

DIVA DOLLARS

VALUE: D$ **10** off a purchase of $50 or more

ISSUED TO:

**2004/2005 Edition
Underground Shopper
Shopping Guide Purchaser**

REDEEMABLE AT:

Closeout Corner
1325 Inwood Rd.
Dallas, TX 75247

214/951-7474

DIVA DOLLARS

CONDITIONS

$75 off on any laser service.

DIVA DOLLARS

CONDITIONS

$10 off on the purchase of a 4 case minimum order.

DIVA DOLLARS

CONDITIONS

10¢ off per foot on any wood.

DIVA DOLLARS

CONDITIONS

$10 off a purchase of $50 or more.

the Underground
● Shopper

1079 W. Round Grove Road
PMB 428, Suite 300
Lewisville, TX 75067
469/293-SHOP

VALUE: DS **5-10** off *(see back)*

ISSUED TO:

2004/2005 Edition
Underground Shopper
Shopping Guide Purchaser

REDEEMABLE AT:

Marsala Restaurant
1618 Hwy. 360 North
Grand Prairie, TX 75050

972/988-1101

---

the Underground
● Shopper

1079 W. Round Grove Road
PMB 428, Suite 300
Lewisville, TX 75067
469/293-SHOP

DIVA DOLLARS

VALUE: DS **100** off purchase

ISSUED TO:

2004/2005 Edition
Underground Shopper
Shopping Guide Purchaser

REDEEMABLE AT:

Nick Mayrath, CPA
13612 Midway, Suite 603
Dallas, TX 75244

972/661-9055

---

the Underground
● Shopper

1079 W. Round Grove Road
PMB 428, Suite 300
Lewisville, TX 75067
469/293-SHOP

DIVA DOLLARS

VALUE: **50%** off a purchase of $25 or more

ISSUED TO:

2004/2005 Edition
Underground Shopper
Shopping Guide Purchaser

REDEEMABLE AT:

Dallas Food Depot
909 S. Tyler
Dallas, TX 75208

214/942-3201

---

the Underground
● Shopper

1079 W. Round Grove Road
PMB 428, Suite 300
Lewisville, TX 75067
469/293-SHOP

DIVA DOLLARS

VALUE: DS **15** off first service call

ISSUED TO:

2004/2005 Edition
Underground Shopper
Shopping Guide Purchaser

REDEEMABLE AT:

Rescue-Tech
3941 Legacy Drive
Plano, TX 75023

972/417-1234 - by appointment only

DIVA DOLLARS

CONDITIONS

$5 off lunch for 2 to 4 diners.
$10 off dinner for 2 to 4 diners.

the Underground Shopper ◇ 469/293-7467 ◇ 1-866/273-SHOP

DIVA DOLLARS

CONDITIONS

$100 off purchase.

the Underground Shopper ◇ 469/293-7467 ◇ 1-866/273-SHOP

DIVA DOLLARS

CONDITIONS

50% off a purchase of $25 or more.

the Underground Shopper ◇ 469/293-7467 ◇ 1-866/273-SHOP

DIVA DOLLARS

CONDITIONS

$15 off of first service call.

the Underground Shopper ◇ 469/293-7467 ◇ 1-866/273-SHOP

the Underground
● Shopper

1079 W. Round Grove Road
PMB 428, Suite 300
Lewisville, TX 75067
469/293-SHOP

VALUE: D$ **5** off initial grooming for first-time customer

ISSUED TO:

2004/2005 Edition
Underground Shopper
Shopping Guide Purchaser

REDEEMABLE AT:

Pet Love
10909 Indian Trail, Suite 101
Dallas, TX 75229

972/243-8331

NO CASH VALUE - NOT REDEEMABLE FOR CASH

---

the Underground
● Shopper

1079 W. Round Grove Road
PMB 428, Suite 300
Lewisville, TX 75067
469/293-SHOP

DIVA DOLLARS

VALUE: D$ **25** off membership fee

ISSUED TO:

2004/2005 Edition
Underground Shopper
Shopping Guide Purchaser

REDEEMABLE AT:

DirectBuy
610 US Highway 80 E.
Sunnyvale, TX 75182

972/203-8881

NO CASH VALUE - NOT REDEEMABLE FOR CASH

---

the Underground
● Shopper

1079 W. Round Grove Road
PMB 428, Suite 300
Lewisville, TX 75067
469/293-SHOP

DIVA DOLLARS

VALUE: **FREE QUILT** with any purchase over $100

ISSUED TO:

2004/2005 Edition
Underground Shopper
Shopping Guide Purchaser

REDEEMABLE AT:

Quilt Factory Outlet
2969 Red Hock Drive
Grand Prairie, TX 75052

972/206-7800

NO CASH VALUE - NOT REDEEMABLE FOR CASH

---

the Underground
● Shopper

1079 W. Round Grove Road
PMB 428, Suite 300
Lewisville, TX 75067
469/293-SHOP

DIVA DOLLARS

VALUE: D$ **100** off whole house carpeting

ISSUED TO:

2004/2005 Edition
Underground Shopper
Shopping Guide Purchaser

REDEEMABLE AT:

S & H Carpet Distributors
8717 Directors Row
Dallas, TX 75247

214/638-3311

NO CASH VALUE - NOT REDEEMABLE FOR CASH

DIVA DOLLARS

CONDITIONS

$5 off initial grooming for first-time customer.

DIVA DOLLARS

CONDITIONS

$25 off of membership fee in DirectBuy buying club.

DIVA DOLLARS

CONDITIONS

One free quilt with any purchase over $100.

DIVA DOLLARS

CONDITIONS

$100 off whole-house carpeting.

the Underground • Shopper

1079 W. Round Grove Road
PMB 428, Suite 300
Lewisville, TX 75067
469/293-SHOP

DIVA DOLLARS

VALUE: **20%** off certain treatments *(see back)*

ISSUED TO:

2004/2005 Edition
Underground Shopper
Shopping Guide Purchaser

REDEEMABLE AT:

John A. Standefer, Jr., M.D.
1014 E. Wheatland Rd.
Duncanville, TX 75116

972/296-1587

---

the Underground • Shopper

1079 W. Round Grove Road
PMB 428, Suite 300
Lewisville, TX 75067
469/293-SHOP

DIVA DOLLARS

VALUE: D$ **20-50** off *(see back)*

ISSUED TO:

2004/2005 Edition
Underground Shopper
Shopping Guide Purchaser

REDEEMABLE AT:

Sears Outlet Store
2724 Realty Road
Carrollton, TX 75006

972/418-2293

---

the Underground • Shopper

1079 W. Round Grove Road
PMB 428, Suite 300
Lewisville, TX 75067
469/293-SHOP

DIVA DOLLARS

VALUE: D$ **155** off Zoom! whitening *(see back)*

ISSUED TO:

2004/2005 Edition
Underground Shopper
Shopping Guide Purchaser

REDEEMABLE AT:

Steven W. Titensor, DDS
1901 Long Prairie Road, Suite 320
Flower Mound, TX 75022

972/355-9545

---

the Underground • Shopper

1079 W. Round Grove Road
PMB 428, Suite 300
Lewisville, TX 75067
469/293-SHOP

DIVA DOLLARS

VALUE: D$ **4** off purchase *(see back)*

ISSUED TO:

2004/2005 Edition
Underground Shopper
Shopping Guide Purchaser

REDEEMABLE AT:

Slim's Discount University
PO Box 5094
Abilene, TX 79608

www.slimsdiscountuniversity.com

DIVA DOLLARS

Choose either 20% off first syringe of Botox® or 20% off first syringe of Restylane®.

DIVA DOLLARS

$20 off of $200 to $499 purchase.
$50 off of $500 or more purchase.

DIVA DOLLARS

$155 off on ZOOM!® whitening treatment, as seen on TV's *Extreme Makeover*.

DIVA DOLLARS

$4 off purchase.

NOTE: Business is done through website, www.slimsdiscountuniversity.com, although payments for goods may be made by mail.

the Underground • Shopper

1079 W. Round Grove Road
PMB 428, Suite 300
Lewisville, TX 75067
469/293-SHOP

DIVA DOLLARS

VALUE: D$ **5** off any purchase

ISSUED TO:

2004/2005 Edition
Underground Shopper
Shopping Guide Purchaser

REDEEMABLE AT:

Small Fry
330 Sunset
Denton, TX 76201

940/387-9915 or 888/442-9002 toll-free

---

the Underground • Shopper

1079 W. Round Grove Road
PMB 428, Suite 300
Lewisville, TX 75067
469/293-SHOP

DIVA DOLLARS

VALUE: D$ **100** off Citizen watches *(see back)*

ISSUED TO:

2004/2005 Edition
Underground Shopper
Shopping Guide Purchaser

REDEEMABLE AT:

Solitaires
7140 Bishop Rd.
Plano, TX 75023

469/241-0590

---

the Underground • Shopper

1079 W. Round Grove Road
PMB 428, Suite 300
Lewisville, TX 75067
469/293-SHOP

DIVA DOLLARS

VALUE: **MANY - SEE BACK**

ISSUED TO:

2004/2005 Edition
Underground Shopper
Shopping Guide Purchaser

REDEEMABLE AT:

Vikon Village Flea Market
2918 South Jupiter
Garland, TX 75041

972/278-7414

---

the Underground • Shopper

1079 W. Round Grove Road
PMB 428, Suite 300
Lewisville, TX 75067
469/293-SHOP

DIVA DOLLARS

VALUE: D$ **50** off purchase of $300 or more

ISSUED TO:

2004/2005 Edition
Underground Shopper
Shopping Guide Purchaser

REDEEMABLE AT:

Thompson's Appliances
2408 S. Cooper
Arlington, TX 76015

817/277-1131 or Metro 817/265-4711

DIVA DOLLARS

CONDITIONS

$5 off of any purchase.

DIVA DOLLARS

CONDITIONS

$100 off of Citizen watches retailing for $250 or more.

DIVA DOLLARS

CONDITIONS

Take this Diva Dollar to the Vikon Village office for an official list of vendors participating in the Diva Dollar Discounts.

DIVA DOLLARS

CONDITIONS

$50 off of purchase of $300 or more.

the Underground
• Shopper

1079 W. Round Grove Road
PMB 428, Suite 300
Lewisville, TX 75067
469/293-SHOP

DIVA DOLLARS

VALUE: D$ **5** off purchase of $40 or more *(see back)*

ISSUED TO:

2004/2005 Edition
Underground Shopper
Shopping Guide Purchaser

REDEEMABLE AT:

Tiny Thru Plus Size Outlet
705 Secretary Drive
Arlington, TX 76015

817/265-3737

NO CASH VALUE - NOT REDEEMABLE FOR CASH

---

the Underground
• Shopper

1079 W. Round Grove Road
PMB 428, Suite 300
Lewisville, TX 75067
469/293-SHOP

DIVA DOLLARS

Expires January 1, 2006

VALUE: **25%** off a RETAIL purchase *(see back)*

ISSUED TO:

2004/2005 Edition
Underground Shopper
Shopping Guide Purchaser

REDEEMABLE AT:

GNS Foods
2109 E. Division St.
Arlington, TX 76011

817/469-7420

NO CASH VALUE - NOT REDEEMABLE FOR CASH

---

the Underground
• Shopper

1079 W. Round Grove Road
PMB 428, Suite 300
Lewisville, TX 75067
469/293-SHOP

DIVA DOLLARS

Expires January 1, 2006

VALUE: D$ **5** off per purchase

ISSUED TO:

2004/2005 Edition
Underground Shopper
Shopping Guide Purchaser

REDEEMABLE AT:

Vantage Shoe Warehouse
2222 Vantage St.
Dallas, TX 75207

214/678-9967

NO CASH VALUE - NOT REDEEMABLE FOR CASH

---

the Underground
• Shopper

1079 W. Round Grove Road
PMB 428, Suite 300
Lewisville, TX 75067
469/293-SHOP

DIVA DOLLARS

Expires January 1, 2006

VALUE: D$ **50** off purchase *(see back)*

ISSUED TO:

2004/2005 Edition
Underground Shopper
Shopping Guide Purchaser

REDEEMABLE AT:

Walt's Appliance
2336 E. Main
Grand Prairie, TX 75050

972/263-3751

NO CASH VALUE - NOT REDEEMABLE FOR CASH

DIVA DOLLARS

$5 off for first-time customer on purchase of **$40** or more (in-house only).

DIVA DOLLARS

25% off a **RETAIL** purchase - purchaser must be retail shopper.

DIVA DOLLARS

$5 off purchase.

DIVA DOLLARS

$50 off of purchase (not valid with any other offers or discounts).

Store Name Index